Standards for showing work and writing conclusions to math problems in MTH 95

Notation is an important part of how we communicate the results to a mathematical problem. Here is a quick reference for how to write your answers for this course:

Problem Type	Special Notes	How to write your answer	Possible Example (Check with your instructor for how they prefer you to show your work.)
Evaluating an expression.	Evaluating means you have an expression (there is no equal sign in the statement of what you are asked to do). You will often times see the word "evaluate," "state," or "find."	Show your substitution step and then work out the arithmetic using equal signs before each line to show equivalency of the expressions.	Evaluate $f(-2)$ for $f(x) = 2x^2 + 5x - 3$. $$f(-2) = 2(-2)^2 + 5(-2) - 3$$ $$= 2(4) - 10 - 3$$ $$= 8 - 10 - 3$$ $$= -5$$
		If you cannot evaluate, state that the value is *undefined*. DO NOT say "no solution" because you are not *solving*.	Evaluate $f(1)$ for $f(x) = \dfrac{1}{x-1}$. $f(1)$ is undefined.
Simplifying an algebraic expression.	Remember, an algebraic expression represents a number which is dependent on the value we choose for the variable. To write an equivalent expression means that both expression hold the same value no matter what we choose for the variable. You will often times see the word "simplify" in the directions.	Since we are writing equivalent expressions we want to use an equal sign to signify that each subsequent expression is equivalent to the previous.	Simplify the expression $\dfrac{\dfrac{3}{x-1}}{\dfrac{1}{x-1} + \dfrac{3}{x}}$. $\dfrac{\dfrac{3}{x-1}}{\dfrac{1}{x-1} + \dfrac{3}{x}} = \dfrac{\dfrac{3}{x-1}}{\dfrac{1}{x-1} + \dfrac{3}{x}} \cdot \dfrac{x \cdot (x-1)}{x \cdot (x-1)}$ $= \dfrac{\dfrac{3}{x-1} \cdot \dfrac{x \cdot (x-1)}{1}}{\dfrac{1}{x-1} \cdot \dfrac{x \cdot (x-1)}{1} + \dfrac{3}{x} \cdot \dfrac{x \cdot (x-1)}{1}}$ $= \dfrac{3x}{x + 3(x-1)} \qquad x \neq 0 \text{ and } x \neq 1$ $= \dfrac{3x}{x + 3x - 3} \qquad x \neq 0 \text{ and } x \neq 1$ $= \dfrac{3x}{4x - 3} \qquad x \neq 0 \text{ and } x \neq 1$

Problem Type	Special Notes	How to write your answer	Possible Example (Check with your instructor for how they prefer you to show your work.)
		Show your work with your equal signs lined up in the middle of each equation.	<u>Solve</u> $f(x) = 10$ when $f(x) = -2x^2 + 4x + 40$.
			$-2x^2 + 4x + 40 = 10$
			$-2x^2 + 4x + 30 = 0$
		Do not put equal signs on the left.	$-2(x^2 - 2x - 15) = 0$
			$-2(x - 5)(x + 3) = 0$
		State what the solution is in a sentence and use either set builder or interval notation as asked for in the directions.	$x - 5 = 0$ OR $x + 3 = 0$
			$x = 5$ OR $x = -3$
			So the solutions are 5 and 3 and the solution set is {5,-3}.
			OR. So the solutions are 5 and 3 and the solution set is $\{x | x = 5 \text{ or } x = -3\}$.
Solving an equation.	You be given an equal sign between two algebraic expressions. You will often times see the word "solve" in the directions.	If there are an infinite number of solutions, communicate this using the "set of all real numbers" symbol.	<u>Solve</u> $3(x - 5) + 1 = 2x - 14 + x$ for x.
			$3(x - 5) + 1 = 2x - 14 + x$
			$3x - 15 + 1 = 3x - 14$
			$3x - 14 = 3x - 14$
			$3x - 14 - 3x = 3x - 14 - 3x$
			$-14 = -14$ Is a true statement.
			So every real number is a solution and the solution set is $\mathbb{R}$.
			OR. So every real number is a solution and the solution set is $\{x | x \in \mathbb{R}\}$.
		If there is no solution, communicate this using either of the empty set symbols.	<u>Solve</u> $x + 2 = x + 1$ for x.
			$x + 2 = x + 1$
			$x + 2 - x = x + 1 - x$
			$2 = 1$ Is not a true statement.
			So there are no solutions and the solution set is $\{\}$.
			OR. So there are no solutions and the solution set is $\emptyset$.

ii

Problem Type	Special Notes	How to write your answer	Possible Example (Check with your instructor for how they prefer you to show your work.)
Solving an inequality.	You be given an inequality symbol ($<, >, \leq,$ or $\geq$) between two algebraic expressions. You will often times see the word "solve" in the directions.	Show your work with your inequality signs lined up in the middle of each inequality. Do not put equal signs on the left. State what the solution is in a sentence and use either set builder or interval notation as asked for in the directions.	Solve $\|w - 2\| \leq 4$ for w. $\quad$ $w - 2 \leq 4$ $\quad$ AND $\quad$ $-(w - 2) \leq 4$ $\quad$ $w \leq 6$ $\qquad\qquad\qquad$ $-w + 2 \leq 4$ $\qquad\qquad\qquad\qquad$ $-w \leq 2$ $\qquad\qquad\qquad\qquad$ $w \geq -2$ So any number greater than or equal to -2 AND less than or equal to 6 is a solution and the solution set is $\{w \mid -2 \leq w \leq 6\}$. OR So any number greater than or equal to -2 AND less than or equal to 6 is a solution and the solution set is $[-2, 6]$.
		If there are an infinite number of solutions, communicate this using the "set of all real numbers" symbol.	Solve $w + 2 \leq w + 4$ for w. $\quad$ $w + 2 \leq w + 4$ $\qquad$ $2 \leq 4$ $\quad$ Is a true statement. So every real number is a solution and the solution set is $\mathbb{R}$. OR So every real number is a solution and the solution set is $(-\infty, \infty)$.
		If there is no solution, communicate this using either of the empty set symbols.	Solve $w + 4 \leq w + 2$ for w. $\quad$ $w + 4 \leq w + 2$ $\qquad$ $4 \leq 2$ $\quad$ Is not a true statement. So there are no solutions and the solution set is $\{\}$. OR So there are no solutions and the solution set is $\emptyset$.

iii

Problem Type	Special Notes	How to write your answer	Possible Example
			Possible Example *(Check with your instructor for how they prefer you to show your work.)*
Solving word problems.	These problems will generally describe a situation and a relationship between two variables with units defined for each variable.	Write your answer as a complete sentence, giving a contextual conclusion which answers the question being asked.	If a rock falls from a height of 20 meters on Earth, the height H, in meters, x seconds after it began to fall is approximately $$H(x) = 20 - 4.9x^2.$$ What is the height of the rock 1 second after beginning its fall? $$H(1) = 20 - 4.9(1)^2$$ $$= 20 - 4.9$$ $$= 15.1$$ The height of the rock 1 second after beginning its fall is approximately 15.1 meters.
Stating the domain and range of a function.	There are different rules for different types of functions. Be sure that you start solving for the domain correctly based on the type of function (often rational or square root) you are dealing with.	Write your answers in either set builder or interval notation (as directed).	State the domain of $f(x) = \dfrac{1}{x-2}$. $f(x)$ is undefined when $x - 2 = 0$. $$x - 2 = 0$$ $$x = 2$$ So the domain of f is $\{x \mid x \neq 2\}$. OR So the domain of f is $(-\infty, 2) \cup (2, \infty)$. State the domain of $f(x) = \sqrt{3x - 6}$. $f(x)$ is only defined when $3x - 6 \geq 0$. $$3x - 6 \geq 0$$ $$3x \geq 6$$ $$x \geq 2$$ So the domain of f is $\{x \mid x \geq 2\}$. OR So the domain of f is $[2, \infty)$.

Problem Type	Special Notes	How to write your answer	Possible Example (Check with your instructor for how they prefer you to show your work.)
Rectangular Coordinate System Guidelines.	Remember, the graph is a picture of the solutions to the equation. The horizontal-axis (often the x-axis) and vertical-axis (often the y-axis) are the *coordinate system* or *coordinate plane* which we draw the graph onto.	Label your *horizontal* and *vertical* axes (often x and y) with an appropriate scale, label the graph with its equation and any points required by your instructor (often the vertical intercept, vertex, horizontal intercept(s) and sometimes others).	Graph the function $f(x) = (x+2)^2 - 1$. The vertex is $(-2, -1)$ and the axis of symmetry is $x = -2$. $f(0) = (0+2)^2 - 1$ $= 4 - 1$ $= 3$ So the y-intercept is $(0, 3)$. $0 = (x+2)^2 - 1$ $1 = (x+2)^2$ $\pm 1 = x + 2$ $-2 \pm 1 = x$ $x = -2 + 1$ OR $x = -2 - 1$ $x = -1$ OR $x = -3$ So the x-intercepts are $(-3, 0)$ and $(-1, 0)$.

Gary K. Rockswold • Terry A. Krieger

Intermediate Algebra with Applications & Visualization

Custom Edition for Portland Community College

Taken from:
Intermediate Algebra with Applications and Visualization, Fourth Edition
by Gary K. Rockswold and Terry A. Krieger

Pearson Learning Solutions, 330 Hudson Street, New York, New York 10013
A Pearson Education Company
www.pearsoned.com

Printed in the United States of America

11   18

000200010271985801

SK

ISBN 10: 1-323-19355-3
ISBN 13: 978-1-323-19355-6

Contents

1 Linear Functions and Models 1

2 Linear Equations and Inequalities 77

3   Polynomial Expressions and Functions   156

6   Quadratic Functions and Equations   415

Preface

Intermediate Algebra with Applications and Visualization, Fourth Edition, connects the real world to mathematics in ways that are both meaningful and motivational. Students using this textbook will have no shortage of realistic and convincing answers to the question, "Why is math important in my life?" Mathematical concepts are introduced by using relevant applications from students' lives that support their conceptual understanding. This textbook does not present math as a sequence of disconnected procedures to be memorized; rather, it shows that math does make sense.

In addition to presenting symbolic techniques, we present mathematical concepts in both visual and numerical ways whenever possible. Graphs, diagrams, and tables of values are often included to provide students with an opportunity to understand math in more than one way. Multiple representations (symbolic, graphical, and numerical) allow students to solve problems using three different methods. This textbook prepares students for future mathematics courses by teaching them both reasoning and problem-solving skills.

As mathematicians, we understand the profound impact that mathematics has on the world around us; as teachers with a combined experience of over 50 years, we know that our students often have difficulty both learning mathematics and recognizing its relevance. We believe that applications and visualization are essential pathways to empowering students with mathematics. Our goal in *Intermediate Algebra with Applications and Visualization* is to help students succeed.

This textbook is one of four textbooks in our series:

■ *Prealgebra*
■ *Beginning Algebra with Applications and Visualization*, Third Edition
■ *Beginning & Intermediate Algebra with Applications and Visualization*, Third Edition
■ *Intermediate Algebra with Applications and Visualization*, Fourth Edition.

New to this Edition

■ **Updated Data** The data in hundreds of exercises and examples have been updated to keep the applications relevant and fresh.
■ **More Visualization** Whenever appropriate, we have made mathematics more visual by using graphs, tables, charts, color, and diagrams to explain important concepts with fewer words.
  • We have added titles to the graphs and also comments on/near the graphs/tables to make them more (immediately) understandable. Now students don't always have to read the text to understand the table or graph.
  • We have added green equation labels, written in standard mathematical notation, to calculator graphs.
■ **Teaching Examples** Every example in the text is now paired with a teaching example in the Annotated Instructor's Edition that instructors can use in class to promote further understanding.
■ **New Vocabulary Checklist** At the start of every section that contains new mathematical definitions, a checklist of new vocabulary has been added to highlight the math concepts that are defined in the section.

- **Updated Glossary** The glossary has been updated to include all New Vocabulary words.
- **Reading Checks** To be sure that students are grasping important concepts, short questions about the material have been added throughout each section.
- **Study Tips** Throughout the text, study tips are now included to give not only general study advice but also pointers that relate to learning specific mathematical concepts.
- **New Application Topics** Students are more engaged when mathematics is tied to current and relevant topics. Several new examples have been added that discuss the mathematics of the Internet, social networks, tablet computers, and other contemporary topics.
- **Online Explorations** New exercises that invite students to use the Internet to explore real-world mathematics are now included throughout the text.
- **Refinement of Content**

CHAPTER 1: In the discussion of slope in Section 1.3, we put more emphasis on visualization to make this important topic more accessible for students.

CHAPTER 2: We put more emphasis on the visualization of the solutions to linear equations and inequalities in Sections 2.1 and 2.3.

CHAPTER 4: We added a new 4-step procedure for solving variation problems, which students can apply to all variation problems.

CHAPTER 5: At the request of reviewers, Section 5.1 was split into two sections so that radical expressions and rational exponents can be taught in two different sections. Section 5.1 was reorganized so that the square root and cube root functions can now be taught in Section 5.1 rather than later in the chapter. Greater emphasis has been given to converting between radical forms and forms with rational exponents.

CHAPTER 6: At the request of reviewers, Sections 6.1 and 6.2 have been reorganized to put topics in better order for student learning. The topic of increasing and decreasing functions is now optional in Section 6.2. In Section 6.5, more visuals for quadratic inequalities have been included to make this topic more accessible for students.

Hallmark Features

Math in the Real World

The Rockswold/Krieger series places an emphasis on teaching algebra in context. Students typically understand best when concepts are tied to the real world or presented visually. We believe that meaningful applications and visualization of important concepts are pathways to success in mathematics.

- **Chapter Openers** Each chapter opens with an application that motivates students by offering insight into the relevance of that chapter's mathematical concepts.
- **A Look into Math** Each section is introduced with a practical application of the math topic students are about to learn.
- **Real World Connection** Where appropriate, we expand on specific math topics and their connections to everyday life.
- **Applications** We integrate applications into both the discussions and the exercises to help students become more effective problem solvers.
- **Modeling Data** We provide opportunities for students to model real and relevant data with their own functions.
- **Online Exploration** NEW These exercises invite students to find data on the Internet and then use mathematics to analyze the data.

Understanding the Concepts

Conceptual understanding is critical to success in mathematics.

- **Math from Multiple Perspectives** Throughout the text, we present concepts by means of verbal, graphical, numerical, and symbolic representations to support multiple learning styles and problem-solving methods.
- **New Vocabulary** At the beginning of each section, we direct the students' attention to important terms before they are discussed in context.
- **Reading Check** Reading Check questions appear along with important concepts, ensuring that students understand the material they have just read.
- **Study Tips** Study Tips offer just-in-time suggestions to help students stay organized and focused on the material at hand.
- **Making Connections** Throughout the text, we help students understand the relationship between previously learned concepts and new concepts.
- **Critical Thinking** One or more Critical Thinking exercises are included in most sections. They pose questions that can be used for classroom discussion or homework assignments.
- **Putting It All Together** At the end of each section, we summarize the techniques and reinforce the mathematical concepts presented in the section.

Multiple types of exercises in this series support the application-based and conceptual nature of the content. These exercise types are designed to reinforce the skills students need to move on to the next concept.

- **Extensive Exercise Sets** The comprehensive exercise sets cover basic concepts, skill-building, writing, applications, and conceptual mastery. These exercise sets are further enhanced by several special types of exercises that appear throughout the text:

  - **Now Try Exercises** Suggested exercises follow every example for immediate reinforcement of skills and concepts.

  - **Checking Basic Concepts** These mixed review exercises appear after every other section and can be used for individual or group review. These exercises require 10–20 minutes to complete and are also appropriate for in-class work.

  - **Thinking Generally** These exercises appear in most exercise sets and offer open-ended conceptual questions that encourage students to synthesize what they have just learned.

  - **Writing About Mathematics** This exercise type is at the end of most sections. Students are asked to explain the concepts behind the mathematics procedures they have just learned.

- **Group Activities: Working with Real Data** This feature occurs once or twice per chapter, and provides an opportunity for students to work collaboratively on a problem that involves real-world data. Most activities can be completed with limited use of class time.

- **Graphing Calculator Exercises** The icon denotes an exercise that requires students to have access to a graphing calculator.

- **Technology Notes** Occurring throughout the book, optional Technology Notes offer students guidance, suggestions, and cautions on the use of a graphing calculator.

By reviewing the material and putting their abilities to the test, students will be able to assess their level of mastery as they complete each chapter.

- **Chapter Summary** In a quick and thorough review, we combine key terms, topics, and procedures with illuminating examples to assist in test preparation.

- **Chapter Review Exercises** Students can work these exercises to gain confidence that they have mastered the material.

- **Extended And Discovery Exercises** These capstone projects at the end of every chapter challenge students to synthesize what they have learned.

- **Chapter Test** Students can reduce math anxiety by using these tests as a rehearsal for the real thing.

- **Chapter Test Prep Videos** Students can prepare for the chapter test by viewing videos of an instructor working through the complete solutions for all Chapter Test exercises for each chapter.

- **Cumulative Review Exercises** Starting with Chapter 2 and appearing in all subsequent chapters, Cumulative Review exercises help students see the big picture of math by reviewing topics and skills they have already learned.

Supplements

STUDENT RESOURCES

Student's Solutions Manual

- Contains solutions for the odd-numbered section-level exercises (excluding Writing About Mathematics and Group Activity exercises), and solutions to all Concepts and Vocabulary exercises, Checking Basic Concepts exercises, Chapter Review Exercises, Chapter Test exercises, and Cumulative Review Exercises.

  ISBNs: 0-321-74784-4, 978-0-321-74784-6

Worksheets

These lab- and classroom-friendly worksheets provide

- Learning objectives and key vocabulary terms for every text section, along with vocabulary practice problems.
- Extra practice exercises for every section of the text with ample space for students to show their work.
- Additional opportunities to explore multiple representation solutions.

  ISBNs: 0-321-74788-7, 978-0-321-74788-4

Video Resources

- A series of lectures correlated directly to the content of each section of the text.
- Material presented in a format that stresses student interaction, often using examples from the text.
- Ideal for distance learning and supplemental instruction.
- Video lectures include English captions.
- The Chapter Test Prep Videos let students watch instructors work through step-by-step solutions to all the Chapter Test exercises from the textbook. Chapter Test Prep videos are available on YouTube™ (search using author name and book title) as well as in MyMathLab.
- Available in MyMathLab.

INSTRUCTOR RESOURCES

Annotated Instructor's Edition

- Contains Teaching Tips, Teaching Examples, and answers to every exercise in the textbook excluding the Writing About Mathematics exercises.
- Answers that do not fit on the same page as the exercises themselves are supplied in the Instructor Answer Appendix at the back of the textbook.

  ISBNs: 0-321-74781-X, 978-0-321-74781-5

Instructor's Resource Manual with Tests and Mini Lectures (Download Only)

Includes resources designed to help both new and adjunct faculty with course preparation and classroom management:

- Teaching tips and additional exercises for selected content.
- Four sets of Cumulative Review Exercises that cover Chapters 1–6.
- Notes for presenting graphing calculator topics as well as supplemental activities.
- Three free-response alternate test forms and one multiple-choice test form per chapter; one free-response and one multiple-choice final exam.
- Available in MyMathLab® and on the Instructor's Resource Center.

Instructor's Solutions Manual (Download Only)

- Provides solutions to all section-level exercises (excluding Writing About Mathematics and Group Activity exercises), and solutions to all Checking Basic Concepts exercises, Chapter Review Exercises, Chapter Test exercises, and Cumulative Review Exercises.
- Available in MyMathLab and on the Instructor's Resource Center.

PowerPoint Slides

- Key concepts and definitions from the text.
- Available in MyMathLab or can be downloaded from the Instructor's Resource Center.

TestGen®

TestGen (www.pearsoned.com/testgen) enables instructors to build, edit, and print, and administer tests using a computerized bank of questions developed to cover all the objectives of the text. TestGen is algorithmically based, allowing instructors to create multiple but equivalent versions of the same question or test with the click of a button. Instructors can also modify test bank questions or add new questions. The software and testbank are available for download from Pearson Education's online catalog.

MathXL® Online Course (access code required)

MathXL is the homework and assessment engine that runs MyMathLab. (MyMathLab is MathXL plus a learning management system.) With MathXL, instructors can:

- Create, edit, and assign online homework and tests using algorithmically generated exercises correlated at the objective level to the textbook.
- Create and assign their own online exercises and import TestGen tests for added flexibility.
- Maintain records of all student work tracked in MathXL's online gradebook.

With MathXL, students can:

- Take chapter tests in MathXL and receive personalized study plans and/or personalized homework assignments based on their test results.
- Use the study plan and/or the homework to link directly to tutorial exercises for the objectives they need to study.
- Access supplemental animations and video clips directly from selected exercises.

MathXL is available to qualified adopters. For more information, visit www.mathxl.com, or contact your Pearson representative.

MyMathLab Online Course (access code required)

MyMathLab delivers **proven results** in helping individual students succeed.

- MyMathLab has a consistently positive impact on the quality of learning in higher education math instruction. MyMathLab can be successfully implemented in any environment–lab-based, hybrid, fully online, traditional–and demonstrates the quantifiable difference that integrated usage has on student retention, subsequent success, and overall achievement.
- MyMathLab's comprehensive online gradebook automatically tracks students' results on tests, quizzes, homework, and in the study plan. Instructors can use the gradebook to quickly intervene if their students have trouble or to provide positive feedback on a job well done. The data within MyMathLab is easily exported to a variety of spreadsheet programs, such as Microsoft Excel. Instructors can determine which points of data they want to export, and then analyze the results to determine success.

MyMathLab provides **engaging experiences** that personalize, stimulate, and measure learning for each student.

- **Tutorial Exercises:** The homework and practice exercises in MyMathLab and MyStatLab are correlated to the exercises in the textbook, and they regenerate algorithmically to give students unlimited opportunity for practice and mastery. The software offers immediate, helpful feedback when students enter incorrect answers.
- **Multimedia Learning Aids:** Exercises include guided solutions, sample problems, animations, videos, and eText clips for extra help at point-of-use.
- **Expert Tutoring:** Although many students describe the whole of MyMathLab as 'like having your own personal tutor," students using MyMathLab and MyStatLab do have access to live tutoring from Pearson, from qualified math and statistics instructors who provide tutoring sessions for students via MyMathLab and MyStatLab."

And, MyMathLab comes from a **trusted partner** with educational expertise and an eye on the future.

Knowing that you are using a Pearson product means knowing that you are using quality content. That means that our eTexts are accurate, that our assessment tools work, and that our questions are error-free. And whether you are just getting started with MyMathLab, or have a question along the way, we're here to help you learn about our technologies and how to incorporate them into your course.

To learn more about how MyMathLab combines proven learning applications with powerful assessment, visit **www.mymathlab.com** or contact your Pearson representative.

Acknowledgments

Many individuals contributed to the development of this textbook. We thank the following reviewers, whose comments and suggestions were invaluable in preparing *Intermediate Algebra with Applications and Visualization,* Fourth Edition.

Mary Kay Abbey, *Montgomery College—Takoma Park*
Raul Aparicio, *Blinn College—Brenham Campus*
David Atwood, *Rochester Community and Technical College*
Alina Coronel, *Miami-Dade College—Kendall Campus*
Emmett Dennis, *Southern Connecticut State University*
James Deveney, *Virginia Commonwealth University*
Christopher Donnelly, *Macomb Community College*
Debbie Garrison, *Valencia Community College—East Campus*
Joan Van Glabek, *Edison Community College—Collier Campus*
Cynthia Gubitose, *Southern Connecticut State University*
Shawna Haider, *Salt Lake Community College*
Kristy Hill, *Hinds Community College—Raymond Campus*
Amy Hlavacek, *Saginaw Valley State University*
Dr. Philip Kaatz, *Mesalands Community College*
Paul Kinion, *Rochester Community and Technical College*
Mike Kirby, *Tidewater Community College—Virginia Beach Campus*
Kim Luna, *Eastern New Mexico University*
Rhonda MacLeod, *Tallahassee Community College*
Toni McCall, *Angelina College*
Lauren McNamara, *Hillsborough Community College*
Benjamin Moulton, *Utah Valley University*
Glenn Noé, *Brookdale Community College*
Mario Scribner, *Tidewater Community College—Virginia Beach Campus*
Robert Shankin, *Santa Fe Community College*
Yvette Stepanian, *Virginia Commonwealth University*
Carol Walker, *Hinds Community College—Raymond Campus*
Elizabeth White, *Trident Technical College*

We would like to welcome Jessica Rockswold to our team. She has been instrumental in developing, writing, and proofing new applications, graphs, and visualizations for this text.

Paul Lorczak, Mitchell Johnson, Lynn Baker, and Mark Rockswold deserve special credit for their help with accuracy checking. Without the excellent cooperation from the professional staff at Pearson Education, this project would have been impossible. Thanks go to Greg Tobin and Maureen O'Connor for giving their support. Particular recognition is due Cathy Cantin who gave essential advice and assistance. The outstanding contributions of Lauren Morse, Sheila Spinney, Joe Vetere, Michelle Renda, Tracy Rabinowitz, Rachel Ross, Ashley Bryan, and Jonathan Wooding are greatly appreciated. Special thanks go to Kathy Diamond, who was instrumental in the success of this project.

Thanks go to Wendy Rockswold and Carrie Krieger, whose unwavering encouragement and support made this project possible. We also thank the many students and instructors who used the previous editions of this textbook. Their suggestions were insightful and helpful.

Please feel free to send us your comments and questions at either of the following e-mail addresses: gary.rockswold@mnsu.edu or terry.krieger@roch.edu. Your opinion is important to us.

Gary K. Rockswold
Terry A. Krieger

1 Linear Functions and Models

> "Our competitive
> advantage is our *math
> skills*, which is prob-
> ably not something
> you would expect of a
> media company."
>
> —Max Levchin,
> CEO of Slide
>
> (Slide is the number one company
> for writing Facebook applications.)

Every day millions of people create trillions of bytes of information. The only way we can make sense out of these data and determine what is occurring within society is to use mathematics. One of the most important mathematical concepts used to discover trends and patterns is that of a *function*. A function typically receives an input (or question), performs a computation, and gives the output (or answer).

Functions have been used in science and engineering for centuries to answer questions related to things like eclipses, communication, and transportation. However, today functions are also being used to describe human behavior and to design social networks. (See Section 1.1, Exercise 79.) In fact, you may have noticed that new features available on Twitter and Facebook are sometimes referred to as applications or *functions*. People are creating thousands of new functions every day. *Math skills are essential* for writing successful applications and functions.

1.1 Functions and Their Representations

Basic Concepts • Representations of a Function • Definition of a Function •
Identifying a Function • Tables, Graphs, and Calculators (Optional)

A LOOK INTO MATH ▶

Numbers are used to describe data. For example, instead of simply saying that there are *a lot* of people on Twitter, we might say that there are about 50 million tweets per day. A number helps explain what "a lot" means. We also showed that data can be summarized with formulas and graphs. Formulas and graphs are sometimes used to represent *functions*, which are essential in mathematics. In this section we introduce functions and their representations.

Basic Concepts

NEW VOCABULARY

☐ Function
☐ Function notation
☐ Input/Output
☐ Name of the function
☐ Dependent variable
☐ Independent variable
☐ Verbal representation
☐ Numerical representation
☐ Symbolic representation
☐ Graphical representation
☐ Diagrams/Diagrammatic
  representation
☐ Domain/Range
☐ Vertical line test

▶ **REAL-WORLD CONNECTION** Functions are used to calculate many important quantities. For example, suppose that a person works for $7 per hour. Then we could use a function *named* f to calculate the amount of money the person earned after working x hours simply by multiplying the *input x* by 7. The result y is called the *output*. This concept is shown visually in the following diagram.

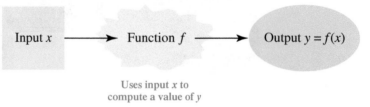

Input x ⟶ Function f ⟶ Output $y = f(x)$

Uses input x to
compute a value of y

For each valid input x, a function computes *exactly one* output y, which may be represented by the ordered pair (x, y). If the input is 5 hours, f outputs $7 \cdot 5 = \$35$; if the input is 8 hours, f outputs $7 \cdot 8 = \$56$. These results can be represented by the ordered pairs $(5, 35)$ and $(8, 56)$. Sometimes an input may not be valid. For example, if $x = -3$, there is no reasonable output because a person cannot work -3 hours.

We say that y *is a function of* x because the output y is determined by and *depends* on the input x. As a result, y is called the *dependent variable* and x is the *independent variable*. To emphasize that y is a function of x, we use the notation $y = f(x)$. The symbol $f(x)$ does not represent multiplication of a variable f and a variable x. The notation $y = f(x)$ is called *function notation*, is read "y equals f of x," and means that function f with input x produces output y. For example, if $x = 3$ hours, $y = f(3) = \$21$.

FUNCTION NOTATION

The notation $y = f(x)$ is called **function notation**. The **input** is x, the **output** is y, and the **name of the function** is f.

Name
↓
$$y = f(x)$$
↗   ↖
Output   Input

The variable y is called the **dependent variable** and the variable x is called the **independent variable**. The expression $f(4) = 28$ is read "*f* of 4 equals 28" and indicates that f outputs 28 when the input is 4. A function computes *exactly one* output for each valid input. The letters f, g, and h are often used to denote names of functions.

NOTE: Functions can be given *meaningful* names and variables. For example, function f could have been defined by $P(h) = 7h$, where function P calculates the pay after working h hours for $7 per hour.

▶ **REAL-WORLD CONNECTION** Functions can be used to compute a variety of quantities. For example, suppose that a boy has a sister who is exactly 5 years older than he is. If the age of the boy is x, then a function g can calculate the age of his sister by adding 5 to x. Thus $g(4) = 4 + 5 = 9$, $g(10) = 10 + 5 = 15$, and in general $g(x) = x + 5$. That is, function g adds 5 to input x to obtain the output $y = g(x)$.

Functions can be represented by an input–output machine, as illustrated in Figure 1.1. This machine represents function g and receives input $x = 4$, adds 5 to this value, and then outputs $g(4) = 4 + 5 = 9$.

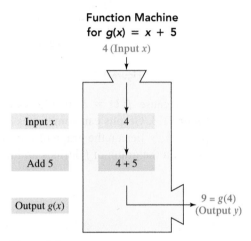

Figure 1.1

Representations of a Function

▶ **REAL-WORLD CONNECTION** A function f forms a relation between inputs x and outputs y that can be represented verbally, numerically, symbolically, and graphically. Functions can also be represented with diagrams. We begin by considering a function f that converts yards to feet.

VERBAL REPRESENTATION (WORDS) To convert x yards to y feet we multiply x by 3. Therefore, if function f computes the number of feet in x yards, a **verbal representation** of f is "Multiply the input x in yards by 3 to obtain the output y in feet."

NUMERICAL REPRESENTATION (TABLE OF VALUES) A function f that converts yards to feet is shown in Table 1.1, where $y = f(x)$.

A *table of values* is called a **numerical representation** of a function. Many times it is impossible to list all valid inputs x in a table. On the one hand, if a table does not contain every x-input, it is a *partial* numerical representation. On the other hand, a *complete* numerical representation includes *all* valid inputs. Table 1.1 is a partial numerical representation of f because many valid inputs, such as $x = 10$ or $x = 5.3$, are not shown in it. Note that for each valid input x there is exactly one output y. *For a function, inputs are not listed more than once in a table.*

SYMBOLIC REPRESENTATION (FORMULA) A *formula* provides a **symbolic representation** of a function. The computation performed by f to convert x yards to y feet is expressed by $y = 3x$. A formula for f is $f(x) = 3x$, where $y = f(x)$. We say that function f is *defined by* or *given by* $f(x) = 3x$. Thus $f(2) = 3 \cdot 2 = 6$.

GRAPHICAL REPRESENTATION (GRAPH) A **graphical representation**, or **graph**, visually associates an x-input with a y-output. The ordered pairs

$$(1, 3), (2, 6), (3, 9), (4, 12), (5, 15), (6, 18), \text{ and } (7, 21)$$

TABLE 1.1

x (yards)	y (feet)
1	3
2	6
3	9
4	12
5	15
6	18
7	21

from Table 1.1 are plotted in Figure 1.2(a). This scatterplot suggests a line for the graph f. For each real number x there is exactly one real number y determined by $y = 3x$. If we restrict inputs to $x \geq 0$ and plot all ordered pairs $(x, 3x)$, then a line with no breaks will appear, as shown in Figure 1.2(b).

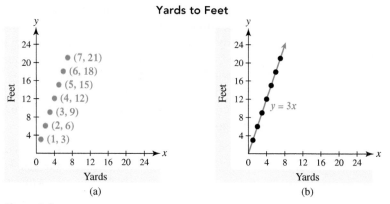

Figure 1.2

Because $f(1) = 3$, it follows that the point $(1, 3)$ lies on the graph of f, as shown in Figure 1.3. Graphs can sometimes be used to define a function f. For example, because the point $(1, 3)$ lies on the graph of f in Figure 1.3, we can conclude that $f(1) = 3$. That is, each point on the graph of f defines an input–output pair for f.

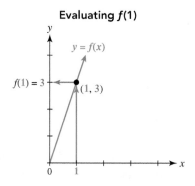

Figure 1.3

MAKING CONNECTIONS

Functions, Points, and Graphs

If $f(a) = b$, then the point (a, b) lies on the graph of f. Conversely, if the point (a, b) lies on the graph of f, then $f(a) = b$. See Figure 1.4(a). Thus each point on the graph of f can be written in the form $(a, f(a))$. See Figure 1.4(b).

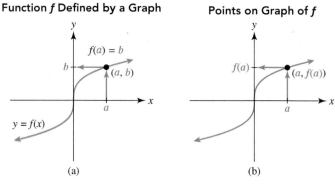

Figure 1.4

Yards to Feet

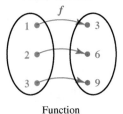

Function

Figure 1.5

DIAGRAMMATIC REPRESENTATION (DIAGRAM) Functions may be represented by **diagrams**. Figure 1.5 is a diagram of a function where an arrow is used to identify the output y associated with input x. For example, an arrow is drawn from input **2** to output **6**, which is written in function notation as $f(2) = 6$. That is, **2** yards are equivalent to **6** feet.

Figure 1.6(a) shows a (different) function f even though $f(1) = 4$ and $f(2) = 4$. Although two inputs for f have the same output, each valid input has exactly one output. In contrast, Figure 1.6(b) shows a relation that is *not* a function because input 2 results in two different outputs, 5 and 6.

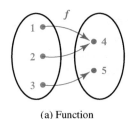

(a) Function   (b) Not a Function

Figure 1.6

MAKING CONNECTIONS

Four Representations of a Function

Symbolic Representation $f(x) = x + 1$

STUDY TIP

Be sure that you understand what verbal, numerical, graphical, and symbolic representations are.

Numerical Representation

x	y
-2	-1
-1	0
0	1
1	2
2	3

Graphical Representation

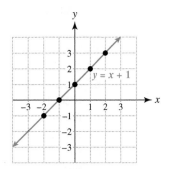

Verbal Representation f adds 1 to an input x to produce an output y.

EXAMPLE 1   Evaluating symbolic representations (formulas)

Evaluate each function f at the given value of x.
(a) $f(x) = 3x - 7$ $x = -2$

(b) $f(x) = \dfrac{x}{x + 2}$ $x = 0.5$

(c) $f(x) = \sqrt{x - 1}$ $x = 10$

Solution
(a) $f(-2) = 3(-2) - 7 = -6 - 7 = -13$

(b) $f(0.5) = \dfrac{0.5}{0.5 + 2} = \dfrac{0.5}{2.5} = 0.2$

(c) $f(10) = \sqrt{10 - 1} = \sqrt{9} = 3$

Now Try Exercises 21, 23, 31

▶ **REAL-WORLD CONNECTION** In the next example we calculate sales tax by evaluating different representations of a function.

EXAMPLE 2   **Calculating sales tax**

Let a function f compute a sales tax of 7% on a purchase of x dollars. Use the given representation to evaluate $f(2)$.

(a) *Verbal Representation* Multiply a purchase of x dollars by 0.07 to obtain a sales tax of y dollars.
(b) *Numerical Representation (partial)* Shown in Table 1.2
(c) *Symbolic Representation* $f(x) = 0.07x$
(d) *Graphical Representation* Shown in Figure 1.7
(e) *Diagrammatic Representation* Shown in Figure 1.8

TABLE 1.2

x	$f(x)$
$1.00	$0.07
$2.00	$0.14
$3.00	$0.21
$4.00	$0.28

Figure 1.7

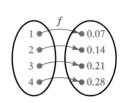

Figure 1.8

Solution

(a) *Verbal* Multiply the input 2 by 0.07 to obtain 0.14. The sales tax on a $2.00 purchase is $0.14.
(b) *Numerical* From Table 1.2, $f(2) = \$0.14$.
(c) *Symbolic* Because $f(x) = 0.07x$, $f(2) = 0.07(2) = 0.14$, or $0.14.
(d) *Graphical* To evaluate $f(2)$ with a graph, first find **2** on the x-axis in Figure 1.7. Then move vertically upward until you reach the graph of f. The point on the graph may be estimated as $(2, 0.14)$, meaning that $f(2) = 0.14$ (see Figure 1.9). Note that it may not be possible to find the exact answer from a graph. For example, one might estimate $f(2)$ to be 0.13 or 0.15 instead of 0.14.

Figure 1.9

(e) *Diagrammatic* In Figure 1.8, follow the arrow from **2** to **0.14**. Thus $f(2) = 0.14$.

Now Try Exercises 25, 33, 53, 59, 61

▶ **REAL-WORLD CONNECTION** There are many examples of functions. To give more meaning to a function, sometimes we change both its name and its input variable. For instance, if we know the radius r of a circle, we can calculate its circumference by using $C(r) = 2\pi r$. The next example illustrates how functions are used in physical therapy.

EXAMPLE 3 ▶ **Computing crutch length**

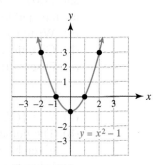

People who sustain leg injuries often require crutches. A proper crutch length can be estimated without using trial and error. The function L, given by $L(t) = 0.72t + 2$, outputs an appropriate crutch length in inches for a person t inches tall. (*Source: Journal of the American Physical Therapy Association.*)
(a) Find $L(60)$ and interpret the result.
(b) If one person is 70 inches tall and another person is 71 inches tall, what should be the difference in their crutch lengths?

Solution
(a) $L(60) = 0.72(60) + 2 = 45.2$. Thus a person 60 inches tall needs crutches that are about 45.2 inches long.
(b) From the formula $L(t) = 0.72t + 2$, we can see that each 1-inch increase in t results in a 0.72-inch increase in $L(t)$. For example,

$$L(71) - L(70) = 53.12 - 52.4 = 0.72.$$

▪ **Now Try Exercise 79**

In the next example we find a formula and then sketch a graph of a function.

EXAMPLE 4 ▶ **Finding representations of a function**

Let function f square the input x and then subtract 1 to obtain the output y.
(a) Write a formula, or symbolic representation, for f.
(b) Make a table of values, or numerical representation, for f. Use $x = -2, -1, 0, 1, 2$.
(c) Sketch a graph, or graphical representation, of f.

Solution
(a) *Symbolic Representation* If we square x and then subtract 1, we obtain $x^2 - 1$. Thus a formula for f is $f(x) = x^2 - 1$.
(b) *Numerical Representation* Make a table of values for $f(x)$, as shown in Table 1.3. For example,

$$f(-2) = (-2)^2 - 1 = 4 - 1 = 3.$$

(c) *Graphical Representation* To obtain a graph of $f(x) = x^2 - 1$, plot the points from Table 1.3 and then connect them with a smooth curve, as shown in Figure 1.10. Note that we need to plot enough points so that we can determine the overall shape of the graph.

TABLE 1.3

x	$f(x)$
-2	3
-1	0
0	-1
1	0
2	3

Figure 1.10

READING CHECK

Give a verbal, numerical, symbolic, and graphical representation of a function that calculates the number of days in x weeks. Choose meaningful variables.

▪ **Now Try Exercise 63**

Definition of a Function

A function is a fundamental concept in mathematics. Its definition should allow for all representations of a function. *A function receives an input x and produces exactly one output y,* which can be expressed as an ordered pair:

$$(x, y).$$

Input   Output

A relation is a set of ordered pairs, and a function is a special type of relation.

FUNCTION

A **function** f is a set of ordered pairs (x, y) where each x-value corresponds to exactly one y-value.

The **domain** of f is the set of all x-values, and the **range** of f is the set of all y-values. For example, a function f that converts 1, 2, 3, and 4 yards to feet could be expressed as

$$f = \{(1, 3), (2, 6), (3, 9), (4, 12)\}.$$

The domain of f is $D = \{1, 2, 3, 4\}$, and the range of f is $R = \{3, 6, 9, 12\}$.

MAKING CONNECTIONS

Relations and Functions

A relation can be thought of as a set of input–output pairs. A function is a special type of relation whereby each input results in exactly one output.

▶ **REAL-WORLD CONNECTION** In the next example, we see how education can improve a person's chances for earning a higher income.

EXAMPLE 5 **Computing average income**

A function f computes the average individual income in dollars in relation to educational attainment. This function is defined by $f(N) = 21,484$, $f(H) = 31,286$, $f(B) = 57,181$, and $f(M) = 70,181$, where N denotes no diploma, H a high school diploma, B a bachelor's degree, and M a master's degree. (*Source: 2010 Statistical Abstract.*)
(a) Write f as a set of ordered pairs.
(b) Give the domain and range of f.
(c) Discuss the relationship between education and income.

Solution
(a) $f = \{(N, 21484), (H, 31286), (B, 57181), (M, 70181)\}$
(b) The domain of function f is given by $D = \{N, H, B, M\}$, and the range of function f is given by $R = \{21484, 31286, 57181, 70181\}$.
(c) Education pays—the greater the educational attainment, the greater are annual earnings.

▌ Now Try Exercise 105

EXAMPLE 6   **Finding the domain and range graphically**

Use the graphs of f shown in Figures 1.11 and 1.12 to find each function's domain and range.

(a)

Figure 1.11

(b)

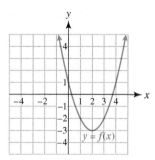

Figure 1.12

READING CHECK

Use the graph in
Figure 1.12 to evaluate $f(3)$.

Solution

(a) The domain is the set of all x-values that correspond to points on the graph of f. Figure 1.13 shows that the domain D includes all x-values satisfying $-3 \leq x \leq 3$. (Recall that the symbol $\leq$ is read "*less than or equal to*.") Because the graph is a semicircle with no breaks, the domain includes all real numbers between and including -3 and 3. The range R is the set of y-values that correspond to points on the graph of f. Thus R includes all y-values satisfying $0 \leq y \leq 3$.

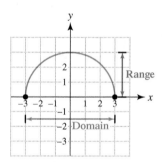

Figure 1.13

Figure 1.14

(b) The arrows on the ends of the graph in Figure 1.12 indicate that the graph extends indefinitely left and right, as well as upward. Thus D includes all real numbers. See Figure 1.14. The smallest y-value on the graph is $y = -3$, which occurs when $x = 2$. Thus the range R is $y \geq -3$. (Recall that the symbol $\geq$ is read "*greater than or equal to*.")

Now Try Exercises 81, 85

CRITICAL THINKING

Suppose that a car travels at 50 miles per hour to a city that is 250 miles away. Sketch a graph of a function f that gives the distance y traveled after x hours. Identify the domain and range of f.

The domain of a function is the set of all valid inputs. To determine the domain of a function from a formula, we must find x-values for which the formula is defined. To do this, we must determine if we can substitute any real number in the formula for $f(x)$. If we can, then the domain of f is *all real numbers*. However, there are situations in which we must limit the domain of f. For example, the domain must often be limited when there is either division or a square root in the formula for f. When division occurs, we must be careful to avoid values of the variable that result in division by 0, which is undefined. When a square root occurs, we must be careful to avoid values of the variable that result in the square root of a negative number, which is not a real number. This concept is demonstrated in the next example.

EXAMPLE 7   **Finding the domain of a function**

Use $f(x)$ to find the domain of f.

(a) $f(x) = 5x$ (b) $f(x) = \dfrac{1}{x - 2}$ (c) $f(x) = \sqrt{x}$

Solution

(a) Because we can always multiply a real number x by 5, $f(x) = 5x$ is defined for all real numbers. Thus the domain of f includes all real numbers.

(b) Because we cannot divide by 0, input $x = 2$ is not valid for $f(x) = \frac{1}{x-2}$. The expression for $f(x)$ is defined for all other values of x. Thus the domain of f includes all real numbers except 2, or $x \neq 2$.

(c) Because square roots of negative numbers are not real numbers, the inputs for $f(x) = \sqrt{x}$ cannot be negative. Thus the domain of f includes all nonnegative numbers, or $x \geq 0$.

▋ Now Try Exercises 91, 95, 99

    Symbolic, numerical, and graphical representations of three common functions are shown in Figure 1.15. Note that their graphs are not lines. For this reason they are called **nonlinear functions**. Use the graphs to find the domain and range of each function.

Absolute value: $f(x) = |x|$

x	-2	-1	0	1	2
$|x|$	2	1	0	1	2

Square: $f(x) = x^2$

x	-2	-1	0	1	2
x^2	4	1	0	1	4

Square root: $f(x) = \sqrt{x}$

x	0	1	4	9
$\sqrt{x}$	0	1	2	3

(a)

(b)

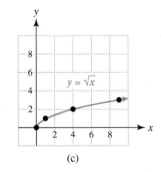

(c)

Figure 1.15

Identifying a Function

Recall that for a function each valid input x produces exactly one output y. In the next three examples we demonstrate techniques for identifying a function.

EXAMPLE 8   **Determining whether a set of ordered pairs is a function**

The set S of ordered pairs (x, y) represents the number of mergers and acquisitions y in 2010 for selected technology companies x.

$$S = \{(\text{IBM}, 12), (\text{HP}, 7), (\text{Oracle}, 5), (\text{Apple}, 5), (\text{Microsoft}, 0)\}$$

Determine if S is a function. (*Source:* cbinsights.)

Solution

The input x is the name of the technology company, and the output y is the number of mergers and acquisitions associated with that company. The set S *is* a function because each company x is associated with exactly one number y. Note that even though there were 5 mergers and acquisitions corresonding to both Oracle and Apple, S is nonetheless a function.

▮ **Now Try Exercise 127**

EXAMPLE 9 **Determining whether a table of values represents a function**

TABLE 1.4

x	y
1	-4
2	8
3	2
1	5
4	-6

Determine whether Table 1.4 represents a function.

Solution

The table does not represent a function because input $x = 1$ produces two outputs: -4 and 5. That is, the following two ordered pairs both belong to this relation.

Same input x

$(1, -4) \qquad (1, 5) \quad \leftarrow$ **Not a function**

Different outputs y

▮ **Now Try Exercise 129**

VERTICAL LINE TEST To determine whether a graph represents a function, we must be convinced that it is impossible for an input x to have two or more outputs y. If two distinct points have the *same* x-coordinate on a graph, then the graph cannot represent a function. For example, the ordered pairs $(-1, 1)$ and $(-1, -1)$ could not lie on the graph of a function because input -1 results in *two* outputs: 1 and -1. When the points $(-1, 1)$ and $(-1, -1)$ are plotted, they lie on the same vertical line, as shown in Figure 1.16(a). A graph passing through these points intersects the vertical line twice, as illustrated in Figure 1.16(b).

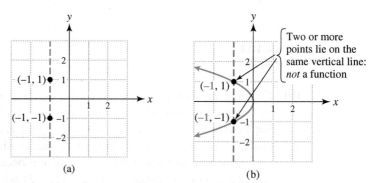

(a)　　　　　(b)

Figure 1.16

To determine whether a graph represents a function, visualize vertical lines moving across the xy-plane. If each vertical line intersects the graph *at most once*, then it is a graph of a function. This test is called the **vertical line test**. Note that the graph in Figure 1.16(b) fails the vertical line test and therefore does not represent a function.

READING CHECK

What is the vertical line test used for?

VERTICAL LINE TEST

If every vertical line intersects a graph at no more than one point, then the graph represents a function.

EXAMPLE 10   **Determining whether a graph represents a function**

Determine whether the graphs shown in Figure 1.17 represent functions.

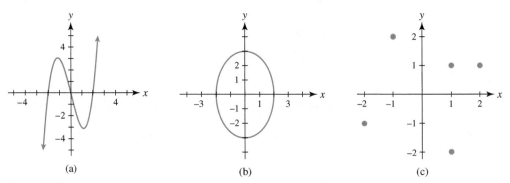

Figure 1.17

Solution

(a) Visualize vertical lines moving across the *xy*-plane from left to right. Any (red) vertical line will intersect the graph at most once, as depicted in Figure 1.18(a). Therefore the graph *does* represent a function.

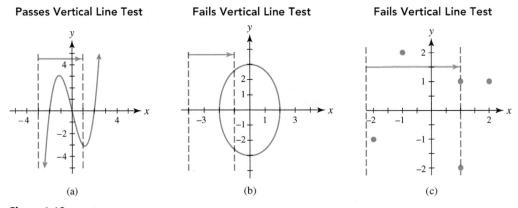

Figure 1.18

(b) Visualize vertical lines moving across the *xy*-plane from left to right. The graph *does not* represent a function because there exist (red) vertical lines that can intersect the graph twice. One such line is shown in Figure 1.18(b).

(c) Visualize vertical lines moving across the *xy*-plane from left to right. The graph is a scatterplot and *does not* represent a function because there exists one (red) vertical line that intersects two points: (1, 1) and (1, −2) with the same *x*-coordinate, as shown in Figure 1.18(c).

Now Try Exercises 115, 117, 123

Tables, Graphs, and Calculators (Optional)

We can use graphing calculators to create graphs and tables, usually more efficiently and reliably than with pencil-and-paper techniques. However, a graphing calculator uses the same techniques that we might use to sketch a graph. For example, one way to sketch a graph of $y = 2x - 1$ is first to make a table of values, as shown in Table 1.5.

We can plot these points in the *xy*-plane, as shown in Figure 1.19. Next we might connect the points, as shown in Figure 1.20.

Plotting Points

Graphing a Line

TABLE 1.5

x	y
-1	-3
0	-1
1	1
2	3

Figure 1.19

Figure 1.20

In a similar manner, a graphing calculator plots numerous points and connects them to make a graph. To create a similar graph with a graphing calculator, we enter the formula $Y_1 = 2X - 1$, set an appropriate viewing rectangle, and graph as shown in Figures 1.21 and 1.22. A table of values can also be generated as illustrated in Figure 1.23.

CALCULATOR HELP

To make a graph, see Appendix A (page AP-5). To make a table, see Appendix A (pages AP-2 and AP-3).

Figure 1.21

$[-10, 10, 1]$ by $[-10, 10, 1]$

Figure 1.22

Figure 1.23

1.1 Putting It All Together

A function calculates exactly one output for each valid input and produces input–output ordered pairs in the form (x, y). A function typically computes something such as area, speed, or sales tax.

CONCEPT	EXPLANATION	EXAMPLES
Function	A set of ordered pairs (x, y), where each x-value corresponds to exactly one y-value	$f = \{(1, 3), (2, 3), (3, 1)\}$ $f(x) = 2x$ A graph of $y = x + 2$ A table of values for $y = 4x$
Independent Variable	The *input* variable for a function	*Function* *Independent Variable* $f(x) = 2x$ x $A(r) = \pi r^2$ r $V(s) = s^3$ s
Dependent Variable	The *output* variable of a function There is exactly one output for each valid input.	*Function* *Dependent Variable* $y = f(x)$ y $T = F(r)$ T $V = g(r)$ V

continued on next page

continued from previous page

CONCEPT	EXPLANATION	EXAMPLES
Domain and Range of a Function	The domain D is the set of all valid inputs. The range R is the set of all outputs.	For $S = \{(-1, 0), (3, 4), (5, 0)\}$, $D = \{-1, 3, 5\}$ and $R = \{0, 4\}$. For $f(x) = \frac{1}{x}$ the domain includes all real numbers except 0, or $x \neq 0$.
Vertical Line Test	If every vertical line intersects a graph at no more than one point, the graph represents a function.	This graph does *not* pass this test and thus does not represent a function. Two points lie on the same vertical line: *not* a function

A function can be represented verbally, symbolically, numerically, and graphically.

REPRESENTATION	EXPLANATION	COMMENTS
Verbal	Precise word description of what is computed	May be oral or written Must be stated *precisely*
Symbolic	Mathematical formula	Efficient and concise way of representing a function (e.g., $f(x) = 2x - 3$)
Numerical	List of specific inputs and their outputs	May be in the form of a table or an explicit set of ordered pairs
Graphical, diagrammatic	Shows inputs and outputs visually	No words, formulas, or tables Many types of graphs and diagrams are possible.

1.1 Exercises

MyMathLab   Math XL   PRACTICE   WATCH   DOWNLOAD   READ   REVIEW

CONCEPTS AND VOCABULARY

1. The notation $y = f(x)$ is called _____ notation.

2. The notation $y = f(x)$ is read _____.

3. The notation $f(x) = x^2 + 1$ is a(n) _____ representation of a function.

4. A table of values is a(n) _____ representation of a function.

5. The set of valid inputs for a function is the _____.

6. The set of outputs for a function is the _____.

7. A function computes _____ output for each valid input.

8. (True or False?) The vertical line test is used to identify graphs of relations.

9. (True or False?) Four ways to represent functions are verbal, numerical, symbolic, and graphical.

10. If $f(3) = 4$, the point _____ is on the graph of f. If $(3, 6)$ is on the graph of f, then $f(\underline{\quad}) = \underline{\quad}$.

11. Thinking Generally If $f(a) = b$, the point _____ is on the graph of f.

12. Thinking Generally If (c, d) is on the graph of g, then $g(c) = \underline{\quad}$.

13. Thinking Generally If a is in the domain of f, then $f(a)$ represents how many outputs?

14. Thinking Generally If $f(x) = x$ for every x in the domain of f, then the domain and range of f are _____.

Exercises 15–20: Determine whether the phrase describes a function.

15. Calculating the square of a number

16. Calculating the low temperature for a day

17. Listing the students who passed a given math exam

18. Listing the children of parent x

19. Finding sales tax on a purchase

20. Naming the people in your class

REPRESENTING AND EVALUATING FUNCTIONS

Exercises 21–32: Evaluate $f(x)$ at the given values of x.

21. $f(x) = 4x - 2$ $\qquad x = -1, 0$

22. $f(x) = 5 - 3x$ $\qquad x = -4, 2$

23. $f(x) = \sqrt{x}$ $\qquad x = 0, \frac{9}{4}$

24. $f(x) = \sqrt[3]{x}$ $\qquad x = -1, 27$

25. $f(x) = x^2$ $\qquad x = -5, \frac{3}{2}$

26. $f(x) = x^3$ $\qquad x = -2, 0.1$

27. $f(x) = 3$ $\qquad x = -8, \frac{7}{3}$

28. $f(x) = 100$ $\qquad x = -\pi, \frac{1}{3}$

29. $f(x) = 5 - x^3$ $\qquad x = -2, 3$

30. $f(x) = x^2 + 5$ $\qquad x = -\frac{1}{2}, 6$

31. $f(x) = \dfrac{2}{x + 1}$ $\qquad x = -5, 4$

32. $f(x) = \dfrac{x}{x - 4}$ $\qquad x = -3, 1$

Exercises 33–38: Do the following.

   (a) Write a formula for the function described.
   (b) Evaluate the function for input 10 and interpret the result.

33. Function I computes the number of inches in x yards.

34. Function A computes the area of a circle with radius r.

35. Function M computes the number of miles in x feet.

36. Function C computes the circumference of a circle with radius r.

37. Function A computes the square feet in x acres. (*Hint:* There are 43,560 square feet in one acre.)

38. Function K computes the number of kilograms in x pounds. (*Hint:* There are about 2.2 pounds in one kilogram.)

Exercises 39–42: Write each function f as a set of ordered pairs. Give the domain and range of f.

39. $f(1) = 3, f(2) = -4, f(3) = 0$

40. $f(-1) = 4, f(0) = 6, f(1) = 4$

41. $f(a) = b, f(c) = d, f(e) = a, f(d) = b$

42. $f(a) = 7, f(b) = 7, f(c) = 7, f(d) = 7$

Exercises 43–52: Sketch a graph of f.

43. $f(x) = -x + 3$ $\qquad$ **44.** $f(x) = -2x + 1$

45. $f(x) = 2x$ $\qquad$ **46.** $f(x) = \frac{1}{2}x - 2$

47. $f(x) = 4 - x$ $\qquad$ **48.** $f(x) = 6 - 3x$

49. $f(x) = x^2$ $\qquad$ **50.** $f(x) = \sqrt{x}$

51. $f(x) = \sqrt{x + 1}$ $\qquad$ **52.** $f(x) = \frac{1}{2}x^2 - 1$

Exercises 53–58: Use the graph of f to evaluate the given expressions.

53. $f(0)$ and $f(2)$ $\qquad$ **54.** $f(-2)$ and $f(2)$

 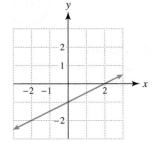

55. $f(-2)$ and $f(1)$ **56.** $f(-1)$ and $f(0)$

    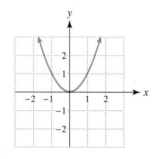

57. $f(1)$ and $f(2)$ **58.** $f(-1)$ and $f(4)$

    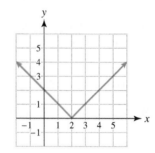

Exercises 59 and 60: Use the table to evaluate the given expressions.

59. $f(0)$ and $f(2)$

x	0	1	2	3	4
$f(x)$	5.5	4.3	3.7	2.5	1.9

60. $f(-10)$ and $f(5)$

x	-10	-5	0	5	10
$f(x)$	23	96	-45	-33	23

Exercises 61 and 62: Use the diagram to evaluate $f(1990)$. Interpret your answer.

61. The function f computes average fuel efficiency of new U.S. passenger cars in miles per gallon during year x. (*Source:* Department of Transportation.)

62. The function f at the top of the next column computes average cost of tuition at public colleges and universities during academic year x. (*Source:* The College Board.)

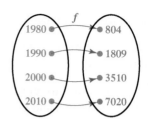

Exercises 63–66: Express the verbal representation for the function f numerically, symbolically, and graphically. Let $x = -3, -2, -1, \ldots, 3$ for the numerical representation (table), and let $-3 \le x \le 3$ for the graph.

63. Add 5 to the input x to obtain the output y.

64. Square the input x to obtain the output y.

65. Multiply the input x by 5 and then subtract 2 to obtain the output y.

66. Divide the input x by 2 and then add 3 to obtain the output y.

Exercises 67–70: Represent the function f numerically and graphically. Let $x = -3, -2, -1, \ldots, 3$ for your numerical representation and use the standard window for your graph.

67. $f(x) = \sqrt{x + 3}$ **68.** $f(x) = x^3 - \frac{1}{2}x^2$

69. $f(x) = \dfrac{5 - x}{5 + x}$ **70.** $f(x) = |2 - x| + \sqrt[3]{x}$

Exercises 71–76: Give a verbal representation for $f(x)$.

71. $f(x) = x - \frac{1}{2}$ **72.** $f(x) = \frac{3}{4}x$

73. $f(x) = \dfrac{x}{3}$ **74.** $f(x) = x^2 + 1$

75. $f(x) = \sqrt{x - 1}$ **76.** $f(x) = 1 - 3x$

77. *Cost of Driving* In 2010, the average cost of driving a new car in the United States was about 50 cents per mile. Symbolically, graphically, and numerically represent a function f that computes the cost in dollars of driving x miles. For the numerical representation (table) let $x = 10, 20, 30, \ldots, 70$. (*Source:* Associated Press.)

78. *Federal Income Taxes* In 2010, the lowest U.S. income tax rate was 10 percent. Symbolically, graphically, and numerically represent a function f that computes the tax on a taxable income of x dollars. For the numerical representation (table) let $x = 1000, 2000, 3000, \ldots, 7000$, and for the graphical representation let $0 \le x \le 10{,}000$. (*Source:* Internal Revenue Service.)

79. *Global Web Searches* The number of World Wide Web searches S in billions during year x can be approximated by $S(x) = 225x - 450{,}650$ from 2009 to 2012. Evaluate $S(2011)$ and interpret the result. (*Source:* RBC Capital Markets Corp.)

80. *Cost of Smartphones* The average cost difference D in dollars between smartphones and all other types of phones during year x can be approximated by $D(x) = -23.5x + 47{,}275$ from 2005 to 2009. Evaluate $D(2009)$ and interpret the result. (*Source:* Business Insider.)

IDENTIFYING DOMAINS AND RANGES

Exercises 81–88: Use the graph of f to estimate its domain and range.

81.

82.

83.

84.

85.

86.

87.

88.
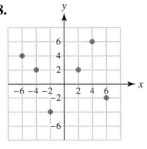

Exercises 89 and 90: Use the diagram to find the domain and range of f.

89.

90.

Exercises 91–104: Find the domain.

91. $f(x) = 10x$ **92.** $f(x) = 5 - x$

93. $f(x) = x^2 - 3$ **94.** $f(x) = \frac{1}{2}x^2$

95. $f(x) = \dfrac{3}{x - 5}$ **96.** $f(x) = \dfrac{x}{x + 1}$

97. $f(x) = \dfrac{2x}{x^2 + 1}$ **98.** $f(x) = \dfrac{6}{1 - x}$

99. $f(x) = \sqrt{x - 1}$ **100.** $f(x) = |x|$

101. $f(x) = |x - 5|$ **102.** $f(x) = \sqrt{2 - x}$

103. $f(x) = \dfrac{1}{x}$ **104.** $f(x) = 1 - 3x^2$

105. *Humpback Whales* The number of humpback whales W sighted in Maui's annual whale census for year x is given by $W(2005) = 649$, $W(2006) = 1265$, $W(2007) = 959$, $W(2008) = 1726$, and $W(2009) = 1010$. (*Source:* Pacific Whale Foundation.)
(a) Evaluate $W(2008)$ and interpret the result.
(b) Identify the domain and range of W.
(c) Describe the pattern in the data.

106. *Digital Music Downloads* The percentage of digital music D that was purchased through downloads during year x is given by $D(2004) = 0.9$, $D(2005) = 5.7$, $D(2006) = 6.7$, $D(2007) = 11.2$, and $D(2008) = 12.8$. (*Source:* The Recording Industry Association of America.)
(a) Evaluate $D(2006)$ and interpret the result.
(b) Identify the domain and range of D.
(c) Describe the pattern in the data.

107. *Cost of Tuition* Suppose that a student can take from 1 to 20 credits at a college and that each credit costs \$200. If function C calculates the cost of taking x credits, determine the domain and range of C.

108. *Falling Ball* Suppose that a ball is dropped from a window that is 64 feet above the ground and that the ball strikes the ground after 2 seconds. If function *H* calculates the height of the ball after *t* seconds, determine a domain and range for *H*, while the ball is falling.

IDENTIFYING A FUNCTION

Exercises 109–112: Determine whether the diagram could represent a function.

109. **110.**

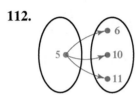

111. **112.**

113. *Average Precipitation* The table lists the monthly average precipitation *P* in Las Vegas, Nevada, where $x = 1$ corresponds to January and $x = 12$ corresponds to December.

x (month)	1	2	3	4	5	6
P (inches)	0.5	0.4	0.4	0.2	0.2	0.1

x (month)	7	8	9	10	11	12
P (inches)	0.4	0.5	0.3	0.2	0.4	0.3

Source: J. Williams.

 (a) Determine the value of *P* during May.
 (b) Is *P* a function of *x*? Explain.
 (c) If $P = 0.4$, find *x*.

114. *Wind Speeds* The table lists the monthly average wind speed *W* in Louisville, Kentucky, where $x = 1$ corresponds to January and $x = 12$ corresponds to December.

x (month)	1	2	3	4	5	6
W (mph)	10.4	12.7	10.4	10.4	8.1	8.1

x (month)	7	8	9	10	11	12
W (mph)	6.9	6.9	6.9	8.1	9.2	9.2

Source: J. Williams.

 (a) Determine the month with the highest average wind speed.
 (b) Is *W* a function of *x*? Explain.
 (c) If $W = 6.9$, find *x*.

Exercises 115–126: Determine whether the graph represents a function. If it does, identify the domain and range.

115. **116.**

117. **118.**

119. **120.**

121. **122.**

123. **124.**

125.

126.

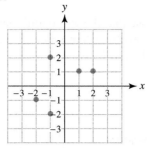

Exercises 127–130: Determine whether S is a function.

127. $S = \{(1, 2), (4, 5), (7, 8), (5, 4), (2, 2)\}$

128. $S = \{(4, 7), (-2, 1), (3, 8), (4, 9)\}$

129. *S* is given by the table.

x	5	10	5
y	2	1	0

130. *S* is given by the table.

x	−3	−2	−1
y	10	10	10

GRAPHICAL INTERPRETATION

Exercises 131 and 132: The graph represents the distance that a person is from home while walking on a straight path. The x-axis represents time and the y-axis represents distance. Interpret the graph.

131.   **132.**

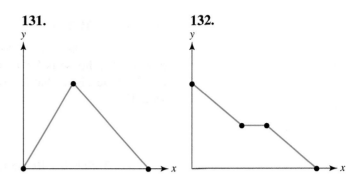

133. *Texting* The average 18- to 24-year-old person texts about 1500 messages per month. Sketch a graph that shows the total number of text messages sent over a period of 4 months. Assume that the same number of texts is sent each day. (*Source:* The Nielsen Company.)

134. *Computer Viruses* In 2000 there were about 50 thousand computer viruses. In 2010 there were about 1.6 million computer viruses. Sketch a graph of this increase from 2000 to 2010. Answers may vary. (*Source:* Symantec.)

WRITING ABOUT MATHEMATICS

135. Give an example of a function. Identify the domain and range of your function.

136. Explain in your own words what a function is. How is a function different from other relations?

137. Explain how to evaluate a function by using a graph. Give an example.

138. Give one difficulty that may occur when you use a table of values to evaluate a function.

1.2 Linear Functions

**Basic Concepts ● Representations of Linear Functions ●
Modeling Data with Linear Functions**

A LOOK INTO MATH ▶

Functions are frequently used to model, or describe, the real world. For example, people are becoming more energy conscious. As a result, there is an increase in the number of *green* buildings that are being constructed. Table 1.6 lists estimated U.S. sales of green building material. Because sales increase by $5 billion each year, a *linear function* can be used to model these data. (See Example 7.) In this section we discuss this important type of function.

NEW VOCABULARY

☐ Linear function
☐ Rate of change
☐ Constant function

TABLE 1.6 Green Material Sales ($ billions)

Year	2010	2011	2012	2013
Sales	65	70	75	80

Source: Freedonia Group, Green Building Material.

Basic Concepts

▶ **REAL-WORLD CONNECTION** Suppose that the air conditioner is turned on when the temperature inside a house is 80°F. The resulting temperatures are listed in Table 1.7 for various elapsed times. Note that for each 1-hour increase in elapsed time, the temperature decreases by 2°F.

TABLE 1.7 House Temperature

Elapsed Time (hours)	0	1	2	3	4	5
Temperature (°F)	80	78	76	74	72	70

We want to determine a function f that models, or calculates, the house temperature after x hours. To do this, we will find numerical, graphical, verbal, and symbolic representations of f.

NUMERICAL REPRESENTATION (TABLE OF VALUES) We can think of Table 1.7 as a numerical representation (table of values) for the function f. A similar numerical representation that uses x and $f(x)$ is shown in Table 1.8.

TABLE 1.8 Numerical Representation of $f(x)$

x	0	1	2	3	4	5
$f(x)$	80	78	76	74	72	70

GRAPHICAL REPRESENTATION (GRAPH) To graph $y = f(x)$, we begin by plotting the points in Table 1.8, as shown in Figure 1.24. This scatterplot suggests that a line models these data, as shown in Figure 1.25. We call f a *linear function* because its graph is a *line*.

Figure 1.24 A Scatterplot

Figure 1.25 A Linear Function

Another graph of $y = f(x)$ with a different y-scale is shown in Figure 1.26. Because the y-values always decrease by the same amount for each 1-hour increase on the x-axis, we say that function f has a *constant rate of change*. In this example, the constant rate of change is −2°F per hour.

Constant Rate of Change

Figure 1.26

VERBAL REPRESENTATION (WORDS) Over a 5-hour period, the air conditioner lowers the initial temperature of 80°F by 2°F for each elapsed hour x. Thus a description of how to calculate the temperature is:

"Multiply x by -2°F and then add 80°F."   Verbal representation of $f(x)$

SYMBOLIC REPRESENTATION (FORMULA) Our verbal representation of $f(x)$ makes it straightforward for us to write a formula.

Elapsed Hours

$$f(x) = -2x + 80$$ Symbolic representation of $f(x)$

Rate of Change   Initial Temperature

For example,

$$f(2.5) = -2(2.5) + 80 = 75$$

means that the temperature is 75°F after the air conditioner has run for 2.5 hours. In this instance, it might be appropriate to *limit the domain* of f to x-values between 0 and 5, inclusive.

LINEAR FUNCTION

A function f defined by $f(x) = mx + b$, where m and b are constants, is a **linear function**.

For $f(x) = -2x + 80$, we have $m = -2$ and $b = 80$. The constant m represents the rate at which the air conditioner cools the building, and the constant b represents the initial temperature.

NOTE: In previous mathematics courses you may have studied slope m. In Section 1.3 we discuss further how m corresponds to the slope of a line and to a linear function's rate of change.

▶ **REAL-WORLD CONNECTION** In general, a linear function defined by $f(x) = mx + b$ changes by m units for each unit increase in x. This **rate of change** is an increase if $m > 0$ and a decrease if $m < 0$. For example, if new carpet costs $20 per square yard, then the linear function defined by $C(x) = 20x$ gives the cost of buying x square yards of carpet. The value of $m = 20$ gives the cost (rate of change) for each additional square yard of carpet. For function C, the value of b is 0 because it costs $0 to buy 0 square yards of carpet.

NOTE: If f is a linear function, then $f(0) = m(0) + b = b$. Thus b can be found by evaluating $f(x)$ at $x = 0$.

EXAMPLE 1 | **Identifying linear functions**

Determine whether f is a linear function. If f is a linear function, find values for m and b so that $f(x) = mx + b$.

(a) $f(x) = 4 - 3x$ (b) $f(x) = 8$ (c) $f(x) = 2x^2 + 8$

Solution
(a) Let $m = -3$ and $b = 4$. Then $f(x) = -3x + 4$, and f is a linear function.
(b) Let $m = 0$ and $b = 8$. Then $f(x) = 0x + 8$, and f is a linear function.
(c) Function f is not linear because its formula contains x^2. The formula for a linear function cannot contain an x with an exponent other than 1.

Now Try Exercises 11, 13, 15

EXAMPLE 2 | **Determining linear functions**

Use each table of values to determine whether $f(x)$ could represent a linear function. If f could be linear, write a formula for f in the form $f(x) = mx + b$.

(a)

x	0	1	2	3
$f(x)$	10	15	20	25

(b)

x	−2	0	2	4
$f(x)$	4	2	0	−2

(c)

x	0	1	2	3
$f(x)$	1	2	4	7

(d)

x	−2	0	3	5
$f(x)$	7	7	7	7

Solution
(a) For each unit increase in x, $f(x)$ increases by 5 units, so $f(x)$ could be linear with $m = 5$. Because $f(0) = 10$, $b = 10$. Thus $f(x) = 5x + 10$.
(b) For each 2-unit increase in x, $f(x)$ decreases by 2 units. Equivalently, each unit increase in x results in a 1-unit decrease in $f(x)$, so $f(x)$ could be linear with $m = -1$. Because $f(0) = 2$, $b = 2$. Thus $f(x) = -x + 2$.
(c) Each unit increase in x does not result in a constant change in $f(x)$. Thus $f(x)$ does *not* represent a linear function.
(d) For any change in x, $f(x)$ does *not* change, so $f(x)$ could be linear with $m = 0$. Because $f(0) = 7$, let $b = 7$. Thus $f(x) = 0x + 7$, or $f(x) = 7$. (When $m = 0$, we say that f is a *constant function*. See Example 8.)

Now Try Exercises 23, 25, 27, 31

Representations of Linear Functions

The graph of a linear function is a line. To graph a linear function f we can start by making a table of values and then plotting three or more points. We can then sketch the graph of f by drawing a line through these points, as demonstrated in the next example.

EXAMPLE 3 | **Graphing a linear function by hand**

Sketch a graph of $f(x) = x - 1$. Use the graph to evaluate $f(-2)$.

Solution

Begin by making a table of values containing at least three points. Pick convenient values of x, such as $x = -1, 0, 1$.

$$f(-1) = -1 - 1 = -2$$
$$f(0) = 0 - 1 = -1$$
$$f(1) = 1 - 1 = 0$$

Display the results, as shown in Table 1.9.

Plot the points $(-1, -2), (0, -1)$, and $(1, 0)$. Sketch a line through these points to obtain the graph of f. A graph of a line results when *infinitely* many points are plotted, as shown in Figure 1.27.

To evaluate $f(-2)$, first find $x = -2$ on the x-axis. See Figure 1.28. Then move downward to the graph of f. By moving across to the y-axis, we see that the corresponding y-value is -3. Thus $f(-2) = -3$.

TABLE 1.9

x	y
-1	-2
0	-1
1	0

Figure 1.27

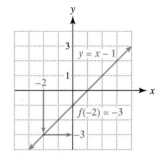

Figure 1.28

Now Try Exercises 39, 57

In the next example a graphing calculator is used to create a graph and table.

EXAMPLE 4 | **Using a graphing calculator**

Give numerical and graphical representations of $f(x) = \frac{1}{2}x - 2$.

Solution

Numerical Representation To make a numerical representation, construct the table for $Y_1 = .5X - 2$, starting at $x = -3$ and incrementing by 1, as shown in Figure 1.29(a). (Other tables are possible.)

Graphical Representation Graph Y_1 in the standard viewing rectangle, as shown in Figure 1.29(b). (Other viewing rectangles may be used.)

CALCULATOR HELP

To make a table, see Appendix A (pages AP-2 and AP-3). To make a graph, see Appendix A (page AP-5).

$[-10, 10, 1]$ by $[-10, 10, 1]$

(a)   (b)

Figure 1.29

Now Try Exercise 75

EXAMPLE 5

Representing a linear function

A linear function is given by $f(x) = -3x + 2$.
(a) Give a verbal representation of f.
(b) Make a numerical representation (table) of f by letting $x = -1, 0, 1$.
(c) Plot the points listed in the table from part (b). Then sketch a graph of $y = f(x)$.

Solution

(a) *Verbal Representation* Multiply the input x by -3 and add 2 to obtain the output.

(b) *Numerical Representation* Evaluate the formula $f(x) = -3x + 2$ at $x = -1, 0, 1$, which results in Table 1.10. Note that $f(-1) = 5$, $f(0) = 2$, and $f(1) = -1$.

(c) *Graphical Representation* To make a graph of f by hand without a graphing calculator, plot the points $(-1, 5)$, $(0, 2)$, and $(1, -1)$ from Table 1.10. Then draw a line passing through these points, as shown in Figure 1.30.

TABLE 1.10

x	$f(x)$
-1	5
0	2
1	-1

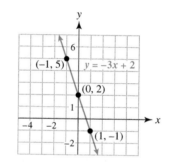

Figure 1.30

Now Try Exercise 71

NOTE: In the next section we use one point and slope m to graph lines rather than plotting three points.

MAKING CONNECTIONS

Mathematics in Newspapers

Think of the mathematics that you see in newspapers or in online publications. Often, percentages are described *verbally*, numbers are displayed in *tables*, and data are shown in *graphs*. Seldom are *formulas* given, which is an important reason to study verbal, numerical, and graphical representations.

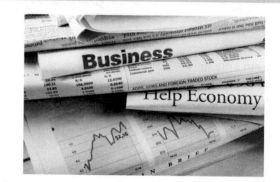

Modeling Data with Linear Functions

▶ **REAL-WORLD CONNECTION** A distinguishing feature of a linear function is that when the input x increases by 1 unit, the output $f(x) = mx + b$ always changes by an amount equal to m. For example, the percentage of wireless households during year x from 2005 to 2010 can be modeled by the linear function

$$f(x) = 4x - 8013,$$

where x is the year. The value of $m = 4$ indicates that the percentage of wireless households has increased, on average, by 4% per year. (*Source: National Center for Health Statistics.*)

The following are other examples of quantities that are modeled by linear functions. Try to determine the value of the constant m.

- The wages earned by an individual working x hours at $8 per hour
- The distance traveled by a jet airliner in x hours if its speed is 500 miles per hour
- The cost of tuition and fees when registering for x credits if each credit costs $200 and the fees are fixed at $300

When we are modeling data with a linear function defined by $f(x) = mx + b$, the following concepts are helpful to determine m and b.

MODELING DATA WITH A LINEAR FUNCTION

The formula $f(x) = mx + b$ may be interpreted as follows.

$$f(x) \quad = \quad mx \quad + \quad b$$

(New amount) = (Change) + (Fixed amount)

When x represents time, *change* equals (rate of change) × (time).

$$f(x) \quad = \quad m \quad \times \quad x \quad + \quad b$$

(Future amount) = (Rate of change) × (Time) + (Initial amount)

▶ **REAL-WORLD CONNECTION** These concepts are applied in the next three examples.

EXAMPLE 6 **Modeling growth of bamboo**

Bamboo is gaining popularity as a *green* building material because of its fast-growing, regenerative characteristics. Under ideal conditions, some species of bamboo grow at an astonishing 2 inches per hour. Suppose a bamboo plant is initially 6 inches tall. (*Source: Cali Bamboo.*)
(a) Find a function H that models the plant's height in inches under ideal conditions after t hours.
(b) Find $H(3)$ and interpret the result.

Solution
(a) The initial height is **6** inches and the rate of change is **2** inches per hour.

$$H(t) \quad = \quad 2 \quad \times \quad t \quad + \quad 6,$$

(Future height) = (Rate of change) × (Time) + (Initial height)

or $H(t) = 2t + 6$.
(b) $H(3) = 2(3) + 6 = 12$. After **3** hours the bamboo plant is **12** inches tall.

Now Try Exercise 89

> EXAMPLE 7   **Modeling demand for building green**

Table 1.11 lists estimated sales of green building material in billions of dollars. (Refer to A Look Into Math at the beginning of this section.)

TABLE 1.11 Green Material Sales ($ billions)

Year	2010	2011	2012	2013
Sales	65	70	75	80

Source: Freedonia Group, Green Building Material.

(a) Make a scatterplot of the data and sketch the graph of a function f that models these data. Let x represent years after 2010. That is, let $x = 0$ correspond to 2010, $x = 1$ to 2011, and so on.

(b) What were the sales in 2010? What was the annual increase in sales each year?

(c) Find a formula for $f(x)$.

(d) Use your formula to estimate sales in 2014.

READING CHECK

How can you determine whether data in a table can be modeled by a linear function?

Solution

(a) In Figure 1.31 the scatterplot suggests that a linear function models the data. A line has been sketched with the data.

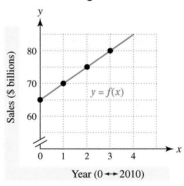

Green Building Material Sales

Figure 1.31 A Linear Model

(b) From Table 1.11, sales for green material were $65 billion in 2010, with sales increasing at a *constant rate* of $5 billion per year.

(c) From part (b) initial sales ($x = 0$) were $**65** billion, and sales increased by $**5** billion per year. Thus

$$f(x) \quad = \quad 5 \quad \times \quad x \quad + \quad 65,$$

(Future sales) = (Rate of change in sales) × (Time) + (Initial sales)

or $f(x) = 5x + 65$.

(d) Because $x = 4$ corresponds to 2014, evaluate $f(4)$.

$$f(4) = 5(4) + 65 = 85$$

This model estimates sales of green building material to be $85 billion in 2014.

Now Try Exercise 91

In the next example, we consider a simple function that models the speed of a car.

EXAMPLE 8 **Modeling with a constant function**

A car travels on a freeway with its speed recorded at regular intervals, as listed in Table 1.12.

TABLE 1.12 Speed of a Car

Elapsed Time (hours)	0	1	2	3	4
Speed (miles per hour)	70	70	70	70	70

(a) Discuss the speed of the car during this time interval.
(b) Find a formula for a function f that models these data.
(c) Sketch a graph of f together with the data.

Solution
(a) The speed of the car appears to be constant at 70 miles per hour.
(b) Because the speed is constant, the rate of change is 0. Thus

$$f(x) \qquad = \qquad 0x \qquad + \qquad 70$$

(Future speed) = (Change in speed) + (Initial speed)

and $f(x) = 70$. We call f a *constant function*.
(c) Because $y = f(x)$, graph $y = 70$ with the data points

$$(0, 70), (1, 70), (2, 70), (3, 70), \text{ and } (4, 70)$$

to obtain Figure 1.32.

Figure 1.32 Speed of a Car

Now Try Exercise 85

The function defined by $f(x) = 70$ is an example of a *constant function*. A **constant function** *is a linear function* with $m = 0$ and can be written as $f(x) = b$. Regardless of the input, a constant function always outputs the same value, b. Its graph is a horizontal line. Its domain is all real numbers and its range is $R = \{b\}$.

CRITICAL THINKING

Find a formula for a function D that calculates the *distance* traveled by the car in Example 8 after x hours. What is the rate of change for $D(x)$?

▶ **REAL-WORLD CONNECTION** The following are three applications of constant functions.

- A thermostat calculates a constant function regardless of the weather outside by maintaining a set temperature.
- A cruise control in a car calculates a constant function by maintaining a fixed speed, regardless of the type of road or terrain.
- A constant function calculates the 1250-foot height of the Empire State Building.

1.2 Putting It All Together

CONCEPT	EXPLANATION	EXAMPLES
Linear Function	Can be represented by $f(x) = mx + b$ Graph is a line.	$f(x) = 2x - 6$, $m = 2$ and $b = -6$ $f(x) = 10$, $m = 0$ and $b = 10$
Constant Function	Can be represented by $f(x) = b$ Graph is a horizontal line.	$f(x) = -7$, $b = -7$ $f(x) = 22$, $b = 22$
Rate of Change for a Linear Function	The output of a linear function changes by a constant amount for each unit increase in the input.	$f(x) = -3x + 8$ decreases 3 units for each unit increase in x. $f(x) = 5$ neither increases nor decreases. The rate of change is 0.

REPRESENTATION	COMMENTS	EXAMPLE
Symbolic	Mathematical formula in the form $f(x) = mx + b$	$f(x) = 2x + 1$, where $m = 2$ and $b = 1$
Verbal	Multiply the input x by m and add b.	Multiply the input x by 2 and then add 1 to obtain the output.
Numerical (table of values)	For each unit increase in x in the table, the output of $f(x) = mx + b$ changes by an amount equal to m.	1-unit increase x: 0, 1, 2 $f(x)$: 1, 3, 5 2-unit increase
Graphical	The graph of a linear function is a line. Plot at least 3 points and then sketch the line.	

1.2 Exercises

CONCEPTS AND VOCABULARY

1. The formula for a linear function is $f(x) =$ _____.

2. The formula for a constant function is $f(x) =$ _____.

3. The graph of a linear function is a(n) _____.

4. The graph of a constant function is a(n) _____ line.

5. If $f(x) = 7x + 5$, each time x increases by 1 unit, $f(x)$ increases by _____ units.

6. If $f(x) = 5$, each time x increases by 1 unit, $f(x)$ increases by _____ units.

7. (True or False?) Every constant function is a linear function.

8. (True or False?) Every linear function is a constant function.

9. If $C(x) = 2x$ calculates the cost in dollars of buying x square feet of carpet, what does 2 represent in the formula? Interpret the fact that the point $(10, 20)$ lies on the graph of C.

10. If $G(x) = 100 - 4x$ calculates the number of gallons of water in a tank after x minutes, what does -4 represent in the formula? Interpret the fact that the point $(5, 80)$ lies on the graph of G.

IDENTIFYING LINEAR FUNCTIONS

Exercises 11–18: Determine whether f is a linear function. If f is linear, give values for m and b so that f may be expressed as $f(x) = mx + b$.

11. $f(x) = \dfrac{1}{2}x - 6$

12. $f(x) = x$

13. $f(x) = \dfrac{5}{2} - x^2$

14. $f(x) = \sqrt{x} + 3$

15. $f(x) = -9$

16. $f(x) = 1.5 - 7.3x$

17. $f(x) = -9x$

18. $f(x) = \dfrac{1}{x}$

Exercises 19–22: Determine whether the graph represents a linear function.

19.

20.

21.

22.
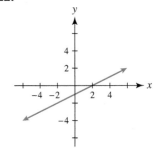

Exercises 23–32: (Refer to Example 2.) Use the table to determine whether $f(x)$ could represent a linear function. If it could, write $f(x)$ in the form $f(x) = mx + b$.

23.

x	0	1	2	3
$f(x)$	-6	-3	0	3

24.

x	0	2	4	6
$f(x)$	-2	2	6	10

25.

x	-2	0	2	4
$f(x)$	6	3	0	-3

26.

x	0	3	6	9
$f(x)$	8	4	2	1

27.

x	-2	-1	0	1
$f(x)$	-5	0	20	40

28.

x	-2	-1	0	1
$f(x)$	6	3	0	-3

29.

x	0	2	3	4
f(x)	0	4	6	8

30.

x	1	2	3	4
f(x)	0	1	3	7

31.

x	−1	0	1	2
f(x)	−4	−4	−4	−4

32.

x	2	5	6	8
f(x)	5	5	5	5

EVALUATING LINEAR FUNCTIONS

Exercises 33–38: Evaluate f(x) at the given values of x.

33. $f(x) = 4x$ $\qquad x = -4, 5$

34. $f(x) = -2x + 1$ $\qquad x = -2, 3$

35. $f(x) = 5 - x$ $\qquad x = -\frac{2}{3}, 3$

36. $f(x) = \frac{1}{2}x - \frac{1}{4}$ $\qquad x = 0, \frac{1}{2}$

37. $f(x) = -22$ $\qquad x = -\frac{3}{4}, 13$

38. $f(x) = 9x - 7$ $\qquad x = -1.2, 2.8$

Exercises 39–44: Use the graph of f to evaluate the given expressions.

39. $f(-1)$ and $f(0)$

40. $f(-2)$ and $f(2)$

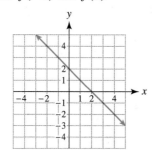

41. $f(-2)$ and $f(4)$

42. $f(0)$ and $f(3)$

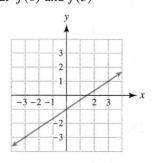

43. $f(-3)$ and $f(1)$

44. $f(1.5)$ and $f(0.5\pi)$

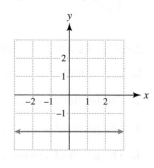

Exercises 45–48: Use the verbal description to write a formula for f(x). Then evaluate f(3).

45. Multiply the input by 6.

46. Multiply the input by −3 and add 7.

47. Divide the input by 6 and subtract $\frac{1}{2}$.

48. Output 8.7 for every input.

REPRESENTING LINEAR FUNCTIONS

Exercises 49–52: Match f(x) with its graph (a.–d.).

49. $f(x) = 3x$ $\qquad\qquad$ **50.** $f(x) = -2x$

51. $f(x) = x - 2$ $\qquad\quad$ **52.** $f(x) = 2x + 1$

a. $\qquad\qquad\qquad\qquad$ **b.**

c. $\qquad\qquad\qquad\qquad$ **d.**

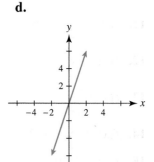

Exercises 53–62: Sketch a graph of y = f(x).

53. $f(x) = 2$ $\qquad\qquad$ **54.** $f(x) = -1$

55. $f(x) = -\frac{1}{2}x$ $\qquad\quad$ **56.** $f(x) = 2x$

57. $f(x) = x + 1$ $\qquad\quad$ **58.** $f(x) = x - 2$

59. $f(x) = 3x - 3$

60. $f(x) = -2x + 1$

61. $f(x) = 3 - x$

62. $f(x) = \frac{1}{4}x + 2$

Exercises 63–68: Write a symbolic representation (formula) for a linear function f that calculates the following.

63. The number of pounds in x ounces

64. The number of dimes in x dollars

65. The distance traveled by a car moving at 65 miles per hour for t hours

66. The long-distance phone bill *in dollars* for calling t minutes at 10 cents per minute and a fixed fee of $4.95

67. The total number of hours in a day during day x

68. The total cost of downhill skiing x times with a $500 season pass

69. Thinking Generally For each 1-unit increase in x with $y = ax + b$ and $a > 0$, y increases by _____ units.

70. Thinking Generally For each 1-unit decrease in x with $y = cx + d$ and $c < 0$, y increases by _____ units.

Exercises 71–74: Do the following.

  (a) *Give a verbal representation of f.*

  (b) *Make a numerical representation (table) of f for $x = -2, 0, 2$.*

  (c) *Plot the points listed in the table from part (b), then sketch a graph of f.*

71. $f(x) = -2x + 1$

72. $f(x) = 1 - x$

73. $f(x) = \frac{1}{2}x - 1$

74. $f(x) = \frac{3}{4}x$

 Exercises 75–78: Do the following.

  (a) *Make a numerical representation (table) of f for $x = -3, -2, -1, \ldots, 3$.*

  (b) *Graph f in the window $[-6, 6, 1]$ by $[-4, 4, 1]$.*

75. $f(x) = \frac{1}{3}x + \sqrt{2}$

76. $f(x) = -\frac{2}{3}x - \sqrt{3}$

77. $f(x) = \frac{x + 2}{5}$

78. $f(x) = \frac{2 - 3x}{7}$

MODELING

Exercises 79–82: Match the situation with the graph (a.–d.) at the top of the next column that models it best, where x-values represent time from 2000 to 2010.

79. The cost of college tuition

80. The cost of 1 gigabyte of computer memory

81. The distance between Chicago and Denver

82. The total distance traveled by a satellite that is orbiting Earth if the satellite was launched in 2000.

83. Online Exploration Look up the fuel efficiency E in miles per gallon for one of your favorite cars. (Answers will vary.)

  (a) Find a function G that calculates the number of gallons required to travel x miles.

  (b) If the cost of gasoline is $3 per gallon, find function C that calculates the cost of fuel to travel x miles.

84. Online Exploration Suppose that you would like to drive to Miami for spring break (if it is possible) in the car that you chose in Exercise 83. Calculate the gallons of gasoline needed for the trip.

APPLICATIONS

85. *Thermostat* Let $y = f(x)$ describe the temperature y of a room that is kept at $70°\text{F}$ for x hours.

  (a) Represent f symbolically and graphically over a 24-hour period for $0 \leq x \leq 24$.

  (b) Construct a table of f for $x = 0, 4, 8, 12, \ldots, 24$.

  (c) What type of function is f?

86. *Cruise Control* Let $y = f(x)$ describe the speed y of an automobile after x minutes if the cruise control is set at 60 miles per hour.
(a) Represent f symbolically and graphically over a 15-minute period for $0 \le x \le 15$.
(b) Construct a table of f for $x = 0, 1, 2, \ldots, 6$.
(c) What type of function is f?

87. *Distance* A car is initially 50 miles south of the Minnesota–Iowa border traveling south on Interstate 35. Distances D between the car and the border are recorded in the table for various elapsed times t. Find a linear function D that models these data.

t (hours)	0	2	3	5
D (miles)	50	170	230	350

88. *Estimating the Weight of a Bass* Sometimes the weight of a fish can be estimated by measuring its length. The table lists typical weights of bass having various lengths.

Length (inches)	12	14	16	18	20	22
Weight (pounds)	1.0	1.7	2.5	3.6	5.0	6.6

Source: Minnesota Department of Natural Resources.

(a) Let x be the length and y be the weight. Make a line graph of the data.
(b) Could the data be modeled accurately with a linear function? Explain your answer.

89. *Texting* In 2010, the average American under age 18 sent approximately 93 texts per day, whereas the average adult over age 65 sent approximately 1 text per day.
(a) Find a formula for a function K that calculates the number of texts sent in x days by the average person under age 18.
(b) Find a formula for a function A that calculates the number of texts sent in x days by the average person over age 65.
(c) Evaluate $K(365)$ and $A(365)$. Interpret your results.

90. *Rain Forests* Rain forests are forests that grow in regions receiving more than 70 inches of rain per year. The world is losing about 49 million acres of rain forest each year. (*Source:* New York Times Almanac.)
(a) Find a linear function f that calculates the change in the acres of rain forest in millions in x years.
(b) Evaluate $f(7)$ and interpret the result.

91. *Car Sales* The table shows the number of U.S. Toyota vehicles sold in millions for past years.

Year	2000	2001	2002	2003	2004
Vehicles	1.6	1.7	1.8	1.9	2.0

Source: Autodata.

(a) What were the sales in 2000?
(b) What was the annual increase in sales?
(c) Find a linear function f that models these data. Let $x = 0$ correspond to 2000, $x = 1$ to 2001, and so on.
(d) Use f to estimate sales in 2006.

92. *Tuition and Fees* Suppose tuition costs \$300 per credit and that student fees are fixed at \$100.
(a) Find a formula for a linear function T that models the cost of tuition and fees for x credits.
(b) Evaluate $T(16)$ and interpret the result.

93. *Skype Users* The number of Skype users S in millions x years after 2006 can be modeled by the formula $S(x) = 110x + 123$.
(a) How many users were there in 2010?
(b) What does the number 123 indicate in the formula?
(c) What does the number 110 indicate in the formula?

94. *Temperature and Volume* If a sample of a gas such as helium is heated, it will expand. The formula $V(T) = 0.147T + 40$ calculates the volume V in cubic inches of a sample of gas at temperature T in degrees Celsius.
(a) Evaluate $V(0)$ and interpret the result.
(b) If the temperature increases by $10°C$, by how much does the volume increase?
(c) What is the volume of the gas when the temperature is $100°C$?

95. *Temperature and Volume* (Refer to the preceding exercise.) A sample of gas at $0°C$ has a volume V of 137 cubic centimeters, which increases in volume by 0.5 cubic centimeter for every $1°C$ increase in temperature T.
(a) Write a formula $V(T) = aT + b$ that gives the volume of the gas at temperature T.
(b) Find the volume of the gas when $T = 50°C$.

96. *Cost* To make a music video it costs \$750 to rent a studio plus \$5 for each copy produced.
(a) Write a formula $C(x) = ax + b$ that calculates the cost of producing x videos.
(b) Find the cost of producing 2500 videos.

97. *Weight Lifting* Lifting weights can increase a person's muscle mass. Each additional pound of muscle burns an extra 40 calories per day. Write a linear function that models the number of calories burned each day by x pounds of muscle. By burning an extra 3500 calories a person can lose 1 pound of fat. How many pounds of muscle are needed to burn 1 pound of fat in 30 days? (*Source: Runner's World.*)

98. *Wireless Households* The percentage P of wireless households x years after 2005 can be modeled by the formula $P(x) = 4x + 7$, where $0 \leq x \leq 7$.
    (a) Evaluate $P(0)$ and $P(3)$. Interpret your results.
    (b) Explain the meaning of 4 and 7 in the formula.

99. *Mobile Data Penetration* The table lists the percentage P of people with cell phones who also subscribed to a data package during year x. (For example, with a data package one can surf the Web and check email.)

Year	2007	2008	2009
Percentage	55%	59%	63%

(a) What was this percentage in 2007?
(b) By how much did this percentage change each year?
(c) Write a function P that models these data. Let x be years after 2007.
(d) Estimate this percentage in 2010.

100. *Wal-Mart Sales* The table shows Wal-Mart's share as a percentage of overall U.S. retail sales for past years. (This percentage excludes restaurants and motor vehicles.)

Year	1998	1999	2000	2001	2002
Share (%)	6	6.5	7	7.5	8

Source: Commerce Department, Wal-Mart.

(a) What was Wal-Mart's share in 1998?
(b) By how much (percent) did Wal-Mart's share increase each year?
(c) Find a linear function f that models these data. Let $x = 0$ correspond to 1998.
(d) Use f to estimate Wal-Mart's share in 2005.

WRITING ABOUT MATHEMATICS

101. Explain how you can determine whether a function is linear by using its
    (a) symbolic representation,
    (b) graphical representation, and
    (c) numerical representation.

102. Describe one way to determine whether data can be modeled by a linear function.

Checking Basic Concepts

1. Find a formula and sketch a graph for a function that squares the input x and then subtracts 1.

2. Use the graph of f to do the following.
    (a) Find the domain and range of f.
    (b) Evaluate $f(0)$ and $f(2)$.
    (c) Is f a linear function? Explain.

3. Determine whether f is a linear function.
    (a) $f(x) = 4x - 2$
    (b) $f(x) = 2\sqrt{x} - 5$
    (c) $f(x) = -7$
    (d) $f(x) = 9 - 2x + 5x$

4. Graph $f(x) = 4 - 3x$. Evaluate $f(-2)$.

5. Find a formula for a linear function that models the data.

x	0	1	2	3	4
$f(x)$	-1	$-\frac{1}{2}$	0	$\frac{1}{2}$	1

6. The median age in the United States from 1970 to 2010 can be approximated by
    $$f(x) = 0.225x + 27.7,$$
    where $x = 0$ corresponds to 1970, $x = 1$ to 1971, and so on.
    (a) Evaluate $f(20)$ and interpret the result.
    (b) Interpret the numbers 0.225 and 27.7.

1.3 The Slope of a Line

Slope • Slope–Intercept Form of a Line • Interpreting Slope in Applications

A LOOK INTO MATH ▶

Figure 1.33 shows some graphs of lines, where the *x*-axis represents time.

Which graph might represent the amount of gas in your car's tank while you are driving?

Which graph might represent the temperature inside a refrigerator?

Which graph might represent the amount of water in a hot tub that is being filled?

To answer these questions, you probably used the concept of slope. In mathematics, slope is a *number* that measures the "tilt" of a line in the *xy*-plane from left to right. We assume throughout the text that lines are always straight. In this section we discuss how slope relates to the graph of a linear function and how to interpret slope.

NEW VOCABULARY

- □ Rise/Change in *y*
- □ Run/Change in *x*
- □ Subscript
- □ Slope
- □ Positive slope
- □ Negative slope
- □ Undefined slope
- □ Zero slope
- □ *y*-intercept
- □ Slope–intercept form
- □ Rate of change

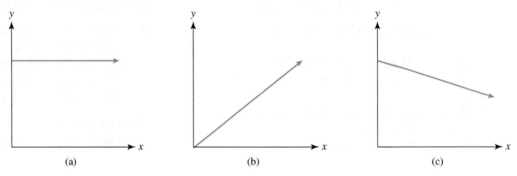

(a)   (b)   (c)

Figure 1.33

Slope

▶ **REAL-WORLD CONNECTION** Suppose we want to construct a stairway where each tread is 12 inches wide and the rise between steps is 6 inches high, as illustrated in Figure 1.34(a). We say that this stairway has a *rise* of 6 inches for each 12 inches of *run*. Next, if we draw a blue line along this stairway and include an *x*- and *y*-axis, as shown in Figure 1.34(b), then this blue line has a *slope* of $\frac{6}{12}$, or $\frac{1}{2}$. That is, the slope of a line equals *rise over run*. For a line, the ratio $\frac{\text{rise}}{\text{run}}$ equals the slope and is always the same regardless of where one is on the line.

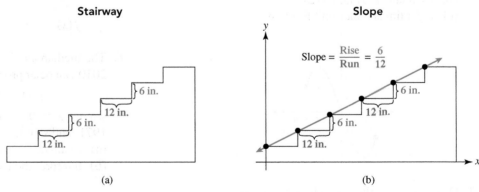

(a)   (b)

Figure 1.34

Slope can also be used to describe other things in real life. The graph shown in Figure 1.35 illustrates the cost of buying *x* pounds of candy. The graph tilts upward from left to right, which indicates that the cost increases as the number of pounds purchased increases. Note that for every 2 additional pounds purchased, the total cost increases by $3. The graph *rises* 3 units for every 2 units of *run*. The slope of this line is $\frac{3}{2}$, or 1.5. That is, for every unit of run along the *x*-axis, the graph rises 1.5 units. A slope of 1.5 indicates that candy costs $1.50 per pound.

Slope and Cost

Figure 1.35 Cost of Candy

CALCULATING SLOPE If we know two points on a line, we can find its slope. A general case is shown in Figure 1.36, where a line passes through the points (x_1, y_1) and (x_2, y_2). The **rise** or **change in y** is $y_2 - y_1$, and the **run** or **change in x** is $x_2 - x_1$. The slope *m* of a line can be found using any of the following three formulas.

$$m = \frac{\text{rise}}{\text{run}}, \quad m = \frac{\text{Change in } y}{\text{Change in } x}, \quad \text{or} \quad m = \frac{y_2 - y_1}{x_2 - x_1}$$

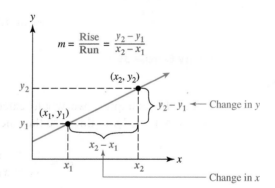

Figure 1.36

NOTE: The expression x_1 has a **subscript** of 1 and is read "*x* sub one" or "*x* one." Thus x_1 and x_2 denote two different *x*-values. Similar comments can be made about y_1 and y_2.

SLOPE

The **slope** *m* of the line passing through the points (x_1, y_1) and (x_2, y_2) is

$$m = \frac{y_2 - y_1}{x_2 - x_1},$$

where $x_1 \neq x_2$. That is, slope equals *rise over run*.

NOTE: *Change in x* is sometimes denoted Δx and equals $x_2 - x_1$. The expression Δx is read "delta *x*." Similarly, *change in y* is sometimes denoted Δy and equals $y_2 - y_1$. Using this notation, we can express slope as $m = \frac{\Delta y}{\Delta x} = \frac{y_2 - y_1}{x_2 - x_1}$.

EXAMPLE 1 **Calculating the slope of a line**

Find the slope of the line passing through the points $(-4, 1)$ and $(2, 4)$. Plot these points and graph the line. Interpret the slope.

Solution

Begin by letting $(x_1, y_1) = (-4, 1)$ and $(x_2, y_2) = (2, 4)$. The slope is

$$m = \frac{y_2 - y_1}{x_2 - x_1} = \frac{4 - 1}{2 - (-4)} = \frac{3}{6} = \frac{1}{2}.$$

A graph of the line passing through these two points is shown in Figure 1.37. A slope of $\frac{1}{2}$ indicates that the line rises 1 unit for every 2 units of run. This slope is equivalent to 3 units of rise for every 6 units of run.

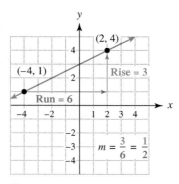

Figure 1.37

▌ Now Try Exercise 35

NOTE: In Example 1 we would calculate the same slope if we let $(x_1, y_1) = (2, 4)$ and $(x_2, y_2) = (-4, 1)$. In this case the calculation would be

$$m = \frac{y_2 - y_1}{x_2 - x_1} = \frac{1 - 4}{-4 - 2} = \frac{-3}{-6} = \frac{1}{2}.$$

READING CHECK

Explain positive slope, negative slope, zero slope, and undefined slope.

If a line has **positive slope**, the line *rises* from *left to right*. In Figure 1.38 the rise is 2 units for each unit of run, so the slope is 2. If a line has **negative slope**, the line *falls* from left to right. In Figure 1.39 the line *falls* 1 unit for every 2 units of run, so the slope is $-\frac{1}{2}$. **Zero slope** indicates that a line is horizontal, as shown in Figure 1.40. If (x_1, y_1) and (x_2, y_2) are two points on a vertical line, $x_1 = x_2$. In Figure 1.41 the run is $x_2 - x_1 = 0$, so a vertical line has **undefined slope** because division by 0 is undefined.

Positive Slope	Negative Slope	Zero Slope	Undefined Slope
			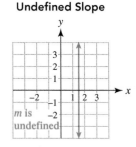
Figure 1.38	**Figure 1.39**	**Figure 1.40**	**Figure 1.41**

STUDY TIP

The information in Making Connections ties concepts together so that you can understand mathematics better.

MAKING CONNECTIONS

Slope, Hills, and Driving

Suppose that one vehicle is going uphill while the other vehicle is going downhill. To avoid any confusion about "uphill" and "downhill," slope is *always calculated by moving left to right* along the *x-axis*. In Figure 1.42, the driver of the orange car is going uphill and experiencing a *positive* slope, while the driver of the purple car is going downhill and experiencing a *negative* slope. Slopes that have large absolute values correspond to steeper hills.

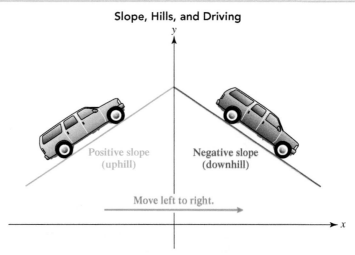

Figure 1.42

EXAMPLE 2 **Calculating slope**

Find the slope of the line passing through each pair of points, if possible.
(a) $(-1, 4), (8, 4)$ **(b)** $\left(-\frac{3}{4}, \frac{1}{4}\right), \left(-\frac{3}{4}, \frac{5}{4}\right)$ **(c)** $(a, 3b), (3a, 5b)$

Solution

(a) For $(-1, 4)$ and $(8, 4)$, $m = \dfrac{y_2 - y_1}{x_2 - x_1} = \dfrac{4 - 4}{8 - (-1)} = \dfrac{0}{9} = 0.$

(b) For $\left(-\frac{3}{4}, \frac{1}{4}\right)$ and $\left(-\frac{3}{4}, \frac{5}{4}\right)$, $m = \dfrac{y_2 - y_1}{x_2 - x_1} = \dfrac{\frac{5}{4} - \frac{1}{4}}{-\frac{3}{4} - \left(-\frac{3}{4}\right)} = \dfrac{1}{0}$, which is undefined.

(c) For $(a, 3b)$ and $(3a, 5b)$, $m = \dfrac{y_2 - y_1}{x_2 - x_1} = \dfrac{5b - 3b}{3a - a} = \dfrac{2b}{2a} = \dfrac{b}{a}.$

Now Try Exercises 21, 23, 31

EXAMPLE 3 **Sketching a line with a given slope**

Sketch a line passing through the point $(0, 4)$ and having slope $-\frac{2}{3}$.

Figure 1.43

Solution

Start by plotting the point $(0, 4)$. Because $m = \dfrac{\text{change in } y}{\text{change in } x}$, a slope of $-\frac{2}{3}$ indicates that the *y*-values *decrease* 2 units each time the *x*-values increase by 3 units. That is, the line *falls* 2 units for every 3-unit increase in the run. The line passes through $(0, 4)$, so a 2-unit decrease in *y* and a 3-unit increase in *x* results in the line passing through the point $(0 + 3, 4 - 2)$ or $(3, 2)$, as shown in Figure 1.43.

Now Try Exercise 39

Slope–Intercept Form of a Line

Suppose we want to graph $f(x) = 2x + 3$. Because $f(0) = 3$ and $f(1) = 5$, the graph is a line that passes through the points $(0, 3)$ and $(1, 5)$, as shown in Figure 1.44. Therefore the slope of this line is

$$m = \frac{5 - 3}{1 - 0} = 2.$$

Note that slope 2 equals the coefficient of x in $f(x) = 2x + 3$. In general, if $f(x) = mx + b$, then the slope of its graph is m.

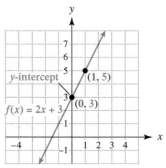

·**Figure 1.44**

The point $(0, 3)$ lies on the graph of $f(x) = 2x + 3$ and is located on the y-axis. The y-value of 3 is called the y-*intercept*. A **y-intercept** is the y-coordinate of a point where a graph intersects the y-axis. Because every point on the y-axis has 0 for its x-coordinate, we can locate the y-intercept by letting $x = 0$ in the formula for $f(x)$. In general, if $f(x) = mx + b$, then the y-intercept is

$$f(0) = m \cdot 0 + b = b.$$

Thus if $f(x) = -4x + 7$, then the y-intercept is 7 and the slope is -4.

Because $y = f(x)$, any linear function is given by $y = mx + b$, where m is the slope and b is the y-intercept. The form $y = mx + b$ is called the *slope–intercept form* of a line.

SLOPE–INTERCEPT FORM

The line with slope m and y-intercept b is given by

$$y = mx + b,$$

the **slope–intercept form** of a line.

EXAMPLE 4   ▶ **Graphing lines**

Identify the slope and y-intercept for the three lines $y = \frac{1}{2}x - 2$, $y = \frac{1}{2}x$, and $y = \frac{1}{2}x + 2$. Graph and compare the lines.

Solution

The graph of $y = \frac{1}{2}x - 2$ has slope $\frac{1}{2}$ and y-intercept -2. This line passes through the point $(0, -2)$ and rises 1 unit for each 2 units of run (see Figure 1.45). The graph of $y = \frac{1}{2}x$ has slope $\frac{1}{2}$ and y-intercept 0, and the graph of $y = \frac{1}{2}x + 2$ has slope $\frac{1}{2}$ and y-intercept 2. These lines are parallel, because the lines all have slope $\frac{1}{2}$, and the vertical distance between adjacent lines is always 2 because their y-intercepts are spaced 2 units apart.

Parallel Lines with Slope $\frac{1}{2}$

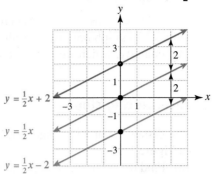

Figure 1.45

Now Try Exercise 49

EXAMPLE 5 | **Using a graph to write the slope–intercept form**

For the graphs shown in Figures 1.46 and 1.47, write the slope–intercept form of the line.

(a)

Figure 1.46

(b)

Figure 1.47

Solution

(a) The graph passes through $(0, -2)$, so the y-intercept is -2. Because the graph rises 3 units for each unit increase in x, the slope is 3. The slope–intercept form is $y = 3x - 2$.

(b) The graph passes through $(0, 2)$, so the y-intercept is 2. Because the graph is a horizontal line, its slope is 0. The slope–intercept form is $y = 0x + 2$, or more simply, $y = 2$.

Now Try Exercises 57, 59

EXAMPLE 6 | **Finding the slope–intercept form**

TABLE 1.13

x	y
-1	1
0	?
2	10

The points listed in Table 1.13 all lie on a line.
(a) Find the missing value in the table.
(b) Write the slope–intercept form of the line.

Solution

(a) The line passes through $(-1, 1)$ and $(2, 10)$, so its slope is

$$m = \frac{10 - 1}{2 - (-1)} = \frac{9}{3} = 3.$$

For each unit increase in x, y increases by 3. When x increases from -1 to 0, y increases from 1 to $1 + 3 = 4$. Therefore the missing value is 4.

(b) Because the line passes through the point $(0, 4)$, its y-intercept is 4. The slope–intercept form is $y = 3x + 4$.

Now Try Exercise 73

Interpreting Slope in Applications

▶ **REAL-WORLD CONNECTION** When a linear function is used to model physical quantities, the slope of its graph provides certain information. Slope can be interpreted as a **rate of change** of a quantity, which we illustrate in the next four examples.

EXAMPLE 7 **Interpreting slope**

The distance y in miles that an athlete riding a bicycle is from home after x hours is shown in Figure 1.48.
(a) Find the y-intercept. What does the y-intercept represent?
(b) The graph passes through the point $(2, 6)$. Discuss the meaning of this point.
(c) Find the slope–intercept form of this line. Interpret the slope as a rate of change.

Distance from Home

Figure 1.48

Solution

(a) The y-intercept is **30**, which indicates that the athlete is initially 30 miles from home.
(b) The point $(2, 6)$ means that after 2 hours the athlete is 6 miles from home.
(c) The line passes through the points $(0, 30)$ and $(2, 6)$. Thus its slope is

$$m = \frac{6 - 30}{2 - 0} = -12,$$

and the slope–intercept form is $y = -12x + 30$. A slope of -12 indicates that the athlete is traveling at 12 miles per hour *toward* home. The negative sign indicates that the distance between the athlete and home is *decreasing*.

Now Try Exercise 83

READING CHECK

Explain how slope can be interpreted as a rate of change.

EXAMPLE 8 **Interpreting slope**

Water is being pumped into a 500-gallon tank during a 10-minute interval. The amount of water W in the tank after t minutes is given by $W(t) = 40t + 100$, where W is in gallons.
(a) Evaluate $W(0)$ and $W(10)$. Interpret each result.
(b) Graph W for $0 \le t \le 10$.
(c) What is the slope of the graph of W? Interpret this slope.

Solution

(a) $W(0) = 40(0) + 100 = 100$; $W(10) = 40(10) + 100 = 500$. Initially, there are 100 gallons of water in the tank. After 10 minutes, there are 500 gallons and the tank is full.
(b) Because $W(0) = 100$ and $W(10) = 500$, plot the points $(0, 100)$ and $(10, 500)$. Function W is linear, so connect these points with a line segment. See Figure 1.49.

Figure 1.49

(c) The slope is 40, which indicates that water is being pumped into the tank at a rate of 40 gallons per minute.

▌ Now Try Exercise 89

EXAMPLE 9 ▌ **Analyzing growth of Wal-Mart**

Table 1.14 lists numbers of Wal-Mart employees.
(a) Make a line graph of the data.
(b) Find the slope of each line segment in the graph.
(c) Interpret these slopes as rates of change.

TABLE 1.14 Wal-Mart Employees (millions)

Year	Employees
1999	1.1
2002	1.4
2007	2.2
2010	2.1

Source: Wal-Mart.

Solution

(a) To make a line graph, start by plotting the points (1999, 1.1), (2002, 1.4), (2007, 2.2), and (2010, 2.1). Connecting these points with line segments results in Figure 1.50.

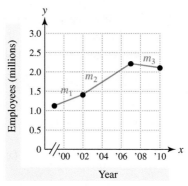

Figure 1.50

(b) The slopes of the line segments in Figure 1.50 are

$$m_1 = \frac{1.4 - 1.1}{2002 - 1999} = 0.1, \quad m_2 = \frac{2.2 - 1.4}{2007 - 2002} = 0.16, \text{ and}$$

$$m_3 = \frac{2.1 - 2.2}{2010 - 2007} = -\frac{1}{30} \approx -0.033.$$

(c) Slope $m_1 = 0.1$ means that, on average, the number of Wal-Mart employees increased by 0.1 million (or 100,000) per year between 1999 and 2002. Slopes m_2 and m_3 can be interpreted similarly. Note that m_3 is *negative* and indicates that the number of employees *decreased*.

▌ Now Try Exercise 79

EXAMPLE 10 **Analyzing growth in computer viruses**

In 2000 there were only 50 thousand computer viruses, but by 2010 this number had grown to 1.6 million. (*Source*: Symantec.)

(a) Calculate the slope m of a line that passes through the points (2000, 50000) and (2010, 1600000).

(b) Interpret m as a rate of change.

Solution

(a) $m = \dfrac{1{,}600{,}000 - 50{,}000}{2010 - 2000} = \dfrac{1{,}550{,}000}{10} = 155{,}000$

(b) *On average*, the number of computer viruses has increased by 155,000 per year from 2000 to 2010.

Now Try Exercise 97

CRITICAL THINKING

An athlete runs away from home at 10 miles per hour for 30 minutes and then jogs back home at 5 miles per hour. Sketch a graph that shows the distance between the athlete and home.

1.3 Putting It All Together

The "tilt" of a line is called the slope and equals rise over run. A positive slope indicates that the line *rises* from left to right, whereas a negative slope indicates that the line *falls* from left to right. A horizontal line has zero slope and a vertical line has undefined slope.

CONCEPT	EXPLANATION	EXAMPLE
Slope	The slope of the line passing through the points (x_1, y_1) and (x_2, y_2) is given by $$m = \frac{\text{rise}}{\text{run}} = \frac{y_2 - y_1}{x_2 - x_1}, (x_1 \neq x_2).$$ rise = change in y run = change in x	The slope of the line passing through $(-2, 3)$ and $(1, 5)$ is $$m = \frac{5 - 3}{1 - (-2)} = \frac{2}{3}.$$ If the x-values increase by 3 units, the y-values increase by 2 units.
Slope–Intercept Form for a Line	The slope equals m, and the y-intercept equals b. $$y = mx + b$$	If $y = \frac{1}{2}x + 1$, the slope of the graph is $\frac{1}{2}$ and the y-intercept is 1.

CONCEPT	EXPLANATION	EXAMPLE
Slope as a Rate of Change	The slope of the graph of a linear function indicates the rate at which a quantity is either increasing or decreasing.	From 1981 to 2010, average public college tuition and fees can be modeled by $$f(x) = 175x + 683,$$ where $x = 1$ corresponds to 1981. The slope of the graph of f is $m = 175$ and indicates that, on average, tuition and fees increased by \$175 per year between 1981 and 2010.

1.3 Exercises

CONCEPTS AND VOCABULARY

1. Slope is equal to *change in* _____ divided by *change in* _____.

2. If two points have the same *y*-coordinates but different *x*-coordinates, then the slope of the line passing through these points is _____.

3. A line with positive slope _____ from left to right.

4. A line with slope 0 is a(n) _____ line.

5. A line with undefined slope is a(n) _____ line.

6. The form $y = mx + b$ is called the _____ form for a line.

INTERPRETATION OF *y*-INTERCEPTS

Exercises 7–10: Explain the meaning of the y-intercept in each situation.

7. $C(x) = \frac{1}{3}x + 9$ models the cost in billions of dollars of pet health care x years after 1999.

8. $A(x) = 1000 - 5x$ models the gallons of water in a large tank.

9. $S(x) = 110x + 123$ models the number of Skype users in millions x years after 2006.

10. $K(x) = 93x$ models the number of texts sent in x days by the average American kid.

SLOPE

Exercises 11–16: Find the slope of the line.

11.

12.

13.

14.

15.

16.

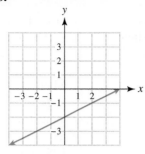

Exercises 17–34: Find the slope of the line passing through the two points.

17. $(1, 2), (2, 4)$

18. $(-3, 2), (2, -3)$

19. $(2, 1), (-1, 3)$

20. $\left(-\frac{3}{5}, -\frac{4}{5}\right), \left(\frac{4}{5}, \frac{3}{5}\right)$

21. $(-3, 6), (4, 6)$

22. $(-3, 5), (-5, 5)$

23. $\left(\frac{1}{2}, -\frac{2}{7}\right), \left(\frac{1}{2}, \frac{13}{17}\right)$

24. $(-1, 6), (-1, -4)$

25. $\left(\frac{1}{3}, -\frac{4}{3}\right), \left(\frac{1}{6}, \frac{1}{3}\right)$

26. $\left(-\frac{1}{2}, \frac{3}{2}\right), \left(2, \frac{1}{2}\right)$

27. $(1989, 10), (1999, 16)$

28. $(1950, 6.1), (2000, 10.6)$

29. $(2.1, 3.6), (-1.2, 4.3)$

30. $(12, -34), (14, 64)$

31. Thinking Generally $(2a, b), (3a, 4b)$

32. Thinking Generally $(-a, -b), (b, a)$

33. Thinking Generally $(a + b, 0), (a, b)$

34. Thinking Generally $(a, b), (b, a)$

Exercises 35–38: Do the following.

    (a) *Find the slope of the line passing through the given points.*
    (b) *Plot these points and graph the line.*
    (c) *Interpret the slope.*

35. $(-1, 2), (3, -1)$

36. $(-2, -2), (1, 3)$

37. $(0, 2), (-3, 0)$

38. $(-1, 2), (1, 2)$

Exercises 39–46: Sketch a line passing through the given point with slope m.

39. $(0, -2), m = 3$

40. $(0, 1), m = -1$

41. $(0, 4), m = -\frac{1}{2}$

42. $(0, -3), m = \frac{2}{3}$

43. $(-1, 1), m = -2$

44. $(2, 1), m = \frac{1}{2}$

45. $(2, -3), m = \frac{1}{2}$

46. $(-2, 3), m = -\frac{3}{5}$

SLOPE–INTERCEPT FORM

Exercises 47–56: Do the following.

    (a) *Find the slope and y-intercept of the line.*
    (b) *Graph the equation.*

47. $y = x + 2$

48. $y = x - 2$

49. $y = -3x + 2$

50. $y = \frac{1}{2}x - 1$

51. $y = \frac{1}{3}x$

52. $y = -2x$

53. $y = 2$

54. $y = -3$

55. $y = -x + 3$

56. $y = \frac{2}{3}x - 2$

Exercises 57–62: Use the graph to express the line in slope–intercept form.

57.

58.

59.

60.

61.

62.

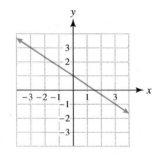

Exercises 63–66: Write the slope–intercept form for a line satisfying the following conditions.

63. Slope 3, y-intercept -5

64. Slope $-\frac{2}{3}$, y-intercept 7

65. Passing through $(1, 0)$ and $\left(0, -\frac{3}{2}\right)$

66. Passing through $(0, 4)$ and $(-2, 0)$

Exercises 67–70: Let f be a linear function. Use the table to find the slope and y-intercept of the graph of f.

67.

x	0	1	2	3
f(x)	−2	0	2	4

68.

x	−1	0	1	2
f(x)	5	10	15	20

69.

x	−2	−1	1	2
f(x)	18	11	−3	−10

70.

x	−4	−2	2	4
f(x)	6	3	−3	−6

Exercises 71–74: Let $f(x)$ represent a linear function.

    (a) *Find the missing value in the table.*
    (b) *Write the slope–intercept form for f.*

71.

x	0	1	2
f(x)	−1	1	?

72.

x	1	2	3
f(x)	12	8	?

73.

x	−2	0	4
f(x)	2	?	11

74.

x	0	5	20
f(x)	?	10	40

INTERPRETING SLOPE

Exercises 75–78: Modeling Choose the graph (a.–d.) at the top of the next column that models the situation best.

75. Money that a person earns after x hours, working for $10 per hour

76. Total acres of rain forests in the world during the past 20 years

77. World population from 1980 to 2010

78. Square miles of land in Nevada from 1950 to 2010

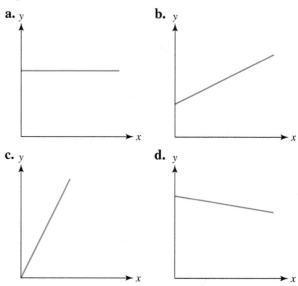

Exercises 79–82: Modeling Each line graph represents the gallons of water in a small swimming pool after x hours. Assume that a pump can either add water to or remove water from the pool.

    (a) *Estimate the slope of each line segment.*
    (b) *Interpret each slope as a rate of change.*
    (c) *Describe what happened to the amount of water in the pool.*

79.

80.

81.

82.

Exercises 83 and 84: Modeling Distance An individual is driving a car along a straight road. The graph shows the distance that the driver is from home after x hours.

   (a) *Find the slope of each line segment in the graph.*
   (b) *Interpret each slope as a rate of change.*
   (c) *Describe both the motion and location of the car.*

83.

84.

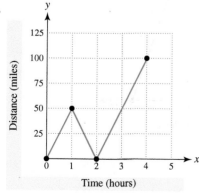

Exercises 85–88: Sketching a Model Sketch a graph that models the given situation.

85. The distance that a bicycle rider is from home if the rider is initially 20 miles away from home and arrives home after riding at a constant speed for 2 hours

86. The distance that an athlete is from home if the athlete runs away from home at 8 miles per hour for 30 minutes and then walks back home at 4 miles per hour

87. The distance that a person is from home if this individual drives (at a constant speed) to a mall, stays 2 hours, and then drives home, assuming that the distance to the mall is 20 miles and that the trip takes 30 minutes

88. The amount of water in a 10,000-gallon swimming pool that is filled at the rate of 1000 gallons per hour, left full for 10 hours, and then drained at the rate of 2000 gallons per hour

APPLICATIONS

89. *Online Ads* Revenues R in billions of dollars for online advertisements from 2005 to 2010 can be estimated by the formula

$$R(x) = \frac{10}{3}x - 6670,$$

where x is the year. (*Source*: Interactive Advertising Bureau.)
   (a) Estimate the revenue in 2005 and in 2008.
   (b) Graph $y = R(x)$.
   (c) What is the slope of the graph?
   (d) Interpret the slope as a rate of change.

90. *Newspaper Ads* Revenues R in billions of dollars for newspaper advertisements from 2005 to 2010 can be estimated by

$$R(x) = -\frac{13}{3}x + 8736,$$

where x is the year. (*Source*: Newspaper Association of America.)
   (a) Estimate the revenue in 2005 and in 2008.
   (b) Graph $y = R(x)$.
   (c) What is the slope of the graph?
   (d) Interpret the slope as a rate of change.

91. *Marathon Finishers* From 2000 to 2010, the number of marathon finishers M in thousands t years after 2000 can be estimated by

$$M(t) = 18.8t + 299.$$

(*Source*: Marathon Guide.)
   (a) How many marathon finishers were there during 2009?
   (b) What is the slope and y-intercept for the graph of the linear function M?

(c) Interpret the slope as a rate of change.
(d) Interpret the *y*-intercept.

92. *Number of Radio Stations* The number of radio stations on the air from 1950 to 2008 may be modeled by

$$f(x) = 201.7x - 390,477,$$

where *x* is the year. (*Source:* National Association of Broadcasters.)
(a) How many radio stations were on the air in 1980?
(b) What is the slope of the graph of *f*?
(c) Interpret the slope as a rate of change.

93. *Filling a Swimming Pool* A 20,000-gallon swimming pool is being filled at a constant rate. Over a 5-hour period the water in the pool increases from $\frac{1}{4}$ full to $\frac{5}{8}$ full. At what rate is water entering the pool?

94. *Speed of an Airplane* An airplane on a 1200-mile trip is flying at a constant rate. Over a 2-hour period the location of the plane changes from covering $\frac{1}{3}$ of the distance to covering $\frac{7}{8}$ of the distance. What is the speed of the airplane?

95. *Cost of Carpet* The graph shows the cost of buying *x* square yards of carpet. Find the slope of this graph and interpret the result.

96. *Cost of Removing Snow* The graph shows the cost of removing *x* tons of snow. Find the slope of this graph and interpret the result.

97. *Pet Health Care* In 1984 spending on health care for pets was $4 billion, and by 2008 it had increased to $12 billion. (*Source:* American Express Institute.)
(a) Calculate the slope *m* of the line that passes through the points $(1984, 4)$ and $(2008, 12)$.
(b) Interpret *m* as a rate of change.

98. *Manufacturing Employment* In 1956, employees of manufacturing firms accounted for 30% of the total employment in the United States. In 2010, this percentage was 9%. (*Source:* U.S. Census Bureau.)
(a) Calculate the slope *m* of the line that passes through $(1956, 30)$ and $(2010, 9)$.
(b) Interpret *m* as a rate of change.

99. *U.S. Median Family Income* In 1990, the median family income was about $35,000, and in 2007 it was about $60,000. (*Source:* Department of the Treasury.)
(a) Let *x* be the number of years after 1990. Find values for *m* and *b* so that $f(x) = mx + b$ models the data.
(b) Estimate the median family income in 2000.

100. *Minimum Wage* In 1980, the minimum wage was about $3.10 per hour, and in 2009 it increased to $7.25. (*Source:* Department of Labor.)
(a) Let *x* be the number of years after 1980. Find values for *m* and *b* so that $f(x) = ax + b$ models the data.
(b) If this trend continues, what should be the minimum wage in 2020?

WRITING ABOUT MATHEMATICS

101. Describe the information that the slope *m* of a line gives. Be as complete as possible.

102. Could one line have two different slope–intercept forms? Explain your answer.

Group Activity Working with Real Data

Directions: Form a group of 2 to 4 people. Select someone to record the group's responses for this activity. All members should work cooperatively to answer the questions. If your instructor asks for the results, each member of the group should be prepared to respond.

U.S. Craigslist Visitors The following table lists the average number of *unique* visitors to Craigslist for selected years.

Year	2006	2007	2008
Visitors	180,000	288,000	420,000

Year	2009	2010
Visitors	516,000	624,000

Soruce: Citi Investment Research and Analysis.

(a) Make a scatterplot of the data. Let *x* represent the number of years after 2006. Discuss any trend in numbers of visitors to Craigslist.

(b) Estimate the slope of a line that could be used to model the data.

(c) Find an equation of a line $y = mx + b$ that models the data.

(d) Interpret the slope as a rate of change.

(e) Use your results to estimate numbers of *unique* visitors to Craigslist in 2012.

1.4 Equations of Lines and Linear Models

Point–Slope Form • Horizontal and Vertical Lines • Parallel and Perpendicular Lines

A LOOK INTO MATH ▶

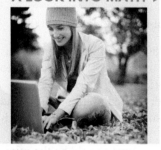

In 2000, there were approximately 124 million Internet users in the United States, and this number grew to about 240 million in 2010. This growth is illustrated in Figure 1.51, where the line passes through the points (2000, 124) and (2010, 240). In this section we discuss how to find the equation of the line that models these data. To do so we start by discussing the *point–slope form* of a line.

NEW VOCABULARY

☐ Equation of a line
☐ Point–slope form
☐ Equivalent equations
☐ *x*-intercept
☐ Horizontal line
☐ Vertical line
☐ Parallel line
☐ Perpendicular line
☐ Negative reciprocals

U.S. Internet Users

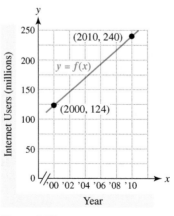

Figure 1.51

Point–Slope Form

If we know the slope m and y-intercept b of a line, we can write its slope–intercept form, $y = mx + b$. The slope–intercept form is an example of an **equation of a line**. The point–slope form is a different form of the equation of a line.

Suppose that a (nonvertical) line with slope m passes through the point (x_1, y_1). If (x, y) is a different point on this line, then $m = \frac{y - y_1}{x - x_1}$ (see Figure 1.52).

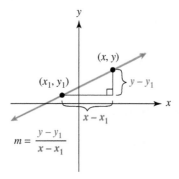

Figure 1.52

We can use this slope formula to find the point–slope form.

$$m = \frac{y - y_1}{x - x_1} \qquad \text{Slope formula}$$

$$m(x - x_1) = y - y_1 \qquad \text{Multiply each side by } (x - x_1).$$

$$y - y_1 = m(x - x_1) \qquad \text{Rewrite the equation.}$$

$$y = m(x - x_1) + y_1 \qquad \text{Add } y_1 \text{ to each side.}$$

The equation $y - y_1 = m(x - x_1)$ is traditionally called the *point–slope form*. We frequently think of y as being a function of x, written $y = f(x)$, so the equivalent form $y = m(x - x_1) + y_1$ is also referred to as the point–slope form.

POINT–SLOPE FORM

The line with slope m passing through the point (x_1, y_1) is given by

$$y = m(x - x_1) + y_1,$$

or, equivalently,

$$y - y_1 = m(x - x_1),$$

the **point–slope form** of a line.

EXAMPLE 1   **Using the point–slope form**

Sketch a line passing through the point $(1, 2)$ with slope -3. Find the point–slope form of this line. Does the point $(2, -1)$ lie on this line?

Solution

First, plot the point $(1, 2)$. Because the slope is -3, this line decreases 3 units along the y-axis for each 1-unit increase along the x-axis. See Figure 1.53.

To find the equation of this line, let $m = -3$ and $(x_1, y_1) = (1, 2)$ in the point–slope form.

$$y = m(x - x_1) + y_1 \qquad \text{Point–slope form}$$

$$y = -3(x - 1) + 2 \qquad \text{Substitute.}$$

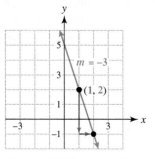

Figure 1.53 Slope $= -3$

To determine whether the point $(2, -1)$ lies on the line, substitute 2 for x and -1 for y in the equation $y = -3(x - 1) + 2$.

$$-1 \stackrel{?}{=} -3(2 - 1) + 2 \qquad \text{Let } x = 2 \text{ and } y = -1.$$

$$-1 \stackrel{?}{=} -3 + 2 \qquad \text{Simplify.}$$

$$-1 = -1 \checkmark \qquad \text{The point satisfies the equation.}$$

The point $(2, -1)$ lies on the line because it satisfies the point–slope form.

▮ Now Try Exercise 39

We can use the point–slope form to find the equation of a line passing through two points.

EXAMPLE 2 **Applying the point–slope form**

Find an equation of the line passing through $(-2, 3)$ and $(6, -1)$.

Solution
Before we can apply the point–slope form, we must find the slope.

$$m = \frac{y_2 - y_1}{x_2 - x_1} \qquad \text{Slope formula}$$

$$= \frac{-1 - 3}{6 - (-2)} \qquad \text{Substitute.}$$

$$= -\frac{1}{2} \qquad \text{Simplify.}$$

We can use either $(-2, 3)$ or $(6, -1)$ for (x_1, y_1) in the point–slope form. If we choose $(-2, 3)$, the point–slope form becomes the following.

$$y = m(x - x_1) + y_1 \qquad \text{Point–slope form}$$

$$y = -\frac{1}{2}(x - (-2)) + 3 \qquad \text{Let } x_1 = -2 \text{ and } y_1 = 3.$$

$$y = -\frac{1}{2}(x + 2) + 3 \qquad \text{Simplify.}$$

If we choose $(6, -1)$, the point–slope form with $x_1 = 6$ and $y_1 = -1$ becomes

$$y = -\frac{1}{2}(x - 6) - 1.$$

Note that, although the two point–slope forms appear to be different, they are **equivalent equations** because their graphs are identical.

▮ Now Try Exercise 33

READING CHECK

Give the slope–intercept and the point–slope forms of a line.

NOTE: Example 2 illustrates the fact that the point–slope form *is not* unique for a given line. However, the slope–intercept form *is* unique because each line has a unique slope and a unique y-intercept. If we simplify both point–slope forms in Example 2, they have the same slope–intercept form.

$$y = -\frac{1}{2}(x + 2) + 3 \qquad y = -\frac{1}{2}(x - 6) - 1 \qquad \text{Different point–slope forms}$$

$$y = -\frac{1}{2}x - 1 + 3 \qquad y = -\frac{1}{2}x + 3 - 1 \qquad \text{Distributive property}$$

$$y = -\frac{1}{2}x + 2 \qquad y = -\frac{1}{2}x + 2 \qquad \text{Identical slope–intercept forms}$$

We can use the *slope–intercept form*, $y = mx + b$, instead of the point–slope form to find the equation of a line, as illustrated in the next example.

EXAMPLE 3 | **Applying the slope–intercept form**

Find the equation of the line that passes through the points $(-3, 9)$ and $(1, 1)$.

Solution

First, find the slope of the line.

$$m = \frac{y_2 - y_1}{x_2 - x_1} = \frac{1 - 9}{1 - (-3)} = -\frac{8}{4} = -2$$

Now substitute -2 for m and $(-3, 9)$ for x and y in the slope–intercept form. (The point $(1, 1)$ could be used instead.)

$$y = mx + b \qquad \text{Slope–intercept form}$$
$$9 = -2(-3) + b \qquad \text{Let } y = 9, m = -2, \text{ and } x = -3.$$
$$9 = 6 + b \qquad \text{Simplify.}$$
$$3 = b \qquad \text{Solve for } b.$$

Thus the slope–intercept form is $y = -2x + 3$.

▌ Now Try Exercise 47

▶ **REAL-WORLD CONNECTION** In the next example we model the data presented in A look Into Math for this section.

EXAMPLE 4 | **Modeling growth in Internet users**

In 2000, there were approximately 124 million Internet users in the United States, and this number grew to about 240 million in 2010 (see Figure 1.51).
(a) Find values for m, x_1, and y_1 so that $f(x) = m(x - x_1) + y_1$ models these data.
(b) Interpret this equation.
(c) Use f to estimate Internet users in 2012.

Solution

(a) The slope of the line passing through $(2000, 124)$ and $(2010, 240)$ is

$$m = \frac{240 - 124}{2010 - 2000} = \frac{116}{10} = 11.6.$$

Thus by choosing the point $(2000, 124)$ for the point–slope form, we can write

$$f(x) = 11.6(x - 2000) + 124.$$

(b) From the point–slope form it is apparent that $m = 11.6$ and that $f(2000) = 124$. This means that in 2000 there were 124 million Internet users and that this number grew, on average, by 11.6 million per year.
(c) $f(2012) = 11.6(2012 - 2000) + 124 \approx 263$ million.

▌ Now Try Exercise 117

Intercepts

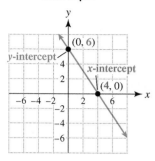

Figure 1.54 *x*-intercept 4; *y*-intercept 6

Modeling and the Dependent Variable *x*

From Example 4, $f(x) = 11.6(x - 2000) + 124$ models the number of Internet users in the United States. In this formula *x* represents the actual year. We could also model the number of Internet users with $g(x) = 11.6x + 124$, where $x = 0$ corresponds to 2000, $x = 1$ to 2001, and so on. Then to estimate the number of Internet users in 2012, we let $x = 12$.

FINDING *x*- AND *y*-INTERCEPTS If a line intersects the *y*-axis at the point (0, 6), the *y-intercept* is 6. Similarly, if the line intersects the *x*-axis at the point (4, 0), the *x-intercept* is 4. This line and its intercepts are illustrated in Figure 1.54. The *x*-coordinate of a point where a graph intersects the *x*-axis is called the ***x*-intercept**. The next example interprets intercepts in a physical situation.

EXAMPLE 5   **Modeling water in a pool**

A small swimming pool containing 6000 gallons of water is emptied by a pump removing 1200 gallons per hour.
(a) How long does it take to empty the pool?
(b) Sketch a function *f* that models the amount of water in the pool after *x* hours.
(c) Identify the *x*-intercept and the *y*-intercept. Interpret each intercept.
(d) Find the slope–intercept form of the line. Interpret the slope as a rate of change.
(e) What are the domain and range of *f*?

Solution
(a) The time needed to empty the pool is $\frac{6000}{1200} = 5$ hours.
(b) Initially the pool contains 6000 gallons, and after 5 hours the pool is empty. Because water is being removed at a constant rate the graph of *f* is a *line* (segment) passing through (0, 6000) and (5, 0), as shown in Figure 1.55.

Water in a Pool

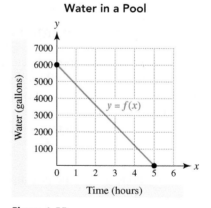

Figure 1.55

Can the graph of a function have more than one *y*-intercept? Explain.

Can the graph of a function have more than one *x*-intercept? Explain.

(c) The *x*-intercept is 5, which means that after 5 hours the pool is empty. The *y*-intercept of 6000 means that initially (when $x = 0$) the pool contained 6000 gallons of water.
(d) To find the equation of the line shown in Figure 1.55, we first find the slope of the line passing through the points (0, 6000) and (5, 0).

$$m = \frac{y_2 - y_1}{x_2 - x_1} \qquad \text{Slope formula}$$

$$= \frac{0 - 6000}{5 - 0} \qquad \text{Substitute.}$$

$$= -1200 \qquad \text{Simplify.}$$

The slope is -1200 and the y-intercept is 6000, so the slope–intercept form is

$$y = -1200x + 6000.$$

The pump *removed* water at the rate of 1200 gallons per hour.

(e) The domain is $D: 0 \le x \le 5$, and the range is $R: 0 \le y \le 6000$.

▌ Now Try Exercise 91

In the next example we introduce a method for modeling linear data by hand.

EXAMPLE 6   Modeling linear data by hand

Find a line $y = mx + b$ that models the data in Table 1.15.

TABLE 1.15

x	10	20	30	40	50
y	15	24	30	39	45

Solution

STEP 1: *Carefully make a scatterplot of the data.* Be sure to properly label the x- and y-axes. For the data in Table 1.15 we can label each axis from 0 to 60 and have each hash mark represent 10 units. A scatterplot of the data is shown in Figure 1.56.

Scatterplot

Figure 1.56

Modeling Linear Data

Figure 1.57

STEP 2: *Sketch a line that models the data.* You may want to use a ruler for this step. In Figure 1.57 a line is drawn that passes through the first and fourth data points. Your line may be slightly different. Note that the line does not have to pass through *any* of the data points.

STEP 3: *Choose two points on the line and find the equation of the line.* The line in Figure 1.57 passes through $(10, 15)$ and $(40, 39)$. Therefore its slope is

$$m = \frac{39 - 15}{40 - 10} = \frac{24}{30} = \frac{4}{5}.$$

The equation of the line is

$$y = \frac{4}{5}(x - 10) + 15 \quad \text{or} \quad y = \frac{4}{5}x + 7.$$

Note that answers may vary because the data are not exactly linear.

▌ Now Try Exercise 103

STUDY TIP

Finding equations of lines is an important skill in this and future math courses.

Modeling, Lines, and Linear Functions

If a set of data is modeled by $y = mx + b$, then the data are also modeled by the linear function defined by $f(x) = mx + b$ because $y = f(x)$. In Example 6 the data set is modeled by $y = \frac{4}{5}x + 7$, so it is also modeled by $f(x) = \frac{4}{5}x + 7$.

Horizontal and Vertical Lines

Table 1.16 represents the constant function $f(x) = 3$. Every output y is 3, regardless of the input x. The graph of a constant function is a horizontal line, and the graph of $f(x) = 3$ is a horizontal line with y-intercept **3**, as shown in Figure 1.58. Its equation may be expressed as $y = 3$, so every point on the line has a y-coordinate of **3**. In general, the equation $y = b$ represents a horizontal line with y-intercept b, as shown in Figure 1.59.

TABLE 1.16

x	y
−4	3
−2	3
0	3
2	3
4	3

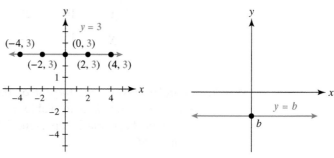

Figure 1.58   Figure 1.59

Table 1.17 represents points on a vertical line. A vertical line cannot be represented by a function because different points on a vertical line have the same x-coordinate. The equation of the vertical line depicted in Figure 1.60 is $x = 3$. Every point on the line $x = 3$ has an x-coordinate equal to **3**. In general, the equation of a vertical line with x-intercept h is $x = h$, as shown in Figure 1.61.

TABLE 1.17

x	y
3	−6
3	−4
3	−2
3	2
3	4
3	6

y is *not* a function of x.

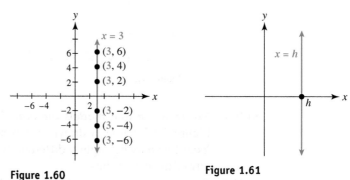

Figure 1.60   Figure 1.61

EQUATIONS OF HORIZONTAL AND VERTICAL LINES

The equation of a horizontal line with y-intercept b is $y = b$.

The equation of a vertical line with x-intercept h is $x = h$.

▶ **REAL-WORLD CONNECTION** Vertical lines are sometimes used in economics. For example, because there is no substitute for insulin, the demand for insulin remains *constant* even though the price may fluctuate. The demand for insulin is said to be *inelastic*. Demand

and price are shown graphically by placing the demand D on the horizontal axis and the price P on the vertical axis. See Figure 1.62, where the vertical line segment shows how the demand remains constant on the horizontal axis even though the price varies along the vertical axis. (See Exercise 95.)

Demand for Insulin

Figure 1.62 Inelastic Demand

EXAMPLE 7   **Finding equations of horizontal and vertical lines**

Find equations of the vertical and horizontal lines that pass through the point $(-3, 4)$. Graph these two lines.

Solution
The x-coordinate of the point $(-3, 4)$ is -3. The vertical line $x = -3$ passes through *every* point in the xy-plane with an x-coordinate of -3, including the point $(-3, 4)$. Similarly, the horizontal line $y = 4$ passes through *every* point with a y-coordinate of 4, including the point $(-3, 4)$. The lines $x = -3$ and $y = 4$ are graphed in Figure 1.63.

Figure 1.63

Now Try Exercises 79, 81

TECHNOLOGY NOTE:

CALCULATOR HELP
To graph a vertical line, see Appendix A (page AP-5).

Graphing Vertical Lines
The equation of a vertical line is $x = h$ and cannot be expressed on a graphing calculator in the form "$Y_1 = $". Some graphing calculators graph a vertical line by accessing the DRAW menu. The accompanying figure shows a calculator graph of Figure 1.63.

$[-6, 6, 1]$ by $[-6, 6, 1]$

Parallel and Perpendicular Lines

Slope is important when we are determining whether two lines are parallel. For example, the lines $y = 2x$ and $y = 2x + 1$ are parallel because they both have slope 2.

> ### PARALLEL LINES
>
> Two lines with the same slope are parallel.
> Two nonvertical parallel lines have the same slope.

EXAMPLE 8 **Finding parallel lines**

Find the slope–intercept form of a line parallel to $y = -2x + 5$, passing through $(-4, 3)$.

Solution
Because the line $y = -2x + 5$ has slope -2, any parallel line also has slope -2. The line passing through $(-4, 3)$ with slope -2 is determined as follows.

$$y = -2(x - (-4)) + 3 \qquad \text{Point–slope form}$$
$$y = -2(x + 4) + 3 \qquad \text{Simplify.}$$
$$y = -2x - 8 + 3 \qquad \text{Distributive property}$$
$$y = -2x - 5 \qquad \text{Slope–intercept form}$$

Now Try Exercise 59

Figure 1.64 shows three pairs of perpendicular lines with their slopes labeled. Note in Figures 1.64(a) and 1.64(b) that the product $m_1 m_2$ equals -1. That is,

$$m_1 m_2 = 1 \cdot (-1) = -1 \quad \text{and} \quad m_1 m_2 = 2 \cdot \left(-\frac{1}{2}\right) = -1.$$

A more general situation for two perpendicular lines is shown in Figure 1.64(c), where

$$m_1 m_2 = m_1 \cdot \left(-\frac{1}{m_1}\right) = -1.$$

That is, if two nonvertical lines are perpendicular, then the product of their slopes is -1.

Perpendicular Lines

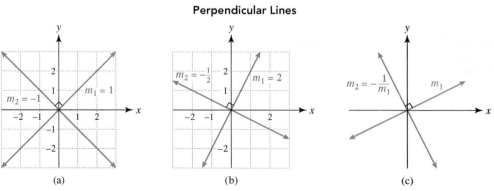

(a) (b) (c)

Figure 1.64

These results are summarized in the following box.

PERPENDICULAR LINES

Two lines with nonzero slopes m_1 and m_2 are perpendicular if $m_1 m_2 = -1$.

If two lines have slopes m_1 and m_2 such that $m_1 \cdot m_2 = -1$, then they are perpendicular.

A vertical line and a horizontal line are perpendicular.

Table 1.18 shows examples of slopes m_1 and m_2 that result in perpendicular lines because $m_1 m_2 = -1$. Note that m_1 and m_2 are **negative reciprocals** of each other; that is, $m_2 = -\frac{1}{m_1}$ and $m_1 = -\frac{1}{m_2}$.

READING CHECK

How are the slopes of two parallel lines related? How are the slopes of two perpendicular lines related?

TABLE 1.18 Slopes of Perpendicular Lines m_1 and m_2

m_1	1	$-\frac{1}{2}$	-4	$\frac{2}{3}$	$\frac{3}{4}$	$-\frac{5}{4}$
m_2	-1	2	$\frac{1}{4}$	$-\frac{3}{2}$	$-\frac{4}{3}$	$\frac{4}{5}$
$m_1 m_2$	-1	-1	-1	-1	-1	-1

EXAMPLE 9   **Finding perpendicular lines**

Find the slope–intercept form of the line perpendicular to $y = -\frac{1}{2}x + 1$, passing through the point $(3, 2)$. Graph the two lines.

Solution

The line $y = -\frac{1}{2}x + 1$ has slope $m_1 = -\frac{1}{2}$. From Table 1.18 the slope of a line that is perpendicular to this line is $m_2 = 2$. The slope–intercept form of a line having slope **2** and passing through $(3, 2)$ can be found as follows.

$$y = 2(x - 3) + 2 \qquad \text{Point–slope form}$$
$$y = 2x - 6 + 2 \qquad \text{Distributive property}$$
$$y = 2x - 4 \qquad \text{Slope–intercept form}$$

A graph of these perpendicular lines is shown in Figure 1.65.

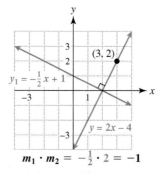

Figure 1.65

Now Try Exercise 71

CALCULATOR HELP

To set a square viewing rectangle, see Appendix A (pages AP-5 and AP-6).

$[-6, 6, 1]$ by $[-4, 4, 1]$

$y = -\frac{1}{2}x + 1$ ← $y = 2x - 4$

TECHNOLOGY NOTE:

Square Viewing Rectangles

The figure to the left shows a square viewing rectangle in which the perpendicular lines from Example 9 intersect at 90°. Try graphing the two perpendicular lines in Example 9 by using the viewing rectangle $[-6, 6, 1]$ by $[-10, 10, 1]$. Do the lines appear perpendicular? For many graphing calculators, a square viewing rectangle results when the distance along the y-axis is about $\frac{2}{3}$ the distance along the x-axis. On some graphing calculators you can create a square viewing rectangle automatically by using the ZOOM menu.

EXAMPLE 10 Equations of perpendicular lines

Find the slope–intercept form of each line shown in Figure 1.66. Verify that the two lines are perpendicular.

Solution

In Figure 1.67, the graph of y_1 is shown to have slope $m_1 = \frac{2}{3}$ because the line rises 2 units for every 3 units of run. Its y-intercept is -2, and its slope–intercept form is $y_1 = \frac{2}{3}x - 2$. Similarly, the graph of y_2 is shown to have slope $m_2 = -\frac{3}{2}$ because the line falls 3 units for every 2 units of run. Its y-intercept is 1, and its slope–intercept form is $y = -\frac{3}{2}x + 1$. To be perpendicular, the product of their slopes must equal -1; that is,

$$m_1 \cdot m_2 = \frac{2}{3} \cdot \left(-\frac{3}{2}\right) = -1. \checkmark \quad \text{It checks.}$$

Figure 1.66 Perpendicular Lines

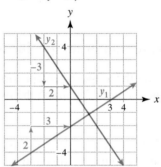

Figure 1.67

Now Try Exercise 75

1.4 Putting It All Together

CONCEPT	EXPLANATION	EXAMPLE
Point–Slope Form	$y = m(x - x_1) + y_1$ or $y - y_1 = m(x - x_1)$ Used to find an equation of a line, given two points or one point and the slope	Given two points $(1, 2)$ and $(3, 5)$, first compute $$m = \frac{5 - 2}{3 - 1} = \frac{3}{2}.$$ An equation of this line is $$y = \frac{3}{2}(x - 1) + 2.$$
Slope–Intercept Form	$y = mx + b$ A unique equation for a line, determined by the slope m and the y-intercept b	An equation of the line with slope $m = 3$ and y-intercept $b = -5$ is $y = 3x - 5$.

The graph of a linear function f is a line. Therefore linear functions can be represented by

$$f(x) = mx + b \quad \text{or} \quad f(x) = m(x - x_1) + y_1.$$

CONCEPT	EQUATION(S)	EXAMPLE
Horizontal Line	$y = b$, where b is a constant	A horizontal line passing through $(-3, 5)$ has the equation $y = 5$.
Vertical Line	$x = h$, where h is a constant	A vertical line passing through $(-3, 5)$ has the equation $x = -3$.
Parallel Lines	$y = m_1x + b_1$ and $y = m_2x + b_2$, where $m_1 = m_2$	The lines $y = 2x - 1$ and $y = 2x + 5$ are parallel because both have slope 2.
Perpendicular Lines	$y = m_1x + b_1$ and $y = m_2x + b_2$, where $m_1m_2 = -1$	The lines $y = 3x - 5$ and $y = -\frac{1}{3}x + 2$ are perpendicular because $m_1m_2 = 3\left(-\frac{1}{3}\right) = -1$.

1.4 Exercises

MyMathLab | Math XL PRACTICE | WATCH | DOWNLOAD | READ | REVIEW

CONCEPTS AND VOCABULARY

1. How many lines are determined by two points?

2. How many lines are determined by a point and a slope?

3. Give the slope–intercept form of a line.

4. Give the point–slope form of a line.

5. Write an equation of a vertical line with x-intercept 5.

6. Write an equation of a horizontal line with y-intercept 2.

7. Give an equation of a horizontal line that has y-intercept b.

8. Give an equation of a vertical line that has x-intercept h.

9. If two parallel lines have slopes m_1 and m_2, what can be said about m_1 and m_2?

10. If two perpendicular lines have slopes m_1 and m_2, then $m_1 \cdot m_2 = $ _____.

11. Give an equation of a line that is parallel to the line $y = -\frac{3}{4}x + 1$.

12. Give an equation of a line that is perpendicular to the line $y = -\frac{3}{4}x$.

13. Give an equation of a line that is perpendicular to the x-axis.

14. Give an equation of a line that is perpendicular to the y-axis.

EQUATIONS OF LINES

Exercises 15–18: Use the labeled point and the slope to find the slope–intercept form of the line.

15.

16.

17.

18.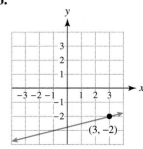

Exercises 19–22: Determine whether the given point lies on the line.

19. $(-3, 4)$ $y = -\frac{2}{3}x + 2$

20. $(4, 2)$ $y = \frac{1}{4}x - 1$

21. $(-4, 3)$ $y = \frac{1}{2}(x + 4) + 2$

22. $(1, -13)$ $y = 3(x - 5) - 1$

Exercises 23–28: Match the equation with its graph (a.–f.), where m and b are constants.

23. $y = mx + b, m > 0$ and $b \neq 0$

24. $y = mx + b, m < 0$ and $b \neq 0$

25. $y = mx, m < 0$

26. $y = b$

27. $y = mx, m > 0$

28. $x = h$

a.

b.

c.

d.

e.

f.

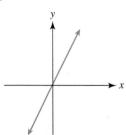

Exercises 29–38: Find a point–slope form of the line satisfying the given conditions.

29. Slope -2, passing through $(2, -3)$

30. Slope $\frac{1}{2}$, passing through $(-4, 1)$

31. Slope 1.3, passing through $(1990, 25)$

32. Slope 45, passing through $(1999, 103)$

33. Passing through $(1, 3)$ and $(-5, -1)$

34. Passing through $(-2, 4)$ and $(3, -1)$

35. Passing through $(1980, 5)$ and $(2000, 45)$

36. Passing through $(1990, 50)$ and $(2000, -10)$

37. Passing through $(6, 0)$ and $(0, 4)$

38. Passing through $(1980, 16)$ and $(2000, 66)$

39. Sketch a line passing through the point $(0, 2)$ with slope $-\frac{1}{2}$. Find the point–slope form of the line. Does the point $(-2, 3)$ lie on this line?

40. Sketch a line passing through the point $(2, 1)$ with slope 2. Find the point–slope form of the line. Does the point $(1, 2)$ lie on this line?

Exercises 41–46: Write in slope–intercept form.

41. $y = 2(x - 1) - 2$

42. $y = -3(x + 2) + 5$

43. $y = \frac{1}{2}(x + 4) + 1$

44. $y = -\frac{2}{3}(x - 3) - 6$

45. $y = 22(x - 1.5) - 10$

46. $y = -30(x + 3) + 106$

Exercises 47–50: (Refer to Example 3.) Use the slope–intercept form to find the equation of the line passing through the given points.

47. $(-3, 7), (2, -8)$

48. $(-6, -3), (3, 3)$

49. $(-4, 1), (4, -5)$

50. $(-1, 14), (4, -6)$

Exercises 51–68: Find the slope–intercept form of the line satisfying the given conditions.

51. Slope $-\frac{1}{3}$, passing through $(0, -5)$

52. Slope 5, passing through $(-1, 4)$

53. Passing through $(3, -2)$ and $(2, -1)$

54. Passing through $(8, 3)$ and $(-7, 3)$

55. x-intercept 2, y-intercept $-\frac{2}{3}$

56. x-intercept -3, y-intercept 4

57. x-intercept 1, y-intercept 3

58. x-intercept -4, y-intercept -5

59. Parallel to $y = 4x - 2$, passing through $(1, 3)$

60. Parallel to $y = -\frac{2}{3}x$, passing through $(0, -10)$

61. Passing through $(-3, 2)$ and parallel to the line passing through $(-2, 3)$ and $(1, -2)$

62. Passing through $\left(\frac{1}{2}, -1\right)$ and parallel to the line passing through $(1, -4)$ and $(-3, 1)$

63. Perpendicular to $y = -\frac{1}{3}x + 4$, passing through the point $(-3, 5)$

64. Perpendicular to $y = \frac{3}{4}(x - 2) + 1$, passing through the point $(-2, -3)$

65. Passing through $\left(-\frac{1}{2}, -2\right)$ and perpendicular to the line passing through $(-1, 6)$ and $(8, -4)$

66. Passing through $(4, -3)$ and perpendicular to the line passing through $(-4, -1)$ and $(2, 7)$

67. Thinking Generally Passing through $(0, b)$ and perpendicular to a line having slope c with $c \neq 0$

68. Thinking Generally Passing through $(a, 0)$ and perpendicular to $y = -mx$ with $m \neq 0$

Exercises 69–74: (Refer to Example 9.) Do the following.

(a) *Find the slope–intercept form of the line perpendicular to the given line, passing through the given point.*
(b) *Graph the two lines.*

69. $y = \frac{1}{2}x$, $(0, 2)$

70. $y = -3x$, $(0, -3)$

71. $y = -2x + 1$, $(-1, 2)$

72. $y = \frac{2}{3}x + 2$, $(-1, 0)$

73. $y = -\frac{1}{3}x + 2$, $(1, 1)$

74. $y = -\frac{4}{3}x + 2$, $(1, -1)$

Exercises 75–78: (Refer to Example 10.) Do the following.

(a) *Find the slope–intercept form of each line.*
(b) *Verify that the two lines are perpendicular.*

75.

76.

77.

78.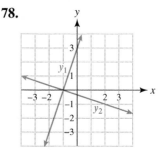

Exercises 79–86: Find an equation of a line satisfying the given conditions.

79. Vertical, passing through $(-1, 6)$

80. Vertical, passing through $(2, -7)$

81. Horizontal, passing through $\left(\frac{3}{4}, -\frac{5}{6}\right)$

82. Horizontal, passing through $(5.1, 6.2)$

83. Perpendicular to $y = \frac{1}{2}$, passing through $(4, -9)$

84. Perpendicular to $x = 2$, passing through $(3, 4)$

85. Parallel to $x = 4$, passing through $\left(-\frac{2}{3}, \frac{1}{2}\right)$

86. Parallel to $y = -2.1$, passing through $(7.6, 3.5)$

Exercises 87–90: Decide whether the points in the table lie on a line. If they do, find the slope–intercept form of the line.

87.

x	1	2	3	4
y	-4	0	4	8

88.

x	-1	0	1	2
y	8	5	4	1

89.

x	-3	0	3	6
y	4	8	14	18

90.

x	-2	2	4	6
y	-6	0	3	6

GRAPHICAL INTERPRETATION

91. *Water Flow* The graph shows the amount of water y in an 80-gallon tank after x minutes have elapsed.
  (a) Is water entering or leaving the tank? How much water is in the tank after 3 minutes?
  (b) Find the x- and y-intercepts. Explain each of their meanings.
  (c) Find a slope–intercept form of the line. Interpret the slope as a rate of change.
  (d) Let $y = f(x)$. Find the domain and range.

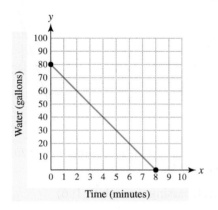

92. *Distance and Speed* A person is driving a car along a straight road. The graph shows the distance y in miles that the driver is from home after x hours.
  (a) Is the person traveling toward or away from home?
  (b) The graph passes through $(1, 35)$ and $(3, 95)$. Discuss the meaning of these points.
  (c) Find a point-slope form of the line. Interpret the slope and y-intercept.

93. *U.S. Population Density* The graph at the top of the next column shows the average number of people living on parcels of land of various sizes in 1960.
  (a) The graph passes through the points $(2, 100)$ and $(4, 200)$. Discuss the meaning of these points.
  (b) Explain why it is reasonable for the graph to pass through the point $(0, 0)$.
  (c) Find the slope–intercept form of the line.
  (d) Interpret the slope as a rate of change.

  (e) Write the equation of this line as a linear function P that outputs the average number of people living on x acres of land.

94. *Cost of Rock* The graph shows the cost of purchasing landscape rock.
  (a) The graph passes through the points $(2, 48)$ and $(5, 120)$. Discuss the meaning of these points.
  (b) Explain why it is reasonable for the graph to pass through the point $(0, 0)$.
  (c) Find the slope–intercept form of the line.
  (d) Interpret the slope as a rate of change.
  (e) Write the equation of this line as a linear function C that outputs the cost of x tons of landscape rock.

95. *Elastic Demand* (Refer to Figure 1.62 and the corresponding Real-World Connection.) If there are a number of gas stations located near each other, then prices for a gallon of gasoline are usually (nearly) equal. If one station were to raise its price by even a small amount, then sales (demand) would likely fall dramatically. In a small area, gasoline exhibits *elastic demand*.
  (a) Sketch a graph of elastic demand, where even though the demand may change, the price remains constant.
  (b) What type of line segment models elastic demand?

96. Online Exploration Find the population in 2000 of the city where you are currently residing. Next, find its current population. Use a linear function P to model these data and then use P to estimate the population in 2007.

APPLICATIONS

97. *Projected Cost of College* The annual cost of the average private college or university is shown in the table. This cost includes tuition, fees, room, and board.

Year	2006	2011
Cost	$28,000	$38,000

Source: Cerulli Associates.

(a) Find the slope–intercept form of a line that passes through these two data points.
(b) Interpret the slope as a rate of change.
(c) Estimate the cost of private college in 2015.

98. *Western Population* In 1950 the western region of the United States had a population of 20 million, and in 2000 it was 63 million. (*Source:* U.S. Census Bureau.)
(a) Find a function f defined by $f(x) = mx + b$ that models this population during year x.
(b) Use f to estimate this population in 1960 and 2010.
(c) Estimate this population in 1900 and discuss your result.

Exercises 99–102: Modeling Data Find $f(x) = mx + b$ so that f models the data, where x is the year. Then use $f(x)$ to make the requested estimate.

99. *Chicken Consumption* In 2005 the average American ate 57 pounds of chicken, and in 2010 this amount increased to 60 pounds. Estimate chicken consumption in 2008. (*Source:* Department of Agriculture.)

100. *Internet* In 2005 the average American spent 9 hours per week on the Internet, and in 2009 this time increased to 13 hours per week. Estimate the time spent on the Internet in 2012. (*Source:* UCLA Center for Communication Policy.)

101. *Life Expectancy* The life expectancy for a baby born in 1910 was 50 years, and in 2010 it was 78 years. Estimate the life expectancy in 1980. (*Source:* U.S. Census Bureau.)

102. *CPI* In 2000 the Consumer Price Index was 178, and in 2010 it was 218. Estimate what this index might be in 2018. (*Source:* Department of Labor.)

Exercises 103–106: Modeling Data (Refer to Example 6.) Find the slope–intercept form of a line that models the data. Because the data are not exactly linear, answers may vary slightly.

103.

x	1	2	3	4
y	1	4	10	13

104.

x	1	3	5	7
y	3	0	−5	−10

105.

x	1	2	3	4	5
y	8	3	0	−1	−6

106.

x	10	20	30	40	50
y	5	20	30	50	60

Exercises 107–110: Modeling Data (Refer to Example 6.) Find the slope–intercept form of a line that models the data. Answers may vary.

107. Population over 85 (millions)

x	1970	1980	1990	2000	2010
y	1.4	2.3	3.0	4.2	5.8

Source: U.S. Census Bureau.

108. Women in Marine Corps

x	1980	1990	2000	2010
y	6000	8600	9500	11,700

Source: Department of Defense.

109. Worldwide Cigarette Consumption (trillions)

x	1950	1970	1990	2010
y	1.7	3.1	5.4	7.1

Source: Department of Agriculture.

110. Global Online Betting Losses ($ billions)

x	2006	2007	2008	2009	2010
y	15	18	20	23	25

Source: Christiansen Capital Advisors.

111. *Cost of Driving* The cost of driving a car includes both fixed costs and mileage costs. Assume that it costs $189.20 per month for insurance and car payments and that it costs $0.30 per mile for gasoline, oil, and routine maintenance.
(a) Find values for a and b so that $f(x) = ax + b$ models the monthly cost of driving x miles.
(b) Interpret the y-intercept on the graph of f.

112. *HIV Infection Rates* In 1999, there were an estimated 24 million HIV infections worldwide, with an annual infection rate of 5.4 million. (*Source:* Centers for Disease Control and Prevention.)
(a) Determine values for m, x_1, and y_1 so that $f(x) = m(x − x_1) + y_1$ models the number of HIV infections in year x.
(b) Estimate the number of HIV infections in 2007.

113. *Ring Sizes* Ring sizes can be modeled by a linear function. If the circumference of a person's finger is 4.9 centimeters, then the ring size is 5; if the circumference is 5.4 centimeters, then the ring size is 7. (*Source:* Overstock.com.)

  (a) Find $R(c) = mc + b$ so that R calculates the ring size for a finger with circumference c.

  (b) A person's finger has a circumference of 6.16 centimeters. What is the ring size?

114. *Hat Sizes* Hat sizes can be modeled by a linear function. If the circumference of a person's head is $21\frac{7}{8}$ inches, the hat size is 7; if the circumference is 25 inches, the hat size is 8. (*Source:* Brentblack.com.)

  (a) Find $H(c) = mc + b$ so that H calculates the hat size for a head with circumference c.

  (b) A person's head has a circumference of 23 inches. What is the hat size to the nearest eighth?

115. *U.S. Population* The population in millions for selected years is shown in the table.

Year	1980	1990	2000	2010
Population	227	249	281	308

Source: U.S. Census Bureau.

  (a) Make a scatterplot of the data.

  (b) Find values for m, x_1, and y_1 so that
$$f(x) = m(x - x_1) + y_1$$
models the data.

  (c) Use f to estimate the population in 2020.

116. *Sexual Partners* The table in the next column shows the percentages of people who had four or more sexual partners in the last 12 months for various years.

Year	2002	2004	2006	2008
Percentage	1.7	1.6	1.5	1.4

Source: National Opinion Research Center.

  (a) Find values for m, x_1, and y_1 so that
$$f(x) = m(x - x_1) + y_1$$
models these data.

  (b) Assuming that trends continued, estimate this percentage in 2014.

117. *Pet Health Care* In 1984 spending on health care for pets was \$4 billion, and by 2008 it had increased to \$12 billion. (*Source:* American Express Institute.)

  (a) Find $f(x) = m(x - x_1) + y_1$ so that f models these data in billions of dollars during year x.

  (b) Estimate health care spending for pets in 2014.

118. *Manufacturing Employment* In 1956, employees of manufacturing firms accounted for 30% of the total employment in the United States. In 2010 this percentage was 9%. (*Source:* U.S. Census Bureau.)

  (a) Find $f(x) = m(x - x_1) + y_1$ so that f models these data during year x.

  (b) Estimate the percentage of people employed by manufacturing in 2014.

WRITING ABOUT MATHEMATICS

119. Explain how you can recognize equations of parallel lines. How can you recognize equations of perpendicular lines?

120. Suppose that some real data can be modeled by a linear function f. Explain what the slope of the graph of f indicates about the data.

SECTIONS 1.3 and 1.4

Checking Basic Concepts

1. Find the slope and a point on each line.
  (a) $y = -3(x - 5) + 7$
  (b) $y = 10$
  (c) $x = -5$
  (d) $y = 5x + 3$

2. (a) Calculate the slope of the line passing through the points $(2, -4)$ and $(5, 2)$.
  (b) Find a point–slope form and the slope–intercept form of the line.
  (c) Find the x-intercept and the y-intercept of the line.

3. Find the equation of a vertical line and the equation of a horizontal line passing through $(-2, 5)$.

4. Find equations of lines that are perpendicular or parallel to $y = -\frac{1}{2}x + 3$, passing through the point $(2, -4)$.

5. The graph to the right shows the distance that a car is from home after x hours.
   (a) Is the car moving toward or away from home?
   (b) Find the slope of the line. Interpret the slope as a rate of change.
   (c) Find the x-intercept and the y-intercept. Explain the meaning of each.
   (d) Determine a and b so that $f(x) = ax + b$ models this situation.
   (e) Give the domain and range of f.

CHAPTER 1   Summary

SECTION 1.1 ■ FUNCTIONS AND THEIR REPRESENTATIONS

Function   A function is a set of ordered pairs (x, y) where each x-value corresponds to exactly one y-value. A function takes a valid input x and computes exactly one output y, forming the ordered pair (x, y).

Domain and Range of a Function   The domain D is the set of all valid inputs, or x-values, and the range R is the set of all outputs, or y-values.

Examples: $f = \{(1, 2), (2, 3), (3, 3)\}$ has $D = \{1, 2, 3\}$ and $R = \{2, 3\}$.

  $f(x) = x^2$ has domain all real numbers and range $y \geq 0$. (See the graph below.)

Function Notation $y = f(x)$ and is read "y equals f of x."

Example: $f(x) = \frac{2x}{x-1}$ implies that $f(3) = \frac{2 \cdot 3}{3-1} = \frac{6}{2} = 3$. Thus the point $(3, 3)$ is on the graph of f.

Function Representations   A function can be represented symbolically, numerically, graphically, or verbally.

> **Symbolic Representation (Formula)** $f(x) = x^2$

> **Numerical Representation (Table)**   **Graphical Representation (Graph)**

x	y
-2	4
-1	1
0	0
1	1
2	4

> **Verbal Representation (Words)** f computes the square of the input x.

Vertical Line Test   If every vertical line intersects a graph at most once, then the graph represents a function.

Linear Function A linear function can be represented by $f(x) = mx + b$. Its graph is a (straight) line. For each unit increase in x, $f(x)$ changes by an amount equal to m.

Example: $f(x) = 2x - 1$ represents a linear function with $m = 2$ and $b = -1$.

Numerical Representation   **Graphical Representation**

Each 1-unit increase in x results in a 2-unit increase in $f(x)$; thus $m = 2$.

NOTE: A numerical representation is a table of values of $f(x)$.

Modeling Data with Linear Functions When data have a constant rate of change, they can be modeled by $f(x) = mx + b$. The constant m represents the *rate of change*, and the constant b represents the *initial amount* or the value when $x = 0$. That is,

$$f(x) = (\text{Rate of change})x + (\text{Initial amount}).$$

Example: In the following table, the y-values decrease by 3 units for each 1-unit increase in x. When $x = 0$, $y = 4$. Thus the data are modeled by $f(x) = -3x + 4$.

x	-2	-1	0	1	2
y	10	7	4	1	-2

Slope The slope m of the line passing through the points (x_1, y_1) and (x_2, y_2) is

$$m = \frac{\text{rise}}{\text{run}} = \frac{y_2 - y_1}{x_2 - x_1}, \qquad \text{where } x_1 \neq x_2.$$

Example: The slope of the line passing through $(-2, 3)$ and $(4, 0)$ is

$$m = \frac{0 - 3}{4 - (-2)} = \frac{-3}{6} = -\frac{1}{2}.$$

Slope–Intercept Form The equation $y = mx + b$ gives the slope m and y-intercept b of a line.

Example: The graph of $y = -\frac{1}{2}x + 1$ has slope $-\frac{1}{2}$ and y-intercept 1.

x	-2	0	2	4
y	2	1	0	-1

y decreases by 1 unit for each 2-unit increase in x.

Slope as a Rate of Change   The slope of the graph of a linear function indicates the rate at which a function is increasing or decreasing.

Example: If $V(t) = 10t$ models the volume of water in a tank in gallons after t minutes, water is *entering* the tank at 10 gallons per minute.

SECTION 1.4 ■ EQUATIONS OF LINES AND LINEAR MODELS

Point–Slope Form

$$y = m(x - x_1) + y_1 \quad \text{or} \quad y - y_1 = m(x - x_1),$$

where m is the slope and (x_1, y_1) is a point on the line.

Example: The point–slope form of the line with slope 4 passing through $(2, -3)$ is

$$y = 4(x - 2) - 3.$$

Equations of Horizontal and Vertical Lines

$$y = b \text{ (horizontal)}, \quad x = h \text{ (vertical)}$$

Example: The equation of the horizontal line passing through $(2, 3)$ is $y = 3$. The equation of the vertical line passing through $(2, 3)$ is $x = 2$.

Parallel Lines
Two lines with the same slope are parallel.

Two nonvertical parallel lines have the same slope.

Example: The lines $y = 2x - 1$ and $y = 2x + 3$ are parallel, with slope 2.

Perpendicular Lines   Two lines with nonzero slopes m_1 and m_2 are perpendicular if $m_1 m_2 = -1$. If two lines have slopes m_1 and m_2 such that $m_1 \cdot m_2 = -1$, then they are perpendicular.

A vertical line and a horizontal line are perpendicular.

Example: The lines $y = 2x - 1$ and $y = -\frac{1}{2}x + 3$ are perpendicular because the product of their slopes equals -1. That is, $2\left(-\frac{1}{2}\right) = -1$.

CHAPTER 1   Review Exercises

SECTION 1.1

Exercises 1–4: Evaluate $f(x)$ for the given values of x.

1. $f(x) = 3x - 1$ $x = -2, \frac{1}{3}$

2. $f(x) = 5 - 3x^2$ $x = -3, 1$

3. $f(x) = \sqrt{x} - 2$ $x = 0, 9$

4. $f(x) = 5$ $x = -5, \frac{7}{5}$

Exercises 5 and 6: Do the following.

  (a) *Write a symbolic representation (formula) for the function described.*

  (b) *Evaluate the function for input 5 and interpret the result.*

5. Function P computes the number of pints in q quarts.

6. Function f computes 3 less than 4 times a number x.

7. If $f(3) = -2$, then the point _____ lies on the graph of f.

8. If $(4, -6)$ lies on the graph of f, then $f(\_\_\_\_) = \_\_\_\_$.

Exercises 9–12: Sketch a graph of f.

9. $f(x) = -2x$ **10.** $f(x) = \frac{1}{2}x - \frac{3}{2}$

11. $f(x) = x^2 - 1$ **12.** $f(x) = \sqrt{x + 1}$

Exercises 13 and 14: Use the graph of f to evaluate the given expressions.

13. $f(0)$ and $f(-3)$ **14.** $f(-2)$ and $f(1)$

          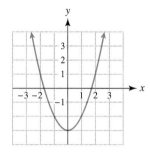

15. Use the table to evaluate $f(-1)$ and $f(3)$.

x	−1	1	3	5
$f(x)$	7	3	−1	−5

16. A function f is represented verbally by "Multiply the input x by 3 and then subtract 2." Give numerical, symbolic, and graphical representations for f. Let $x = -3, -2, -1, \ldots, 3$ in the table of values, and let $-3 \le x \le 3$ for the graph.

Exercises 17 and 18: Use the graph of f to estimate its domain and range.

17.   **18.**

          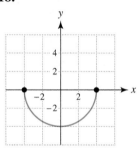

Exercises 19 and 20: Does the graph represent a function?

19.   **20.**

          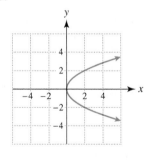

Exercises 21 and 22: Find the domain and range of S. Then state whether S defines a function.

21. $S = \{(-3, 4), (-1, 4), (2, 3), (4, -1)\}$

22. $S = \{(-1, 5), (0, 3), (1, -2), (-1, 2), (2, 4)\}$

Exercises 23–30: Find the domain.

23. $f(x) = -3x + 7$ **24.** $f(x) = \sqrt{x}$

25. $f(x) = \frac{3}{x}$ **26.** $f(x) = x^2 + 2$

27. $f(x) = \sqrt{5 - x}$ **28.** $f(x) = \dfrac{x}{x + 2}$

29. $f(x) = |2x + 1|$ **30.** $f(x) = x^3$

SECTION 1.2

Exercises 31 and 32: Does the graph represent a linear function?

31.   **32.**

          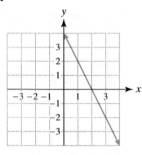

Exercises 33–36: Determine whether f is a linear function. If f is linear, give values for m and b so that f may be expressed as $f(x) = mx + b$.

33. $f(x) = -4x + 5$ **34.** $f(x) = 7 - x$

35. $f(x) = \sqrt{x}$ **36.** $f(x) = 6$

Exercises 37 and 38: Use the table to determine whether $f(x)$ could represent a linear function. If it could, write the formula for f in the form $f(x) = mx + b$.

37.

x	0	2	4	6
$f(x)$	−3	0	3	6

38.

x	−1	0	1	2
$f(x)$	−5	0	10	15

39. Evaluate $f(x) = \frac{1}{2}x + 3$ at $x = -4$.

40. Use the graph to evaluate $f(-2)$ and $f(1)$.

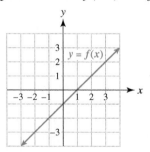

Exercises 41–44: Sketch a graph of $y = f(x)$.

41. $f(x) = x + 1$ **42.** $f(x) = 1 - 2x$

43. $f(x) = -\frac{1}{3}x$ **44.** $f(x) = -1$

45. Write a symbolic representation (formula) for a linear function H that calculates the number of hours in x days. Evaluate $H(2)$ and interpret the result.

46. Let $f(x) = \sqrt{x + 2} - x^2$.
  (a) Make a numerical representation (table) for the function f with $x = 1, 2, 3, \ldots, 7$.
  (b) Graph f in the standard window. What is the domain of f?

SECTION 1.3

Exercises 47–50: Find the slope of the line.

47.

48.

49.

50.

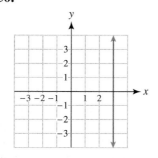

Exercises 51–54: Calculate the slope of the line passing through the given points, if possible.

51. $(-1, 2), (3, 8)$ **52.** $\left(-3, \frac{5}{2}\right), \left(1, -\frac{1}{2}\right)$

53. $(3, -4), (5, -4)$ **54.** $(-2, 6), (-2, 8)$

55. Sketch a line passing through $(1, 2)$ with slope $-\frac{1}{2}$.

56. Find the slope and y-intercept of the line $y = -\frac{2}{3}x$. Graph the line.

57. Use the graph to express the line in slope–intercept form.

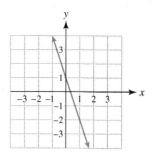

58. Write the slope–intercept form of a line passing through $(0, 2)$ and $(-1, 0)$.

59. Let f be a linear function. Use the table to find the slope and y-intercept of the graph of f.

x	-2	0	3
$f(x)$	3	1	-2

60. The line graph represents the gallons of water in a small swimming pool after x hours.
  (a) Estimate the slope of each line segment.
  (b) Interpret each slope as a rate of change.
  (c) Describe what happens to the amount of water in the pool.

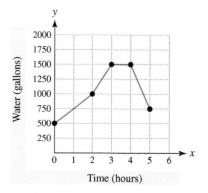

61. *Sketching a Model* A distance runner starts at home and runs at a constant speed. After 1.5 hours she is 12 miles from home. She then turns around and runs home at the same speed. Sketch a graph that shows the distance that the runner is from home after x hours.

62. Let $f(x) = \frac{1}{2}x - 2$.
  (a) Find the slope and y-intercept of the graph of f.
  (b) Sketch a graph of f.

SECTION 1.4

63. Determine whether the point (2, 1) lies on the graph of $y = \frac{3}{2}x - 2$.

64. Let f be a linear function. Find the slope, x-intercept, and y-intercept of the graph of f.

x	-1	0	1	2
$f(x)$	6	4	2	0

65. Write $y = -3(x - 2) + 1$ in slope–intercept form.

66. Write the point–slope form and the slope–intercept form of the line with slope -3, passing through the point $(-2, 3)$.

Exercises 67–72: Write the slope–intercept form of a line satisfying the given conditions.

67. x-intercept 2, y-intercept -3

68. Passing through $(-1, 4)$ and $(2, -2)$

69. Parallel to $y = 4x - 3$, passing through $\left(-\frac{3}{5}, \frac{1}{5}\right)$

70. Perpendicular to $y = \frac{1}{2}x$, passing through $(-1, 1)$

71. Passing through $(3, 1)$ and perpendicular to the line passing through $(-2, 3)$ and $(2, 1)$

72. Passing through $(3, 3)$ and parallel to the line passing through $(-3, -4)$ and $(3, 0)$

Exercises 73 and 74: Find the slope–intercept form of the line shown in the graph.

73.

74.

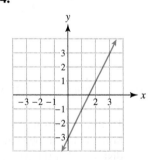

Exercises 75 and 76: Determine whether the given point lies on the line.

75. $(2, -1)$ $y = -2(x - 1) + 3$

76. $\left(4, -\frac{5}{2}\right)$ $y = \frac{1}{4}(x + 2) - 4$

Exercises 77–80: Find an equation of a line satisfying the given conditions.

77. Vertical, passing through $(-4, 14)$

78. Horizontal, passing through $\left(\frac{11}{13}, -\frac{7}{13}\right)$

79. Perpendicular to $x = -3$, passing through $(-2, 1)$

80. Parallel to $y = 5$, passing through $(4, -8)$

Exercises 81 and 82: Decide whether the points in the table lie on a line. If they do, find its slope–intercept form.

81.

x	1	2	3	4
y	6	7	8	7

82.

x	-2	0	2	4
y	1	5	9	13

APPLICATIONS

83. *U.S. Population* The following line graph shows the population of the United States in millions.
(a) Find the slope of each line segment.
(b) Interpret each slope as a rate of change.

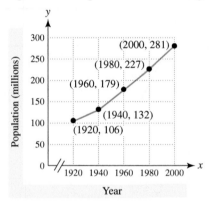

84. *Flow Rates* A water tank has an inlet pipe with a flow rate of 10 gallons per minute and an outlet pipe with a flow rate of 6 gallons per minute. A pipe can be either completely closed or open. The following graph shows the number of gallons of water in the tank after x minutes. Interpret the graph.

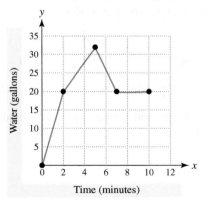

85. *Age at First Marriage* The median age at the first marriage for men from 1890 to 1960 can be modeled by $f(x) = -0.0492x + 119.1$, where x is the year.
(*Source:* National Center of Health Statistics.)

(a) Find the median age in 1910.

(b) Graph f in [1885, 1965, 10] by [22, 26, 1]. What happened to the median age?

(c) What is the slope of the graph of f? Interpret the slope as a rate of change.

86. *Marriages* From 2002 to 2008 the number of U.S. marriages in millions could be modeled by the formula $f(x) = 2.2$, where x is the year.

(a) Estimate the number of marriages in 2006.

(b) What information does f give about the number of marriages from 2002 to 2008?

87. *Fat Grams* A cup of milk contains 8 grams of fat.

(a) Give a formula for $f(x)$ that calculates the number of fat grams in x cups of milk.

(b) What is the slope of the graph of f?

(c) Interpret the slope as a rate of change.

88. *Birth Rate* The U.S. birth rate per 1000 people for selected years is shown in the table.

Year	1950	1970	1990	2010
Birth Rate	24.1	18.4	16.7	13.5

Source: U.S. Census Bureau.

(a) Make a scatterplot of the data.

(b) Model the data with $f(x) = mx + b$, where x is the year. Answers may vary.

(c) Use f to estimate the birth rate in 2000.

89. *Unhealthy Air Quality* The Environmental Protection Agency (EPA) monitors air quality in U.S. cities. The function f gives the annual number of days with unhealthy air quality in Los Angeles, California, for selected years.

x	1995	1999	2000	2003	2007
$f(x)$	113	56	87	88	100

Source: Environmental Protection Agency.

(a) Find $f(1995)$ and interpret your result.

(b) Identify the domain and range of f.

(c) Discuss the trend of air pollution in Los Angeles.

90. *Temperature Scales* The following table shows equivalent temperatures in degrees Celsius and degrees Fahrenheit.

°C	−40	0	15	35	100
°F	−40	32	59	95	212

(a) Plot the data. Let the x-axis correspond to the Celsius temperature and the y-axis correspond to the Fahrenheit temperature. What type of relation exists between the data?

(b) Find $f(x) = mx + b$ so that f receives the Celsius temperature x as input and outputs the corresponding Fahrenheit temperature. Interpret the slope of the graph of f.

(c) If the temperature is 20°C, what is the equivalent temperature in degrees Fahrenheit?

Exercises 91–96: Modeling Match the situation to the graph (a.–f.) that models it best.

91. The total federal debt y from 2001 to 2010

92. The distance y from New York City to Seattle, Washington, during year x

93. The amount of money y earned working for x hours at a fixed hourly rate

94. The sales of 8-millimeter movie projectors from 1970 to 1990

95. The average Celsius temperature y in a freezer

96. The height above sea level of a rocket launched from a submarine during the first minute of flight

a.   b.

c.   d.

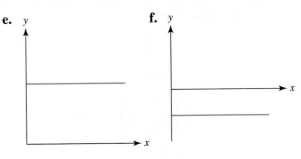

e.   f.

97. *Graphical Model* A 500-gallon water tank is initially full and then emptied at a constant rate of 50 gallons per minute. Ten minutes after the tank is empty, it is filled by a pump that supplies 25 gallons per minute. Sketch a graph that depicts the amount of water in the tank after x minutes.

98. *HIV/AIDS* In 2006 there were a total of 1.1 million people living with HIV/AIDS in the United States,

with an annual infection rate of 56,000. (*Source:* Centers for Disease Control and Prevention.)

(a) Assuming that this trend continues, determine $f(x) = m(x - x_1) + y_1$ so that f models the number of AIDS cases to date during year x.

(b) Find $f(2015)$ and interpret the result.

CHAPTER 1   Test

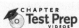 CHAPTER Test Prep VIDEOS   Step-by-step test solutions are found on the Chapter Test Prep Videos available via the Video Resources on DVD, in *MyMathLab*, and on You Tube (search "RockswoldInterAlg" and click on "Channels").

1. Evaluate $f(4)$ if $f(x) = 3x^2 - \sqrt{x}$. Give a point on the graph of f.

2. Write a symbolic representation (formula) for a function C that calculates the cost of buying x pounds of candy at \$4 per pound. Evaluate $C(5)$ and interpret your result.

3. Sketch a graph of f.
  (a) $f(x) = -2x + 1$ **(b)** $f(x) = x^2 + 1$
  (c) $f(x) = \sqrt{x + 3}$ **(d)** $f(x) = |x + 1|$

4. Use the graph of f to evaluate $f(-3)$ and $f(0)$. Determine the domain and range of f.

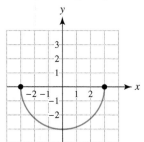

5. A function f is represented verbally by "Square the input x and then subtract 5." Give symbolic, numerical, and graphical representations of f. Let $x = -3, -2, -1, \ldots, 3$ in the numerical representation (table) and let $-3 \le x \le 3$ for the graph.

6. Determine whether the graph represents a function. Explain your reasoning.

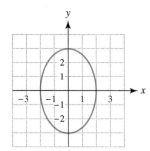

7. Find the domain of function f.
  (a) $f = \{(-2, 3), (-1, 5), (0, 3), (5, 7)\}$
  (b) $f(x) = \frac{3}{4}x - 5$
  (c) $f(x) = \sqrt{x + 4}$
  (d) $f(x) = 2x^2 - 1$
  (e) $f(x) = \frac{3x}{5 - x}$

8. Determine if $f(x) = 6 - 8x$ is a linear function. If it is, write it in the form $f(x) = mx + b$.

9. Find the slope of the line passing through $(-3, 7)$ and $(6, -2)$.

10. Determine the slope of the line shown in the graph.

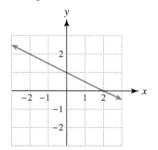

11. Write the slope–intercept form of a line satisfying the given conditions.
  (a) x-intercept -2, y-intercept -4
  (b) Passing through $(-5, 2)$ and perpendicular to the line passing through $(-2, 5)$ and $(-1, 3)$
  (c) Passing through $(1, -2)$ and $\left(-5, \frac{3}{2}\right)$

12. Let f be a linear function. Find the slope, x-intercept, and y-intercept of the graph of f.

x	-2	-1	0	2
$f(x)$	8	6	4	0

13. Give the slope–intercept form of a line parallel to $y = 1 - 3x$, passing through $\left(\frac{1}{3}, 2\right)$.

14. Find the slope–intercept form for the line shown in the graph. Then find the equation of a line that passes through the origin and is perpendicular to the given line.

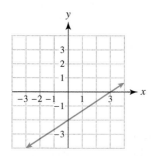

15. Find equations of the vertical line and the horizontal line passing through the point $\left(\frac{2}{3}, -\frac{1}{7}\right)$.

16. *Modeling* The line graph shows the number of welfare beneficiaries in millions for selected years. (*Source:* Administration for Children and Families.)
(a) Find the slope of each line segment.
(b) Interpret each slope as a rate of change.

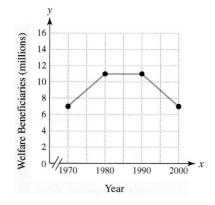

17. *Distance from Home* Starting at home, a driver travels away from home on a straight highway for 2 hours at 60 miles per hour, stops for 1 hour, and then drives home at 40 miles per hour. Sketch a graph that shows the distance between the driver and home.

18. *iPod Sales* The table shows the number of worldwide iPod sales in millions for selected years.

Year	2004	2005	2006	2007
Sales	5	22	39	52

Source: Apple Corporation.

(a) Make a scatterplot of the data.
(b) Determine values for m, x_1, and y_1 so that $f(x) = m(x - x_1) + y_1$ models these data.
(c) Use f to estimate iPod sales in 2008.

CHAPTER 1   Extended and Discovery Exercises

1. *Developing a Model* Two identical cylindrical tanks, A and B, each contain 100 gallons of water. Tank A has a pump that begins removing water at a constant rate of 8 gallons per minute. Tank B has a plug removed from its bottom and water begins to flow out—faster at first and then more slowly.
(a) Assuming that the tanks become empty at the same time, sketch a graph that models the amount of water in each tank. Explain your graphs.
(b) Which tank is half empty first? Explain.

2. *Modeling Real Data* Per capita personal incomes in the United States are listed in the following table.

Year	2002	2003	2004
Income	$31,461	$32,271	$33,881

Year	2005	2006	2007
Income	$35,424	$37,698	$39,458

Source: Department of Commerce.

(a) Make a scatterplot of the data.
(b) Find a function f that models the data. Explain your reasoning.
(c) Use f to estimate per capita income in 2000.

3. *Graphing a Rectangle* One side of a rectangle has vertices (0, 0) and (5, 3). If the point (0, 5) lies on a different side of this rectangle, as shown in the figure, write the equation of each line.

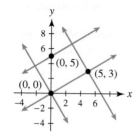

Exercises 4–6: (Refer to Exercise 3.) Graph the rectangle that satisfies the given conditions. Write the equation of each line.

4. Vertices (0, 0), (2, 2), and (1, 3)

5. Vertices (1, 1), (5, 1), and (1, 5)

6. Vertices (4, 0), (0, 4), (0, −4), and (−4, 0)

7. *Remaining Life Expectancy* The table lists the average *remaining* life expectancy E in years for females at age x.

x (year)	0	10	20	30	40
E (year)	72.3	69.9	60.1	50.4	40.9

x (year)	50	60	70	80
E (year)	31.6	23.1	15.5	9.2

Source: Department of Health and Human Services.

(a) Make a line graph of the data.

(b) Assume that the graph represents a function f. Calculate the slope of each line segment and interpret each slope as a rate of change.

(c) Determine the life expectancy (not the remaining life expectancy) of a 20-year-old woman. What is the life expectancy of a 70-year-old woman? Discuss reasons why these two expectancies are not equal.

8. *Weight of a Small Fish* The graph at the top of the next column shows a function f that models the weight in milligrams of a small fish, *Lebistes reticulatus*, during the first 14 weeks of its life. (*Source:* D. Brown and P. Rothery, *Models in Biology.*)

(a) Estimate the weight of the fish when it hatches, at 6 weeks, and at 12 weeks.

(b) If (x_1, y_1) and (x_2, y_2) are points on the graph of a function, the **average rate of change of f from x_1 to x_2** is given by $\frac{y_2 - y_1}{x_2 - x_1}$. Approximate the average rates of change of f from hatching to 6 weeks and from 6 weeks to 12 weeks.

(c) Interpret these rates of change.

(d) During which time period does the fish gain weight the fastest?

9. *Interpreting Carbon Dioxide Levels* Carbon dioxide is a greenhouse gas that may cause Earth's climate to change. Plants absorb carbon dioxide during daylight and release carbon dioxide at night. The burning of fossil fuels, such as gasoline, produces carbon dioxide. At Mauna Loa, Hawaii, atmospheric carbon dioxide levels in parts per million have been measured regularly since 1958. The accompanying figure shows a graph of the carbon dioxide levels between 1960 and 2000. (*Source:* A. Nilsson, *Greenhouse Earth.*)

(a) What is the overall trend in these carbon dioxide levels?

(b) Discuss what happens to these carbon dioxide levels each year.

(c) Give an explanation for the shape of this graph.

10. *Carbon Dioxide in Alaska* (Refer to Exercise 9.) The atmospheric carbon dioxide levels at Barrow, Alaska, in parts per million from 1970 to 2000 are shown in the figure to the right. (*Source:* M. Zeilik, S. Gregory, and D. Smith, *Introductory Astronomy and Astrophysics.*)

(a) Compare this graph with the graph in Exercise 9.

(b) Discuss possible reasons for their similarities and differences.

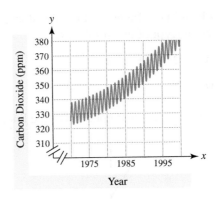

CHAPTER 1   Cumulative Review Exercises

Exercises 1 and 2: Classify each real number as one or more of the following: natural number, whole number, integer, rational number, or irrational number.

1. $-3, \frac{3}{4}, \sqrt{7}, -5.8, \sqrt[3]{8}$

2. $0, -5, \frac{1}{2}, -\sqrt{9}, \frac{50}{10}, \sqrt{8}$

Exercises 3 and 4: State whether the equation illustrates an identity, commutative, associative, or distributive property.

3. $6x + 8x = 14x$

4. $a + (b + c) = (b + c) + a$

5. Evaluate $-5^2 + 3 + 4 \cdot 5$ by hand.

6. Write $(x + 1)x + (x + 1)5$ as a product of two factors by using the distributive property.

7. Find the opposite of $a - b$.

8. Find the reciprocal of $\frac{a + b}{c}$.

9. Evaluate $\frac{1}{3} \div \left(\frac{3}{4} \cdot \frac{7}{8}\right) + \frac{5}{6}$ with a calculator.

10. Simplify each expression. Write the result using positive exponents.

(a) $\left(\dfrac{2^{-3}}{3^{-2}}\right)^2$ **(b)** $\dfrac{(3x^2y^{-3})^4}{x^3(y^4)^{-2}}$

(c) $\left(\dfrac{ab^{-2}}{a^{-3}b^4}\right)^{-2}$

11. Write 9540 in scientific notation.

12. Find $f(4)$ if $f(x) = 2x^2 + \sqrt{x}$.

13. Evaluate $B = \frac{1}{2}bh^2$ for $b = 4$ and $h = 3$.

14. Identify the domain of each function f.

(a) $f = \{(-3, 4), (0, 3), (2, -1)\}$

(b) $f(x) = \dfrac{3}{x + 6}$

(c) $f(x) = \sqrt{x + 4}$

Exercises 15–20: Graph f by hand.

15. $f(x) = -2x + 1$ **16.** $f(x) = -\frac{1}{2}x^2$

17. $f(x) = |x - 2|$ **18.** $f(x) = \sqrt{-x}$

19. $f(x) = -1$ **20.** $f(x) = \frac{1}{3}x$

21. Use the graph of f to do the following.

(a) Determine if the graph represents a function.

(b) Identify the domain and range.

(c) Evaluate $f(-1)$ and $f(0)$.

(d) Identify the x- and y-intercepts.

(e) Find the slope of the line.

(f) Find a formula for $f(x)$.

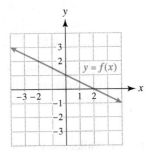

22. Find the slope–intercept form of the line that passes through $(-4, 5)$ and $(2, -4)$.

23. Find the slope–intercept form of the line that passes through $(-1, 2)$ and is perpendicular to the line that passes through $(1, -3)$ and $(2, 0)$.

24. Write an equation of a line that is perpendicular to the x-axis and passes through $(-2, 4)$.

25. Let f be a linear function. Find the slope, x-intercept, and y-intercept of the graph of f.

x	-2	-1	1	2
$f(x)$	9	6	0	-3

26. Write the slope–intercept form of the line.

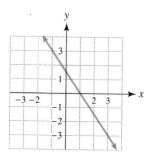

APPLICATIONS

27. *Earnings* Earning $120 one day and $80 the next day is equivalent to earning $80 the first day and $120 the second day. What property of real numbers is illustrated?

28. *Storage in a Box* A rectangular box contains 400 cubic inches. If a similar box has the same width but double the length and double the height, how many cubic inches does this box contain?

29. *Foreign-Born Population* The table shows the percentage of the U.S. population that is foreign-born for selected years.

Year	1970	1980	1990	2000	2010
Percentage	4.7	6.2	7.9	10.4	12.7

Source: U.S. Census Bureau.

    (a) Find a linear function f that models the data.
    (b) Estimate the percentage of the U.S. population that may be foreign-born in 2017.

30. *Calculating Wages* The amount A that a person makes in dollars after working x hours is given by $A(x) = 9x$. Interpret the slope of the graph of A as a rate of change.

31. *Distance* A person walks away from home at 4 miles per hour for 30 minutes, rests in a park for 1 hour, and then takes 1 hour to walk back home at a constant speed. Sketch a graph that models the distance y that the person is from home after x hours.

32. *Age in the United States* The median age of the population for each year x between 1970 and 2010 can be approximated by

$$f(x) = 0.243x - 450.8.$$

(Source: U.S. Census Bureau.)

    (a) What type of function is f?
    (b) Evaluate $f(2005)$ and interpret your result.
    (c) What is the slope of the graph of f?
    (d) Interpret this slope as a rate of change.

33. *Fat Grams* Some slices of pizza contain 10 grams of fat.
    (a) Find a formula $f(x)$ that calculates the number of fat grams in x slices of pizza.
    (b) Graph f for $0 \le x \le 6$.
    (c) What is the slope of the graph of f?
    (d) Interpret the slope as a rate of change.

34. *Two-Cycle Engines* Two-cycle engines used in many snowmobiles, jet skis, chain saws, and outboard motors require a mixture of gas and oil to run properly. For certain engines, the amount of oil in pints that should be added to x gallons of gasoline is computed by $f(x) = \frac{4}{25}x$. (*Source:* Johnson Outboard Motor Company.)
    (a) How many pints of oil should be added to 6 gallons of gasoline?
    (b) Graph f for $0 \le x \le 25$.
    (c) What is the slope of the graph of f?
    (d) Interpret the slope as a rate of change.

35. *Municipal Waste* From 1960 to 1995, municipal solid waste in millions of tons can be modeled by

$$f(x) = 3.4(x - 1960) + 87.8,$$

where x is the year. (*Source:* EPA.)
    (a) Find the tons of waste in 1960.
    (b) Graph f in the viewing rectangle [1960, 1995, 5] by [60, 220, 20].
    (c) What is the slope of the graph of f? Interpret the slope as a rate of change.

36. *Modeling Distance* An individual is driving a car along a straight road. The graph shows the distance that the driver is from home after x hours.
    (a) Find the slope of each line segment in the graph.
    (b) Interpret each slope as a rate of change.
    (c) Describe both the motion and location of the car.

2 Linear Equations and Inequalities

Say it, I'll forget. Demonstrate it, I may recall. But if I do it, I'll understand.

—OLD CHINESE PROVERB

Global consumption of seafood has increased from 42 million tons in 1960 to 157 million tons in 2008. This trend is due to a dramatic increase in world population living near the ocean, to an increase in per capita consumption, and to unsustainable fishing practices. These data are modeled by using a linear function f in the figure.

Global Seafood Consumption

By 2027, worldwide consumption may increase by at least 45 million tons. How are predictions like this one made? Mathematics plays an essential role in predictions and in analyzing environmental issues. (See Section 2.1, Exercise 117.) Before we can make predictions of our own, we need to discuss linear equations. Linear equations are fundamental to understanding many concepts in mathematics.

Source: Lischewski, C., "The Global Seafood Industry: A Perspective on Consumption and Supply," 2008.

2.1   Linear Equations

Equations • Symbolic Solutions • Numerical and Graphical Solutions •
Identities and Contradictions • Intercepts of a Line

A LOOK INTO MATH ▶

In Chapter 1, functions were introduced as a way to model a variety of data. Society uses functions to answer important questions and make predictions. To do this, equations need to be solved. As a result, a primary objective of mathematics is to solve equations. In this section we focus on methods for solving one type of equation called a *linear equation*.

Equations

NEW VOCABULARY

- ☐ Linear equation
- ☐ Solution/Solution set
- ☐ Addition property
- ☐ Multiplication property
- ☐ Symbolic solution
- ☐ Expression/Equation
- ☐ Graphical solution
- ☐ Numerical solution
- ☐ Identity/Contradiction
- ☐ Conditional equation
- ☐ Standard form

▶ **REAL-WORLD CONNECTION** In 2010, sales of green building materials were $65 billion and growing at a constant rate of $5 billion per year. We modeled these sales in billions of dollars with the *linear function* $f(x) = 5x + 65$, where x is the number of years after 2010. (See Example 7, Section 1.2.)

Now suppose we want to predict when sales of green building materials might reach $80 billion. To answer this question, set the expression $5x + 65$ equal to 80 and form the following *linear equation*. (You may be able to solve this particular equation in your head, but many times equations are more complicated.)

Forming a Linear Equation

Expression for linear function   Constant amount

$$5x + 65 = 80$$

Find x so that the left side equals **80**.

Finding the value of x that makes the left side of the equation equal to 80 is called *solving the equation,* and this value of x is called the *solution.* For this example, the solution tells us how many years after 2010 green building sales will reach $80 billion.

Equations like this one can be solved *symbolically, graphically,* and *numerically.* The basic idea behind these three methods is illustrated by the following. (These three methods will be explained more fully throughout this section.)

Symbolically

$5x + 65 = 80$

$5x = 15$

$x = 3$

Start by subtracting 65 from each side, and then divide each side by 5 to get the solution of 3.

Graphically

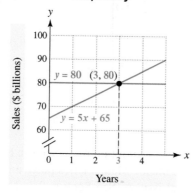

$y = 80$ $(3, 80)$

$y = 5x + 65$

Years

Graph each side of the equation. Find the point of intersection.

Numerically (table)

x	$5x + 65 \stackrel{?}{=} 80$	T or F
1	$5(1) + 65 \stackrel{?}{=} 80$	F
2	$5(2) + 65 \stackrel{?}{=} 80$	F
3	$5(3) + 65 \stackrel{?}{=} 80$	T ✓
4	$5(4) + 65 \stackrel{?}{=} 80$	F

Find an x-value that makes the equation true.

LINEAR EQUATION IN ONE VARIABLE

A **linear equation** in one variable is an equation that can be written in the form

$$ax + b = 0,$$

where a and b are constants with $a \neq 0$.

Examples of linear equations include

$$2x - 1 = 0, \quad -5x = 10 + x, \quad \text{and} \quad 3x + 8 = 2.$$

Although the second and third equations do not appear to be in the form $ax + b = 0$, they can be transformed by using properties of algebra, which we discuss later in this section.

To *solve* an equation means to find all values for a variable that make the equation a true statement. Such values are called **solutions**, and the set of all solutions is called the **solution set**. For example, substituting 2 for x in the equation $3x - 1 = 5$ results in $3(2) - 1 = 5$, which is a true statement. The value 2 *satisfies* the equation $3x - 1 = 5$ and is the only solution. The solution set is $\{2\}$. Two equations are *equivalent* if they have the same solution set.

LINEAR EQUATIONS AND SOLUTIONS Any linear equation can be written as $ax + b = 0$ with $a \neq 0$, so every linear equation has exactly *one solution*. To understand why, consider the linear equation $\frac{1}{2}x - 1 = 0$. The graph of $y = \frac{1}{2}x - 1$ (Figure 2.1) is a line with slope $\frac{1}{2}$ that intersects the x-axis *once* at the point $(2, 0)$. Thus 2 is the solution because when $x = 2$, the y-value is 0 and the linear equation

$$\frac{1}{2}x - 1 = 0 \quad \text{simplifies to} \quad \frac{1}{2}(2) - 1 = 0. \quad \longleftarrow \text{True statement}$$

In fact, any line with *nonzero* slope must intersect the x-axis at exactly one point $(k, 0)$. This value of k is the only solution to the linear equation $ax + b = 0$.

Linear Equation: $\frac{1}{2}x - 1 = 0$

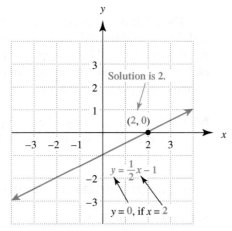

Figure 2.1 One Solution: 2

READING CHECK

Give an example of a linear function. Use the formula for this function to write a linear equation.

MAKING CONNECTIONS

Linear Functions and Equations

A linear function can be written as $f(x) = ax + b$ ($a = $ slope m).

A linear equation can be written as $ax + b = 0$ ($a \neq 0$).

Symbolic Solutions

Linear equations can be solved symbolically, graphically, and numerically. One advantage of a symbolic method is that *the solution is always exact*. To solve an equation symbolically, we write a sequence of equivalent equations, using algebraic properties. For example, to solve $3x - 5 = 0$, we might add 5 to *each side* of the equation and then divide *each side* by 3 to obtain $x = \frac{5}{3}$.

$$3x - 5 = 0 \qquad \text{Given equation}$$
$$3x - 5 + 5 = 0 + 5 \qquad \text{Add 5 to each side.}$$
$$3x = 5 \qquad \text{Simplify.}$$
$$\frac{3x}{3} = \frac{5}{3} \qquad \text{Divide each side by 3.}$$
$$x = \frac{5}{3} \qquad \text{Simplify.}$$

The solution is $\frac{5}{3}$. That is, $3\left(\frac{5}{3}\right) - 5 = 0$ is a true statement.

Adding 5 to each side is an example of the *addition property of equality,* and dividing each side by 3 is an example of the *multiplication property of equality*. Note that dividing each side by 3 is equivalent to multiplying each side by $\frac{1}{3}$.

PROPERTIES OF EQUALITY

Addition Property of Equality
If a, b, and c are real numbers, then

$$a = b \quad \text{is equivalent to} \quad a + c = b + c.$$

Multiplication Property of Equality
If a, b, and c are real numbers with $c \neq 0$, then

$$a = b \quad \text{is equivalent to} \quad ac = bc.$$

The addition property states that an equivalent equation results if the same number is added to (or subtracted from) each side of an equation. That is, "equals added to equals are equal." Similarly, the multiplication property states that an equivalent equation results if each side of an equation is multiplied (or divided) by the same *nonzero* number. That is, "equals multiplied by equals are equal."

NOTE: Loosely speaking, these properties say that the same "thing" or "action" must be done to each side of the equation so that the equation "remains balanced."

EXAMPLE 1 **Applying properties of equality**

Solve each equation. Check your answer.
(a) $x - 4 = 5$ **(b)** $5x = 13$

Solution

(a) Isolate x in the equation $x - 4 = 5$ by applying the addition property of equality. To do this, we add 4 to *each side* of the equation.

$$x - 4 = 5 \qquad \text{Given equation}$$
$$x - 4 + 4 = 5 + 4 \qquad \text{Add 4 to each side.}$$
$$x = 9 \qquad \text{Simplify.}$$

Check: To check that 9 is the solution, we substitute 9 in the *given* equation.

$$x - 4 = 5 \qquad \text{Given equation}$$

$$9 - 4 \overset{?}{=} 5 \qquad \text{Let } x = 9.$$

$$5 = 5 \checkmark \qquad \text{It checks.}$$

(b) Isolate x in the equation $5x = 13$ by applying the multiplication property of equality. To do this, we multiply *each side* of the equation by $\frac{1}{5}$, the reciprocal of 5. Note that this step is equivalent to dividing *each side* of the equation by **5**.

$$5x = 13 \qquad \text{Given equation}$$

$$\frac{5x}{5} = \frac{13}{5} \qquad \text{Divide each side by 5.}$$

$$x = \frac{13}{5} \qquad \text{Simplify: } \tfrac{5}{5} = 1.$$

Check: To check that $\frac{13}{5}$ is the solution, we substitute $\frac{13}{5}$ in the *given* equation.

$$5x = 13 \qquad \text{Given equation}$$

$$5 \cdot \frac{13}{5} \overset{?}{=} 13 \qquad \text{Let } x = \tfrac{13}{5}.$$

$$13 = 13 \checkmark \qquad \text{It checks.}$$

▌ **Now Try Exercises 23, 29**

STUDY TIP

When you solve an equation, be sure that you can explain, or justify, each step.

Sometimes both properties are needed, as in the next example.

EXAMPLE 2 **Solving a linear equation symbolically**

Solve $2 - \frac{1}{2}x = 1$.

Solution

To solve, we write a sequence of equivalent equations by using the properties of equality.

$$2 - \frac{1}{2}x = 1 \qquad \text{Given equation}$$

$$-2 + 2 - \frac{1}{2}x = 1 + (-2) \qquad \text{Add } -2 \text{ to each side.}$$

$$-\frac{1}{2}x = -1 \qquad \text{Simplify.}$$

$$-2\left(-\frac{1}{2}x\right) = -1(-2) \qquad \text{Multiply each side by } -2, \text{ the reciprocal of } -\tfrac{1}{2}.$$

$$x = 2 \qquad \text{Simplify.}$$

The solution is 2.

▌ **Now Try Exercise 35**

Expressions and Equations

Expressions and equations are *different* mathematical concepts. An expression does *not* contain an equals sign, whereas an equation *always* contains an equals sign. *An equation is a statement that two expressions are equal.* For example,

$$2x - 1 \quad \text{and} \quad x + 1 \qquad \text{Expressions}$$

are two different expressions, and

$$2x - 1 = x + 1 \qquad \text{Equation}$$

is an equation. We often *solve an equation* for a value of x that makes the equation a true statement, but we *do not solve an expression.* We sometimes *simplify* an expression.

READING CHECK

Explain the difference between an expression and an equation.

In the next example we use the distributive property to solve a linear equation.

EXAMPLE 3   Solving a linear equation symbolically

Solve $2(x - 1) = 4 - \frac{1}{2}(4 + x)$. Check your answer.

Solution
We begin by applying the distributive property.

$$2(x - 1) = 4 - \frac{1}{2}(4 + x) \qquad \text{Given equation}$$

$$2x - 2 = 4 - 2 - \frac{1}{2}x \qquad \text{Distributive property}$$

$$2x - 2 = 2 - \frac{1}{2}x \qquad \text{Simplify.}$$

Next, we move the constant terms to the right and the x-terms to the left.

$$2x - 2 + 2 = 2 - \frac{1}{2}x + 2 \qquad \text{Add 2 to each side.}$$

$$2x = 4 - \frac{1}{2}x \qquad \text{Simplify.}$$

$$2x + \frac{1}{2}x = 4 - \frac{1}{2}x + \frac{1}{2}x \qquad \text{Add } \tfrac{1}{2}x \text{ to each side.}$$

$$\frac{5}{2}x = 4 \qquad \text{Simplify.}$$

Finally, we multiply by $\frac{2}{5}$, which is the reciprocal of $\frac{5}{2}$.

$$\frac{2}{5} \cdot \frac{5}{2}x = 4 \cdot \frac{2}{5} \qquad \text{Multiply each side by } \tfrac{2}{5}.$$

$$x = \frac{8}{5} = 1.6 \qquad \text{Simplify.}$$

The solution is $\frac{8}{5}$.

To check our answer, we substitute $x = \frac{8}{5}$ in the *given* equation.

$$2(x - 1) = 4 - \frac{1}{2}(4 + x) \quad \text{Given equation}$$

$$2\left(\frac{8}{5} - 1\right) \stackrel{?}{=} 4 - \frac{1}{2}\left(4 + \frac{8}{5}\right) \quad \text{Let } x = \frac{8}{5}.$$

$$\frac{16}{5} - 2 \stackrel{?}{=} 4 - 2 - \frac{4}{5} \quad \text{Distributive property}$$

$$\frac{6}{5} = \frac{6}{5} \checkmark \quad \text{It checks.}$$

Now Try Exercise 53

The equation in Example 3 contained a fraction. Sometimes it is easier to avoid working with fractions. To clear fractions we can multiply each side by a common denominator.

EXAMPLE 4 **Solving equations involving fractions or decimals**

Solve each equation.

(a) $\frac{1}{3}(2z - 3) - \frac{1}{2}z = -2$ **(b)** $0.4t + 0.3 = 0.75 - 0.05t$

Solution

(a) The least common denominator of $\frac{1}{3}$ and $\frac{1}{2}$ is 6, so multiply each side (or equivalently, every term) of the equation by 6. This step will clear, or eliminate, fractions.

$$\frac{1}{3}(2z - 3) - \frac{1}{2}z = -2 \quad \text{Given equation}$$

$$6\left(\frac{1}{3}(2z - 3) - \frac{1}{2}z\right) = 6(-2) \quad \text{Multiply each side by 6.}$$

$$2(2z - 3) - 3z = -12 \quad \text{Distributive property}$$

$$4z - 6 - 3z = -12 \quad \text{Distributive property}$$

$$z - 6 = -12 \quad \text{Combine like terms.}$$

$$z = -6 \quad \text{Add 6 to each side.}$$

The solution is -6.

(b) The decimals 0.4, 0.3, 0.75, and 0.05 can be written as $\frac{4}{10}, \frac{3}{10}, \frac{75}{100}$, and $\frac{5}{100}$. A common denominator is 100, so multiply each side by 100.

$$0.4t + 0.3 = 0.75 - 0.05t \quad \text{Given equation}$$

$$100(0.4t + 0.3) = 100(0.75 - 0.05t) \quad \text{Multiply each side by 100.}$$

$$40t + 30 = 75 - 5t \quad \text{Distributive property}$$

$$45t + 30 = 75 \quad \text{Add } 5t \text{ to each side.}$$

$$45t = 45 \quad \text{Subtract 30 from each side.}$$

$$t = 1 \quad \text{Divide each side by 45.}$$

The solution is 1.

Now Try Exercises 57, 61

▶ **REAL-WORLD CONNECTION** In the next example, we model some real data with a linear function and then use this function to make an estimate.

EXAMPLE 5 **Modeling numbers of LCD screens**

Flat screens or LCD (liquid crystal display) screens are becoming increasingly popular. In 2002 about 30 million LCD screens were manufactured, and this number increased to 102 million in 2008.

(a) Find a linear function that models these data.

(b) Estimate the year when 150 million LCD screens were manufactured.

Solution

(a) The graph of this linear function must pass through (**2002**, **30**) and (**2008**, **102**). Its slope is

$$m = \frac{102 - 30}{2008 - 2002} = \frac{72}{6} = 12.$$

Using the point (**2002**, **30**) in the point–slope form gives

Expression for $f(x)$

$$f(x) = 12(x - 2002) + 30.$$

(b) To determine when 150 million LCD screens were manufactured, we can set the expression for $f(x)$ equal to **150**.

$$12(x - 2002) + 30 = 150 \qquad \text{Equation to be solved}$$
$$12(x - 2002) = 120 \qquad \text{Subtract 30 from each side.}$$
$$x - 2002 = 10 \qquad \text{Divide each side by 12.}$$
$$x = 2012 \qquad \text{Add 2002 to each side.}$$

In 2012, 150 million LCD screens may have been manufactured.

▌ Now Try Exercise 117

Numerical and Graphical Solutions

Linear equations can also be solved numerically (with a table) and graphically. The disadvantage of using a table or graph is that the solution is often an estimate, rather than exact. In the next example these two methods are applied to the equation in Example 2.

EXAMPLE 6 **Solving an equation numerically and graphically**

Solve $2 - \frac{1}{2}x = 1$ numerically and graphically.

Solution

Numerical Solution Begin by constructing a table for the expression $2 - \frac{1}{2}x$, as shown in Table 2.1. This expression equals **1** when $x = 2$. That is, the solution to $2 - \frac{1}{2}x = 1$ is **2**.

TABLE 2.1 **A Numerical Solution**

x	0	1	2	3	4	5	6
$2 - \frac{1}{2}x$	2	1.5	1	0.5	0	−0.5	−1

↑ Exact solution is 2.

A Numerical Solution

X	Y1
0	2
1	1.5
2	1
3	.5
4	0
5	-.5
6	-1

Y₁■2−(1/2)X

Figure 2.2

In Figure 2.2 a calculator has been used to create the same table.

A Graphical Solution

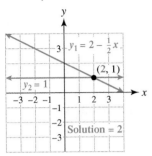

Figure 2.3

Graphical Solution One way to find a graphical solution is to let y_1 equal the left side of the equation, to let y_2 equal the right side of the equation, and then to graph $y_1 = 2 - \frac{1}{2}x$ and $y_2 = 1$, as shown in Figure 2.3. The graphs intersect at the point $(2, 1)$. We are seeking an x-value that satisfies $2 - \frac{1}{2}x = 1$, so 2 is the solution.

■ **Now Try Exercise 91**

TECHNOLOGY NOTE

Finding a Numerical Solution
The solution to the equation $2(x - 1) = 4 - \frac{1}{2}(4 + x)$ in Example 3 is the decimal number 1.6. It is possible to find it numerically. Let

$$Y_1 = 2(X - 1) \quad \text{and} \quad Y_2 = 4 - (1/2)(4 + X)$$

and increment the x-values by 1. There is no value where $y_1 = y_2$, as shown in the left-hand figure below. However, note that when $x = 1$, $y_1 < y_2$ and when $x = 2$, $y_1 > y_2$. This change indicates that there is a solution *between* $x = 1$ and $x = 2$. When x is incremented by 0.1, $y_1 = y_2$ when $x = 1.6$, as shown in the right-hand figure below.

Sometimes a graphical solution gives an *approximate* solution because it depends on how accurately a graph can be read. To verify that a graphical solution is exact, check it by substituting it in the given equation, as is done in the next two examples.

EXAMPLE 7 **Solving a linear equation graphically**

Figure 2.4 shows graphs of $y_1 = 2x + 1$ and $y_2 = -x + 4$. Use the graphs to solve the equation $2x + 1 = -x + 4$. Check your answer.

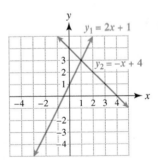

Figure 2.4

Solution
The graphs of y_1 and y_2 intersect at the point $(1, 3)$. Therefore 1 is the solution. We can check this solution by substituting $x = 1$ in the equation.

$$2x + 1 = -x + 4 \quad \text{Given equation}$$
$$2(1) + 1 \overset{?}{=} -1 + 4 \quad \text{Let } x = 1.$$
$$3 = 3 \checkmark \quad \text{The answer checks.}$$

■ **Now Try Exercise 77**

EXAMPLE 8

Solving a linear equation graphically

Solve $3(1 - x) = 2$ graphically.

Solution

We begin by graphing $y_1 = 3(1 - x)$ and $y_2 = 2$, as shown in Figure 2.5. Their graphs intersect near the point $(0.3333, 2)$. Because $\frac{1}{3} = 0.\overline{3}$, the solution appears to be $\frac{1}{3}$. Note that this graphical solution is *approximate*. We can verify our result as follows.

$$3(1 - x) = 2 \qquad \text{Given equation}$$

$$3\left(1 - \frac{1}{3}\right) \stackrel{?}{=} 2 \qquad \text{Substitute } x = \frac{1}{3}.$$

$$2 = 2 \ \checkmark \qquad \text{It checks.}$$

[−6, 6, 1] by [−4, 4, 1]

Figure 2.5

Now Try Exercise 87

CALCULATOR HELP

To find a point of intersection, see Appendix A (page AP-6).=

Technology can be helpful when we are solving an equation that is more complicated. In the next example, we solve an application graphically and symbolically.

EXAMPLE 9

Analyzing numbers of Facebook and Google visitors

From 2009 to 2014, the number of unique visitors F to Facebook in millions x years after 2009 is expected to be $F(x) = 202x + 300$. Similarly, the number of unique visitors G to Google is expected to be $G(x) = 83x + 800$.
(a) Evaluate $F(3)$ and interpret the result.
(b) Does Facebook or Google have a greater rate of growth? Explain.
(c) Estimate graphically the year when Facebook and Google could have the same number of unique visitors.
(d) Solve part (c) symbolically. Do your answers agree?

Solution

(a) $F(3) = 202(3) + 300 = 906$. Facebook is expected to have 906 million unique visitors in the year $2009 + 3 = 2012$.
(b) Facebook is growing faster. From $F(x) = 202x + 300$ and $G(x) = 83x + 800$, we can see that unique Facebook visitors are growing at a rate of 202 million per year, whereas Google is growing at a rate of 83 million per year.
(c) *Graphically* To determine the year when the numbers of unique visitors to Facebook and Google are equal, we must find an x such that $F(x) = G(x)$. That is, we must solve

$$202x + 300 = 83x + 800.$$

Start by graphing the equations $y_1 = 202x + 300$ and $y_2 = 83x + 800$, as shown in Figure 2.6. The graphs intersect near $(4.2, 1149)$. This model predicts that during 2013 $(2009 + 4.2 = 2013.2)$, there will be about $1,149,000,000$ unique visitors to both Facebook and Google.

[0, 8, 1] by [0, 2000, 500]

(a)

(b)

Figure 2.6

(d) *Symbolically* As in part (c), we must find an x such that $F(x) = G(x)$.

$$202x + 300 = 83x + 800 \quad \text{Solve } F(x) = G(x).$$
$$202x = 83x + 500 \quad \text{Subtract 300 from each side.}$$
$$119x = 500 \quad \text{Subtract } 83x \text{ from each side.}$$
$$x = \frac{500}{119} \approx 4.2 \quad \text{Divide each side by 119.}$$

Our graphical and symbolic answers agree. Note that the symbolic answer of $\frac{500}{119}$ is exact, while the graphical answer of 4.2 is approximate.

Now Try Exercise 123

Identities and Contradictions

A linear equation ($ax + b = 0$, $a \neq 0$) has exactly one solution. However, there are other types of equations, called *identities* and *contradictions*. An **identity** is an equation that is always *true*, regardless of the values of any variables. For example, $x + x = 2x$ is an identity, because it is true for all real numbers x. A **contradiction** is an equation that is always *false*, regardless of the values of any variables. For example, $x = x + 1$ is a contradiction because no real number x can be equal to itself plus 1. If an equation is true for some but not all values of any variable, then it is called a **conditional equation**. The equation $x + 1 = 4$ is conditional because 3 is the only solution. Thus far, we have only discussed conditional equations.

EXAMPLE 10 **Determining identities and contradictions**

Determine whether each equation is an identity, contradiction, or conditional equation.
(a) $0 = 1$ **(b)** $5 = 5$ **(c)** $2x = 6$ **(d)** $2(z - 1) + z = 3z + 2$

Solution
(a) The equation $0 = 1$ is always false. It is a contradiction.
(b) The equation $5 = 5$ is always true. It is an identity.
(c) The equation $2x = 6$ is true only when $x = 3$. It is a conditional equation.
(d) Simplify the equation to obtain the following.

$$2(z - 1) + z = 3z + 2 \quad \text{Given equation}$$
$$2z - 2 + z = 3z + 2 \quad \text{Distributive property}$$
$$3z - 2 = 3z + 2 \quad \text{Combine like terms.}$$
$$-2 = 2 \;\text{✗} \quad \text{Subtract } 3z \text{ from each side.}$$

Because $-2 = 2$ is always false, the given equation is a contradiction.

Now Try Exercises 95, 97

Intercepts of a Line

Equations of lines can be written in slope–intercept form or point–slope form. A third form for the equation of a line is called *standard form*, which is defined as follows.

STANDARD FORM OF A LINE

An equation for a line is in **standard form** when it is written as

$$ax + by = c,$$

where a, b, and c are constants with a and b not both 0.

Standard Form

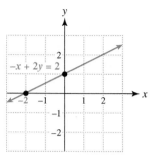

Figure 2.7

Examples of lines in standard form include

$$3x - 7y = -2, \quad -5x - 6y = 0, \quad 2y = 5, \quad \text{and} \quad \tfrac{1}{2}x + y = 4.$$

To graph a line in standard form, we often start by locating the x- and y-intercepts. For example, the graph of $-x + 2y = 2$ is shown in Figure 2.7. All points on the x-axis have a y-coordinate of 0. To find the x-intercept, we let $y = 0$ in the equation $-x + 2y = 2$ and then solve for x.

$$-x + 2(0) = 2 \quad \text{or} \quad x = -2 \quad \text{Let } y = 0.$$

The x-intercept is -2. Note that the graph intersects the x-axis at $(-2, 0)$. Similarly, all points on the y-axis have an x-coordinate of 0. To find the y-intercept, we let $x = 0$ in the equation $-x + 2y = 2$ and then solve for y to obtain 1. Note that the graph intersects the y-axis at the point $(0, 1)$. This discussion is summarized by the following.

FINDING INTERCEPTS

To find the x-intercept of a line, let $y = 0$ in its equation and solve for x.

To find the y-intercept of a line, let $x = 0$ in its equation and solve for y.

NOTE: In some texts, intercepts are defined to be points rather than real numbers. In this case the x-intercept in Figure 2.7 is $(-2, 0)$ and the y-intercept is $(0, 1)$.

EXAMPLE 11   **Finding intercepts of a line in standard form**

Let the equation of a line be $3x - 2y = 6$.
(a) Find the x- and y-intercepts.
(b) Graph the line.
(c) Solve the equation for y to obtain the slope–intercept form.

Solution
(a) **x-intercept:** Let $y = 0$ in $3x - 2y = 6$ to obtain $3x - 2(0) = 6$, or $x = 2$. The x-intercept is 2.
    y-intercept: Let $x = 0$ in $3x - 2y = 6$ to obtain $3(0) - 2y = 6$, or $y = -3$. The y-intercept is -3.
(b) Sketch a line passing through $(2, 0)$ and $(0, -3)$, as shown in Figure 2.8.
(c) To solve for y, start by subtracting $3x$ from each side.

$$
\begin{aligned}
3x - 2y &= 6 && \text{Given equation} \\
-2y &= -3x + 6 && \text{Subtract } 3x \text{ from each side.} \\
-\tfrac{1}{2}(-2y) &= -\tfrac{1}{2}(-3x + 6) && \text{Multiply each side by } -\tfrac{1}{2}. \\
y &= \tfrac{3}{2}x - 3 && \text{Distributive property}
\end{aligned}
$$

The slope–intercept form is $y = \tfrac{3}{2}x - 3$.

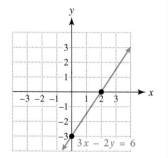

Figure 2.8

Now Try Exercise 107

2.1 Putting It All Together

CONCEPT	EXPLANATION	EXAMPLES
Linear Equations	Can be written as $ax + b = 0$, where $a \neq 0$; has *one solution*	$3x - 4 = 0$, $\quad 2(x + 3) = -2$, $\quad$ and $2x = \dfrac{2}{3} - 5x$
Solution Set	The set of all solutions	The solution set for $x - 4 = 0$ is $\{4\}$ because 4 is the only solution to the equation.
Addition Property of Equality	$a = b$ is equivalent to $a + c = b + c$. "Equals added to equals are equal."	If 2 is added to each side of $x - 2 = 1$, the equation becomes $x = 3$.
Multiplication Property of Equality	$a = b$ is equivalent to $ac = bc$ for $c \neq 0$. "Equals multiplied by equals are equal."	If each side of $\frac{1}{2}x = 3$ is multiplied by 2, the resulting equation is $x = 6$.
Standard Form for a Line	$ax + by = c$, where a, b, and c are constants with a and b not both zero	$3x + 5y = 10$, $\quad -2x + y = 0$, $3y = 18$, $\quad$ and $\quad x = 4$
Finding Intercepts	To find the x-intercept, let $y = 0$ and solve for x. To find the y-intercept, let $x = 0$ and solve for y.	Let $2x + 4y = 8$. x-intercept: $2x + 4(0) = 8$, $\quad$ or $\quad x = 4$ y-intercept: $2(0) + 4y = 8$, $\quad$ or $\quad y = 2$

Linear equations can be solved symbolically, graphically, and numerically. The following illustrates how to solve the equation $2x - 1 = 3$ with each method.

Symbolic Solution

$$2x - 1 = 3$$
$$2x = 4$$
$$x = 2$$

The solution is **2**.

Graphical Solution

The solution is **2**.

Numerical Solution

x	$2x - 1$
0	-1
1	1
2	**3**
3	5

Because $2x - 1$ equals 3 when $x = 2$, the solution to $2x - 1 = 3$ is **2**.

2.1 Exercises

CONCEPTS AND VOCABULARY

1. Give the general form of a linear equation.

2. How many solutions does a linear equation have?

3. Is 1 the solution to $4x - 1 = 3x$?

4. Are $3x = 6$ and $x = 2$ equivalent equations?

5. The solution to $x + 6 = 10$ is _____.

6. The solution to $7x = -14$ is _____.

7. What symbol must occur in every equation?

8. Name three methods for solving a linear equation.

9. If a graphical solution to a linear equation results in the point of intersection $(3, 4)$, then the solution to the equation is _____.

10. The standard form for the equation of a line is _____.

11. The addition property of equality states that $a = b$ is equivalent to _____.

12. The multiplication property of equality states that $a = b$ is equivalent to _____.

Exercises 13–16: Classify each statement as true or false.

13. The equation $2x - 1 = 2x$ is a contradiction.

14. The equation $3(x - 5) = 3x - 15$ is an identity.

15. The equation $x + 7 = 9$ is an identity.

16. The equation $4x - 6 = x$ is a contradiction.

Exercises 17–22: Decide whether the given value for the variable is a solution to the equation.

17. $x - 6 = -2$ $x = 5$

18. $-\frac{1}{2}x + 1 = \frac{1}{3}x - \frac{2}{3}$ $x = 2$

19. $3(2t + 3) = \frac{13}{3} - t$ $t = -\frac{2}{3}$

20. $t - 1 = 2 - (t + 1)$ $t = 2$

21. $-(2z - 3) + 2z = 1 - z$ $z = -2$

22. $-\frac{1}{3}(4 - z) + \frac{2}{5}(z + 1) = -\frac{1}{5}$ $z = 1$

SYMBOLIC SOLUTIONS

Exercises 23–64: Solve the equation symbolically. Check your answer.

23. $x - 4 = 10$ **24.** $x - \frac{1}{2} = \frac{3}{2}$

25. $5 + x = 3$ **26.** $8 + x = -5$

27. $\frac{1}{2} - x = 2$ **28.** $10 - x = -5$

29. $-6x = -18$ **30.** $-5x = 15$

31. $-\frac{1}{3}x = 4$ **32.** $\frac{3}{4}x = 9$

33. $2x + 3 = 13$ **34.** $6x - 4 = -10$

35. $7 - 3x = -8$ **36.** $5 - 2x = -2$

37. $2x = 8 - \frac{1}{2}x$ **38.** $-7 = 3.5x$

39. $3x - 1 = 11(1 - x)$

40. $4 - 3x = -5(1 + 2x)$

41. $x + 4 = 2 - \frac{1}{3}x$

42. $2x - 5 = 6 - \frac{5}{2}x$ **43.** $2(x - 1) = 5 - 2x$

44. $-(x - 4) = 4(x + 1) + 3(x - 2)$

45. $\dfrac{2x + 1}{3} = \dfrac{2x - 1}{2}$ **46.** $\dfrac{3 - 4x}{5} = \dfrac{3x - 1}{2}$

47. $4.2x - 6.2 = 1 - 1.1x$

48. $8.4 - 2.1x = 1.4x$ **49.** $\frac{1}{2}x - \frac{3}{2} = 4$

50. $5 - \frac{1}{3}x = x - 3$

51. $4(x - 1980) + 6 = 18$

52. $-5(x - 1900) - 55 = 145$

53. $2(y - 3) + 5(1 - 2y) = 4y + 1$

54. $4(y + 1) - (3 - 5y) = -2(y - 2)$

55. $-\left(5 - (z + 1)\right) = 9 - \left(5 - (2z - 3)\right)$

56. $-3(2 - 3z) + 2z = 1 - 3z$

57. $\frac{2}{3}(t - 3) + \frac{1}{2}t = 5$ **58.** $\frac{1}{5}t + \frac{3}{10} = 2 - \frac{1}{2}t$

59. $\dfrac{3k}{4} - \dfrac{2k}{3} = \dfrac{1}{6}$ **60.** $\dfrac{k + 1}{3} - \dfrac{1}{2} = \dfrac{3k - 3}{6}$

61. $0.2(n - 2) + 0.4n = 0.05$

62. $0.15(n + 1) = 0.1n + 1$

63. $0.7y - 0.8(y - 1) = 2$

64. $0.2y + 0.3(5 - 2y) = -0.2y$

65. Thinking Generally Solve the general linear equation $ax + b = 0$ for x, if $a \neq 0$.

66. Thinking Generally Solve the general linear equation $ax - b = cx$ for x, if $a \neq c$.

NUMERICAL SOLUTIONS

Exercises 67–70: Complete the table. Then use the table to solve the equation.

67. $-4x + 8 = 0$

x	1	2	3	4	5
$-4x + 8$	4				

68. $3x + 2 = 5$

x	-2	-1	0	1	2
$3x + 2$	-4				

69. $4 - 2x = x + 7$

x	-2	-1	0	1	2
$4 - 2x$	8				0
$x + 7$	5				9

70. $3(x - 1) = -2(1 - x)$

x	-2	-1	0	1	2
$3(x - 1)$	-9				
$-2(1 - x)$	-6				

Exercises 71–76: Solve the linear equation numerically.

71. $x - 3 = 7$

72. $2x + 1 = 11$

73. $2t - \frac{1}{2} = \frac{3}{2}$

74. $7 - 4t = -5$

 75. $3(z - 1) + 1.5 = 2z$

 76. $-3z - 6 = z + 2$

GRAPHICAL SOLUTIONS

Exercises 77–80: A linear equation is solved graphically by letting y_1 equal the left side of the equation and y_2 equal the right side of the equation. Find the solution. Check your answer.

77.

78.

79.

80.

Exercises 81–90: Solve the equation graphically. Check your answer.

81. $5 - 2x = 7$

82. $-2x + 3 = -7$

83. $2x - (x - 2) = 2$

84. $x + 1 = 3 - x$

85. $3(x + 2) + 1 = x + 1$

86. $x + 5 = 2x + 2$

 87. $5(x - 1990) + 15 = 100$

88. $10(x - 1985) - 20 = 55$

89. $\sqrt{2} + 4(x - \pi) = \frac{1}{7}x$

90. $\pi(x - \sqrt{5}) = \frac{7x + 5}{3}$

SOLVING LINEAR EQUATIONS BY MORE THAN ONE METHOD

*Exercises 91–94: Solve the equation **(a)** numerically, **(b)** graphically, and **(c)** symbolically.*

91. $2x - 1 = 13$

92. $9 - x = 3x + 1$

93. $3x - 5 - (x + 1) = 0$

94. $\frac{1}{2}x - 1 = \frac{5 - x}{2}$

IDENTITIES AND CONTRADICTIONS

Exercises 95–102: Determine whether the equation is an identity, contradiction, or conditional equation.

95. $2x + 3 = 2x$

96. $x + 5 = x - 4$

97. $2x + 3x = 5x$

98. $-3x = 4x - 7x$

99. $2(x - 1) = 2x - 2$

100. $3x - 10 = 2(x - 5) + x$

101. $5 - 7(4 - 3x) = x - 4(2 - 4x)$

102. $7 - 2(x + 3) - x = -4(x - 5) - 22$

103. Thinking Generally Let f and g be linear functions satisfying $f(-4) = 9$, $f(1) = -1$, $g(-3) = 1$, and $g(0) = 13$. Determine the point where their graphs intersect.

104. Thinking Generally Let f and g be linear functions where $f(-2) = -2$, $f(8) = -7$, $g(-4) = -11$, and $g(12) = 1$. Determine the point where their graphs intersect.

FINDING INTERCEPTS

Exercises 105–116: Do the following.

    (a) Find the x- and y-intercepts.
    (b) Graph the line.
    (c) Solve the equation for y to obtain the slope–intercept form.

105. $x + y = 4$

106. $x - y = -2$

107. $2x + 5y = 10$

108. $-3x + 4y = -6$

109. $2x - 3y = 9$

110. $\frac{1}{2}x - \frac{1}{4}y = 1$

111. $-\frac{2}{3}x - y = 2$

112. $-x - \frac{2}{5}y = 2$

113. $2x + 5y = 7$

114. $3x - 4y = 2$

115. $5x - 6y = -3$

116. $-8x + 9y = -10$

APPLICATIONS

117. *Global Seafood Consumption* (Refer to the chapter introduction.) In 1960 global seafood consumption was 42 million tons, and it increased to 157 million tons in 2008.
   (a) Determine $S(x) = m(x - x_1) + y_1$, where x is the year, so that S models these data.
   (b) Use $S(x)$ to estimate the amount of seafood that was consumed in 2000.
   (c) Assuming that trends continue, when might the 2008 amount increase by 45 million tons?

118. *Centenarians* In 1990 there were 37,306 centenarians, people age 100 or older, in the United States. The number of centenarians is estimated to increase by 8260 per year. (*Source:* U.S. Census Bureau.)
   (a) Find values for m, x_1, and y_1 so that the formula $f(x) = m(x - x_1) + y_1$ models the number of centenarians during year x.
   (b) Estimate the year when there will be 450,000 centenarians.

119. *State and Federal Inmates* From 1995 to 2009 the number of state and federal prison inmates in millions can be modeled by $f(x) = 0.0338x - 66.5$ during year x. (*Source:* Department of Justice.)
   (a) Determine symbolically the year when there were 1.3 million inmates.
   (b) Solve part (a) numerically.
   (c) Solve part (a) graphically.

120. *Asian-American Population* In 1998 there were 10.5 million Asian-Americans, and by 2009 this number grew to 14.9 million. (*Source:* U.S. Census Bureau.)
   (a) Find a linear function P that approximates this population in millions x years after 1998.
   (b) Interpret the y-intercept on the graph of P.
   (c) Estimate symbolically when this population was 13.7 million.
   (d) Solve part (c) graphically.

121. *College Degrees* In 1970 there were 1.1 million college degrees awarded. This number increased to 1.9 million in 2010. (*Source:* The College Board.)
   (a) Find a linear function D that approximates degree numbers in millions x years after 1970.
   (b) Interpret the y-intercept on the graph of D.
   (c) Estimate symbolically when this number was 1.7 million.
   (d) Solve part (c) graphically.

122. *Injured at Work* In 2006 there were 4.2 fatal work injuries per 100,000 full-time workers. By 2009 this number decreased to 2.3 per 100,000 full-time workers. (*Source:* Department of Labor.)
   (a) Find a linear function D that models these data x years after 2006.
   (b) If trends continue, estimate symbolically when this rate could be 2.1.
   (c) Solve part (b) graphically.

123. *Online Versus Newspaper Ads* From 2005 to 2012 the revenue in billions of dollars from newspaper ads N is given by $N(x) = -3.285x + 47.5$, where x is the number of years after 2005. Similarly, the revenue from online ads O can be calculated by $O(x) = 2.244x + 13$. (*Source:* Newspaper Association of America and Interactive Advertising Bureau.)
   (a) Evaluate $N(3)$ and interpret the result.
   (b) Do newspaper ads or online ads have a greater rate of growth? Explain.
   (c) Estimate graphically the year when newspaper and online ads had the same revenue.
   (d) Solve part (c) symbolically. Do your answers agree?

124. *Hip Hop Versus Rock and Roll* From 1987 to 2005 the (combined) percentage of music sales from rap and hip hop music can be calculated by $H(x) = \frac{83}{170}x + 3.8$, where x represents years after 1987. Similarly, $R(x) = -\frac{22}{17}x + 46$ can calculate the percentage of music sales from rock and roll music. (*Source:* Recording Industry of America.)
   (a) Evaluate $R(3)$ and interpret the result.
   (b) Estimate graphically the year when rap and hip hop sales equal rock and roll sales.
   (c) Solve part (b) symbolically. Do your answers agree?

125. *Smartphones* From 2008 to 2012 the percentage of mobile phone owners S with a smartphone can be modeled by $S(x) = 9.76x + 10$, where x is the number of years after 2008. Similarly, $F(x) = -9.76x + 90$ models the percentage of mobile phone owners with a feature phone. (*Source: Nielsen Company.*)

    (a) Evaluate $S(2)$ and interpret the result.

    (b) Interpret the y-intercept on the graph of S.

    (c) Estimate the year when smartphone ownership will exceed feature phone ownership.

126. *Craigslist Visitors* From 2006 to 2011 the number of *monthly* unique visitors to Craigslist C can be modeled by $C(x) = 7660x + 13{,}000$, where x is the number of years after 2006. Similarly, $E(x) = -5176x + 75{,}000$ models the number of monthly unique visitors to eBay. (*Source: Citi Investment Research Analysis.*)

    (a) Describe the rate of change in monthly unique visitors for Craigslist and eBay.

    (b) Interpret the y-intercept on the graph of C.

    (c) Estimate the year when Craigslist visitors could exceed eBay visitors.

127. *CD and LP Record Sales* From 1985 to 1990, sales of CDs (compact discs) in the United States can be modeled by $y_1 = 51.6(x - 1985) + 9.1$, and sales of LPs (vinyl records) can be modeled by $y_2 = -31.9(x - 1985) + 167.7$. All sales are in millions. Determine the year when sales of CDs and LPs were equal.

128. *U.S. Population Density* In 1900 there were, on average, 22 people per square mile in the United States. By 2008 the population density had increased to 86 people per square mile. (*Source: U.S. Census Bureau.*)

    (a) Find a linear function f that models the population density during year x.

    (b) Determine the year when the population density was 58 people per square mile.

129. Online Exploration Look up the U.S. divorce rate for two different years, such as 1990 and 2005. Find a linear function D that models these rates and then use D to estimate the year when the divorce rate was 5.0 per 1000 population.

130. Online Exploration Look up the federal debt for 2001 and the current year. Find a linear function that models these debts and use it to estimate when the debt was \$8 trillion. Look up the true value.

WRITING ABOUT MATHEMATICS

131. Explain each of the following terms: linear equation, solution, solution set, and equivalent equations. Give an example of each.

132. Explain how to solve the equation $ax + b = 0$ symbolically and graphically. Use both methods to solve the equation $5x + 10 = 0$.

Group Activity   Working with Real Data

Directions: Form a group of 2 to 4 people. Select someone to record the group's responses for this activity. All members of the group should work cooperatively to answer the questions. If your instructor asks for your results, each member of the group should be prepared to respond.

Older Mothers The table lists the number of births per 1000 for women ages 40–44.

Year	1980	1990	1995	2000	2007
Births	3.9	5.5	6.6	7.9	9.5

Source: U.S. Census Bureau.

(a) Make a scatterplot of the data.

(b) Comment on any trends in the data.

(c) Find a linear function B in the form
$$B(x) = m(x - x_1) + y_1$$
that models the data. Answers may vary.

(d) Interpret the slope as a rate of change.

(e) If this trend continues, estimate when the birth rate might reach 12.

2.2 Introduction to Problem Solving

Solving a Formula for a Variable • Steps for Solving a Problem • Percentages

A LOOK INTO MATH ▶ Problem-solving skills are essential because every day we must solve problems—both small and large—for survival. A logical approach to a problem is often helpful, which is especially true in mathematics. In this section we discuss steps that can be used to solve mathematical problems. We begin the section by discussing how to solve a formula for a variable.

NEW VOCABULARY

☐ Percentage
☐ Percent form
☐ Decimal form

Solving a Formula for a Variable

The perimeter P of a rectangle with width W and length L is given by $P = 2W + 2L$, as illustrated in Figure 2.9. Suppose that we know the perimeter P and length L of this rectangle. Even though the formula is written to calculate P, we can still use it to find the width W. This technique is demonstrated in the next example.

W

L

Figure 2.9 $P = 2W + 2L$

EXAMPLE 1 **Finding the width of a rectangle**

A rectangle has a perimeter of 80 inches and a length of 23 inches.
(a) Write a formula to find the width W of a rectangle with known perimeter P and length L.
(b) Use the formula to find W.

Solution
(a) We must solve $P = 2W + 2L$ for W.

$$P = 2W + 2L \qquad \text{Given formula}$$

$$P - 2L = 2W \qquad \text{Subtract } 2L \text{ from each side.}$$

$$\frac{1}{2}(P - 2L) = \frac{1}{2}(2W) \qquad \text{Multiply each side by } \tfrac{1}{2}.$$

$$\frac{P}{2} - L = W \qquad \text{Distributive property}$$

The required formula is $W = \frac{P}{2} - L$.
(b) Substitute $P = 80$ and $L = 23$ into this formula. The width is

$$W = \frac{80}{2} - 23 = 17 \text{ inches.}$$

▌ Now Try Exercise 45

▶ **REAL-WORLD CONNECTION** In the next example we use a formula that converts degrees Fahrenheit to degrees Celsius to find a formula that converts degrees Celsius to degrees Fahrenheit.

EXAMPLE 2 **Converting temperature**

The formula $C = \frac{5}{9}(F - 32)$ is used to convert degrees Fahrenheit to degrees Celsius.
(a) Use this formula to convert $212°F$ to an equivalent Celsius temperature.
(b) Solve the formula for F to obtain a formula that can convert degrees Celsius to degrees Fahrenheit. Interpret the slope of the graph of F.
(c) Use this new formula to convert $25°C$ to an equivalent Fahrenheit temperature.

Solution
(a) $C = \frac{5}{9}(212 - 32) = \frac{5}{9}(180) = 100°C$

(b)
$$C = \frac{5}{9}(F - 32) \quad \text{Given formula}$$
$$\frac{9}{5}C = \frac{9}{5} \cdot \frac{5}{9}(F - 32) \quad \text{Multiply each side by } \frac{9}{5}.$$
$$\frac{9}{5}C = F - 32 \quad \text{Simplify.}$$
$$\frac{9}{5}C + 32 = F \quad \text{Add 32 to each side.}$$

Because $F = \frac{9}{5}C + 32$, the slope of the graph of F is $\frac{9}{5}$, which indicates that a $1°$ increase in Celsius temperature is equivalent to a $\frac{9°}{5}$ increase in Fahrenheit temperature.

(c) Substitute 25 for C in this formula to obtain $F = \frac{9}{5}(25) + 32 = 77°F$.

Now Try Exercise 49

Sometimes an equation in two variables can be used to determine the formula for a function. To do so, we must let one variable be the dependent variable and the other variable be the independent variable. For example, $2x - 5y = 10$ is the equation of a line written in standard form. Solving for y gives the following result.

$$-5y = -2x + 10 \quad \text{Subtract } 2x \text{ from each side.}$$
$$-\frac{1}{5}(-5y) = -\frac{1}{5}(-2x + 10) \quad \text{Multiply each side by } -\frac{1}{5}.$$
$$y = \frac{2}{5}x - 2 \quad \text{Distributive property}$$

If y is the dependent variable, x is the independent variable, and $y = f(x)$, then
$$f(x) = \frac{2}{5}x - 2$$
defines a function f whose graph is the line determined by $2x - 5y = 10$.

EXAMPLE 3 **Writing a function defined by an equation**

Solve each equation for y and write a formula for a function f defined by $y = f(x)$.

(a) $4(x - 2y) = -3x$ \qquad (b) $\frac{x + y}{2} - 5 = 20$

Solution

(a)
$$4(x - 2y) = -3x \quad \text{Given equation}$$
$$4x - 8y = -3x \quad \text{Distributive property}$$
$$-8y = -7x \quad \text{Subtract } 4x \text{ from each side.}$$
$$y = \frac{7}{8}x \quad \text{Divide each side by } -8.$$

Thus $f(x) = \frac{7}{8}x$.

(b)

$$\frac{x + y}{2} - 5 = 20 \qquad \text{Given equation}$$

$$\frac{x + y}{2} = 25 \qquad \text{Add 5 to each side.}$$

$$\frac{2(x + y)}{2} = 2(25) \qquad \text{Multiply each side by 2.}$$

$$x + y = 50 \qquad \text{Simplify.}$$

$$y = 50 - x \qquad \text{Subtract } x \text{ from each side.}$$

Thus $f(x) = 50 - x$.

Now Try Exercises 21, 23

Steps for Solving a Problem

Solving problems in mathematics can be challenging, especially when formulas and equations are not given to us. In these situations we have to write them, but to do so, we need a strategy. The following steps are often a helpful strategy. They are based on George Polya's (1888–1985) four-step process for problem solving.

STEPS FOR SOLVING A PROBLEM

STEP 1: Read the problem carefully to be sure that you understand it. (You may need to read the problem more than once.) Assign a variable to what you are being asked to find. If necessary, write other quantities in terms of this variable.

STEP 2: Write an equation that relates the quantities described in the problem. You may need to sketch a diagram, make a table, or refer to known formulas.

STEP 3: Solve the equation and determine the solution.

STEP 4: Look back and check your answer. Does it seem reasonable? Did you find the required information?

STUDY TIP

These four steps can make it easier to solve word problems.

In the next example we apply these steps to a word problem involving unknown numbers.

EXAMPLE 4   **Solving a number problem**

The sum of three consecutive *even* integers is 108. Find the three numbers.

Solution

STEP 1: *Start by assigning a variable to an unknown quantity.*

$$n: \text{smallest of the three integers}$$

Next, write the other two numbers in terms of n.

$$n + 2: \text{next consecutive } even \text{ integer}$$

$$n + 4: \text{largest of the three even integers}$$

STEP 2: *Write an equation that relates these unknown quantities.* As the sum of these three even integers is 108, the needed equation is

$$n + (n + 2) + (n + 4) = 108.$$

STEP 3: *Solve the equation in Step 2.*

$n + (n + 2) + (n + 4) = 108$	Equation to be solved
$(n + n + n) + (2 + 4) = 108$	Commutative and associative properties
$3n + 6 = 108$	Combine like terms.
$3n = 102$	Subtract 6 from each side.
$n = 34$	Divide each side by 3.

The smallest of the three numbers is 34, so the three numbers are 34, 36, and 38.

STEP 4: *Check your answer.* The sum of these three consecutive even integers is

$$34 + 36 + 38 = 108.$$

The answer checks.

▌ Now Try Exercise 53

In the next example we apply this procedure to find the dimensions of a room.

EXAMPLE 5 **Solving a geometry problem**

The length of a rectangular room is 2 feet more than its width. If the perimeter of the room is 80 feet, find the width and length of the room.

Solution
STEP 1: *Start by assigning a variable to an unknown quantity.* See Figure 2.10.

x: width of the room

$x + 2$: length of the room

STEP 2: *Write an equation that relates these unknown quantities.* The perimeter is the distance around the room and equals 80 feet. Thus

$$2x + 2(x + 2) = 80,$$

which simplifies to $4x + 4 = 80$.

STEP 3: *Solve the equation in Step 2.*

Figure 2.10 Perimeter = 80

$4x + 4 = 80$	Equation to be solved
$4x = 76$	Subtract 4 from each side.
$\dfrac{4x}{4} = \dfrac{76}{4}$	Divide each side by 4.
$x = 19$	Simplify.

The width is 19 feet and the length is $19 + 2 = 21$ feet.

STEP 4: *Check your answer.* The perimeter is $2(19) + 2(21) = 80$ feet. The answer checks.

▌ Now Try Exercise 57

EXAMPLE 6   **Solving a geometry problem**

A wire, 100 inches long, needs to be cut into two pieces so that it can be bent into a circle and a square. The length of a side of the square must equal the diameter of the circle. Approximate where the 100-inch wire should be cut.

Solution

STEP 1: *Assign a variable.* Let x be both the diameter of the circle and the length of a side of the square, as shown in Figure 2.11.

STEP 2: *Write an equation.* Because $C = \pi d$, the circumference of the circle is $C = \pi x$, and the perimeter of the square is $P = 4x$. The wire is 100 inches long, so

$$\pi x + 4x = 100.$$

STEP 3: *Solve the equation in Step 2.*

$$\pi x + 4x = 100 \qquad \text{Equation to be solved}$$
$$(\pi + 4)x = 100 \qquad \text{Distributive property}$$
$$x = \frac{100}{\pi + 4} \qquad \text{Divide by } \pi + 4.$$
$$x \approx 14 \qquad \text{Approximate.}$$

Figure 2.11

The wire should be cut so that the piece for the square is about $4 \times 14 = 56$ inches and the piece for the circle is about $100 - 56 = 44$ inches.

STEP 4: *Check the answer.* If the square's perimeter is 56 inches, then each of its sides is $\frac{56}{4} = 14$ inches. If the diameter of the circle is 14 inches, then its circumference is $C = \pi(14) \approx 43.98$, or about 44 inches. Because $56 + 44 = 100$, the answer checks.

Now Try Exercise 59

EXAMPLE 7   **Solving a motion problem**

Two cars are traveling in opposite directions on a freeway. Three hours after meeting, they are 420 miles apart. If one car is traveling 10 miles per hour faster than the other car, find the speeds of the two cars.

Solution

STEP 1: *Assign a variable.*

$$x: \text{speed of the slower car}$$

$$x + 10: \text{speed of the faster car}$$

STEP 2: *Write an equation.* The information is summarized in Table 2.2.

NOTE: Distance = Rate × Time.

TABLE 2.2

	Rate	Time	Distance	
Slower Car	x	3	$3x$	← Sum equals
Faster Car	$x + 10$	3	$3(x + 10)$	← 420 miles.
Total			420	

The sum of the distances traveled by the cars is 420 miles. Thus

$$3x + 3(x + 10) = 420.$$

STEP 3: *Solve the equation in Step 2.*

$$3x + 3(x + 10) = 420 \qquad \text{Equation to be solved}$$
$$3x + 3x + 30 = 420 \qquad \text{Distributive property}$$
$$6x + 30 = 420 \qquad \text{Combine like terms.}$$
$$6x = 390 \qquad \text{Subtract 30 from each side.}$$
$$x = 65 \qquad \text{Divide each side by 6.}$$

The speed of the slower car is 65 miles per hour and the speed of the faster car is 10 miles per hour faster, or 75 miles per hour.

STEP 4: *Check the answer.* The difference in the cars' speeds is $75 - 65 = 10$ miles per hour.

$$\text{Distance traveled by the slower car: } 65 \times 3 = 195 \text{ miles}$$

$$\text{Distance traveled by the faster car: } 75 \times 3 = 225 \text{ miles}$$

The total distance is $195 + 225 = 420$ miles, so it checks.

▎ Now Try Exercise 61

▶ **REAL-WORLD CONNECTION** Many times we are called upon to solve a mixture problem. Such problems may involve a mixture of acid solutions, a mixture of loan amounts, or some other mixture. In the next example an athlete jogs at two different speeds, and mathematics is used to determine how much time is spent jogging at each speed.

EXAMPLE 8 ## Solving a "mixture" problem

An athlete begins jogging at 8 miles per hour and then jogs at 7 miles per hour, traveling 10.9 miles in 1.5 hours. How long did the athlete jog at each speed?

Solution

STEP 1: *Assign a variable.* Let t represent the time spent jogging at 8 miles per hour. Because total time spent jogging is 1.5 hours, the time spent jogging at 7 miles per hour must be $1.5 - t$.

STEP 2: *Write an equation.* A table is often helpful in solving a mixture problem. Because $d = rt$, Table 2.3 shows that the distance the athlete jogs at 8 miles per hour is $8t$. The distance traveled at 7 miles per hour is $7(1.5 - t)$, and the total distance traveled is 10.9 miles. From the "Distance" column, we can write the equation as

$$8t + 7(1.5 - t) = 10.9.$$

TABLE 2.3

	Rate	Time	Distance
First Part	8	t	$8t$
Second Part	7	$1.5 - t$	$7(1.5 - t)$
Total		1.5	10.9

Sum equals 10.9 miles.

STEP 3: *Solve the equation in Step 2.*

$$8t + 7(1.5 - t) = 10.9 \qquad \text{Equation to be solved}$$
$$8t + 10.5 - 7t = 10.9 \qquad \text{Distributive property}$$
$$t + 10.5 = 10.9 \qquad \text{Combine like terms.}$$
$$t = 0.4 \qquad \text{Subtract 10.5 from each side.}$$

The athlete jogged 0.4 hour at 8 miles per hour and $1.5 - 0.4 = 1.1$ hours at 7 miles per hour.

STEP 4: *Check your answer.* Start by calculating the distance traveled at each speed.

$$8 \cdot 0.4 = 3.2 \text{ miles} \quad \text{Distance at 8 mph}$$
$$7 \cdot 1.1 = 7.7 \text{ miles} \quad \text{Distance at 7 mph}$$

The total distance is $3.2 + 7.7 = 10.9$ miles and the total time is $0.4 + 1.1 = 1.5$ hours. The answer checks.

Now Try Exercise 65

Percentages

A **percentage** can be written either in **percent form** or in **decimal form**. For example, the percent form of 15% can be also written in decimal form as 0.15. To change a percent form $R\%$ to a decimal form r we divide R by 100. That is, $r = \frac{R}{100}$.

EXAMPLE 9 ▶ **Writing percentages as decimals**

Write each percentage as a decimal.
(a) 37%   **(b)** 0.02%   **(c)** 320%   **(d)** -1.45% **(e)** $\frac{2}{5}\%$

Solution
(a) Let $R = 37$. Then $r = \frac{37}{100} = 0.37$.

(b) Let $R = 0.02$. Then $r = \frac{0.02}{100} = 0.0002$.

   NOTE: Dividing a number by 100 is equivalent to moving the decimal point two places to the *left*.

(c) Let $R = 320$. Then $r = \frac{320}{100} = 3.2$

(d) Let $R = -1.45$. Then $r = \frac{-1.45}{100} = -0.0145$. A negative percentage generally corresponds to a quantity decreasing rather than increasing.

(e) Let $R = \frac{2}{5}$. Then $r = \frac{2/5}{100} = \frac{2}{500} = 0.004$.

Now Try Exercises 35, 37, 39, 41, 43

▶ **REAL-WORLD CONNECTION** Applications involving percentages often make use of linear equations. Taking r percent of x is given by rx, where r is written in decimal form. For example, to calculate 35% of x, we compute $0.35x$. As a result, 35% of $150 is $0.35(150) = 52.5$, or $52.50.

NOTE: The word *of* often indicates multiplication when working with percentages.

EXAMPLE 10 ▶ **Analyzing smoking data**

In 2010 an estimated 19.8% of Americans age 18 and older, or 46.2 million people, were smokers. Use these data to estimate the number of Americans age 18 and older in 2010.
(*Source:* Department of Health and Human Services.)

Solution
STEP 1: *Assign a variable.* Let x be the number of Americans age 18 and older.
STEP 2: *Write an equation.* Note that 19.8% of x equals 46.2 million. Thus

$$0.198x = 46.2.$$

STEP 3: *Solve the equation in Step 2.*

$$0.198x = 46.2 \qquad \text{Equation to be solved}$$

$$\frac{0.198x}{\mathbf{0.198}} = \frac{46.2}{\mathbf{0.198}} \qquad \text{Divide each side by 0.198.}$$

$$x \approx 233.3 \qquad \text{Approximate with a calculator.}$$

In 2010 there were about 232.3 million Americans age 18 and older.

STEP 4: *Check your answer.* If there were 232.3 million Americans age 18 and older, then 19.8% of 232.3 million would equal $0.198 \times 233.3 \approx 46.2$ million. The answer checks.

▌ Now Try Exercise 77

EXAMPLE 11 **Solving a percent problem**

In 2010 an estimated $280 billion was spent on advertising in the United States. This was an increase of 409% over the amount spent in 1980. Determine how much was spent on advertising in 1980. (*Source: Advertising Age.*)

Solution

STEP 1: *Assign a variable.* Let x be the amount spent on advertising in 1980.

STEP 2: *Write an equation.* Note that the increase was 409% of x, or $4.09x$.

$$x \quad + \quad 4.09x \quad = \quad 280$$

$$\text{Amount in 1980} \; + \; \text{Increase} \; = \; \text{Amount in 2010}$$

STEP 3: *Solve the equation in Step 2.*

$$x + 4.09x = 280 \qquad \text{Equation to be solved}$$

$$5.09x = 280 \qquad \text{Add like terms.}$$

$$x = \frac{280}{5.09} \qquad \text{Divide each side by 5.09.}$$

$$x \approx 55 \qquad \text{Simplify.}$$

In 1980, about $55 billion was spent on advertising.

STEP 4: *Check your answer.* An increase of 409% of $55 billion is $4.09 \times 55 \approx \$225$ billion. Thus the amount spent in 2010 would be $55 + 225 = \$280$ billion. The answer checks.

▌ Now Try Exercise 79

EXAMPLE 12 **Solving an interest problem**

A college student takes out two loans to pay tuition. The first loan is for 3% annual interest and the second loan is for 7% annual interest. If the total of the two loans is $4000 and the student must pay $170 in interest at the end of the first year, determine the amount borrowed at each interest rate.

Solution

STEP 1: *Assign a variable.*

$$x: \text{the loan amount at 3\%}$$

$$4000 - x: \text{the loan amount at 7\%}$$

STEP 2: *Write an equation.* Note that the total interest is $170.

$$0.03x \quad + \quad 0.07(4000 - x) \quad = \quad 170$$

$$\text{Interest at 3\%} \; + \; \text{Interest at 7\%} \; = \; \text{Total Interest}$$

STEP 3: *Solve the equation in Step 2.*

$$0.03x + 0.07(4000 - x) = 170 \qquad \text{Equation to be solved}$$
$$3x + 7(4000 - x) = 17{,}000 \qquad \text{Multiply by 100 to clear decimals.}$$
$$3x + 28{,}000 - 7x = 17{,}000 \qquad \text{Distributive property}$$
$$-4x + 28{,}000 = 17{,}000 \qquad \text{Combine like terms.}$$
$$-4x = -11{,}000 \qquad \text{Subtract 28,000.}$$
$$x = 2750 \qquad \text{Divide by } -4.$$

The amount at 3% is $2750, and the amount at 7% is 4000 − 2750 = $1250.

STEP 4: *Check the answer.* The sum is 2750 + 1250 = $4000. Also, 3% of $2750 is $82.50 and 7% of $1250 is $87.50. The total interest is $82.50 + $87.50 = $170. The answer checks.

▌ Now Try Exercise 69

▶ **REAL-WORLD CONNECTION** In chemistry acids are frequently mixed. In the next example, percentages are used to determine how to mix an acid solution with a specified concentration.

EXAMPLE 13 ▎ **Mixing acid**

A chemist mixed 2 liters of 20% sulfuric acid with another sample of 60% sulfuric acid to obtain a sample of 50% sulfuric acid. How much of the 60% sulfuric acid was used? See Figure 2.12.

Figure 2.12 Mixing acid

Solution

STEP 1: *Assign a variable.* Let *x* be as follows.

$$x:\ \text{liters of 60\% sulfuric acid}$$
$$x + 2:\ \text{liters of 50\% sulfuric acid}$$

STEP 2: *Write an equation.* Table 2.4 can be used to organize our calculations. The total amount of pure sulfuric acid in the 20% and 60% samples must equal the amount of pure sulfuric acid in the final 50% acid solution.

TABLE 2.4 Mixing Acid

Concentration (as a decimal)	Solution Amount (liters)	Pure Acid (liters)
20% = 0.20	2	0.20(2)
60% = 0.60	x	0.60x
50% = 0.50	x + 2	0.50(x + 2)

From the third column, we can write the equation

$$0.20(2) \quad + \quad 0.60x \quad = \quad 0.50(x + 2).$$

Pure acid in 20% solution + Pure acid in 60% solution = Pure acid in 50% solution

STEP 3: *Solve the equation in Step 2.*

$$0.20(2) + 0.60x = 0.50(x + 2)$$ Equation to be solved

$$2(2) + 6x = 5(x + 2)$$ Multiply by 10.

$$4 + 6x = 5x + 10$$ Distributive property

$$x = 6$$ Subtract $5x$ and 4 from each side.

Six liters of the 60% acid solution were added to the 2 liters of 20% acid solution.

STEP 4: *Check your answer.* If 6 liters of 60% acid solution are added to 2 liters of 20% solution, then there will be 8 liters of acid solution containing

$$0.60(6) + 0.20(2) = 4 \text{ liters}$$

of pure acid. The concentration is $\frac{4}{8} = 0.50$, or 50%. The answer checks.

Now Try Exercise 63

2.2 Putting It All Together

When solving an application problem, follow the *Steps for Solving a Problem* discussed on page 96. Be sure to read the problem carefully and check your answer. The following table summarizes some other important concepts from this section.

CONCEPT	EXPLANATION	EXAMPLES
Writing a Function	If possible, solve an equation for a variable. Express the result in function notation.	$5x + y = 10$ $y = -5x + 10$ If $y = f(x)$, then $f(x) = -5x + 10$.
Changing a Percentage to a Decimal	Move the decimal point two places to the left and remove the percent symbol.	$73\% = 0.73$, $5.3\% = 0.053$, and $125\% = 1.25$
Percent Problems	To find $P\%$ of a quantity Q, change $P\%$ to a decimal and multiply by Q.	To find 45% of $200, calculate $0.45 \times 200 = \$90$.

2.2 Exercises

MathXL PRACTICE   WATCH   DOWNLOAD   READ   REVIEW

CONCEPTS AND VOCABULARY

1. If we solve $2y = x$ for y, we obtain $y = $ _____.

2. If $y = 4x - 7$ and $y = f(x)$, then $f(x) = $ _____.

3. If a rectangle has width W and length L, then its perimeter is $P = $ _____.

4. The first step in solving an application is to _____.

5. Write 42.1% as a decimal.

6. Find 20% of 50.

SOLVING FOR A VARIABLE

Exercises 7–14: Solve the equation for the given variable.

7. $4x + 3y = 12$ for y **8.** $6x - 3y = 6$ for y

9. $5(2x - 3y) = 2x$ for x

10. $-2(2x + y) = 3y$ for x

11. $S = 6ab$ for b **12.** $S = 2\pi rh$ for r

13. $\dfrac{r + t}{2} = 7$ for t **14.** $\dfrac{2 + a + b}{3} = 8$ for a

Exercises 15–24: Solve the equation for y. Let $y = f(x)$ and write a formula for $f(x)$.

15. $-3x + y = 8$ **16.** $2x - 5y = 10$

17. $4x = 2\pi y$ **18.** $\dfrac{x}{2} = \dfrac{y}{3}$

19. $\dfrac{3y}{8} = x$ **20.** $\dfrac{3x + 2y}{4} = 3$

21. $3(2x + 3y) = -x$ **22.** $-(x - 2y) = 5x + 1$

23. $\dfrac{2x - 3y}{5} = 4$ **24.** $\dfrac{2y + 5x + 1}{5} = 2x$

WRITING AND SOLVING EQUATIONS

Exercises 25–34: Do the following.

(a) Translate the sentence into an equation by using the variable x.

(b) Solve the resulting equation.

25. The sum of a number and 2 is 12.

26. Twice a number plus 7 equals 9.

27. A number divided by 5 equals the number plus 1.

28. 25 times a number is 125.

29. If a number is increased by 5 and then divided by 2, the result equals 7.

30. A number subtracted from 8 is 5.

31. The quotient of a number and 2 is 17.

32. The product of 5 and a number equals 95.

33. The sum of three consecutive integers is 30.

34. A rectangle that is 5 inches longer than it is wide has a perimeter of 60 inches.

PERCENTAGES

Exercises 35–44: Write each percentages as a decimal.

35. 55%   **36.** 67%

37. 0.04%   **38.** 0.056%

39. 341%   **40.** 243%

41. −1.67%   **42.** −0.5%

43. $\frac{1}{4}$%   **44.** $\frac{3}{10}$%

APPLICATIONS

45. *Perimeter of a Rectangle* A rectangle has a perimeter of 86 feet and a width of 19 feet.
(a) Write a formula to find the length L of a rectangle with perimeter P and width W.
(b) Use the formula to find L.

46. *Perimeter of a Triangle* The perimeter P of a triangle with sides a, b, and c is $P = a + b + c$.

(a) Solve this formula for a.
(b) Find a if $b = 5$, $c = 7$, and $P = 15$.

47. *Area of a Cylinder* The area A of the *side* of a cylinder with height h and radius r is $A = 2\pi rh$. Solve this formula for h.

48. *Volume of a Cylinder* The volume V of a cylinder with height h and radius r is $V = \pi r^2 h$. Solve this formula for h.

49. *Temperature* (Refer to Example 2.) Solve the formula $F = \frac{9}{5}C + 32$ for C.

50. *Area of a Parallelogram* The area A of a parallelogram with base b and height h is $A = bh$. Solve this formula for b.

51. *Area of a Triangle* The area A of a triangle with base b and height h is $A = \frac{1}{2}bh$. Solve this formula for h.

52. *Volume of a Box* The volume V of a box with length L, width W, and height H is $V = WLH$. Solve this formula for L.

53. *Number Problem* The sum of three consecutive integers is 135. Find the three integers.

54. *Number Problem* Are there three consecutive *even integers* whose sum is 82? If so, find them.

55. *Number Problem* Twice the sum of three consecutive *odd integers* is 150. Find the three integers.

56. *Number Problem* Ten plus twice the sum of two consecutive integers is 196. Find the two integers.

57. *Geometry* Find the value of x in the figure if the perimeter of the room is 48 feet.

58. *Distance and Time* A train 100 miles west of St. Louis, Missouri, is traveling east at 60 miles per hour. How long will it take for the train to be 410 miles east of St. Louis?

59. *Geometry* A wire 41 inches long needs to be cut into three pieces so that it can be formed into two identical circles and a square. The length of the side of the square must equal the diameter of the circles. Approximate where the wire should be cut.

60. *Fencing* Three identical pens for dogs are to be enclosed with 120 feet of fence, as illustrated in the figure. If the length of each pen is twice its width plus 2 feet, find the dimensions of each pen.

61. *Distance and Time* Two cars are traveling in opposite lanes on a freeway. Two and a half hours after they meet they are 355 miles apart. If one car is traveling 6 miles per hour faster than the other car, find the speed of each car.

62. *Distance and Time* At first an athlete jogs at 6 miles per hour and then jogs at 5 miles per hour, traveling 7 miles in 1.3 hours. How long did the athlete jog at each speed?

63. *Chemical Mixture* A chemist mixed 3 liters of 30% sulfuric acid with a sample of 80% sulfuric acid to obtain a sample of 60% sulfuric acid. How much of the 80% sulfuric acid was used?

64. *Antifreeze Mixture* A radiator holds 4 gallons of fluid. If it is full with a 20% solution, how much fluid should be drained and replaced with a 70% antifreeze mixture to result in a 50% mixture of antifreeze?

65. *Distance and Time* A car travels at 74 miles per hour and then 63 miles per hour, traveling 248 miles in 2.5 hours. How long did the driver travel at each speed?

66. *Distance and Time* Two vehicles are beside each other on a freeway. After 1 hour and 30 minutes, the faster car is 12 miles ahead of the slower car. During this time the two cars travel a total of 198 miles. Find the speed of each car.

67. *Chemical Mixture* A chemist needs to mix 6 liters of a 50% acid solution with some 20% solution to obtain a 38% solution. How much of the 20% solution should the chemist use?

68. *Herbicide Solution* How much water should be added to 4 gallons of a 5% herbicide solution to dilute it to a 2.2% herbicide solution?

69. *Loan Interest* A student takes out two student loans, one at 6% annual interest and the other at 4% annual interest. The total amount of the two loans is $5000, and the total interest after 1 year is $244. Find the amount of each loan.

70. *Investment Interest* A person invests two amounts of money at 5% and 6% interest. The total amount of money invested is $2400 and the total interest after 1 year is $130.50. Find the amount invested at each rate.

71. *Angles in a Triangle* The measure of the largest angle in a triangle is twice the measure of the smallest angle. The third angle is 10° less than the largest angle. Find the measure of each angle.

72. *Angles in a Triangle* The sum of the degree measures of the angles in a triangle equals 180°. Find the measure of *x* in the triangle shown.

73. *Classroom Ventilation* Ventilation is effective at removing air pollutants. A classroom should have a ventilation rate of 900 cubic feet of air per hour for each person in the classroom. (*Source: ASHRAE.*)
(a) What ventilation rate should a classroom containing 40 people have?
(b) If a ventilation system moves 60,000 cubic feet of air per hour, find the maximum number of people that should be in the classroom.

74. *Lead Poisoning* According to the EPA, the maximum amount of lead that can be ingested by a person without becoming ill is 36.5 milligrams per year.
(a) Write an expression that gives the maximum amount of lead in milligrams that can be "safely" ingested over *x* years.
(b) Under these guidelines what is the minimum number of years that the consumption of 500 milligrams should be spread over?

75. *Hybrid Cars* The 2011 model of the Honda Civic Hybrid averages about 40 miles per gallon and has an annual fuel cost of $1050. If it is assumed that a Hybrid owner drives 15,000 miles per year, what is the average cost of a gallon of gasoline? (*Source: Honda Corporation.*)

76. *Hybrid Cars* The 2011 Toyota Camry Hybrid has an annual fuel cost of $1320. If it is assumed that gasoline costs $3.00 per gallon and that a Hybrid owner drives 15,000 miles per year, estimate the average mileage for this vehicle. (*Source: Toyota Corporation.*)

77. *Solar Energy in Nevada* The U.S. Department of Energy has estimated that solar power plants covering 9900 square miles, or 9% of Nevada, could generate enough electricity to meet the needs of the entire United States. Find the area of Nevada.

78. *Energy Efficiency Rating* The Energy Efficiency Rating (EER) of an air conditioner must be at least 8.0. Changing to an air conditioner with an EER of 10.0 can cut electrical bills by 20%. Suppose that a person's monthly electrical bill is $125 and that the more efficient air conditioner costs an extra $275. How many months will it take to recover this added cost? (*Source: Energy Service Office, Springfield, Illinois.*)

79. *Wireless Expenditures* In 2009, Verizon Wireless spent $7.1 billion on capital, such as new cell towers, a 492% increase over the amount that Sprint spent on capital in 2009. How much did Sprint spend on capital in 2009? (*Source: Business Insider.*)

80. *Watching Online Advertisements* In 2010 on theWB.com, each viewer watched about 20 ads per month, on average. This number is a 138% increase over the average number of ads each viewer watched on NBC.com in 2010. How many ads per month would someone view on NBC.com? (*Source: comScore.*)

81. *Meeting a Future Mate* In a survey, about 32% of adult Americans believe that they will meet their mates on the Internet. In this survey 480 respondents held this belief. Determine the number of people participating in the survey. (*Source: Men's Health.*)

82. *Financial Advice* In a survey, about 34% of adult Americans believe that they have gotten the best financial advice from the media. In this survey, about 5608 respondents held this belief. Determine the number of people participating in this survey. (*Source: CNNMoney.com.*)

83. *Grade Point Averages* The average GPA at public colleges and universities is 3.0, or 9.1% less than the average GPA at private colleges and universities. What is the average GPA at private colleges and universities? (*Source: New York Times.*)

84. *Grades* To receive an A in a college course a student must average 90 percent correct on four exams of 100 points each and on a final exam of 200 points. If a student scores 83, 87, 94, and 91 on the 100-point exams, what minimum score on the final exam is necessary for the student to receive an A?

WRITING ABOUT MATHEMATICS

85. A student solves the following equation for *y*. What is the student's mistake?

$$\frac{x + 2y}{2} = 5$$
$$x + y \overset{?}{=} 5$$
$$y \overset{?}{=} 5 - x$$

86. Explain how to find *P*% of a quantity *Q*. Give an example.

SECTIONS
2.1 and 2.2 **Checking Basic Concepts**

1. How many solutions does a linear equation have?

2. Solve $\frac{1}{2}z - (1 - 2z) = \frac{2}{3}z$.

3. Solve $2(3x + 4) + 3 = -1$
   (a) symbolically,
   (b) graphically, and
   (c) numerically.
   Do your answers agree?

4. At first an athlete jogs at 10 miles per hour and then jogs at 8 miles per hour, traveling 10.2 miles in 1.2 hours. How long did the athlete jog at each speed?

5. Find the x- and y-intercepts for the graph of the equation $5x - 4y = 20$.

6. Classify each equation as either an identity or a contradiction.
   (a) $3(x - 2) = 3x - 6$
   (b) $2x + 3x = 5x - 2$

7. The length of a rectangular room is 5 feet more than its width. If the perimeter of a room is 82 feet, find the length and width of the room.

2.3 Linear Inequalities

Basic Concepts • Symbolic Solutions • Numerical and Graphical Solutions • An Application

A LOOK INTO MATH ▶

On a freeway, the speed limit might be 70 miles per hour. A driver traveling x miles per hour is obeying the speed limit if $x \leq 70$ and breaking the speed limit if $x > 70$. A speed of $x = 70$ represents the boundary between obeying the speed limit and breaking it. A posted speed limit, or *boundary*, allows drivers to easily determine whether they are speeding.

Solving linear inequalities is closely related to solving linear equations because equality is the boundary between *greater than* and *less than*. In this section we discuss techniques needed to solve linear inequalities.

NEW VOCABULARY

☐ Inequality
☐ Solution
☐ Solution set
☐ Set-builder notation
☐ Linear inequality
☐ Break-even point
☐ Properties of inequalities

Basic Concepts

An **inequality** results whenever the equals sign in an equation is replaced with any one of the symbols $<$, $\leq$, $>$, or $\geq$. Examples of *linear equations* include

$$2x + 1 = 0, \quad 1 - x = 6, \quad \text{and} \quad 5x + 1 = 3 - 2x, \quad \text{Equations}$$

and, therefore, examples of *linear inequalities* include

$$2x + 1 < 0, \quad 1 - x \geq 6, \quad \text{and} \quad 5x + 1 \leq 3 - 2x. \quad \text{Inequalities}$$

A **solution** to an inequality is a value of the variable that makes the statement true. The set of all solutions is called the **solution set**. Two inequalities are *equivalent* if they have the same solution set. Inequalities frequently have *infinitely many solutions*. For example, the solution set to the inequality $x - 5 > 0$ includes all real numbers greater than 5, which can be written as $x > 5$. Using **set-builder notation**, we can write the solution set as $\{x \mid x > 5\}$. This expression is read as "the set of all real numbers x such that x is greater than 5." The vertical line | in set-builder notation is read "such that." To summarize, we have the following.

Inequality	Set-Builder Notation	Meaning
$t \leq 3$	$\{t \mid t \leq 3\}$	The set of all real numbers t such that t is less than or equal to 3
$z > 8$	$\{z \mid z > 8\}$	The set of all real numbers z such that z is greater than 8

Next we more formally define a linear inequality in one variable.

LINEAR INEQUALITY IN ONE VARIABLE

A **linear inequality** in one variable is an inequality that can be written in the form

$$ax + b > 0,$$

where $a \neq 0$. (The symbol $>$ may be replaced with $\geq$, $<$, or $\leq$.)

MAKING CONNECTIONS

Linear Functions, Equations, and Inequalities

Concept	Can be written as:
Linear function	$f(x) = ax + b$ (a = slope m)
Linear equation	$ax + b = 0$ ($a \neq 0$)
Linear inequality	$ax + b > 0$ ($a \neq 0$)

A linear equation has *one* solution, while a linear inequality has *infinitely many* solutions

▶ **REAL-WORLD CONNECTION** To better understand linear inequalities, suppose that it costs a student $100 to make a large batch of candy. If the student sells bags of this candy for $5 each, then the profit y is $y = 5x - 100$, where x represents the number of bags sold. The graph of y is a line with slope 5 and y-intercept -100, as shown in Figure 2.13.

Figure 2.13

Because the x-intercept is 20, the student will *break even* when $5x - 100 = 0$, or when 20 bags of candy are sold. (The **break-even point** occurs when the *revenue* from selling the candy equals the *cost* of making the candy.) Note that the student incurs a **loss** when the line is below the *x*-axis, or when $5x - 100 < 0$. This situation corresponds to selling less than 20 bags, or $x < 20$. A **profit** occurs when the graph is above the *x*-axis, or when $5x - 100 > 0$. This situation corresponds to selling more than 20 bags, or $x > 20$. Selling $x = 20$ bags of candy represents the *boundary* between **loss** and **profit**.

To better understand linear inequalities more generally, let the graph of $y = ax + b$ with slope $a \neq 0$ ($m = a$) be a line that intersects the *x*-axis at $x = k$. Figure 2.14(a) shows this line with positive slope ($a > 0$), and Figure 2.14(b) shows this line with negative slope ($a < 0$). The solution to the *equation* $ax + b = 0$ is *k*, and the solution set to the *inequality* $ax + b > 0$ is either all *x*-values greater than *k*, as shown in Figure 2.14(a), or all *x*-values less than *k*, as shown in Figure 2.14(b). (See also Example 4.)

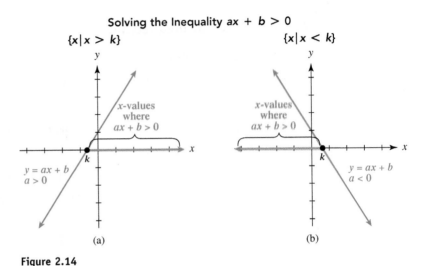

Figure 2.14

Symbolic Solutions

The inequality $3 < 5$ is equivalent to $3 + 1 < 5 + 1$. That is, we can add the same number to each side of an inequality. This is an example of one property of inequalities.

PROPERTIES OF INEQUALITIES

Let *a*, *b*, and *c* be real numbers.

1. $a < b$ and $a + c < b + c$ are equivalent.
   (The same number may be added to or subtracted from each side of an inequality.)
2. If $c > 0$, then $a < b$ and $ac < bc$ are equivalent.
   (Each side of an inequality may be multiplied or divided by the same positive number.)
3. If $c < 0$, then $a < b$ and $ac > bc$ are equivalent.
   (Each side of an inequality may be multiplied or divided by the same negative number provided the inequality symbol is reversed.)

Similar properties exist for the $\leq$ and $\geq$ symbols.

STUDY TIP

Be sure you understand Property 2 and Property 3.

When applying Property 2 or 3, we need to determine whether the inequality symbol should be reversed. For example, if each side of the inequality $3 < 5$ is multiplied by the *positive* number 2, we obtain

$$3 < 5 \quad \text{or} \quad 2 \cdot 3 < 2 \cdot 5 \quad \text{or} \quad 6 < 10,$$

which is a true statement. However, if each side of the inequality $3 < 5$ is multiplied by the *negative* number -2, we obtain

$$3 < 5 \quad \text{or} \quad -2 \cdot 3 > -2 \cdot 5 \quad \text{or} \quad -6 > -10,$$

$$\uparrow$$

Reverse the inequality symbol.

which is a true statement because the inequality symbol is reversed from $<$ to $>$.

To solve an inequality we apply properties of inequalities to find a simpler, equivalent inequality, as illustrated in the next example.

EXAMPLE 1 **Solving linear inequalities**

Solve each inequality.

(a) $2x - 1 > 4$ **(b)** $\frac{1}{2}(z - 3) - (2 - z) \leq 1$

Solution

(a) Begin by adding 1 to each side of the inequality.

$2x - 1 > 4$	Given inequality
$2x - 1 + 1 > 4 + 1$	Add 1 to each side.
$2x > 5$	Simplify.
$\dfrac{2x}{2} > \dfrac{5}{2}$	Divide by 2; do *not* reverse the inequality symbol because $2 > 0$.
$x > \dfrac{5}{2}$	Simplify.

The solution set is $\left\{ x \mid x > \frac{5}{2} \right\}$.

(b) To clear (eliminate) fractions multiply each term by 2.

$\dfrac{1}{2}(z - 3) - (2 - z) \leq 1$	Given inequality
$(z - 3) - 2(2 - z) \leq 2$	Multiply by 2; do *not* reverse the inequality symbol because $2 > 0$.
$z - 3 - 4 + 2z \leq 2$	Distributive property
$3z - 7 \leq 2$	Combine like terms.
$3z - 7 + 7 \leq 2 + 7$	Add 7 to each side.
$3z \leq 9$	Simplify.
$z \leq 3$	Divide by 3; do *not* reverse the inequality symbol because $3 > 0$.

The solution set is $\{ z \mid z \leq 3 \}$.

Now Try Exercises 19, 27

EXAMPLE 2 **Solving linear inequalities**

Solve each inequality.
(a) $5 - 3x \leq x - 3$

(b) $\dfrac{2t - 3}{5} \geq \dfrac{t + 1}{3} + 3t$

Solution

(a) Begin by subtracting 5 from each side of the inequality.

$$5 - 3x \le x - 3 \qquad \text{Given inequality}$$

$$5 - 3x - 5 \le x - 3 - 5 \qquad \text{Subtract 5 from each side.}$$

$$-3x \le x - 8 \qquad \text{Simplify.}$$

$$-3x - x \le x - 8 - x \qquad \text{Subtract } x \text{ from each side.}$$

$$-4x \le -8 \qquad \text{Simplify.}$$

Next divide each side by -4. As we are dividing by a *negative* number, Property 3 requires reversing the inequality by changing $\le$ to $\ge$.

$$\frac{-4x}{-4} \ge \frac{-8}{-4} \qquad \begin{array}{l}\text{Divide by } -4; \text{ reverse the} \\ \text{inequality because } -4 < 0.\end{array}$$

$$x \ge 2 \qquad \text{Simplify.}$$

The solution set is $\{x \mid x \ge 2\}$.

(b) To clear (eliminate) fractions multiply each term by 15.

$$\frac{2t - 3}{5} \ge \frac{t + 1}{3} + 3t \qquad \text{Given inequality}$$

$$15 \cdot \left(\frac{2t - 3}{5}\right) \ge 15 \cdot \left(\frac{t + 1}{3}\right) + 15 \cdot 3t \qquad \begin{array}{l}\text{Multiply each term by 15; do not} \\ \text{reverse the inequality symbol because} \\ 15 > 0.\end{array}$$

$$3(2t - 3) \ge 5(t + 1) + 45t \qquad \text{Simplify: } \tfrac{15}{5} = 3 \text{ and } \tfrac{15}{3} = 5$$

$$6t - 9 \ge 5t + 5 + 45t \qquad \text{Distributive property}$$

$$6t - 9 + 9 \ge 50t + 5 + 9 \qquad \text{Add 9; combine like terms.}$$

$$6t \ge 50t + 14 \qquad \text{Simplify.}$$

$$6t - 50t \ge 50t - 50t + 14 \qquad \text{Subtract } 50t \text{ from each side.}$$

$$-44t \ge 14 \qquad \text{Simplify.}$$

$$t \le \frac{14}{-44} \qquad \begin{array}{l}\text{Divide by } -44; \text{ reverse the inequality} \\ \text{symbol because } -44 < 0.\end{array}$$

$$t \le -\frac{7}{22} \qquad \text{Simplify.}$$

The solution set is $\left\{t \mid t \le -\frac{7}{22}\right\}$.

Now Try Exercises 23, 29

READING CHECK

When do you reverse the inequality symbol?

Numerical and Graphical Solutions

In Section 2.1 we solved linear equations with symbolic, numerical, and graphical methods. We can also use these methods to solve linear inequalities.

NOTE: Numerical and graphical solutions can sometimes be difficult to find if the x-value that determines equality is not an integer. Symbolic methods work well in such situations.

EXAMPLE 3 **Solving linear inequalities numerically**

Use Table 2.5 to find the solution set to each equation or inequality.

(a) $-\frac{1}{2}x + 1 = 0$ **(b)** $-\frac{1}{2}x + 1 > 0$ **(c)** $-\frac{1}{2}x + 1 < 0$

TABLE 2.5

x	-1	0	1	2	3	4	5
$-\frac{1}{2}x + 1$	$\frac{3}{2}$	1	$\frac{1}{2}$	0	$-\frac{1}{2}$	-1	$-\frac{3}{2}$

Solution

(a) The expression $-\frac{1}{2}x + 1$ equals 0 when $x = 2$. Thus the solution set is $\{x \mid x = 2\}$.

(b) The expression $-\frac{1}{2}x + 1$ is positive when $x < 2$. Thus the solution set is $\{x \mid x < 2\}$.

(c) The expression $-\frac{1}{2}x + 1$ is negative when $x > 2$. Thus the solution set is $\{x \mid x > 2\}$.

Now Try Exercise 53

EXAMPLE 4 **Solving linear inequalities graphically**

Graph $y = -\frac{1}{2}x + 1$ and find the solution set to each equation or inequality.

(a) $-\frac{1}{2}x + 1 = 0$ **(b)** $-\frac{1}{2}x + 1 > 0$ **(c)** $-\frac{1}{2}x + 1 < 0$

Solution

(a) The graph of $y = -\frac{1}{2}x + 1$ in Figure 2.15 crosses the x-axis at $x = 2$. Thus the solution set to $-\frac{1}{2}x + 1 = 0$ is $\{x \mid x = 2\}$.

(b) The graph is *above* the x-axis when $x < 2$. Thus the solution set is $\{x \mid x < 2\}$.

(c) The graph is *below* the x-axis when $x > 2$. Thus the solution set is $\{x \mid x > 2\}$.

Graphical Solution

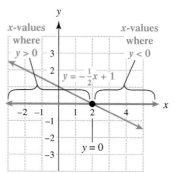

Figure 2.15

Now Try Exercise 59

CRITICAL THINKING

A linear equation has one solution that can be easily checked. A linear inequality has infinitely many solutions. Discuss ways that the solution set to a linear inequality could be checked.

Sometimes linear inequalities are written in the form $y_1 < y_2$, $y_1 \leq y_2$, $y_1 > y_2$, or $y_1 \geq y_2$, where both y_1 and y_2 represent expressions containing variables. These types of inequalities can also be solved graphically or numerically.

▶ **REAL-WORLD CONNECTION** Figure 2.16 shows the distances that two cars are from Chicago, Illinois, after x hours while traveling in the same direction on a freeway. The distance for Car 1 is denoted y_1, and the distance for Car 2 is denoted y_2.

Distance from Chicago

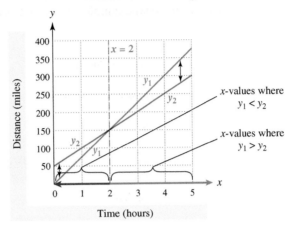

Figure 2.16

When $x = 2$ hours, $y_1 = y_2$ and both cars are 150 miles from Chicago. To the left of the dashed vertical line $x = 2$, the graph of y_1 is *below* the graph of y_2, so Car 1 is *closer* to Chicago than Car 2. Thus

$$y_1 < y_2 \quad \text{when} \quad x < 2.$$

To the right of the dashed vertical line $x = 2$, the graph of y_1 is *above* the graph of y_2, so Car 1 is *farther* from Chicago than Car 2. Thus

$$y_1 > y_2 \quad \text{when} \quad x > 2.$$

EXAMPLE 5   **Solving an inequality graphically**

Use a graph to solve $5 - 3x \geq x - 3$.

Solution

The graphs of $y_1 = 5 - 3x$ and $y_2 = x - 3$ intersect at the point $(2, -1)$, as shown in Figure 2.17(a). Equality, or $y_1 = y_2$, occurs when $x = 2$. The graph of y_1 is above the graph of y_2 to the left of the vertical line, or when $x < 2$. Thus $5 - 3x \geq x - 3$ is satisfied when $x \leq 2$. The solution set is $\{x \mid x \leq 2\}$. Figure 2.17(b) shows the same graph generated with a graphing calculator.

CRITICAL THINKING

Use the results from Example 5 to write the solution set for $5 - 3x \leq x - 3$.

(a)

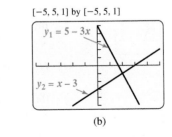

(b)

Figure 2.17

▌ Now Try Exercise 63

An Application

▶ **REAL-WORLD CONNECTION** Air generally becomes colder as the altitude increases. See Figure 2.18. One mile above Earth's surface the temperature is about 19°F colder than the ground-level temperature. As the air temperature cools, the chance of clouds forming increases. In the next example we estimate the altitudes at which clouds will *not* form.

3 miles ⟶ 33°F

2 miles ⟶ 52°F

1 mile ⟶ 71°F

0 miles ⟶ 90°F

Figure 2.18

EXAMPLE 6   **Finding the altitude of clouds**

If ground-level temperature is 90°F, the temperature *T* above Earth's surface is modeled by $T(x) = 90 - 19x$, where *x* is the altitude in miles. Suppose that clouds will form only if the temperature is 53°F or colder. (*Source:* A. Miller and R. Anthes, *Meteorology.*)
(a) Determine symbolically the altitudes at which there are no clouds.
(b) Give graphical support for your answer.
(c) Give numerical support for your answer.

Solution
(a) *Symbolic Solution* Clouds will not form at altitudes at which the temperature is greater than 53°F. Thus we must solve the inequality $T(x) > 53$.

$$90 - 19x > 53 \qquad \text{Inequality to be solved}$$
$$90 - 19x - 90 > 53 - 90 \qquad \text{Subtract 90 from each side.}$$
$$-19x > -37 \qquad \text{Simplify.}$$
$$\frac{-19x}{-19} < \frac{-37}{-19} \qquad \text{Divide by} -19; \text{reverse inequality.}$$
$$x < \frac{37}{19} \qquad \text{Simplify.}$$

[0, 3, 1] by [0, 100, 20]

$y_1 = 90 - 19x$

$y_2 = 53$

Intersection
X=1.9473684 Y=53

(a)

The result, $\frac{37}{19} \approx 1.95$, indicates that clouds will not form below about 1.95 miles. Note that models are usually not exact, so rounding values is appropriate.

(b) *Graphical Solution* Graph $y_1 = 90 - 19x$ and $y_2 = 53$. In Figure 2.19(a) their graphs intersect near the point (1.95, 53). The graph of y_1 is above the graph of y_2 when $x < 1.95$.

X	Y₁	Y₂
0	90	53
1	71	53
2	52	53
3	33	53
4	14	53
5	-5	53
6	-24	53

X=2

(b)

Figure 2.19

(c) *Numerical Solution* Make a table of y_1 and y_2, as shown in Figure 2.19(b). When $x = 2$, the air temperature is 52°F. Thus the air temperature would be 53°F when the altitude is slightly less than 2 miles, which supports our symbolic solution of $x \approx 1.95$.

CALCULATOR HELP

To find a point of intersection, see Appendix A (page AP-6).

Now Try Exercise 105

2.3   Putting It All Together

CONCEPT	EXPLANATION	EXAMPLES
Linear Inequalities in One Variable	Can be written as $$ax + b > 0,$$ where $a \neq 0$ and $>$ may be replaced by $<$, $\leq$, or $\geq$; has infinitely many solutions	$3x - 4 > 0$, $-(x - 5) < 2$, $2x \geq 5 - x$, and $4 - 2(x + 1) \leq 7x - 1$
Set-Builder Notation	Used to express sets of real numbers	$\{x \mid x > 4\}$ represents the set of real numbers x such that x is greater than 4.
Properties of Inequalities	See the box on page 109. Be sure to note Property 3: When multiplying or dividing by a negative number, *reverse* the inequality symbol.	*Property 1*: (Add 3.) $x - 3 \geq 2$ is equivalent to $x \geq 5$. *Property 2*: (Divide by 2.) $2x \leq 6$ is equivalent to $x \leq 3$. *Property 3*: (Divide by -3) $-3x < 6$ is equivalent to $x > -2$.

Symbolic, graphical, and numerical methods are used to solve $2x - 4 \geq 0$.

Symbolic Solution

$$2x - 4 \geq 0$$
$$2x \geq 4$$
$$x \geq 2$$

Graphical Solution

The graph of $y = 2x - 4$ is above or intersects the x-axis when $x \geq 2$.

Numerical Solution

x	$2x - 4$
0	-4
1	-2
2	0
3	2
4	4

The values of $2x - 4$ are greater than or equal to 0 when $x \geq 2$.

2.3   Exercises

MyMathLab Math XL PRACTICE WATCH DOWNLOAD READ REVIEW

CONCEPTS AND VOCABULARY

1. Give an example of a linear inequality.

2. Can a linear inequality have infinitely many solutions? Explain.

3. Are $x + 5 < y + 5$ and $x < y$ equivalent?

4. Are $x - 7 \geq y - 7$ and $x \geq y$ equivalent?

5. Are $2x > 6$ and $x > 3$ equivalent? Explain.

6. Are $-4x < 8$ and $x < -2$ equivalent? Explain.

7. Distinguish between an equation and an inequality.

8. Name three methods for solving a linear inequality.

9. Write the set of real numbers x less than 6 in set-builder notation.

10. Write the set of real numbers x greater than or equal to -0.7 in set-builder notation.

Exercises 11–14: Decide whether the given value for the variable is a solution to the inequality.

11. $x - 5 \leq 3$ $\qquad\qquad x = 2$

12. $\frac{3}{2}x - \frac{1}{2} \geq 1 - x$ $\qquad x = -2$

13. $2t - 3 > 5t - (2t + 1)$ $\quad t = 5$

14. $2(z - 1) < 3(z + 1)$ $\qquad z = \pi$

SYMBOLIC SOLUTIONS

Exercises 15–18: Solve each equation or inequality.

$\quad$ *(a)* $y_1 = 0$ $\quad$ *(b)* $y_1 < 0$ $\quad$ *(c)* $y_1 > 0$

15. $y_1 = x - 2$

16. $y_1 = x + 5$

17. $y_1 = -2x + 6$

18. $y_1 = -6 - 6x$

Exercises 19–44: Solve the inequality symbolically.

19. $x + 3 \leq 5$ $\qquad\qquad$ **20.** $x - 5 \geq -3$

21. $\frac{1}{4}x > 9$ $\qquad\qquad$ **22.** $14 < -3.5x$

23. $4 - 3x \leq -\frac{2}{3}$ $\qquad$ **24.** $4x - 2 \geq \frac{5}{2}$

25. $7 - \frac{1}{2}x < x - \frac{3}{2}$ $\qquad$ **26.** $4x - 6 > 12 - 10x$

27. $\frac{5}{2}(2x - 3) < 6 - 2x$

28. $1 - \left(\frac{3}{2}x - 4\right) > \frac{1}{2}(x + 1)$

29. $\frac{3x - 2}{-2} \leq \frac{x - 4}{-5}$ $\qquad$ **30.** $\frac{5 - 2x}{2} \geq \frac{2x + 1}{4}$

31. $3(x - 2000) + 15 < 45$

32. $-2(x - 1990) + 75 > 25$

33. $0.4x - 0.7 < 1.3$ $\qquad$ **34.** $-0.3(x - 5) + 0.2 > 2$

35. $\frac{4}{5}x - \frac{1}{5} \geq -5$ $\qquad$ **36.** $\frac{3x}{4} - \frac{1}{2} \leq \frac{1}{4}(2x + 1)$

37. $-\frac{1}{3}(z - 3) - \frac{1}{4} \geq \frac{1}{4}(5 - z)$

38. $2(3 - 2z) - (1 - z) \leq 4z - (1 + z)$

39. $\frac{3}{4}(2t - 5) \leq \frac{1}{2}(4t - 6) + 1$

40. $\frac{5}{6}x + (3 - x) \geq \frac{x - 3}{3}$

41. $\frac{1}{2}\left(4 - (x + 3)\right) + 4 > -\frac{1}{3}\left(2x - (1 - x)\right)$

42. $\frac{x - (2 - 3x)}{2} < \frac{1 - (4 - 5x)}{6}$

43. $0.05 + 0.08x < 0.01x - 0.04(3 - 4x)$

44. $-0.2(5x + 2) \geq 0.4 + 1.5x$

DOMAINS OF FUNCTIONS

Exercises 45–52: Write the domain of f in set-builder notation.

45. $f(x) = \sqrt{2x - 1}$ $\qquad$ **46.** $f(x) = \sqrt{1 - x}$

47. $f(x) = \frac{x}{5 - 2x}$ $\qquad$ **48.** $f(x) = \frac{x - 1}{4x + 1}$

49. $f(x) = \sqrt{5(x - 2) + 1}$

50. $f(x) = \sqrt{-(2x + 5) - x}$

51. $f(x) = \frac{1}{\sqrt{1 + 2x}}$

52. $f(x) = \frac{\sqrt{x}}{x + 1}$

NUMERICAL SOLUTIONS

Exercises 53 and 54: Complete the table. Then use the table to solve the inequality.

53. $-2x + 6 \leq 0$

x	1	2	3	4	5
$-2x + 6$	4				-4

54. $3x - 1 < 8$

x	0	1	2	3	4
$3x - 1$					

Exercises 55–58: Solve the inequality numerically.

55. $x - 3 > 0$ $\qquad\qquad$ **56.** $2x < 0$

57. $2x - 1 \geq 3$ $\qquad\qquad$ **58.** $2 - 3x \leq -4$

GRAPHICAL SOLUTIONS

Exercises 59–62: Use the graph of y_1 to solve each equation or inequality.

(a) $y_1 = 0$ (b) $y_1 < 0$ (c) $y_1 > 0$

59.

60.

61.

62.

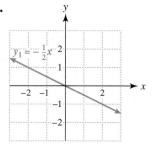

Exercises 63–66: Use the graph to solve the inequality.

63. $y_1 \le y_2$

64. $y_2 > y_1$

65. $y_1 > y_2$

66. $y_1 \le y_2$

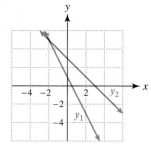

67. *Distance Between Cars* Car 1 and Car 2 are traveling in the same direction. Their distances in miles north of St. Louis, Missouri, after x hours are shown in the graph in the next column, where $x \le 8$.

(a) Which car is traveling faster? Explain.

(b) How many hours elapse before the two cars are the same distance from St. Louis? How far are they from St. Louis when this equality occurs?

(c) During what time interval is Car 2 farther from St. Louis than Car 1?

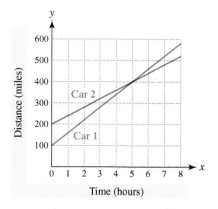

68. *Distance Between Cars* Two cars are traveling on a freeway. The distance in miles between Chicago and each car after x hours is shown in the graph.

(a) Are the cars moving toward or away from Chicago?

(b) Interpret the y-intercept of Car 2.

(c) When is Car 1 farther from Chicago than Car 2?

(d) When are Car 1 and Car 2 the same distance from Chicago?

69. Use the following graph to solve each equation or inequality.

(a) $f(x) = g(x)$ (b) $f(x) < g(x)$

(c) $f(x) \ge g(x)$ (d) $f(x) \le g(x)$

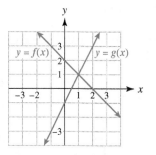

70. Use the following graph to solve each inequality.
    (a) $f(x) > g(x)$ **(b)** $f(x) \le g(x)$

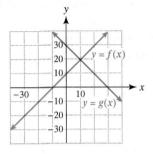

Exercises 71–82: Solve the inequality graphically.

71. $x - 1 < 0$ **72.** $4 - 2x \le 0$

73. $2x \ge 0$ **74.** $3x + 6 > 0$

75. $4 - 2x \le 8$ **76.** $-2x + 3 < -3$

77. $x - (2x + 4) > 0$ **78.** $2x + 1 \ge 3x - 4$

79. $2(x + 2) + 5 < -x$

80. $\dfrac{x + 5}{3} \ge \dfrac{1 - x}{2}$

81. $25(x - 1995) + 100 \le 0$

82. $5(x - 1980) - 20 > 50$

Exercises 83 and 84: Solve the inequality graphically. Approximate boundary numbers to the nearest thousandth.

83. $\pi(\sqrt{2}x - 1.2) + \sqrt{3}x > \dfrac{\pi + 1}{3}$

84. $3.1x - 0.5(\pi - x) \le \sqrt{5} - 0.4x$

CONCEPTS

85. Thinking Generally Let y_1 be a (nonconstant) linear function. If $y_1 < b$ when $x > a$, then solve $y_1 > b$.

86. Thinking Generally Let y_1 be a (nonconstant) linear function and $y_1 = 0$ when $x = a$. What are the possible solution sets to $y_1 \le 0$?

87. Online Exploration Determine when the world average life expectancy exceeded 60 years.

88. Online Exploration Determine when the national debt was $9 trillion or more.

SOLVING LINEAR INEQUALITIES BY MORE THAN ONE METHOD

*Exercises 89–92: Solve the inequality **(a)** numerically, **(b)** graphically, and **(c)** symbolically.*

89. $5x - 2 < 8$ **90.** $2x - 4 - 3(x + 3) \le 0$

91. $2x \ge 3x - 3$ **92.** $x - 1 > \dfrac{4 - x}{2}$

INEQUALITIES AND FUNCTIONS

Exercises 93–98: Solve each equation or inequality for the given $f(x)$.

93. $f(x) = x - 5$
    (a) $f(x) = 7$
    (b) $f(x) > 7$

94. $f(x) = 4x$
    (a) $f(x) = -2$
    (b) $f(x) < -2$

95. $f(x) = 4 - 3x$
    (a) $f(x) \ge 11$
    (b) $f(x) \le 11$

96. $f(x) = 9 - 3x$
    (a) $f(x) < 0$
    (b) $f(x) > 0$

97. $f(x) = 3(x + 7) + 1$
    (a) $f(x) \le -5$
    (b) $f(x) \ge -5$

98. $f(x) = -2(4 - 3x)$
    (a) $f(x) > 16$
    (b) $f(x) < 16$

APPLICATIONS

99. *Profit* A band buys 500 blank DVDs and records a music video on them. The band sells the DVDs to earn a profit. Refer to the graph to answer the following questions.

(a) How much did the band pay for the blank DVDs?
(b) How much did the band charge for their DVDs?
(c) Write an equation that gives the profit P from selling x DVDs.
(d) Determine the break-even point.
(e) When will the band make a profit?

100. *Average Temperature* On March 1 the average high temperature in Minnesota is about 21°F. On March 30 this average increases to about 46°F. Use a linear function to estimate the days in March when the average high temperature is 31°F or less.

101. *Geometry* Find values for x so that the perimeter of the figure is less than 50 feet.

102. *Geometry* A rectangle is twice as long as it is wide. If the rectangle is to have a perimeter of 36 inches or less, what values for the width are possible?

103. *Distance and Time* Two cars are traveling in the same direction along a freeway. After x hours, the first car's distance in miles from a rest stop is given by $y_1 = 70x$ and the second car's distance in miles is given by $y_2 = 60x + 35$.
(a) What is the speed of each car?
(b) When are the cars the same distance from the rest stop?
(c) At what times is the first car farther from the rest stop than the second? Assume that $x \geq 0$.

 104. *Sales of CDs and LP Records* From 1985 to 1990 sales of CDs, in millions, in the United States can be modeled by
$$y_1 = 51.6(x - 1985) + 9.1,$$
and sales of vinyl LP records, in millions, can be modeled by
$$y_2 = -31.9(x - 1985) + 167.7.$$
(a) Graph y_1 and y_2 in the viewing rectangle given by [1984, 1991, 1] by [0, 350, 50].
(b) Estimate the years when CD sales were greater than or equal to LP record sales.
(c) Solve part (b) symbolically.

105. *Altitude and Temperature* (Refer to Example 6.) If the temperature on the ground is $60°$F, the air temperature x miles high is given by $T(x) = 60 - 19x$. Determine the altitudes at which the air temperature is greater than $0°$F. Support your answer graphically or numerically. (*Source:* A. Miller.)

106. *Altitude and Dew Point* If the dew point on the ground is $70°$F, then the dew point x miles high is given by $D(x) = 70 - 5.8x$. (*Source:* A. Miller.)
(a) For each 1-mile increase in altitude, how much does the dew point change?
(b) Determine the altitudes at which the dew point is greater than $30°$F.
(c) Interpret the y-intercept on the graph of D.

107. *Body Mass Index* Body mass index, BMI, gives a recommended relationship between a person's height H in inches and weight W in pounds and is given by
$$\text{BMI} = \frac{705W}{H^2}.$$
If a person is 70 inches tall, approximate the range of weights W that result in a BMI between 19 and 25, inclusive.

108. *Grades* A student scores 75, 86, and 72 on three 100-point exams. If the final is worth 150 points, find the range of final exam scores S that gives the student an overall percentage of 80% or higher.

109. *Amazon versus eBay* From 2006 to 2012, the formula $A(x) = 4124x + 45,000$ gives the number of monthly *unique* visitors to Amazon x years after 2006. Similarly, $E(x) = -5176x + 75,000$ calculates the number of monthly unique visitors to eBay. Use each method to find the years when the number of visitors to Amazon is greater than the number of visitors to eBay. (*Source:* comScore.)
(a) Graphical   (b) Numerical   (c) Symbolical

110. *Computers Sold* From 2006 to 2012, the formula $A(x) = 7.2x + 10$ calculates the number of personal computers sold in millions by Acer x years after 2006. Similarly, $D(x) = -1.6x + 43$ calculates the number of personal computers sold in millions by Dell. Use each method to find the years when the number of computers sold by Dell was more than the number sold by Acer. (*Source:* Gartner.)
(a) Graphical   (b) Numerical   (c) Symbolical

WRITING ABOUT MATHEMATICS

111. Explain the following terms and give examples.
(a) Linear function   (b) Linear equation
(c) Linear inequality

112. Suppose that a student says that a linear equation and a linear inequality can be solved symbolically in exactly the same way. How would you respond?

Group Activity   Working with Real Data

Directions: Form a group of 2 to 4 people. Select someone to record the group's responses for this activity. All members of the group should work cooperatively to answer the questions. If your instructor asks for your results, each member of the group should be prepared to respond.

1. *Born Outside the United States* The foreign-born portion of the population increased from 5% in 1970 to 12% in 2010. This increase could be modeled by a linear function. Use these data to estimate the year when this percentage was 8.5%. (*Source:* U.S. Census Bureau.)

2. When do you expect the foreign-born population to be 15%?

3. What does your model say about the foreign-born population in 1940 and in 2600? Are your answers reasonable? What do these results say about your model?

2.4 Compound Inequalities

Basic Concepts • Symbolic Solutions and Number Lines •
Numerical and Graphical Solutions • Interval Notation

A LOOK INTO MATH ▶ A person weighing 143 pounds and needing to purchase a life vest for white-water rafting is not likely to find one designed exactly for this weight. Life vests are manufactured to support a range of body weights. A vest approved for weights between 100 and 160 pounds might be appropriate for this person. In other words, if a person's weight is w, this life vest is safe if $w \geq 100$ *and* $w \leq 160$. This example illustrates the concept of a *compound inequality*.

Basic Concepts

A **compound inequality** consists of two inequalities joined by the words *and* or *or*. The following are two examples of compound inequalities.

NEW VOCABULARY

☐ Compound inequality
☐ Intersection
☐ Three-part inequality
☐ Union
☐ Interval notation
☐ Infinity
☐ Negative infinity

1. $2x \geq -3$ and $2x < 5$

First compound inequality

2. $x + 2 \geq 3$ or $x - 1 < -5$

Second compound inequality

If a compound inequality contains the word *and*, a solution must satisfy *both* inequalities. For example, 1 is a solution to the first compound inequality because

$$2(1) \geq -3 \quad \text{and} \quad 2(1) < 5 \qquad \text{First compound inequality}$$
$$\text{True} \qquad\qquad\quad \text{True} \qquad\qquad \text{with } x = 1$$

are both true statements.

If a compound inequality contains the word *or*, a solution must satisfy *at least one* of the two inequalities. Thus 5 is a solution to the second compound inequality, because the first statement is true.

$$5 + 2 \geq 3 \quad \text{or} \quad 5 - 1 < -5 \qquad \text{Second compound inequality}$$
$$\text{True} \qquad\qquad \text{False} \qquad\qquad \text{with } x = 5$$

Note that 5 does not need to satisfy both statements for this compound inequality to be true.

EXAMPLE 1 **Determining solutions to compound inequalities**

Determine whether the given x-values are solutions to the compound inequalities.
(a) $x + 1 < 9$ and $2x - 1 > 8$ $\qquad x = 5, -5$
(b) $5 - 2x \leq -4$ or $5 - 2x \geq 4$ $\qquad x = 2, -3$

Solution
(a) Substitute $x = 5$ in the compound inequality $x + 1 < 9$ and $2x - 1 > 8$.

$$5 + 1 < 9 \quad \text{and} \quad 2(5) - 1 > 8$$
$$\text{True} \qquad\qquad \text{True}$$

Both inequalities are true, so 5 is a solution. Now substitute $x = -5$.

$$-5 + 1 < 9 \quad \text{and} \quad 2(-5) - 1 > 8$$
$$\text{True} \qquad\qquad\quad \text{False}$$

To be a solution both inequalities must be true, so -5 is *not* a solution.

(b) Substitute $x = 2$ into the compound inequality $5 - 2x \leq -4$ or $5 - 2x \geq 4$.

$$5 - 2(2) \leq -4 \quad \text{or} \quad 5 - 2(2) \geq 4$$
False   False

Neither inequality is true, so 2 is *not* a solution. Now substitute $x = -3$.

$$5 - 2(-3) \leq -4 \quad \text{or} \quad 5 - 2(-3) \geq 4$$
False   True

At least one of the two inequalities is true, so -3 is a solution.

▌ Now Try Exercises 7, 9

CRITICAL THINKING

Graph the following inequalities and discuss your results.
1. $x < 2$ and $x > 5$
2. $x > 2$ or $x < 5$

Symbolic Solutions and Number Lines

We can use a number line to graph solutions to compound inequalities, such as

$$x \leq 6 \quad \text{and} \quad x > -4.$$

The solution set for $x \leq 6$ is shaded to the left of 6, with a bracket placed at $x = 6$, as shown in Figure 2.20. The solution set for $x > -4$ can be shown by shading a different number line to the right of -4 and placing a left parenthesis at -4. Because the inequalities are connected by *and*, the solution set consists of all numbers that are shaded on *both* number lines. The final number line represents the intersection of the two solution sets. That is, the solution set includes real numbers where the graphs "overlap." For any two sets A and B, the **intersection** of A and B, denoted $A \cap B$, is defined by

$$A \cap B = \{x \mid x \text{ is an element of } A \text{ and an element of } B\}.$$

Graphing a Compound Inequality

Figure 2.20

NOTE: A bracket, either [or], is used when an inequality contains $\leq$ or $\geq$. A parenthesis, either (or), is used when an inequality contains $<$ or $>$. This notation makes clear whether an endpoint is included in the inequality.

EXAMPLE 2 ▌ **Solving a compound inequality containing "and"**

Solve $2x + 4 > 8$ and $5 - x < 9$. Graph the solution set.

Solution
First solve each linear inequality separately.

$$2x + 4 > 8 \quad \text{and} \quad 5 - x < 9$$
$$2x > 4 \quad \text{and} \quad -x < 4$$
$$x > 2 \quad \text{and} \quad x > -4$$

Graph $x > 2$ and $x > -4$ on two different number lines. On a third number line, shade solutions that appear on both of the first two number lines. As shown in Figure 2.21, the solution set is $\{x \mid x > 2\}$.

$x > 2$

$x > -4$

$x > 2$ and $x > -4$ Solution set

Figure 2.21

■ Now Try Exercise 43

READING CHECK

What is a three-part inequality?

Sometimes a compound inequality containing the word *and* can be combined into a three-part inequality. For example, rather than writing

$$x > 5 \quad \text{and} \quad x \leq 10,$$

we could write the **three-part inequality**

$$5 < x \leq 10.$$

This three-part inequality is represented by the number line shown in Figure 2.22.

$5 < x \leq 10$

Figure 2.22

EXAMPLE 3   **Solving three-part inequalities**

Solve each inequality. Graph each solution set.

(a) $4 < t + 2 \leq 8$ **(b)** $-3 \leq 3z \leq 6$ **(c)** $-\dfrac{5}{2} < \dfrac{1 - m}{2} < 4$

Solution

(a) To solve a three-part inequality, isolate the variable by applying properties of inequalities to each part of the inequality.

$$4 < t + 2 \leq 8 \qquad \text{Given three-part inequality}$$
$$4 - 2 < t + 2 - 2 \leq 8 - 2 \qquad \text{Subtract 2 from each part.}$$
$$2 < t \leq 6 \qquad \text{Simplify each part.}$$

The solution set is $\{t \mid 2 < t \leq 6\}$. See Figure 2.23.

$2 < t \leq 6$ Solution set

Figure 2.23

(b) To simplify, divide each part by 3.

$$-3 \leq 3z \leq 6 \qquad \text{Given three-part inequality}$$
$$\frac{-3}{3} \leq \frac{3z}{3} \leq \frac{6}{3} \qquad \text{Divide each part by 3.}$$
$$-1 \leq z \leq 2 \qquad \text{Simplify each part.}$$

The solution set is $\{z \mid -1 \le z \le 2\}$. See Figure 2.24.

$-1 \le z \le 2$ Solution set

Figure 2.24

(c) Multiply each part by 2 to clear (eliminate) fractions.

$$-\frac{5}{2} < \frac{1 - m}{2} < 4 \qquad \text{Given three-part inequality}$$

$$2 \cdot \left(-\frac{5}{2}\right) < 2 \cdot \left(\frac{1 - m}{2}\right) < 2 \cdot 4 \qquad \text{Multiply each part by 2.}$$

$$-5 < 1 - m < 8 \qquad \text{Simplify each part.}$$

$$-5 - 1 < 1 - m - 1 < 8 - 1 \qquad \text{Subtract 1 from each part.}$$

$$-6 < -m < 7 \qquad \text{Simplify each part.}$$

$$-1 \cdot (-6) > -1 \cdot (-m) > -1 \cdot 7 \qquad \begin{array}{l}\text{Multiply each part by } -1;\\ \textit{reverse} \text{ inequality symbols.}\end{array}$$

$$6 > m > -7 \qquad \text{Simplify each part.}$$

$$-7 < m < 6 \qquad \text{Rewrite inequality.}$$

The solution set is $\{m \mid -7 < m < 6\}$. See Figure 2.25.

$-7 < m < 6$ Solution set

Figure 2.25

NOTE: Either $6 > m > -7$ or $-7 < m < 6$ is a correct way to write a three-part inequality. *However*, we usually write the smaller number on the left side and the larger number on the right side.

▌ Now Try Exercises **59, 63, 79**

▶ **REAL-WORLD CONNECTION** Three-part inequalities occur frequently in applications. In the next example we find altitudes at which the air temperature is within a certain range.

EXAMPLE 4 ▌ **Solving a three-part inequality**

If the ground-level temperature is 80°F, the air temperature x miles above Earth's surface is cooler and can be modeled by $T(x) = 80 - 19x$. Find the altitudes at which the air temperature ranges from 42°F down to 23°F. (*Source*: A. Miller and R. Anthes, *Meteorology*.)

Solution
We write and solve the three-part inequality $23 \le T(x) \le 42$.

$$23 \le 80 - 19x \le 42 \qquad \text{Substitute for } T(x).$$

$$-57 \le -19x \le -38 \qquad \text{Subtract 80 from each part.}$$

$$\frac{-57}{-19} \ge x \ge \frac{-38}{-19} \qquad \text{Divide by } -19; \textit{reverse} \text{ inequality symbols.}$$

$$3 \ge x \ge 2 \qquad \text{Simplify.}$$

$$2 \le x \le 3 \qquad \text{Rewrite inequality.}$$

The air temperature ranges from 42°F to 23°F for altitudes between 2 and 3 miles.

▌ Now Try Exercise **119**

Writing Three-Part Inequalities

The inequality $-2 < x < 1$ means that $x > -2$ *and* $x < 1$. A three-part inequality should *not* be used when *or* connects a compound inequality. Writing $x < -2$ or $x > 1$ as $1 < x < -2$ is **incorrect** because it states that x must be both greater than 1 *and* less than -2. It is impossible for any value of x to satisfy this statement.

We can also solve compound inequalities containing the word *or*. To write the solution to such an inequality we sometimes use *union* notation. For any two sets A and B, the **union** of A and B, denoted $A \cup B$, is defined by

$$A \cup B = \{x \mid x \text{ is an element of } A \text{ } or \text{ an element of } B\}.$$

If the solution to an inequality is $\{x \mid x < 1\}$ or $\{x \mid x \geq 3\}$, then it can also be written as

$$\{x \mid x < 1\} \cup \{x \mid x \geq 3\}.$$

That is, we can replace the word *or* with the $\cup$ symbol.

EXAMPLE 5 **Solving a compound inequality containing "or"**

Solve $x + 2 < -1$ or $x + 2 > 1$. Graph the solution set.

Solution
We first solve each linear inequality.

$$x + 2 < -1 \quad \text{or} \quad x + 2 > 1 \qquad \text{Given compound inequality}$$
$$x < -3 \quad \text{or} \quad x > -1 \qquad \text{Subtract 2.}$$

We can graph the simplified inequalities on different number lines, as shown in Figure 2.26. A solution must satisfy at least one of the two inequalities. Thus the solution set for the compound inequality results from taking the *union* of the first two number lines. We can write the solution, using set-builder notation, as $\{x \mid x < -3\} \cup \{x \mid x > -1\}$ or as $\{x \mid x < -3 \text{ or } x > -1\}$.

Figure 2.26

Now Try Exercise 47

CRITICAL THINKING

Carbon dioxide is emitted when human beings breathe. In one study of college students, the amount of carbon dioxide exhaled in grams per hour was measured during both lectures and exams. The average amount exhaled during lectures L satisfied $25.33 \leq L \leq 28.17$, whereas the average amount exhaled during exams E satisfied $36.58 \leq E \leq 40.92$. What do these results indicate? Explain. (*Source:* T. Wang, *ASHRAE Trans.*)

Numerical and Graphical Solutions

Compound inequalities can also be solved graphically and numerically, as illustrated in the next example.

EXAMPLE 6 ▶ **Estimating numbers of Internet users**

The number of U.S. Internet users in millions during year x can be modeled by the formula $f(x) = 11.6(x - 2000) + 124$. Estimate the years when the number of users is expected to be between 240 and 275 million. (*Source: The Nielsen Company.*)

Solution

Numerical Solution Let $y_1 = 11.6(x - 2000) + 124$. Make a table of values, as shown in Figure 2.27(a). In 2010 the number of Internet users was 240 million, and in 2013 this number is about 275 million. Thus from 2010 to about 2013 the number of Internet users is expected to be between 240 million and 275 million.

Graphical Solution The graph of $y_1 = 11.6(x - 2000) + 124$ is shown between the graphs of $y_2 = 240$ and $y_3 = 275$ in Figures 2.27(b) and 2.27(c) from 2010 to about 2013, or when $2010 \le x \le 2013$.

CALCULATOR HELP

To find a point of intersection, see Appendix A (page AP-6).

[2006, 2015, 1] by [150, 350, 50]   [2006, 2015, 1] by [150, 300, 50]

(a)   (b)   (c)

Figure 2.27

▮ Now Try Exercise 113 (a) and (b)

Interval Notation

Figure 2.28

The solution set in Example 4 was $\{x \mid 2 \le x \le 3\}$. This solution set can be graphed on a number line, as shown in Figure 2.28.

A convenient notation for number line graphs is called **interval notation**. Instead of drawing the entire number line as in Figure 2.28, the solution set can be expressed as [2, 3] in interval notation. Because the solution set includes the endpoints 2 and 3, brackets are used. A solution set that includes all real numbers satisfying $-2 < x < 3$ can be expressed as $(-2, 3)$. Parentheses indicate that the endpoints are *not* included. The interval $0 \le x < 4$ is represented by [0, 4).

MAKING CONNECTIONS

Points and Intervals

The expression (1, 2) may represent a point in the xy-plane or the interval $1 < x < 2$. To alleviate confusion, phrases such as "the point (1, 2)" or "the interval (1, 2)" are used.

Table 2.6 on the next page provides examples of interval notation. The symbol ∞ refers to **infinity**, and it does not represent a real number. The interval $(5, \infty)$ represents $x > 5$, which has no maximum x-value, so ∞ is used for the right endpoint. The symbol $-\infty$ may be used similarly and denotes **negative infinity**. Real numbers are denoted $(-\infty, \infty)$.

TABLE 2.6 Interval Notation

Inequality	Interval Notation	Number Line Graph
$-1 < x < 3$	$(-1, 3)$	
$-3 < x \leq 2$	$(-3, 2]$	
$-2 \leq x \leq 2$	$[-2, 2]$	
$x < -1$ or $x > 2$	$(-\infty, -1) \cup (2, \infty)$ ($\cup$ is the union symbol.)	
$x > -1$	$(-1, \infty)$	
$x \leq 2$	$(-\infty, 2]$	

EXAMPLE 7 **Writing inequalities in interval notation**

Write each expression in interval notation.
(a) $-2 \leq x < 5$ **(b)** $x \geq 3$ **(c)** $x < -5$ or $x \geq 2$
(d) $\{x \mid x > 0 \text{ and } x \leq 3\}$ **(e)** $\{x \mid x \leq 1 \text{ or } x \geq 3\}$

Solution
(a) $[-2, 5)$ **(b)** $[3, \infty)$ **(c)** $(-\infty, -5) \cup [2, \infty)$
(d) $(0, 3]$ **(e)** $(-\infty, 1] \cup [3, \infty)$

▌ Now Try Exercises 13, 17, 23, 27, 37

EXAMPLE 8 **Solving an inequality**

Solve $2x + 1 \leq -1$ or $2x + 1 \geq 3$. Write the solution set in interval notation.

Solution
First solve each inequality.

$$\begin{array}{lll} 2x + 1 \leq -1 & \text{or} & 2x + 1 \geq 3 & \text{Given compound inequality} \\ 2x \leq -2 & \text{or} & 2x \geq 2 & \text{Subtract 1.} \\ x \leq -1 & \text{or} & x \geq 1 & \text{Divide by 2.} \end{array}$$

The solution set may be written as $(-\infty, -1] \cup [1, \infty)$.

▌ Now Try Exercise 55

EXAMPLE 9 **Writing domains in interval notation**

Write the domain of each function in interval notation.
(a) $f(x) = \sqrt{x - 1}$ **(b)** $g(x) = \frac{1}{2x + 1}$

Solution
(a) The square root $\sqrt{x - 1}$ is undefined when $x - 1$ is negative. Thus x is in the domain of f whenever $x - 1 \geq 0$, or $x \geq 1$. In interval notation the domain of f is $[1, \infty)$.

(b) The ratio $\frac{1}{2x + 1}$ is undefined when $2x + 1 = 0$. The solution to this equation is $-\frac{1}{2}$. Thus the domain of f is all real numbers except $-\frac{1}{2}$. In interval notation the domain of f is $\left(-\infty, -\frac{1}{2}\right) \cup \left(-\frac{1}{2}, \infty\right)$.

Now Try Exercises 99, 101

2.4	Putting It All Together

CONCEPT	EXPLANATION	EXAMPLES
Compound Inequality	Two inequalities joined by *and* or *or*	$2x \geq 10$ and $x + 2 < 16$; $x < -1$ or $x > 2$
Three-Part Inequality	Can be used to write some types of compound inequalities involving *and*	$x > -2$ and $x \leq 3$ is equivalent to $-2 < x \leq 3$.
Interval Notation	Notation used to write sets of real numbers rather than using number lines or inequalities	$-2 \leq z \leq 4$ is equivalent to $[-2, 4]$. $x < 4$ is equivalent to $(-\infty, 4)$. $x \leq -2$ or $x > 0$ is equivalent to $(-\infty, -2] \cup (0, \infty)$.

TYPE OF INEQUALITY	METHOD TO SOLVE THE INEQUALITY
Solving a Compound Inequality Containing *and*	**STEP 1:** First solve each inequality individually. **STEP 2:** The solution set includes values that satisfy *both* inequalities from Step 1.
Solving a Compound Inequality Containing *or*	**STEP 1:** First solve each inequality individually. **STEP 2:** The solution set includes values that satisfy *at least one* of the inequalities from Step 1.
Solving a Three-Part Inequality	Work on all three parts at the same time. Be sure to perform the same step on each part. Continue until the variable is isolated in the middle part.

2.4	Exercises

PRACTICE   WATCH   DOWNLOAD   READ   REVIEW

CONCEPTS AND VOCABULARY

1. Give an example of a compound inequality containing the word *and*.

2. Give an example of a compound inequality containing the word *or*.

3. Is 1 a solution to $x > 3$ and $x \leq 5$?

4. Is 1 a solution to $x < 3$ or $x \geq 5$?

5. Is the compound inequality $x \geq -5$ and $x \leq 5$ equivalent to $-5 \leq x \leq 5$?

6. Name three ways to solve a compound inequality.

Exercises 7–12: Determine whether the given values of x are solutions to the compound inequality.

7. $x - 1 < 5$ and $2x > 3$ $x = 2, x = 6$

8. $2x + 1 \geq 4$ and $1 - x \leq 3$ $x = -2, x = 3$

9. $3x < -5$ or $2x \geq 3$ $x = 0, x = 3$

10. $x + 1 \leq -4$ or $x + 1 \geq 4$ $x = -5, x = 2$

11. $2 - x > -5$ and $2 - x \leq 4$ $x = -3, x = 0$

12. $x + 5 \geq 6$ or $3x \leq 3$ $x = -1, x = 1$

INTERVAL NOTATION

Exercises 13–38: Write the inequality in interval notation.

13. $2 \leq x \leq 10$ 14. $-1 < x < 5$

15. $5 < x \leq 8$ 16. $-\frac{1}{2} \leq x \leq \frac{5}{6}$

17. $x < 4$ 18. $x \leq -3$

19. $x > -2$ 20. $x \geq 6$

21. $x \geq -2$ and $x < 5$ 22. $x \leq 6$ and $x \geq 2$

23. $x \leq 8$ and $x > -8$ 24. $x \geq -4$ and $x < 3$

25. $x \geq 6$ or $x > 3$ 26. $x \leq -4$ or $x < -3$

27. $x \leq -2$ or $x \geq 4$ 28. $x \leq -1$ or $x > 6$

29. $x < 1$ or $x \geq 5$ 30. $x < -3$ or $x > 3$

31.

32.

33.

34.

35. $\{x \mid x < 4\}$ 36. $\{x \mid -1 \leq x < 4\}$

37. $\{x \mid x < 1 \text{ or } x > 2\}$ 38. $\{x \mid -\infty < x < \infty\}$

SYMBOLIC SOLUTIONS

Exercises 39–48: Solve the compound inequality. Graph the solution set on a number line.

39. $x \leq 3$ and $x \geq -1$ 40. $x \geq 5$ and $x > 6$

41. $2x < 5$ and $2x > -4$

42. $2x + 1 < 3$ and $x - 1 \geq -5$

43. $x + 2 > 5$ and $3 - x < 10$

44. $x + 2 > 5$ or $3 - x < 10$

45. $x \leq -1$ or $x \geq 2$

46. $2x \leq -6$ or $x \geq 6$

47. $5 - x > 1$ or $x + 3 \geq -1$

48. $1 - 2x > 3$ or $2x - 4 \geq 4$

Exercises 49–58: Solve the compound inequality. Write your answer in interval notation.

49. $x - 3 \leq 4$ and $x + 5 \geq -1$

50. $2z \geq -10$ and $z < 8$

51. $3t - 1 > -1$ and $2t - \frac{1}{2} > 6$

52. $2(x + 1) < 8$ and $-2(x - 4) > -2$

53. $x - 4 \geq -3$ or $x - 4 \leq 3$

54. $1 - 3n \geq 6$ or $1 - 3n \leq -4$

55. $-x < 1$ or $5x + 1 < -10$

56. $7x - 6 > 0$ or $-\frac{1}{2}x \leq 6$

57. $1 - 7x < -48$ and $3x + 1 \leq -9$

58. $3x - 4 \leq 8$ or $4x - 1 \leq 13$

Exercises 59–80: Solve the three-part inequality. Write your answer in interval notation.

59. $-2 \leq t + 4 < 5$ 60. $5 < t - 7 < 10$

61. $-\frac{5}{8} \leq y - \frac{3}{8} < 1$ 62. $-\frac{1}{2} < y - \frac{3}{2} < \frac{1}{2}$

63. $-27 \leq 3x \leq 9$ 64. $-4 < 2y < 22$

65. $\frac{1}{2} < -2y \leq 8$ 66. $-16 \leq -4x \leq 8$

67. $-4 < 5z + 1 \leq 6$ 68. $-3 \leq 3z + 6 < 9$

69. $3 \leq 4 - n \leq 6$ 70. $-1 < 3 - n \leq 1$

71. $-1 < 2z - 1 < 3$ 72. $2 \leq 4z + 5 \leq 6$

73. $-2 \leq 5 - \frac{1}{3}m < 2$ 74. $-\frac{3}{2} < 4 - 2m < \frac{7}{2}$

75. $100 \leq 10(5x - 2) \leq 200$

76. $-15 < 5(x - 1990) < 30$

77. $-3 < \dfrac{3z + 1}{4} < 1$ 78. $-3 < \dfrac{z - 1}{2} < 5$

79. $-\dfrac{5}{2} \leq \dfrac{2 - m}{4} \leq \dfrac{1}{2}$

80. $\dfrac{4}{5} \leq \dfrac{4 - 2m}{10} \leq 2$

NUMERICAL AND GRAPHICAL SOLUTIONS

Exercises 81–84: Use the table to solve the three-part inequality. Write your answer in interval notation.

81. $-3 \le 3x \le 6$

X	Y₁	
-2	-6	
-1	-3	
0	0	
1	3	
2	6	
3	9	
4	12	
Y₁■3X		

82. $-5 \le 2x - 1 \le 1$

X	Y₁	
-4	-9	
-3	-7	
-2	-5	
-1	-3	
0	-1	
1	1	
2	3	
Y₁■2X−1		

83. $-1 < 1 - x < 2$

X	Y₁	
-2	3	
-1	2	
0	1	
1	0	
2	-1	
3	-2	
4	-3	
Y₁■1−X		

84. $-2 \le -2x < 4$

X	Y₁	
-3	6	
-2	4	
-1	2	
0	0	
1	-2	
2	-4	
3	-6	
Y₁■-2X		

Exercises 85–88: Use the graph to solve the compound inequality. Write your answer in interval notation.

85. $-2 \le y_1 \le 2$

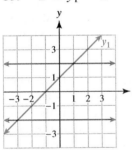

86. $1 \le y_1 < 3$

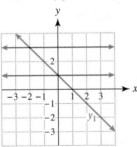

87. $y_1 < -2$ or $y_1 > 2$

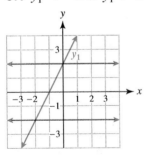

88. $y_1 \le -2$ or $y_1 \ge 4$

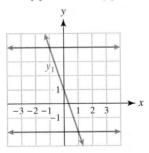

89. *Distance* The function f, shown in the figure at the top of the next column, gives the distance y in miles between a car and Omaha, Nebraska, after x hours, where $0 \le x \le 6$.
  (a) Is the car moving toward or away from Omaha? Explain.
  (b) Determine the times when the car is 100 miles or 200 miles from Omaha.
  (c) When is the car from 100 to 200 miles from Omaha?

(d) When is the car's distance from Omaha greater than or equal to 200 miles?

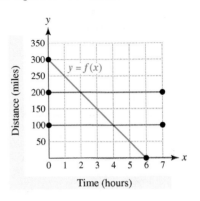

90. *Distance* The function g, shown in the figure, gives the distance y in miles between a train and Seattle after x hours, where $0 \le x \le 5$.
  (a) Is the train moving toward or away from Seattle? Explain.
  (b) Determine the times when the train is 150 miles or 300 miles from Seattle.
  (c) When is the train from 150 to 300 miles from Seattle?
  (d) When is the train's distance from Seattle less than or equal to 150 miles?

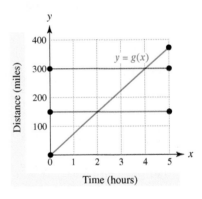

91. Use the figure to solve each equation or inequality. Let the domains of $y_1, y_2,$ and y_3 be $0 \le x \le 8$.
  (a) $y_1 = y_2$ **(b)** $y_2 = y_3$
  (c) $y_1 \le y_2 \le y_3$ **(d)** $y_2 < y_1$

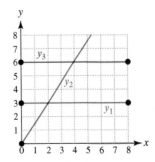

92. Use the figure to solve each equation or inequality. Let the domains of y_1, y_2, and y_3 be $0 \le x \le 5$.
 (a) $y_1 = y_2$ **(b)** $y_2 = y_3$
 (c) $y_1 \le y_2 \le y_3$ **(d)** $y_2 < y_3$

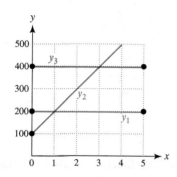

Exercises 93–98: Solve numerically or graphically. Write your answer in interval notation.

93. $-2 \le 2x - 4 \le 4$ **94.** $-1 \le 1 - x \le 3$

95. $x + 1 < -1$ or $x + 1 > 1$

96. $2x - 1 < -3$ or $2x - 1 > 5$

97. $95 \le 25(x - 2000) + 45 \le 295$

98. $42 \le -13(x - 2005) + 120 \le 94$

DOMAINS OF FUNCTIONS

Exercises 99–104: Write the domain of f in interval notation.

99. $f(x) = \sqrt{5 - x}$ **100.** $f(x) = \sqrt{3x + 6}$

101. $f(x) = \frac{1}{x + 1}$ **102.** $f(x) = \frac{x}{2x - 3}$

103. $f(x) = \frac{1}{\sqrt{x}}$ **104.** $f(x) = \frac{x}{\sqrt{x - 1}}$

USING MORE THAN ONE METHOD

Exercises 105–110: Solve symbolically, graphically, and numerically. Write the solution set in interval notation.

105. $4 \le 5x - 1 \le 14$ **106.** $-4 < 2x < 4$

107. $4 - x \ge 1$ or $4 - x < 3$

108. $x + 3 \ge -2$ or $x + 3 \le 1$

109. $2x + 1 < 3$ or $2x + 1 \ge 7$

110. $3 - x \le 4$ or $3 - x > 8$

111. **Thinking Generally** Solve $c < x + b \le d$ for x.

112. **Thinking Generally** Solve $c \le ax + b \le d$ for x, if $a < 0$.

APPLICATIONS

113. *Online Betting* Global online betting losses in billions can be modeled by $L(x) = 2.5x - 5000$, where x is a year from 2006 to 2011. Use each method to estimate when losses ranged from \$15 billion to \$20 billion. (*Source:* Christiansen Capital Advisors.)
 (a) Numerical
 (b) Graphical
 (c) Symbolical

114. *College Tuition* From 1980 to 2000, college tuition and fees at private colleges could be modeled by the linear function $f(x) = 575(x - 1980) + 3600$. Use each method to estimate when the average tuition and fees ranged from \$8200 to \$10,500. (*Source:* The College Board.)
 (a) Numerical
 (b) Graphical
 (c) Symbolical

115. *Altitude and Dew Point* If the dew point D on the ground is 60°F, then the dew point x miles high is given by $D(x) = 60 - 5.8x$. Find the altitudes where the dew point ranges from 57.1°F to 51.3°F. (*Source:* A. Miller.)

116. *Cigarette Consumption* Worldwide cigarette consumption in trillions from 1950 to 2010 can be modeled by $C(x) = 0.09x - 173.8$, where x is the year. Estimate the years when cigarette consumption was between 5.3 and 6.2 trillion. (*Source:* Department of Agriculture.)

117. *Geometry* For what values of x is the perimeter of the rectangle from 40 to 60 feet?

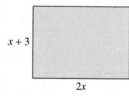

118. *Geometry* A rectangle is three times as long as it is wide. If the perimeter ranges from 100 to 160 inches, what values for the width are possible?

119. *Altitude and Temperature* If the air temperature at ground level is 70°F, the air temperature x miles high is given by $T(x) = 70 - 19x$. Determine the altitudes at which the air temperature is from 41.5°F to 22.5¡F. (*Source:* A. Miller and R. Anthes, *Meteorology.*)

120. *Distance* A car's distance in miles from a rest stop after x hours is given by $f(x) = 70x + 50$.
 (a) Make a table for $f(x)$ for $x = 4, 5, 6, \ldots, 10$ and use the table to solve the inequality $470 \le f(x) \le 680$. Explain your result.
 (b) Solve the inequality in part (a) symbolically.

121. *Medicare Costs* In 2000 Medicare cost taxpayers $250 billion, and in 2010 it cost $500 billion. (*Source: Department of Health and Human Services.*)

(a) Find a linear function M that models these data x years after 2000

(b) Estimate when Medicare costs were from $300 billion to $400 billion.

122. *Temperature Conversion* Water freezes at 32°F, or 0°C, and boils at 212°F, or 100°C.

(a) Find a linear function $C(F)$ that converts Fahrenheit temperature to Celsius temperature.

(b) The greatest temperature ranges on Earth are recorded in Siberia, where temperature has varied from about −70°C to 35°C. Find this temperature range in Fahrenheit.

WRITING ABOUT MATHEMATICS

123. Suppose that the solution set for a compound inequality can be written as $x < -3$ or $x > 2$. A student writes it as $2 < x < -3$. Is the student's three-part inequality correct? Explain your answer.

124. How can you determine whether an x-value is a solution to a compound inequality containing the word *and*? Give an example. Repeat the question for a compound inequality containing the word *or*.

SECTIONS 2.3 and 2.4 **Checking Basic Concepts**

1. Solve the linear inequality $4 - 3x < \frac{1}{2}x$.

2. Use the graph to solve each equation or inequality.

(a) $\frac{1}{2}x - 1 = 2 - x$ (b) $\frac{1}{2}x - 1 < 2 - x$

(c) $\frac{1}{2}x - 1 \geq 2 - x$

3. (a) Is 3 a solution to the compound inequality $x + 2 < 4$ or $2x - 1 \geq 3$?

(b) Is 3 a solution to the compound inequality $x + 2 < 4$ and $2x - 1 \geq 3$?

4. Solve each compound inequality. Write your answers in interval notation.

(a) $-5 \leq 2x + 1 \leq 3$

(b) $1 - x \leq -2$ or $1 - x > 2$

(c) $-2 < \dfrac{4 - 3x}{2} \leq 6$

2.5   Absolute Value Equations and Inequalities

Basic Concepts • Absolute Value Equations • Absolute Value Inequalities

A LOOK INTO MATH ▶

Monthly average temperatures can vary greatly from one month to another, whereas yearly average temperatures remain fairly constant from one year to the next. In Boston, Massachusetts, the yearly average temperature is 50°F, but monthly average temperatures can vary from 28°F to 72°F. Because 50°F − 28°F = 22°F and 72°F − 50°F = 22°F, the monthly average temperatures are always within 22°F of the yearly average temperature. If T represents a monthly average temperature, we can model this situation by using the *absolute value inequality*

$$|T - 50| \leq 22.$$

The absolute value is necessary because a monthly average temperature T can be either greater than or less than 50°F by as much as 22°F. In this section we discuss absolute value equations and inequalities. (*Source:* A. Miller and J. Thompson, *Elements of Meteorology.*)

NEW VOCABULARY

☐ Absolute value function
☐ Absolute value equation
☐ Absolute value inequality

Basic Concepts

We can define the **absolute value function** by $f(x) = |x|$. To graph $y = |x|$, we begin by making a table of values, as shown in Table 2.7. Next we plot these points and then sketch the graph shown in Figure 2.29. Note that the graph is V-shaped.

TABLE 2.7

x	$|x|$
-2	2
-1	1
0	0
1	1
2	2

Absolute Value Function

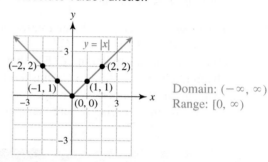

Domain: $(-\infty, \infty)$
Range: $[0, \infty)$

Figure 2.29

Because the input for $f(x) = |x|$ is any real number, the domain of f is all real numbers, or $(-\infty, \infty)$. The graph of the absolute value function shows that the output y (range) is any real number greater than or equal to 0. That is, the range is $[0, \infty)$.

EXAMPLE 1   **Graphing an absolute value equation**

Graph the equation $y = |3x + 3|$

Solution

Begin by making a table of values for $y = |3x + 3|$, as shown in Table 2.8. Plot these points in the xy-plane, and sketch the resulting V-shaped graph, as shown in Figure 2.30.

TABLE 2.8

x	$|3x + 3|$
-3	6
-2	3
-1	0
0	3
1	6

Graph of Absolute Value Equation

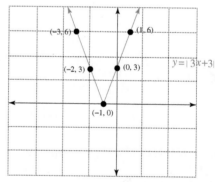

Figure 2.30

Now Try Exercise 7

Making Connections

Graphs and the Absolute Value

The graph of $y = |ax + b|$ is a reflection of the line $y = ax + b$ across the x-axis whenever $ax + b < 0$, which is shown in red. Otherwise, when $ax + b \geq 0$, their graphs are identical, which is shown in blue. Note that the graph of $y = |ax + b|$ is *always* V-shaped and *never* goes below the x-axis, whereas the graph of $y = ax + b$ is a line with slope $m = a$.

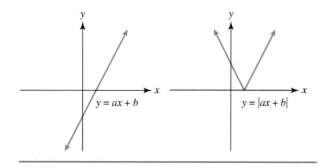

Absolute Value Equations

An equation that contains an absolute value is an **absolute value equation**. Examples are

$$|x| = 2, \quad |2x - 1| = 5, \quad \text{and} \quad |5 - 3x| - 3 = 1.$$

Consider the absolute value equation $|x| = 2$. This equation has *two* solutions: -2 and 2 because $|-2| = 2$ and $|2| = 2$. We can also demonstrate this result with a table of values or a graph. Refer back to Table 2.7: $|x| = 2$ when $x = -2$ or $x = 2$. In Figure 2.31 the blue graph of $y_1 = |x|$ intersects the red graph of $y_2 = 2$ at the points $(-2, 2)$ and $(2, 2)$. The x-values at these points of intersection correspond to the solutions -2 and 2.

Solving |x| = 2 Graphically

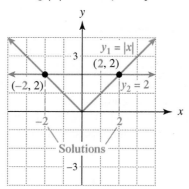

Figure 2.31

We generalize this discussion in the following manner.

SOLVING $|x| = k$

1. If $k > 0$, then $|x| = k$ is equivalent to $x = k$ or $x = -k$.

2. If $k = 0$, then $|x| = k$ is equivalent to $x = 0$.

3. If $k < 0$, then $|x| = k$ has no solutions.

EXAMPLE 2   **Solving absolute value equations**

Solve each equation.
(a) $|x| = 20$ **(b)** $|x| = -5$

Solution
(a) The solutions are -20 and 20.   **(b)** There are no solutions because $|x|$ is never negative.

Now Try Exercises 23, 25

EXAMPLE 3 **Solving an absolute value equation**

Solve $|2x - 5| = 3$
(a) symbolically, **(b)** numerically, and **(c)** graphically.

Solution

(a) *Symbolic Solution*

If $|2x - 5| = 3$, then either $2x - 5 = 3$ or $2x - 5 = -3$. Solve each equation separately.

$$2x - 5 = 3 \quad \text{or} \quad 2x - 5 = -3 \qquad \text{Equations to be solved}$$
$$2x = 8 \quad \text{or} \quad 2x = 2 \qquad \text{Add 5.}$$
$$x = 4 \quad \text{or} \quad x = 1 \qquad \text{Divide by 2.}$$

The solutions are **1** and **4**.

(b) *Numerical Solution*

A table of values can also be used to solve the equation $|2x - 5| = 3$. Table 2.9 shows that $|2x - 5| = 3$ when $x = 1$ or $x = 4$

TABLE 2.9 $|2x - 5| = 3$

x	0	1	2	3	4	5	6
$|2x - 5|$	5	3	1	1	3	5	7

Solutions are **1** and **4**.

(c) *Graphical Solution*

The equation $|2x - 5| = 3$ can be solved by graphing $y_1 = |2x - 5|$ and $y_2 = 3$. To graph y_1, first plot some of the points from Table 2.9. Its graph is V-shaped, as shown in Figure 2.32. Note that the x-coordinate of the "point" or vertex of the V can be found by solving the equation $2x - 5 = 0$ to obtain $\frac{5}{2}$. The graph of y_1 intersects the graph of y_2 at the points $(1, 3)$ and $(4, 3)$, giving the solutions **1** and **4**, so the graphical solutions agree with the numerical and symbolic solutions.

Graphical Solution

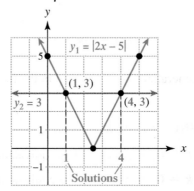

Figure 2.32

Now Try Exercises 31

This discussion leads to the following result.

ABSOLUTE VALUE EQUATIONS

If $k > 0$, then

$$|ax + b| = k$$

is equivalent to

$$ax + b = k \quad \text{or} \quad ax + b = -k.$$

EXAMPLE 4   **Solving absolute value equations**

Solve.
(a) $|5 - x| - 2 = 8$ **(b)** $\left|\frac{1}{2}(x - 6)\right| = \frac{3}{4}$

Solution

(a) Start by adding 2 to each side to obtain $|5 - x| = 10$. This new equation is satisfied by the solution from either of the following equations.

$5 - x = 10$	or	$5 - x = -10$	Equations to be solved
$-x = 5$	or	$-x = -15$	Subtract 5.
$x = -5$	or	$x = 15$	Multiply by -1.

The solutions are -5 and 15.

(b) This equation is satisfied by the solution from either of the following equations.

$\frac{1}{2}(x - 6) = \frac{3}{4}$	or	$\frac{1}{2}(x - 6) = -\frac{3}{4}$	Equations to be solved
$4 \cdot \frac{1}{2}(x - 6) = 4 \cdot \frac{3}{4}$	or	$4 \cdot \frac{1}{2}(x - 6) = 4\left(-\frac{3}{4}\right)$	Multiply by 4 to clear fractions.
$2(x - 6) = 3$	or	$2(x - 6) = -3$	Simplify.
$2x - 12 = 3$	or	$2x - 12 = -3$	Distributive property
$2x = 15$	or	$2x = 9$	Add 12.
$x = \frac{15}{2}$	or	$x = \frac{9}{2}$	Divide by 2.

The solutions are $\frac{9}{2}$ and $\frac{15}{2}$.

Now Try Exercises 33, 37

EXAMPLE 5   **Solving absolute value equations with no solutions and one solution**

Solve.
(a) $|2x - 1| = -2$ **(b)** $|4 - 2x| = 0$

Solution

(a) Because an absolute value is never negative, there are no solutions. Figure 2.33 shows that the graph of $y_1 = |2x - 1|$ never intersects the graph of $y_2 = -2$.

(b) If $|y| = 0$, then $y = 0$. Thus $|4 - 2x| = 0$ when $4 - 2x = 0$ or when $x = 2$. The only solution is 2.

Now Try Exercises 35, 39

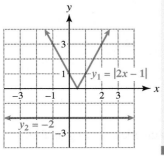

Figure 2.33

Sometimes an equation can have an absolute value on each side. An example would be $|2x| = |x - 3|$. In this situation either $2x = x - 3$ (the two expressions are equal) or $2x = -(x - 3)$ (the two expressions are opposites).

These concepts are summarized as follows.

SOLVING $|ax + b| = |cx + d|$

Let a, b, c, and d be constants. Then $|ax + b| = |cx + d|$ is equivalent to

$$ax + b = cx + d \quad \text{or} \quad ax + b = -(cx + d).$$

EXAMPLE 6   **Solving an absolute value equation**

Solve $|2x| = |x - 3|$.

Solution
Solve the following equalities.

$$2x = x - 3 \quad \text{or} \quad 2x = -(x - 3)$$
$$x = -3 \quad \text{or} \quad 2x = -x + 3$$
$$3x = 3$$
$$x = 1$$

The solutions are -3 and 1.

Now Try Exercise 43

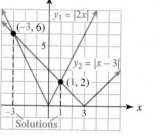

Figure 2.34

Example 6 is solved graphically in Figure 2.34. The graphs of $y_1 = |2x|$ and $y_2 = |x - 3|$ are V-shaped and intersect at $(-3, 6)$ and $(1, 2)$. The solutions are -3 and 1.

Absolute Value Inequalities

Numerical and Graphical Solutions We can solve absolute value inequalities numerically and graphically. For example, to solve $|x| < 3$ graphically, let $y_1 = |x|$ and $y_2 = 3$ (see Figure 2.35). Their graphs intersect at $(-3, 3)$ and $(3, 3)$. The V-shaped graph of y_1 is *below* the graph of y_2 for x-values *between*, but not including, $x = -3$ and $x = 3$. The solution set for $|x| < 3$ is $(-3, 3)$ in interval notation and is shaded on the x-axis.

$$|x| < 3$$

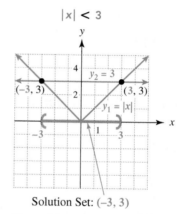

Solution Set: $(-3, 3)$

Figure 2.35

In the next example we solve absolute value inequalities both numerically and graphically.

EXAMPLE 7   **Solving inequalities numerically and graphically**

Solve each inequality numerically and graphically.
(a) $|2x - 1| < 3$ **(b)** $|2x - 1| > 3$

Solution

(a) Numerical Solution Table 2.10 shows a table of values for $y_1 = |2x - 1|$. Note that when $x = -1$ and $x = 2$, the absolute value $|2x - 1| = 3$ From this table we see that $|2x - 1| < 3$ when $-1 < x < 2$.

TABLE 2.10

x	$\lvert 2x-1 \rvert$	
-3	7	$\left.\vphantom{\begin{matrix}7\\5\end{matrix}}\right\}$ $\leftarrow \lvert 2x-1 \rvert > 3$
-2	5	
-1	3	$\leftarrow \lvert 2x-1 \rvert = 3$
0	1	$\left.\vphantom{\begin{matrix}1\\1\end{matrix}}\right\}$ $\leftarrow \lvert 2x-1 \rvert < 3$
1	1	
2	3	$\leftarrow \lvert 2x-1 \rvert = 3$
3	5	$\left.\vphantom{\begin{matrix}5\\7\end{matrix}}\right\}$ $\leftarrow \lvert 2x-1 \rvert > 3$
4	7	

Graphical Solution In Figure 2.36 the V-shaped graph of $y_1 = \lvert 2x - 1 \rvert$ lies *below* the horizontal line $y_2 = 3$ between $x = -1$ and $x = 2$, or when $-1 < x < 2$. Thus, the solution set to $\lvert 2x - 1 \rvert < 3$ is $(-1, 2)$ in interval notation and the graphical and numerical solutions agree.

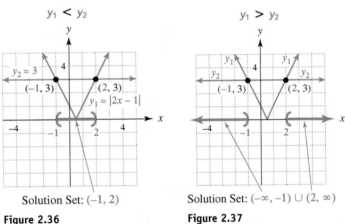

Solution Set: $(-1, 2)$

Figure 2.36

Solution Set: $(-\infty, -1) \cup (2, \infty)$

Figure 2.37

(b) Numerical Solution From Table 2.10 we see that $\lvert 2x - 1 \rvert > 3$ when $x < -1$ or when $x > 2$. Thus the solution set is $(-\infty, -1) \cup (2, \infty)$.

Graphical Solution In Figure 2.37 the V-shaped graph of $y_1 = \lvert 2x - 1 \rvert$ lies *above* the horizontal line $y_2 = 3$ to the left of $x = -1$ and to the right of $x = 2$. Thus, the solution set to $\lvert 2x - 1 \rvert > 3$ is $(-\infty, -1) \cup (2, \infty)$, and the graphical and numerical solutions agree.

▌ Now Try Exercise 101

Symbolic Solutions The absolute value of a number gives its distance from the origin on a number line. For example, $\lvert 3 \rvert = 3$ and $\lvert -3 \rvert = 3$ because both 3 and -3 are located 3 units from the origin, as shown in Figure 2.38.

Figure 2.38 Absolute Values of -3 and 3

Now suppose we want to find the solution set to $|x| < 3$ An x-value that satisfies this inequality has a distance that is less than 3 from the origin. For example, both x = 1 and $x = -2$ are solutions because $|1| < 3$ and $|-2| < 3$. In general, solutions to $|x| < 3$ satisfy $-3 < x < 3$, as shown in Figure 2.39.

Distance from Origin Is Less Than 3: $|x| < 3$
$$-3 < x < 3$$

Figure 2.39

Next suppose we want to find the solution set to $|x| > 3$. An x-value that satisfies this inequality has a distance that is greater than 3 from the origin. For example, both x = 4 and $x = -4$ are solutions because $|4| > 3$ and $|-4| > 3$. In general, solutions to $|x| > 3$ satisfy $x < -3$ or $x > 3$, as shown in 2.40.

Distance from Origin Is Greater Than 3: $|x| > 3$
$$x < -3 \text{ or } x > 3$$

Figure 2.40

From the preceding discussion it follows that if $|ax + b| < 3$, then $-3 < ax + b < 3$. Similarly, if $|ax + b| > 3$, then either $ax + b < -3$ or $ax + b > 3$. This method for solving absolute value inequalities symbolically is summarized by the following.

CRITICAL THINKING

How many solutions are there to $|2x + 1| < 4$? How many solutions are there to $|2x + 1| < -4$? Explain.

ABSOLUTE VALUE INEQUALITIES

Let k be a positive number.

1. $|ax + b| < k$ is equivalent to $-k < ax + b < k$.
2. $|ax + b| > k$ is equivalent to $ax + b < -k$ or $ax + b > k$.

Similar statements can be made for inequalities involving $\leq$ or $\geq$.

EXAMPLE 8 **Solving absolute value inequalities symbolically**

Solve each absolute value inequality. Write your answer in interval notation.
(a) $|4 - 5x| \leq 3$
(b) $|-4x - 6| > 2$

Solution
(a) $|4 - 5x| \leq 3$ is equivalent to the following three-part inequality.

$$-3 \leq 4 - 5x \leq 3 \qquad \text{Equivalent inequality}$$

$$-7 \leq -5x \leq -1 \qquad \text{Subtract 4 from each part.}$$

$$\frac{7}{5} \geq x \geq \frac{1}{5} \qquad \text{Divide each part by } -5; \text{ reverse the inequality.}$$

In interval notation the solution is $\left[\frac{1}{5}, \frac{7}{5}\right]$.

(b) $|-4x - 6| > 2$ is equivalent to the following compound inequality.

$$-4x - 6 < -2 \quad \text{or} \quad -4x - 6 > 2 \quad \text{Equivalent compound inequality}$$

$$-4x < 4 \quad \text{or} \quad -4x > 8 \quad \text{Add 6 to each side.}$$

$$x > -1 \quad \text{or} \quad x < -2 \quad \text{Divide each by -4; reverse the inequality.}$$

In interval notation the solution set is $(-\infty, -2) \cup (-1, \infty)$.

Now Try Exercises 61 and 63

EXAMPLE 9 **Solving absolute value equations and inequalities**

Solve each absolute value equation and inequality.

(a) $|2 - 3x| = 4$ **(b)** $|2 - 3x| < 4$ **(c)** $|2 - 3x| > 4$

Solution

(a) The given equation is equivalent to the following equations.

$$2 - 3x = 4 \quad \text{or} \quad 2 - 3x = -4 \quad \text{Equations to be solved}$$

$$-3x = 2 \quad \text{or} \quad -3x = -6 \quad \text{Subtract 2.}$$

$$x = -\frac{2}{3} \quad \text{or} \quad x = 2 \quad \text{Divide by } -3.$$

The solutions are $-\frac{2}{3}$ and 2.

(b) The solution set to $|2 - 3x| < 4$ is found by solving the following three-part inequality.

$$-4 < 2 - 3x < 2 \qquad \text{Three-part inequality}$$

$$-6 < -3x < 2 \qquad \text{Subtract 2 from each part.}$$

$$2 > x > -\frac{2}{3} \qquad \text{Divide by } -3; \text{ Reverse the inequality symbols.}$$

Thus the solution set is $\{x \mid -\frac{2}{3} < x < 2\}$, or in interval notation, $(-\frac{2}{3}, 2)$.

(c) The solution set to $|2 - 3x| > 4$ is found by solving the following compound inequality.

$$2 - 3x > 4 \text{ or } 2 - 3x < -4 \quad \text{Compound inequality}$$

$$-3x > 4 \quad \text{or } -3x < -6 \quad \text{Subtract 2 from each inequality.}$$

$$x < -\frac{2}{3} \quad \text{or } x < 2 \quad \text{Divide by } -3; \text{ Reverse the inequality symbols.}$$

Thus the solution set is $\{x \mid x < -\frac{2}{3} \text{ or } x > 2\}$, or in interval notation, $(-\infty, -\frac{2}{3}) \cup (2, \infty)$.

Now Try Exercise 51

EXAMPLE 10 **Solving an absolute value inequality**

Solve $\left|\frac{2x-5}{3}\right| > 3$. Write the solution set in interval notation.

Solution

Start by solving $\left|\frac{2x-5}{3}\right| > 3$ as follows.

$$\frac{2x-5}{3} > 3 \quad \text{or} \quad \frac{2x-5}{3} < -3 \qquad \text{Compound inequality to be solved}$$

$$2x-5 > 9 \quad \text{or} \quad 2x-5 < -9 \qquad \text{Multiply by 3.}$$

$$2x > 14 \quad \text{or} \qquad 2x < -4 \qquad \text{Add 5.}$$

$$x > 7 \quad \text{or} \qquad x < -2 \qquad \text{Divide by 2.}$$

The solution set is $x < -2$ or $x > 7$, or in interval notation, $(-\infty, -2) \cup (7, \infty)$.

Now Try Exercise 79

EXAMPLE 11 **Analyzing error**

An engineer is designing a circular cover for a container. The diameter d of the cover is to be 4.25 inches and must be accurate to within 0.01 inch. Write an absolute value inequality that gives acceptable values for d.

Solution

The diameter d must satisfy $4.24 \le d \le 4.26$. Subtracting 4.25 from each part gives

$$-0.01 \le d - 4.25 \le 0.01,$$

CALCULATOR HELP

To graph an absolute value, see Appendix A (page AP-8).

which is equivalent to $|d - 4.25| \le 0.01$. The "distance" or difference between 4.25 and the diameter is less than or equal to 0.01.

Now Try Exercise 121

EXAMPLE 12 **Modeling temperature in Boston**

In A Look Into Math at the beginning of this section we discussed how the inequality $|T - 50| \le 22$ models the range for the monthly average temperatures T in Boston.
(a) Solve this inequality and interpret the result.
(b) Give graphical support for part (a).

[0, 100, 10] by [0, 70, 10]

(a)

[0, 100, 10] by [0, 70, 10]

(b)

Figure 2.41

Solution

(a) **Symbolic Solution** To solve $|T - 50| \le 22$, we can solve the three-part inequality $-22 \le T - 50 \le 22$.

$$-22 \le T - 50 \le 22 \qquad \text{Inequality to be solved}$$

$$28 \le T \le 72 \qquad \text{Add 50 to each part.}$$

Thus the solution set to $|T - 50| \le 22$ is $\{T \mid 28 \le T \le 72\}$. Monthly average temperatures in Boston vary from 28°F to 72°F.

(b) **Graphical Solution** The graphs of $y_1 = |x - 50|$ and $y_2 = 22$ intersect at (28, 22) and (72, 22), as shown in Figures 2.41(a) and (b). The V-shaped graph of y_1 intersects the horizontal graph of y_2, or is below it, when $28 \le x \le 72$. Thus the solution set is $\{T \mid 28 \le T \le 72\}$. This result agrees with the symbolic result.

Now Try Exercise 113

Sometimes the solution set to an absolute value inequality can be either empty or the set of all real numbers. These two situations are illustrated in the next example.

EXAMPLE 13   **Solving absolute value inequalities**

Solve if possible.
(a) $|2x - 5| > -1$ **(b)** $|5x - 1| + 3 \le 2$

Solution
(a) Because the absolute value of an expression cannot be negative, $|2x - 5|$ is greater than -1 for every x-value. The solution set is all real numbers, or $(-\infty, \infty)$.
(b) Subtracting 3 from each side results in $|5x - 1| \le -1$. Because the absolute value is always greater than or equal to 0, no x-values satisfy this inequality. There are no solutions.

Now Try Exercises 75, 77

2.5   Putting It All Together

PROBLEM	SYMBOLIC SOLUTION	GRAPHICAL SOLUTION
$\|ax + b\| = k, k > 0$	Solve the equations $$ax + b = k$$ and $$ax + b = -k.$$	Graph $y_1 = \|ax + b\|$ and $y_2 = k$. Find the x-values of the two points of intersection.
$\|ax + b\| < k, k > 0$	The solutions to $$\|ax + b\| < k$$ are found by solving the three-part inequality $$-k < ax + b < k$$	Graph $y_1 = \|ax + b\|$ and $y_2 = k$. Find the x-values of the two points of intersection. The solutions are between these x-values on the number line, where the graph of y_1 lies below the graph of y_2.
$\|ax + b\| > k, k > 0$	The solutions to $$\|ax + b\| > k$$ are found by solving the compound inequality $$ax + b > k \text{ or } ax + b < -k$$	Graph $y_1 = \|ax + b\|$ and $y_2 = k$. Find the x-values of the two points of intersection. The solutions are "outside" (left or right of) these x-values on the number line, where the graph of y_1 is above the graph of y_2.

2.5   Exercises

CONCEPTS AND VOCABULARY

1. Give an example of an absolute value equation.

2. Give an example of an absolute value inequality.

3. Is -3 a solution to $|x| = 3$?

4. Is -4 a solution to $|x| > 3$?

5. Is the solution set to $|x| = 5$ equal to $\{-5, 5\}$?

6. Is $|x| < 3$ equivalent to $x < -3$ or $x > 3$? Explain.

7. How many times does the graph of $y = |2x - 1|$ intersect the graph of $y = 5$?

8. How many times does the graph of $y = |2x - 1|$ intersect the graph of $y = -5$?

Exercises 9–14: Determine whether the given values of x are solutions to the absolute value equation or inequality.

9. $|2x - 5| = 1$ $x = -3, x = 3$

10. $|5 - 6x| = 1$ $x = 1, x = 0$

11. $|7 - 4x| \le 5$ $x = -2, x = 2$

12. $|2 + x| < 2$ $x = -4, x = -1$

13. $|7x + 4| > -1$ $x = -\frac{4}{7}, x = 2$

14. $|12x + 3| \ge 3$ $x = -\frac{1}{4}, x = 2$

Exercises 15 and 16: Use the graph to solve the equation.

15. $|x - 2| = 2$ 16. $|2x + 1| = 3$

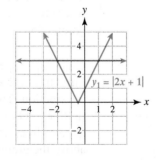

Exercises 17–22: Solve each equation or inequality.

17. $|x| = 3$ 18. $|x| = 5$

19. $|x| < 3$ 20. $|x| < 5$

21. $|x| > 3$ 22. $|x| > 5$

SYMBOLIC SOLUTIONS

Exercises 23–48: Solve the absolute value equation.

23. $|x| = 7$ 24. $|x| = 4$

25. $|x| = -6$ 26. $|x| = 0$

27. $|4x| = 9$ 28. $|-3x| = 7$

29. $|-2x| - 6 = 2$ 30. $|5x| + 1 = 5$

31. $|2x + 1| = 11$ 32. $|1 - 3x| = 4$

33. $|-2x + 3| + 3 = 4$

34. $|6x + 2| - 2 = 6$

35. $|3 - 4x| = 0$ 36. $|5x - 3| = -1$

37. $\left|\frac{1}{2}x - 1\right| = 5$ 38. $\left|6 - \frac{3}{4}x\right| = 3$

39. $|2x - 6| = -7$ 40. $\left|1 - \frac{2}{3}x\right| = 0$

41. $\left|\frac{2}{3}z - 1\right| - 3 = 8$ 42. $|1 - 2z| + 5 = 10$

43. $|z - 1| = |2z|$ 44. $|2z + 3| = |2 - z|$

45. $|3t + 1| = |2t - 4|$

46. $\left|\frac{1}{2}t - 1\right| = \left|3 - \frac{3}{2}t\right|$ 47. $\left|\frac{1}{4}x\right| = \left|3 + \frac{1}{4}x\right|$

48. $|2x - 1| = |2x + 2|$

Exercises 49–52: Solve each equation or inequality.

49. (a) $|2x| = 8$ (b) $|2x| < 8$
    (c) $|2x| > 8$

50. (a) $|3x - 9| = 6$
    (b) $|3x - 9| \le 6$
    (c) $|3x - 9| \ge 6$

51. (a) $|5 - 4x| = 3$
    (b) $|5 - 4x| \le 3$
    (c) $|5 - 4x| \ge 3$

52. (a) $\left|\dfrac{x - 5}{2}\right| = 2$ (b) $\left|\dfrac{x - 5}{2}\right| < 2$

    (c) $\left|\dfrac{x - 5}{2}\right| > 2$

Exercises 53–84: Solve the absolute value inequality. Write your answer in interval notation.

53. $|x| \le 3$ 54. $|x| < 2$

55. $|k| > 4$ 56. $|k| \ge 5$

57. $|t| \le -3$

58. $|t| < -1$

59. $|z| > 0$

60. $|2z| \ge 0$

61. $|2x| > 7$

62. $|-12x| < 30$

63. $|-4x + 4| < 16$

64. $|-5x - 8| > 2$

65. $2|x + 5| \ge 8$

66. $-3|x - 1| \ge -9$

67. $|8 - 6x| - 1 \le 2$

68. $4 - \left|\dfrac{2x}{3}\right| < -7$

69. $5 + \left|\dfrac{2 - x}{3}\right| \le 9$

70. $\left|\dfrac{x + 3}{5}\right| \le 12$

71. $|2x - 1| \le -3$

72. $|x + 6| \ge -5$

73. $|x + 1| - 1 > -3$

74. $-2|1 - 7x| \ge 2$

75. $|2z - 4| + 2 \le 1$

76. $|4 - z| \le 0$

77. $|3z - 1| > -3$

78. $|2z| \ge -2$

79. $\left|\dfrac{2 - t}{3}\right| \ge 5$

80. $\left|\dfrac{2t + 3}{5}\right| \ge 7$

81. $|t - 1| \le 0.1$

82. $|t - 2| \le 0.01$

83. $|b - 10| > 0.5$

84. $|b - 25| \ge 1$

NUMERICAL AND GRAPHICAL SOLUTIONS

Exercises 85 and 86: Use the table of $y = |ax + b|$ to solve each equation or inequality. Write your answers in interval notation for parts (b) and (c).

85. **(a)** $y = 2$ **(b)** $y < 2$ **(c)** $y > 2$

x	−2	−1	0	1	2	3	4
y	3	2	1	0	1	2	3

86. **(a)** $y = 6$ **(b)** $y \le 6$ **(c)** $y \ge 6$

x	−12	−6	0	6	12	18	24
y	9	6	3	0	3	6	9

Exercises 87 and 88: Use the graph of y_1 at the top of the next column to solve each equation or inequality. Write your answers in interval notation for parts (b) and (c).

87. **(a)** $|2x + 1| = 1$

   (b) $|2x + 1| \le 1$

   (c) $|2x + 1| \ge 1$

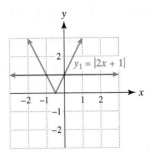

88. **(a)** $|x - 1| = 3$ **(b)** $|x - 1| < 3$

   (c) $|x - 1| > 3$

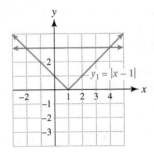

Exercises 89–98: Solve the inequality graphically. Write your answer in interval notation.

89. $|x| \ge 1$

90. $|x| < 2$

91. $|x - 1| \le 3$

92. $|x + 5| \ge 2$

93. $|4 - 2x| > 2$

94. $|1.5x - 3| \ge 6$

95. $|10 - 3x| < 4$

96. $|7 - 4x| \le 2.5$

97. $|8.1 - x| > -2$

98. $\left|\dfrac{5x - 9}{2}\right| \le -1$

USING MORE THAN ONE METHOD

Exercises 99–102: Solve the absolute value inequality

   (a) *symbolically,*
   (b) *graphically, and*
   (c) *numerically.*

Write your answer in set-builder notation.

99. $|3x| \le 9$

100. $|5 - x| \ge 3$

101. $|2x - 5| > 1$

102. $|-8 - 4x| < 6$

WRITING ABSOLUTE VALUE INEQUALITIES

Exercises 103–110: Write each compound inequality as an absolute value inequality. Do not simplify Exercises 107–110.

103. $-4 \le x \le 4$

104. $-0.1 < y < 0.1$

105. $y < -2$ or $y > 2$

106. $-0.1 \le x \le 0.1$

107. $-0.3 \le 2x + 1 \le 0.3$

108. $4x < -5$ or $4x > 5$ **109.** $\pi x \leq -7$ or $\pi x \geq 7$

110. $-0.9 \leq x - \sqrt{2} \leq 0.9$

111. Thinking Generally If $a \neq 0$ and $k > 0$, then the graph of $y = |ax + b|$ intersects the graph of $y = k$ at _____ points.

112. Thinking Generally If a and k are positive, then the solution set to $|ax + b| < k$ is _____.

APPLICATIONS

Exercises 113–116: Average Temperatures (Refer to Example 9.) The given inequality models the range for the monthly average temperatures T in degrees Fahrenheit at the location specified.

(a) Solve the inequality.
(b) Give a possible interpretation of the inequality.

113. $|T - 43| \leq 24$, Marquette, Michigan

114. $|T - 62| \leq 19$, Memphis, Tennessee

115. $|T - 10| \leq 36$, Chesterfield, Canada

116. $|T - 61.5| \leq 12.5$, Buenos Aires, Argentina

117. *Highest Elevations* The table lists the highest elevation in each continent.

Continent	Elevation (feet)
Asia	29,028
S. America	22,834
N. America	20,320
Africa	19,340
Europe	18,510
Antarctica	16,066
Australia	7,310

Source: National Geographic.

(a) Calculate the average A of these elevations.
(b) Which continents have their highest elevations within 1000 feet of A?
(c) Which continents have their highest elevations within 5000 feet of A?
(d) Let E be an elevation. Write an absolute value inequality that says that E is within 5000 feet of A.

118. *Distance* Suppose that two cars, both traveling at a constant speed of 60 miles per hour, approach each other on a straight highway.

(a) If the two cars are initially 4 miles apart, sketch a graph of the distance between the two cars after x minutes, where $0 \leq x \leq 4$. (*Hint:* 60 miles per hour = 1 mile per minute.)
(b) Write an absolute value equation whose solution gives the times when the cars are 2 miles apart.
(c) Solve your equation from part (b).

119. *Error in Measurements* (Refer to Example 11.) The maximum error in the diameter of the can is restricted to 0.002 inch, so an acceptable diameter d must satisfy the absolute value inequality

$$|d - 2.5| \leq 0.002.$$

Solve this inequality for d and interpret the result.

120. *Error in Measurements* Suppose that a person can operate a stopwatch accurately to within 0.02 second. If Byron Dyce's time in the 800-meter race is recorded as 105.30 seconds, write an absolute value inequality that gives the possible values for the actual time t.

121. *Error in Measurements* A circular lid is being designed for a container. The diameter d of the lid is to be 3.8 inches and must be accurate to within 0.03 inch. Write an absolute value inequality that gives acceptable values for d.

122. *Manufacturing a Tire* An engineer is designing a tire for a truck. The diameter d of the tire is to be 36 inches and the *circumference* must be accurate to within 0.1 inch. Write an absolute value inequality that gives acceptable values for d.

123. *Relative Error* If a quantity is measured to be x and the true value is t, then the relative error in the measurement is $\left|\frac{x - t}{t}\right|$. If the true measurement is $t = 20$ and you want the relative error to be less than 0.05 (5%), what values for x are possible?

124. *Relative Error* (Refer to the preceding exercise.) The volume V of a box is 50 cubic inches. How accurately must you measure the volume of the box for the relative error to be less than 3%?

WRITING ABOUT MATHEMATICS

125. If $a \neq 0$, how many solutions are there to the equation $|ax + b| = k$ when
(a) $k > 0$,   (b) $k = 0$, and   (c) $k < 0$?
Explain each answer.

126. Suppose that you know two solutions to the equation $|ax + b| = k$. How can you use these solutions to solve the inequalities $|ax + b| < k$ and $|ax + b| > k$? Give an example.

Checking Basic Concepts

Write answers in interval notation whenever possible.

1. Solve $\left|\frac{3}{4}x - 1\right| - 3 = 5$.

2. Solve the absolute value equation and inequalities.
(a) $|3x - 6| = 8$
(b) $|3x - 6| < 8$
(c) $|3x - 6| > 8$

3. Solve the inequality $|-2(3 - x)| < 6$, and then solve $|-2(3 - x)| \geq 6$.

4. Use the graph to solve the equation and inequalities.

(a) $|2x - 4| = 2$ (b) $|2x - 4| \leq 2$
(c) $|2x - 4| \geq 2$

CHAPTER 2   Summary

SECTION 2.1 ■ LINEAR EQUATIONS

Linear Equations in One Variable
Can be written as $ax + b = 0$, where $a \neq 0$. Linear equations have *one* solution.

Examples: $3x - 5 = 0$ and $x + 2 = 1 - 3x$

Symbolic, Graphical, and Numerical Solutions

Example: Solve $3x - 1 = 2$.

Symbolic Solution

$3x - 1 = 2$
$3x = 3$
$x = 1$

The solution is 1.

Numerical Solution

x	$3x - 1$
0	-1
1	2
2	5
3	8

$3x - 1 = 2$ when $x = 1$.

Graphical Solution

The solution is 1.

Lines

Standard Form	$ax + by = c$, where a, b, and c are constants with a and b not both 0.
Finding x-intercepts	Let $y = 0$ and solve for x.
Finding y-intercepts	Let $x = 0$ and solve for y.

Example: $3x - 4y = 24$

$3x - 4(0) = 24$ implies $x = 8$; the x-intercept is 8.

$3(0) - 4y = 24$ implies $y = -6$; the y-intercept is -6.

Identities and Contradictions

An *identity* is an equation that is always true, regardless of the values of any variables. A *contradiction* is an equation that is always false, regardless of the values of any variables.

Examples: $x + 3x = 4x$ (identity); $4x + 5 = 4x + 1$ (contradiction)

SECTION 2.2 ■ INTRODUCTION TO PROBLEM SOLVING

Solving a Formula for a Variable Use properties of algebra to solve for a variable.

Example: Solve $N = \dfrac{a + b}{2}$ for b.

$$2N = a + b \qquad \text{Multiply by 2.}$$
$$2N - a = b \qquad \text{Subtract } a.$$

Steps for Solving a Problem

STEP 1: Read the problem carefully and be sure that you understand it. (You may need to read the problem more than once.) Assign a variable to what you are being asked to find. If necessary, write other quantities in terms of this variable.

STEP 2: Write an equation that relates the quantities described in the problem. You may need to sketch a diagram, make a table, or refer to known formulas.

STEP 3: Solve the equation and determine the solution.

STEP 4: Look back and check your answer. Does it seem reasonable? Did you find the required information?

SECTION 2.3 ■ LINEAR INEQUALITIES

Linear Inequalities in One Variable Can be written as $ax + b > 0$, where $a \neq 0$; the symbol $>$ can be replaced with $<$, $\leq$, or $\geq$. Linear inequalities have *infinitely many* solutions.

Examples: $3x - 5 < 0$, $x + 2 \geq 1 - 3x$

Symbolic, Numerical, and Graphical Solutions

Example: Solve $4 - 2x \geq 0$.

Symbolic Solution

$$4 - 2x \geq 0$$
$$-2x \geq -4$$
$$x \leq 2$$

Reverse inequality.

Numerical Solution

x	$4 - 2x$
0	4
1	2
2	0
3	-2
4	-4

$4 - 2x \geq 0$ when $x \leq 2$.

Graphical Solution

Graph is above or intersects the x-axis for $x \leq 2$.

Compound Inequality Two inequalities connected by *and* or *or*.

Examples: For $x + 1 < 3$ *or* $x + 1 > 6$, a solution satisfies *at least* one of the inequalities.

For $2x + 1 < 3$ *and* $1 - x > 6$, a solution satisfies *both* inequalities.

Three-Part Inequality A compound inequality in the form $x > a$ *and* $x < b$ can be written as the three-part inequality $a < x < b$.

Example: $1 \leq x < 7$ means $x \geq 1$ *and* $x < 7$.

Interval Notation Can be used to identify intervals on the real number line

Examples: $-2 < x \leq 3$ is equivalent to $(-2, 3]$.

$x < 5$ is equivalent to $(-\infty, 5)$.

All real numbers are denoted $(-\infty, \infty)$.

Absolute Value Equations The graph of $y = |ax + b|, a \neq 0$, is V-shaped and intersects the horizontal line $y = k$ twice if $k > 0$. In this case there are two solutions to the equation $|ax + b| = k$ determined by $ax + b = k$ or $ax + b = -k$.

Example: The equation $|2x - 1| = 5$ has two solutions.

Symbolic Solution

$$2x - 1 = 5 \quad \text{or} \quad 2x - 1 = -5$$
$$2x = 6 \quad \text{or} \quad 2x = -4 \qquad \text{Add 1.}$$
$$x = 3 \quad \text{or} \quad x = -2 \qquad \text{Divide by 2.}$$

Graphical Solution

The solutions are -2 and 3.

Numerical Solution

x	-3	-2	-1	0	1	2	3
$|2x - 1|$	7	5	3	1	1	3	5

The solutions are -2 and 3.

Absolute Value Inequalities The solution set to $|ax + b| < k$ can be found by solving the three-part inequality $-k < ax + b < k$. The solution set to $|ax + b| > k$ can be found by solving the compound inequality $ax + b < -k$ or $ax + b > k$.

Examples: $|3 - x| < 5$ is equivalent to $-5 < 3 - x < 5$ and

$|3 - x| > 5$ is equivalent to $3 - x < -5$ or $3 - x > 5$.

CHAPTER 2 Review Exercises

SECTION 2.1

Exercises 1 and 2: Complete the table and then use the table to solve the equation.

1. $3x - 6 = 0$

x	0	1	2	3	4
$3x - 6$	-6				6

2. $5 - 2x = 3$

x	-1	0	1	2	3
$5 - 2x$					

3. Decide whether $-\frac{2}{3}$ is a solution to the linear equation $\frac{1}{2}z - 2(2z + 3) = 4z - 1$.

4. Use the graph to solve the equation $y_1 = y_2$.

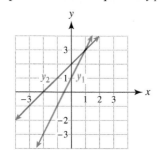

5. Solve $5 - 2x = -1 + x$ graphically.

6. Solve $4x - 3 = 5 + 2x$ graphically or numerically.

Exercises 7–16: Solve the equation.

7. $2x - 7 = 21$ **8.** $1 - 7x = -\frac{5}{2}$

9. $-2(4x - 1) = 1 - x$

10. $-\frac{3}{4}(x - 1) + 5 = 6$

11. $\dfrac{x - 4}{3} = 2$ **12.** $\dfrac{2x - 3}{2} = \dfrac{x + 3}{5}$

13. $-2(z - 1960) + 32 = 8$

14. $5 - (3 - 2z) + 4 = 5(2z - 3) - (3z - 2)$

15. $\dfrac{2}{3}\left(\dfrac{t - 3}{2}\right) + 4 = \dfrac{1}{3}t - (1 - t)$

16. $0.3r - 0.12(r - 1) = 0.4r + 2.1$

Exercises 17 and 18: Determine whether the equation is an identity or a contradiction.

17. $-4(5 - 3x) = 12x - 20$

18. $4x - (x - 3) = 3x - 3$

Exercises 19 and 20: Find the x- and y-intercepts. Then write the equation in slope–intercept form.

19. $4x - 5y = 20$

20. $2x + \frac{1}{2}y = -6$

SECTION 2.2

Exercises 21–26: Solve the equation for the given variable.

21. $5x - 4y = 20$ for y **22.** $-\frac{1}{3}x + \frac{1}{2}y = 1$ for y

23. $2a + 3b = a$ for a

24. $4m - 5n = 6m + 2n$ for n

25. $A = \frac{1}{2}h(a + b)$ for b **26.** $V = \frac{1}{3}\pi r^2 h$ for h

Exercises 27–30: Solve the equation for y. Let $y = f(x)$ and write a formula for $f(x)$.

27. $\frac{1}{2}x - \frac{3}{4}y = 2$ **28.** $-7(x - 4y) = y + 1$

29. $3x + 4y = 10 - y$ **30.** $\dfrac{y}{x} = 3$

Exercises 31 and 32: Translate the sentence into an equation and then solve the equation.

31. The sum of twice x and 25 is 19.

32. If 5 is subtracted from twice x, it equals x plus 1.

SECTION 2.3

33. Use the table to solve $f(x) < 5$, where $f(x)$ represents a linear function.

x	-2	-1	0	1	2
$f(x)$	7	5	3	1	-1

34. Solve $2(3 - x) + 4 < 0$.

35. Solve the inequality $y_1 \geq y_2$, using the graph.

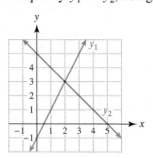

36. Solve each equation or inequality.
   (a) $5 - 4x = -2$ **(b)** $5 - 4x < -2$
   (c) $5 - 4x > -2$

Exercises 37–44: Solve the inequality.

37. $-2x + 1 \le 3$

38. $x - 5 \ge 2x + 3$

39. $\dfrac{3x - 1}{4} > \dfrac{1}{2}$

40. $-3.2(x - 2) < 1.6x$

41. $\dfrac{2}{5}t - (5 - t) + 3 > 2\left(\dfrac{3 - t}{5}\right)$

42. $\dfrac{2(3x - 5)}{5} - 3 \ge \dfrac{2 - x}{3} + 2$

43. $0.05t - 0.15 \le 0.03 - 0.75(t - 2)$

44. $0.6z - 1.55(z + 5) < 1 - 0.35(2z - 1)$

 Exercises 45 and 46: Solve the inequality graphically. Approximate boundary numbers to the nearest thousandth.

45. $0.72(\pi - 1.3x) \ge 0.54$

46. $\sqrt{2} - (4 - \pi x) > \sqrt{7}$

SECTION 2.4

Use interval notation whenever possible for the remaining exercises.

Exercises 47–50: Solve the compound inequality. Graph the solution set on a number line.

47. $x + 1 \le 3$ and $x + 1 \ge -1$

48. $2x + 7 < 5$ and $-2x \ge 6$

49. $5x - 1 \le 3$ or $1 - x < -1$

50. $3x + 1 > -1$ or $3x + 1 < 10$

51. Use the table to solve $-2 \le 2x + 2 \le 4$.

x	-3	-2	-1	0	1	2	3
$2x + 2$	-4	-2	0	2	4	6	8

52. Use the following figure to solve each equation and inequality.

  (a) $y_1 = y_2$ (b) $y_2 = y_3$
  (c) $y_1 \le y_2 \le y_3$ (d) $y_2 < y_3$

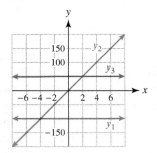

53. The graphs of y_1 and y_2 are shown at the top of the next column. Solve each equation and inequality.

  (a) $y_1 = y_2$ (b) $y_1 < y_2$
  (c) $y_1 > y_2$

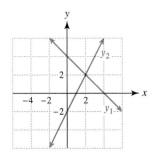

54. The graphs of three linear functions f, g, and h are shown in the following figure. Solve each equation and inequality.

  (a) $f(x) = g(x)$ (b) $g(x) = h(x)$
  (c) $f(x) < g(x) < h(x)$

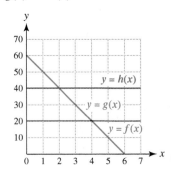

Exercises 55–60: Write the given inequality in interval notation.

55. $-3 \le x \le \frac{2}{3}$

56. $-6 < x \le 45$

57. $x < \frac{7}{2}$

58. $x \ge 1.8$

59. $x > -3$ and $x < 4$

60. $x < 4$ or $x > 10$

Exercises 61–66: Solve the three-part inequality. Write the solution set in interval notation.

61. $-4 < x + 1 < 6$

62. $20 \le 2x + 4 \le 60$

63. $-3 < 4 - \frac{1}{3}x < 7$

64. $2 \le \frac{1}{2}x - 2 \le 12$

65. $-3 \le \dfrac{4 - 5x}{3} - 2 < 3$

66. $30 \le \dfrac{2x - 6}{5} - 4 < 50$

SECTION 2.5

Exercises 67–70: Determine whether the given values of x are solutions to the absolute value equation or inequality.

67. $|12x - 24| = 24$ $x = -3; x = 2$

68. $|5 - 3x| > 3$ $x = \frac{4}{3}; x = 0$

69. $|3x - 6| \le 6$ $x = -3; x = 4$

70. $|2 + 3x| + 4 < 11$ $x = -3; x = \frac{2}{3}$

71. Use the accompanying table to solve each equation or inequality.

(a) $y_1 = 2$ **(b)** $y_1 < 2$ **(c)** $y_1 > 2$

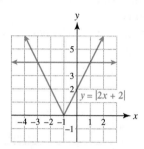

72. Use the graph of $y = |2x + 2|$ to solve each equation or inequality.
   (a) $|2x + 2| = 4$ **(b)** $|2x + 2| \le 4$
   (c) $|2x + 2| \ge 4$

Exercises 73–78: Solve the absolute value equation.

73. $|x| = 22$ **74.** $|2x - 9| = 7$

75. $\left|4 - \frac{1}{2}x\right| = 17$ **76.** $\frac{1}{3}|3x - 1| + 1 = 9$

77. $|2x - 5| = |5 - 3x|$

78. $|-3 + 3x| = |-2x + 6|$

Exercises 79 and 80: Solve each absolute value equation or inequality.

79. (a) $|x + 1| = 7$ **(b)** $|x + 1| \le 7$

   (c) $|x + 1| \ge 7$

80. (a) $|1 - 2x| = 6$ **(b)** $|1 - 2x| \le 6$

   (c) $|1 - 2x| \ge 6$

Exercises 81–88: Solve the absolute value inequality.

81. $|x| > 3$ **82.** $|-5x| < 20$

83. $|4x - 2| \le 14$ **84.** $\left|1 - \frac{4}{5}x\right| \ge 3$

85. $|t - 4.5| \le 0.1$ **86.** $-2|13t - 5| \ge -4$

87. $|5 - 4x| > -5$ **88.** $|2t - 3| \le 0$

Exercises 89 and 90: Solve the inequality graphically.

89. $|2x| \ge 3$ **90.** $\left|\frac{1}{2}x - 1\right| \le 2$

Exercises 91 and 92: Write each compound inequality as an absolute value inequality.

91. $-0.05 \le x \le 0.05$

92. $5x - 1 < -4$ or $5x - 1 > 4$

APPLICATIONS

93. *Loan Interest* A student takes out two loans, one at 5% and the other at 7% annual interest. The total amount for both loans is $7700, and the total interest after one year is $469. Find the amount of each loan.

94. *Distance and Time* At first an athlete runs at 8 miles per hour and then runs at 10 miles per hour, traveling 12.8 miles in 1.4 hours. How long did the athlete run at each speed?

95. *Expensive Homes* A typical 2200-square-foot house in Honolulu costs $415,000, which is only 54% of the cost of the same house in San Francisco. (San Francisco has the most expensive housing in the United States.) How much would this Honolulu house cost in San Francisco? (*Source:* Runzheimer International.)

96. *Violent Crimes in the U.S.* The number of violent crimes reported has dropped from 10 million in 1992 to 5 million in 2008.
   (a) Find a linear function $f(x) = mx + b$ that models the data x years after 1992.
   (b) Use $f(x)$ to estimate the number of violent crimes in 2005.

97. *Distance Between Bicyclists* The following graph shows the distance between two bicyclists traveling toward each other along a straight road after x hours.
   (a) After how long did the bicycle riders meet?
   (b) When were they 20 miles apart?
   (c) Find the times when they were less than 20 miles apart.
   (d) Estimate the sum of the speeds of the bicyclists.

98. *Distance* Two cars, Car 1 and Car 2, are traveling in the same direction on a straight highway. Their distances in miles north of Austin, Texas, after x hours are shown in the following graph.
   (a) Which car is traveling faster? Explain.
   (b) How many hours elapse before the two cars are the same distance from Austin? How far are they from Austin?
   (c) During what time interval is Car 1 closer to Austin than Car 2?

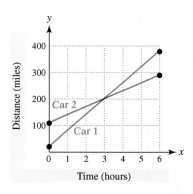

Time (hours)

99. *Weight of a Fish* If a walleye has a length of x inches, where $30 \leq x \leq 35$, its weight W in pounds can be *estimated* by $W(x) = 1.11x - 23.3$. (*Source: Minnesota Department of Natural Resources.*)

   (a) What length of walleye weighs 12 pounds?

   (b) What lengths of walleye weigh less than 12 pounds?

100. *Air Temperature* Suppose that the air temperature at ground level is $60°\,F$ and that the air cools $19°\,F$ for each one-mile increase in altitude.

   (a) Write $T(x) = ax + b$ so that T gives the temperature at an altitude of x miles.

   (b) Estimate the altitudes at which the air temperature is from $40°\,F$ to $20°\,F$.

101. *Age in the United States* The median age from 1970 to 2010 can be approximated by $f(x) = 0.238x + 27.9$, where x is the number of years after 1970.

   (a) Estimate the year(s) when this number was 30 years.

(b) Interpret the slope and y-intercept.

102. *Geometry* A rectangle is 5 feet longer than twice its width. If the rectangle has a perimeter of 88 feet, what are the dimensions of the rectangle?

103. *Temperature* The formula $F = \frac{9}{5}C + 32$ may be used to convert Fahrenheit temperature to Celsius temperature. The temperature range at Houghton Lake, Michigan, has varied between $-48°\,F$ and $107°\,F$. Solve a three-part inequality to find this temperature range in Celsius.

104. *Error in Measurements* A square garden is being fenced along its 160-foot perimeter. If the length L of the fence must be within 1 foot of the garden's perimeter, write an absolute value inequality that gives acceptable values for L. Solve your inequality.

105. *Average Precipitation* The average rainfall in Houston, Texas, is 3.9 inches per month. Each month's average A is within 1.7 inches of 3.9 inches. (*Source:* J. Williams, *The Weather Almanac 1995.*)

   (a) Write an absolute value inequality that models this situation.

   (b) Solve the inequality.

106. *Relative Error* If a quantity is measured to be T and the actual value is A, then the relative error in this measurement is $\left|\frac{T - A}{A}\right|$. If $A = 35$ and the relative error is to be less than 0.08 (8%), what values for T are possible?

CHAPTER 2 **Test**   **Test Prep** CHAPTER VIDEOS   Step-by-step test solutions are found on the Chapter Test Prep Videos available via the Video Resources on DVD, in *MyMathLab*, and on *YouTube* (search "RockswoldInterAlg" and click on "Channels").

1. Is $\frac{1}{6}$ a solution to $3 - 4(1 - 2x) = 2x$?

2. Complete the table and then solve $2 - 3x \leq -1$.

x	-2	-1	0	1	2
$2 - 3x$					

3. Solve $3 - 5x = 18$. Check your answer.

4. Use the graph to the right to solve each equation and inequality. Write your answers for parts (b) and (c) in interval notation.

   (a) $y_1 = y_2$ **(b)** $y_1 \geq y_2$

   (c) $y_1 \leq y_2$

5. Solve $4 - 2x = 1 + x$ graphically.

6. Solve each equation.

   (a) $-\frac{2}{3}(3x - 2) + 1 = x$

   (b) $\dfrac{2z + 1}{3} = \dfrac{3(1 - z)}{2}$

   (c) $0.4(2 - 3x) = 0.5x - 0.2$

7. Find the x- and y-intercepts for the graph of the equation $-6x + 3y = 9$. Then write the equation in slope–intercept form.

8. Translate the sentence into an equation and then solve. "If 2 is added to 5 times x, it equals x minus 4."

9. Solve $3x - 2y = 6$ for y. Let $y = f(x)$ and write a formula for $f(x)$.

Exercises 10 and 11: Solve the inequality. Write your answer in interval notation.

10. $-5x + 1 \leq 4$ **11.** $3.1(3 - x) < 2.9x$

12. Graph the solution set to $2x + 6 < 2$ and $-3x \geq 3$ on a number line.

13. Use the table to solve the compound inequality $-3x < -3$ or $-3x > 6$. Write your answer in interval notation.

x	-3	-2	-1	0	1	2	3
$-3x$	9	6	3	0	-3	-6	-9

14. Use the following figure to solve the equations and inequalities. Write your answers for parts (c) and (d) in interval notation.
- **(a)** $y_1 = y_2$ **(b)** $y_2 = y_3$
- **(c)** $y_1 \leq y_2 \leq y_3$ **(d)** $y_2 < y_3$

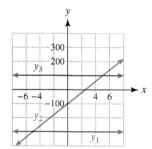

15. Solve $-2 < 2 + \frac{1}{2}x < 2$ and write the solution set in interval notation.

16. Solve the equation $\left| 2 - \frac{1}{3}x \right| = 6$.

17. Solve each inequality. Write your answer in interval notation.
- **(a)** $|x| \leq 5$
- **(b)** $|x| > 0$
- **(c)** $|2x + 7| \leq -2$
- **(d)** $|5x| > 10$
- **(e)** $-2|2 - 5x| + 1 \leq 5$
- **(f)** $|3 - x| < 5$

18. Solve each equation or inequality. Write your answers for parts (b) and (c) in interval notation.
- **(a)** $|1 - 5x| = 3$ **(b)** $|1 - 5x| \leq 3$
- **(c)** $|1 - 5x| \geq 3$

19. *Sport Drinks* The following graph shows a relationship between the calories in an 8-ounce serving of a sport drink and the corresponding grams of carbohydrates. Estimate the number of calories x in 8 ounces of a sport drink with the following grams of carbohydrates. (*Source: Runner's World.*)
- **(a)** 16 grams of carbohydrates
- **(b)** More than 16 grams of carbohydrates

(c) Less than 16 grams of carbohydrates

(d) Interpret the slope of the graph.

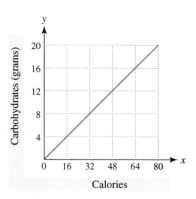

20. *Drinking Fluids and Exercise* To determine the number of ounces of fluid that a person should drink in a day, divide his or her weight in pounds by 2 and then add 0.4 ounce for every minute of exercise.
- **(a)** Write a function that gives the fluid requirements for a person weighing 150 pounds and exercising x minutes a day.
- **(b)** If a 150-pound runner needs 89 ounces of fluid each day, determine the runner's daily minutes of exercise.

21. *Solving a Formula* Solve the formula $d = \frac{1}{2}gt^2$ for g.

22. *Loan Interest* A student takes out two loans, one at 4% and the other at 6% annual interest. The total amount for both loans is $5000, and the total interest after one year is $230. Find the amount of each loan.

23. *Angles in a Triangle* The measure of the largest angle in a triangle is twice the measure of the smallest angle. The third angle is 16° more than the smallest angle. Find the measure of each angle.

24. *Prices* The sale price of a jacket is $81. If the retail price had been reduced by 25%, find the retail price of the jacket.

25. *Women Marines* The number of women in the Marine Corps from 1980 to 2010 can be approximated by $f(x) = 190x + 6000$, where x is the number of years after 1980.
- **(a)** Estimate the years when this number was from 7900 to 9800.
- **(b)** Interpret the slope and y-intercept.

CHAPTER 2   Extended and Discovery Exercises

1. *Clouds and Temperature* If the air temperature is greater than the dew point, clouds do not form. If the air temperature cools to the dew point, fog or clouds may appear. Suppose that the Fahrenheit temperature x miles high is given by $T(x) = 90 - 19x$ and that the dew point x miles high is given by $D(x) = 70 - 5.8x$. (*Source:* A. Miller.)
   - (a) Find the temperature and dew point at ground level.
   - (b) At what altitude are the air temperature and dew point equal?
   - (c) Find the altitudes at which clouds do not form.
   - (d) Find the altitudes at which clouds may form.

2. *Critical Thinking* (Refer to Exercise 1.) At ground level the dew point is usually less than the air temperature. However, if the air temperature reaches the dew point, fog or clouds may form.
   - (a) Discuss why clouds are likely to form at some altitude in the sky.
   - (b) Suppose that the dew point is slightly less than the air temperature near the ground. How does that affect the altitude at which clouds form?

3. *Recording Music* A compact disc (CD) can hold approximately 700 million bytes. One *byte* is capable of storing one letter of the alphabet. For example, the word "function" requires 8 bytes to store in computer

memory. One million bytes is commonly referred to as a *megabyte* (MB). Recording music requires an enormous amount of memory. The accompanying table lists the megabytes x needed to record y seconds (sec) of music.

x (MB)	0.129	0.231	0.415	0.491
y (sec)	6.010	10.74	19.27	22.83

x (MB)	0.667	1.030	1.160	1.260
y (sec)	31.00	49.00	55.25	60.18

Source: Gateway 2000 System CD.

   - (a) Make a scatterplot of the data.
   - (b) What relationship seems to exist between x and y? Why does this relationship seem reasonable?
   - (c) Find the slope–intercept form of a line that models the data. Interpret the slope of this line as a rate of change. Answers may vary.
   - (d) Check your answer in part (c) by graphing the line and data in the same graph.
   - (e) Write a linear equation whose solution gives the megabytes needed to record 120 seconds of music.
   - (f) Solve the equation in part (e) graphically or symbolically.

CHAPTERS 1–2   Cumulative Review Exercises

Exercises 1 and 2: Classify each real number as one or more of the following: natural number, whole number, integer, rational number, or irrational number.

1. $-7, -\frac{3}{5}, 0, \sqrt{5}, \frac{8}{2}, 5.\overline{12}$

2. $-\frac{6}{3}, \frac{0}{9}, \sqrt{9}, \pi, 4.\overline{6}$

Exercises 3 and 4: State whether the equation illustrates an identity, commutative, associative, or distributive property.

3. $8x - 2x = 6x$

4. $(6 + z) + 3 = 6 + (z + 3)$

Exercises 5 and 6: Use properties of real numbers to evaluate the expression mentally.

5. $11 + 26 + (-1) + 14$

6. $7 \cdot 99$

7. Plot the numbers $-4, -\frac{5}{2}, 0,$ and 3 on a number line.

8. Find the opposite of $-5y - 4$.

Exercises 9 and 10: Simplify the expression. Write the result using positive exponents.

9. $\dfrac{24x^{-4}y^2}{8xy^{-5}}$

10. $\left(\dfrac{3a^2}{4b^3}\right)^{-3}$

11. Evaluate the expression $15 - 2^3 \div 4$.

12. Write the number 0.000059 in scientific notation.

Exercises 13 and 14: Evaluate the formula for the given value of the variable.

13. $J = \sqrt{38 - t} \quad t = 13$

14. $r = 3 - z^3 \qquad z = -3$

15. Select the formula that best models the data in the table.

x	-2	-1	0	1	2
y	7	5	3	1	-1

(i) $y = 2x + 11$ (ii) $y = -2x + 3$
(iii) $y = x - 5$

16. Identify the domain and range of the given relation $S = \{(-2, 4), (0, 2), (1, 4), (3, 0)\}$.

Exercises 17 and 18: Evaluate the given formula for $x = -2, -1, 0, 1,$ and 2. Plot these ordered pairs.

17. $y = -2x + 1$ **18.** $y = \dfrac{x^3 + 4}{2}$

19. Sketch the graph of $f(x) = x^2 - 3$ by hand.

20. Find the domain of $f(x) = \dfrac{4}{x}$.

Exercises 21 and 22: Use the graph or table to evaluate $f(0)$ and $f(-2)$.

21.

22.

x	-2	-1	0	1	2
$f(x)$	-4	-1	2	5	8

Exercises 23 and 24: Determine whether f is a linear function. If f is linear, give values for m and b so that f may be expressed as $f(x) = mx + b$.

23. $f(x) = 11 - 3x$

24. $f(x) = \sqrt{x} + 2$

25. Use the table to write the formula for $f(x) = mx + b$.

x	-2	-1	0	1	2
$f(x)$	-5	-1	3	7	11

26. Sketch a graph of $f(x) = 3$.

27. Find the slope and the y-intercept of the graph of $f(x) = 5x - 4$.

28. Calculate the slope of the line passing through the points $(3, -2)$ and $(-1, 6)$.

29. Sketch a line passing through the point $(1, 3)$ with slope $m = 2$.

30. Use the graph to express the equation of the line in slope–intercept form.

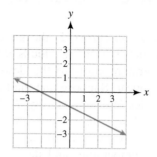

31. Let f be a linear function. Find the slope, x-intercept, and y-intercept of the graph of f.

x	-2	-1	0	1	2
$f(x)$	-3	0	3	6	9

32. Write the equation of the vertical line that passes through the point $(5, 7)$.

Exercises 33 and 34: Write the slope–intercept equation for a line satisfying the given conditions.

33. Parallel to $y = 3x - 4$, passing through $(2, 1)$

34. Perpendicular to $y = -x - 5$, passing through the point $(-3, 0)$

35. Determine whether $\frac{8}{5}$ is a solution to the equation $\frac{1}{2}x - 4(x - 1) = \frac{1}{4}x - 2$.

36. Use the graph to solve the equation $y_1 = y_2$.

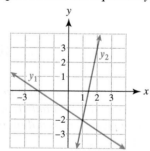

Exercises 37 and 38: Solve the equation.

37. $\frac{3}{4}(x - 2) + 4 = 2$

38. $\dfrac{2}{3}\left(\dfrac{t - 7}{4}\right) - 2 = \dfrac{1}{3}t - (2t + 3)$

Exercises 39 and 40: Find the x- and y-intercepts. Write the equation in slope–intercept form.

39. $x - \frac{1}{3}y = 2$

40. $5x - 4y = -10$

41. Use the table to solve $y < 2$, where y represents a linear function. Write the solution set in set-builder notation.

x	−2	−1	0	1	2
y	12	7	2	−3	−8

42. Use the graph to solve the inequality $y_1 \le y_2$. Write the solution set in interval notation.

Exercises 43 and 44: Solve the inequality symbolically. Write the solution set in interval notation.

43. $\dfrac{4x - 9}{6} > \dfrac{1}{2}$

44. $\frac{2}{3}z - 2 \le \frac{1}{4}z - (2z + 2)$

Exercises 45 and 46: Solve the compound inequality. Graph the solution set on a number line.

45. $x + 2 > 1$ and $2x - 1 \le 9$

46. $4x + 7 < 1$ or $3x + 2 \ge 11$

Exercises 47 and 48: Solve the three-part inequality. Write the solution set in interval notation.

47. $-7 \le 2x - 3 \le 5$

48. $-8 \le -\frac{1}{2}x - 3 \le 5$

Exercises 49 and 50: Solve the absolute value inequality. Write the solution set in interval notation.

49. $|3x + 5| > 13$

50. $-3|2t - 11| \ge -9$

51. Use the graph to solve the equation and inequalities.
  (a) $y_1 = 2$ **(b)** $y_1 \le 2$
  (c) $y_1 \ge 2$

52. Solve the absolute value equation $\left|\frac{2}{3}x - 4\right| = 8$.

APPLICATIONS

53. *Calculating Interest* If P dollars are deposited in a savings account paying 5% annual interest, then the amount A in the account after t years is given by the formula $A = P(1.05)^t$. Find A for the given values of P and t. Round your answer to the nearest cent.
  (a) $P = \$4300$, $t = 10$ years
  (b) $P = \$11{,}000$, $t = 6$ years

54. *Modeling Motion* The table lists the distance d in miles traveled by a car for various elapsed times t in hours. Find an equation that models these data.

t (hours)	3	5	7	9
d (miles)	195	325	455	585

55. *Sodium Content* Some types of diet soda contain 120 milligrams of sodium per 12-ounce can.
  (a) Give a formula for $f(x)$ that calculates the number of milligrams of sodium in x ounces of this type of diet soda.
  (b) What is the slope of the graph of f?
  (c) Interpret the slope as a rate of change.

56. *Graphical Model* A 150-liter aquarium is initially empty. A small hose attached to a faucet begins to fill the aquarium at a constant rate of 5 liters per minute. After 10 minutes, the faucet is turned off for 15 minutes and the small hose is replaced by a larger hose that can fill the aquarium at a rate of 10 liters per minute. The faucet is turned back on until the aquarium is full. Sketch a graph that depicts the amount of water in the aquarium after x minutes.

57. *Distance* A motorcyclist and a bicyclist are traveling toward each other on a straight road. Their distances in miles south of Euclid, Ohio, after x hours are shown in the graph to the right.
  (a) Is the bicyclist traveling toward or away from Euclid? Explain.
  (b) How many hours elapse before they are the same distance from Euclid?
  (c) During what time period is the motorcyclist farther away from Euclid than the bicyclist?

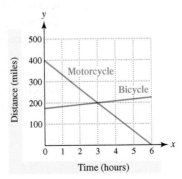

58. *Women Officers* The number of women officers in the Marine Corps from 1960 to 2010 may be modeled by $f(x) = 17(x - 1960) + 56$, where x represents the year. Estimate the years in which the number of women officers was between 600 and 800. (*Source:* Department of Defense.)

3 Polynomial Expressions and Functions

The book of nature is written in the language of mathematics.

— GALILEO

Video games have been available to consumers for many years. However, most of these older games lacked the graphic capability to make the action appear real on a screen. During the past three decades the computing power of processors has *doubled every 2 years*. Now video game systems, such as PlayStation 3, Wii, and Xbox 360, are taking advantage of the new generation of powerful processors to make action scenes look incredibly realistic. Thousands of objects can be tracked and manipulated simultaneously, making the experience more lifelike to the user.

Video games are mathematically intensive because separate equations must be formed and solved in real time to determine the position of each person and object on the screen. Whether it is an athlete, a football, or an exploding object, *mathematics is essential* to making the movements look real.

Because flying objects do not follow straight-line paths, we cannot use linear functions and equations to model their paths. Instead, we need functions whose graphs are curves. Polynomial functions are frequently used in modeling *nonlinear motion* of objects and are excellent at describing flying objects. In this chapter you will begin to learn about polynomials and how they can be used to model the motion of objects like golf balls in flight. (See Section 3.3, Example 6.)

Source: Microsoft.

3.1 Polynomial Functions

Monomials and Polynomials • Addition and Subtraction of Polynomials • Polynomial Functions • Evaluating Polynomials • Operations on Functions • Applications and Models

A LOOK INTO MATH ▶

Many quantities in applications cannot be modeled with linear functions and equations. If data points do not lie on a line, we say that the data are *nonlinear*. For example, a scatterplot of the *cumulative* number of AIDS deaths from 1981 through 2007 is nonlinear, as shown in Figure 3.1. Monomials and polynomials are often used to model nonlinear data such as these. (*Source:* U.S. Department of Health and Human Services.)

U.S. AIDS Deaths

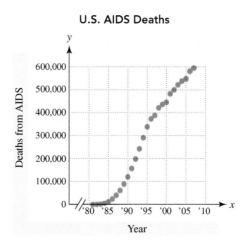

Figure 3.1

NEW VOCABULARY

☐ Term
☐ Monomial
☐ Degree of monomial
☐ Coefficient
☐ Leading coefficient
☐ Degree of a polynomial
☐ Linear polynomial
☐ Quadratic polynomial
☐ Cubic polynomial
☐ Like terms
☐ Opposite of a polynomial
☐ Linear function
☐ Quadratic function
☐ Cubic function

Monomials and Polynomials

A **term** is a number, a variable, or a *product* of numbers and variables raised to powers. Examples of terms include

Terms: $-15, \quad y, \quad 4x^2, \quad 3x^{-2}, \quad -xy^2, \quad x^3y^{-2}, \quad \dfrac{5}{x}, \quad \text{and} \quad \dfrac{x}{2}.$

If the variables in a term have only *nonnegative integer* exponents, the term is called a **monomial**. Examples of monomials include

Monomials: $-15, \quad y, \quad 4x^2, \quad 3\cancel{x^{-2}}, \quad -xy^2, \quad \cancel{x^3y^{-2}}, \quad \cancel{\dfrac{5}{x}}, \quad \text{and} \quad \dfrac{x}{2}.$

Not monomials

NOTE: Although a monomial can have a negative sign, it cannot contain any addition or subtraction signs. Also, a monomial cannot have division by a variable.

EXAMPLE 1 **Identifying monomials**

Determine whether the expression is a monomial.

(a) $-8x^3y^5$ **(b)** xy^{-1} **(c)** $9 + x^2$ **(d)** $\dfrac{2}{x}$

Solution

(a) The expression $-8x^3y^5$ represents a monomial because it is a product of the number -8 and the variables x and y, which have the nonnegative integer exponents 3 and 5.

(b) The expression xy^{-1} is not a monomial because y has a negative exponent.

(c) The expression $9 + x^2$ is not a monomial; it is the sum of two monomials, 9 and x^2.

(d) The expression $\frac{2}{x}$ is not a monomial because it involves division by a variable. Note also that $\frac{2}{x} = 2x^{-1}$, which has a negative exponent.

▌ Now Try Exercises 15, 17, 19, 21

Monomials occur in applications involving geometry, as illustrated in the next example.

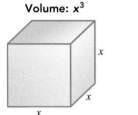

Volume: x^3

Figure 3.2

EXAMPLE 2 ▎ Writing monomials

Write a monomial that represents the volume of a cube with sides of length x.

Solution

The volume of a rectangular box equals the product of its length, width, and height. For a cube with sides of length x, its volume is given by $x \cdot x \cdot x = x^3$. See Figure 3.2.

▌ Now Try Exercise 23

The **degree of a monomial** equals the sum of the exponents of the variables. A constant term has degree 0, unless the term is 0 (which has an undefined degree). The numeric constant in a monomial is called its **coefficient**. Table 3.1 shows the degree and coefficient of several monomials.

TABLE 3.1

Monomial	64	$4x^2y^3$	$-5x^2$	xy^3
Degree	0	5	2	4
Coefficient	64	4	-5	1

A **polynomial** is either a monomial or a sum of monomials. Examples include

$$5x^4z^2, \quad 9x^4 - 5, \quad 4x^2 + 5xy - y^2, \quad \text{and} \quad 4 - y^2 + 5y^4 + y^5.$$
$$\text{1 term} \qquad \text{2 terms} \qquad \text{3 terms} \qquad\qquad\qquad \text{4 terms}$$

Polynomials containing one variable are called **polynomials of one variable**. The second and fourth polynomials shown are examples of polynomials of one variable. The **leading coefficient** of a polynomial of one variable is the coefficient of the monomial with greatest degree. The **degree of a polynomial** equals the degree of the monomial with greatest degree. Table 3.2 shows several polynomials of one variable along with their degrees and leading coefficients. A polynomial of degree 1 is a **linear polynomial**, a polynomial of degree 2 is a **quadratic polynomial**, and a polynomial of degree 3 is a **cubic polynomial**.

STUDY TIP

Study Table 3.2 carefully. It will help you understand the vocabulary of this section.

TABLE 3.2

Polynomial	Degree	Leading Coefficient	Type
-98	0	-98	Constant
$2x - 7$	1	2	Linear
$-5z + 9z^2 + 7$	2	9	Quadratic
$-2x^3 + 4x^2 + x - 1$	3	-2	Cubic
$7 - x + 4x^2 + x^5$	5	1	Fifth degree

Addition and Subtraction of Polynomials

Suppose that we have 3 rectangles of the same dimension having length x and width y, as shown in Figure 3.3. The total area is given by

$$xy + xy + xy.$$

This area is equivalent to 3 times xy, which can be expressed as $3xy$. In symbols we write

$$xy + xy + xy = 3xy.$$

Total Area: 3xy

$$x \quad A = xy \qquad x \quad A = xy \qquad x \quad A = xy$$

$$y \qquad\qquad y \qquad\qquad y$$

Figure 3.3

We can add these three terms because they are *like terms*. If two or more terms contain the *same variables raised to the same powers*, we call them **like terms**. We can add or subtract *like* terms but not *unlike* terms. For example, if one cube has sides of length x and another cube has sides of length y, their respective volumes are x^3 and y^3. The total volume equals

$$x^3 + y^3,$$

but we cannot combine these terms into one term because they are unlike terms. See Figure 3.4.

Unlike Terms

$$x^3 \qquad\qquad y^3$$

$$x \qquad + \qquad y \qquad = ?$$

$$x \quad x \qquad\qquad y \quad y$$

Figure 3.4

However, the distributive property can be used to simplify the expression $2x^3 + 3x^3$ as

$$2x^3 + 3x^3 = (2 + 3)x^3 = 5x^3$$

because $2x^3$ and $3x^3$ are like terms. See Figure 3.5.

Like Terms

$$2x^3 \qquad\qquad\qquad 3x^3$$

$$\qquad + \qquad\qquad\qquad = 5x^3$$

Figure 3.5

READING CHECK

What are like terms? Give examples.

Table 3.3 lists examples of like terms and unlike terms.

TABLE 3.3

Like terms	$-x^4, 2x^4$	$-2x^2y, 4x^2y$	$a^2b^4, \frac{1}{2}a^2b^4$
Unlike terms	$-x^3, 2x^4$	$-2xy^2, 4x^2y$	$ab^5, \frac{1}{2}a^2b^4$

To add or subtract monomials we simply apply the distributive property.

EXAMPLE 3 **Adding and subtracting monomials**

Simplify each expression by combining like terms.
(a) $8x^2 - 4x^2 + x^3$ **(b)** $9x - 6xy^2 + 2xy^2 + 4x$ **(c)** $5ab^2 - 4a^2 - ab^2 + a^2$

Solution
(a) The terms $8x^2$ and $-4x^2$ are like terms, so they can be combined.

$$8x^2 - 4x^2 + x^3 = (8 - 4)x^2 + x^3 \qquad \text{Combine like terms.}$$
$$= 4x^2 + x^3 \qquad \text{Simplify.}$$

However, $4x^2$ and x^3 are unlike terms and cannot be combined.
(b) The terms $9x$ and $4x$ can be combined, as can $-6xy^2$ and $2xy^2$.

$$9x - 6xy^2 + 2xy^2 + 4x = 9x + 4x - 6xy^2 + 2xy^2 \qquad \text{Commutative property}$$
$$= (9 + 4)x + (-6 + 2)xy^2 \qquad \text{Combine like terms.}$$
$$= 13x - 4xy^2 \qquad \text{Simplify.}$$

(c) The terms $5ab^2$ and $-ab^2$ are like terms, as are $-4a^2$ and a^2, so they can be combined.

$$5ab^2 - 4a^2 - ab^2 + a^2 = 5ab^2 - 1ab^2 - 4a^2 + 1a^2 \qquad \text{Commutative property}$$
$$= (5 - 1)ab^2 + (-4 + 1)a^2 \qquad \text{Combine like terms.}$$
$$= 4ab^2 - 3a^2 \qquad \text{Simplify.}$$

▌ Now Try Exercises 41, 47, 49

To add two polynomials we combine like terms, as in the next example.

EXAMPLE 4 **Adding polynomials**

Simplify each expression.
(a) $(2x^2 - 3x + 7) + (3x^2 + 4x - 2)$ **(b)** $(z^3 + 4z + 8) + (4z^2 - z + 6)$

Solution
(a) $(2x^2 - 3x + 7) + (3x^2 + 4x - 2) = 2x^2 + 3x^2 - 3x + 4x + 7 - 2$
$$= (2 + 3)x^2 + (-3 + 4)x + (7 - 2)$$
$$= 5x^2 + x + 5$$
(b) $(z^3 + 4z + 8) + (4z^2 - z + 6) = z^3 + 4z^2 + 4z - z + 8 + 6$
$$= z^3 + 4z^2 + (4 - 1)z + (8 + 6)$$
$$= z^3 + 4z^2 + 3z + 14$$

▌ Now Try Exercises 55, 57

We can also add polynomials vertically, as in the next example.

EXAMPLE 5 | **Adding polynomials vertically**

Find the sum.
(a) $(3x^2 - 5xy - 7y^2) + (xy + 4y^2 - x^2)$
(b) $(3x^3 - 2x + 7) + (x^3 + 5x^2 - 9)$

Solution
(a) Polynomials can be added vertically by placing like terms in the same columns and then adding each column.

$$
\begin{array}{r}
3x^2 - 5xy - 7y^2 \\
-x^2 + xy + 4y^2 \\
\hline
2x^2 - 4xy - 3y^2
\end{array}
\qquad \text{Add each column.}
$$

(b) Note that the first polynomial does not contain an x^2-term and that the second polynomial does not contain an x-term. When you are adding vertically, leave a blank for a missing term.

$$
\begin{array}{r}
3x^3 - 2x + 7 \\
x^3 + 5x^2 - 9 \\
\hline
4x^3 + 5x^2 - 2x - 2
\end{array}
\qquad \text{Add each column.}
$$

Now Try Exercises 59, 63

Recall that to subtract integers we add the first integer and the *additive inverse* or *opposite* of the second integer. For example, to evaluate $3 - 5$ we perform the following operations.

$$
\begin{aligned}
3 - 5 &= 3 + (-5) \qquad \text{Add the opposite.} \\
&= -2 \qquad\qquad\;\; \text{Simplify.}
\end{aligned}
$$

Similarly, to subtract two polynomials we add the first polynomial and the opposite of the second polynomial. To find the **opposite of a polynomial**, we negate each term. For example, the opposite of $2x - 1$ can be found as follows.

Opposite of 2x − 1

Multiplying by -1 is equivalent to negating an expression.

$$-(2x - 1) = -1(2x - 1) = -2x + 1$$

Thus to find the opposite of $2x - 1$ we *negate* each term and get $-2x + 1$. Table 3.4 shows three polynomials and their opposites.

TABLE 3.4

Polynomial	Opposite
$9 - x$	$-9 + x$
$5x^2 + 4x - 1$	$-5x^2 - 4x + 1$
$-x^4 + 5x^3 - x^2 + 5x - 1$	$x^4 - 5x^3 + x^2 - 5x + 1$

EXAMPLE 6 **Subtracting polynomials**

Simplify.

(a) $(y^5 + 3y^3) - (-y^4 + 2y^3)$ (b) $(5x^3 + 9x^2 - 6) - (5x^3 - 4x^2 - 7)$

Solution

(a) The opposite of the polynomial $(-y^4 + 2y^3)$ is $(y^4 - 2y^3)$. Rather than subtracting, we add the opposite.

$$(y^5 + 3y^3) - (-y^4 + 2y^3) = (y^5 + 3y^3) + (y^4 - 2y^3)$$
$$= y^5 + y^4 + (3 - 2)y^3$$
$$= y^5 + y^4 + y^3$$

(b) The opposite of the polynomial $(5x^3 - 4x^2 - 7)$ is $(-5x^3 + 4x^2 + 7)$.

$$(5x^3 + 9x^2 - 6) - (5x^3 - 4x^2 - 7) = (5x^3 + 9x^2 - 6) + (-5x^3 + 4x^2 + 7)$$
$$= (5 - 5)x^3 + (9 + 4)x^2 + (-6 + 7)$$
$$= 0x^3 + 13x^2 + 1$$
$$= 13x^2 + 1$$

Now Try Exercises 71, 73

The following summarizes addition and subtraction of polynomials.

ADDITION AND SUBTRACTION OF POLYNOMIALS

1. To *add* two polynomials, combine like terms.

2. To *subtract* two polynomials, add the first polynomial and the opposite of the second polynomial.

NOTE: The *opposite* of a polynomial is found by changing the sign of every term.

CRITICAL THINKING

Is the sum of two quadratic polynomials always a quadratic polynomial? Explain.

Polynomial Functions

The following expressions are examples of polynomials of one variable.

$$1 - 5x, \quad 3x^2 - 5x + 1, \quad \text{and} \quad x^3 + 5$$

As a result, we say that the following are *symbolic representations* of polynomial functions of one variable.

$$f(x) = 1 - 5x, \quad g(x) = 3x^2 - 5x + 1, \quad \text{and} \quad h(x) = x^3 + 5$$

Function f is a **linear function** because it has degree 1, function g is a **quadratic function** because it has degree 2, and function h is a **cubic function** because it has degree 3.
NOTE: The domain of *every* polynomial function is *all* real numbers.

EXAMPLE 7 **Identifying polynomial functions**

Determine whether $f(x)$ represents a polynomial function. If possible, identify the type of polynomial function and its degree.
(a) $f(x) = 5x^3 - x + 10$
(b) $f(x) = x^{-2.5} + 1$
(c) $f(x) = 1 - 2x$
(d) $f(x) = \dfrac{3}{x - 1}$

Solution

(a) The expression $5x^3 - x + 10$ is a cubic polynomial, so $f(x)$ represents a cubic polynomial function. It has degree 3.
(b) $f(x)$ does not represent a polynomial function because the variables in a polynomial must have *nonnegative integer* exponents.
(c) $f(x) = 1 - 2x$ represents a polynomial function that is linear. It has degree 1.
(d) $f(x)$ does not represent a polynomial function because $\dfrac{3}{x - 1}$ is not a polynomial.

▌ Now Try Exercises 79, 81, 83, 85

Evaluating Polynomials

Frequently, monomials and polynomials represent functions or formulas that can be evaluated. This situation is illustrated in the next three examples.

EXAMPLE 8 **Evaluating a polynomial function graphically and symbolically**

A graph of $f(x) = 4x - x^3$ is shown in Figure 3.6. Evaluate $f(-1)$ graphically and check your result symbolically.

Figure 3.6

Solution

Graphical Evaluation To evaluate $f(-1)$ graphically, find -1 on the x-axis and move down until the graph of f is reached. Then move horizontally to the y-axis, as shown in Figure 3.7. Thus when $x = -1$, $y = -3$ and $f(-1) = -3$.

Symbolic Evaluation When $x = -1$, evaluation of $f(x) = 4x - x^3$ is performed as follows.

$$f(-1) = 4(-1) - (-1)^3 = -4 - (-1) = -3$$

Figure 3.7

▌ Now Try Exercises 93, 97

EXAMPLE 9   **Writing and evaluating a polynomial**

Write a polynomial that represents the total volume of two identical boxes having square bases. Make a sketch to illustrate your formula. Find the total volume of the boxes if each base is 11 inches on a side and the height of each box is 5 inches.

Solution

Let b be the length (width) of the square base and h be the height of a side. The volume of one box is length times width times height, or b^2h, as illustrated in Figure 3.8, and the volume of two boxes is $2b^2h$. To calculate their total volumes, let $b = 11$ and $h = 5$ in the expression $2b^2h$. Then

$$2 \cdot 11^2 \cdot 5 = 1210 \text{ cubic inches.}$$

Figure 3.8 Volume: b^2h

▮ Now Try Exercise 125

EXAMPLE 10   **Evaluating a polynomial function symbolically**

Evaluate $f(x)$ at the given value of x.
(a) $f(x) = -3x^4 - 2$, $x = 2$ **(b)** $f(x) = -2x^3 - 4x^2 + 5$, $x = -3$

Solution
(a) Be sure to evaluate exponents before multiplying.

$$f(2) = -3(2)^4 - 2 = -3 \cdot 16 - 2 = -50$$

(b) $f(-3) = -2(-3)^3 - 4(-3)^2 + 5 = -2(-27) - 4(9) + 5 = 23$

▮ Now Try Exercises 101, 105

Operations on Functions

▶ **REAL-WORLD CONNECTION** A business incurs a *cost* to make its product and then it receives *revenue* from selling this product. For example, suppose a small business reconditions motorcycles. The graphs of its cost and of its revenue for reconditioning and selling x motorcycles are shown in Figure 3.9.

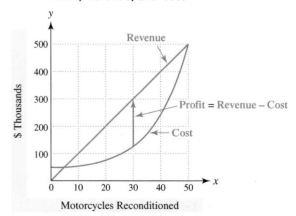

Figure 3.9

In general, *profit equals revenue minus cost.* In Figure 3.9, profit is shown visually as the length of the vertical green arrow between the graphs of **revenue** and **cost**. For any x-value, the distance by which revenue is above cost is called the profit for reconditioning and selling x motorcycles. *Maximum profit* for the company occurs at the x-value where the *length of the vertical green arrow is greatest.*

If we let $C(x)$, $R(x)$, and $P(x)$ be functions that calculate the cost, revenue, and profit, respectively, for reconditioning and selling x motorcycles, then

$$P(x) = R(x) - C(x).$$

Profit *equals* Revenue *minus* Cost.

This example helps explain why we subtract functions in the real world. Functions can be added in a similar manner.

Given two functions, f and g, we define the sum, $f + g$, and difference, $f - g$, as follows.

SUM AND DIFFERENCE OF TWO FUNCTIONS

The sum and difference of two functions f and g are defined as

$$(f + g)(x) = f(x) + g(x)$$

$$(f - g)(x) = f(x) - g(x)$$

provided both $f(x)$ and $g(x)$ are defined.

EXAMPLE 11   **Calculating sums and differences of functions**

Let $f(x) = 2x^2 + 1$ and $g(x) = 5 - x^2$. Find each sum or difference.
(a) $(f + g)(1)$ **(b)** $(f - g)(-2)$
(c) $(f + g)(x)$ **(d)** $(f - g)(x)$

Solution
(a) Because $f(1) = 2 \cdot 1^2 + 1 = 3$ and $g(1) = 5 - 1^2 = 4$, it follows that

$$(f + g)(1) = f(1) + g(1) = 3 + 4 = 7.$$

(b) Because $f(-2) = 2 \cdot (-2)^2 + 1 = 9$ and $g(-2) = 5 - (-2)^2 = 1$, it follows that

$$(f - g)(-2) = f(-2) - g(-2) = 9 - 1 = 8.$$

(c) $(f + g)(x) = f(x) + g(x)$ Addition of functions

$\qquad\qquad = (2x^2 + 1) + (5 - x^2)$ Substitute for $f(x)$ and $g(x)$.

$\qquad\qquad = x^2 + 6$ Combine like terms.

(d) $(f - g)(x) = f(x) - g(x)$ Subtraction of functions

$\qquad\qquad = (2x^2 + 1) - (5 - x^2)$ Substitute for $f(x)$ and $g(x)$.

$\qquad\qquad = (2x^2 + 1) + (-5 + x^2)$ Add the opposite.

$\qquad\qquad = 3x^2 - 4$ Combine like terms.

Now Try Exercise 115

Applications and Models

▶ **REAL-WORLD CONNECTION** Polynomials are used to model a wide variety of data. A scatterplot of the cumulative number of reported AIDS cases in thousands from 1984 to 1994 is shown in Figure 3.10. In this graph $x = 4$ corresponds to 1984, $x = 5$ to 1985, and so on until $x = 14$ represents 1994. These data can be modeled with a quadratic function, as shown in Figure 3.11, where $f(x) = 4.1x^2 - 25x + 46$ is graphed with the data. Note that $f(x)$ was found by using a graphing calculator. (*Source:* U.S. Department of Health and Human Services.)

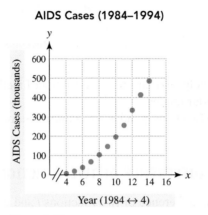

| Figure 3.10 | Figure 3.11 |

Limits on Modeling: After 1994, effective drugs and education greatly slowed the spread of AIDS in the United States. As a result, the modeling function f does *not* accurately describe the data after 1994. In general, we have to be careful about using a modeling function to predict too far into the future.

EXAMPLE 12 ▶ **Modeling AIDS cases in the United States**

Use $f(x) = 4.1x^2 - 25x + 46$ to model the number of AIDS cases.
(a) Estimate the number of AIDS cases reported by 1987. Compare it to the actual value of 71.4 thousand.
(b) By 1997, the total number of AIDS cases reported was 631 thousand. What estimate does $f(x)$ give? Discuss your result.

Solution
(a) The value $x = 7$ corresponds to 1987. Let $f(x) = 4.1x^2 - 25x + 46$ and evaluate $f(7)$, which gives

$$f(7) = 4.1(7)^2 - 25(7) + 46 = 71.9.$$

This model estimates that a cumulative total of 71.9 thousand AIDS cases were reported by 1987. This result compares favorably to the actual value of 71.4 thousand cases.
(b) To estimate the number in 1997, we evaluate $f(17)$ because $x = 17$ corresponds to 1997, obtaining

$$f(17) = 4.1(17)^2 - 25(17) + 46 = 805.9.$$

This result is considerably more than the actual value of 631 thousand. The reason is that f models data only from 1984 through 1994. After 1994, f gives estimates that are too large because the growth in AIDS cases has slowed more in recent years.

Now Try Exercise 123

▶ **REAL-WORLD CONNECTION** A well-conditioned athlete's heart rate can reach 200 beats per minute during strenuous physical activity. Upon quitting, a typical heart rate decreases rapidly at first and then more gradually after a few minutes, as illustrated in the next example.

EXAMPLE 13   **Modeling heart rate of an athlete**

Let $P(t) = 1.875t^2 - 30t + 200$ model an athlete's heart rate (or pulse P) in beats per minute (bpm) t minutes after strenuous exercise has stopped, where $0 \le t \le 8$. (Source: V. Thomas, *Science and Sport.*)

(a) What is the initial heart rate when the athlete stops exercising?
(b) What is the heart rate after 8 minutes?
(c) A graph of P is shown in Figure 3.12. Interpret this graph.

Athlete's Heart Rate

Figure 3.12

Solution
(a) To find the initial heart rate, evaluate $P(t)$ at $t = 0$, or

$$P(0) = 1.875(0)^2 - 30(0) + 200 = 200.$$

When the athlete stops exercising, the heart rate is 200 beats per minute. (This result agrees with the graph.)
(b) $P(8) = 1.875(8)^2 - 30(8) + 200 = 80$ beats per minute.
(c) The heart rate does not drop at a constant rate; rather, it drops rapidly at first and then gradually begins to level off.

Now Try Exercise 121

3.1   Putting It All Together

CONCEPT	EXAMPLES
Addition of Polynomials	$(-3x^2 + 2x - 7) + (4x^2 - x + 1) = -3x^2 + 4x^2 + 2x - x - 7 + 1$ $= (-3 + 4)x^2 + (2 - 1)x + (-7 + 1)$ $= x^2 + x - 6$ $(x^4 + 8x^3 - 7x) + (5x^4 - 3x) = x^4 + 5x^4 + 8x^3 - 7x - 3x$ $= (1 + 5)x^4 + 8x^3 + (-7 - 3)x$ $= 6x^4 + 8x^3 - 10x$
Opposite of a Polynomial	The opposite of $-5x^2 + 3x - 5$ is $5x^2 - 3x + 5$. The opposite of $-6x^6 + 4x^4 - 8x^2 - 17$ is $6x^6 - 4x^4 + 8x^2 + 17$.

continued on next page

continued from previous page

CONCEPT	EXAMPLES
Subtraction of Polynomials (Add the Opposite.)	$(5x^2 - 6x + 1) - (-5x^2 + 3x - 5) = (5x^2 - 6x + 1) + (5x^2 - 3x + 5)$ $= (5 + 5)x^2 + (-6 - 3)x + (1 + 5)$ $= 10x^2 - 9x + 6$ $(x^4 - 6x^2 + 5x) - (x^4 - 5x + 7) = (x^4 - 6x^2 + 5x) + (-x^4 + 5x - 7)$ $= (1 - 1)x^4 - 6x^2 + (5 + 5)x - 7$ $= -6x^2 + 10x - 7$
Polynomial Functions	The following represent polynomial functions. $f(x) = 3$ Degree $= 0$ Constant $f(x) = 5x - 3$ Degree $= 1$ Linear $f(x) = x^2 - 2x - 1$ Degree $= 2$ Quadratic $f(x) = 3x^3 + 2x^2 - 6$ Degree $= 3$ Cubic
Evaluating a Polynomial Function	To evaluate $f(x) = -4x^2 + 3x - 1$ at $x = 2$, substitute 2 for x. $f(2) = -4(2)^2 + 3(2) - 1 = -16 + 6 - 1 = -11$
Sums and Differences of Functions	Let $f(x) = 2x + 3$ and $g(x) = x + 2$. $(f + g)(x) = (2x + 3) + (x + 2) = 3x + 5$ $(f - g)(x) = (2x + 3) - (x + 2) = x + 1$

3.1   Exercises

MyMathLab | Math XL PRACTICE   WATCH   DOWNLOAD   READ   REVIEW

CONCEPTS AND VOCABULARY

1. Give an example of a monomial.

2. What are the degree and leading coefficient of the polynomial $3x^2 - x^3 + 1$?

3. Are $-5x^3y$ and $6xy^3$ like terms? Explain.

4. Give an example of a polynomial that has 3 terms and is degree 4.

5. Does the opposite of $x^2 + 1$ equal $-x^2 + 1$? Explain.

6. Evaluate $4x^3y$ when $x = 2$ and $y = 3$.

7. When you evaluate a polynomial function at one value of x, can you calculate two answers? Explain.

8. Could the graph of a polynomial function be a line? Explain.

9. If $f(x) = x^2 + x$, then $f(2) =$ _____.

10. If $f(x) = x^2$ and $g(x) = 2x^2$, then it follows that $(f + g)(x) =$ _____.

11. If $f(x) = 3x^2 + 7$ and $g(x) = 2x^2 - 5$, then it follows that $(f - g)(x) =$ _____.

12. Identify which entries in the following list are terms.

$7, \ 3 - x^2, -5x^6, \ xy^3, \ \dfrac{1}{2x}, \ x^{-3}$

MONOMIALS AND POLYNOMIALS

Exercises 13–22: Determine whether the expression is a monomial.

13. x^4

14. x^{-4}

15. $2x^2y + y^2$

16. $5 - \sqrt{x}$

17. $-4x^3y^3$

18. xy

19. $\dfrac{3}{x - 2}$

20. $\pi x^4 y^2 z$

21. $x^{-3}y$

22. x^{-2}

Exercises 23–28: Write a monomial that represents the described quantity.

23. The area of a square with sides equal to x

24. The circumference of a circle with diameter d

25. The area of a circle with radius r

26. The area of three congruent triangles with base b and height h

27. The number of members in a marching band that has x rows with y people in each row

28. The revenue from selling w items for z dollars each

Exercises 29–34: Identify the degree and coefficient.

29. $3x^7$ **30.** $-5y^3$

31. $-3x^2y^5$ **32.** xy^5

33. $-x^3y^3$ **34.** $\sqrt{2}xy$

Exercises 35–40: Identify the degree and leading coefficient of the polynomial.

35. $5x^2 - 4x + \frac{3}{4}$ **36.** $-9y^4 + y^2 + 5$

37. $5 - x + 3x^2 - \frac{2}{5}x^3$ **38.** $7x + 4x^4 - \frac{4}{3}x^3$

39. $8x^4 + 3x^3 - 4x + x^5$ **40.** $5x^2 - x^3 + 7x^4 + 10$

Exercises 41–52: Combine like terms whenever possible.

41. $x^2 + 4x^2$ **42.** $-3z + 5z$

43. $6y^4 - 3y^4$ **44.** $9xy - 7xy$

45. $5x^2y + 8xy^2$ **46.** $5x + 4y$

47. $9x^2 - x + 4x - 6x^2$ **48.** $-xy^2 - \frac{1}{2}xy^2$

49. $x^2 + 9xy - y^2 + 4x^2 + y^2$

50. $6xy + 4x - 6xy$

51. $4x + 7x^3y^7 - \frac{1}{2}x^3y^7 + 9x - \frac{3}{2}x^3y^7$

52. $19x^3 + x^2 - 3x^3 + x - 4x^2 + 1$

Exercises 53–64: Add the polynomials.

53. $(3x + 1) + (-x + 1)$

54. $(5y^3 + y) + (12y^3 - 5y)$

55. $(x^2 - 2x + 15) + (-3x^2 + 5x - 7)$

56. $(4x) + (1 - 4.5x)$

57. $(3x^3 - 4x + 3) + (5x^2 + 4x + 12)$

58. $(y^5 + y) + \left(5 - y + \frac{1}{3}y^2\right)$

59. $(x^4 - 3x^2 - 4) + \left(-8x^4 + x - \frac{1}{2}\right)$

60. $(3z + z^4 + 2) + (-3z^4 - 5 + z^2)$

61. $(4r^4 - r + 2) + (r^3 - 5r)$

62. $(5t^3 + 3t) + (4t^4 - 3t^3 + 1)$

63. $(4xy - x^2 + y^2) + (4y^2 - 8xy - x^2)$

64. $(3x^2 + 6xy - y^2) + (8y^2 - xy - 2x^2)$

Exercises 65–70: Find the opposite of the polynomial.

65. $6x^5$ **66.** $-5y^7$

67. $19x^5 - 5x^3 + 3x$ **68.** $-x^2 - x - 5$

69. $-7z^4 + z^2 - 8$ **70.** $6 - 4x + 5x^2 - \frac{1}{10}x^3$

Exercises 71–78: Subtract the polynomials.

71. $(5x - 3) - (2x + 4)$

72. $(10x + 5) - (-6x - 4)$

73. $(x^2 - 3x + 1) - (-5x^2 + 2x - 4)$

74. $(-x^2 + x - 5) - (x^2 - x + 5)$

75. $3(4x^4 + 2x^2 - 9) - 4(x^4 - 2x^2 - 5)$

76. $2(8x^3 + 5x^2 - 3x + 1) - 5(-5x^3 + 6x - 11)$

77. $4(x^4 - 1) - (4x^4 + 3x + 7)$

78. $(5x^4 - 6x^3 + x^2 + 5) - (x^3 + 11x^2 + 9x - 3)$

Exercises 79–86: Determine whether $f(x)$ represents a polynomial function. If possible, identify the degree and type of polynomial function.

79. $f(x) = x^4 + 5x^2$ **80.** $f(x) = 5x^3 + 1$

81. $f(x) = x^{-2}$ **82.** $f(x) = |x|$

83. $f(x) = \dfrac{1}{x^2 + 1}$ **84.** $f(x) = 5x - 7$

85. $f(x) = 3x - x^2$ **86.** $f(x) = x + 3x^{-2}$

EVALUATING POLYNOMIALS

Exercises 87–92: Evaluate the polynomial at the given value(s) of the variable(s).

87. $-4x^2$ $x = 2$

88. $-2y^3$ $y = -3$

89. $2x^2y$ $x = 2, y = 3$

90. $-xy^3$ $x = 4, y = -1$

91. $a^2b - ab^2$ $a = -3, b = 4$

92. $3a^3 + 2b^3$ $a = -2, b = 3$

Exercises 93–96: Evaluate the expressions graphically.

93. $f(1)$ and $f(-2)$ ⬛ **94.** $f(0)$ and $f(2)$

 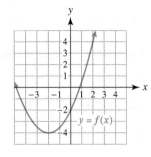

95. $f(-1)$ and $f(2)$ ⬛ **96.** $f(-1)$ and $f(0)$

 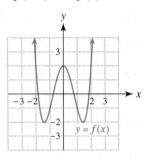

Exercises 97–110: Evaluate $f(x)$ at the given x-value.

97. $f(x) = 3x^2$ $x = -2$

98. $f(x) = x^2 - 2x$ $x = 3$

99. $f(x) = 5 - 4x$ $x = -\frac{1}{2}$

100. $f(x) = x^2 + 4x - 5$ $x = -3$

101. $f(x) = 0.5x^4 - 0.3x^3 + 5$ $x = -1$

102. $f(x) = 6 - 2x + x^3$ $x = 0$

103. $f(x) = -x^3$ $x = -1$

104. $f(x) = 3 - 2x$ $x = \frac{3}{10}$

105. $f(x) = -x^2 - 3x$ $x = -3$

106. $f(x) = 2x^3 - 4x + 1$ $x = 1$

107. $f(x) = 1 - 2x + x^2$ $x = 2.4$

108. $f(x) = 4x^2 - 20x + 25$ $x = 1.8$

109. $f(x) = x^5 - 5$ $x = -1$

110. $f(x) = 1.2x^4 - 5.7x + 3$ $x = \frac{3}{2}$

111. Thinking Generally If $f(x) = x^2 - 2x$, then it follows that $f(a) = $ _____.

112. Thinking Generally If $f(x) = 2x - 1$, then it follows that $f(a + 2) = $ _____.

Exercises 113–120: For the given $f(x)$ and $g(x)$, find the following and simplify.

   (a) $(f + g)(2)$ **(b)** $(f - g)(-1)$
   (c) $(f + g)(x)$ **(d)** $(f - g)(x)$

113. $f(x) = 3x - 1, g(x) = 5 - x$

114. $f(x) = -4x + 3, g(x) = 5x$

115. $f(x) = -3x^2, g(x) = x^2 + 1$

116. $f(x) = 2x^2 - 2, g(x) = 3 - x^2$

117. $f(x) = -x^3, g(x) = 3x^3$

118. $f(x) = x^3 + x, g(x) = 2x - 3x^3$

119. $f(x) = x^2 - 2x + 1, g(x) = 4x^2 + 3x$

120. $f(x) = 3 + x - 2x^2, g(x) = 5x + 8$

APPLICATIONS

121. *Women on the Run* The number of women participating in the New York City Marathon has increased dramatically in recent years. The polynomial function $f(x) = 3.56x^2 + 360x + 1300$ models the number of women running each year from 1980 through 2010, where $x = 0$ corresponds to 1980, $x = 10$ to 1990, and $x = 30$ to 2010. See the accompanying figure. (*Source: Runner's World.*)

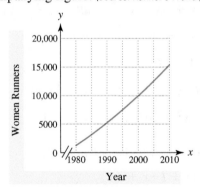

  (a) Use the graph to estimate the number of women running in 1980 and in 2000.
  (b) Answer part (a) using the polynomial. How do your answers compare with your answers in part (a)?
  (c) Use the polynomial to find the increase in women runners from 1980 to 2000.

122. *A PC for All?* Worldwide sales of computers have climbed as prices have continued to drop. The function $f(x) = 0.29x^2 + 8x + 19$ models the number of personal computers sold in millions during year x, where $x = 0$ corresponds to 1990, $x = 1$ to 1991, and so on until $x = 25$ corresponds to 2015.

Estimate the number of personal computers sold in 2010, using both the graph and the polynomial. (*Source:* eTForcasts.)

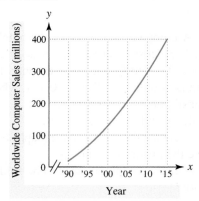

123. *U.S. AIDS Deaths* The following scatterplot shows the cumulative number of reported AIDS deaths. The data may be modeled x years after 1980 by $f(x) = 2.4x^2 - 14x + 23$, where the output is in thousands of deaths.

(a) Use $f(x)$ to estimate the cumulative total of AIDS deaths in 1990. Compare it with the actual value of 121.6 thousand.

(b) In 1997 the cumulative number of AIDS deaths was 390 thousand. What estimate does $f(x)$ give? Discuss your result.

124. *Geometry* A house has 8-foot-high ceilings. Three rooms are x feet by y feet and two rooms are x feet by z feet. Write a polynomial that gives the total volume of the five rooms. Find their total volume if $x = 10$ feet, $y = 12$ feet, and $z = 7$ feet.

125. Write a monomial that represents the volume of five identical cubes with sides having length s.

126. Write a monomial that represents the area of six identical rectangles with length L and width W.

127. *Squares and Circles* Write a polynomial that gives the sum of the areas of a square with sides of length x and a circle with radius x. Find the combined area when $x = 10$ inches.

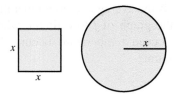

128. *Spheres* Write a monomial that gives the volume of 9 spheres with radius y. Find the combined volumes when $y = 3$ feet. (*Hint:* $V = \frac{4}{3}\pi r^3$.)

129. *Heart Rate* (Refer to Example 13.) Make a table of $f(t) = 1.875t^2 - 30t + 200$, starting at $t = 3$ and incrementing by 1. When was the athlete's heart rate between 80 and 110, inclusive?

130. *Life Expectancy* The life expectancy of a female born in 1970 is 75 years, and in 2015 it is expected to be 84 years. (*Source:* Bureau of the Census.)

(a) Find values for a and b so that $f(x) = ax + b$ models the data. (*Hint:* The graph of f should pass through the point (1970, 75) and the point (2015, 84).)

(b) Estimate the life expectancy in 2010.

131. *Microsoft Stocks* If a person had bought $2500 of Microsoft stock in 1986, it would have been worth about $1.2 million in 1999. The following table shows the cost of this stock (adjusted for splits) in various years.

Year	1986	1994	1999
Cost ($)	0.19	20	90

Source: USA Today.

Which of the following polynomials models the data best, where $x = 6$ corresponds to 1986, $x = 14$ to 1994, and $x = 19$ to 1999? Explain how you made your decision.

(i) $f(x) = 0.886x^2 - 15.25x + 59.79$

(ii) $g(x) = 0.882x^2 - 15.4x + 60.15$

132. *Ocean Temperatures* The cubic polynomial

$$f(x) = -0.064x^3 + 0.56x^2 + 2.9x + 61$$

models the ocean temperature in degrees Fahrenheit at Naples, Florida. In this formula $x = 1$ corresponds to January, $x = 2$ to February, and so on. (*Source:* J. Williams.)

(a) What is the average ocean temperature in April?

(b) Use the graph of f to estimate when the maximum ocean temperature occurs. What is this maximum?

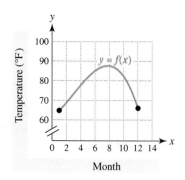

Month

133. *Profit from DVDs* Suppose that the cost in dollars for a band to produce x DVDs is given by the function $C(x) = 4x + 2000$. If the band sells DVDs for $16 each, complete the following.

(a) Write a function R that gives the revenue for selling x DVDs.

(b) If profit equals revenue minus cost, write a formula $P(x)$ for the profit.

(c) Evaluate $P(3000)$ and interpret the answer.

134. *Profit* A company makes and sells sailboats. The company's cost function in thousands of dollars is $C(x) = 2x + 20$, and the revenue function in thousands of dollars is $R(x) = 4x$, where x is the number of sailboats.

(a) Evaluate and interpret $C(5)$.

(b) Interpret the y-intercepts on the graphs of C and R.

(c) Give the profit function $P(x)$.

(d) How many sailboats need to be sold to break even?

135. *Profit* A company makes and sells notebook computers. Their cost function in thousands of dollars is $C(x) = 0.3x + 100$, and their revenue function in thousands of dollars is $R(x) = 0.75x$, where x is the number of notebook computers.

(a) Evaluate and interpret $C(100)$.

(b) Interpret the y-intercepts on the graphs of C and R.

(c) Give the profit function $P(x)$.

(d) How many computers need to be sold to make a profit?

136. *Income Tax* Let the state tax be 7% and the federal tax be 15%.

(a) Find a function T that calculates the total tax on a taxable income of x dollars.

(b) Evaluate $T(4000)$ and interpret the result.

WRITING ABOUT MATHEMATICS

137. Discuss how to subtract two polynomials. Demonstrate your method with an example.

138. Explain the difference between a monomial and a polynomial. Give examples of each and an example that is neither a monomial nor a polynomial.

139. If a polynomial function has degree 1, what can be said about its graph? If a polynomial function has degree greater than 1, what can be said about its graph?

140. Explain how to evaluate a function graphically. Use your method to evaluate $f(x) = x^2$ at $x = -2$.

Group Activity   Working with Real Data

Directions: Form a group of 2 to 4 people. Select someone to record the group's responses for this activity. All members of the group should work cooperatively to answer the questions. If your instructor asks for the results, each member of the group should be prepared to respond.

Female Graduates The table shows the number of bachelor degrees awarded to women for various years

Year	1992	2002	2012
Degrees (thousands)	533	632	968

Source: National Center for Education Statistics.

(a) Verify that $f(x) = 1.185x^2 - 6.69x + 541.64$ models the data by evaluating $f(2)$, $f(12)$, and $f(22)$, where x is years *after* 1990.

(b) Interpret the y-intercept.

(c) Evaluate $f(15)$ and $f(50)$. Interpret each answer. Which one is more accurate?

3.2 Multiplication of Polynomials

Review of Basic Properties • Multiplying Polynomials • Some Special Products • Multiplying Functions

A LOOK INTO MATH ▶ In 2010 Serena Williams claimed her thirteenth Grand Slam title at Wimbledon. Her serves reached speeds of 122 miles per hour, and her first serves had a 66% chance of being in bounds. More and more, mathematics is being used to evaluate an athlete's performance. In Exercise 133 we use a polynomial to estimate the likelihood that either the first serve or the second serve will be in bounds. (*Source: The Associated Press.*)

Review of Basic Properties

Distributive properties are used frequently in the multiplication of polynomials. For all real numbers a, b, and c

$$a(b + c) = ab + ac \quad \text{and} \qquad \text{Distributive properties}$$
$$a(b - c) = ab - ac.$$

In the next example we use these distributive properties to multiply expressions.

NEW VOCABULARY

☐ Monomial
☐ Binomial
☐ Trinomial

EXAMPLE 1 ▶ **Using distributive properties**

Multiply.
(a) $4(5 + x)$ **(b)** $-3(x - 4y)$ **(c)** $(2x - 5)(6)$

Solution
(a) $4(5 + x) = 4 \cdot 5 + 4 \cdot x = 20 + 4x$
(b) $-3(x - 4y) = -3 \cdot x - (-3) \cdot (4y) = -3x + 12y$
(c) $(2x - 5)(6) = 2x \cdot 6 - 5 \cdot 6 = 12x - 30$

Now Try Exercises 21, 23, 27

VISUALIZING THE DISTRIBUTIVE PROPERTY We can visualize the distributive property in Example 1(a) by using rectangles. In Figure 3.13(a) there is a large rectangle having width 4 and length $5 + x$, so its area must be $4(5 + x)$. In Figure 3.13(b) the large rectangle has been split into two smaller rectangles having equivalent total areas of $4(5)$ and $4(x)$. Finally, in Figure 3.13(c), small squares and rectangles have been sketched to show that the total area is 20 squares, each having area 1, plus 4 rectangles with area x.

The Distributive Property

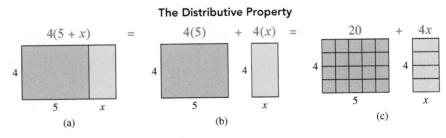

Figure 3.13

In Section 1.3 we discussed several properties of exponents. The following three properties of exponents are frequently used in the multiplication of polynomials.

PROPERTIES OF EXPONENTS

For any numbers a and b and integers m and n,

$$a^m \cdot a^n = a^{m+n}, \quad (a^m)^n = a^{mn}, \quad \text{and} \quad (ab)^n = a^n b^n.$$

We use these three properties to simplify expressions in the next two examples.

EXAMPLE 2 ▶ **Multiplying powers of variables**

Multiply each expression.
(a) $-2x^3 \cdot 4x^5$ (b) $(3xy^3)(4x^2y^2)$ (c) $6y^3(2y - y^2)$ (d) $-mn(m^2 - n)$

Solution
(a) $-2x^3 \cdot 4x^5 = (-2)(4)x^3 x^5 = -8x^{3+5} = -8x^8$
(b) $(3xy^3)(4x^2y^2) = (3)(4)xx^2y^3y^2 = 12x^{1+2}y^{3+2} = 12x^3y^5$

   NOTE: We cannot simplify $12x^3y^5$ further because x^3 and y^5 have different bases.

(c) $6y^3(2y - y^2) = 6y^3 \cdot 2y - 6y^3 \cdot y^2 = 12y^4 - 6y^5$
(d) $-mn(m^2 - n) = -mn \cdot m^2 + mn \cdot n = -m^3n + mn^2$

▌ Now Try Exercises 13, 17, 29, 31

EXAMPLE 3 ▶ **Using properties of exponents**

Simplify.
(a) $(x^2)^5$ (b) $(2x)^3$ (c) $(5x^3)^2$ (d) $(-mn^3)^2$

Solution
(a) $(x^2)^5 = x^{2 \cdot 5} = x^{10}$ (b) $(2x)^3 = 2^3x^3 = 8x^3$
(c) $(5x^3)^2 = 5^2(x^3)^2 = 25x^6$ (d) $(-mn^3)^2 = (-m)^2(n^3)^2 = m^2n^6$

▌ Now Try Exercises 83, 85, 87

Multiplying Polynomials

A polynomial with one term is a **monomial**, with two terms a **binomial**, and with three terms a **trinomial**. Examples are shown in Table 3.5.

TABLE 3.5

Monomials	$2x^2$		$-3x^4y$		9
Binomials	$3x - 1$		$2x^3 - x$		$x^2 + 5$
Trinomials	$x^2 - 3x + 5$		$5x^4 - 2x + 10$		$2x^3 - x^2 - 2$

In the next example we multiply binomials, using geometric and symbolic techniques.

EXAMPLE 4 ▶ **Multiplying binomials**

Multiply $(x + 1)(x + 3)$
(a) geometrically and   (b) symbolically.

Area: (x + 1)(x + 3)

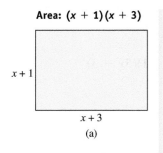

(a)

Area: x² + 4x + 3

(b)

Figure 3.14

Solution

(a) To multiply $(x + 1)(x + 3)$ geometrically, draw a rectangle $x + 1$ wide and $x + 3$ long, as shown in Figure 3.14(a). The area of the rectangle equals the product $(x + 1)(x + 3)$. This large rectangle can be divided into four smaller rectangles as shown in Figure 3.14(b). The sum of the areas of these four smaller rectangles equals the area of the large rectangle. The smaller rectangles have areas of x^2, x, $3x$, and 3. Thus

$$(x + 1)(x + 3) = x^2 + x + 3x + 3$$
$$= x^2 + 4x + 3.$$

(b) To multiply $(x + 1)(x + 3)$ symbolically we apply the distributive property.

$$(x + 1)(x + 3) = (x + 1)(x) + (x + 1)(3)$$
$$= x \cdot x + 1 \cdot x + x \cdot 3 + 1 \cdot 3$$
$$= x^2 + x + 3x + 3$$
$$= x^2 + 4x + 3$$

▌ Now Try Exercise 37

GRAPHICAL AND NUMERICAL SUPPORT It is possible to give graphical and numerical support to our result in Example 4 by letting $y_1 = (x + 1)(x + 3)$ and by letting $y_2 = x^2 + 4x + 3$. The graphs of y_1 and y_2 appear to be identical in Figures 3.15(a) and 3.15(b). Figure 3.15(c) shows that $y_1 = y_2$ for each value of x in the table.

[−6, 6, 1] by [−4, 4, 1]   [−6, 6, 1] by [−4, 4, 1]

$y_1 = (x + 1)(x + 3)$ $y_2 = x^2 + 4x + 3$

(a)   (b)   (c)

Figure 3.15

FOIL One way to multiply $(x + 1)$ by $(x + 3)$ is to multiply every term in $x + 1$ by every term in $x + 3$. That is,

$$(x + 1)(x + 3) = x^2 + 3x + x + 3$$
$$= x^2 + 4x + 3.$$

NOTE: This process of multiplying binomials is sometimes called *FOIL*, which reminds us to multiply the first terms (*F*), outside terms (*O*), inside terms (*I*), and last terms (*L*).

Multiply the *First terms* to obtain x^2. $(x + 1)(x + 3)$

Multiply the *Outside terms* to obtain $3x$. $(x + 1)(x + 3)$

Multiply the *Inside terms* to obtain x. $(x + 1)(x + 3)$

Multiply the *Last terms* to obtain 3. $(x + 1)(x + 3)$

The following method summarizes how to multiply two polynomials in general.

MULTIPLICATION OF POLYNOMIALS

The product of two polynomials may be found by multiplying every term in the first polynomial by every term in the second polynomial.

EXAMPLE 5 **Multiplying polynomials**

Multiply each binomial.
(a) $(2x - 1)(x + 2)$ **(b)** $(1 - 3x)(2 - 4x)$ **(c)** $(x^2 + 1)(5x - 3)$

Solution

(a) $(2x - 1)(x + 2) = 2x \cdot x + 2x \cdot 2 - 1 \cdot x - 1 \cdot 2$
$= 2x^2 + 4x - x - 2$
$= 2x^2 + 3x - 2$

(b) $(1 - 3x)(2 - 4x) = 1 \cdot 2 - 1 \cdot 4x - 3x \cdot 2 + 3x \cdot 4x$
$= 2 - 4x - 6x + 12x^2$
$= 2 - 10x + 12x^2$

(c) $(x^2 + 1)(5x - 3) = x^2 \cdot 5x - x^2 \cdot 3 + 1 \cdot 5x - 1 \cdot 3$
$= 5x^3 - 3x^2 + 5x - 3$

■ **Now Try Exercises 53, 57, 63**

EXAMPLE 6 **Multiplying polynomials**

Multiply each expression.
(a) $3x(x^2 + 5x - 4)$ **(b)** $-x^2(x^4 - 2x + 5)$ **(c)** $(x + 2)(x^2 + 4x - 3)$

Solution
(a) Multiply each term in the second polynomial by $3x$.

$$3x(x^2 + 5x - 4) = 3x \cdot x^2 + 3x \cdot 5x - 3x \cdot 4$$
$$= 3x^3 + 15x^2 - 12x$$

(b) $-x^2(x^4 - 2x + 5) = -x^2 \cdot x^4 + x^2 \cdot 2x - x^2 \cdot 5$
$= -x^6 + 2x^3 - 5x^2$

(c) $(x + 2)(x^2 + 4x - 3) = x \cdot x^2 + x \cdot 4x - x \cdot 3 + 2 \cdot x^2 + 2 \cdot 4x - 2 \cdot 3$
$= x^3 + 4x^2 - 3x + 2x^2 + 8x - 6$
$= x^3 + 6x^2 + 5x - 6$

■ **Now Try Exercises 67, 69, 73**

EXAMPLE 7 **Multiplying polynomials**

Multiply each expression.
(a) $2ab^3(a^2 - 2ab + 3b^2)$ **(b)** $4m(mn^2 + 3m)(m^2n - 4n)$

Solution
(a) Multiply each term in the second polynomial by $2ab^3$.

$$2ab^3(a^2 - 2ab + 3b^2) = 2ab^3 \cdot a^2 - 2ab^3 \cdot 2ab + 2ab^3 \cdot 3b^2$$
$$= 2a^3b^3 - 4a^2b^4 + 6ab^5$$

(b) Start by multiplying every term in $(mn^2 + 3m)$ by $4m$.

$$4m(mn^2 + 3m)(m^2n - 4n) = (4m \cdot mn^2 + 4m \cdot 3m)(m^2n - 4n)$$
$$= (4m^2n^2 + 12m^2)(m^2n - 4n)$$
$$= 4m^2n^2 \cdot m^2n - 4m^2n^2 \cdot 4n + 12m^2 \cdot m^2n - 12m^2 \cdot 4n$$
$$= 4m^4n^3 - 16m^2n^3 + 12m^4n - 48m^2n$$

■ **Now Try Exercises 75, 77**

$$
\begin{array}{r}
212 \\
\times\ 32 \\
\hline
424 \\
636 \\
\hline
6784
\end{array}
$$

MULTIPLYING POLYNOMIALS VERTICALLY Before we demonstrate a second way to multiply polynomials in Example 8, we will review how to multiply 212 and 32 vertically, as shown in the margin. First, we multiply 2 and 212 to get 424. Second, we multiply 3 and 212 to get 636, but we must move 636 one place to the left so that the ones, tens, and hundreds digits are aligned correctly. Finally, we add to get 6784.

EXAMPLE 8   **Multiplying polynomials vertically**

Multiply $(3x - 4y)(2x^2 + xy - 4y^2)$.

Solution

Start by stacking the polynomials as follows. Note that unlike terms can be multiplied but not added.

$$
\begin{array}{r}
2x^2 + xy - 4y^2 \qquad \text{First row} \\
3x - 4y \\
\hline
-8x^2y - 4xy^2 + 16y^3 \qquad \text{Multiply first row by } -4y. \\
6x^3 + 3x^2y - 12xy^2 \qquad\qquad\ \text{Multiply first row by } 3x. \\
\hline
6x^3 - 5x^2y - 16xy^2 + 16y^3 \qquad \text{Add columns.}
\end{array}
$$

▌ **Now Try Exercise 73**

▶ **REAL-WORLD CONNECTION**   Polynomials frequently occur in business applications. For example, the **demand** D for buying a new video game might vary with its price. If the price is high, fewer games are sold, and if the price is low, more games are sold. The revenue R from selling D games at price p is given by $R = pD$. This concept is used in the next example.

EXAMPLE 9   **Using polynomials in a business application**

Let the demand D, or number of games sold in thousands, be given by $D = 30 - \frac{1}{5}p$, where $p \geq 10$ is the price of the game in dollars.
(a) Find the demand when $p = \$30$ and when $p = \$60$.
(b) Write an expression for the revenue R. Multiply your expression.
(c) Find the revenue when $p = \$40$.

Solution
(a) When $p = 30, D = 30 - \frac{1}{5}(30) = 24$ thousand games.

   When $p = 60, D = 30 - \frac{1}{5}(60) = 18$ thousand games.

(b) $R = pD = p(30 - \frac{1}{5}p) = 30p - \frac{1}{5}p^2$

(c) Let $R = 30p - \frac{1}{5}p^2$. When $p = 40, R = 30(40) - \frac{1}{5}(40)^2 = \$880$ thousand.

▌ **Now Try Exercise 131**

Some Special Products

The product of a sum and a difference often occurs in mathematics.

$$
\begin{aligned}
(a + b)(a - b) &= a \cdot a - a \cdot b + b \cdot a - b \cdot b \\
&= a^2 - ab + ba - b^2 \\
&= a^2 - b^2
\end{aligned}
$$

That is, the product of a sum and difference of two numbers equals the difference of their squares.

PRODUCT OF A SUM AND DIFFERENCE

For any real numbers a and b,

$$(a + b)(a - b) = a^2 - b^2.$$

EXAMPLE 10 **Finding the product of a sum and difference**

Multiply.
(a) $(x + 3)(x - 3)$ **(b)** $(5 - 4x^2)(5 + 4x^2)$

Solution
(a) If we let $a = x$ and $b = 3$, we can apply the rule

$$(a + b)(a - b) = a^2 - b^2.$$

Thus

$$(x + 3)(x - 3) = (x)^2 - (3)^2$$
$$= x^2 - 9.$$

(b) Because $(a - b)(a + b) = a^2 - b^2$, we can multiply as follows.

$$(5 - 4x^2)(5 + 4x^2) = (5)^2 - (4x^2)^2$$
$$= 25 - 16x^4$$

▌ Now Try Exercises 91, 93

EXAMPLE 11 **Finding the product of a sum and difference**

Multiply each expression.
(a) $4rt(r - 4t)(r + 4t)$ **(b)** $(2z + 5k^4)(2z - 5k^4)$

Solution
(a) Start by finding the product of the difference and sum, then simplify.

$$4rt(r - 4t)(r + 4t) = 4rt(r^2 - 16t^2)$$
$$= 4rt \cdot r^2 - 4rt \cdot 16t^2$$
$$= 4r^3t - 64rt^3$$

(b) $(2z + 5k^4)(2z - 5k^4) = (2z)^2 - (5k^4)^2$
$$= 4z^2 - 25k^8$$

▌ Now Try Exercises 107, 109

Two other special products involve *squaring a binomial*.

$$\begin{array}{ll}
(a + b)^2 = (a + b)(a + b) & \quad (a - b)^2 = (a - b)(a - b) \\
\quad = a^2 + ab + ba + b^2 & \quad\quad = a^2 - ab - ba + b^2 \\
\quad = a^2 + 2ab + b^2 & \quad\quad = a^2 - 2ab + b^2
\end{array}$$

The first product is illustrated geometrically in Figure 3.16, where each side of a square has length $(a + b)$. The area of the square is

$$(a + b)(a + b) = (a + b)^2.$$

$(a + b)^2 = a^2 + 2ab + b^2$

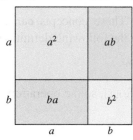

Figure 3.16

This area can also be computed by adding the areas of the four small rectangles.

$$a^2 + ab + ba + b^2 = a^2 + 2ab + b^2$$

Thus $(a + b)^2 = a^2 + 2ab + b^2$. *To obtain the middle term, multiply the two terms in the binomial and double the result.*

SQUARE OF A BINOMIAL

For any real numbers a and b,

$$(a + b)^2 = a^2 + 2ab + b^2 \quad \text{and} \quad (a - b)^2 = a^2 - 2ab + b^2.$$

NOTE: $(a + b)^2 \neq a^2 + b^2 \quad \text{and} \quad (a - b)^2 \neq a^2 - b^2$

EXAMPLE 12

Squaring a binomial

Multiply.
(a) $(x + 5)^2$ **(b)** $(3 - 2x)^2$ **(c)** $(2m^3 + 4n)^2$ **(d)** $\big((2z - 3) + k\big)\big((2z - 3) - k\big)$

Solution
(a) If we let $a = x$ and $b = 5$, we can apply $(a + b)^2 = a^2 + 2ab + b^2$. Thus

$$(x + 5)^2 = (x)^2 + 2(x)(5) + (5)^2 \qquad \text{To find the middle term, multiply}$$
$$\qquad\qquad\qquad\qquad\qquad x \text{ and } 5 \text{ and double the result.}$$
$$= x^2 + 10x + 25.$$

(b) Applying the formula $(a - b)^2 = a^2 - 2ab + b^2$, we find

$$(3 - 2x)^2 = (3)^2 - 2(3)(2x) + (2x)^2$$
$$= 9 - 12x + 4x^2.$$

(c) $(2m^3 + 4n)^2 = (2m^3)^2 + 2(2m^3)(4n) + (4n)^2$
$$= 4m^6 + 16m^3n + 16n^2$$

(d) If $a = 2z - 3$ and $b = k$, we can use $(a + b)(a - b) = a^2 - b^2$.

$$\big((2z - 3) + k\big)\big((2z - 3) - k\big) = (2z - 3)^2 - k^2$$
$$= (2z)^2 - 2(2z)(3) + (3)^2 - k^2$$
$$= 4z^2 - 12z + 9 - k^2$$

Now Try Exercises 97, 99, 111, 117

NOTE: If you forget these special products, you can still use techniques learned earlier to multiply the polynomials in Examples 10–12. Consider Example 12(b).

$$(3 - 2x)^2 = (3 - 2x)(3 - 2x)$$
$$= 3 \cdot 3 - 3 \cdot 2x - 2x \cdot 3 + 2x \cdot 2x$$
$$= 9 - 6x - 6x + 4x^2$$
$$= 9 - 12x + 4x^2 \checkmark$$

CRITICAL THINKING

Suppose that a friend is convinced that the expressions

$$(x + 3)^2 \quad \text{and} \quad x^2 + 9$$

are equivalent. How could you convince your friend that $(x + 3)^2 \neq x^2 + 9$?

Multiplying Functions

In Section 3.1 we discussed how to add and subtract functions. These concepts can be extended to include multiplication of two functions, f and g, by using the following definition.

$$(fg)(x) = f(x)g(x) \qquad \text{Multiplying functions}$$

NOTE: There is no operation symbol written between f and g in $(fg)(x)$, so the operation is assumed to be multiplication, just as in the expression xy.

STUDY TIP

Examples like this are sometimes useful for helping to understand why we multiply two functions in real life.

▶ **REAL-WORLD CONNECTION** When would someone ever need to multiply two functions? Consider the following example. From 1980 to 2010, the average person used $G(x) = -24x + 1900$ gallons of water per day, where x is years after 1980. (Note that G includes all types of water usage in the United States, not just residential usage.) During the same time period, the population P of the United States in millions was $P(x) = 2.6x + 230$. If we multiply the gallons G of water each person used by the number of people P, we get the total amount of water used per day (in millions of gallons). That is, we multiply $G(x)$ and $P(x)$ to obtain the total water consumption $T(x)$.

$$\begin{aligned} T(x) &= G(x)P(x) \\ &= (-24x + 1900)(2.6x + 230) \end{aligned}$$

You are asked to multiply these binomials and interpret your answer in Exercise 135.

EXAMPLE 13 **Multiplying polynomial functions**

Let $f(x) = x^2 - x$ and $g(x) = 2x^2 + 4$. Find $(fg)(3)$ and $(fg)(x)$.

Solution
To find $(fg)(3)$, evaluate $f(3)$ and $g(3)$. Then multiply the results.

$$(fg)(3) = f(3)g(3) = (3^2 - 3)(2 \cdot 3^2 + 4) = (6)(22) = 132$$

To find $(fg)(x)$, multiply the formulas for $f(x)$ and $g(x)$.

$$(fg)(x) = f(x)g(x) = (x^2 - x)(2x^2 + 4) = 2x^4 - 2x^3 + 4x^2 - 4x$$

▌ **Now Try Exercise 121**

3.2 Putting It All Together

CONCEPT	EXPLANATION	EXAMPLES
Distributive Properties	For all real numbers a, b, and c, $$a(b + c) = ab + ac \quad \text{and}$$ $$a(b - c) = ab - ac.$$	$4(3 + a) = 12 + 4a, \quad 5(x - 1) = 5x - 5$, and $-(b - 5) = -1(b - 5) = -b + 5$
Multiplying Polynomials	The product of two polynomials may be found by multiplying every term in the first polynomial by every term in the second polynomial.	$(2x + 3)(x - 7) = 2x \cdot x - 2x \cdot 7 + 3 \cdot x - 3 \cdot 7$ $= 2x^2 - 14x + 3x - 21$ $= 2x^2 - 11x - 21$

CONCEPT	EXPLANATION	EXAMPLES
Properties of Exponents	For numbers a and b and integers m and n, $$a^m \cdot a^n = a^{m+n},$$ $$(a^m)^n = a^{mn}, \quad \text{and}$$ $$(ab)^n = a^n b^n.$$	$5^2 \cdot 5^6 = 5^8,$ $(2^3)^2 = 2^6,$ $(5y^4)^2 = 25y^8,$ $(a^2b^3)^4 = a^8b^{12},$ and $(-4rt^3)^2 = 16r^2t^6$
Special Products of Binomials	Product of a sum and difference $$(a + b)(a - b) = a^2 - b^2$$ Squares of binomials $$(a + b)^2 = a^2 + 2ab + b^2$$ $$(a - b)^2 = a^2 - 2ab + b^2$$	$(x + 2)(x - 2) = x^2 - 4,$ $(7y - 6z^2)(7y + 6z^2) = 49y^2 - 36z^4,$ $(x + 4)^2 = x^2 + 8x + 16,$ $(x - 4)^2 = x^2 - 8x + 16,$ and $(2m - 3n^2)^2 = 4m^2 - 12mn^2 + 9n^4$
Multiplication of Functions	$(fg)(x) = f(x)g(x)$	If $f(x) = x^2$ and $g(x) = x + 2$, then $(fg)(x) = x^2(x + 2) = x^3 + 2x^2.$

3.2   Exercises

CONCEPTS AND VOCABULARY

1. $5(x - 4) = 5x - 20$ illustrates what property?

2. Give an example of a monomial, a binomial, and a trinomial.

3. Simplify the expression $x^3 \cdot x^5$.

4. Simplify $(2x)^3$ and $(x^2)^3$.

5. $(a + b)(a - b) = $ _____

6. $(a + b)^2 = $ _____

7. $x(x - 1) = $ _____

8. Does $(x + 1)^2$ equal $x^2 + 1$? Explain.

9. (True or False?) $x^3(x^2 - x^4)$ equals $x^6 - x^{12}$.

10. (True or False?) b^3b^5 equals b^8.

11. Which of the following (a. – d.) simplifies to $4x^2y^6$?
  a. $-(2xy^3)^2$ **b.** $-2^2(xy^3)^2$
  c. $4x^2(y^3)^3$ **d.** $(-2xy^3)^2$

12. Which of the following (a. – d.) simplifies to $4x^3 - 4x$?
  a. $4x(x + 1)(x - 1)$ **b.** $4(x - 1)(x + 1)$
  c. $x(x + 2)(x - 2)$ **d.** $4(x^2 - x)$

MULTIPLYING POLYNOMIALS

Exercises 13–20: Multiply the monomials.

13. $x^4 \cdot x^8$ **14.** $2x \cdot 4x^3$

15. $-5y^7 \cdot 4y$ **16.** $3xy^2 \cdot 6x^3y^2$

17. $(-xy)(4x^3y^5)$

18. $(4z^3)(-5z^2)$

19. $(5y^2z)(4x^2yz^5)$

20. $x^2(-xy^2)$

Exercises 21–32: Multiply.

21. $5(y + 2)$ **22.** $4(y - 7)$

23. $-2(5x + 9)$ **24.** $-3x(5 + x)$

25. $-6y(y - 3)$ **26.** $(2y - 5)8y^3$

27. $(9 - 4x)3$ **28.** $-(5 - x^2)$

29. $-ab(a^2 - b^2)$ **30.** $a^2b^2(1 - 4ab)$

31. $-5m(n^3 + m)$ **32.** $7n(3n - 2m^2)$

Exercises 33–36: Use the figure to write the product. Find the area of the rectangle if x = 5 inches.

33. $(x + 1)(x + 2)$

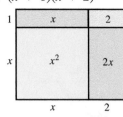

34. $(x + 3)(x + 4)$

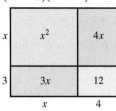

35. $(2x + 1)(x + 1)$

36. $(2x + 4)(3x + 2)$

Exercises 37–40: (Refer to Example 4.) Multiply geometrically and symbolically. Support your answer graphically or numerically.

37. $(x + 5)(x + 6)$

38. $(x + 1)(x + 4)$

39. $(2x + 1)(2x + 1)$

40. $(x + 3)(2x + 4)$

Exercises 41 and 42: The pair of graphing calculator screens show graphs of y_1 and y_2. Does $y_1 = y_2$? Interpret this result in general.

41. $y_1 = (x + 1)^2$, $y_2 = x^2 + 1$

[−4, 4, 1] by [−4, 4, 1]   [−4, 4, 1] by [−4, 4, 1]

42. $y_1 = (x − 2)^2$, $y_2 = x^2 − 4$

[−4, 4, 1] by [−4, 4, 1]   [−4, 4, 1] by [−4, 4, 1]

Exercises 43–48: Determine whether the equation is an identity. (Hint: If it is an identity, the equation must be true for all x-values.)

43. $(x − 2)^2 = x^2 − 4$

44. $(x + 4)^2 = x^2 + 16$

45. $(x + 3)(x − 2) = x^2 + x − 6$

46. $(5x − 1)^2 = 25x^2 − 10x + 1$

47. $2z(3z + 1) = 6z^2 + 1$ **48.** $−(z^2 + 4z) = −z^2 + 4z$

Exercises 49–66: Multiply the binomials.

49. $(x + 5)(x + 10)$ **50.** $(x − 5)(x − 10)$

51. $(x − 3)(x − 4)$ **52.** $(x + 3)(x + 4)$

53. $(2z − 1)(z + 2)$ **54.** $(2z + 1)(z − 2)$

55. $(y + 3)(y − 4)$ **56.** $(2y + 1)(5y + 1)$

57. $(4x − 3)(4 − 9x)$ **58.** $(1 − x)(1 + 2x)$

59. $(−2z + 3)(z − 2)$ **60.** $(z − 2)(4z + 3)$

61. $\left(z − \frac{1}{2}\right)\left(z + \frac{1}{4}\right)$ **62.** $\left(z − \frac{1}{3}\right)\left(z − \frac{1}{6}\right)$

63. $(x^2 + 1)(2x^2 − 1)$ **64.** $(x^2 − 2)(x^2 + 4)$

65. $(x + y)(x − 2y)$ **66.** $(x^2 + y^2)(x − y)$

Exercises 67–80: Multiply the polynomials.

67. $4x(x^2 − 2x − 3)$ **68.** $2x(3 − x + x^2)$

69. $−x(x^4 − 3x^2 + 1)$

70. $−3m^2(4m^3 + m^2 − 2m)$

71. $(2n^2 − 4n + 1)(3n^2)$

72. $(x − y + 5)(xy)$

73. $(x + 1)(x^2 + 2x − 3)$

74. $(2x − 1)(3x^2 − x + 6)$

75. $z(2 + z)(1 − z − z^2)$

76. $z^2(1 − z)(2 + z)$

77. $2ab^2(2a^2 − ab + 3b^2)$

78. $2n(mn^2 + 2n)(3m^2n − 3n)$

79. $(2r − 4t)(3r^2 + rt − t^2)$

80. $−2(x − y)(x^2 + xy + y^2)$

Exercises 81–90: Simplify the expression.

81. $(2^3)^2$ **82.** $(x^3)^5$

83. $2(z^3)^6$ **84.** $(5y)^3$

85. $(−5x)^2$ **86.** $(2y)^4$

87. $(−2xy^2)^3$ **88.** $(3x^2y^3)^4$

89. $(−4a^2b^3)^2$ **90.** $−(5r^3t)^2$

Exercises 91–118: Multiply the expression.

91. $(x − 4)(x + 4)$ **92.** $(x + 5)(x − 5)$

93. $(3 − 2x)(3 + 2x)$ **94.** $(4 − 5x)(4 + 5x)$

95. $(x - y)(x + y)$ **96.** $(2x + 2y)(2x - 2y)$

97. $(x + 2)^2$ **98.** $(y + 5)^2$

99. $(2x + 1)^2$ **100.** $(3x + 5)^2$

101. $(x - 1)^2$

102. $(x - 7)^2$

103. $(3x - 2)^2$

104. $(6x - 5)^2$

105. $3x(x + 1)(x - 1)$

106. $-4x(3x - 5)^2$

107. $3rt(t - 2r)(t + 2r)$

108. $5r^2t^2(t - 4)(t + 4)$

109. $(a^2 + 2b^2)(a^2 - 2b^2)$

110. $(2a + 5b^4)(2a - 5b^4)$

111. $(3m^3 + 5n^2)^2$

112. $(6m + 4n^2)^2$

113. $(x^3 - 2y^3)^2$

114. $(6m - n^4)^2$

115. $\big((x - 3) + y\big)\big((x - 3) - y\big)$

116. $\big((2m - 1) + n\big)\big((2m - 1) - n\big)$

117. $\big(r - (t + 2)\big)\big(r + (t + 2)\big)$

118. $\big(y - (z + 1)\big)\big(y + (z + 1)\big)$

Exercises 119 and 120: **Thinking Generally** *Use*

$$(a + b)(a - b) = a^2 - b^2$$

to multiply the pair of integers mentally.

119. $102, 98$

120. $51, 49$

Exercises 121–126: Find $(fg)(2)$ and $(fg)(x)$.

121. $f(x) = x + 1, g(x) = x - 2$

122. $f(x) = 2x + 3, g(x) = 4 - x$

123. $f(x) = x^2, g(x) = 3 - 5x$

124. $f(x) = x^2 - 4x, g(x) = x^2 - 5$

125. $f(x) = 2x^2 + 1, g(x) = x^2 + x - 3$

126. $f(x) = x^3 - 3x^2, g(x) = 2x^2 + 4x$

AREA

Exercises 127–130: Express the shaded area of the given figure in terms of x. Find the area if $x = 20$ feet.

127.

128.

129.

130.

APPLICATIONS

Exercises 131 and 132: **Price and Demand** *(Refer to Example 9.) Let D be the demand in thousands of units and p be the price in dollars of one unit.*

  (a) *Find D when $p = 20$.*
  (b) *Write an expression for the revenue R. Multiply your expression.*
  (c) *Find the revenue when $p = 30$.*

131. $D = 40 - \frac{1}{2}p$ **132.** $D = 20 - \frac{1}{10}p$

133. *Tennis Serves* Serena Williams hit 66% of her first serves *in* bounds at Wimbledon 2010, or, equivalently, 34% of these serves were *out* of bounds. If x represents the percentage of a player's serves that are *out* of bounds, then the percent chance that two consecutive serves will be *in* bounds is given by $100\big(1 - \frac{x}{100}\big)^2$.
  (a) Multiply this expression.
  (b) Evaluate both the given expression and the expression you found in part (a) with $x = 34$. Are your answers the same?
  (c) Interpret your answer from part (b).

134. *Interest* If the annual interest rate r is expressed as a decimal and N dollars are deposited into an account, then the amount in the account after two years is $N(1 + r)^2$.
  (a) Multiply this expression.
  (b) Let $r = 0.10$ and $N = 200$. Use both the given expression and the expression you obtained in part (a) to find the amount of money in the account after 2 years. Do your answers agree?

135. *Water Usage* (Refer to the Real-World Connection preceding Example 13.)
  (a) Interpret the numbers -24 and 1900 in the formula $G(x) = -24x + 1900$.
  (b) Let $P(x) = 2.6x + 230$. Find $T(x) = G(x)P(x)$.
  (c) Evaluate $T(30)$ and interpret your answer.

136. *Numbers* Write a polynomial that represents the product of two consecutive even integers, where x is the greater even integer. Multiply your answer.

137. *Numbers* Write a polynomial that represents the product of two consecutive integers, where x is the smaller integer. Multiply your answer.

138. *Revenue* Write a polynomial that represents the revenue received from selling $2y + 1$ items at a price of x dollars each.

139. *Rectangular Pen* A rectangular pen has a perimeter of 100 feet. If x represents its width, write a polynomial that gives the area of the pen in terms of x.

140. *Numbers* Find an expression that represents the product of the sum and difference of two numbers. Let the two numbers be x and y.

WRITING ABOUT MATHEMATICS

141. Suppose that a student insists that

$$(x + 5)(x + 5)$$

equals $x^2 + 25$. Explain how you could convince the student otherwise.

142. Explain how to multiply two polynomials. Give an example of how your method works. Does your method give the correct result for any two polynomials?

Checking Basic Concepts

1. Combine like terms.
  (a) $8x^2 + 4x - 5x^2 + 3x$
  (b) $(5x^2 - 3x + 2) - (3x^2 - 5x^3 + 1)$

2. Write a polynomial that represents the revenue from ticket sales if $x + 120$ tickets are sold for x dollars each. Evaluate the polynomial for $x = 10$ and interpret the result.

3. An athlete's heart rate t minutes after exercise is stopped is modeled by

$$f(t) = 2t^2 - 25t + 160,$$

where $0 \le t \le 6$.
  (a) What was the initial heart rate?
  (b) What was the heart rate after 4 minutes?

4. Multiply the expressions.
  (a) $-5(x - 6)$
  (b) $4x^3(3x^2 - 5x)$
  (c) $(2x - 1)(x + 3)$

5. Multiply the following special products.
  (a) $(5x - 6)(5x + 6)$
  (b) $(3x - 4)^2$

6. Make a sketch of a rectangle whose area illustrates that $(x + 2)(x + 4) = x^2 + 6x + 8$.

3.3 Factoring Polynomials

Common Factors • Factoring and Equations • Factoring by Grouping

Video games involving sports frequently have to show a ball traveling through the air. To make the motion look realistic, the game must solve an equation in real time to determine when the ball hits the ground. For example, suppose that a golf ball is hit with an *upward* velocity of 88 feet per second, or 60 miles per hour. Then its height h in feet above the ground after t seconds is modeled by the *quadratic function* $h(t) = 88t - 16t^2$. To estimate when the ball strikes the ground, we can solve the *quadratic equation*

$$88t - 16t^2 = 0. \qquad \text{At ground level, } h = 0.$$

One method for solving this equation is factoring (see Example 6). In this section we discuss factoring and how it is used to solve equations.

NEW VOCABULARY

☐ Greatest common
   factor (GCF)
☐ Zero-product property
☐ Zero
☐ Expressions/equations
☐ Parabola

Common Factors

When factoring a polynomial, we first look for factors that are common to each term. By applying a distributive property, we can write a polynomial as two factors. For example, each term in $2x^2 + 4x$ contains a factor of $2x$.

$$2x^2 = 2x \cdot x$$
$$4x = 2x \cdot 2$$

Thus the polynomial $2x^2 + 4x$ can be factored as follows.

$$2x^2 + 4x = 2x(x + 2)$$
$$\qquad\qquad\qquad \text{↑}$$
$$\qquad\qquad\quad \text{Common factor}$$

EXAMPLE 1 **Finding common factors**

Factor.
(a) $4x^2 + 5x$ **(b)** $12x^3 - 4x^2$ **(c)** $6z^3 - 2z^2 + 4z$ **(d)** $4x^3y^2 + x^2y^3$

Solution
(a) Both $4x^2$ and $5x$ contain a common factor of x. That is,

$$4x^2 = x \cdot 4x \quad \text{and} \quad 5x = x \cdot 5.$$

Thus $4x^2 + 5x = x(4x + 5)$.
(b) Both $12x^3$ and $4x^2$ contain a common factor of $4x^2$. That is,

$$12x^3 = 4x^2 \cdot 3x \quad \text{and} \quad 4x^2 = 4x^2 \cdot 1.$$

Thus $12x^3 - 4x^2 = 4x^2(3x - 1)$.
(c) Each of the terms $6z^3$, $2z^2$, and $4z$ contains a common factor of $2z$. That is,

$$6z^3 = 2z \cdot 3z^2, \quad 2z^2 = 2z \cdot z, \quad \text{and} \quad 4z = 2z \cdot 2.$$

Thus $6z^3 - 2z^2 + 4z = 2z(3z^2 - z + 2)$.
(d) Both $4x^3y^2$ and x^2y^3 contain a common factor of x^2y^2. That is,

$$4x^3y^2 = x^2y^2 \cdot 4x \quad \text{and} \quad x^2y^3 = x^2y^2 \cdot y.$$

Thus $4x^3y^2 + x^2y^3 = x^2y^2(4x + y)$.

▌ Now Try Exercises 9, 17, 21, 27

Many times we factor out the *greatest common factor*. For example, the polynomial $15x^4 - 5x^2$ has a common factor of $5x$. We could write this polynomial as

$$15x^4 - 5x^2 = 5x(3x^3 - x).$$

However, we can also factor out $5x^2$ to obtain

$$15x^4 - 5x^2 = 5x^2(3x^2 - 1).$$

Because $5x^2$ is the common factor with the greatest degree and largest (integer) coefficient, we say that $5x^2$ is the **greatest common factor** (GCF) of $15x^4 - 5x^2$. In Example 1, we factored out the GCF in each case.

EXAMPLE 2 **Factoring greatest common factors**

Factor.
(a) $24x^5 + 12x^3 - 6x^2$ **(b)** $6m^3n^2 - 3mn^2 + 9m$ **(c)** $-9x^3 + 6x^2 - 3x$

Solution
(a) The GCF of $24x^5$, $12x^3$, and $6x^2$ is $6x^2$.

$$24x^5 = 6x^2 \cdot 4x^3, \quad 12x^3 = 6x^2 \cdot 2x, \quad \text{and} \quad 6x^2 = 6x^2 \cdot 1$$

Thus $24x^5 + 12x^3 - 6x^2 = 6x^2(4x^3 + 2x - 1)$.
(b) The GCF of $6m^3n^2$, $3mn^2$, and $9m$ is $3m$.

$$6m^3n^2 = 3m \cdot 2m^2n^2, \quad 3mn^2 = 3m \cdot n^2, \quad \text{and} \quad 9m = 3m \cdot 3$$

Thus $6m^3n^2 - 3mn^2 + 9m = 3m(2m^2n^2 - n^2 + 3)$.
(c) Rather than factoring out $3x$, we can also factor out $-3x$ and make the leading coefficient of the remaining expression positive.

$$-9x^3 = -3x \cdot 3x^2, \quad 6x^2 = -3x \cdot -2x, \quad \text{and} \quad -3x = -3x \cdot 1$$

Thus $-9x^3 + 6x^2 - 3x = -3x(3x^2 - 2x + 1)$.

Now Try Exercises 25, 33, 39

Factoring and Equations

To solve equations by using factoring, we use the **zero-product property**. It states that if the product of two numbers is 0, then at least one of the numbers must equal 0.

ZERO-PRODUCT PROPERTY

For all real numbers a and b, if $ab = 0$, then $a = 0$ or $b = 0$ (or both).

NOTE: The zero-product property works only for 0. If $ab = 1$, then it does *not* follow that $a = 1$ or $b = 1$. For example, $a = \frac{1}{3}$ and $b = 3$ also satisfy the equation $ab = 1$.

Sometimes factoring needs to be performed on an equation before the zero-product property can be applied. For example, the left side of the equation

$$2x^2 + 4x = 0$$

may be factored to obtain

$$2x(x + 2) = 0.$$

Note that $2x$ times $(x + 2)$ equals 0. By the zero-product property, we must have either

$$2x = 0 \quad \text{or} \quad x + 2 = 0.$$

Solving each equation for x gives

$$x = 0 \quad \text{or} \quad x = -2.$$

The x-values of 0 and -2 are called **zeros** of the polynomial $2x^2 + 4x$ because when they are substituted in $2x^2 + 4x$, the result is 0. That is, $2(0)^2 + 4(0) = 0$ and $2(-2)^2 + 4(-2) = 0$.

READING CHECK

What are the differences between expressions and equations?

MAKING CONNECTIONS

Expressions and Equations

There are important distinctions between expressions and equations. We often *factor expressions* and *solve equations*. For example, when we solved the *equation* $2x^2 + 4x = 0$, we started by factoring the *expression* $2x^2 + 4x$, as $2x(x + 2)$. The equivalent equation, $2x(x + 2) = 0$, resulted. Then the zero-product property was used to obtain the *solutions to the equation*: 0 and -2.

An equation is a statement that two expressions are equal. Equations *always* have an equals sign. We often solve equations, but we do *not* solve expressions.

EXAMPLE 3   **Applying the zero-product property**

Solve.
(a) $x(x - 1) = 0$ (b) $2x(x + 3) = 0$ (c) $(2x - 1)(3x + 2) = 0$

Solution
(a) The expression $x(x - 1)$ is the product of x and $(x - 1)$. By the zero-product property, either $x = 0$ or $x - 1 = 0$. The solutions are 0 and 1.

(b)
$$2x(x + 3) = 0 \qquad \text{Given equation}$$
$$2x = 0 \quad \text{or} \quad x + 3 = 0 \qquad \text{Zero-product property}$$
$$x = 0 \quad \text{or} \quad x = -3 \qquad \text{Solve each equation.}$$

The solutions are 0 and -3.

(c)
$$(2x - 1)(3x + 2) = 0 \qquad \text{Given equation}$$
$$2x - 1 = 0 \quad \text{or} \quad 3x + 2 = 0 \qquad \text{Zero-product property}$$
$$2x = 1 \quad \text{or} \quad 3x = -2 \qquad \text{Add 1; subtract 2.}$$
$$x = \frac{1}{2} \quad \text{or} \quad x = -\frac{2}{3} \qquad \text{Divide by 2; divide by 3.}$$

The solutions are $\frac{1}{2}$ and $-\frac{2}{3}$.

Now Try Exercises 45, 49

EXAMPLE 4   **Solving polynomial equations with factoring**

Solve each polynomial equation.
(a) $x^2 + 3x = 0$ (b) $4x^2 = 16x$ (c) $2x^3 + 2x^2 = 0$

Solution
(a) We begin by factoring out the greatest common factor x.

$$x^2 + 3x = 0 \qquad \text{Given equation}$$
$$x(x + 3) = 0 \qquad \text{Factor out } x.$$
$$x = 0 \quad \text{or} \quad x + 3 = 0 \qquad \text{Zero-product property}$$
$$x = 0 \quad \text{or} \quad x = -3 \qquad \text{Solve.}$$

The solutions are 0 and -3.

(b) Write the equation $4x^2 = 16x$ so that there is a 0 on its right side before applying the zero-product property.

$$
\begin{aligned}
4x^2 &= 16x && \text{Given equation} \\
4x^2 - 16x &= 0 && \text{Subtract } 16x \text{ from each side.} \\
4x(x - 4) &= 0 && \text{Factor out } 4x. \\
4x = 0 \quad \text{or} \quad x - 4 &= 0 && \text{Zero-product property} \\
x = 0 \quad \text{or} \quad x &= 4 && \text{Solve.}
\end{aligned}
$$

The solutions are 0 and 4.

(c) Start by factoring out the GCF of $2x^2$.

$$
\begin{aligned}
2x^3 + 2x^2 &= 0 && \text{Given equation} \\
2x^2(x + 1) &= 0 && \text{Factor out } 2x^2. \\
2x^2 = 0 \quad \text{or} \quad x + 1 &= 0 && \text{Zero-product property} \\
x = 0 \quad \text{or} \quad x &= -1 && \text{Solve.}
\end{aligned}
$$

The solutions are -1 and 0.

❚ Now Try Exercises 67, 71, 75

Polynomial equations can also be solved numerically and graphically. For example, to find a graphical solution to $x^2 - 2x = 0$, graph $y = x^2 - 2x$ by making a table of values, as shown in Table 3.6. When the points are plotted and connected, a U-shaped curve results, with x-intercepts 0 and 2. This curve shown in Figure 3.17 is called a *parabola*.

NOTE: The zeros, 0 and 2, of $x^2 - 2x$ in Table 3.6; the x-intercepts, 0 and 2, in Figure 3.17; and the solutions, 0 and 2, to the equation $x^2 - 2x = 0$ are *identical*.

Numerical Solution

TABLE 3.6

$y = x^2 - 2x$

x	y
-1	3
0	0
1	-1
2	0
3	3

Zeros: 0, 2

Graphical Solution

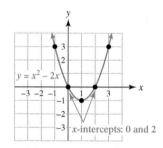

Figure 3.17

Symbolic Solution

$$
\begin{aligned}
x^2 - 2x &= 0 \\
x(x - 2) &= 0 \\
x = 0 \quad \text{or} \quad x - 2 &= 0 \\
x = 0 \quad \text{or} \quad x &= 2
\end{aligned}
$$

Solutions: 0, 2

These concepts are generalized in the following.

MAKING CONNECTIONS

Zeros, x-Intercepts, and Solutions

The following statements are *equivalent*, where k is a real number and $P(x)$ is a polynomial.

1. A *zero* of a polynomial $P(x)$ is k.
2. An *x-intercept* on the graph of $y = P(x)$ is k.
3. A *solution* to the equation $P(x) = 0$ is k.

See the Making Connections after the solution to Example 5.

In the next example we solve an equation numerically, graphically, and symbolically.

EXAMPLE 5   **Solving an equation**

Solve the equation $4x - x^2 = 0$ numerically, graphically, and symbolically.

Solution

Numerical Solution Make a table of values for $y = 4x - x^2$, as shown in Table 3.7. Note that 0 and 4 are zeros of $4x - x^2$ and solutions to $4x - x^2 = 0$, because $4(0) - 0^2 = 0$ and $4(4) - 4^2 = 0$.

Graphical Solution Plot the points given in Table 3.7 and sketch a curve through them, as shown in Figure 3.18. The curve is a ∩-shaped graph, or parabola, with x-intercepts 0 and 4, which are the solutions to the given equation.

Numerical Solution

TABLE 3.7

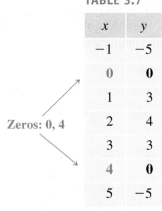

x	y
-1	-5
0	0
1	3
2	4
3	3
4	0
5	-5

Zeros: 0, 4

Graphical Solution

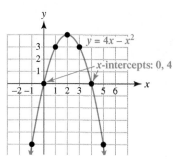

Figure 3.18

Symbolic Solution Start by factoring the left side of the equation.

$$4x - x^2 = 0 \quad \text{Given equation}$$
$$x(4 - x) = 0 \quad \text{Factor out } x.$$
$$x = 0 \quad \text{or} \quad 4 - x = 0 \quad \text{Zero-product property}$$
$$x = 0 \quad \text{or} \quad x = 4 \quad \text{Solve each equation.}$$

Solutions: 0, 4

NOTE: The numerical and graphical solutions agree with the symbolic solutions.

Now Try Exercise 77

MAKING CONNECTIONS

1. The *zeros* of $4x - x^2$ are 0 and 4, as shown in Table 3.7.
2. The *x-intercepts* for $y = 4x - x^2$ are 0 and 4, as shown in Figure 3.18.
3. The *solutions* to $4x - x^2 = 0$ are 0 and 4, as shown in the *Symbolic Solution*.

GRAPH OF $y = ax^2 + bx + c$

The graph of $y = ax^2 + bx + c$ is a **parabola**. It is a ∪-shaped graph if $a > 0$ and a ∩-shaped graph if $a < 0$. This graph can have zero, one, or two x-intercepts.

CALCULATOR HELP

To find an x-intercept or zero, see Appendix A (page AP-10).

TECHNOLOGY NOTE:

Locating x-intercepts
Many calculators have the capability to locate an x-intercept or zero. This method is illustrated in the accompanying figures, where the solution 2 to the equation $x^2 - 4 = 0$ is found.

$[-9, 9, 1]$ by $[-6, 6, 1]$

In the next example we use factoring to estimate when a golf ball strikes the ground.

EXAMPLE 6   **Modeling the flight of a golf ball**

If a golf ball is hit upward at 88 feet per second, or 60 miles per hour, its height h in feet after t seconds is modeled by $h(t) = 88t - 16t^2$.
(a) Use factoring to determine when the golf ball strikes the ground.
(b) Solve part (a) graphically and numerically.

Solution
(a) *Symbolic Solution* The golf ball strikes the ground when its height is 0.

$$88t - 16t^2 = 0 \qquad \text{Set the formula equal to 0.}$$
$$8t(11 - 2t) = 0 \qquad \text{Factor out } 8t.$$
$$8t = 0 \quad \text{or} \quad 11 - 2t = 0 \qquad \text{Zero-product property}$$
$$t = 0 \quad \text{or} \quad t = \frac{11}{2} \qquad \text{Solve for } t.$$

The ball strikes the ground after $\frac{11}{2}$, or 3.5 seconds. The solution of $t = 0$ is not used in this problem because it corresponds to when the ball is initially hit from the ground.

(b) *Graphical and Numerical Solutions* Graph $y_1 = 88x - 16x^2$. Using a graphing calculator to find an x-intercept (or zero) yields the solution, 3.5. See Figure 3.19(a). Numerical support is shown in Figure 3.19(b), where $y_1 = 0$ when $x = 5.5$.

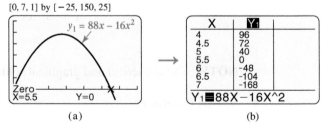

$[0, 7, 1]$ by $[-25, 150, 25]$

(a)

(b)

Figure 3.19

▮ **Now Try Exercise 101**

Factoring by Grouping

Factoring by grouping is a technique that makes use of the associative and distributive properties. The next example illustrates the first step in this factoring technique.

EXAMPLE 7   **Factoring out binomials**

Factor.
(a) $2x(x + 1) + 3(x + 1)$ **(b)** $2x^2(3x - 2) - x(3x - 2)$

Solution

(a) Both terms in the expression $2x(x + 1) + 3(x + 1)$ contain the binomial $(x + 1)$. Therefore the distributive property can be used to factor out this expression.

$$2x(x + 1) + 3(x + 1) = (2x + 3)(x + 1)$$

(b) Both terms in the expression $2x^2(3x - 2) - x(3x - 2)$ contain the binomial $(3x - 2)$. Therefore the distributive property can be used to factor this expression.

$$2x^2(3x - 2) - x(3x - 2) = (2x^2 - x)(3x - 2)$$

▌ **Now Try Exercises 81, 83**

Now consider the polynomial

$$3t^3 + 6t^2 + 2t + 4.$$

We can factor this polynomial by first grouping it into two binomials.

$$(3t^3 + 6t^2) + (2t + 4) \quad \text{Associative property}$$
$$3t^2(t + 2) + 2(t + 2) \quad \text{Factor out common factors.}$$
$$(3t^2 + 2)(t + 2) \quad \text{Factor out } (t + 2).$$

The following steps summarize factoring a polynomial with four terms by grouping.

FACTORING BY GROUPING

STEP 1: Use parentheses to group the terms into binomials with common factors. Begin by writing the expression with a plus sign between the binomials.

STEP 2: Factor out the common factor in each binomial.

STEP 3: Factor out the common binomial. If there is no common binomial, try a different grouping.

These steps are used in Example 8.

EXAMPLE 8 ▌ **Factoring by grouping**

Factor each polynomial.
(a) $x^3 - 2x^2 + 3x - 6$ **(b)** $12x^3 - 9x^2 - 8x + 6$ **(c)** $2x - 2y + ax - ay$

Solution

(a)
$$\begin{aligned}
x^3 - 2x^2 + 3x - 6 &= (x^3 - 2x^2) + (3x - 6) & &\text{Group terms.}\\
&= x^2(x - 2) + 3(x - 2) & &\text{Factor out } x^2 \text{ and } 3.\\
&= (x^2 + 3)(x - 2) & &\text{Factor out } x - 2.
\end{aligned}$$

(b)
$$\begin{aligned}
12x^3 - 9x^2 - 8x + 6 &= (12x^3 - 9x^2) + (-8x + 6) & &\text{Write with a plus sign between binomials.}\\
&= 3x^2(4x - 3) - 2(4x - 3) & &\text{Factor out } 3x^2 \text{ and } -2.\\
&= (3x^2 - 2)(4x - 3) & &\text{Factor out } 4x - 3.
\end{aligned}$$

(c)
$$\begin{aligned}
2x - 2y + ax - ay &= (2x - 2y) + (ax - ay) & &\text{Group terms.}\\
&= 2(x - y) + a(x - y) & &\text{Factor out } 2 \text{ and } a.\\
&= (2 + a)(x - y) & &\text{Factor out } x - y.
\end{aligned}$$

▌ **Now Try Exercises 85, 93, 95**

CRITICAL THINKING

Solve
$xy - 4x - 3y + 12 = 0.$

3.3   Putting It All Together

CONCEPT	EXPLANATION	EXAMPLES
Greatest Common Factor (GCF)	We can sometimes factor the greatest common factor out of a polynomial. The GCF has the largest (integer) coefficient and greatest degree possible.	$3x^4 - 9x^3 + 12x^2 = 3x^2(x^2 - 3x + 4)$ The terms in the expression $(x^2 - 3x + 4)$ have no common factor, so $3x^2$ is called the *greatest common factor* of $3x^4 - 9x^3 + 12x^2$.
Zero-Product Property	If the product of two numbers is 0, then at least one of the numbers equals 0.	$xy = 0$ implies that $x = 0$ or $y = 0$. $x(2x + 1) = 0$ implies that $x = 0$ or $2x + 1 = 0$.
Factoring and Equations	Factoring may be used to solve equations.	$$6x^2 - 9x = 0$$ $$3x(2x - 3) = 0 \quad \text{Common factor, } 3x$$ $$3x = 0 \quad \text{or} \quad 2x - 3 = 0 \quad \text{Zero-product property}$$ $$x = 0 \quad \text{or} \quad x = \tfrac{3}{2} \quad \text{Solve for } x.$$
Factoring by Grouping	Factoring by grouping is a method that can be used to factor four terms into a product of two binomials. It involves the associative and distributive properties.	$$4x^3 + 6x^2 + 10x + 15 = (4x^3 + 6x^2) + (10x + 15)$$ $$= 2x^2(2x + 3) + 5(2x + 3)$$ $$= (2x^2 + 5)(2x + 3)$$
Zeros, x-Intercepts, and Solutions	An x-intercept for the graph of $y = P(x)$ corresponds to a zero of $P(x)$ and to a solution to the equation $P(x) = 0$. These three concepts are closely connected.	x-Intercepts: **0, 1** Zeros of $x^2 - x$: **0, 1** Solutions to $x^2 - x = 0$: **0, 1**

3.3   Exercises

CONCEPTS AND VOCABULARY

1. Give one reason for factoring expressions.

2. If $x(x - 3) = 0$, what can be said about either x or $(x - 3)$? What property did you use?

3. Is $2x$ a common factor of $(4x^3 - 12x^2)$? Explain.

4. Is $2x$ the GCF of $(4x^3 - 12x^2)$? Explain.

5. If $ab = 2$, must either $a = 2$ or $b = 2$? Explain.

6. If $xy = 0$, must either $x = 0$ or $y = 0$? Explain.

7. Which of the following (a.–d.) is a factorization of $4x^3 - 6x^2$?
    a. $2x(2x - 3)$ **b.** $4x(x^2 - 2x)$
    c. $2x^2(2x + 3)$ **d.** $2x^2(2x - 3)$

8. Which of the following (a.–d.) is a factorization of $36a^2b^3 - 24a^3b^2$?
    a. $12ab(3b - 2a)$ **b.** $12a^2b^2(3b - 2a)$
    c. $6a^2b(6b - 4a)$ **d.** $12a^2b^2(3b + 2a)$

FACTORING AND EQUATIONS

Exercises 9–36: Factor out the greatest common factor.

9. $10x - 15$ **10.** $32 - 16x$

11. $4x + 6y$ **12.** $50a + 20b$

13. $9r - 15t$ **14.** $16m - 24n$

15. $2x^3 - 5x$ **16.** $3y - 9y^2$

17. $8a^3 + 10a$ **18.** $20b^3 + 25b^2$

19. $6r^3 - 18r^5$ **20.** $7n^2 - 21n^4$

21. $8x^3 - 4x^2 + 16x$ **22.** $5x^3 - x^2 + 4x$

23. $9n^4 - 6n^2 + 3n$ **24.** $5n^4 + 10n^2 - 25n$

25. $6t^6 - 4t^4 + 2t^2$ **26.** $15t^6 + 25t^4 - 20t^2$

27. $5x^2y^2 - 15x^2y^3$ **28.** $21xy + 14x^3y^3$

29. $6a^3b^2 - 15a^2b^3$ **30.** $45a^2b + 30a^3b^2$

31. $18mn^2 + 12m^2n^3$ **32.** $24m^2n^3 - 36m^3n^2$

33. $15x^2y + 10xy - 25x^2y^2$

34. $14a^3b^2 - 21a^2b^2 + 35a^2b$

35. $4a^2 - 2ab + 6ab^2$

36. $5a^2 + 10a^2b^2 - 15ab$

Exercises 37–42: (Refer to Example 2(c).) Factor out the negative of the greatest common factor.

37. $-2x^2 + 4x - 6$ **38.** $-7x^5 - 21x^3 - 14x^2$

39. $-8z^4 - 16z^3$ **40.** $-8z^5 - 24z^4$

41. $-4m^2n^3 - 6mn^2 - 8mn$

42. $-13m^4n^4 - 13m^3n^3 + 26m^2n^2$

Exercises 43–52: Use the zero-product property to solve the equation.

43. $mn = 0$ **44.** $xyz = 0$

45. $3z(z + 4) = 0$ **46.** $2z(z - 1) = 0$

47. $(r - 1)(r + 3) = 0$ **48.** $(2r + 3)(r - 5) = 0$

49. $(x + 2)(3x - 1) = 0$ **50.** $(4y - 3)(2y + 1) = 0$

51. $3x(y - 6) = 0$ **52.** $7m(3n + 1) = 0$

Exercises 53–58: Use the graph of $y = P(x)$ to do the following.

    (a) Find the x-intercepts.
    (b) Solve the equation $P(x) = 0$.
    (c) Find the zeros of $P(x)$.

53.

54.

55.

56.

57.

58.
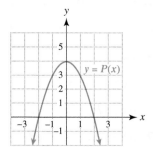

Exercises 59–64: Solve the equation graphically. Check your answers.

59. $x^2 - 2x = 0$ **60.** $x^2 + x = 0$

61. $x - x^2 = 0$ **62.** $3x - x^2 = 0$

63. $x^2 + 4x = 0$ **64.** $x^2 - 4x = 0$

Exercises 65–76: Solve the equation.

65. $x^2 - x = 0$ **66.** $4x - 2x^2 = 0$

67. $5x^2 - x = 0$ **68.** $4x^2 + 3x = 0$

69. $10x^2 + 5x = 0$

70. $6x - 12x^2 = 0$

71. $15x^2 = 10x$

72. $4x = 8x^2$

73. $25x = 10x^2$

74. $34x^2 = 51x$

75. $32x^4 - 16x^3 = 0$

76. $45x^4 - 30x^3 = 0$

 Exercises 77–80: Solve the equation numerically, graphically, and symbolically.

77. $x^2 + 2x = 0$

78. $x^2 + 3x = 0$

79. $2x^2 - 3x = 0$

80. $2x - 3x^2 = 0$

FACTORING BY GROUPING

Exercises 81–98: Factor the polynomial.

81. $2x(x + 2) + 3(x + 2)$ **82.** $5(x - 1) - 2x(x - 1)$

83. $(x - 5)x^2 - (x - 5)2$

84. $7x(x - 1) - 3(x - 1)$

85. $x^3 + 3x^2 + 2x + 6$

86. $4x^3 + 3x^2 + 8x + 6$

87. $6x^3 - 4x^2 + 9x - 6$

88. $x^3 - 3x^2 - 5x + 15$

89. $2x^3 - 3x^2 + 2x - 3$

90. $8x^3 - 2x^2 + 12x - 3$

91. $x^3 - 7x^2 - 3x + 21$

92. $6x^3 - 15x^2 - 4x + 10$

93. $3x^3 - 15x^2 + 5x - 25$

94. $2x^4 - x^3 + 4x - 2$

95. $xy + x + 3y + 3$

96. $ax + bx - ay - by$

97. $ab - 3a + 2b - 6$

98. $2ax - 6bx - ay + 3by$

99. *Graphical Interpretation* Which graph might represent the height h of a golf ball in flight after t seconds? Which graph might represent the height h of a yo-yo above the ground after t seconds?

a.

b.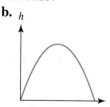

100. **Thinking Generally** The zero-product property states $ab = 0$ implies that either $a = 0$ or $b = 0$.
(a) Why isn't there a "five-product" property?
(b) Solve $ax^2 - bx = 0$, where $a \neq 0$.

APPLICATIONS

101. *Flight of a Golf Ball* (Refer to Example 6.) If a golf ball is hit with an upward velocity of 128 feet per second (about 87 mph), its height h in feet above the ground can be modeled by

$$h(t) = -16t^2 + 128t,$$

where t is in seconds.
(a) Use factoring to determine when the golf ball strikes the ground.
(b) Use the graph of $y = h(t)$ to estimate when the golf ball strikes the ground.

(c) Make a table of h, starting at $t = 3$ and incrementing by 1. Does the table support your answer in part (a)?
(d) Use the table and graph of h to determine the maximum height of the golf ball. At what value of t does this occur?

102. *Flight of a Golf Ball* The height h in feet reached by a golf ball after t seconds is given by

$$h(t) = -16t^2 + 96t.$$

After how many seconds does the golf ball strike the ground?

 Exercises 103 and 104: Climate Change Atmospheric carbon dioxide (CO_2) in parts per million (ppm) from 1958 to 2010 is modeled by $f(x) = 0.0148x^2 + 0.686x + 315$, where x represents years after 1958. Do the following. (*Source:* The Honolulu Advertiser.)

103. Evaluate $f(52)$ and interpret the result.

104. Solve the equation $f(x) = 340$ graphically. Interpret the result.

105. *Geometry* The area of a rectangle with width y and length 8 is $A = 8y$. A circle with radius y has area $A = \pi y^2$. For what positive value of y are these two areas equal?

106. *Mobile Data Subscribers* The number of mobile data subscribers S in millions x years after 2000 is approximated by $S(x) = 1.368x^2 + 6x + 19$. (*Source: Business Insider.*)

(a) Evaluate $S(9)$ and interpret your answer.

(b) Estimate graphically when there were 100 million subscribers.

107. *Space Shuttle Altitude* Approximate altitudes y in feet reached by the space shuttle *Endeavour*, t seconds after liftoff, are shown in the table.

t (seconds)	20	30	40
y (feet)	4500	10,000	18,000

t (seconds)	50	60
y (feet)	28,000	40,000

Source: NASA.

(a) The function $f(t) = 11t^2 + 6t$ models the data, where $y = f(t)$. Make a table of f, starting at $t = 20$ and incrementing by 10. Comment on how well f models the data.

(b) Predict the altitude reached by the shuttle 70 seconds after liftoff. Round your answer to the nearest thousand feet.

(c) Solve the equation $11t^2 + 6t = 0$. Do your results have any physical meaning? Explain.

108. *Average Temperature* Suppose that the monthly average temperatures T in degrees Fahrenheit for a city are given by $T(x) = 24x - 2x^2$, where $x = 1$ corresponds to January, $x = 2$ to February, and so on.

(a) What is the average temperature in October?

(b) Use factoring to solve the quadratic equation $24x - 2x^2 = 0$. Do your results have any physical meaning?

(c) Support your results in part (b) either graphically or numerically.

109. *Area* Suppose that the area of a rectangular room is 216 square feet. Can you find the dimensions of the room from this information? Explain.

110. *Area* Suppose that the area of a rectangular room is $4x^2 + 8x$ square feet. If the length of the room is $4x$, is it possible to determine the width of the room in terms of x? Explain.

111. Online Exploration Go online and search for images of parabolas. Using these images, discuss two real-world applications of parabolas.

112. Online Exploration Go online and search for images of cubic polynomials. Using these images, discuss one real-world situation in which cubic polynomials occur.

WRITING ABOUT MATHEMATICS

113. A student solves the following equation *incorrectly*.

$$x^2 - 5x \overset{?}{=} 1$$
$$x(x - 5) \overset{?}{=} 1$$
$$x \overset{?}{=} 1 \quad \text{or} \quad x - 5 \overset{?}{=} 1$$
$$x \overset{?}{=} 1 \quad \text{or} \quad x \overset{?}{=} 6$$

What is the student's mistake? Explain.

114. Explain how you would solve $ax^2 + bx = 0$ symbolically and graphically.

3.4   Factoring Trinomials

Factoring $x^2 + bx + c$ • Factoring Trinomials by Grouping •
Factoring Trinomials with FOIL • Factoring with Graphs and Tables

A LOOK INTO MATH ▶

Items usually sell better at a lower price. At a higher price fewer items are sold, but more money is made on each item. For example, suppose that if concert tickets are priced at $100 no one will buy a ticket, but for each $1 reduction in price 100 additional tickets will be sold. If the promoters of the concert need to gross $240,000 from ticket sales, what ticket price accomplishes this goal? To solve this problem we need to set up and solve a polynomial equation. In this section we describe how to solve polynomial equations by factoring trinomials in the form $x^2 + bx + c$ and $ax^2 + bx + c$. See Example 3.

NEW VOCABULARY

☐ Symbolic factoring
☐ Numerical factoring
☐ Graphical factoring

Factoring $x^2 + bx + c$

The product $(x + 3)(x + 4)$ can be found as follows.

$$(x + 3)(x + 4) = x^2 + 4x + 3x + 12 \quad \text{Multiplication}$$
$$= x^2 + \quad 7x \quad + 12$$

The middle term $7x$ is found by calculating the sum $4x + 3x$, and the last term is found by calculating the product $3 \cdot 4 = 12$.

When we factor polynomials, we are *reversing* the process of multiplication. To factor $x^2 + 7x + 12$ we must find m and n that satisfy

$$x^2 + 7x + 12 = (x + m)(x + n).$$

Because

$$(x + m)(x + n) = x^2 + (m + n)x + mn,$$

it follows that $mn = 12$ and $m + n = 7$. To determine m and n we list factors of 12 and their sum, as shown in Table 3.8.

Because $3 \cdot 4 = 12$ and $3 + 4 = 7$, we can write the factored form as

$$x^2 + 7x + 12 = (x + 3)(x + 4). \quad \text{Factoring}$$

This result can always be checked by multiplying the two binomials.

$$(x + 3)(x + 4) = x^2 + 7x + 12$$

$$3x$$
$$+4x$$
$$7x \longleftarrow \text{ The middle term checks. } ✓$$

TABLE 3.8
Factor Pairs for 12

Factors	Sum
1, 12	13
2, 6	8
3, 4	7

FACTORING $x^2 + bx + c$

To factor the trinomial $x^2 + bx + c$, find numbers m and n that satisfy

$$m \cdot n = c \quad \text{and} \quad m + n = b.$$

Then $x^2 + bx + c = (x + m)(x + n)$. Note that the coefficient of x^2 is 1.

Factoring $\longrightarrow$
NOTE: $x^2 + 7x + 12 = (x + 3)(x + 4)$ Multiplying and factoring
$\longleftarrow$ **Multiplying**   are reverse operations.

EXAMPLE 1 **Factoring the form $x^2 + bx + c$**

TABLE 3.9
Factor Pairs for 16

Factors	Sum
1, 16	17
2, 8	10
4, 4	8

Factor each trinomial.
(a) $x^2 + 10x + 16$ (b) $x^2 - 5x - 24$ (c) $x^2 + 7x - 30$

Solution

(a) We need to find a factor pair for 16 whose sum is 10. From Table 3.9 the required factor pair is $m = 2$ and $n = 8$. Thus

$$x^2 + 10x + 16 = (x + 2)(x + 8).$$

(b) Factors of -24 whose sum equals -5 are 3 and -8. Thus

$$x^2 - 5x - 24 = (x + 3)(x - 8).$$

(c) Factors of -30 whose sum equals 7 are -3 and 10. Thus

$$x^2 + 7x - 30 = (x - 3)(x + 10).$$

Now Try Exercises 17, 23, 25

EXAMPLE 2 **Removing common factors first**

Factor completely.
(a) $3x^2 + 15x + 18$ (b) $5x^3 + 5x^2 - 60x$

Solution

(a) If we first factor out the common factor of 3, the resulting trinomial is easier to factor.

$$3x^2 + 15x + 18 = 3(x^2 + 5x + 6)$$

Now we find m and n such that $mn = 6$ and $m + n = 5$. These numbers are 2 and 3.

$$3x^2 + 15x + 18 = 3(x^2 + 5x + 6)$$
$$= 3(x + 2)(x + 3)$$

(b) First, we factor out the common factor of $5x$. Then we factor the resulting trinomial.

$$5x^3 + 5x^2 - 60x = 5x(x^2 + x - 12)$$
$$= 5x(x - 3)(x + 4)$$

Now Try Exercises 55, 67

▶ **REAL-WORLD CONNECTION** Factoring may be used to solve the problem presented in A Look Into Math for this section. To do so we let x be the number of dollars that the price of a ticket is reduced below \$100. Then $100 - x$ represents the price of a ticket. For each \$1 reduction in price, 100 additional tickets will be sold, so the number of tickets sold is given by $100x$. Because the number of tickets sold times the price of each ticket equals the total revenue, we need to solve

Number sold ⌐   ⌐ Price

$$100x(100 - x) = 240{,}000 \quad \text{Revenue equals \$240,000.}$$

to determine when gross sales will reach \$240,000. We cannot immediately apply the zero-product property because the right side of the equation is *not* 0.

EXAMPLE 3 **Determining ticket price**

Solve the equation $100x(100 - x) = 240{,}000$ symbolically. What should be the price of the tickets and how many tickets will be sold? Support your answer graphically.

CRITICAL THINKING

In Example 3 what price will maximize the revenue from ticket sales? (*Hint:* See Figure 3.20.)

Solution

Symbolic Solution Begin by applying the distributive property.

$$100x(100 - x) = 240,000 \qquad \text{Given equation}$$
$$10,000x - 100x^2 = 240,000 \qquad \text{Distributive property}$$
$$-100x^2 + 10,000x - 240,000 = 0 \qquad \text{Subtract 240,000; rewrite.}$$
$$-100(x^2 - 100x + 2400) = 0 \qquad \text{Factor out } -100.$$
$$-100(x - 40)(x - 60) = 0 \qquad \text{Factor.}$$
$$x = 40 \quad \text{or} \quad x = 60 \qquad \text{Solve.}$$

If $x = 40$, the price is $100 - 40 = \$60$ per ticket and $100 \cdot 40 = 4000$ tickets are sold at \$60 each. If $x = 60$, the price is $100 - 60 = \$40$ and $100 \cdot 60 = 6000$ tickets are sold at \$40 each. Either price gives the desired ticket revenue of \$240,000.

Graphical Solution The graphs of $y_1 = 100x(100 - x)$ and $y_2 = 240,000$ intersect in Figure 3.20 at $x = 40$ and $x = 60$, which agrees with the symbolic solution.

CALCULATOR HELP

To find a point of intersection, see Appendix A (page AP-6).

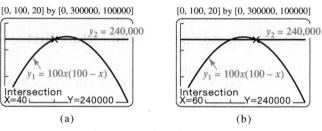

(a)   (b)

Figure 3.20

NOTE: These graphs also illustrate how revenue increases to a maximum value and then decreases as the price of the tickets decreases from \$100 to \$0.

Now Try Exercise 103

Factoring Trinomials by Grouping

In this subsection we use grouping to factor trinomials $ax^2 + bx + c$ with $a \neq 1$.

FACTORING $ax^2 + bx + c$ BY GROUPING

To factor $ax^2 + bx + c$ perform the following steps. (Assume that a, b, and c have no factor in common.)

1. Find numbers m and n such that $mn = ac$ and $m + n = b$. (This step may require trial and error.)
2. Write the trinomial as $ax^2 + mx + nx + c$.
3. Use grouping to factor this expression as two binomials.

For example, one way to factor $3x^2 + 14x + 8$ is to find two numbers m and n such that $mn = 3 \cdot 8 = 24$ and $m + n = 14$. Because $2 \cdot 12 = 24$ and $2 + 12 = 14$, $m = 2$ and $n = 12$. Using grouping, we can now factor this trinomial.

$$3x^2 + 14x + 8 = 3x^2 + 2x + 12x + 8 \qquad \text{Write } 14x \text{ as } 2x + 12x.$$
$$= (3x^2 + 2x) + (12x + 8) \qquad \text{Associative property}$$
$$= x(3x + 2) + 4(3x + 2) \qquad \text{Factor out } x \text{ and } 4.$$
$$= (x + 4)(3x + 2) \qquad \text{Factor out } 3x + 2.$$

EXAMPLE 4 **Factoring $ax^2 + bx + c$ by grouping**

Factor each trinomial.
(a) $3x^2 + 17x + 10$ **(b)** $12y^2 + 5y - 3$ **(c)** $6r^2 - 19r + 10$

Solution

(a) In this trinomial $a = 3, b = 17$, and $c = 10$. Because $mn = ac$ and $m + n = b$, the numbers m and n satisfy $mn = 30$ and $m + n = 17$. Thus $m = 2$ and $n = 15$.

$$3x^2 + \mathbf{17}x + 10 = 3x^2 + \mathbf{2}x + \mathbf{15}x + 10 \qquad \text{Write } 17x \text{ as } 2x + 15x.$$
$$= (3x^2 + 2x) + (15x + 10) \qquad \text{Associative property}$$
$$= x(3x + 2) + 5(3x + 2) \qquad \text{Factor out } x \text{ and } 5.$$
$$= (x + 5)(3x + 2) \qquad \text{Distributive property}$$

(b) In this trinomial $a = 12, b = 5$, and $c = -3$. Because $mn = ac$ and $m + n = b$, the numbers m and n satisfy $mn = -36$ and $m + n = 5$. Thus $m = 9$ and $n = -4$.

$$12y^2 + \mathbf{5}y - 3 = 12y^2 + \mathbf{9}y - \mathbf{4}y - 3 \qquad \text{Write } 5y \text{ as } 9y - 4y.$$
$$= (12y^2 + 9y) + (-4y - 3) \qquad \text{Associative property}$$

Be sure to factor out the GCF from each quantity. $\rightarrow$
$$= 3y(4y + 3) - 1(4y + 3) \qquad \text{Factor out } 3y \text{ and } -1.$$
$$= (3y - 1)(4y + 3) \qquad \text{Distributive property}$$

(c) In this trinomial $a = 6, b = -19$, and $c = 10$. Because $mn = ac$ and $m + n = b$, the numbers m and n satisfy $mn = 60$ and $m + n = -19$. Thus $m = -4$ and $n = -15$.

$$6r^2 - \mathbf{19}r + 10 = 6r^2 - \mathbf{4}r - \mathbf{15}r + 10 \qquad \text{Write } -19r \text{ as } -4r - 15r.$$
$$= (6r^2 - 4r) + (-15r + 10) \qquad \text{Associative property}$$
$$= 2r(3r - 2) - 5(3r - 2) \qquad \text{Factor out } 2r \text{ and } -5.$$
$$= (2r - 5)(3r - 2) \qquad \text{Distributive property}$$

Now Try Exercises 35, 41, 43

Factoring Trinomials with FOIL

An alternative to factoring trinomials by grouping is to use FOIL in reverse. For example, the factors of $3x^2 + 7x + 2$ are two binomials.

$$3x^2 + 7x + 2 \stackrel{?}{=} (\_\_\_ + \_\_\_)(\_\_\_ + \_\_\_)$$

The expressions to be placed in the four blanks are yet to be found. By the FOIL method, we know that the product of the first terms is $3x^2$. Because $3x^2 = 3x \cdot x$, we can write

$$3x^2 + 7x + 2 \stackrel{?}{=} (\underline{\,3x\,} + \_\_\_)(\underline{\,x\,} + \_\_\_).$$

The product of the last terms in each binomial must equal 2. Because $2 = 1 \cdot 2$, we can put the 1 and 2 in the blanks, but we must be sure to place them correctly so that the product of the *outside terms* plus the product of the *inside terms* equals $7x$.

$$(3x + 1)(x + 2) = 3x^2 + 7x + 2$$

$$\text{1}x$$
$$+6x$$
$$\overline{7x} \longleftarrow \text{ Middle term checks. } \checkmark$$

If we had interchanged the 1 and 2, we would have obtained an incorrect result.

$$(3x + 2)(x + 1) = 3x^2 + 5x + 2$$

$$\text{2}x$$
$$+3x$$
$$\overline{5x} \longleftarrow \text{ Middle term is } not \; 7x. \; ✗$$

In the next example we factor expressions of the form $ax^2 + bx + c$, where $a \neq 1$. In this situation, we may need to *guess and check* or use *trial and error* a few times before finding the correct factors.

EXAMPLE 5 **Factoring the form $ax^2 + bx + c$**

Factor each trinomial.
(a) $2x^2 + 9x + 4$ (b) $6x^2 - x - 2$ (c) $4x^3 - 14x^2 + 6x$

Solution
(a) The factors of $2x^2$ are $2x$ and x, so we begin by writing

$$2x^2 + 9x + 4 \stackrel{?}{=} (2x + \underline{\ \ })(x + \underline{\ \ }).$$

The factors of the last term, 4, are either 1 and 4 or 2 and 2. Selecting the factors 2 and 2 results in a middle term of $6x$ rather than $9x$.

$$(2x + 2)(x + 2) = 2x^2 + 6x + 4$$

Next we try the factors 1 and 4.

$$(2x + 4)(x + 1) = 2x^2 + 6x + 4$$

Again we obtain the wrong middle term. By interchanging the 1 and 4, we find the correct factorization.

$$(2x + 1)(x + 4) = 2x^2 + 9x + 4$$

(b) The factors of $6x^2$ are either $2x$ and $3x$ or $6x$ and x. The factors of -2 are either -1 and 2 or 1 and -2. To obtain a middle term of $-x$ we use the following factors.

$$(3x - 2)(2x + 1) = 6x^2 - x - 2$$

To find the correct factorization we may need to guess and check a few times.
(c) Each term contains a common factor of $2x$, so we do the following step first.

$$4x^3 - 14x^2 + 6x = 2x(2x^2 - 7x + 3)$$

Next we factor $2x^2 - 7x + 3$. The factors of $2x^2$ are $2x$ and x. Because the middle term is negative, we use -1 and -3 for factors of 3.

$$4x^3 - 14x^2 + 6x = 2x(2x^2 - 7x + 3)$$
$$= 2x(2x - 1)(x - 3)$$

Now Try Exercises 37, 39, 69

NOTE: If a trinomial does not have any common factors, then its binomial factors will not have any common factors either. Thus in Example 5(a), $(2x + 2)$ and $(2x + 4)$ cannot be factors of $2x^2 + 9x + 4$. These factors can be eliminated without checking.

EXAMPLE 6   **Estimating passing distance**

A car traveling 48 miles per hour accelerates at a constant rate to pass a car in front of it. A no-passing zone begins 2000 feet away. The distance d traveled in feet by the car after t seconds is $d(t) = 3t^2 + 70t$. How long does it take the car to reach the no-passing zone?

Solution

We must determine the time when $3t^2 + 70t = 2000$.

$$3t^2 + 70t = 2000 \qquad \text{Equation to be solved}$$
$$3t^2 + 70t - 2000 = 0 \qquad \text{Subtract 2000.}$$
$$(3t - 50)(t + 40) = 0 \qquad \text{Factor.}$$
$$3t - 50 = 0 \quad \text{or} \quad t + 40 = 0 \qquad \text{Zero-product property}$$
$$t = \frac{50}{3} \quad \text{or} \quad t = -40 \qquad \text{Solve.}$$

The car reaches the no-passing zone after $\frac{50}{3} \approx 16.7$ seconds. (The solution $t = -40$ has no physical meaning in this problem.)

▌ **Now Try Exercise 107**

CRITICAL THINKING

Can every trinomial be factored with the methods discussed in this section? Try to factor the following trinomials and then make a conjecture.

$$x^2 + 2x + 2, \quad x^2 - x + 1, \quad \text{and} \quad 2x^2 + x + 2.$$

Factoring with Graphs and Tables

Polynomials can also be factored graphically. One way to do so is to use a graph of the polynomial to find its zeros. A number p is a *zero* if a value of 0 results when p is substituted in the polynomial. For example, both -2 and 2 are zeros of $x^2 - 4$ because

$$(-2)^2 - 4 = 0 \quad \text{and} \quad (2)^2 - 4 = 0.$$

Now consider the trinomial $x^2 - 3x + 2$, whose graph is shown in Figure 3.21. Its x-intercepts or zeros are 1 and 2, and this trinomial factors as

$$x^2 - 3x + 2 = (x - 1)(x - 2).$$

We generalize these concepts as follows.

Figure 3.21
$y = x^2 - 3x + 2$

$f(x) = a(x - p)(x - q)$

Figure 3.22
$y = f(x)$
$a > 0$

FACTORING WITH A GRAPH OR A TABLE OF VALUES

To factor the trinomial $x^2 + bx + c$, either graph or make a table of $y = x^2 + bx + c$. If the zeros of the trinomial are p and q, then the trinomial can be factored as

$$x^2 + bx + c = (x - p)(x - q).$$

If the trinomial $ax^2 + bx + c$ has zeros p and q, then it may be factored as

$$ax^2 + bx + c = a(x - p)(x - q).$$

See Figure 3.22.

NOTE: If the coefficient a of x^2 is not 1, then a must be included in the factoring. For example, the zeros of $2x^2 - 8x + 6$ are 1 and 3, so it can be factored as $2(x - 1)(x - 3)$. Note that the leading coefficient 2 must be included as part of the factorization.

EXAMPLE 7   **Factoring with technology**

Factor each trinomial graphically or numerically.
(a) $x^2 - 2x - 24$ (b) $2x^2 - 51x + 220$

Solution

(a) Graph $y_1 = x^2 - 2x - 24$. When the trace feature is used, the zeros of the trinomial are -4 and 6, as shown in Figure 3.23. Thus the trinomial factors as follows.

$$x^2 - 2x - 24 = \big(x - (-4)\big)(x - 6)$$
$$= (x + 4)(x - 6)$$

Figure 3.23

(b) Construct a table for $y_1 = 2x^2 - 51x + 220$. Figure 3.24 reveals that the zeros are **3.5** and **20**. The leading coefficient of $2x^2 - 51x + 220$ is **2**, so we factor this expression as follows.

$$2x^2 - 51x + 220 = 2(x - 5.5)(x - 20)$$
$$= (2x - 11)(x - 20)$$

Figure 3.24

Now Try Exercises 95, 99

READING CHECK

If you know the zeros and leading coefficient of a polynomial, how can you factor it?

3.4	**Putting It All Together**

Equations of the form $ax^2 + bx + c = 0$ occur in applications. One way to solve such equations is to factor the trinomial $ax^2 + bx + c$. This factorization may be done symbolically, graphically, or numerically. The following table includes an explanation and examples of each technique. To factor by grouping, see the box on page 196.

TECHNIQUE	EXPLANATION	EXAMPLE
Symbolic Factoring	To factor $x^2 + bx + c$ find two factors of c whose sum is b. To factor $ax^2 + bx + c$ find factors of ax^2 and c so that the middle term is bx. Grouping can also be used. With grouping we start by finding two numbers whose product is ac and whose sum is b.	To factor $x^2 - 3x - 4$, find two factors of -4 whose sum is -3. These factors are 1 and -4. $$x^2 - 3x - 4 = (x + 1)(x - 4)$$ It checks. $\longrightarrow$ $-3x$ ✓ To factor $2x^2 + 3x - 2$ find factors of $2x^2$ and -2 so that the middle term is $3x$. $$2x^2 + 3x - 2 = (2x - 1)(x + 2)$$ It checks. $\longrightarrow$ $3x$ ✓
Graphical Factoring	If p and q are zeros of $x^2 + bx + c$, then the expression factors as $$(x - p)(x - q).$$ If p and q are zeros of $ax^2 + bx + c$, then the expression factors as $$a(x - p)(x - q).$$	To factor $x^2 - 3x - 4$ ($a = 1$), graph $y = x^2 - 3x - 4$. The zeros (x-intercepts) are -1 and 4, and it follows that $$x^2 - 3x - 4 = (x + 1)(x - 4).$$
Numerical Factoring	If p and q are zeros of $x^2 + bx + c$, then the expression factors as $$(x - p)(x - q).$$ If p and q are zeros of $ax^2 + bx + c$, then the expression factors as $$a(x - p)(x - q).$$	To factor $2x^2 + 3x - 2$, make a table for $y_1 = 2x^2 + 3x - 2$. The zeros are 0.5 and -2. $$2x^2 + 3x - 2 = 2(x - 0.5)(x + 2)$$ $$= (2x - 1)(x + 2)$$

X	Y₁
-2	0
-1.5	-2
-1	-3
-.5	-3
0	-2
.5	0
1	3

$Y_1 = 2X^2 + 3X - 2$

3.4 Exercises

 MyMathLab | Math XL PRACTICE | WATCH | DOWNLOAD | READ | REVIEW

CONCEPTS AND VOCABULARY

1. What is a trinomial? Give an example.

2. Name two methods for factoring $ax^2 + bx + c$.

3. The trinomial $3x^2 - x - 3$ is written in the form $ax^2 + bx + c$. Identify a, b, and c.

4. If you factor the trinomial $x^2 + 3x + 2$, do you obtain $(x + 1)(x + 2)$? Explain.

5. Suppose that the graph of $y = x^2 + bx + c$ has x-intercepts -3 and 1. Factor $x^2 + bx + c$.

6. The graph of $y = 6x^2 - 15x + 6$ has x-intercepts $\frac{1}{2}$ and 2. Factor $6x^2 - 15x + 6$.

7. Which of the following (a.–d.) is a factorization of $x^2 - 3x - 18$?
a. $(x - 2)(x + 9)$ **b.** $(x + 6)(x + 3)$
c. $(x + 3)(x - 6)$ **d.** $(x - 9)(4x + 2)$

8. Which of the following (a.–d.) is a factorization of $12x^2 - 7x - 12$?
a. $(6x - 3)(2x + 4)$ **b.** $(x - 1)(12x + 6)$
c. $(3x + 4)(4x - 3)$ **d.** $(3x - 4)(4x + 3)$

FACTORING TRINOMIALS

Exercises 9–16: Determine whether the factors of the trinomial are the given binomials.

9. $x^2 + 5x + 6$ $(x + 2)(x + 3)$

10. $x^2 - 13x + 30$ $(x - 10)(x - 3)$

11. $x^2 - x - 20$ $(x + 5)(x - 4)$

12. $x^2 + 3x - 28$ $(x + 4)(x - 7)$

13. $6z^2 - 11z + 4$ $(2z - 1)(3z - 4)$

14. $4z^2 - 19z + 12$ $(2z - 4)(2z - 3)$

15. $10m^2 - 21m + 10$ $(5m + 2)(2m - 5)$

16. $12n^2 + 5n - 2$ $(3n + 2)(4n - 1)$

Exercises 17–72: Factor completely.

17. $x^2 + 7x + 10$ **18.** $x^2 + 3x - 10$

19. $x^2 + 8x + 12$ **20.** $x^2 - 8x + 12$

21. $x^2 - 13x + 36$ **22.** $x^2 + 11x + 24$

23. $x^2 - 7x - 8$ **24.** $x^2 - 21x - 100$

25. $z^2 + z - 72$ **26.** $z^2 + 6z - 55$

27. $t^2 - 15t + 56$ **28.** $t^2 - 14t + 40$

29. $y^2 - 18y + 72$ **30.** $y^2 - 15y + 54$

31. $m^2 - 18m - 40$ **32.** $m^2 - 22m - 75$

33. $n^2 - 20n - 300$ **34.** $n^2 - 13n - 30$

35. $2x^2 + 7x + 3$ **36.** $2x^2 - 5x - 3$

37. $6x^2 - 7x - 5$ **38.** $10x^2 + 3x - 1$

39. $4z^2 + 19z + 12$ **40.** $4z^2 + 17z + 4$

41. $6t^2 - 17t + 12$ **42.** $6t^2 - 13t + 6$

43. $10y^2 + 13y - 3$ **44.** $10y^2 + 23y - 5$

45. $6m^2 - m - 12$ **46.** $20m^2 - m - 12$

47. $42n^2 + 5n - 25$ **48.** $42n^2 + 65n + 25$

49. $1 + x - 2x^2$ **50.** $3 - 5x - 2x^2$

51. $20 + 7x - 6x^2$ **52.** $4 + 13x - 12x^2$

53. $5y^2 + 5y - 30$ **54.** $3y^2 - 27y + 24$

55. $2z^2 + 12z + 16$ **56.** $4z^2 + 32z + 60$

57. $z^3 + 9z^2 + 14z$ **58.** $z^3 + 7z^2 + 12z$

59. $t^3 - 10t^2 + 21t$ **60.** $t^3 - 11t^2 + 24t$

61. $m^4 + 6m^3 + 5m^2$ **62.** $m^4 - m^3 - 2m^2$

63. $5x^3 + x^2 - 6x$ **64.** $2x^3 + 8x^2 - 24x$

65. $6x^3 + 21x^2 + 9x$ **66.** $12x^3 - 8x^2 - 20x$

67. $2x^3 - 14x^2 + 20x$ **68.** $7x^3 + 35x^2 + 42x$

69. $60z^3 + 230z^2 - 40z$ **70.** $24z^3 + 8z^2 - 80z$

71. $4x^4 + 10x^3 - 6x^2$ **72.** $30x^4 + 3x^3 - 9x^2$

Exercises 73–76: Thinking Generally Factor the given expression completely.

73. $x^2 + (2 + 3)x + 2 \cdot 3$

74. $x^2 - (3 + 4)x + 3 \cdot 4$

75. $x^2 + (a + b)x + ab$

76. $x^2 - (a + b)x + ab$

77. Thinking Generally If $x^2 + bx + c = 0$ for $x = 1$ and $x = 2$, find b and c.

78. Thinking Generally If $x^2 + bx = 0$ for $x = -4$, find b.

Exercises 79–82: Multiplying Functions Use factoring to find $f(x)$ and $g(x)$ so that $h(x) = f(x)\,g(x)$.

79. $h(x) = x^2 + 3x + 2$

80. $h(x) = x^2 - 4x + 3$

81. $h(x) = x^2 - 2x - 8$

82. $h(x) = x^2 + 3x - 10$

FACTORING WITH GRAPHS AND TABLES

Exercises 83–88: Factor the expression by using the graph of $y = f(x)$, where $f(x)$ is the given expression. Check your answer by multiplying.

83. $x^2 - 6x + 8$

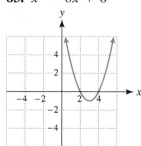

84. $x^2 - x - 6$

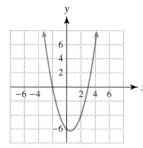

85. $2x^2 - 2x - 4$

86. $3x^2 + 3x - 18$

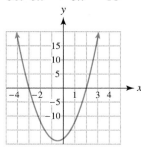

87. $2 + x - x^2$

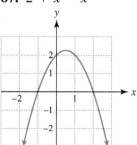

88. $3 - 2x - x^2$

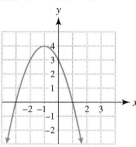

Exercises 89–92: Use the table to factor the expression. Check your answer by multiplying.

89. $x^2 - 3x - 4$

90. $x^2 - 40x + 300$

91. $2x^2 - 2x - 4$

92. $3x^2 - 18x + 24$

Exercises 93–102: Factor graphically or numerically.

93. $x^2 + 3x - 10$ **94.** $x^2 + 7x + 12$

95. $x^2 - 3x - 28$ **96.** $x^2 - 25x + 100$

97. $2x^2 - 14x + 20$ **98.** $12x^2 - 6x - 6$

99. $5x^2 - 30x - 200$ **100.** $12x^2 - 30x + 12$

101. $8x^2 - 44x + 20$ **102.** $20x^2 + 3x - 9$

APPLICATIONS

103. *Ticket Prices* (Refer to Example 3.) If tickets are sold for \$35, 1200 tickets are expected to be sold. For each \$1 reduction in ticket price, an additional 100 tickets will be sold.
  (a) Find the revenue from ticket sales when ticket prices are reduced by x dollars.
  (b) Find the ticket prices that give sales of \$54,000.

104. *Ticket Prices* One airline ticket costs \$295. For each additional ticket sold to a group of up to 30 people, the price of every ticket is reduced by \$5. For example, 2 tickets cost $2 \cdot \$290 = \$580$ and 3 tickets cost $3 \cdot \$285 = \$855$.
  (a) Find the cost of x tickets.
  (b) What is the cost of 20 tickets?
  (c) How many tickets are sold if the total cost is \$2500?

105. *Area of a Rectangle* A rectangle has an area of 91 square feet. Its length is 6 feet more than its width. Find the dimensions of the rectangle.

106. *Area of a Triangle* The base of a triangle is 2 inches less than its height. If the area of the triangle is 60 square inches, find its height.

107. *Passing Distances* (Refer to Example 6.) The distance traveled in feet by a car passing another car after t seconds is given by $2t^2 + 88t$.
  (a) Use factoring to determine how long it takes for the car to travel 600 feet.
  (b) Solve part (a) either graphically or numerically.

108. *Numbers* Find the two consecutive positive integers whose product is 132.

109. A student factors each trinomial into the given pair of binomials.

  (i) $x^2 - 5x - 6$ $(x - 1)(x + 6)$
  (ii) $10x^2 - 11x - 6$ $(5x - 3)(2x + 2)$
  (iii) $12x^2 + 13x + 3$ $(6x + 1)(2x + 3)$

  Explain the error that the student is making.

110. Suppose that a graph of $y = x^2 + bx + c$ intersects the x-axis at p and at q. Explain how you could use the graph to factor $x^2 + bx + c$.

SECTIONS 3.3 and 3.4 — Checking Basic Concepts

1. Factor out the greatest common factor.
  (a) $3x^2 - 6x$ (b) $16x^3 - 8x^2 + 4x$

2. Use factoring to solve each equation.
  (a) $x^2 - 2x = 0$ (b) $9x^2 = 81x$

3. Factor each trinomial.
  (a) $x^2 + 3x - 10$ (b) $x^2 - 3x - 10$
  (c) $8x^2 + 14x + 3$

4. Solve $x^2 + 3x + 2 = 0$.

5. A baseball is thrown upward at 64 feet per second or approximately 44 miles per hour. Its height above the ground after t seconds is given by

$$h(t) = -16t^2 + 64t + 8.$$

Determine when the baseball is 56 feet above the ground.

3.5   Special Types of Factoring

Difference of Two Squares • Perfect Square Trinomials •
Sum and Difference of Two Cubes

A LOOK INTO MATH ▶

Polynomials are frequently used to estimate and model things in real life, such as the curved shape of a car's exterior. Because of this fact, people have spent a lot of time developing factoring methods for polynomials. Two primary reasons for factoring are to *solve equations* and to *simplify expressions*. Although not all polynomials can be factored easily, many polynomials can be factored. In this section we focus on some special types of factoring.

Difference of Two Squares

NEW VOCABULARY

☐ Difference of two squares
☐ Perfect square trinomials
☐ Sum/difference of cubes

When we factor polynomials, we are *reversing* the process of multiplying polynomials. In Section 3.2 we discussed the equation

$$(a - b)(a + b) = a^2 - b^2. \quad \text{Multiplying}$$

We can use this equation to factor a **difference of two squares**. For example, if we want to factor $x^2 - 25$, we can substitute x for a and 5 for b in

$$a^2 - b^2 = (a - b)(a + b) \quad \text{Factoring}$$

to get

$$x^2 - 5^2 = (x - 5)(x + 5).$$

> ## DIFFERENCE OF TWO SQUARES
>
> For any real numbers a and b,
> $$a^2 - b^2 = (a - b)(a + b).$$

NOTE: The sum of two squares *cannot* be factored completely using real numbers. For example, $x^2 + y^2$ cannot be factored, whereas $x^2 - y^2$ can be factored. *It is important to remember that* $x^2 + y^2 \neq (x + y)^2$.

EXAMPLE 1   **Factoring the difference of two squares**

Factor each polynomial, if possible.
(a) $9x^2 - 64$ **(b)** $4x^2 + 9y^2$ **(c)** $9x^4 - y^6$ **(d)** $4a^3 - 4a$

Solution
(a) Note that $9x^2 = (3x)^2$ and $64 = 8^2$.

$$9x^2 - 64 = (3x)^2 - (8)^2 \qquad \text{Write as } a^2 - b^2.$$
$$= (3x - 8)(3x + 8) \qquad \text{Factor as } (a - b)(a + b).$$

(b) Because $4x^2 + 9y^2$ is the *sum* of two squares, it *cannot* be factored.
(c) If we let $a^2 = 9x^4$ and $b^2 = y^6$, then $a = 3x^2$ and $b = y^3$. Thus

$$9x^4 - y^6 = (3x^2)^2 - (y^3)^2 \qquad \text{Write as } a^2 - b^2.$$
$$= (3x^2 - y^3)(3x^2 + y^3). \qquad \text{Factor as } (a - b)(a + b).$$

(d) Start by factoring out the common factor of $4a$.

$$4a^3 - 4a = 4a(a^2 - 1)$$
$$= 4a(a - 1)(a + 1)$$

▮ Now Try Exercises 17, 19, 25, 29

EXAMPLE 2   **Applying the difference of two squares**

Factor each expression.
(a) $(n + 1)^2 - 9$ **(b)** $x^4 - y^4$ **(c)** $6r^2 - 24t^4$ **(d)** $x^3 + 3x^2 - 4x - 12$

Solution
(a) Use $a^2 - b^2 = (a - b)(a + b)$, with $a = n + 1$ and $b = 3$.

$$(n + 1)^2 - 9 = (n + 1)^2 - 3^2 \qquad\qquad 9 = 3^2$$
$$= \big((n + 1) - 3\big)\big((n + 1) + 3\big) \qquad \text{Difference of squares}$$
$$= (n - 2)(n + 4) \qquad \text{Combine terms.}$$

(b) Use $a^2 - b^2 = (a - b)(a + b)$, with $a = x^2$ and $b = y^2$.

$$x^4 - y^4 = (x^2)^2 - (y^2)^2 \qquad\qquad \text{Write as squares.}$$
$$= (x^2 - y^2)(x^2 + y^2) \qquad \text{Difference of squares}$$
$$= (x - y)(x + y)(x^2 + y^2) \qquad \text{Difference of squares again}$$

(c) Start by factoring out the common factor of 6.

$$6r^2 - 24t^4 = 6(r^2 - 4t^4) \qquad \text{Factor out 6.}$$
$$= 6\left(r^2 - (2t^2)^2\right) \qquad \text{Write as squares.}$$
$$= 6(r - 2t^2)(r + 2t^2) \qquad \text{Difference of squares}$$

(d) Start factoring by using *grouping* and then factor the difference of squares.

$$x^3 + 3x^2 - 4x - 12 = (x^3 + 3x^2) + (-4x - 12) \qquad \text{Associative property}$$
$$= x^2(x + 3) - 4(x + 3) \qquad \text{Factor out } x^2 \text{ and } -4.$$
$$= (x^2 - 4)(x + 3) \qquad \text{Factor out } (x + 3).$$
$$= (x - 2)(x + 2)(x + 3) \qquad \text{Difference of squares}$$

> Now Try Exercises 23, 31, 37, 39

Perfect Square Trinomials

In Section 3.2 we also showed how to multiply $(a + b)^2$ and $(a - b)^2$.

$$(a + b)^2 = a^2 + 2ab + b^2 \quad \text{and} \quad (a - b)^2 = a^2 - 2ab + b^2$$

The expressions $a^2 + 2ab + b^2$ and $a^2 - 2ab + b^2$ are **perfect square trinomials**. If we can recognize a perfect square trinomial, we can use these formulas to factor it.

PERFECT SQUARE TRINOMIALS

For any real numbers a and b,

$$a^2 + 2ab + b^2 = (a + b)^2 \quad \text{and}$$
$$a^2 - 2ab + b^2 = (a - b)^2.$$

EXAMPLE 3   **Factoring perfect square trinomials**

Factor.
(a) $x^2 + 6x + 9$ **(b)** $81x^2 - 72x + 16$

Solution

(a) Let $a^2 = x^2$ and $b^2 = 3^2$. For a *perfect square trinomial*, the middle term must be $2ab$.

$$2ab = 2(x)(3) = 6x, \checkmark$$

which equals the given middle term. Thus $a^2 + 2ab + b^2 = (a + b)^2$ implies

$$x^2 + 6x + 9 = (x + 3)^2.$$

(b) Let $a^2 = (9x)^2$ and $b^2 = 4^2$. Again, the middle term must be $2ab$.

$$2ab = 2(9x)(4) = 72x, \checkmark$$

which equals the given middle term. Thus $a^2 - 2ab + b^2 = (a - b)^2$ implies

$$81x^2 - 72x + 16 = (9x - 4)^2.$$

> Now Try Exercises 51, 57

EXAMPLE 4   **Factoring perfect square trinomials**

Factor each expression.
(a) $4x^2 + 4xy + y^2$ (b) $9r^2 - 12rt + 4t^2$ (c) $25a^3 + 10a^2b + ab^2$

Solution
(a) Let $a^2 = (2x)^2$ and $b^2 = y^2$. The middle term must be $2ab$.

$$2ab = 2(2x)(y) = 4xy, \checkmark$$

which equals the given middle term. Thus $a^2 + 2ab + b^2 = (a + b)^2$ implies

$$4x^2 + 4xy + y^2 = (2x + y)^2.$$

(b) Let $a^2 = (3r)^2$ and $b^2 = (2t)^2$. The middle term must be $2ab$.

$$2ab = 2(3r)(2t) = 12rt, \checkmark$$

which equals the given middle term. Thus $a^2 - 2ab + b^2 = (a - b)^2$ implies

$$9r^2 - 12rt + 4t^2 = (3r - 2t)^2.$$

(c) Factor out the common factor of a. Then factor the resulting perfect square trinomial.

$$25a^3 + 10a^2b + ab^2 = a(25a^2 + 10ab + b^2)$$
$$= a(5a + b)^2$$

▌ Now Try Exercises 63, 65, 67

MAKING CONNECTIONS

Special Factoring and General Techniques

If you do *not* recognize a polynomial as being either the difference of two squares or a perfect square trinomial, then you can factor the polynomial by using the methods discussed in earlier sections.

Sum and Difference of Two Cubes

The **sum or difference of two cubes** may be factored. This fact is justified by the following two equations.

$$(a + b)(a^2 - ab + b^2) = a^3 + b^3 \quad \text{and} \qquad \text{Sum of cubes}$$
$$(a - b)(a^2 + ab + b^2) = a^3 - b^3 \qquad\qquad \text{Difference of cubes}$$

These equations can be verified by multiplying the left side to obtain the right side. For example,

$$(a + b)(a^2 - ab + b^2) = a \cdot a^2 - a \cdot ab + a \cdot b^2 + b \cdot a^2 - b \cdot ab + b \cdot b^2$$
$$= a^3 - a^2b + ab^2 + a^2b - ab^2 + b^3$$
$$= a^3 + b^3.$$

SUM AND DIFFERENCE OF TWO CUBES

For any real numbers a and b,

$$a^3 + b^3 = (a + b)(a^2 - ab + b^2) \quad \text{and}$$
$$a^3 - b^3 = (a - b)(a^2 + ab + b^2).$$

EXAMPLE 5   **Factoring a sum or difference of two cubes**

Factor each polynomial.
(a) $x^3 + 8$ (b) $27x^3 - 64y^3$

Solution

(a) Because $x^3 = (x)^3$ and $8 = 2^3$, we let $a = x$, $b = 2$, and factor. Substituting in

$$a^3 + b^3 = (a + b)(a^2 - ab + b^2)$$

gives

$$x^3 + 2^3 = (x + 2)(x^2 - x \cdot 2 + 2^2)$$
$$= (x + 2)(x^2 - 2x + 4).$$

Note that $x^2 - 2x + 4$ does not factor further.

(b) Here, $27x^3 = (3x)^3$ and $64y^3 = (4y)^3$, so

$$27x^3 - 64y^3 = (3x)^3 - (4y)^3.$$

Substituting $a = 3x$ and $b = 4y$ in

$$a^3 - b^3 = (a - b)(a^2 + ab + b^2)$$

gives

$$(3x)^3 - (4y)^3 = (3x - 4y)\big((3x)^2 + 3x \cdot 4y + (4y)^2\big)$$
$$= (3x - 4y)(9x^2 + 12xy + 16y^2).$$

▮ Now Try Exercises 69, 75

EXAMPLE 6   **Factoring a sum or difference of two cubes**

Factor each expression.
(a) $x^6 + 8y^3$ (b) $27p^9 - 8q^6$

Solution

(a) Let $a^3 = (x^2)^3$ and $b^3 = (2y)^3$. Then $a^3 + b^3 = (a + b)(a^2 - ab + b^2)$ implies

$$x^6 + 8y^3 = (x^2 + 2y)(x^4 - 2x^2y + 4y^2).$$

(b) Let $a^3 = (3p^3)^3$ and $b^3 = (2q^2)^3$. Then $a^3 - b^3 = (a - b)(a^2 + ab + b^2)$ implies

$$27p^9 - 8q^6 = (3p^3 - 2q^2)(9p^6 + 6p^3q^2 + 4q^4).$$

▮ Now Try Exercises 81, 83

3.5 Putting It All Together

In this section we presented three special types of factoring, which are summarized in the following table.

TYPE OF FACTORING	DESCRIPTION	EXAMPLE
The Difference of Two Squares	To factor the difference of two squares, use $a^2 - b^2 = (a - b)(a + b)$. **NOTE:** $a^2 + b^2$ cannot be factored.	$25x^2 - 16 = (5x - 4)(5x + 4)$ $a = 5x, b = 4$ $4x^2 + y^2$ cannot be factored.
A Perfect Square Trinomial	To factor a perfect square trinomial, use $a^2 + 2ab + b^2 = (a + b)^2$ or $a^2 - 2ab + b^2 = (a - b)^2$.	$x^2 + 4x + 4 = (x + 2)^2$ $a = x, b = 2$ $16x^2 - 24x + 9 = (4x - 3)^2$ $a = 4x, b = 3$ Be sure to check the middle term.
The Sum and Difference of Two Cubes	The sum and difference of two cubes can be factored as $a^3 + b^3 = (a + b) \cdot (a^2 - ab + b^2)$ or $a^3 - b^3 = (a - b) \cdot (a^2 + ab + b^2)$.	$x^3 + 8y^3 = (x + 2y)\left(x^2 - x \cdot 2y + (2y)^2\right)$ $= (x + 2y)(x^2 - 2xy + 4y^2)$ $a = x, b = 2y$ $125x^3 - 64 = (5x - 4)\left((5x)^2 + 5x \cdot 4 + 4^2\right)$ $= (5x - 4)(25x^2 + 20x + 16)$ $a = 5x, b = 4$

3.5 Exercises

PRACTICE   WATCH   DOWNLOAD   READ   REVIEW

CONCEPTS AND VOCABULARY

1. Give an example of a difference of two squares.

2. Give an example of a perfect square trinomial.

3. Give an example of the sum of two cubes.

4. Factor $a^2 - b^2$.

5. Factor $a^2 + 2ab + b^2$.

6. Factor $a^3 - b^3$.

7. Which of the following (a.–d.) is a factorization of $25x^2 - 16$?
   a. $(5x - 8)(5x + 8)$ **b.** $(5x - 4)(5x - 4)$
   c. $(5x - 4)(5x + 4)$ **d.** $(25x - 1)(x - 16)$

8. Which of the following (a.–d.) is a factorization of $36x^2 - 48x + 16$?
   a. $(9x - 8)(2x - 2)$ **b.** $4(3x - 2)^2$
   c. $(12x + 4)(3x + 4)$ **d.** $4(3x + 2)^2$

DIFFERENCE OF TWO SQUARES

Exercises 9–12: Determine whether the expression represents a difference of two squares. Factor the expression.

9. $x^2 - 25$

10. $16x^2 - 100$

11. $x^3 + y^3$

12. $9x^2 + 36y^2$

Exercises 13–38: Factor the expression, if possible.

13. $x^2 - 36$ 14. $y^2 - 144$

15. $25 - z^2$ 16. $36 - y^2$

17. $4z^2 + 25$ 18. $9z^2 + 64$

19. $36x^2 - 100$ 20. $4y^2 - 64$

21. $49a^2 - 64b^2$ 22. $9x^2 - 4y^2$

23. $64z^2 - 25z^4$

24. $64z^4 - 49z^2$

25. $5x^3 - 125x$

26. $100x^3 - x$

27. $4r^4 + t^6$

28. $9t^4 - 25r^6$

29. $16t^4 - r^2$

30. $t^4 + 9r^2$

31. $(x + 1)^2 - 25$

32. $(x - 2)^2 - 9$

33. $100 - (n - 4)^2$

34. $81 - (n + 3)^2$

35. $y^4 - 16$

36. $16z^4 - 1$

37. $16x^4 - y^4$

38. $r^4 - 81t^4$

Exercises 39–42: Use grouping to help factor the expression completely.

39. $x^3 + x^2 - x - 1$

40. $x^3 + x^2 - 9x - 9$

41. $4x^3 - 8x^2 - x + 2$

42. $9x^3 - 18x^2 - 16x + 32$

PERFECT SQUARE TRINOMIALS

Exercises 43–50: Determine whether the trinomial is a perfect square. If it is, factor it.

43. $x^2 + x + 16$

44. $4x^2 - 2x + 25$

45. $x^2 + 8x + 16$

46. $x^2 - 4x + 4$

47. $4z^2 - 4z + 1$

48. $9z^2 + 6z + 4$

49. $16t^2 - 12t + 9$

50. $4t^2 + 12t + 9$

Exercises 51–68: Factor the expression.

51. $x^2 + 2x + 1$

52. $x^2 - 6x + 9$

53. $4x^2 + 20x + 25$

54. $x^2 + 10x + 25$

55. $x^2 - 12x + 36$

56. $x^2 + 20x + 100$

57. $9z^2 - 24z + 16$

58. $36z^2 + 12z + 1$

59. $4y^4 + 4y^3 + y^2$

60. $16z^4 - 24z^3 + 9z^2$

61. $9z^3 - 6z^2 + z$

62. $49y^2 + 42y + 9$

63. $9x^2 + 6xy + y^2$

64. $25x^2 + 30xy + 9y^2$

65. $49a^2 - 28ab + 4b^2$

66. $64a^2 - 16ab + b^2$

67. $4x^4 - 4x^3y + x^2y^2$

68. $4x^3y + 12x^2y^2 + 9xy^3$

SUM AND DIFFERENCE OF TWO CUBES

Exercises 69–86: Factor the expression.

69. $x^3 - 8$

70. $x^3 + 8$

71. $y^3 + z^3$

72. $y^3 - z^3$

73. $27x^3 - 8$

74. $64 - y^3$

75. $64z^3 + 27t^3$

76. $125t^3 - 64r^3$

77. $8x^4 + 125x$

78. $x^3y^2 + 8y^5$

79. $27y - 8x^3y$

80. $x^3y^3 + 1$

81. $z^6 - 27y^3$

82. $z^6 + 27y^3$

83. $125z^6 + 8y^9$

84. $125z^6 - 8y^9$

85. $5m^6 + 40n^3$

86. $10m^9 - 270n^6$

GENERAL FACTORING

Exercises 87–120: Factor the expression completely.

87. $25x^2 - 64$

88. $25x^2 - 30x + 9$

89. $x^3 + 27$

90. $4 - 16y^2$

91. $64x^2 + 16x + 1$

92. $2x^2 - 5x + 3$

93. $3x^2 + 14x + 8$

94. $125x^3 - 1$

95. $x^4 + 8x$

96. $2x^3 - 12x^2 + 18x$

97. $64x^3 + 8y^3$

98. $54 - 16x^3$

99. $2r^2 - 8t^2$

100. $a^3 - ab^2$

101. $a^3 + 4a^2b + 4ab^2$

102. $8r^4 + rt^3$

103. $x^2 - 3x + 2$

104. $x^2 + 4x - 5$

105. $4z^2 - 25$

106. $(z + 1)^2 - 49$

107. $x^4 + 16x^3 + 64x^2$

108. $4x^2 - 12xy + 9y^2$

109. $z^3 - 1$

110. $8z^3 + 1$

111. $3t^2 - 5t - 8$

112. $15t^2 - 11t + 2$

113. $7a^3 + 20a^2 - 3a$

114. $b^3 - b^2 - 2b$

115. $x^6 - y^6$

116. $a^8 - b^8$

117. $100x^2 - 1$

118. $4x^2 + 28x + 49$

119. $p^3q^3 - 27$

120. $a^2b^2 - c^2d^2$

121. *Difference of Two Squares* Write the difference in the areas between the large square with sides of length x and a smaller square with sides of length 5, using factored form.

122. *Difference of Two Cubes* Write the difference in the volumes between a large cube with sides of length 2 and a smaller cube with sides of length x, using factored form.

WRITING ABOUT MATHEMATICS

123. Explain how factoring $x^3 + y^3$ is similar to factoring $x^3 - y^3$.

124. Can $x^2 - y^2$ be factored? Can $x^2 + y^2$ be factored? Explain your answers.

Group Activity   Working with Real Data

Directions: Form a group of 2 to 4 people. Select someone to record the group's responses for this activity. All members of the group should work cooperatively to answer the questions. If your instructor asks for your results, each member of the group should be prepared to respond.

Exercises 1–6: *Geometric Factoring* The polynomial $x^2 + 4x + 3$ can be factored by grouping.

$$x^2 + 4x + 3 = x^2 + x + 3x + 3$$
$$= (x^2 + x) + (3x + 3)$$
$$= x(x + 1) + 3(x + 1)$$
$$= (x + 3)(x + 1)$$

This factorization is represented geometrically in the accompanying figure. Note that the outside dimensions of the large rectangle are $x + 3$ by $x + 1$ and therefore its area is $(x + 3)(x + 1)$. This area equals the sum of the four smaller rectangles inside the large rectangle. Thus

$$(x + 3)(x + 1) = x^2 + x + 3x + 3 = x^2 + 4x + 3.$$

Factor the following expressions geometrically. If the rectangle turns out to be a square, what can you say about the trinomial?

1. $x^2 + 3x + 2$ **2.** $x^2 + 6x + 5$

3. $4x^2 + 4x + 1$ **4.** $x^2 + 6x + 9$

5. $6x^2 + 29x + 20$ **6.** $8x^2 + 59x + 21$

3.6   Summary of Factoring

Guidelines for Factoring Polynomials • Factoring Polynomials

A LOOK INTO MATH ▶ Mathematics is being used more and more to model all types of situations. Modeling is not only used in science; it is also used to describe consumer behavior and to search the Internet. To model the world around us, mathematical equations need to be solved. One important technique for solving equations is to set an expression equal to 0 and then factor. Factoring is an important method for solving equations and for simplifying complicated expressions. In this section, we discuss general guidelines that can be used to factor polynomials.

Guidelines for Factoring Polynomials

The following guidelines can be used to factor polynomials in general.

FACTORING POLYNOMIALS

STEP 1: Factor out the greatest common factor, if possible.

STEP 2: A. If the polynomial has *four terms*, try factoring by grouping.

    B. If the polynomial is a *binomial*, try one of the following.

      1. $a^2 - b^2 = (a - b)(a + b)$ Difference of two squares

      2. $a^3 - b^3 = (a - b)(a^2 + ab + b^2)$ Difference of two cubes

      3. $a^3 + b^3 = (a + b)(a^2 - ab + b^2)$ Sum of two cubes

    C. If the polynomial is a *trinomial*, check for a perfect square.

      1. $a^2 + 2ab + b^2 = (a + b)^2$ Perfect square trinomial

      2. $a^2 - 2ab + b^2 = (a - b)^2$ Perfect square trinomial

    Otherwise, apply FOIL or grouping, as described in Section 3.4.

STEP 3: Check to make sure that the polynomial is *completely* factored.

These guidelines give a general strategy for factoring a polynomial by hand. It is important to always perform Step 1 first. Factoring out the greatest common factor first usually makes it easier to factor the resulting polynomial. In the next subsection we apply these guidelines to several polynomials.

Factoring Polynomials

In the first example, we apply Step 1 to a polynomial with a common factor.

EXAMPLE 1 **Factoring out a common factor**

Factor $3x^3 - 9x^2$.

Solution

STEP 1: The greatest common factor is $3x^2$.

$$3x^3 - 9x^2 = 3x^2(x - 3)$$

STEP 2B: The binomial, $x - 3$, cannot be factored further.

STEP 3: The completely factored polynomial is $3x^2(x - 3)$.

❚ Now Try Exercise 19

In several of the next examples we apply more than one factoring technique.

EXAMPLE 2 **Factoring a difference of squares**

Factor $5x^3 - 20x$.

Solution

STEP 1: The greatest common factor is $5x$.

$$5x^3 - 20x = 5x(x^2 - 4)$$

STEP 2B: We can factor the binomial $x^2 - 4$ as a difference of squares.

$$5x(x^2 - 4) = 5x(x - 2)(x + 2)$$

STEP 3: The completely factored polynomial is $5x(x - 2)(x + 2)$.

❚ Now Try Exercise 21

EXAMPLE 3

Factoring a difference of squares

Factor $5x^4 - 80$.

Solution

STEP 1: The greatest common factor is 5.

$$5x^4 - 80 = 5(x^4 - 16)$$

STEP 2B: We can factor $x^4 - 16$ as a difference of squares *twice*.

$$5(x^4 - 16) = 5(x^2 - 4)(x^2 + 4) = 5(x - 2)(x + 2)(x^2 + 4)$$

The sum of squares, $x^2 + 4$, cannot be factored further.

STEP 3: The completely factored polynomial is $5(x - 2)(x + 2)(x^2 + 4)$.

▌ Now Try Exercise 23

EXAMPLE 4

Factoring a perfect square trinomial

Factor $12x^3 + 36x^2 + 27x$.

Solution

STEP 1: The greatest common factor is $3x$.

$$12x^3 + 36x^2 + 27x = 3x(4x^2 + 12x + 9)$$

STEP 2C: The trinomial $4x^2 + 12x + 9$ is a perfect square trinomial.

$$3x(4x^2 + 12x + 9) = 3x(2x + 3)(2x + 3)$$

STEP 3: The completely factored polynomial is $3x(2x + 3)^2$.

▌ Now Try Exercise 37

EXAMPLE 5

Factoring a sum of cubes

Factor $-8x^4 - 27x$.

Solution

STEP 1: The negative of the greatest common factor is $-x$.

$$-8x^4 - 27x = -x(8x^3 + 27)$$

STEP 2B: The binomial $8x^3 + 27$ can be factored as a sum of cubes.

$$-x(8x^3 + 27) = -x(2x + 3)(4x^2 - 6x + 9)$$

The trinomial, $4x^2 - 6x + 9$, cannot be factored further.

STEP 3: The completely factored polynomial is $-x(2x + 3)(4x^2 - 6x + 9)$.

▌ Now Try Exercise 43

EXAMPLE 6

Factoring by grouping

Factor $x^3 - 2x^2 + x - 2$.

Solution

STEP 1: There are no common factors.

STEP 2A: Because there are four terms, we apply grouping.

$$x^3 - 2x^2 + x - 2 = (x^3 - 2x^2) + (x - 2) \qquad \text{Associative property}$$
$$= x^2(x - 2) + 1(x - 2) \qquad \text{Factor out } x^2 \text{ and 1.}$$
$$= (x^2 + 1)(x - 2) \qquad \text{Distributive property}$$

The sum of squares, $x^2 + 1$, cannot be factored further.

STEP 3: The completely factored polynomial is $(x^2 + 1)(x - 2)$.

▌ Now Try Exercise 31

EXAMPLE 7 ▌ **Factoring a trinomial**

Factor $2x^4 - 7x^3 + 6x^2$.

Solution

STEP 1: The greatest common factor is x^2.

$$2x^4 - 7x^3 + 6x^2 = x^2(2x^2 - 7x + 6)$$

STEP 2C: We can factor the resulting trinomial by using FOIL.

$$x^2(2x^2 - 7x + 6) = x^2(x - 2)(2x - 3)$$

STEP 3: The completely factored polynomial is $x^2(x - 2)(2x - 3)$.

▌ Now Try Exercise 27

EXAMPLE 8 ▌ **Factoring with two variables**

Factor $12x^2 - 27a^2$.

Solution

STEP 1: The greatest common factor is 3.

$$12x^2 - 27a^2 = 3(4x^2 - 9a^2)$$

STEP 2B: We can factor the binomial as the difference of squares.

$$3(4x^2 - 9a^2) = 3(2x - 3a)(2x + 3a)$$

STEP 3: The completely factored polynomial is $3(2x - 3a)(2x + 3a)$.

▌ Now Try Exercise 49

In the next example we use common factors, grouping, the difference of two cubes, and the difference of two squares to factor a polynomial.

EXAMPLE 9 ▌ **Applying several techniques**

Factor $2x^5 - 8x^3 - 2x^2 + 8$.

Solution

STEP 1: The expression has a greatest common factor of 2.

$$2x^5 - 8x^3 - 2x^2 + 8 = 2(x^5 - 4x^3 - x^2 + 4)$$

STEP 2A: The resulting four terms can be factored by grouping.

$$2(x^5 - 4x^3 - x^2 + 4) = 2\left((x^5 - 4x^3) + (-x^2 + 4)\right) \quad \text{Associative property}$$
$$= 2\left(x^3(x^2 - 4) - 1(x^2 - 4)\right) \quad \text{Factor out } x^3 \text{ and } -1.$$
$$= 2(x^3 - 1)(x^2 - 4) \quad \text{Distributive property}$$

STEP 2B: Both of the resulting binomials can be factored further, one as the difference of two cubes and the other as the difference of two squares.

$$2(x^3 - 1)(x^2 - 4) = 2(x - 1)(x^2 + x + 1)(x - 2)(x + 2)$$

The trinomial, $x^2 + x + 1$, cannot be factored further.

STEP 3: The completely factored polynomial is $2(x - 1)(x^2 + x + 1)(x - 2)(x + 2)$.

▮ Now Try Exercise 57

3.6 Putting It All Together

When using the guidelines presented in this section for general factoring strategy, the following rules can be helpful.

CONCEPT	EXPLANATION	EXAMPLES
Greatest Common Factor	Factor out the greatest common factor, or monomial, that occurs in each term.	$4x^2 - 8x = 4x(x - 2)$ $2x^2 - 4x + 8 = 2(x^2 - 2x + 4)$ $x^5 + x^3 = x^3(x^2 + 1)$
Factoring by Grouping	Use the associative and distributive properties to factor a polynomial with four terms.	$x^3 - 2x^2 + 3x - 6$ $= (x^3 - 2x^2) + (3x - 6)$ $= x^2(x - 2) + 3(x - 2)$ $= (x^2 + 3)(x - 2)$
Factoring Binomials	Use the difference of squares, the difference of cubes, or the sum of cubes.	$4x^2 - 9 = (2x - 3)(2x + 3)$ $x^3 - 8 = (x - 2)(x^2 + 2x + 4)$ $x^3 + 8 = (x + 2)(x^2 - 2x + 4)$
Factoring Trinomials	Use FOIL or grouping to factor a trinomial after factoring out the greatest common factor.	$x^2 - 3x + 2 = (x - 1)(x - 2)$ $6x^2 + 13x + 5 \quad \text{(grouping)}$ $= (6x^2 + 3x) + (10x + 5)$ $= 3x(2x + 1) + 5(2x + 1)$ $= (3x + 5)(2x + 1)$

3.6 Exercises

MyMathLab

CONCEPTS AND VOCABULARY

1. When factoring a polynomial, what is a good first step?

2. What is the greatest common factor for $4x^2 + 2x$?

3. Can you factor $x^2 + 4$? Explain.

4. What method might you use to factor a polynomial with four terms?

WARM UP

Exercises 5–18: Factor completely, if possible.

5. $a^2 - a$ 6. $2x - 4$

7. $a^2 - 9$ 8. $4b^2 - 1$

9. $x^2 - 2x + 1$ 10. $a^2 + 2ab + b^2$

11. $x^3 - a^3$ 12. $x^3 + a^3$

13. $a^2 + 4$ 14. $36x^2 + y^2$

15. $x(x + 2) - 3(x + 2)$ 16. $2x(x - 3) + (x - 3)$

17. $x^3 + 2x^2 + x + 2$ 18. $x^3 - x^2 + 2x - 2$

FACTORING

Exercises 19–58: Factor completely.

19. $6x^2 - 14x$ 20. $-27x^3 - 15x$

21. $2x^3 - 18x$ 22. $8x^2 - 18$

23. $4a^4 - 64$ 24. $b^4 - 81$

25. $6x^3 - 13x^2 - 15x$ 26. $10x^4 + 13x^3 - 3x^2$

27. $2x^4 - 5x^3 - 25x^2$ 28. $10x^3 + 28x^2 - 6x$

29. $2x^4 + 5x^2 + 3$ 30. $2x^4 + 2x^2 - 4$

31. $x^3 + 3x^2 + x + 3$ 32. $x^3 + 5x^2 + 4x + 20$

33. $5x^3 - 5x^2 + 10x - 10$

34. $5x^4 - 20x^3 + 10x - 40$

35. $ax + bx - ay - by$ 36. $ax - bx - ay + by$

37. $18x^2 + 12x + 2$ 38. $-3x^2 + 30x - 75$

39. $-4x^3 + 24x^2 - 36x$ 40. $18x^3 - 60x^2 + 50x$

41. $8x^3 - 27$ 42. $27x^3 + 8$

43. $-x^4 - 8x$ 44. $x^5 - 27x^2$

45. $x^4 - 2x^3 - x + 2$ 46. $x^4 + 3x^3 + x + 3$

47. $r^4 - 16$ 48. $r^4 - 81$

49. $25x^2 - 4a^2$ 50. $9y^2 - 16z^2$

51. $2x^4 - 2y^4$ 52. $a^4 - b^4$

53. $9x^3 + 6x^2 - 3x$ 54. $8x^3 + 28x^2 - 16x$

55. $(z - 2)^2 - 9$ 56. $(y + 2)^2 - 4$

57. $3x^5 - 27x^3 + 3x^2 - 27$

58. $2x^5 - 8x^3 - 16x^2 + 64$

APPLICATIONS

59. *Greenhouse Gas Puzzle* Worldwide atmospheric carbon dioxide levels continue to increase and are suspected to contribute to climate change. The solution to the polynomial equation

$$x^3 - 390x^2 + 2x - 780 = 0$$

gives the record high amount of carbon dioxide in parts per million (ppm) in 2010, as measured at Mauna Loa Observatory. (*Source: The Honolulu Advertiser.*)
(a) Factor the expression on the left side of the equation.
(b) Solve the equation and determine this record amount.

60. *Greenhouse Gas Puzzle* (Refer to the preceding exercise.) The solution to the polynomial equation

$$2x^3 - 620x^2 + x - 310 = 0$$

gives the amount of carbon dioxide in parts per million (ppm) in 1958, as measured at Mauna Loa Observatory. (*Source: The Honolulu Advertiser.*)
(a) Factor the expression on the left side of the equation.
(b) Solve the equation and determine this amount.

61. *Dimensions of a Box* A box has a volume of 6 cubic feet. The height of the box is 1 foot more than its length, and its length is 1 foot more than its width. Let x be the height.
(a) Write a polynomial that gives the volume of the box in terms of x.
(b) Write an equation whose solution gives the height of the box.
(c) Solve the equation by using factoring.

62. *Dimensions of a Rectangle* The length of a rectangle is 2 inches more than its width, and the area is 24 square inches. Let x be the width.
(a) Write a polynomial that gives the area of the rectangle in terms of x.
(b) Write an equation whose solution gives the width of the rectangle.
(c) Solve the equation by using factoring.

WRITING ABOUT MATHEMATICS

63. Give the basic guidelines for factoring a polynomial.

64. What are some ways to recognize that a polynomial is completely factored?

Checking Basic Concepts

1. Factor each special type of polynomial.
(a) $25x^2 - 16$
(b) $x^2 + 12x + 36$
(c) $9x^2 - 30x + 25$
(d) $x^3 - 27$
(e) $81x^4 - 16$

2. Factor each expression.
(a) $x^3 - 2x^2 + 3x - 6$
(b) $x^2 - 4x - 21$
(c) $12x^3 + 2x^2 - 4x$

3.7   Polynomial Equations

Quadratic Equations ● Higher Degree Equations ● Equations in Quadratic Form ● Applications

A LOOK INTO MATH ▶ Polynomials are used to solve important problems. One example is found in highway construction where the elevations of hills and valleys are modeled by quadratic polynomials. (*Source:* F. Mannering and W. Kilareski, *Principles of Highway Engineering and Traffic Analysis.*)

The quadratic polynomial

$$h(x) = -0.0001x^2 + 100$$

could model the height of a hill, where $x = 0$ corresponds to the peak or crest of the hill, as illustrated in Figure 3.25. To determine any locations where the height of the hill is 75 feet, we can solve the *quadratic equation*

$$-0.0001x^2 + 100 = 75.$$

See Example 3.

Figure 3.25

NEW VOCABULARY

☐ Quadratic equation
☐ Quadratic form

Quadratic Equations

Any **quadratic equation** can be written as $ax^2 + bx + c = 0$, where a, b, and c are constants, with $a \neq 0$. Quadratic equations can sometimes be solved by factoring and then applying the zero-product property. They can also be solved graphically. These techniques are demonstrated in the next two examples.

EXAMPLE 1 **Solving a quadratic equation**

Solve $x^2 - 4 = 0$ symbolically and graphically.

Solution

Symbolic Solution Start by factoring the left side of the equation.

$$x^2 - 4 = 0 \qquad \text{Given equation}$$

$$(x - 2)(x + 2) = 0 \qquad \text{Difference of squares}$$

$$x - 2 = 0 \quad \text{or} \quad x + 2 = 0 \qquad \text{Zero-product property}$$

$$x = 2 \quad \text{or} \quad x = -2 \qquad \text{Solve each equation.}$$

The solutions are -2 and 2.

Graphical Solution Start by making Table 3.10. Plot these points and connect them with a smooth curve called a parabola, as shown in Figure 3.26. The x-intercepts, or zeros, are -2 and 2, which are also the solutions to the equation.

Zeros: $-2, 2$

Figure 3.26

TABLE 3.10 $y = x^2 - 4$

x	-3	-2	-1	0	1	2	3
y	5	$\mathbf{0}$	-3	-4	-3	$\mathbf{0}$	5

└── Zeros are -2 and 2. ──┘

Now Try Exercise 7

EXAMPLE 2 **Solving quadratic equations**

Solve each equation.
(a) $4x^2 - 20x + 25 = 0$ **(b)** $3x^2 + 11x = 20$ **(c)** $x^2 + 25 = 0$

Solution

(a) Start by factoring the left side, which is a perfect square trinomial.

$$4x^2 - 20x + 25 = 0 \qquad \text{Given equation}$$

$$(2x - 5)(2x - 5) = 0 \qquad \text{Factor.}$$

$$2x - 5 = 0 \qquad \text{Zero-product property}$$

$$x = \frac{5}{2} \qquad \text{Solve.}$$

The only solution is $\frac{5}{2}$.

(b) Start by subtracting 20 from each side to obtain a 0 on the right side.

$$3x^2 + 11x = 20 \qquad \text{Given equation}$$

$$3x^2 + 11x - 20 = 0 \qquad \text{Subtract 20.}$$

$$(x + 5)(3x - 4) = 0 \qquad \text{Factor.}$$

$$x + 5 = 0 \quad \text{or} \quad 3x - 4 = 0 \qquad \text{Zero-product property}$$

$$x = -5 \quad \text{or} \quad x = \frac{4}{3} \qquad \text{Solve.}$$

The solutions are -5 and $\frac{4}{3}$.

(c) $x^2 + 25 = 0$ implies that $x^2 = -25$, which has no solutions because $x^2 \geq 0$ for all real numbers.

Now Try Exercises 25, 29, 33

MAKING CONNECTIONS

Quadratic Equations and Solutions

Example 2 demonstrates that a quadratic equation can have no solutions, one solution, or two solutions. The following graphs illustrate this concept.

No solutions
$x^2 + 25 = 0$

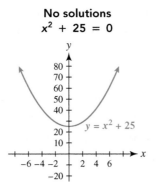

One solution
$4x^2 - 20x + 25 = 0$

Two solutions
$3x^2 + 11x + 20$

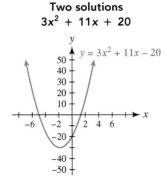

READING CHECK

How many solutions can a quadratic equation have? Explain your answer graphically.

EXAMPLE 3

Determining highway elevations

Solve the equation $-0.0001x^2 + 100 = 75$, which is discussed in A Look Into Math for this section. See Figure 3.25 repeated in the margin.

Figure 3.25 (Repeated)

Solution
Start by subtracting 75 from each side of the equation. Then multiply each side by $-10,000$ to clear decimals.

$$-0.0001x^2 + 100 = 75 \qquad \text{Given equation}$$
$$-0.0001x^2 + 25 = 0 \qquad \text{Subtract 75.}$$
$$-10,000(-0.0001x^2 + 25) = -10,000(0) \qquad \text{Multiply by } -10,000.$$
$$x^2 - 250,000 = 0 \qquad \text{Distributive property}$$
$$(x - 500)(x + 500) = 0 \qquad \sqrt{250,000} = 500$$
$$x - 500 = 0 \quad \text{or} \quad x + 500 = 0 \qquad \text{Zero-product property}$$
$$x = 500 \quad \text{or} \quad x = -500 \qquad \text{Solve each equation.}$$

Thus the highway elevation is 75 feet at a distance of 500 feet on either side of the crest of the hill.

Now Try Exercise 75

Higher Degree Equations

Using the techniques of factoring that we discussed in earlier sections, we can solve equations that involve higher degree polynomials. These higher degree equations can have more than two solutions.

EXAMPLE 4   **Solving higher degree equations**

Solve each equation.
(a) $x^3 = 4x$ **(b)** $2x^3 + 2x^2 - 12x = 0$ **(c)** $x^3 - 5x^2 - x + 5 = 0$

Solution

(a) Start by subtracting $4x$ from each side of $x^3 = 4x$ to obtain a 0 on the right side. (Do *not* divide each side by x because the solution $x = 0$ will be lost.)

$$x^3 = 4x \qquad \text{Given equation}$$
$$x^3 - 4x = 0 \qquad \text{Subtract } 4x.$$
$$x(x^2 - 4) = 0 \qquad \text{Factor out } x.$$
$$x(x - 2)(x + 2) = 0 \qquad \text{Difference of squares}$$
$$x = 0 \quad \text{or} \quad x - 2 = 0 \quad \text{or} \quad x + 2 = 0 \qquad \text{Zero-product property}$$
$$x = 0 \quad \text{or} \quad x = 2 \quad \text{or} \quad x = -2 \qquad \text{Solve each equation.}$$

The solutions are $-2, 0,$ and 2.

(b) Start by factoring out the common factor $2x$.

$$2x^3 + 2x^2 - 12x = 0 \qquad \text{Given equation}$$
$$2x(x^2 + x - 6) = 0 \qquad \text{Factor out } 2x.$$
$$2x(x + 3)(x - 2) = 0 \qquad \text{Factor the trinomial.}$$
$$2x = 0 \quad \text{or} \quad x + 3 = 0 \quad \text{or} \quad x - 2 = 0 \qquad \text{Zero-product property}$$
$$x = 0 \quad \text{or} \quad x = -3 \quad \text{or} \quad x = 2 \qquad \text{Solve each equation.}$$

The solutions are $-3, 0,$ and 2.

(c) To solve this equation use *grouping* to factor the left side.

$$x^3 - 5x^2 - x + 5 = 0 \qquad \text{Given equation}$$
$$(x^3 - 5x^2) + (-x + 5) = 0 \qquad \text{Associative property}$$
$$x^2(x - 5) - 1(x - 5) = 0 \qquad \text{Factor out } x^2 \text{ and } -1.$$
$$(x^2 - 1)(x - 5) = 0 \qquad \text{Distributive property}$$
$$(x - 1)(x + 1)(x - 5) = 0 \qquad \text{Difference of squares}$$
$$x - 1 = 0 \quad \text{or} \quad x + 1 = 0 \quad \text{or} \quad x - 5 = 0 \qquad \text{Zero-product property}$$
$$x = 1 \quad \text{or} \quad x = -1 \quad \text{or} \quad x = 5 \qquad \text{Solve each equation.}$$

The solutions are $-1, 1,$ and 5.

Now Try Exercises 43, 47, 51

In the next example, we demonstrate how an equation can be solved symbolically, graphically, and numerically with the aid of a graphing calculator.

EXAMPLE 5   **Solving a polynomial equation**

Solve $16x^4 - 64x^3 + 64x^2 = 0$ symbolically, graphically, and numerically.

Solution

Symbolic Solution Begin by factoring out the common factor $16x^2$.

$$16x^4 - 64x^3 + 64x^2 = 0 \qquad \text{Given equation}$$
$$16x^2(x^2 - 4x + 4) = 0 \qquad \text{Factor out } 16x^2.$$
$$16x^2(x - 2)^2 = 0 \qquad \text{Perfect square trinomial}$$

Solving results in

$$16x^2 = 0 \quad \text{or} \quad (x - 2)^2 = 0 \qquad \text{Zero-product property}$$
$$x = 0 \quad \text{or} \quad x = 2. \qquad \text{Solve.}$$

Graphical Solution Graph $y_1 = 16x^4 - 64x^3 + 64x^2$, as shown in Figures 3.27(a) and 3.27(b). When the trace feature is used, solutions to $y_1 = 0$ occur when $x = 0$ and $x = 2$.

Numerical Solution Construct the table for $y_1 = 16x^4 - 64x^3 + 64x^2$, as shown in Figure 3.27(c). Solutions occur at $x = 0$ and $x = 2$.

(a)   (b)   (c)

Figure 3.27

▎ **Now Try Exercise 61**

Equations in Quadratic Form

Sometimes equations do not appear to be quadratic, but they can be solved by using factoring techniques that we have already applied to quadratic equations. Such equations have **quadratic form** and sometimes need to be factored more than once, as demonstrated in the next example.

EXAMPLE 6   **Solving equations in quadratic form**

Solve each equation.
(a) $x^4 - 81 = 0$ **(b)** $x^4 - 5x^2 + 4 = 0$

Solution
(a) To solve this equation use the difference of squares twice.

$$(x^2)^2 - 9^2 = 0 \qquad \text{Rewrite given equation.}$$
$$(x^2 - 9)(x^2 + 9) = 0 \qquad \text{Difference of squares}$$
$$(x - 3)(x + 3)(x^2 + 9) = 0 \qquad \text{Difference of squares again}$$
$$x - 3 = 0 \quad \text{or} \quad x + 3 = 0 \quad \text{or} \quad x^2 + 9 = 0 \qquad \text{Zero-product property}$$
$$x = 3 \quad \text{or} \quad x = -3 \quad \text{or} \quad x^2 = -9 \qquad \text{Solve each equation.}$$

The solutions are -3 and 3 because $x^2 = -9$ has no real number solutions.
(b) To solve this equation start by factoring the trinomial.

$$x^4 - 5x^2 + 4 = 0 \qquad \text{Given equation}$$
$$(x^2 - 4)(x^2 - 1) = 0 \qquad \text{Factor.}$$
$$(x - 2)(x + 2)(x - 1)(x + 1) = 0 \qquad \text{Difference of squares twice}$$
$$x = 2 \quad \text{or} \quad x = -2 \quad \text{or} \quad x = 1 \quad \text{or} \quad x = -1 \qquad \text{Solve.}$$

The solutions are $-2, -1, 1,$ and 2.

▎ **Now Try Exercises 65, 69**

NOTE: To factor the equation in Example 6(a), it may be helpful to let $z = x^2$ and $z^2 = x^4$. Then the given equation becomes $z^2 - 81 = 0$, or $(z - 9)(z + 9) = 0$ after factoring. Substituting $z = x^2$ gives the factored equation $(x^2 - 9)(x^2 + 9) = 0$. Similar comments can be made for Example 6(b).

MAKING CONNECTIONS

Symbolic, Graphical, and Numerical Solutions

The following illustrates how to solve $x^3 - 4x = 0$ with each method. Note that the solutions to $x^3 - 4x = 0$, the x-intercepts of the graph of $y = x^3 - 4x$, and the zeros of $x^3 - 4x$ are *all identical*.

READING CHECK

Explain how solutions, zeros, and x-intercepts are related when solving a polynomial equation.

Symbolic Solution	Graphical Solution	Numerical Solution

Symbolic Solution

$$x^3 - 4x = 0$$
$$x(x^2 - 4) = 0$$
$$x(x - 2)(x + 2) = 0$$
$$x = 0, \ x = 2, \ x = -2$$

Solutions: $-2, 0, 2$

Graphical Solution

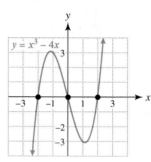

x-intercepts: $-2, 0, 2$

Numerical Solution

x	$x^3 - 4x$
-3	-15
-2	$\mathbf{0}$
-1	3
0	$\mathbf{0}$
1	-3
2	$\mathbf{0}$
3	15

Zeros: $-2, 0, 2$

Applications

▶ **REAL-WORLD CONNECTION** Many times applications involving geometry make use of quadratic equations. In the next example we solve a quadratic equation to find the dimensions of a picture.

EXAMPLE 7 **Finding the dimensions of a picture**

A frame surrounding a picture is 3 inches wide. The picture inside the frame is 5 inches wider than it is high. If the overall area of the picture and frame is 336 square inches, find the dimensions of the picture inside the frame.

Solution

Let x be the height of the picture and $x + 5$ be its width. The dimensions of the picture and frame, in inches, are illustrated in Figure 3.28.

The overall area is given by $(x + 6)(x + 11)$, which equals 336 square inches.

$$(x + 6)(x + 11) = 336 \qquad \text{Equation to solve}$$
$$x^2 + 17x + 66 = 336 \qquad \text{Multiply binomials.}$$
$$x^2 + 17x - 270 = 0 \qquad \text{Subtract 336.}$$
$$(x - 10)(x + 27) = 0 \qquad \text{Factor.}$$
$$x = 10 \quad \text{or} \quad x = -27 \qquad \text{Zero-product property; solve.}$$

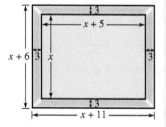

Figure 3.28

The only valid solution for x is 10 inches. Because the width is 5 inches more than the height, the dimensions are 10 inches by 15 inches.

Now Try Exercise 73

▶ **REAL-WORLD CONNECTION** Highway engineers often use quadratic functions to calculate stopping distances for cars. The faster a car is traveling, the farther it takes for the car to stop. The stopping distance for a car can be used to estimate its speed, as demonstrated in the next example. (*Source:* F. Mannering.)

EXAMPLE 8 **Finding the speed of a car**

For a car traveling at x miles per hour on wet, level pavement, highway engineers sometimes estimate stopping distance d in feet by

$$d(x) = \frac{1}{9}x^2 + \frac{11}{3}x.$$

Use this formula to approximate the speed of a car that takes 180 feet to stop.

Solution
We need to solve the equation $\frac{1}{9}x^2 + \frac{11}{3}x = 180$. Start by multiplying by 9 to eliminate fractions.

$$\frac{1}{9}x^2 + \frac{11}{3}x = 180 \qquad \text{Equation to be solved}$$

$$9\left(\frac{1}{9}x^2 + \frac{11}{3}x\right) = 9 \cdot 180 \qquad \text{Multiply by 9.}$$

$$x^2 + 33x = 1620 \qquad \text{Distributive property}$$

$$x^2 + 33x - 1620 = 0 \qquad \text{Subtract 1620.}$$

$$(x - 27)(x + 60) = 0 \qquad \text{Factor.}$$

$$x = 27 \quad \text{or} \quad x = -60 \qquad \text{Zero-product property; solve.}$$

The speed of the car is 27 miles per hour.

▮ **Now Try Exercise 81**

NOTE: To factor $x^2 + 33x - 1620$ in Example 8, we find values for m and n such that $mn = -1620$ and $m + n = 33$, which may require some trial and error.

EXAMPLE 9 **Finding the dimensions of an iPod Mini**

The width of an iPod Mini is 1.5 inches more than its thickness, and its length is 3 inches more than its thickness. If the volume of an iPod Mini is 3.5 cubic inches, find its dimensions graphically.

[−6, 6, 1] by [−2, 6, 1]

Figure 3.29

Solution
Let x be its thickness, $x + 1.5$ be its width, and $x + 3$ be its length. Because volume equals thickness times width times length, we have

$$x(x + 1.5)(x + 3) = 3.5.$$

The graphs of $y_1 = x(x + 1.5)(x + 3)$ and $y_2 = 3.5$ intersect at $(0.5, 3.5)$, as shown in Figure 3.29. Thus the iPod Mini is 0.5 inch thick, 2 inches wide, and 3.5 inches long.

▮ **Now Try Exercise 83**

3.7   Putting It All Together

The following is a typical strategy for solving a polynomial equation. When you have finished, *be sure to check your answers*.

STEP 1: If necessary, rewrite the equation so that a 0 appears on one side of the equation.

STEP 2: Factor out common factors.

STEP 3: Factor the remaining polynomial using the techniques presented in this chapter.

STEP 4: Apply the *zero-product* property.

STEP 5: Solve each resulting equation.

The following table summarizes how to solve three types of higher degree polynomial equations.

CONCEPT	EXPLANATION	EXAMPLE
Higher Degree Equations	Factor out common factors; then use the techniques for factoring.	$2x^3 - 32x = 0$ $2x(x^2 - 16) = 0$ $2x(x - 4)(x + 4) = 0$ $x = 0$ or $x = 4$ or $x = -4$
Equations in Quadratic Form	Factor these forms as $ax^2 + bx + c$.	$x^4 - 13x^2 + 36 = 0$ $(x^2 - 4)(x^2 - 9) = 0$ $(x - 2)(x + 2)(x - 3)(x + 3) = 0$ $x = 2$ or $x = -2$ or $x = 3$ or $x = -3$
Solving by Grouping	Use grouping to help factor a cubic expression having four terms. Apply the distributive property.	$x^3 - 7x^2 - 16x + 112 = 0$ $(x^3 - 7x^2) + (-16x + 112) = 0$ $x^2(x - 7) - 16(x - 7) = 0$ $(x^2 - 16)(x - 7) = 0$ $(x - 4)(x + 4)(x - 7) = 0$ $x = 4$ or $x = -4$ or $x = 7$

3.7   Exercises

CONCEPTS AND VOCABULARY

1. Explain why factoring is important in mathematics.

2. Factoring a polynomial is the *reverse* of _____ polynomials.

3. When you are solving $x^2 = 16$ by factoring, what is a good first step?

4. To solve $x^2 - 3x - 3 = 1$ could you start by factoring the left side of the equation? Explain.

5. What is the solution to $(x - 1)^2 = 0$?

6. Does the equation $x^2 + 4 = 0$ have any real number solutions? Explain.

SOLVING QUADRATIC EQUATIONS

Exercises 7–12: Solve the equation graphically. Then solve the equation symbolically.

7. $x^2 - 1 = 0$ **8.** $x^2 - 9 = 0$

9. $\frac{1}{4}x^2 - 1 = 0$ **10.** $\frac{1}{16}x^2 - 1 = 0$

11. $x^2 - x - 2 = 0$ **12.** $x^2 - x - 6 = 0$

Exercises 13–34: Solve the given quadratic equation, if possible.

13. $z^2 - 64 = 0$ **14.** $z^2 - 100 = 0$

15. $4y^2 - 1 = 0$ **16.** $9y^2 - 36 = 0$

17. $x^2 - 3x - 4 = 0$ **18.** $x^2 - 8x + 7 = 0$

19. $x^2 + 4x - 12 = 0$ **20.** $x^2 - 3x - 28 = 0$

21. $2x^2 + 5x - 3 = 0$ **22.** $3x^2 + 8x + 4 = 0$

23. $2x^2 = 32$ **24.** $4x^2 = 64$

25. $z^2 + 14z + 49 = 0$ **26.** $z^2 + 64 = 16z$

27. $9t^2 + 1 = 6t$ **28.** $49t^2 + 28t + 4 = 0$

29. $15n^2 = 7n + 2$ **30.** $7n^2 + 57n + 8 = 0$

31. $24m^2 + 23m = 12$ **32.** $11m^2 = 31m + 6$

33. $x^2 + 12 = 0$ **34.** $2x^2 + 3 = 0$

Exercises 35–38: Use the graph to solve the equation. Then solve the equation by factoring.

35. $x^2 + x - 6 = 0$ **36.** $x^2 - 2x - 3 = 0$

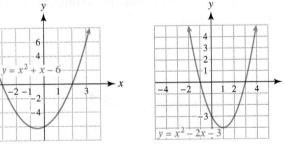

37. $2x^2 - 4x - 16 = 0$ **38.** $2x^2 + 3x - 2 = 0$

Exercises 39–42: The graph of the quadratic expression $y = ax^2 + bx + c$ is $\cap$-shaped when $a < 0$. If possible, sketch a graph of a quadratic expression with $a < 0$ that satisfies the condition.

39. No x-intercepts   **40.** One x-intercept

41. Two x-intercepts   **42.** Three x-intercepts

HIGHER DEGREE EQUATIONS

Exercises 43–54: Solve the equation.

43. $z^3 = 9z$ **44.** $2z^3 + 8z = 0$

45. $x^3 + x = 0$ **46.** $x^3 = x$

47. $2x^3 - 6x^2 = 20x$

48. $3x^3 + 15x^2 + 12x = 0$

49. $t^4 - 4t^3 - 5t^2 = 0$ **50.** $2t^4 - 8t^3 + 6t^2 = 0$

51. $x^3 + 7x^2 - 4x - 28 = 0$

52. $x^3 + 5x^2 = 9x + 45$

53. $n^3 - 2n^2 - 36n + 72 = 0$

54. $n^3 - 10n^2 - 4n + 40 = 0$

Exercises 55–62: (Refer to Example 5.) Solve the equation

(a) symbolically,
(b) graphically, and
(c) numerically.

55. $x^2 - 2x - 15 = 0$ **56.** $x^2 + 7x + 10 = 0$

57. $2x^2 - 3x = 2$ **58.** $4t^2 + 25 = 20t$

59. $3t^2 + 18t + 15 = 0$ **60.** $4z^2 = 16$

61. $4x^4 + 16x^2 = 16x^3$

62. $2x^3 + 12x^2 + 18x = 0$

EQUATIONS IN QUADRATIC FORM

Exercises 63–72: Solve the equation.

63. $x^4 - 2x^2 - 8 = 0$ **64.** $x^4 - 8x^2 - 9 = 0$

65. $x^4 - 26x^2 + 25 = 0$

66. $x^4 - 21x^2 - 100 = 0$

67. $x^4 - 13x^2 + 36 = 0$

68. $x^4 - 18x^2 + 81 = 0$

69. $x^4 - 16 = 0$ **70.** $4x^4 = x^2 + 18$

71. $9x^4 - 13x^2 + 4 = 0$

72. $64x^4 - 180x^2 + 81 = 0$

APPLICATIONS

73. *Picture Frame* (Refer to Example 7.) A rectangular frame surrounding a picture is made from boards that are 2 inches wide. The picture inside the frame is 4 inches wider than it is high. If the overall area of the picture and frame is 525 square inches, find the dimensions of the picture.

74. *Picture Frame* The outside measurements of a rectangular frame for a picture are 30 inches by 40 inches. The area of the rectangular picture inside the frame is 936 square inches. Find the width of the frame that surrounds the picture.

75. *Modeling a Hill* (Refer to Example 3.) The elevation E in feet of a highway x feet along a hill is modeled by

$$E(x) = -0.0001x^2 + 500,$$

where $-2000 \le x \le 2000$. Determine the x-values where the elevation is 400 feet.

76. *Numbers* If a positive number n is increased by 3, its square equals 121. Find n.

77. *Sidewalk Around a Pool* A 5-foot-wide sidewalk around a rectangular swimming pool has a total area of 900 square feet. Find the dimensions of the swimming pool if the pool is 20 feet longer than it is wide.

78. *Height Reached by a Baseball* The height in feet reached by a batted baseball after t seconds is given by

$$h(t) = -16t^2 + 88t + 4.$$

Determine when the baseball is 100 feet in the air.

79. *Height Reached by a Baseball* The height in feet reached by a batted baseball after t seconds is given by

$$h(t) = -16t^2 + 66t + 2.$$

A graph of $y = h(t)$ is shown.
(a) Interpret the y-intercept.
(b) Use the graph to estimate when the baseball is 70 feet in the air.
(c) Solve part (b) symbolically.
(d) Why are symbolic solutions important?

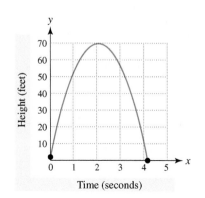

Time (seconds)

80. *Geometry* A rectangle is 2 inches longer than it is wide. If each side is increased by 3 inches, the area increases by 183 square inches. Find the dimensions of the rectangle.

Exercises 81 and 82: (Refer to Example 8.) On dry, level pavement, the stopping distance d in feet for a car traveling at x miles per hour can be estimated by

$$d(x) = \frac{1}{11}x^2 + \frac{11}{3}x.$$

Use this formula to approximate the speed of a car that takes d feet to stop.

81. $d = 220$ feet   **82.** $d = 638$ feet

83. *iPod Dimensions* The width of a classic iPod is 1.8 inches more than its thickness, and its length is 3.5 inches more than its thickness. If the volume of an iPod is 5.904 cubic inches, find its dimensions graphically.

84. *Box Dimensions* The width of a rectangular mailing box is 9 inches more than its height, and its length is 11 inches more than its height. If the volume of the box is 286 cubic inches, find its dimensions graphically.

85. *Modeling a Highway* In highway design, quadratic polynomials are used not only to model hills but also to model valleys. Valleys or sags in the road are sometimes referred to as *sag curves*. Suppose that the elevation E in feet of the sag curve x (horizontal) feet along a proposed route is modeled by

$$E(x) = 0.0002x^2 - 0.3x + 500,$$

where $0 \le x \le 1500$. See the accompanying figure.
(*Source:* F. Mannering.)

(a) Make a table of the elevations for $x = 0,\ 300,\ 600,\ \ldots,\ 1500$ and interpret these values.
(b) Determine where the elevation is 400 feet.

86. *Biology* Some types of worms have a remarkable ability to live without moisture. The following table from one study shows the number of worms y surviving after x days without moisture.

x (days)	0	20	40
y (worms)	50	48	45

x (days)	80	120	160
y (worms)	36	20	3

Source: D. Brown and P. Rothery, *Models in Biology.*

(a) Plot the data and graph

$$y = -0.00138x^2 - 0.076x + 50.1$$

in the same viewing rectangle.

(b) Discuss how well the equation models the data.

(c) Estimate the day x when 10 worms remained.

WRITING ABOUT MATHEMATICS

87. Explain why the graph of $y = ax^2 + bx + c$ is used to model a dip or valley in a highway rather than the graph of $y = |ax + b|$. Make a sketch to support your reasoning. Assume that $a > 0$.

88. Explain the basic steps that you would use to solve the quadratic equation $ax^2 + bx + c = 0$ graphically and numerically. Assume that the equation has two solutions.

SECTION 3.7 **Checking Basic Concepts**

1. Use the graph to solve $x^2 + 4x + 3 = 0$. Then solve the equation symbolically.

2. Solve $x^2 - 9 = 0$ graphically. Then solve the equation by factoring.

3. If possible, solve each equation.
   (a) $x^2 + 9 = 6x$
   (b) $x^2 + 9 = 0$
   (c) $12x^2 + 7x - 10 = 0$

4. Solve each equation.
   (a) $x^3 + 5x = 0$
   (b) $x^4 - 81 = 0$
   (c) $z^4 + z^2 = 20$
   (d) $x^3 + 2x^2 - 49x = 98$

CHAPTER 3 Summary

SECTION 3.1 • POLYNOMIAL FUNCTIONS

Monomials and Polynomials A monomial is a term with only *nonnegative integer* exponents. A polynomial is either a monomial or a sum of monomials.

Examples: Monomial: $-4x^3y^2$ has degree 5 and coefficient -4

Polynomial: $3x^2 - 4x + 2$ has degree 2 and leading coefficient 3

Addition and Subtraction of Polynomials To add two polynomials, combine like terms. When subtracting two polynomials, add the first polynomial and the opposite of the second polynomial. Combine like terms.

Examples:
$$(3x^3 - 4x) + (-5x^3 + 7x) = (3 - 5)x^3 + (-4 + 7)x$$
$$= -2x^3 + 3x$$

$$(3xy^2 + 4x^2) - (4xy^2 - 6x) = (3xy^2 + 4x^2) + (-4xy^2 + 6x)$$
$$= 3xy^2 - 4xy^2 + 4x^2 + 6x$$
$$= -xy^2 + 4x^2 + 6x$$

Polynomial Functions If the formula for a function f is a polynomial, then f is a polynomial function. The following are examples of polynomial functions.

$$f(x) = 2x - 7 \qquad \text{Linear} \qquad \text{Degree 1}$$
$$f(x) = 4x^2 - 5x + 1 \qquad \text{Quadratic} \qquad \text{Degree 2}$$
$$f(x) = 9x^3 + 6x \qquad \text{Cubic} \qquad \text{Degree 3}$$

Example: $f(x) = 4x^3 - 2x^2 + 4$ represents a polynomial function of one variable.

$$f(2) = 4(2)^3 - 2(2)^2 + 4 = 32 - 8 + 4 = 28$$

SECTION 3.2 • MULTIPLICATION OF POLYNOMIALS

Product of Two Polynomials The product of two polynomials may be found by multiplying every term in the first polynomial by every term in the second polynomial.

Example: $(2x + 3)(3x - 4) = 6x^2 - 8x + 9x - 12 = 6x^2 + x - 12$

Special Products

Product of a Sum and Difference $\qquad (a + b)(a - b) = a^2 - b^2$

$\qquad\qquad\qquad\qquad\qquad\qquad$ **Example:** $(x + 3)(x - 3) = x^2 - 9$

Square of a Binomial $\qquad\qquad (a + b)^2 = a^2 + 2ab + b^2$

$\qquad\qquad\qquad\qquad\qquad\qquad (a - b)^2 = a^2 - 2ab + b^2$

$\qquad\qquad\qquad\qquad\qquad\qquad$ **Examples:** $(x + 3)^2 = x^2 + 6x + 9$

$\qquad\qquad\qquad\qquad\qquad\qquad\qquad\qquad\quad (x - 3)^2 = x^2 - 6x + 9$

SECTION 3.3 • FACTORING POLYNOMIALS

Common Factors When factoring a polynomial, start by factoring out the greatest common factor (GCF).

Examples: $8z^3 - 12z^2 + 16z = 4z(2z^2 - 3z + 4)$

$\qquad\qquad 18x^2y^3 - 12x^3y^2 = 6x^2y^2(3y - 2x)$

Zero-Product Property For all real numbers a and b, if $ab = 0$, then $a = 0$ or $b = 0$ (or both).

Example: $(x - 3)(x + 2) = 0$ implies that either $x - 3 = 0$ or $x + 2 = 0$.

Solving Polynomial Equations by Factoring Obtain a zero on one side of the equation. Factor the other side of the equation and apply the zero-product property.

Example: $\qquad x^2 - 7x = 0$

$\qquad\qquad\qquad x(x - 7) = 0 \qquad$ Factor out common factor.

$\qquad\quad x = 0 \quad \text{or} \quad x = 7 \qquad$ Zero-product property; solve.

Factoring by Grouping Grouping can be used to factor some polynomial expressions with four terms by applying the distributive and associative properties.

Example: $x^3 + x^2 + 5x + 5 = (x^3 + x^2) + (5x + 5) \qquad$ Associative property

$\qquad\qquad\qquad\qquad\qquad = x^2(x + 1) + 5(x + 1) \qquad$ Distributive property

$\qquad\qquad\qquad\qquad\qquad = (x^2 + 5)(x + 1) \qquad$ Distributive property

SECTION 3.4 • FACTORING TRINOMIALS

Factoring $x^2 + bx + c$ Find integers m and n that satisfy $mn = c$ and $m + n = b$. Then $x^2 + bx + c = (x + m)(x + n)$.

Example: $x^2 + 3x + 2 = (x + 1)(x + 2)$ $m = 1, n = 2$

Factoring $ax^2 + bx + c$ Either grouping or FOIL (in reverse) can be used to factor $ax^2 + bx + c$. Trinomials can also be factored graphically or numerically.

Examples: *Grouping* Find m and n so that $mn = ac = 30$ and $m + n = b = 17$.

$$6x^2 + 17x + 5 = (6x^2 + 2x) + (15x + 5)   \quad m = 2, n = 15$$
$$\underset{a}{\uparrow} \quad \underset{b}{\uparrow} \quad \underset{c}{\uparrow}$$
$$= 2x(3x + 1) + 5(3x + 1)$$
$$= (2x + 5)(3x + 1)$$

FOIL Correctly factoring a trinomial requires checking the middle term.

$$2x^2 + 3x - 14 = (2x + 7)(x - 2)$$

$$\underbrace{7x}$$
$$-4x$$
$$\overline{3x} \checkmark$$

It checks. $\longrightarrow$ $3x$ ✓

Graphically or Numerically The x-intercepts on the graph of $f(x) = 2x^2 + x - 1$ are $x = 0.5$ and $x = -1$. The zeros of f are 0.5 and -1. Thus $f(x)$ can be factored as

$$2x^2 + x - 1 = 2(x - 0.5)(x + 1)$$
$$= (2x - 1)(x + 1).$$

SECTION 3.5 • SPECIAL TYPES OF FACTORING

Difference of Two Squares $a^2 - b^2 = (a - b)(a + b)$

Example: $49x^2 - 36y^2 = (7x)^2 - (6y)^2 = (7x - 6y)(7x + 6y)$ $a = 7x, b = 6y$

Perfect Square Trinomials

$$a^2 + 2ab + b^2 = (a + b)^2 \quad \text{and} \quad a^2 - 2ab + b^2 = (a - b)^2$$

Examples: $x^2 + 2xy + y^2 = (x + y)^2$ and $9r^2 - 12r + 4 = (3r - 2)^2$

Sum and Difference of Two Cubes

$$a^3 + b^3 = (a + b)(a^2 - ab + b^2) \quad \text{and}$$
$$a^3 - b^3 = (a - b)(a^2 + ab + b^2)$$

Examples: $x^3 + y^3 = (x + y)(x^2 - xy + y^2)$ $\qquad a = x, b = y$
$\qquad\qquad$ $8t^3 - 27r^6 = (2t - 3r^2)(4t^2 + 6tr^2 + 9r^4)$ $a = 2t, b = 3r^2$

SECTION 3.6 • SUMMARY OF FACTORING

Factoring Polynomials The following steps can be used as general guidelines for factoring a polynomial.

STEP 1: Factor out the greatest common factor, if possible.

STEP 2: **A.** If the polynomial has four terms, try factoring by grouping.

$\qquad$ **B.** If the polynomial is a binomial, consider the difference of two squares, difference of two cubes, or sum of two cubes.

$\qquad$ **C.** If the polynomial is a trinomial, check for a perfect square. Otherwise, apply FOIL or grouping, as described in Section 3.4.

STEP 3: Check to make sure that the polynomial is *completely* factored.

Solving Polynomial Equations Follow the strategy presented in Putting It All Together for Section 3.7.

Example:

$x^4 = 2x^2 + 8$	Given equation
$x^4 - 2x^2 - 8 = 0$	Subtract $2x^2 + 8$ from each side.
$(x^2 - 4)(x^2 + 2) = 0$	Factor trinomial.
$(x - 2)(x + 2)(x^2 + 2) = 0$	Difference of squares
$x = 2$ or $x = -2$	Zero-product property; solve.

CHAPTER 3   Review Exercises

SECTION 3.1

1. Give an example of a binomial and of a trinomial.

2. Write a monomial that represents the volume of 10 identical boxes x inches tall with square bases y inches on a side. What is the total volume of the boxes if $x = 5$ and $y = 8$?

Exercises 3–6: Identify the degree and coefficient.

3. $-4x^5$

4. y^3

5. $5xy^6$

6. $-9y^{10}$

Exercises 7–9: Combine like terms.

7. $5x - 4x + 10x$

8. $9x^3 - 5x^3 + x^2$

9. $6x^3y - 4x^3 + 8x^3y + 5x^3$

10. Evaluate $2x^3y^2 - 3y$ when $x = 2$ and $y = -1$.

Exercises 11 and 12: Identify the degree and leading coefficient of the polynomial.

11. $5x^2 - 3x + 5$

12. $x^3 - 5x + 5 + 2x^4$

Exercises 13–16: Combine the polynomials.

13. $(3x^2 - x + 7) + (5x^2 + 4x - 8)$

14. $(6z^3 + z) + (17z^3 - 4z^2)$

15. $(-4x^2 - 6x + 1) - (-3x^2 - 7x + 1)$

16. $(3x^3 - 5x + 7) - (8x^3 + x^2 - 2x + 1)$

Exercises 17 and 18: Evaluate $f(x)$ at the value of x.

17. $f(x) = 2x^2 - 3x + 2$ $x = -1$

18. $f(x) = 1 - x - 4x^3$ $x = 4$

19. Use the graph to evaluate $f(2)$.

20. If $f(x) = x^2 - 1$ and $g(x) = x - 3x^2$, then find $(f + g)(-2)$ and $(f - g)(x)$.

SECTION 3.2

Exercises 21 and 22: Multiply.

21. $5(3x - 4)$

22. $-2x(1 + x - 4x^2)$

Exercises 23–26: Multiply the monomials.

23. $x^3 \cdot x^5$

24. $-2x^3 \cdot 3x$

25. $(-7xy^7)(6xy)$

26. $(12xy^4)(5x^2y)$

Exercises 27–38: Multiply the expressions.

27. $(x + 4)(x + 5)$

28. $(x - 7)(x - 8)$

29. $(6x + 3)(2x - 9)$

30. $\left(y - \frac{1}{3}\right)\left(y + \frac{1}{3}\right)$

31. $4x^2(2x^2 - 3x - 1)$ **32.** $-x(4 + 5x - 7x^2)$

33. $(4x + y)(4x - y)$ **34.** $(x + 3)^2$

35. $(2y - 5)^2$

36. $(a - b)(a^2 + ab + b^2)$

37. $(5m - 2n^4)^2$

38. $\big((r - 1) + t\big)\big((r - 1) - t\big)$

SECTION 3.3

Exercises 39 and 40: Factor out the greatest common factor.

39. $25x^2 - 30x$ **40.** $12x^4 + 8x^3 - 16x^2$

Exercises 41–44: Use factoring to solve the equation.

41. $x^2 + 3x = 0$ **42.** $7x^4 = 28x^2$

43. $2t^2 - 3t + 1 = 0$

44. $4z(z - 3) + 4(z - 3) = 0$

Exercises 45–47: Use grouping to factor the polynomial.

45. $2x^3 + 2x^2 - 3x - 3$

46. $z^3 + z^2 + z + 1$ **47.** $ax - bx + ay - by$

48. If $f(x) = x + 1$ and $g(x) = x - 3$, find $(fg)(4)$ and $(fg)(x)$.

Exercises 49 and 50: Use the graph to do the following.

(a) *Find the x-intercepts.*
(b) *Solve the equation $P(x) = 0$.*
(c) *Find the zeros of $P(x)$.*

49. **50.**

 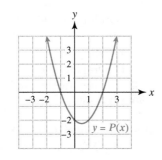

SECTION 3.4

Exercises 51–58: Factor completely.

51. $x^2 + 8x + 12$ **52.** $x^2 - 5x - 50$

53. $9x^2 + 25x - 6$ **54.** $4x^2 - 22x + 10$

55. $x^3 - 4x^2 + 3x$ **56.** $2x^4 + 14x^3 + 20x^2$

57. $5x^4 + 15x^3 - 90x^2$ **58.** $10x^3 - 90x^2 + 200x$

Exercises 59 and 60: Use the table to factor the expression. Check your answer by multiplying.

59. $x^2 - 2x - 15$ **60.** $x^2 - 24x + 143$

  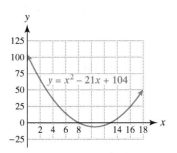

61. Use the graph to factor $x^2 + 3x - 28$. Check your answer by multiplying.

62. Use the graph to solve $x^2 - 21x + 104 = 0$. Check your solutions.

SECTION 3.5

Exercises 63–76: Factor completely.

63. $t^2 - 49$ **64.** $4y^2 - 9x^2$

65. $x^2 + 4x + 4$ **66.** $16x^2 - 8x + 1$

67. $x^3 - 27$ **68.** $64x^3 + 27y^3$

69. $10y^3 - 10y$ **70.** $4r^4 - t^6$

71. $m^4 - 16n^4$ **72.** $n^3 - 2n^2 - n + 2$

73. $25a^2 - 30ab + 9b^2$ **74.** $2r^3 - 12r^2t + 18rt^2$

75. $a^6 + 27b^3$ **76.** $8p^6 - q^3$

SECTION 3.6

Exercises 77–86: Factor completely.

77. $5x^3 - 10x^2$ **78.** $-2x^3 + 32x$

79. $x^4 - 16y^4$ **80.** $4x^3 + 8x^2 - 12x$

81. $-2x^3 + 11x^2 - 12x$ **82.** $x^4 - 8x^2 - 9$

83. $64a^3 + b^3$ **84.** $8 - y^3$

85. $(z + 3)^2 - 16$

86. $x^4 - 5x^3 - 4x^2 + 20x$

SECTION 3.7

Exercises 87 and 88: Solve the equation symbolically and graphically.

87. $x^2 - 16 = 0$ **88.** $x^2 - 2x - 3 = 0$

Exercises 89–98: Solve the equation.

89. $4x^2 - 28x + 49 = 0$

90. $x^2 + 8 = 0$

91. $3x^2 = 2x + 5$

92. $4x^2 + 5x = 6$

93. $x^3 = x$

94. $x^3 - 6x^2 + 11x = 6$

95. $x^3 + x^2 - 72x = 0$

96. $x^4 - 15x^3 + 56x^2 = 0$

97. $x^4 = 16$

98. $x^4 + 5x^2 = 36$

APPLICATIONS

99. *Profit from DVDs* Suppose a band produces x music videos with cost C in dollars of $C(x) = 3x + 9000$. If they sell each DVD for $15, do the following.
(a) Write a revenue function R that gives the amount the band makes for selling x DVDs.
(b) If profit equals revenue minus cost, write a formula $P(x)$ for the profit function.
(c) Evaluate $P(4000)$ and interpret the answer.

100. *Dimensions of a Box* The length of a box is 5 inches more than its width, its width is 5 inches more than its height, and its volume is 168 cubic inches. Let x be the height.
(a) Write an expression that gives the volume of the box in terms of x.
(b) Write an equation whose solution gives the height of the box.
(c) Find the dimensions of the box.

101. *Picture Frame* A rectangular frame surrounding a picture is made from boards that are 3 inches wide. The picture inside the frame is 2 inches wider than it is high. If the overall area of the picture and frame is 224 square inches, find the dimensions of the picture.

102. *Geometry* Suppose that a triangle has base $x + 2$ and height $x - 3$. Find a polynomial that gives the area of the triangle.

103. *High Temperatures* The formula

$$f(x) = -1.466x^2 + 20.25x + 9$$

models the monthly average high temperatures in degrees Fahrenheit at Columbus, Ohio. In this formula, let $x = 1$ be January, $x = 2$ be February, and so on. (*Source:* J. Williams, *The Weather Almanac.*)

(a) What is the average high temperature in May?
(b) Make a table of $f(x)$, starting at $x = 1$ and incrementing by 1. During what month is the average temperature the greatest?
(c) Graph f in [1, 12, 1] by [30, 90, 10] and interpret the graph.

104. *Softball Pitching* Suppose that the likelihood, or chance, that a pitch in softball will be a strike is x percent. Then the likelihood, as a percentage, that two consecutive pitches will *not* be strikes is given by $100\left(1 - \frac{x}{100}\right)^2$.
(a) Multiply this expression.
(b) Let $x = 70$. Use both the given expression and the expression you found in part (a) to obtain the likelihood that two consecutive pitches are not strikes.

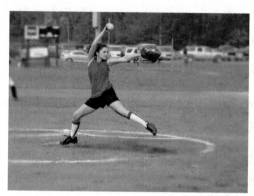

105. *Numbers* Write a polynomial that represents the product of three consecutive integers, where x corresponds to the largest integer.

106. *Area* Use the area of a rectangle to illustrate that $(x + 2)(x + 7) = x^2 + 9x + 14$.

107. *Area* Suppose that the area of the floor of a small building is 144 square feet and its length is 7 feet longer than its width. Find the dimensions of the building
(a) graphically,
(b) numerically, and
(c) symbolically.

108. *Rectangular Pen* A rectangular pen has a perimeter of 50 feet. If x represents its width, write a polynomial that gives the area of the pen in terms of x.

109. *Flight of a Golf Ball* If a golf ball is hit upward with a velocity of 66 feet per second (45 mph), its height h in feet above the ground after t seconds can be modeled by

$$h(t) = -16t^2 + 66t.$$

(a) Determine when the ball strikes the ground.
(b) When is the height of the ball 50 feet?

110. *Ticket Prices* If tickets are sold for $50, then 600 tickets are expected to be sold. For each $1 reduction in price, an additional 20 tickets will be sold.
 (a) Write an equation that gives the revenue R from ticket sales when ticket prices are reduced by x dollars.
 (b) Determine the ticket price that results in sales of $32,000.

111. *Modeling a Hill* The elevation E of a hill x feet along a highway can be modeled by

$$E(x) = -0.0001x^2 + 500,$$

where E is in feet. The crest of the hill corresponds to $x = 0$. Find values of x where E is 400 feet.

CHAPTER 3 **Test** CHAPTER Test Prep VIDEOS Step-by-step test solutions are found on the Chapter Test Prep Videos available via the Video Resources on DVD, in *MyMathLab*, and on YouTube (search "RockswoldInterAlg" and click on "Channels").

Exercises 1 and 2: Simplify by combining like terms.

1. $x^2y^2 - 4x + 9x - 5x^2y^2$

2. $(-2x^3 - 6x + 1) - (5x^3 - x^2 + x - 10)$

3. Evaluate $f(x) = 2x^3 - x^2 - 5x + 2$ at $x = -2$.

4. Use the graph to evaluate $f(2)$.

5. Give the degree and coefficient of $3x^3y$.

6. Write a monomial that gives the volume of 8 identical boxes with width x, length y, and height z.

7. Evaluate $-x^2y + 3xy^2$ when $x = -2$ and $y = 3$.

8. If $f(x) = 2x - 5$ and $g(x) = 1 - x^3$, then find $(f - g)(4)$ and $(f + g)(x)$.

Exercises 9–16: Multiply and simplify.

9. $-\frac{2}{5}x^2(10x - 5)$ 10. $2xy^7 \cdot 7xy$

11. $(2x + 1)(5x - 7)$ 12. $(5 - 3x)^2$

13. $(5x - 4y)(5x + 4y)$ 14. $-2x^2(x^2 - 3x + 2)$

15. $(x - 2y)(x^2 + 2xy + 4y^2)$

16. $2x^2(x - 1)(x + 1)$

Exercises 17–25: Factor completely.

17. $x^2 - 3x - 10$ 18. $2x^3 + 6x$

19. $3x^2 + 7x - 20$ 20. $5x^4 - 5x^2$

21. $2x^3 + x^2 - 10x - 5$

22. $49x^2 - 14x + 1$ 23. $x^3 + 8$

24. $4x^2y^4 + 8x^4y^2$ 25. $a^2 - 3ab + 2b^2$

26. Identify the degree and leading coefficient of the polynomial $5 - 4x + x^3$.

27. When we multiply $(2m^3 - 4n^2)^2$ we get which of the following (a.–d.)?
 a. $4m^6 - 8m^3n^2 + 16n^4$ b. $4m^6 - 16n^4$
 c. $4m^6 - 16m^3n^2 + 16n^4$ d. $4m^6 + 16n^4$

28. Use the graph to factor $x^2 + 2x - 48$.

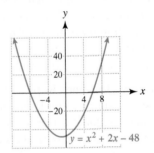

29. *Numbers* Write a polynomial that represents the product of two consecutive even integers, where x is the smaller integer. Multiply the expression.

Exercises 30–34: Use factoring to solve the polynomial equation.

30. $5x^2 = 15x$ 31. $4t^2 + 19t - 5 = 0$

32. $2z^4 - 8z^2 = 0$ 33. $x^4 - 2x^2 + 1 = 0$

34. $x(x - 3) + (x - 3) = 0$

35. *Area* A rectangular picture frame is 4 inches wider than it is high and has an area of 221 square inches.
 (a) Write an equation whose solution gives the height of the picture frame.
 (b) Solve the equation in part (a).
 (c) Find the perimeter of the picture frame.

36. *Dew Point* The formula

$$f(x) = -0.091x^3 + 0.66x^2 + 5.78x + 23.5$$

models the monthly average dew point in degrees Fahrenheit in Birmingham, Alabama. In this formula $x = 1$ corresponds to January, $x = 2$ to February, and so on. (**Source:** J. Williams, *The Weather Almanac.*)

(a) What is the average dew point in May?

(b) Use the graph of f to discuss how the dew point changes during the year.

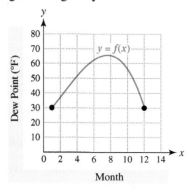

Month

37. *Geometry* Multiply $(x + 2)(x + 3)$ geometrically by drawing a rectangle.

38. *Height Reached by a Baseball* After a baseball is hit, the height h in feet reached after t seconds is given by

$$h(t) = -16t^2 + 96t + 3.$$

Determine when the baseball is 131 feet in the air.

CHAPTER 3   Extended and Discovery Exercises

MODELING NONLINEAR DATA

Exercises 1–3: Real-world data often do not lie on a line when they are plotted. Such data are called nonlinear data, and nonlinear functions are used to model this type of data. In the next three exercises you will be asked to find your own functions that model real-world data.

 1. *Planetary Orbits* Johannes Kepler (1571–1630) was the first person to find a formula that models the relationship between a planet's average distance from the sun and the time it takes to orbit the sun. The following table lists a planet's average distance x from the sun and the number of years y it takes to orbit the sun. In this table distances have been normalized so that Earth's distance is exactly 1. For example, Saturn is 9.54 times farther from the sun than Earth is and requires 29.5 years to orbit the sun.

Planet	x (distance)	y (period)
Mercury	0.387	0.241
Venus	0.723	0.615
Earth	1.00	1.00
Mars	1.52	1.88
Jupiter	3.20	11.9
Saturn	9.54	29.5

Source: C. Ronan, *The Natural History of the Universe.*

(a) Make a scatterplot of the data. Are the data linear or nonlinear?

(b) Kepler discovered a formula having the form $y = x^k$, which models the data in the table. Graph $y = x^{2.5}$ and the data in the same viewing rectangle. Does y model the data accurately? Explain.

(c) Try to discover a value for k so that $y = x^k$ models the data.

(d) Online Exploration The average distances of Neptune and Pluto (no longer a planet) from the sun are 30.1 and 39.4, respectively. Estimate how long it takes for each of them to orbit the sun. Go online to see whether your answers are accurate.

2. *Aging of America* Americans are living longer. The table shows the number of Americans who were more than 100 years old for various years.

Year	1994	1996	1998
Number (thousands)	50	56	65

Year	2000	2002	2004
Number (thousands)	75	94	110

Source: U.S. Census Bureau.

(a) Make a scatterplot of the data. Choose an appropriate viewing rectangle.

(b) Use trial and error to find a value for k so that
$$y = k(x - 1994)^2 + 50$$
models the data.

(c) Use y to estimate the number of Americans that were more than 100 years old in 2006.

 3. *Charitable Giving* Average charitable giving varies according to income. The average amount given for three different incomes is listed in the table.

Income	$10,000	$40,000	$100,000
Giving	$412	$843	$2550

Source: Gallup for Independent Sector.

(a) Let x be income and y be charitable giving. Set up an augmented matrix whose solution gives values for a, b, and c so that the graph of $y = ax^2 + bx + c$ passes through the points $(10000, 412)$, $(40000, 843)$, and $(100000, 2550)$.

(b) Use a graphing calculator to solve this system of linear equations.

(c) Estimate the average charitable giving for someone earning $20,000. Compare your answer to the actual value of $525.

CHAPTERS 1–3   Cumulative Review Exercises

1. Evaluate $A = \frac{1}{2}ab$ when $a = 5$ and $b = \frac{3}{2}$.

2. Find the reciprocal of $\frac{a}{b - a}$.

3. Simplify each expression. Write the result using positive exponents.

(a) $\left(\dfrac{x^{-3}}{y}\right)^2$ **(b)** $\dfrac{(3r^{-1}t)^{-4}}{r^2(t^2)^{-2}}$ **(c)** $(ab^{-2})^4(ab^3)^{-1}$

4. Write 5.859×10^4 in standard (decimal) form.

5. Find $f(-3)$, if $f(x) = -2x^2 + 3x$.

6. Find the domain of $f(x) = \sqrt{x - 4}$.

Exercises 7 and 8: Graph f by hand.

7. $f(x) = 3 - 2x$ **8.** $f(x) = x^2 - x - 2$

9. Use the graph to answer the following.
(a) Does the graph represent a function?
(b) Identify the domain and range.
(c) Evaluate $f(1)$ and $f(2)$.
(d) Identify the x-intercepts.
(e) Solve the equation $f(x) = 0$.
(f) Write $f(x)$ completely factored, if $f(x)$ is quadratic with leading coefficient 1.

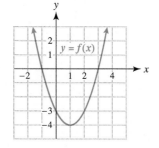

10. Find the slope–intercept form of the line that passes through $(-2, 5)$ and is parallel to $2x - y = 4$.

11. Let f be a linear function. Find a formula for $f(x)$.

x	-2	-1	1	2
$f(x)$	12	7	-3	-8

12. Solve $-2(5x - 1) = 1 - (5 - x)$.

13. Solve $3x + 4 \le x - 1$.

14. Solve $|5x - 10| > 5$.

15. Solve $-2 < 2 - 7x \le 2$.

16. Solve the system graphically or numerically.
$$4x + 2y = 10$$
$$-x + 5y = 3$$

17. Solve each system symbolically.
(a) $-x - 2y = 5$ **(b)** $3x + 2y = 7$
   $2x + 4y = -10$ $2x - 2y = 3$

18. Shade the solution set in the xy-plane.
$$2x + y \le 4$$
$$x - 2y < -2$$

19. Solve the system.
$$x + y - z = -2$$
$$x - y + z = -6$$
$$x - y - 2z = 3$$

20. Use Gauss–Jordan elimination to solve the system.

$$
\begin{aligned}
x - y - z &= -2 \\
2x + y + z &= 8 \\
-x - y + 2z &= 0
\end{aligned}
$$

21. Calculate $\det \begin{bmatrix} 0 & 1 & -3 \\ 1 & 0 & -1 \\ 3 & 1 & 0 \end{bmatrix}$

22. Solve $x^2 + 4 = 0$, if possible.

Exercises 23–28: Multiply the expression.

23. $-2x(x^2 - 2x + 5)$

24. $(2a + b)(2a - b)$

25. $(x - 1)(x + 1)(x + 3)$

26. $(4x + 9)(2x - 1)$

27. $(x^2 + 3y^3)^2$

28. $-2x(1 - x^2)$

Exercises 29–34: Factor the expression.

29. $x^2 - 8x - 33$

30. $10x^3 + 65x^2 - 35x$

31. $4x^2 - 100$

32. $49x^2 - 70x + 25$

33. $r^4 - r$

34. $x^3 + 2x^2 + x + 2$

Exercises 35–38: Solve the equation.

35. $4x^2 - 1 = 0$

36. $3x^2 + 14x - 5 = 0$

37. $x^3 + 4x = 4x^2$

38. $x^4 = x^2$

Exercises 39 and 40: Solve each equation graphically or numerically to the nearest tenth.

39. $\sqrt{2x} - 1.1(x - \pi) = 1 - 2x$

40. $(\pi - 1)x^2 - \sqrt{3} = 5 - 1.3x$

APPLICATIONS

41. *Investment* Suppose $4000 is deposited in two accounts paying 6% and 7% annual interest. If the interest after 1 year is $257, how much is invested at each rate?

42. *Cost of a Car* Suppose the cost C of an antique car from 1990 to 2010 is modeled by

$$C(x) = 750(x - 1990) + 6800.$$

(a) Evaluate $C(1995)$ and interpret the result.

(b) Interpret the slope of the graph of C.

43. *Geometry* A rectangular box with a square base has a volume of 1008 cubic inches. If its height is 5 inches less than the length of an edge of the base, find the dimensions of the box.

44. *Angles in a Triangle* The measure of the largest angle in a triangle is 20° less than the sum of the measures of the two smaller angles. The sum of the measures of the two larger angles is 100° greater than the measure of the smaller angle. Find the measure of each angle.

4

Rational Expressions and Functions

The future belongs to those who believe in the beauty of their dreams.

—ELEANOR ROOSEVELT

O n average, a person spends an estimated 45 to 60 minutes waiting each day. This waiting could be at the doctor's office, at the grocery store, in airports, or stuck in traffic. In a 70-year life span, a person might spend as much as 3 years waiting!

Motorists in the nation's top 68 urban areas spend about 50 percent more time stuck in traffic than they did 10 years ago. Traffic congestion delays travelers 3.7 billion hours and wastes 2.3 billion gallons of fuel at a cost of $63 billion each year. Many urban areas are not adding enough roads and highways to keep traffic moving.

The time spent waiting in lines is subject to a *nonlinear effect*. For example, you can put more cars on the road up to a point. Then, if the traffic intensity increases even slightly, congestion and long lines increase dramatically. See the graph below. This phenomenon cannot be modeled by linear or polynomial functions. Instead we need a new function, called a rational function, to describe this type of behavior. (See Example 6 in Section 4.4.)

Sources: Phillip J. Longman,
"American Gridlock," *U.S. News &
World Report*, May 28, 2001;
answers.google.com; CBS/AP, 2007.

Waiting in Traffic

Rational Function →

Time Waiting

Traffic Intensity

4.1 Introduction to Rational Functions and Equations

Recognizing and Using Rational Functions • Solving Rational Equations • Operations on Functions

A LOOK INTO MATH ▶

Suppose that you are trying to exit a parking ramp. If the parking attendant can wait on 5 cars per minute and cars are randomly leaving the parking ramp at a rate of 4 cars per minute, how long is your wait? What happens to your wait if cars start arriving randomly at nearly the parking attendant's rate of 5 cars per minute? Using a new function, called a *rational function*, we can answer these questions and also describe such things as how people participate in social networks. (See Example 8 and Exercise 105.)

Recognizing and Using Rational Functions

NEW VOCABULARY

☐ Rational expression
☐ Rational function
☐ Vertical asymptote
☐ Rational equation
☐ Extraneous solution

In Chapter 3 we discussed polynomials. Examples of polynomials include

$$4, \quad x, \quad x^2, \quad 2x - 5, \quad 3x^2 - 6x + 1, \quad \text{and} \quad 3x^4 - 7.$$

Rational expressions result when a polynomial is divided by a nonzero polynomial. Three examples of rational expressions are

$$\frac{4}{x}, \quad \frac{x^2}{2x - 5}, \quad \text{and} \quad \frac{3x^2 - 6x + 1}{3x^4 - 7}. \quad \text{Rational expressions}$$

EXAMPLE 1 **Recognizing a rational expression**

Determine whether each expression is rational.

(a) $\dfrac{4 - x}{5x^2 + 3}$ **(b)** $\dfrac{x^2 - 1}{\sqrt{x} + 2x}$ **(c)** $\dfrac{6}{x - 1}$

Solution

(a) This expression is rational because both $4 - x$ and $5x^2 + 3$ are polynomials.
(b) This expression is not rational because $\sqrt{x} + 2x$ is not a polynomial.
(c) This expression is rational because both 6 and $x - 1$ are polynomials.

Now Try Exercises 11, 13, 15

Rational expressions are used to define *rational functions*. For example, $\frac{6}{x - 1}$ is a rational *expression*, so $f(x) = \frac{6}{x - 1}$ represents a rational *function*.

A Rational Function

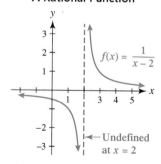

Figure 4.1

RATIONAL FUNCTION

Let $p(x)$ and $q(x)$ be polynomials. Then a **rational function** is given by

$$f(x) = \frac{p(x)}{q(x)}.$$

The domain of f includes all x-values such that $q(x) \neq 0$.

Formulas for linear and polynomial functions are *defined* for all x-values. However, formulas for a rational function are *undefined* for x-values that make the denominator equal to 0. (Division by 0 is undefined.) For example, if $f(x) = \frac{1}{x - 2}$, then $f(2) = \frac{1}{2 - 2} = \frac{1}{0}$ is undefined because the denominator equals 0. A graph of $y = f(x)$ is shown in Figure 4.1.

READING CHECK

How can you determine the domain of a rational function?

The graph does not cross the dashed vertical line $x = 2$, because $f(x)$ is *undefined* at $x = 2$. The red vertical dashed line $x = 2$ is called a *vertical asymptote*, and is used as an aid for sketching a graph of f. It is not actually part of the graph of the function.

EXAMPLE 2 | **Identifying the domain of rational functions**

Identify the domain of each function.

(a) $f(x) = \dfrac{1}{x + 2}$ **(b)** $g(x) = \dfrac{2x}{x^2 - 3x + 2}$ **(c)** $h(t) = \dfrac{4}{t^3 - t}$

Solution

(a) The domain of f includes all x-values for which the expression $f(x) = \dfrac{1}{x + 2}$ is defined. Thus we must *exclude* values of x for which the denominator equals 0.

$$x + 2 = 0 \quad \text{Set denominator equal to 0.}$$
$$x = -2 \quad \text{Subtract 2.}$$

In set-builder notation, $D = \{x \mid x \neq -2\}$.

(b) The domain of g includes all values of x except where the denominator equals 0.

$$x^2 - 3x + 2 = 0 \quad \text{Set denominator equal to 0.}$$
$$(x - 1)(x - 2) = 0 \quad \text{Factor.}$$
$$x = 1 \quad \text{or} \quad x = 2 \quad \text{Zero-product property; solve.}$$

Thus $D = \{x \mid x \neq 1, x \neq 2\}$.

(c) The domain of h includes all values of t except where the denominator equals 0.

$$t^3 - t = 0 \quad \text{Set denominator equal to 0.}$$
$$t(t^2 - 1) = 0 \quad \text{Factor out } t.$$
$$t(t - 1)(t + 1) = 0 \quad \text{Factor difference of squares.}$$
$$t = 0 \quad \text{or} \quad t = 1 \quad \text{or} \quad t = -1 \quad \text{Zero-product property; solve.}$$

Thus $D = \{t \mid t \neq 0, t \neq 1, t \neq -1\}$.

Now Try Exercises 21, 27, 29

To graph a rational function by hand, we usually start by making a table of values, as demonstrated in the next example. Because the graphs of rational functions are typically nonlinear, it is a good idea to plot at least 3 points on each side of an x-value where the formula is undefined, that is, where the denominator equals 0.

EXAMPLE 3 | **Graphing a rational function**

Graph $f(x) = \dfrac{1}{x}$. State the domain of f.

Solution

Make a table of values for $f(x) = \frac{1}{x}$, as shown in Table 4.1. Notice that $x = 0$ is not in the domain of f, and a dash can be used to denote this undefined value. The domain of f is all real numbers such that $x \neq 0$. Start by picking three x-values on each side of 0.

TABLE 4.1

x	-2	-1	$-\frac{1}{2}$	0	$\frac{1}{2}$	1	2
$\frac{1}{x}$	$-\frac{1}{2}$	-1	-2	—	2	1	$\frac{1}{2}$

↑―――― Undefined

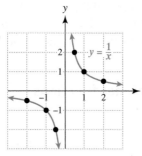

Figure 4.2

TABLE 4.1 **(Repeated)**

x	-2	-1	$-\frac{1}{2}$	0	$\frac{1}{2}$	1	2
$\frac{1}{x}$	$-\frac{1}{2}$	-1	-2	—	2	1	$\frac{1}{2}$

↑———— Undefined

Plot the points shown in Table 4.1 and then connect the points with a smooth curve, as shown in Figure 4.2. Because $f(0)$ is undefined, the graph of $f(x) = \frac{1}{x}$ does not cross the line $x = 0$ (the y-axis). The line $x = 0$ is a vertical asymptote.

Now Try Exercise 31

In the next example we evaluate a rational function in three ways.

EXAMPLE 4 **Evaluating a rational function**

Use Table 4.2, the formula for $f(x)$, and Figure 4.3 to evaluate $f(-1)$, $f(1)$, and $f(2)$.

(a) **TABLE 4.2**

x	$f(x)$
-3	$\frac{3}{2}$
-2	$\frac{4}{3}$
-1	1
0	0
1	—
2	4
3	3

(b) $f(x) = \dfrac{2x}{x - 1}$

(c)

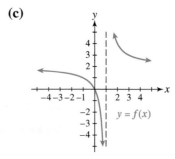

Figure 4.3

Solution

(a) *Numerical Evaluation* Table 4.2 shows that

$$f(-1) = 1, \quad f(1) \text{ is undefined}, \quad \text{and} \quad f(2) = 4.$$

(b) *Symbolic Evaluation*

$$f(-1) = \frac{2(-1)}{-1 - 1} = 1$$

$$f(1) = \frac{2(1)}{1 - 1} = \frac{2}{0}, \text{ which is undefined. Input 1 is } not \text{ in the domain of } f.$$

$$f(2) = \frac{2(2)}{2 - 1} = 4$$

(c) *Graphical Evaluation* To evaluate $f(-1)$ graphically, find $x = -1$ on the x-axis and move upward to the graph of f. The y-value is 1 at the point of intersection, so $f(-1) = 1$, as shown in Figure 4.4(a). In Figure 4.4(b) the red, dashed vertical line $x = 1$ is called a vertical asymptote. Because the graph of f does not intersect this line, $f(1)$ is undefined. Figure 4.4(c) reveals that $f(2) = 4$.

Evaluating a Rational Function Graphically

Figure 4.4

Now Try Exercises 43, 49, 53

MAKING CONNECTIONS

Asymptotes and Graphs of Rational Functions

A **vertical asymptote** often occurs at x-values in the graph of a rational function $y = f(x)$ where the denominator equals 0. A vertical asymptote can be used as an aid to sketch the graph of a rational function. However, the graph of a rational function *never* crosses a vertical asymptote, so a vertical asymptote is *not* part of the graph of f.

On either side of a vertical asymptote, the y-values on the graph of a rational function typically become either very large (approach ∞) or very small (approach $-\infty$). See the figure below.

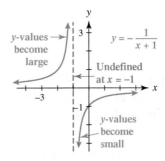

TECHNOLOGY NOTE

Asymptotes, Dot Mode, and Decimal Windows
When a rational function is graphed on a graphing calculator in connected mode, pseudo-asymptotes often occur because the calculator is simply connecting dots to draw a graph. The accompanying figures show the graph of $y = \frac{2}{x-2}$ in connected mode, in dot mode, and with a *decimal*, or *friendly*, window. In dot mode, pixels in the calculator screen are not connected. With dot mode (and sometimes with a decimal window) pseudo-asymptotes do not appear. To learn more about these features, consult your owner's manual.

CALCULATOR HELP

To set a calculator in dot mode or to set a decimal window, see Appendix A (pages AP-10 and AP-11).

▶ **REAL-WORLD CONNECTION** Applications involving rational functions are numerous. One instance is in the design of curves for train tracks, which we discuss in the next example.

EXAMPLE 5

Modeling a train track curve

When curves are designed for train tracks, sometimes the outer rail is elevated, or banked, so that a locomotive and its cars can safely negotiate the curve at a higher speed than if the tracks were level. Suppose that a circular curve with a radius of r feet is being designed for a train traveling 60 miles per hour. Then $f(r) = \frac{2540}{r}$ calculates the proper elevation y in inches for the outer rail, where $y = f(r)$. See Figure 4.5. (*Source:* L. Haefner, *Introduction to Transportation Systems.*)

(a) Evaluate $f(300)$ and interpret the result.
(b) A graph of f is shown in Figure 4.6. Discuss how the elevation of the outer rail changes as the radius r increases.

Figure 4.5

Figure 4.6

Solution

(a) $f(300) = \frac{2540}{300} \approx 8.5$. Thus the outer rail on a curve with a radius of 300 feet should be elevated about 8.5 inches for a train to safely travel through it at 60 miles per hour.
(b) As the radius r increases (and the curve becomes less sharp), the outer rail needs less elevation.

Now Try Exercise 101(a)

Solving Rational Equations

▶ **REAL-WORLD CONNECTION** When working with rational functions, we commonly encounter rational equations. In Example 5, we used $f(r) = \frac{2540}{r}$ to calculate the elevation of the outer rail in a train track curve. Now suppose that the outer rail for a curve is elevated 6 inches. What should be the radius of the curve? To answer this question, we need to solve the **rational equation**

$$\frac{2540}{r} = 6. \quad \text{Rational equation}$$

We solve this equation in the next example.

EXAMPLE 6

Determining the proper radius for a train track curve

Solve the rational equation $\frac{2540}{r} = 6$ and interpret the result.

Solution

We begin by multiplying each side of the equation by r.

$$r \cdot \frac{2540}{r} = 6 \cdot r \qquad \text{Multiply by } r.$$

$$2540 = 6r \qquad \text{Simplify.}$$

$$\frac{2540}{6} = r \qquad \text{Divide by 6.}$$

$$r = 423.\overline{3} \qquad \text{Rewrite.}$$

A train track curve designed for 60 miles per hour and banked 6 inches should have a radius of about 423 feet.

Now Try Exercise 101(d)

Multiplying each side of the rational equation in the form $\frac{N}{D} = C$ by the denominator D is often a good step for solving this equation (see Example 6), because

$$D \cdot \frac{N}{D} = C \cdot D \quad \text{simplifies to} \quad N = CD,$$

provided that $D \neq 0$. For example, to solve

$$\frac{x}{12} = 5,$$

we multiply each side of the equation by 12, because

$$12 \cdot \frac{x}{12} = 5 \cdot 12 \quad \text{simplifies to} \quad x = 5 \cdot 12 = 60.$$

We use this technique in Example 7. Be sure to check your answer.

EXAMPLE 7   **Solving rational equations**

Solve each rational equation and check your answer.

(a) $\dfrac{3x}{2x - 1} = 3$ **(b)** $\dfrac{x + 1}{x - 2} = \dfrac{3}{x - 2}$ **(c)** $\dfrac{6}{x + 1} = x$

Solution

(a) First note that $\frac{1}{2}$ cannot be a solution to this equation because $x = \frac{1}{2}$ results in the left side of the equation being undefined; division by 0 is not possible. Multiply each side of the equation by the denominator, $2x - 1$.

$$(2x - 1) \cdot \frac{3x}{2x - 1} = 3 \cdot (2x - 1) \qquad \text{Multiply by } (2x - 1).$$

$$3x = 6x - 3 \qquad \text{Simplify.}$$

$$-3x = -3 \qquad \text{Subtract } 6x.$$

$$x = 1 \qquad \text{Divide by } -3.$$

To check your answer, substitute 1 in the given equation for x.

$$\frac{3(1)}{2(1) - 1} = 3 \ \checkmark \qquad \text{The answer checks.}$$

(b) Each side of the equation is undefined when $x = 2$. Thus 2 cannot be a solution. Begin by multiplying each side of the equation by the denominator, $x - 2$.

$$(x - 2) \cdot \frac{x + 1}{x - 2} = \frac{3}{x - 2} \cdot (x - 2) \qquad \text{Multiply by } x - 2.$$

$$x + 1 = 3 \qquad \text{Simplify.}$$

$$x = 2 \qquad \text{Subtract 1.}$$

In this case 2 is not a valid solution. There are no solutions. Instead, 2 is called an **extraneous solution**, which cannot be used. It is *important* to check your answers, as follows.

$$\frac{2 + 1}{2 - 2} \stackrel{?}{=} \frac{3}{2 - 2} \qquad \text{Let } x = 2 \text{ in given equation.}$$

$$\frac{3}{0} \stackrel{?}{=} \frac{3}{0} \; \text{✗} \qquad \text{Division by 0 is undefined.}$$

READING CHECK

Why is it important to check your answer when solving a rational equation?

(c) The left side of the equation is undefined when $x = -1$. Thus -1 cannot be a solution. To solve this equation start by multiplying each side by the denominator, $x + 1$.

$$(x + 1) \cdot \frac{6}{x + 1} = x \cdot (x + 1) \qquad \text{Multiply by } x + 1.$$

$$6 = x^2 + x \qquad \text{Simplify.}$$

$$x^2 + x - 6 = 0 \qquad \text{Rewrite the equation.}$$

$$(x + 3)(x - 2) = 0 \qquad \text{Factor.}$$

$$x = -3 \quad \text{or} \quad x = 2 \qquad \text{Zero-product property}$$

Checking these results confirms that both -3 and 2 are solutions.

> Now Try Exercises 57, 65, 69

Like other equations, rational equations can be solved symbolically, graphically, and numerically, as shown in this Making Connections.

MAKING CONNECTIONS

Symbolic, Numerical, and Graphical Solutions to a Rational Equation

Symbolic Solution

$$\frac{x + 3}{2x} = 2$$

$$2x \cdot \frac{x + 3}{2x} = 2 \cdot 2x$$

$$x + 3 = 4x$$

$$3 = 3x$$

$$x = 1$$

The solution is **1**.

Numerical Solution

x	$(x + 3)/(2x)$
-2	-0.25
-1	-1
0	—
1	2
2	1.25

When $x = 1$, $\frac{x + 3}{2x} = 2$.

Graphical Solution

The graphs intersect at **(1, 2)**.

STUDY TIP

It can be helpful to talk and study with other students. However, make sure that others are not "doing the work for you."

▶ **REAL-WORLD CONNECTION** You may have noticed that a relatively small percentage of people do the vast majority of postings on social networks, such as Facebook and Twitter. This phenomenon is called *participation inequality*. That is, a vast majority of the population falls under the category of "lurkers," who are on the network but are not posting material. This characteristic of a social network can be modeled approximately by a rational function, as illustrated in the next example. (*Source:* Wu, Michael, *The Economics of 90–9–1.*)

EXAMPLE 8

Modeling social network participation

The rational function given by

$$f(x) = \frac{100}{101 - x}, \ 5 \le x \le 100,$$

models participation inequality in a social network. In this formula, $f(x)$ outputs the percentage of the postings done by the least active (bottom) x percent of the population.
(a) Evaluate $f(95)$. Interpret your answer.
(b) A graph of $y = f(x)$ is shown in Figure 4.7. Interpret the graph.

Participation in a Social Network

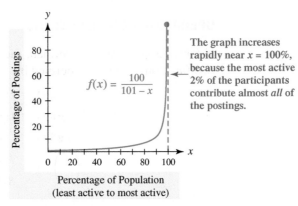

The graph increases rapidly near $x = 100\%$, because the most active 2% of the participants contribute almost *all* of the postings.

Figure 4.7 Participation Inequality

(c) Solve the rational equation $\frac{100}{101 - x} = 9$. Interpret your answer.

Solution

(a) $f(95) = \dfrac{100}{101 - 95} = \dfrac{100}{6} \approx 16.7\%$ Let $x = 95$.

This means that the least active 95% of the population contributes only 14.7% of the postings, so the most active 5% of the population is responsible for the remaining 83.3% of the postings.

(b) The graph shows participation inequality visually. The graph remains at a relatively low percentage until $x = 90\%$. This means that the bottom 90% of the population does very few postings. For $x \ge 90\%$ the graph rises rapidly because the top 10% contributes a vast majority of the postings.

(c) To solve this equation, we begin by multiplying each side by $(101 - x)$.

$$\frac{100}{101 - x} = 9 \qquad \text{Given equation}$$

$$(101 - x) \cdot \frac{100}{101 - x} = 9(101 - x) \qquad \text{Multiply by } (101 - x).$$

$$100 = 9(101 - x) \qquad \text{Simplify left side.}$$

$$100 = 909 - 9x \qquad \text{Distributive property}$$

$$9x + 100 - 100 = 909 - 100 + 9x - 9x \qquad \text{Add } 9x. \text{ Subtract 100.}$$

$$9x = 809 \qquad \text{Simplify.}$$

$$x = \frac{809}{9} \approx 90\% \qquad \text{Simplify.}$$

This result indicates that the least active 90% of the population contributes only 9% of the postings.

CRITICAL THINKING

Suppose that a social network had *participation equality*, in which every member contributed an equal number of postings. Sketch a graph like Figure 4.7 that describes this social network.

Now Try Exercise 105

Operations on Functions

▶ **REAL-WORLD CONNECTION** The ratio of two functions can give us information. For example, suppose that $G(x)$ gives the revenue for Google x years after its startup, and that $F(x)$ gives the revenue for Facebook x years after its startup. The function of their ratios, $R(x) = \frac{G(x)}{F(x)}$, gives a measure of how their revenues compare in size. (See Exercises 111 and 112.)

We have performed addition, subtraction, multiplication, and division on numbers and variables. In Chapter 3, we performed addition, subtraction, and multiplication on functions. In this subsection we will review these operations and also perform division on functions.

OPERATIONS ON FUNCTIONS

If $f(x)$ and $g(x)$ are both defined, then the sum, difference, product, and quotient of two functions f and g are defined by

$$(f + g)(x) = f(x) + g(x) \qquad \text{Sum}$$

$$(f - g)(x) = f(x) - g(x) \qquad \text{Difference}$$

$$(fg)(x) = f(x) \cdot g(x) \qquad \text{Product}$$

$$\left(\frac{f}{g}\right)(x) = \frac{f(x)}{g(x)}, \text{ where } g(x) \neq 0. \qquad \text{Quotient}$$

EXAMPLE 9 **Performing arithmetic on functions**

Use $f(x) = x^2$ and $g(x) = 2x - 4$ to evaluate each of the following.

(a) $(f + g)(3)$ **(b)** $(fg)(-1)$ **(c)** $\left(\frac{f}{g}\right)(0)$ **(d)** $(f/g)(2)$

Solution
(a) $(f + g)(3) = f(3) + g(3) = 3^2 + (2 \cdot 3 - 4) = 9 + 2 = 11$
(b) $(fg)(-1) = f(-1) \cdot g(-1) = (-1)^2 \cdot (2 \cdot (-1) - 4) = 1 \cdot (-6) = -6$
(c) $\left(\frac{f}{g}\right)(0) = \frac{f(0)}{g(0)} = \frac{0^2}{2 \cdot 0 - 4} = \frac{0}{-4} = 0$

(d) Note that $(f/g)(2)$ is equivalent to $\left(\frac{f}{g}\right)(2)$.

$$(f/g)(2) = \frac{f(2)}{g(2)} = \frac{2^2}{2 \cdot 2 - 4} = \frac{4}{0},$$

which is not possible because division by 0 is undefined. Thus $(f/g)(2)$ is *undefined*.

Now Try Exercise 89

In the next example, we find the sum, difference, product, and quotient of two functions for a general x.

EXAMPLE 10 **Performing arithmetic on functions**

Use $f(x) = 4x - 5$ and $g(x) = 3x + 1$ to evaluate each of the following.

(a) $(f + g)(x)$ **(b)** $(f - g)(x)$ **(c)** $(fg)(x)$ **(d)** $\left(\frac{f}{g}\right)(x)$

Solution

(a) $(f + g)(x) = f(x) + g(x) = (4x - 5) + (3x + 1) = 7x - 4$
(b) $(f - g)(x) = f(x) - g(x) = (4x - 5) - (3x + 1) = x - 6$
(c) $(fg)(x) = f(x) \cdot g(x) = (4x - 5)(3x + 1) = 12x^2 - 11x - 5$

(d) $\left(\dfrac{f}{g}\right)(x) = \dfrac{f(x)}{g(x)} = \dfrac{4x - 5}{3x + 1}$

▌ **Now Try Exercise 93**

4.1 Putting It All Together

CONCEPT	EXPLANATION	EXAMPLE
Rational Function	Let $p(x)$ and $q(x)$ be polynomials with $q(x) \neq 0$. Then a *rational function* is given by $$f(x) = \dfrac{p(x)}{q(x)}.$$	$$f(x) = \dfrac{3x}{x + 2}$$ The domain of f includes all real numbers except $x = -2$. A vertical asymptote occurs at $x = -2$ in the graph of f.
Rational Equation	An equation that contains rational expressions is a *rational equation*. When you are solving a rational equation, multiplication is often a good first step. *Be sure to check your results.*	To solve $\dfrac{3x}{x + 1} = 6$, begin by multiplying each side by $x + 1$. $$(x + 1) \cdot \dfrac{3x}{x + 1} = 6 \cdot (x + 1)$$ $$3x = 6x + 6$$ $$-3x = 6$$ $$x = -2$$
Division of Functions	$$(f/g)(x) = \dfrac{f(x)}{g(x)}, \ g(x) \neq 0$$	If $f(x) = x^2$ and $g(x) = x + 1$, then $$(f/g)(x) = \dfrac{x^2}{x + 1}.$$

4.1 Exercises

CONCEPTS AND VOCABULARY

1. What is a rational expression? Give an example.

2. If $f(x) = \dfrac{6}{x - 4}$, for what input x is $f(x)$ undefined?

3. What would be a good first step in solving the rational equation $\dfrac{3}{x + 7} = x$?

4. Is 5 a solution to $\dfrac{x + 5}{x - 5} = \dfrac{10}{x - 5}$? Explain.

5. Does $x \cdot \dfrac{5 + x}{x}$ simplify to $5x$? Explain.

6. If $x \neq 3$, then $\dfrac{x - 3}{x - 3} = $ _____.

7. If $b \neq 0$, then $b \cdot \dfrac{a}{b} = $ _____.

8. The domain of $f(x) = \frac{p(x)}{q(x)}$ includes all x-values such that $q(x) \neq$ _____.

9. Which of the following expressions (a.–d.) is not a rational function?

a. $f(x) = \frac{1}{x}$ **b.** $f(x) = x^2 + 1$

c. $f(x) = \sqrt{x}$ **d.** $f(x) = \frac{2x^2}{x - 1}$

10. Which (a.–d.) is the domain of $f(x) = \frac{2x}{2x - 1}$?

a. $\{x \mid x \neq \frac{1}{2}\}$ **b.** $\{x \mid x \neq 1\}$
c. $\{x \mid x \neq 0\}$ **d.** $\{x \mid x = 1\}$

Exercises 11–16: Determine if the expression is rational.

11. $\frac{2}{x}$ **12.** $\frac{5 - 2x}{x^2}$

13. $\frac{3x - 5}{2x + 1}$ **14.** $|x| + \frac{4}{|x|}$

15. $\frac{\sqrt{x}}{x^2 - 1}$ **16.** $\frac{4x^2 - 3x + 1}{x^3 - 4x}$

RATIONAL FUNCTIONS

Exercises 17–20: Write a symbolic representation (or formula) for the rational function f described.

17. Divide x by the quantity x plus 1.

18. Add 2 to x and then divide the result by the quantity x plus 5.

19. Divide x squared by the quantity x minus 2.

20. Compute the reciprocal of twice x.

Exercises 21–30: Identify the domain of f. Write your answer in set-builder notation.

21. $f(x) = \frac{x + 1}{x + 2}$ **22.** $f(x) = \frac{2x}{x - 4}$

23. $f(x) = \frac{1 - x}{3x - 1}$ **24.** $f(x) = \frac{x}{5x + 4}$

25. $f(t) = \frac{2}{t^2 - 4}$ **26.** $f(t) = \frac{5t}{9 - t^2}$

27. $f(x) = \frac{x^2 + 1}{x^2 - 3x + 2}$ **28.** $f(x) = \frac{2x^2 + x + 5}{2x^2 - x - 15}$

29. $f(x) = \frac{5}{x^3 - 4x}$ **30.** $f(x) = \frac{x^2 + 4}{9x - x^3}$

Exercises 31–42: Graph $y = f(x)$. Be sure to include any vertical asymptotes as dashed lines. State the domain of f in set-builder notation.

31. $f(x) = \frac{1}{x - 1}$ **32.** $f(x) = \frac{1}{x + 3}$

33. $f(x) = \frac{1}{2x}$ **34.** $f(x) = \frac{2}{x}$

35. $f(x) = \frac{1}{x + 2}$ **36.** $f(x) = \frac{1}{x - 2}$

37. $f(x) = \frac{4}{x^2 + 1}$ **38.** $f(x) = \frac{6}{x^2 + 2}$

39. $f(x) = \frac{3}{2x - 3}$ **40.** $f(x) = \frac{1}{3x + 2}$

41. $f(x) = \frac{1}{x^2 - 1}$ **42.** $f(x) = \frac{4}{4 - x^2}$

Exercises 43–48: Evaluate $f(x)$ at the given value of x.

43. $f(x) = \frac{1}{x - 1}$ $x = -2$

44. $f(x) = \frac{3x}{x^2 - 1}$ $x = 2$

45. $f(x) = \frac{x + 1}{x - 1}$ $x = -3$

46. $f(x) = \frac{2x + 1}{3x - 1}$ $x = 0$

47. $f(x) = \frac{x^2 - 3x + 5}{x^2 + 1}$ $x = -2$

48. $f(x) = \frac{5}{x^2 - x}$ $x = -1$

Exercises 49–52: Use the graph to evaluate each expression. Give the equation of any vertical asymptotes.

49. $f(-3)$ and $f(1)$ **50.** $f(-3)$ and $f(2)$

51. $f(-1)$ and $f(2)$ **52.** $f(-1)$ and $f(1)$

    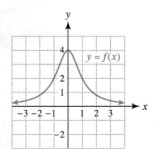

Exercises 53 and 54: Complete the table. Then evaluate $f(1)$.

53.

x	-2	-1	0	1	2
$f(x) = \dfrac{1}{x-1}$					

54.

x	-2	-1	0	1	2
$f(x) = \dfrac{2x}{x+2}$					

RATIONAL EQUATIONS

Exercises 55–74: Solve. Check your result.

55. $\dfrac{3}{x} = 5$

56. $\dfrac{5}{x} = 7$

57. $\dfrac{1}{x-2} = -1$

58. $\dfrac{-5}{x+4} = -5$

59. $\dfrac{x}{x+1} = 2$

60. $\dfrac{3x}{x+3} = -6$

61. $\dfrac{2x+1}{3x-2} = 1$

62. $\dfrac{x+3}{4x+1} = \dfrac{3}{5}$

63. $\dfrac{3}{x+2} = x$

64. $\dfrac{6}{2x+1} = x$

65. $\dfrac{6}{x+1} = 3x$

66. $\dfrac{4}{x-3} = x$

67. $\dfrac{1}{x^2-1} = -1$

68. $\dfrac{5x}{x^2-5} = \dfrac{x+2}{x^2-5}$

69. $\dfrac{x}{x-5} = \dfrac{2x-5}{x-5}$

70. $\dfrac{x}{x+1} = \dfrac{2x+1}{x+1}$

71. $\dfrac{4x}{x+2} = \dfrac{-8}{2x+4}$

72. $\dfrac{6x}{3x-2} = \dfrac{4}{4-6x}$

73. $\dfrac{2x}{x+2} = \dfrac{x-4}{x+2}$

74. $\dfrac{x+3}{x+1} = \dfrac{3x+4}{x+1}$

Exercises 75–80: Solve the rational equation either graphically or numerically. Check your answer.

75. $\dfrac{4+x}{2x} = -0.5$

76. $\dfrac{2x-1}{x-5} = -\dfrac{5}{2}$

77. $\dfrac{2x}{x^2-4} = -\dfrac{2}{3}$

78. $\dfrac{x-1}{x+2} = x$

79. $\dfrac{1}{x-1} = x-1$

80. $\dfrac{2}{x+2} = x+1$

USING MORE THAN ONE METHOD

Exercises 81–84: Solve the equation (a) symbolically, (b) graphically, and (c) numerically.

81. $\dfrac{1}{x+2} = 1$

82. $\dfrac{3}{x-1} = 2$

83. $\dfrac{x}{2x+1} = \dfrac{2}{5}$

84. $\dfrac{4x-2}{x+1} = \dfrac{3}{2}$

Exercises 85 and 86: Solve to the nearest hundredth.

85. $\dfrac{x^3}{x-1} = \dfrac{-1}{x+1}$

86. $\dfrac{x^2-1}{2x^2} = \dfrac{x+2}{1-x}$

87. Thinking Generally If $a = \dfrac{x}{b}$, then $x =$ _____.

88. Thinking Generally If $\dfrac{a}{b} = \dfrac{c}{d}$, then $ad =$ _____.

OPERATIONS ON FUNCTIONS

Exercises 89–92: Use $f(x)$ and $g(x)$ to evaluate each of the following.

(a) $(f+g)(3)$ (b) $(f-g)(-2)$
(c) $(fg)(5)$ (d) $(f/g)(0)$

89. $f(x) = 5x, g(x) = x+1$

90. $f(x) = x^2+2, g(x) = -2x$

91. $f(x) = 2x-1, g(x) = 4x^2$

92. $f(x) = x^2-1, g(x) = x+2$

Exercises 93–96: Use $f(x)$ and $g(x)$ to find each of the following.

(a) $(f+g)(x)$ (b) $(f-g)(x)$
(c) $(fg)(x)$ (d) $(f/g)(x)$

93. $f(x) = x+1, g(x) = x+2$

94. $f(x) = -3x, g(x) = x-1$

95. $f(x) = 1-x, g(x) = x^2$

96. $f(x) = x^2+4, g(x) = 6x$

APPLICATIONS

Exercises 97–100: Graphical Interpretation Match the physical situation with the graph (a.–d.) of the rational function that models it best.

97. A population of fish that increases and then levels off

98. An insect population that dies out

99. The length of a ticket line as the rate at which people arrive in line increases

100. The wind speed during a day that is initially calm, becomes windy, and then is calm again

a.

b.

c.

d.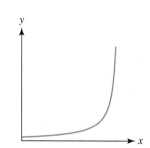

101. *Train Track Curves* (Refer to Example 5.) Let $f(r) = \frac{2540}{r}$ compute the elevation of the outer rail in inches for a curve designed for 60 miles per hour with a radius of r feet. (*Source:* L. Haefner.)
 (a) Evaluate $f(400)$ and interpret the result.
 (b) Construct a table of f, starting at $r = 100$ and incrementing by 50.
 (c) From the table, if the radius of the curve doubles, what happens to the elevation of the outer rail?
 (d) If the outer rail is elevated 5 inches, what should be the radius of the curve?

102. *Highway Curves* Engineers need to calculate a minimum safe radius for highway curves. To make a sharp curve safer, the road can be banked, or elevated, as illustrated in the figure at the top of the next column. If a curve is designed for a speed of 40 miles per hour and is banked with slope m, then a minimum radius R is computed by

$$R(m) = \frac{1600}{15m + 2}.$$

(*Source:* N. Garber.)

 (a) Evaluate $R(0.1)$ and interpret the result.
 (b) A graph of R is shown in the figure. Describe what happens to the radius of the curve as the slope of the banking increases.

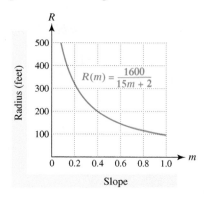

 (c) If the curve has a radius of 320 feet, what is m?

103. *Uphill Highway Grade* The *grade x* of a hill is a measure of its steepness and corresponds to the slope of the road. For example, if a road rises 10 feet for every 100 feet of horizontal distance, it has an uphill grade of $x = \frac{10}{100}$, or 10%, as illustrated in the figure.

The braking distance for a car traveling 30 miles per hour on a wet, *uphill* grade x is given by

$$D(x) = \frac{900}{10.5 + 30x}.$$

(*Source:* N. Garber.)

 (a) Evaluate $D(0.05)$ and interpret the result.

 (b) If the braking distance for this car is 60 feet, find the uphill grade x.

104. *Downhill Highway Grade* (See Exercise 103.) The braking distance for a car traveling 30 miles per hour on a wet, *downhill* grade x is given by

$$S(x) = \frac{900}{10.5 - 30x}.$$

 (a) Evaluate $S(0.05)$ and interpret the result.

(b) Make a table for $D(x)$ from Exercise 103 and $S(x)$, starting at $x = 0$ and incrementing by 0.05.

(c) How do the braking distances for uphill and downhill grades compare? Does this result agree with your driving experience?

105. *Time Spent in Line* If a parking lot attendant can wait on 5 vehicles per minute and vehicles are leaving the lot randomly at an average rate of x vehicles per minute, then the average time T in minutes spent waiting in line *and* paying the attendant is given by

$$T(x) = \frac{1}{5 - x},$$

where $x < 5$. (*Source:* N. Garber.)

(a) Evaluate $T(4)$ and interpret the result.

(b) A graph of T is shown in the figure. Interpret the graph as x increases from 0 to 5. Does this result agree with your intuition?

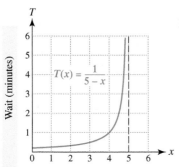

Traffic Rate (vehicles per minute)

(c) Find x if the waiting time is 3 minutes.

106. *People Waiting in Line* At a post office, workers can wait on 50 people per hour. If people arrive randomly at an average rate of x per hour, then the average number of people N waiting in line is given by

$$N(x) = \frac{x^2}{2500 - 50x},$$

where $x < 50$. (*Source:* N. Garber.)

(a) Evaluate $N(30)$ and interpret the result.

(b) A graph of N is shown in the figure. Interpret the graph as x increases from 0 to 50. Does this result agree with your intuition?

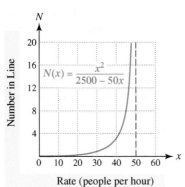

Rate (people per hour)

(c) Find x if $N = 8$.

107. *Winning Number* A jar contains x balls. Each ball has a unique number written on it and only one ball has the winning number. The likelihood, or probability P, of *not* drawing the winning ball is given by

$$P(x) = \frac{x - 1}{x},$$

where $x > 0$. For example, if $P = 0.99$, then there is a 99% chance of not drawing the winning ball.

(a) Evaluate $P(1)$ and $P(50)$ and interpret the result.

(b) Graph P in [0, 100, 10] by [0, 1, 0.1].

(c) What happens to the probability of not winning as the number of balls increases? Does this result agree with your intuition? Explain.

(d) How many balls are in the jar if the probability of not winning is 0.975?

108. *Insect Population* Suppose that an insect population in thousands per acre is modeled by

$$P(x) = \frac{5x + 2}{x + 1},$$

where $x \geq 0$ is time in months.

(a) Evaluate $P(10)$ and interpret the result.

(b) Graph P in [0, 50, 10] by [0, 6, 1].

(c) What happens to the insect population after several years?

(d) After how many months is the insect population 4.8 thousand per acre?

Exercises 109 and 110: Remembering What You Learn After a test students often forget what they learned. The rational function

$$R(x) = \frac{100}{1.2x + 1}, \quad 0 \leq x \leq 5,$$

gives an estimate of the percentage of the material a student remembers x days after a test.

109. Evaluate $R(1)$ and $R(3)$. Interpret your results.

110. If a student takes notes in class, these percentages increase by 30% for $1 \leq x \leq 5$. Write another function $N(x)$ that models this result. Evaluate $N(3)$.

111. *Google and Facebook Revenues* (Refer to the Real-World Connection that is discussed before Example 9.) The function $G(x) = 350(x - 3)^2 + 50$ gives the revenue for Google x years after its startup, and $F(x) = 206(x - 3)^2 + 150$ gives the revenue for Facebook x years after its startup. Both revenues are in millions of dollars and $x \geq 3$.

(a) Write a formula for $R(x) = \frac{G(x)}{F(x)}$.

(b) Evaluate $R(6)$ and interpret your result.

112. *Google and Yahoo Revenues* (Refer to Exercise 111.) The function $G(x) = 350(x - 3)^2 + 50$ gives the revenue for Google x years after its startup, and $Y(x) = 117(x - 3)^2 + 50$ gives the revenue for Yahoo x years after its startup. Both revenues are in millions of dollars and $x \geq 3$.
(a) Write a formula for $R(x) = \frac{G(x)}{Y(x)}$.
(b) Evaluate $R(5)$ and interpret your result.

WRITING ABOUT MATHEMATICS

113. Is every polynomial function a rational function? Explain your answer.

114. The domain of a polynomial function includes all real numbers. Does the domain of a rational function include all real numbers? Explain your answer and give an example.

Group Activity   Working with Real Data

Directions: Form a group of 2 to 4 people. Select someone to record the group's responses for this activity. All members of the group should work cooperatively to answer the questions. If your instructor asks for your results, each member of the group should be prepared to respond.

Slippery Roads If a car is moving on a level highway, its stopping distance depends on road conditions. If the road is slippery, stopping may take longer. A measure of the slipperiness of a road is the coefficient of friction x between the tire and the road, where x satisfies $0 < x \leq 1$. A smaller value for x indicates that the road is slipperier. The stopping distance D in feet for a car traveling at 50 miles per hour on a road with a coefficient of friction x is given by

$$D(x) = \frac{250}{3x}.$$

(*Source:* L. Haefner.)

(a) Graph D. Identify any vertical asymptotes.
(b) What happens to the stopping distance as x increases to 1? Explain.
(c) What happens to the stopping distance as x decreases to 0? Explain.
(d) In reality, could $x = 0$? Explain. What would happen if a road could have $x = 0$ and a car tried to stop?

4.2   Multiplication and Division of Rational Expressions

Simplifying Rational Expressions • Review of Multiplication and Division of Fractions • Multiplication of Rational Expressions • Division of Rational Expressions

A LOOK INTO MATH ▶

Rational expressions are sometimes used by businesses to describe the average cost to produce a particular item. If a business knows the average cost to produce each item and also knows the number of items produced, then they can easily determine the total cost by multiplying the two expressions. See Example 5 and Exercises 109 and 110.

Simplifying Rational Expressions

NEW VOCABULARY

☐ Basic principle of fractions
☐ Lowest terms
☐ Reciprocal of a polynomial
☐ Reciprocal of a rational expression

When simplifying fractions, we often use the **basic principle of fractions**, which states that

$$\frac{a \cdot c}{b \cdot c} = \frac{a}{b}.$$

This principle holds because $\frac{c}{c} = 1$ and $\frac{a}{b} \cdot 1 = \frac{a}{b}$. That is,

$$\frac{a \cdot c}{b \cdot c} = \frac{a}{b} \cdot \frac{c}{c} = \frac{a}{b} \cdot 1 = \frac{a}{b}.$$

For example, this principle can be used to simplify a fraction.

$$\frac{6}{44} = \frac{3 \cdot 2}{22 \cdot 2} = \frac{3}{22}$$

This same principle can also be used to simplify rational expressions. For example,

$$\frac{(z+1)(z+3)}{z(z+3)} = \frac{z+1}{z}, \quad \text{provided } z \neq -3.$$

SIMPLIFYING RATIONAL EXPRESSIONS

The following principle can be used to simplify rational expressions, where A, B, and C are polynomials.

$$\frac{A \cdot C}{B \cdot C} = \frac{A}{B} \qquad B \text{ and } C \text{ not zero}$$

To *simplify* a rational expression, we *completely factor* the numerator and the denominator and then apply the principle for simplifying rational expressions until the expression is in **lowest terms**. These concepts are illustrated in the next example.

EXAMPLE 1 **Simplifying rational expressions**

Simplify each expression.

(a) $\dfrac{9x}{3x^2}$ (b) $\dfrac{5y-10}{10y-20}$ (c) $\dfrac{2z^2-3z-9}{z^2+2z-15}$ (d) $\dfrac{a^2-b^2}{a+b}$

Solution
(a) First factor out the greatest common factor, $3x$, in the numerator and denominator.

$$\frac{9x}{3x^2} = \frac{3 \cdot 3x}{x \cdot 3x} = \frac{3}{x}$$

(b) Use the distributive property and then simplify the rational expressions.

$$\frac{5y-10}{10y-20} = \frac{5(y-2)}{10(y-2)} = \frac{5}{10} = \frac{1}{2} \qquad \text{Provided } y \neq 2$$

(c) Start by factoring the numerator and denominator.

$$\frac{2z^2-3z-9}{z^2+2z-15} = \frac{(2z+3)(z-3)}{(z+5)(z-3)} = \frac{2z+3}{z+5} \qquad \text{Provided } z \neq 3$$

(d) Start by factoring the numerator as the difference of squares.

$$\frac{a^2-b^2}{a+b} = \frac{(a-b)(a+b)}{a+b} = a-b \qquad \text{Provided } a+b \neq 0$$

Now Try Exercises 23, 25, 39, 43

NOTE: In Example 1(b) the expressions $\frac{5y-10}{10y-20}$ and $\frac{1}{2}$ are equal, *provided* that $y \neq 2$. If $y = 2$, then $\frac{5y-10}{10y-20}$ is not defined but $\frac{1}{2}$ is defined. When we simplify rational expressions, we will usually not list these excluded values; nonetheless, be aware that the given expression may *not* be defined for some values of the variable, whereas the simplified expression may be defined for these same values.

There are a number of ways that a negative sign can be placed in a fraction. For example,

$$-\frac{2}{3} = \frac{-2}{3} = \frac{2}{-3}$$

illustrates three fractions that are equal.

STUDY TIP

If you tried to solve a problem but need help, ask a question in class. Other students will likely have the same question.

To simplify some types of rational expressions, it may be helpful to factor out -1.

$$2 - x = -1(-2 + x) = -(x - 2) \qquad \text{Factor out } -1.$$

Thus $2 - x = -(x - 2)$. As a result, the following rational expression simplifies to -1.

$$\frac{2 - x}{x - 2} = \frac{-(x - 2)}{x - 2} = -\frac{x - 2}{x - 2} = -1$$

Some examples of this result are the following.

$$\frac{4 - y}{y - 4} = -1, \quad \frac{z - 3}{3 - z} = -1, \quad \text{and} \quad \frac{x - y}{y - x} = -1$$

These concepts are applied in the next example.

EXAMPLE 2 **Distributing or factoring out a negative sign**

Simplify each expression.

(a) $-\dfrac{1 - z}{z - 1}$ (b) $\dfrac{-y - 2}{4y + 8}$ (c) $\dfrac{3 - x}{x - 3}$

Solution

(a) Start by distributing the negative sign over the numerator.

$$-\frac{1 - z}{z - 1} = \frac{-(1 - z)}{z - 1} = \frac{-1 + z}{z - 1} = \frac{z - 1}{z - 1} = 1$$

Note that the negative sign could also be distributed over the denominator.

(b) Factor -1 out of the numerator and 4 out of the denominator.

$$\frac{-y - 2}{4y + 8} = \frac{-1(y + 2)}{4(y + 2)} = -\frac{1}{4}$$

(c) Start by factoring -1 out of the numerator.

$$\frac{3 - x}{x - 3} = \frac{-1(-3 + x)}{x - 3} = \frac{-1(x - 3)}{x - 3} = -1$$

Now Try Exercises 47, 49, 51

MAKING CONNECTIONS

Negative Signs and Rational Expressions

In general, $(b - a)$ equals $-1(a - b)$. As a result, if $a \neq b$, then

$$\frac{b - a}{a - b} = \frac{-1(a - b)}{a - b} = -1.$$

See Example 2(c).

Review of Multiplication and Division of Fractions

Recall that to multiply two fractions we use the property

$$\frac{a}{b} \cdot \frac{c}{d} = \frac{ac}{bd}.$$

For example, $\dfrac{2}{5} \cdot \dfrac{3}{7} = \dfrac{2 \cdot 3}{5 \cdot 7} = \dfrac{6}{35}.$

EXAMPLE 3   **Multiplying fractions**

Multiply and simplify the product.

(a) $\dfrac{4}{9} \cdot \dfrac{3}{8}$ (b) $\dfrac{2}{3} \cdot \dfrac{3}{4} \cdot \dfrac{5}{6}$

Solution

(a) $\dfrac{4}{9} \cdot \dfrac{3}{8} = \dfrac{4 \cdot 3}{9 \cdot 8} = \dfrac{12}{72} = \dfrac{1 \cdot 12}{6 \cdot 12} = \dfrac{1}{6}$ (b) $\dfrac{2}{3} \cdot \dfrac{3}{4} \cdot \dfrac{5}{6} = \dfrac{6 \cdot 5}{12 \cdot 6} = \dfrac{5}{12}$

Now Try Exercises 11, 13

Recall that to divide two fractions we "invert and multiply." That is, we change a division problem to a multiplication problem, using the property

$$\frac{a}{b} \div \frac{c}{d} = \frac{a}{b} \cdot \frac{d}{c}. \quad \text{"Invert and multiply."}$$

For example, $\dfrac{3}{4} \div \dfrac{5}{4} = \dfrac{3}{4} \cdot \dfrac{4}{5} = \dfrac{3 \cdot 4}{5 \cdot 4} = \dfrac{3}{5}.$

$\uparrow$ —— "Invert and multiply."

Multiplication of Rational Expressions

Multiplying rational expressions is similar to multiplying fractions.

READING CHECK

How do you multiply rational expressions?

PRODUCTS OF RATIONAL EXPRESSIONS

To multiply two rational expressions, multiply numerators and multiply denominators.

$$\frac{A}{B} \cdot \frac{C}{D} = \frac{AC}{BD} \quad B \text{ and } D \text{ not zero}$$

EXAMPLE 4   **Multiplying rational expressions**

Multiply. Leave your answer in factored form when appropriate.

(a) $\dfrac{1}{x} \cdot \dfrac{x + 1}{2x}$ (b) $\dfrac{x - 1}{x} \cdot \dfrac{x - 1}{x + 2}$

Solution

(a) $\dfrac{1}{x} \cdot \dfrac{x + 1}{2x} = \dfrac{1 \cdot (x + 1)}{x \cdot 2x} = \dfrac{x + 1}{2x^2}$

(b) $\dfrac{x - 1}{x} \cdot \dfrac{x - 1}{x + 2} = \dfrac{(x - 1)(x - 1)}{x(x + 2)} = \dfrac{(x - 1)^2}{x(x + 2)}$

Now Try Exercises 61, 63

In the next example we see how rational expressions are sometimes multiplied to help businesses calculate costs.

EXAMPLE 5   **Finding total cost of producing earbuds**

The average cost (per item) in dollars to produce x pairs of earbuds is given by

$$C(x) = \frac{12x + 6000}{x}.$$

(a) A company expects to sell 2000 pairs. Evaluate $C(2000)$ and interpret the result.

(b) Write an expression $T(x)$ that gives the total cost of producing x pairs. Simplify it.

(c) Evaluate $T(2000)$ and interpret the result.

Solution

(a) Because $C(x) = \frac{12x + 6000}{x}$, $C(2000) = \frac{12(2000) + 6000}{2000} = \$15$. When 2000 earbuds are made, the average cost is $15 per pair.

(b) To find the total cost we must multiply the average cost $C(x)$ by the number of pairs x of earbuds sold.

$$T(x) = C(x) \cdot x$$
$$= \frac{12x + 6000}{x} \cdot \frac{x}{1}$$
$$= 12x + 6000$$

(c) $T(2000) = 12(2000) + 6000 = \$30{,}000$. It costs $30,000 to make 2000 pairs of earbuds.

▌ Now Try Exercise 109

Many times the product of two rational expressions can be simplified. This process is demonstrated in the next two examples.

EXAMPLE 6 **Multiplying rational expressions**

Multiply and simplify. Leave your answer in factored form when appropriate.

(a) $\dfrac{5x}{8} \cdot \dfrac{4}{10x^2}$ **(b)** $\dfrac{x - 2}{2x - 1} \cdot \dfrac{x + 1}{2x - 4}$ **(c)** $\dfrac{x^2 - 1}{x^2 - 4} \cdot \dfrac{x + 2}{x - 1}$

Solution

(a) $\dfrac{5x}{8} \cdot \dfrac{4}{10x^2} = \dfrac{20x}{80x^2}$ Multiply rational expressions.

$\qquad\qquad = \dfrac{1}{4x}$ Simplify.

(b) $\dfrac{x - 2}{2x - 1} \cdot \dfrac{x + 1}{2x - 4} = \dfrac{(x - 2)(x + 1)}{(2x - 1)(2x - 4)}$ Multiply rational expressions.

$\qquad\qquad = \dfrac{(x - 2)(x + 1)}{(2x - 1)2(x - 2)}$ Factor $2x - 4$.

$\qquad\qquad = \dfrac{(x + 1)(x - 2)}{2(2x - 1)(x - 2)}$ Commutative property

$\qquad\qquad = \dfrac{x + 1}{2(2x - 1)}$ Simplify.

(c) $\dfrac{x^2 - 1}{x^2 - 4} \cdot \dfrac{x + 2}{x - 1} = \dfrac{(x^2 - 1)(x + 2)}{(x^2 - 4)(x - 1)}$ Multiply rational expressions.

$\qquad\qquad = \dfrac{(x - 1)(x + 1)(x + 2)}{(x - 2)(x + 2)(x - 1)}$ Difference of squares

$\qquad\qquad = \dfrac{(x + 1)(x - 1)(x + 2)}{(x - 2)(x - 1)(x + 2)}$ Commutative property

$\qquad\qquad = \dfrac{x + 1}{x - 2}$ Simplify.

▌ Now Try Exercises 65, 71, 73

EXAMPLE 7 **Multiplying rational expressions**

Multiply and simplify. Leave your answer in factored form when appropriate.

(a) $\dfrac{2x^2y^3}{3xy^2} \cdot \dfrac{(2x^3y)^2}{2(xy)^3}$　　(b) $\dfrac{x^3 - x}{x - 1} \cdot \dfrac{x + 1}{x}$　　(c) $\dfrac{a}{b} \cdot \dfrac{a^2 - b^2}{2} \cdot \dfrac{b}{a + b}$

Solution

(a)
$$\frac{2x^2y^3}{3xy^2} \cdot \frac{(2x^3y)^2}{2(xy)^3} = \frac{2x^2y^3 \cdot 4x^6y^2}{3xy^2 \cdot 2x^3y^3} \qquad \text{Multiply; properties of exponents.}$$

$$= \frac{8x^8y^5}{6x^4y^5} \qquad \text{Multiply; properties of exponents.}$$

$$= \frac{4x^4}{3} \qquad \text{Simplify.}$$

(b)
$$\frac{x^3 - x}{x - 1} \cdot \frac{x + 1}{x} = \frac{(x^3 - x)(x + 1)}{x(x - 1)} \qquad \text{Multiply.}$$

$$= \frac{x(x^2 - 1)(x + 1)}{x(x - 1)} \qquad \text{Factor out } x.$$

$$= \frac{x(x - 1)(x + 1)(x + 1)}{x(x - 1)} \qquad \text{Difference of squares}$$

$$= (x + 1)(x + 1) \qquad \text{Simplify.}$$

$$= (x + 1)^2 \qquad \text{Rewrite.}$$

(c)
$$\frac{a}{b} \cdot \frac{a^2 - b^2}{2} \cdot \frac{b}{a + b} = \frac{a(a^2 - b^2)b}{b(2)(a + b)} \qquad \text{Multiply.}$$

$$= \frac{a(a - b)(a + b)b}{2(a + b)b} \qquad \text{Difference of squares}$$

$$= \frac{a(a - b)}{2} \qquad \text{Simplify.}$$

Now Try Exercises 69, 75, 83

Division of Rational Expressions

When dividing two rational expressions, *multiply* the first expression by the reciprocal of the second expression. This technique is similar to the division of fractions.

READING CHECK

How do you divide rational expressions?

QUOTIENTS OF RATIONAL EXPRESSIONS

To divide two rational expressions, multiply by the reciprocal of the divisor.

$$\frac{A}{B} \div \frac{C}{D} = \frac{A}{B} \cdot \frac{D}{C} \qquad B, C, \text{ and } D \text{ not zero}$$

NOTE: This technique of multiplying the first rational expression and the reciprocal of the second rational expression is sometimes summarized as "invert and multiply."

The **reciprocal of a polynomial** $p(x)$ is $\frac{1}{p(x)}$, and the **reciprocal of a rational expression** $\frac{p(x)}{q(x)}$ is $\frac{q(x)}{p(x)}$. The next example demonstrates how to find reciprocals.

EXAMPLE 8 **Finding reciprocals**

Write the reciprocal of each expression.

(a) $3x + 4$ (b) $\dfrac{5}{x^2 + 1}$ (c) $\dfrac{x - 7}{x + 7}$

Solution

(a) The reciprocal of $3x + 4$ is $\dfrac{1}{3x + 4}$. (b) The reciprocal of $\dfrac{5}{x^2 + 1}$ is $\dfrac{x^2 + 1}{5}$.

(c) The reciprocal of $\dfrac{x - 7}{x + 7}$ is $\dfrac{x + 7}{x - 7}$.

■ Now Try Exercises 53, 57, 59

EXAMPLE 9 **Dividing two rational expressions**

Divide and simplify.

(a) $\dfrac{2}{x} \div \dfrac{2x - 1}{4x}$ (b) $\dfrac{x^2 - 1}{x^2 + x - 6} \div \dfrac{x - 1}{x + 3}$

Solution

(a)
$$\dfrac{2}{x} \div \dfrac{2x - 1}{4x} = \dfrac{2}{x} \cdot \dfrac{4x}{2x - 1} \qquad \text{"Invert and multiply."}$$

$$= \dfrac{8x}{x(2x - 1)} \qquad \text{Multiply.}$$

$$= \dfrac{8}{2x - 1} \qquad \text{Simplify.}$$

(b) $\dfrac{x^2 - 1}{x^2 + x - 6} \div \dfrac{x - 1}{x + 3} = \dfrac{x^2 - 1}{x^2 + x - 6} \cdot \dfrac{x + 3}{x - 1}$ "Invert and multiply."

$$= \dfrac{(x + 1)(x - 1)}{(x - 2)(x + 3)} \cdot \dfrac{x + 3}{x - 1} \qquad \text{Factor completely.}$$

$$= \dfrac{(x + 1)(x - 1)(x + 3)}{(x - 2)(x - 1)(x + 3)} \qquad \text{Commutative property}$$

$$= \dfrac{x + 1}{x - 2} \qquad \text{Simplify.}$$

■ Now Try Exercises 85, 99

EXAMPLE 10 **Dividing rational expressions**

Divide and simplify. Leave your answer in factored form when appropriate.

(a) $\dfrac{7a^2}{4b^3} \div \dfrac{21a}{8b^4}$ (b) $\dfrac{2x + 2}{x - 1} \div (x + 1)$ (c) $\dfrac{x^2 - 25}{x^2 + 5x + 4} \div \dfrac{x^2 - 10x + 25}{2x^2 + 8x}$

Solution

(a) $\dfrac{7a^2}{4b^3} \div \dfrac{21a}{8b^4} = \dfrac{7a^2}{4b^3} \cdot \dfrac{8b^4}{21a}$ "Invert and multiply."

$$= \dfrac{56a^2b^4}{84ab^3} \qquad \text{Multiply rational expressions.}$$

$$= \dfrac{2ab}{3} \qquad \text{Simplify.}$$

(b) $\dfrac{2x+2}{x-1} \div (x+1) = \dfrac{2x+2}{x-1} \cdot \dfrac{1}{x+1}$ "Invert and multiply."

$\qquad\qquad\qquad = \dfrac{2(x+1)}{x-1} \cdot \dfrac{1}{x+1}$ Factor.

$\qquad\qquad\qquad = \dfrac{2(x+1)}{(x-1)(x+1)}$ Multiply rational expressions.

$\qquad\qquad\qquad = \dfrac{2}{x-1}$ Simplify.

(c) $\dfrac{x^2-25}{x^2+5x+4} \div \dfrac{x^2-10x+25}{2x^2+8x} = \dfrac{x^2-25}{x^2+5x+4} \cdot \dfrac{2x^2+8x}{x^2-10x+25}$

$\qquad\qquad\qquad\qquad = \dfrac{(x-5)(x+5)}{(x+1)(x+4)} \cdot \dfrac{2x(x+4)}{(x-5)(x-5)}$

$\qquad\qquad\qquad\qquad = \dfrac{2x(x+5)(x-5)(x+4)}{(x+1)(x-5)(x-5)(x+4)}$

$\qquad\qquad\qquad\qquad = \dfrac{2x(x+5)}{(x+1)(x-5)}$

| Now Try Exercises 87, 89, 97

In the next example, we divide three rational expressions. It is important to realize that *the associative property does not apply to division*. For example,

$$(24 \div 6) \div 2 = 4 \div 2 = 2 \quad \text{but} \quad 24 \div (6 \div 2) = 24 \div 3 = 8.$$

The order in which we do division *does matter*. As a result, we perform division from *left to right*, so

$$24 \div 6 \div 2 = 2.$$

EXAMPLE 11   **Dividing three fractions**

Divide and simplify $\dfrac{4x}{y} \div \dfrac{x^2}{y} \div \dfrac{3y}{2x}$.

Solution

$\dfrac{4x}{y} \div \dfrac{x^2}{y} \div \dfrac{3y}{2x} = \left(\dfrac{4x}{y} \div \dfrac{x^2}{y} \right) \div \dfrac{3y}{2x}$ Divide left to right.

$\qquad\qquad\qquad = \left(\dfrac{4x}{y} \cdot \dfrac{y}{x^2} \right) \div \dfrac{3y}{2x}$ "Invert and multiply."

$\qquad\qquad\qquad = \dfrac{4xy}{x^2y} \div \dfrac{3y}{2x}$ Multiply fractions.

$\qquad\qquad\qquad = \dfrac{4xy}{x^2y} \cdot \dfrac{2x}{3y}$ "Invert and multiply."

$\qquad\qquad\qquad = \dfrac{8x^2y}{3x^2y^2}$ Multiply fractions.

$\qquad\qquad\qquad = \dfrac{8}{3y}$ Simplify.

| Now Try Exercise 101

In the next example, we find the length of a rectangle when its area and width are expressed as polynomials.

EXAMPLE 12 **Finding the dimensions of a rectangle**

The area A of a rectangle is $3x^2 + 14x + 15$ and its width W is $x + 3$. See Figure 4.8.
(a) Find the length L of the rectangle.
(b) Find the length if the width is 12 inches.

$$x + 3 \quad\boxed{\quad A = 3x^2 + 14x + 15 \quad}$$
$$L$$

Figure 4.8

Solution
(a) Because the area equals length times width, $A = LW$, length equals area divided by width, or $L = \frac{A}{W}$. To determine L, factor the expression for A and then simplify.

$$L = \frac{3x^2 + 14x + 15}{x + 3} = \frac{(3x + 5)(x + 3)}{x + 3} = 3x + 5.$$

The length of the rectangle is $3x + 5$.
(b) If the width is 12 inches, then $x + 3 = 12$ or $x = 9$. The length is

$$L = 3x + 5 = 3(9) + 5 = 32 \text{ inches.}$$

▌ Now Try Exercise 111

4.2   Putting It All Together

CONCEPT	EXPLANATION	EXAMPLES
Simplifying Rational Expressions	Use the principle $$\frac{A \cdot C}{B \cdot C} = \frac{A}{B}.$$ B and C not zero	$\frac{5a(a + b)}{7b(a + b)} = \frac{5a}{7b}$ and $\frac{x^2 - 1}{x - 1} = \frac{(x + 1)(x - 1)}{x - 1} = x + 1$
Multiplying Rational Expressions	To multiply two rational expressions, multiply numerators and multiply denominators. $$\frac{A}{B} \cdot \frac{C}{D} = \frac{AC}{BD}$$ B and D not zero	$\frac{5a}{4b^2} \cdot \frac{2b^3}{10a^3} = \frac{10ab^3}{40a^3b^2} = \frac{b}{4a^2}$
Dividing Rational Expressions	To divide two rational expressions, multiply by the reciprocal of the divisor. ("Invert and multiply.") $$\frac{A}{B} \div \frac{C}{D} = \frac{A}{B} \cdot \frac{D}{C}$$ B, C, and D not zero — "Invert and multiply."	$\frac{x}{x + 1} \div \frac{x + 2}{x + 1} = \frac{x}{x + 1} \cdot \frac{x + 1}{x + 2}$ $= \frac{x(x + 1)}{(x + 2)(x + 1)}$ $= \frac{x}{x + 2}$

4.2   Exercises

CONCEPTS AND VOCABULARY

1. Simplify $\frac{2x + 3}{2x + 3}$.

2. Simplify $\frac{x - 3}{3 - x}$.

3. Is $\frac{x^2 - 1}{x - 1}$ equal to x? Explain.

4. Is $\frac{3}{3 + x}$ equal to $\frac{1}{x}$? Is it equal to $1 + \frac{3}{x}$?

5. To divide $\frac{2}{3}$ by $\frac{5}{7}$ multiply _____ by _____.

6. $\frac{a}{b} \cdot \frac{c}{d} =$ _____.

7. $\frac{a}{b} \div \frac{c}{d} =$ _____.

8. $\frac{ac}{bc} =$ _____.

9. Which of the following expressions (a.–d.) is equal to the quotient $\frac{x^2 - 1}{x^2 + 2x + 1}$?

    a. $\frac{1}{2x + 1}$

    b. $\frac{x + 1}{x - 1}$

    c. $\frac{x - 1}{x + 1}$

    d. $x - 1$

10. Which of the following expressions (a.–d.) is equal to the quotient $\frac{5x}{y} \div \frac{15x - 15}{3y^2}$?

    a. $\frac{75x(x - 1)}{3y^3}$

    b. $\frac{xy}{x - 1}$

    c. $\frac{3xy}{x - 1}$

    d. $\frac{y}{x(x - 1)}$

REVIEW OF FRACTIONS

Exercises 11–22: Simplify.

11. $\frac{1}{2} \cdot \frac{4}{5}$

12. $\frac{5}{6} \cdot \frac{3}{10}$

13. $\frac{7}{8} \cdot \frac{4}{3} \cdot (-3)$

14. $4 \cdot \frac{7}{4} \cdot \frac{1}{2}$

15. $\frac{3}{8} \cdot 2$

16. $-5 \cdot \frac{2}{7}$

17. $-\frac{7}{11} \div 14$

18. $6 \div \frac{6}{5}$

19. $\frac{5}{7} \div \frac{15}{14}$

20. $-\frac{2}{3} \div 2$

21. $6 \div \left(-\frac{1}{3}\right)$

22. $\frac{10}{9} \div \frac{5}{3}$

SIMPLIFYING RATIONAL EXPRESSIONS

Exercises 23–52: Simplify the rational expression.

23. $\frac{5x}{x^2}$

24. $\frac{18t^3}{6t}$

25. $\frac{3z + 6}{z + 2}$

26. $\frac{6}{12x + 6}$

27. $\frac{2z + 2}{3z + 3}$

28. $\frac{4x - 12}{2x - 6}$

29. $\frac{(x - 1)(x + 1)}{x - 1}$

30. $(x + 2) \cdot \frac{x - 6}{x + 2}$

31. $\frac{x^2 - 4}{x + 2}$

32. $\frac{(x + 2)(x - 5)}{(x + 10)(x + 2)}$

33. $\frac{x(x - 1)}{(x + 1)(x - 1)}$

34. $\frac{(2x - 1)(x - 3)}{(x - 3)(2x + 5)}$

35. $\frac{(3x + 1)(x + 2)}{(x + 2)(5x - 2)}$

36. $\frac{(3x + 2)(x - 7)}{x(x - 7)}$

37. $\frac{x + 5}{x^2 + 2x - 15}$

38. $\frac{x^2 - 9}{x^2 + 6x + 9} \cdot (x + 3)$

39. $\frac{x^2 + 2x}{x^2 + 3x + 2}$

40. $\frac{x^2 - 3x - 10}{x^2 - 6x + 5}$

41. $\frac{6x^2 + 7x - 5}{2x^2 - 11x + 5}$

42. $\frac{30x^2 - 7x - 15}{6x^2 + 7x - 10}$

43. $\frac{a^2 - b^2}{a - b}$

44. $\frac{a^2 + 2ab + b^2}{a + b}$

45. $\frac{m^3 + n^3}{m + n}$

46. $\frac{m^3 - n^3}{m - n}$

47. $-\frac{4 - t}{t - 4}$

48. $-\frac{t - r}{r - t}$

49. $\frac{4m - n}{-4m + n}$

50. $\frac{2n + 10m}{-n - 5m}$

51. $\frac{5 - y}{y - 5}$

52. $\frac{a - b}{b - a}$

RECIPROCALS

Exercises 53–60: Write the reciprocal of the expression.

53. $4x$

54. $5x - 2$

55. $\frac{2a}{5b}$

56. $\frac{5b^3}{7a^2}$

57. $\frac{3 - x}{5 - x}$

58. $\frac{x^2 - 4}{3x + 1}$

59. $\frac{1}{x^2 + 1}$

60. $\frac{-1}{5 - x}$

MULTIPLICATION AND DIVISION OF RATIONAL EXPRESSIONS

Exercises 61–104: Multiply or divide. Leave your answer in factored form when appropriate.

61. $\dfrac{2}{x} \cdot \dfrac{x-1}{3x}$

62. $\dfrac{2}{x-3} \cdot \dfrac{x}{x+1}$

63. $\dfrac{x-2}{x} \cdot \dfrac{x-3}{x+4}$

64. $\dfrac{x}{x+5} \cdot \dfrac{x-6}{x+4}$

65. $\dfrac{1}{2x} \cdot \dfrac{4x}{2}$

66. $\dfrac{5a^2}{7} \cdot \dfrac{7}{10a}$

67. $\dfrac{5a}{4} \cdot \dfrac{12}{5a}$

68. $\dfrac{a^2b}{4c} \cdot \dfrac{8c^2}{3ab^2}$

69. $\dfrac{9x^2y^4}{8xy^6} \cdot \dfrac{(2xy^2)^3}{3(xy)^4}$

70. $\dfrac{(7rt)^2}{8} \cdot \dfrac{8r}{49(rt^2)^3}$

71. $\dfrac{x+1}{2x-5} \cdot \dfrac{2x-5}{x}$

72. $\dfrac{x+1}{x} \cdot \dfrac{x}{x+2}$

73. $\dfrac{b^2+1}{b^2-1} \cdot \dfrac{b-1}{b+1}$

74. $\dfrac{(x-5)(x+3)}{3x-1} \cdot \dfrac{x(3x-1)}{(x-5)}$

75. $\dfrac{x^2-2x-35}{2x^3-3x^2} \cdot \dfrac{x^3-x^2}{2x-14}$

76. $\dfrac{2x+4}{x+1} \cdot \dfrac{x^2+3x+2}{4x+2}$

77. $\dfrac{3n-9}{n^2-9} \cdot (n^3+27)$

78. $(10n+15) \cdot \dfrac{n+1}{6n+9}$

79. $\dfrac{3n-9}{n^2-9} \cdot \dfrac{n^3+27}{12}$

80. $\dfrac{10n+15}{n^2-1} \cdot \dfrac{n+1}{6n+9}$

81. $\dfrac{x}{y} \cdot \dfrac{2y}{x} \cdot \dfrac{2}{xy}$

82. $\dfrac{4z^2}{r^3} \cdot \dfrac{5r}{2z} \cdot \dfrac{r}{z}$

83. $\dfrac{x-1}{y} \cdot \dfrac{y(x+y)}{2} \cdot \dfrac{y}{x+y}$

84. $\dfrac{x}{y^2} \cdot \dfrac{y^3-y^2}{x+y} \cdot \dfrac{x^2+xy}{5x^2}$

85. $\dfrac{3x}{2} \div \dfrac{2x}{5}$

86. $\dfrac{x^2+x}{2x+6} \div \dfrac{x}{x+3}$

87. $\dfrac{8a^4}{3b} \div \dfrac{a^5}{9b^2}$

88. $\dfrac{5m^4}{n^2} \div 5m$

89. $(2n+4) \div \dfrac{n+2}{n-1}$

90. $\dfrac{n+1}{n+3} \div \dfrac{n+1}{n+3}$

91. $\dfrac{6b}{b+2} \div \dfrac{3b^4}{2b+4}$

92. $\dfrac{5x^5}{x-2} \div \dfrac{10x^3}{5x-10}$

93. $\dfrac{3a+1}{a^7} \div \dfrac{a+1}{3a^8}$

94. $\dfrac{16-x^2}{x+3} \div \dfrac{x+4}{9-x^2}$

95. $\dfrac{x+5}{x-x^3} \div \dfrac{25-x^2}{x^3}$

96. $\dfrac{x^2+x-12}{2x^2-9x-5} \div \dfrac{x^2+7x+12}{2x^2-7x-4}$

97. $\dfrac{x^2-3x+2}{x^2+5x+6} \div \dfrac{x^2+x-2}{x^2+2x-3}$

98. $\dfrac{2x^2+x-1}{6x^2+x-2} \div \dfrac{2x^2+5x+3}{6x^2+13x+6}$

99. $\dfrac{x^2-4}{x^2+x-2} \div \dfrac{x-2}{x-1}$

100. $\dfrac{x^2+2x+1}{x-2} \div \dfrac{x+1}{2x-4}$

101. $\dfrac{3y}{x^2} \div \dfrac{y^2}{x} \div \dfrac{y}{5x}$

102. $\dfrac{x+1}{y-2} \div \dfrac{2x+2}{y-2} \div \dfrac{x}{y}$

103. $\dfrac{x-3}{x-1} \div \dfrac{x^2}{x-1} \div \dfrac{x-3}{x}$

104. $\dfrac{2x}{x-2} \div \dfrac{x+2}{x} \div \dfrac{7x}{x^2-4}$

OPERATIONS ON FUNCTIONS

105. If $f(x) = \dfrac{x+2}{x^2-3x+2}$ and $g(x) = \dfrac{x-1}{x+2}$, then find $(fg)(x)$.

106. If $f(x) = \dfrac{2}{x^2 - 5x + 4}$ and $g(x) = \dfrac{x - 4}{x + 1}$, then find $(fg)(x)$.

107. Find $(f/g)(x)$ if $f(x) = x^2 - 1$ and $g(x) = x + 1$.

108. Find $(f/g)(x)$ if $f(x) = \dfrac{2x - 4}{5}$ and $g(x) = \dfrac{4 - 2x}{15}$.

APPLICATIONS

109. *Total Production Cost* (Refer to Example 5.) The average cost per item in dollars for a company to produce x digital cameras is given by

$$C(x) = \frac{50x + 20{,}000}{x}.$$

(a) The company expects to sell 5000 cameras. Evaluate $C(5000)$ and interpret the result.
(b) Write an expression $T(x)$ that gives the total cost of producing x cameras. Simplify it.
(c) Evaluate $T(5000)$ and interpret the result.

110. *Total Production Cost* (Refer to Example 5.) The average cost per item in dollars for a company to produce x flash drives is given by

$$C(x) = \frac{18x + 36{,}000}{x}.$$

(a) The company expects to sell 9000 flash drives. Evaluate $C(9000)$ and interpret the result.
(b) Write an expression for $T(x)$ that gives the total cost of producing x flash drives. Simplify this expression.
(c) Evaluate $T(9000)$ and interpret the result.

GEOMETRY

111. *Area of a Rectangle* The area A of a rectangle is $5x^2 + 12x + 4$ and its width W is $x + 2$, as shown in the figure.
(a) Find the length L of the rectangle.
(b) Find the length if the width is 8 feet.

112. *Area of a Rectangle* The area A of a rectangle is given by $x^2 - 1$.
(a) Find its length if its width is $x - 1$.
(b) Find the dimensions and area of the rectangle when $x = 15$.

113. *Volume of a Box* The volume V of a box with a square bottom is $4x^3 + 4x^2 + x$.
(a) If its height is x, find the area of the bottom.
(b) Find the dimensions of the box when $x = 10$.

114. *Area of a Triangle* The area A of a triangle is $6x^2 - x - 15$. Find its height if the base of the triangle is $2x + 3$.

WRITING ABOUT MATHEMATICS

115. A student does the following to simplify a rational expression. Is the work correct? Explain any errors and how you would correct them.

$$\frac{3x + x^2}{3x} \overset{?}{=} 1 + x^2$$

116. Explain how to multiply two rational expressions and how to divide two rational expressions.

| SECTIONS 4.1 and 4.2 | **Checking Basic Concepts** |

1. Let $f(x) = \dfrac{x}{x - 1}$.
(a) Evaluate $f(2)$.
(b) Find the domain of f.
(c) Graph f. Identify any vertical asymptotes.

2. Solve each equation. Check your answers.
(a) $\dfrac{6}{2x + 3} = 3$
(b) $\dfrac{2}{x - 1} = x$

3. Simplify $\dfrac{x^2 - 6x - 7}{x^2 - 1}$.

4. Multiply or divide each expression.
(a) $\dfrac{2x^2}{x^2 - 1} \cdot \dfrac{x + 1}{4x}$
(b) $\dfrac{1}{x - 2} \div \dfrac{3}{(x - 2)(x + 3)}$

4.3 Addition and Subtraction of Rational Expressions

Least Common Multiples ● Review of Addition and Subtraction of Fractions ●
Addition of Rational Expressions ● Subtraction of Rational Expressions

A LOOK INTO MATH ▶

Rational expressions occur in many real-world applications. For example, addition of rational expressions is used in the design of electrical circuits. (See Example 8.) They are also used in business to analyze average cost. (See Exercises 91 and 92.) In this section we demonstrate how to add and subtract rational expressions. These techniques are similar to techniques used to add and subtract fractions. We begin by discussing least common multiples, which are used to find least common denominators.

Least Common Multiples

▶ **REAL-WORLD CONNECTION** Two friends work part-time at a store. The first person works every fourth day and the second person works every sixth day. If they are both working today, how many days pass before they both work on the same day again?

We can answer this question by listing the days that each person works.

First person: 4,   8,   **12**,   16,   20,   **24**,   28,   32,   **36**,   40,…
Second person: 6,   **12**,   18,   **24**,   30,   **36**,   42,…

After 12 days, the two friends work on the same day and the next time is after 24 days. The numbers 12 and 24 are *common multiples* of 4 and 6. (Find two more.) However, **12** is the **least common multiple** (LCM) of 4 and 6. Note that 12 is the smallest positive number that has both 4 and 6 as factors.

Another way to find the least common multiple for 4 and 6 is to first factor each number into prime numbers:

$$4 = 2 \cdot 2 \quad \text{and} \quad 6 = 2 \cdot 3.$$

To find the least common multiple, list each factor the *greatest* number of times that it occurs in either factorization. Then find the product of the listed numbers. For our example, the factor 2 occurs two times in the factorization of 4 and only once in the factorization of 6, so list 2 two times. The factor 3 appears only once in the factorization of 6 and not at all in the factorization of 4, so list it once:

$$2, 2, 3.$$

The least common multiple is their product: $2 \cdot 2 \cdot 3 = 12$. This same procedure can also be used to find the least common multiple for two (or more) polynomials.

NEW VOCABULARY

☐ Least common multiple
☐ Common denominator
☐ Least common denominator

FINDING THE LEAST COMMON MULTIPLE

The least common multiple (LCM) of two polynomials can be found as follows.

STEP 1: Factor each polynomial completely.

STEP 2: List each factor the greatest number of times that it occurs in either factorization.

STEP 3: Find the product of this list of factors. The result is the LCM.

The next example illustrates how to use this procedure.

EXAMPLE 1   **Finding least common multiples**

Find the least common multiple for each pair of expressions.
(a) $4x, 5x^3$ **(b)** $x^2 - 2x, (x - 2)^2$
(c) $x + 2, x - 1$ **(d)** $x^2 + 4x + 4, x^2 + 3x + 2$

Solution
(a) STEP 1: Factor each polynomial completely.

$$4x = 2 \cdot 2 \cdot x \quad \text{and} \quad 5x^3 = 5 \cdot x \cdot x \cdot x$$

STEP 2: The factor 2 occurs twice, the factor 5 occurs once, and the factor x occurs at most three times. The list is **2, 2, 5, x, x,** and x.
STEP 3: The LCM is the product $2 \cdot 2 \cdot 5 \cdot x \cdot x \cdot x$, or $20x^3$.

(b) STEP 1: Factor each polynomial completely.

$$x^2 - 2x = x(x - 2) \quad \text{and} \quad (x - 2)^2 = (x - 2)(x - 2)$$

STEP 2: The factor x occurs once, and the factor $(x - 2)$ occurs at most twice. The list of factors is $x, (x - 2)$, and $(x - 2)$.
STEP 3: The LCM is the product $x(x - 2)^2$, which is left in factored form.

(c) STEP 1: Neither polynomial can be factored.
STEP 2: The list of factors is $(x + 2)$ and $(x - 1)$.
STEP 3: The LCM is the product $(x + 2)(x - 1)$, or $x^2 + x - 2$.

(d) STEP 1: Factor each polynomial as follows.

$$x^2 + 4x + 4 = (x + 2)(x + 2) \quad \text{and} \quad x^2 + 3x + 2 = (x + 1)(x + 2)$$

STEP 2: The factor $(x + 1)$ occurs once and $(x + 2)$ occurs at most twice.
STEP 3: The LCM is the product $(x + 1)(x + 2)^2$, which is left in factored form.

Now Try Exercises 15, 17, 19, 21

Review of Addition and Subtraction of Fractions

Recall that to add two fractions we use the property

$$\frac{a}{c} + \frac{b}{c} = \frac{a + b}{c}. \qquad \text{Like denominators}$$

This property requires that the fractions have like denominators. For example,

$$\frac{1}{5} + \frac{3}{5} = \frac{1 + 3}{5} = \frac{4}{5}. \qquad \text{Like denominators}$$

When the denominators are not alike, we must find a common denominator. Before adding two fractions, such as $\frac{1}{6}$ and $\frac{3}{4}$, we write them with 12 as their common denominator. That is, we multiply each fraction by 1, written in an appropriate form. For example, to write $\frac{1}{6}$ with a denominator of 12 we multiply $\frac{1}{6}$ by 1, written as $\frac{2}{2}$.

$$\frac{1}{6} = \frac{1}{6} \cdot \frac{2}{2} = \frac{2}{12} \quad \text{and} \quad \frac{3}{4} = \frac{3}{4} \cdot \frac{3}{3} = \frac{9}{12}$$

Once the fractions have a common denominator, we can add them, as in

$$\frac{1}{6} + \frac{3}{4} = \frac{2}{12} + \frac{9}{12} = \frac{11}{12}.$$

Note that a **common denominator** for $\frac{1}{6}$ and $\frac{3}{4}$ is also a *common multiple* of 6 and 4. The **least common denominator** (LCD) for $\frac{1}{6}$ and $\frac{3}{4}$ is equal to the *least common multiple* (LCM) of 6 and 4. Thus the least common denominator is **12**.

EXAMPLE 2 **Adding fractions**

Find the sum.

(a) $\dfrac{3}{4} + \dfrac{1}{8}$ **(b)** $\dfrac{3}{5} + \dfrac{2}{7}$

Solution

(a) The LCD is 8.

$$\frac{3}{4} + \frac{1}{8} = \frac{3}{4} \cdot \frac{2}{2} + \frac{1}{8} = \frac{6}{8} + \frac{1}{8} = \frac{7}{8}$$

(b) The LCD is 35.

$$\frac{3}{5} + \frac{2}{7} = \frac{3}{5} \cdot \frac{7}{7} + \frac{2}{7} \cdot \frac{5}{5} = \frac{21}{35} + \frac{10}{35} = \frac{31}{35}$$

Now Try Exercises 23, 25

Recall that subtraction of fractions is similar to addition of fractions. To subtract two fractions with like denominators we use the property

$$\frac{a}{c} - \frac{b}{c} = \frac{a - b}{c}. \quad \text{Like denominators}$$

For example, $\frac{3}{11} - \frac{7}{11} = \frac{3 - 7}{11} = -\frac{4}{11}$.

EXAMPLE 3 **Subtracting fractions**

Find the difference.

(a) $\dfrac{3}{10} - \dfrac{2}{15}$ **(b)** $\dfrac{3}{8} - \dfrac{5}{6}$

Solution

(a) The LCD is 30.

$$\frac{3}{10} - \frac{2}{15} = \frac{3}{10} \cdot \frac{3}{3} - \frac{2}{15} \cdot \frac{2}{2} = \frac{9}{30} - \frac{4}{30} = \frac{5}{30} = \frac{1}{6}$$

(b) The LCD is 24.

$$\frac{3}{8} - \frac{5}{6} = \frac{3}{8} \cdot \frac{3}{3} - \frac{5}{6} \cdot \frac{4}{4} = \frac{9}{24} - \frac{20}{24} = -\frac{11}{24}$$

Now Try Exercises 27, 29

Addition of Rational Expressions

Addition of rational expressions is similar to addition of fractions.

SUMS OF RATIONAL EXPRESSIONS

To add two rational expressions with like denominators, add their numerators. The denominator does not change.

$$\frac{A}{C} + \frac{B}{C} = \frac{A + B}{C} \quad C \text{ not zero}$$

EXAMPLE 4   **Adding rational expressions with like denominators**

Add and simplify.

(a) $\dfrac{x}{x+2} + \dfrac{3x-1}{x+2}$ (b) $\dfrac{x}{3x^2+4x-4} + \dfrac{2}{3x^2+4x-4}$

Solution

(a) The expressions have like denominators, so add the numerators.

$$\dfrac{x}{x+2} + \dfrac{3x-1}{x+2} = \dfrac{x+3x-1}{x+2} \qquad \text{Add numerators.}$$

$$= \dfrac{4x-1}{x+2} \qquad \text{Combine like terms.}$$

(b) The expressions have like denominators, so add the numerators. The resulting sum can be simplified by factoring the denominator.

$$\dfrac{x}{3x^2+4x-4} + \dfrac{2}{3x^2+4x-4} = \dfrac{x+2}{3x^2+4x-4} \qquad \text{Add numerators.}$$

$$= \dfrac{x+2}{(3x-2)(x+2)} \qquad \text{Factor denominator.}$$

$$= \dfrac{1}{3x-2} \qquad \text{Simplify.}$$

Now Try Exercises 31, 45

READING CHECK

How do you add rational expressions with unlike denominators?

To add rational expressions with *unlike denominators*, we must first write each expression so that it has the same common denominator. For example, the least common denominator for $\frac{1}{x+2}$ and $\frac{2}{x-1}$ equals the least common multiple of $x+2$ and $x-1$, which was shown to be their product $(x+2)(x-1)$ in Example 1(c). To rewrite $\frac{1}{x+2}$ with the new denominator, we multiply it by 1, expressed as $\frac{x-1}{x-1}$.

$$\dfrac{1}{x+2} \cdot 1 = \dfrac{1}{x+2} \cdot \dfrac{x-1}{x-1} = \dfrac{x-1}{(x+2)(x-1)}$$

Similarly, we multiply $\frac{2}{x-1}$ by 1, expressed as $\frac{x+2}{x+2}$.

$$\dfrac{2}{x-1} \cdot 1 = \dfrac{2}{x-1} \cdot \dfrac{x+2}{x+2} = \dfrac{2x+4}{(x-1)(x+2)}$$

Now the two rational expressions have like denominators and can be added.

$$\dfrac{1}{x+2} + \dfrac{2}{x-1} = \dfrac{x-1}{(x+2)(x-1)} + \dfrac{2x+4}{(x-1)(x+2)} \qquad \text{Write with LCD.}$$

$$= \dfrac{x-1+2x+4}{(x+2)(x-1)} \qquad \text{Add numerators.}$$

$$= \dfrac{3x+3}{(x+2)(x-1)} \qquad \text{Combine like terms.}$$

EXAMPLE 5   **Adding rational expressions with unlike denominators**

Add and simplify. Leave your answer in factored form when appropriate.

(a) $\dfrac{1}{x} + \dfrac{2}{x^2}$ (b) $\dfrac{1}{x^2-9} + \dfrac{2}{x+3}$

(c) $\dfrac{a}{a-b} + \dfrac{b}{a+b}$ (d) $\dfrac{1}{x-1} + \dfrac{1}{1-x}$

Solution

(a) The LCD for $\dfrac{1}{x} + \dfrac{2}{x^2}$ is x^2.

$$\dfrac{1}{x} \cdot \dfrac{x}{x} + \dfrac{2}{x^2} = \dfrac{x}{x^2} + \dfrac{2}{x^2} \qquad \text{Write with LCD.}$$

$$= \dfrac{x + 2}{x^2} \qquad \text{Add numerators.}$$

(b) The LCD for $\dfrac{1}{x^2 - 9} + \dfrac{2}{x + 3}$ is $x^2 - 9 = (x - 3)(x + 3)$.

$$\dfrac{1}{x^2 - 9} + \dfrac{2}{x + 3} \cdot \dfrac{x - 3}{x - 3} = \dfrac{1}{(x + 3)(x - 3)} + \dfrac{2x - 6}{(x + 3)(x - 3)} \qquad \text{Write with LCD.}$$

$$= \dfrac{2x - 5}{(x + 3)(x - 3)} \qquad \text{Add numerators.}$$

(c) The LCD for $\dfrac{a}{a - b} + \dfrac{b}{a + b}$ is $(a - b)(a + b)$.

$$\dfrac{a}{a - b} \cdot \dfrac{a + b}{a + b} + \dfrac{b}{a + b} \cdot \dfrac{a - b}{a - b} = \dfrac{a^2 + ab}{(a - b)(a + b)} + \dfrac{ab - b^2}{(a - b)(a + b)} \qquad \text{Write with LCD.}$$

$$= \dfrac{a^2 + 2ab - b^2}{(a - b)(a + b)} \qquad \text{Add numerators.}$$

(d) For $\dfrac{1}{x - 1} + \dfrac{1}{1 - x}$, multiply the second expression by $\dfrac{-1}{-1}$.

$$\dfrac{1}{x - 1} + \dfrac{1}{1 - x} \cdot \dfrac{-1}{-1} = \dfrac{1}{x - 1} + \dfrac{-1}{(1 - x)(-1)} \qquad \text{Write with LCD.}$$

$$= \dfrac{1}{x - 1} + \dfrac{-1}{x - 1} \qquad \text{Distributive property}$$

$$= \dfrac{0}{x - 1} \qquad \text{Add numerators.}$$

$$= 0 \qquad \text{Simplify.}$$

Now Try Exercises 49, 55, 59

NOTE: When one denominator is the opposite of the other, try multiplying one expression by 1 in the form $\dfrac{-1}{-1}$.

Subtraction of Rational Expressions

Subtraction of rational expressions is similar to subtraction of fractions.

DIFFERENCES OF RATIONAL EXPRESSIONS

To subtract two rational expressions with like denominators, subtract their numerators. The denominator does not change.

$$\dfrac{A}{C} - \dfrac{B}{C} = \dfrac{A - B}{C} \qquad C \text{ not zero}$$

When you are subtracting numerators of rational expressions, it is *essential* to apply the distributive property correctly: subtract every term in the numerator of the second rational expression. For example,

$$\frac{1}{x+1} - \frac{2x-1}{x+1} = \frac{1-(2x-1)}{x+1} = \frac{1-2x+1}{x+1} = \frac{2-2x}{x+1}.$$

Be sure to place parentheses around the second numerator before subtracting.

EXAMPLE 6 **Subtracting rational expressions with like denominators**

Subtract and simplify.

(a) $\dfrac{3}{x^2} - \dfrac{x+3}{x^2}$ **(b)** $\dfrac{2x}{x^2-1} - \dfrac{x+1}{x^2-1}$

Solution

(a) The expressions have like denominators, so subtract the numerators.

$$\frac{3}{x^2} - \frac{x+3}{x^2} = \frac{3-(x+3)}{x^2} \qquad \text{Subtract numerators.}$$

$$= \frac{3-x-3}{x^2} \qquad \text{Distributive property}$$

$$= \frac{-x}{x^2} \qquad \text{Subtract.}$$

$$= -\frac{1}{x} \qquad \text{Simplify.}$$

READING CHECK

How do you subtract rational expressions with like denominators?

(b) The expressions have like denominators, so subtract the numerators.

$$\frac{2x}{x^2-1} - \frac{x+1}{x^2-1} = \frac{2x-(x+1)}{x^2-1} \qquad \text{Subtract numerators.}$$

$$= \frac{2x-x-1}{x^2-1} \qquad \text{Distributive property}$$

$$= \frac{x-1}{(x+1)(x-1)} \qquad \text{Combine like terms; factor.}$$

$$= \frac{1}{x+1} \qquad \text{Simplify.}$$

Now Try Exercises 33, 41

TECHNOLOGY NOTE

Graphical and Numerical Support
We can give support to our work in Example 6(a) by letting $Y_1 = 3/X^2 - (X+3)/X^2$, the given expression, and $Y_2 = -1/X$, the simplified expression. In Figures 4.9(a) and 4.9(b) the graphs of y_1 and y_2 appear to be identical. In Figure 4.9(c) numerical support is given, where $y_1 = y_2$ for each value of x.

[−4.7, 4.7, 1] by [−3.1, 3.1, 1] [−4.7, 4.7, 1] by [−3.1, 3.1, 1]

(a) (b) (c)

Figure 4.9

EXAMPLE 7   **Subtracting rational expressions with unlike denominators**

Subtract and simplify. Leave your answer in factored form when appropriate.

(a) $\dfrac{5a}{b^2} - \dfrac{4b}{a^2}$ **(b)** $\dfrac{x-1}{x} - \dfrac{5}{x+5}$ **(c)** $\dfrac{1}{x^2-3x+2} - \dfrac{1}{x^2-x-2}$

Solution
(a) The LCD is $a^2 b^2$.

$$\frac{5a}{b^2}\cdot\frac{a^2}{a^2} - \frac{4b}{a^2}\cdot\frac{b^2}{b^2} = \frac{5a^3}{b^2 a^2} - \frac{4b^3}{a^2 b^2} \qquad \text{Write with LCD.}$$

$$= \frac{5a^3 - 4b^3}{a^2 b^2} \qquad \text{Subtract numerators.}$$

(b) The LCD is $x(x+5)$.

$$\frac{x-1}{x}\cdot\frac{x+5}{x+5} - \frac{5}{x+5}\cdot\frac{x}{x} \qquad \text{Write with LCD.}$$

$$= \frac{(x-1)(x+5)}{x(x+5)} - \frac{5x}{x(x+5)} \qquad \text{Multiply.}$$

$$= \frac{(x-1)(x+5) - 5x}{x(x+5)} \qquad \text{Subtract numerators.}$$

$$= \frac{x^2 + 4x - 5 - 5x}{x(x+5)} \qquad \text{Multiply binomials.}$$

$$= \frac{x^2 - x - 5}{x(x+5)} \qquad \text{Combine like terms.}$$

(c) Because $x^2 - 3x + 2 = (x-2)(x-1)$ and $x^2 - x - 2 = (x-2)(x+1)$, the LCD is $(x-1)(x+1)(x-2)$.

$$\frac{1}{(x-2)(x-1)}\cdot\frac{(x+1)}{(x+1)} - \frac{1}{(x-2)(x+1)}\cdot\frac{(x-1)}{(x-1)} \qquad \text{Write with LCD.}$$

$$= \frac{(x+1)}{(x-2)(x-1)(x+1)} - \frac{(x-1)}{(x-2)(x+1)(x-1)} \qquad \text{Multiply.}$$

$$= \frac{(x+1) - (x-1)}{(x-2)(x-1)(x+1)} \qquad \text{Subtract numerators.}$$

$$= \frac{x+1-x+1}{(x-2)(x-1)(x+1)} \qquad \text{Distributive property}$$

$$= \frac{2}{(x-2)(x-1)(x+1)} \qquad \text{Simplify numerator.}$$

Now Try Exercises 47, 51, 69

The following procedure summarizes how to add or subtract rational expressions.

STEPS FOR FINDING SUMS AND DIFFERENCES OF RATIONAL EXPRESSIONS

STEP 1: If the denominators are not common, multiply each expression by 1 written in the appropriate form to obtain the LCD.

STEP 2: Add or subtract the numerators. Combine like terms.

STEP 3: If possible, simplify the final expression.

Figure 4.10

▶ **REAL-WORLD CONNECTION** Sums of rational expressions occur in applications such as electrical circuits. Suppose that two light bulbs are wired in parallel so that electricity can flow through either light bulb, as depicted in Figure 4.10. If their resistances are R_1 and R_2, their combined resistance R can be computed by the equation

$$\frac{1}{R} = \frac{1}{R_1} + \frac{1}{R_2}.$$

Resistance is often measured in a unit called *ohms*. A standard 60-watt light bulb might have a resistance of about 200 ohms. (*Source:* R. Weidner and R. Sells, *Elementary Classical Physics, Vol. 2.*)

EXAMPLE 8 **Modeling electrical resistance**

A 100-watt light bulb with a resistance of $R_1 = 120$ ohms and a 75-watt light bulb with a resistance of $R_2 = 160$ ohms are placed in an electrical circuit, as shown in Figure 4.10. Find their combined resistance.

Solution
Let $R_1 = 120$ and $R_2 = 160$ in the given equation and solve for R.

$$\frac{1}{R} = \frac{1}{R_1} + \frac{1}{R_2} \qquad \text{Given equation}$$

$$= \frac{1}{120} + \frac{1}{160} \qquad \text{Substitute for } R_1 \text{ and } R_2.$$

$$= \frac{1}{120} \cdot \frac{4}{4} + \frac{1}{160} \cdot \frac{3}{3} \qquad \text{LCD is 480.}$$

$$= \frac{4}{480} + \frac{3}{480} \qquad \text{Multiply.}$$

$$= \frac{7}{480} \qquad \text{Add.}$$

Because $\frac{1}{R} = \frac{7}{480}$, $R = \frac{480}{7} \approx 69$ ohms.

▍ **Now Try Exercise 95**

CRITICAL THINKING

If $\frac{1}{R} = \frac{1}{R_1} + \frac{1}{R_2}$, does it follow that $R = R_1 + R_2$? Explain your answer.

4.3	**Putting It All Together**

CONCEPT	EXPLANATION	EXAMPLE
Least Common Multiple (LCM)	To find the LCM, follow the three-step procedure presented on page 264.	To find the LCM of $2x^2 - 2x$ and $8x^2$, factor each expression: $2x^2 - 2x = 2 \cdot x \cdot (x - 1)$ and $8x^2 = 2 \cdot 2 \cdot 2 \cdot x \cdot x.$ The LCM is $2 \cdot 2 \cdot 2 \cdot x \cdot x \cdot (x - 1) = 8x^2(x - 1).$
Least Common Denominator (LCD)	*The* LCD *equals the* LCM *of the* denominators.	The LCD for $$\frac{3x}{2x^2 - 2x} \text{ and } \frac{5}{8x^2}$$ is $8x^2(x - 1)$.

continued on next page

continued from previous page

CONCEPT	EXPLANATION	EXAMPLE
Addition and Subtraction of Rational Expressions	To add (or subtract) two rational expressions with like denominators, add (or subtract) their numerators. The denominator does not change. $$\frac{A}{C} + \frac{B}{C} = \frac{A+B}{C}$$ $$\frac{A}{C} - \frac{B}{C} = \frac{A-B}{C} \quad C \text{ not zero}$$ If the denominators are *not alike*, write each term with the LCD first.	*Like denominators* $$\frac{x}{x+1} + \frac{3x}{x+1} = \frac{4x}{x+1}$$ *Unlike denominators* $$\frac{1}{x} - \frac{2x}{x+1} = \frac{1}{x} \cdot \frac{x+1}{x+1} - \frac{2x}{x+1} \cdot \frac{x}{x}$$ $$= \frac{x+1}{x(x+1)} - \frac{2x^2}{x(x+1)}$$ $$= \frac{-2x^2 + x + 1}{x(x+1)}$$

4.3 Exercises

MyMathLab

CONCEPTS AND VOCABULARY

1. What is the LCM for 6 and 9?

2. What is the LCD for $\frac{1}{6}$ and $\frac{1}{9}$?

3. What is the LCM for $x^2 - 25$ and $x + 5$?

4. What is the LCD for $\frac{1}{x^2 - 25}$ and $\frac{1}{x + 5}$?

5. What do you need to find before you can add $\frac{1}{4}$ and $\frac{1}{3}$?

6. What do you need to find before you can add the expressions $\frac{2}{x}$ and $\frac{1}{2x-1}$?

7. $\frac{a}{c} + \frac{b}{c} = $ _____.

8. $\frac{a}{c} - \frac{b}{c} = $ _____.

9. Which of the following (a.–d.) equals $\frac{1-x}{2+x} + \frac{x}{2+x}$?

a. $\frac{1}{4+2x}$

b. $\frac{1}{2+x}$

c. $\frac{1}{(2+x)^2}$

d. $\frac{x-x^2}{2+x}$

10. Which of the following (a.–d.) equals $\frac{1}{x} - \frac{2-x}{2x}$?

a. $\frac{1}{2}$

b. $\frac{x-1}{2x}$

c. $\frac{1+x}{x}$

d. $\frac{x}{2}$

LEAST COMMON MULTIPLES

Exercises 11–22: Find the least common multiple.

11. 10, 15

12. 9, 12

13. 34, 51

14. 24, 36

15. $6a, 9a^2$

16. $12ab, 6a^2$

17. $10x^2, 25(x^2 - x)$

18. $x^2 - 4, x^2 + 2x$

19. $x^2 + 2x + 1, x^2 - 4x - 5$

20. $4x^2 + 20x + 25, 2x^2 + 5x$

21. $x + y, x - y$

22. $(x - y)^2, x^2 - y^2$

REVIEW OF FRACTIONS

Exercises 23–30: Simplify.

23. $\frac{1}{7} + \frac{4}{7}$

24. $\frac{2}{5} + \frac{1}{2}$

25. $\frac{2}{3} + \frac{5}{6} + \frac{1}{4}$

26. $\frac{3}{11} + \frac{1}{2} + \frac{1}{6}$

27. $\frac{1}{10} - \frac{3}{10}$

28. $\frac{2}{9} - \frac{1}{11}$

29. $\frac{3}{2} - \frac{1}{8}$

30. $\frac{3}{12} - \frac{5}{16}$

ADDITION AND SUBTRACTION OF RATIONAL EXPRESSIONS

Exercises 31–84: Add or subtract. Leave your answer in factored form when appropriate.

31. $\frac{1}{x} + \frac{3}{x}$

32. $\frac{2}{x-1} + \frac{x}{x-1}$

33. $\frac{2}{x^2 - 4} - \frac{x+1}{x^2 - 4}$

34. $\frac{2x-1}{x^2+6} - \frac{2x+1}{x^2+6}$

35. $\frac{4}{x^2} + \frac{5}{x^2}$

36. $\frac{8}{b^3} - \frac{5}{b^3}$

37. $\frac{4}{xy} - \frac{7}{xy}$

38. $\frac{9}{a^2b} + \frac{1}{a^2b}$

39. $\dfrac{x}{x+1} + \dfrac{1}{x+1}$ **40.** $\dfrac{1}{2x-1} - \dfrac{2x}{2x-1}$

41. $\dfrac{2z}{4-z} - \dfrac{3z-4}{4-z}$ **42.** $\dfrac{z}{z^2-9} - \dfrac{3}{z^2-9}$

43. $\dfrac{4r}{5t^2} + \dfrac{r}{5t^2}$ **44.** $\dfrac{1}{2ab} + \dfrac{1}{2ab}$

45. $\dfrac{3t}{t^2-t-6} + \dfrac{2-2t}{t^2-t-6}$

46. $\dfrac{t}{t^2+5t} + \dfrac{5}{t^2+5t}$ **47.** $\dfrac{5b}{3a} - \dfrac{7b}{5a}$

48. $\dfrac{a}{ab^2} - \dfrac{b}{a^2b}$ **49.** $\dfrac{4}{n-4} + \dfrac{3}{2-n}$

50. $\dfrac{3}{2n-1} - \dfrac{3}{1-2n}$ **51.** $\dfrac{x}{x+4} - \dfrac{x+1}{x}$

52. $\dfrac{4x}{x+2} + \dfrac{x-5}{x-2}$ **53.** $\dfrac{2}{x^2} - \dfrac{4x-1}{x}$

54. $\dfrac{2x}{x-5} - \dfrac{x}{x+5}$ **55.** $\dfrac{x+3}{x-5} + \dfrac{5}{x-3}$

56. $\dfrac{x}{2x-1} + \dfrac{1-x}{3x}$ **57.** $\dfrac{4n}{n^2-9} - \dfrac{8}{n-3}$

58. $\dfrac{3n}{(4n-3)^2} - \dfrac{1}{4n-3}$ **59.** $\dfrac{x}{x^2-9} + \dfrac{5x}{x-3}$

60. $\dfrac{a^2+1}{a^2-1} + \dfrac{a}{1-a^2}$ **61.** $\dfrac{b}{2b-4} - \dfrac{b-1}{b-2}$

62. $\dfrac{y^2}{2-y} - \dfrac{y}{y^2-4}$

63. $\dfrac{2x}{x-5} + \dfrac{2x-1}{3x^2-16x+5}$

64. $\dfrac{x+3}{2x-1} + \dfrac{3}{10x^2-5x}$ **65.** $\dfrac{4x}{x-y} - \dfrac{9}{x+y}$

66. $\dfrac{1}{a-b} - \dfrac{3a}{a^2-b^2}$

67. $\dfrac{3}{(x-1)(x-2)} + \dfrac{4x}{(x+1)(x-2)}$

68. $\dfrac{x}{(x-1)^2} - \dfrac{1}{(x-1)(x+3)}$

69. $\dfrac{3}{x^2-x-6} - \dfrac{2}{x^2+5x+6}$

70. $\dfrac{x}{x^2-5x+4} + \dfrac{2}{x^2-2x-8}$

71. $\dfrac{3}{x^2-2x+1} + \dfrac{1}{x^2-3x+2}$

72. $\dfrac{x}{x^2-4} - \dfrac{1}{x^2+4x+4}$

73. $\dfrac{3x}{x^2+2x-3} + \dfrac{1}{x^2-2x+1}$

74. $\dfrac{3x}{x-y} - \dfrac{3y}{x^2-2xy+y^2}$

75. $\dfrac{4c}{ab} + \dfrac{3b}{ac} - \dfrac{2a}{bc}$ **76.** $x + \dfrac{1}{x-1} - \dfrac{1}{x+1}$

77. $5 - \dfrac{6}{n^2-36} + \dfrac{3}{n-6}$

78. $\dfrac{6}{t-1} + \dfrac{2}{t-2} + \dfrac{1}{t}$

79. $\dfrac{3}{x-5} - \dfrac{1}{x-3} - \dfrac{2x}{x-5}$

80. $\dfrac{2x+1}{x-1} - \dfrac{3}{x+1} + \dfrac{x}{x-1}$

81. $\dfrac{5}{2x-3} + \dfrac{x}{x+1} - \dfrac{x}{2x-3}$

82. $\dfrac{1}{x-3} - \dfrac{2}{x+3} + \dfrac{x}{x^2-9}$

83. $\dfrac{1}{x-1} - \dfrac{2}{x+1} + \dfrac{x}{x^2-1}$

84. $\dfrac{2}{x-2} + \dfrac{1}{x+3} - \dfrac{1}{x-1}$

Exercises 85 and 86: Thinking Generally *Add or subtract.*

85. $\dfrac{a-b}{a+b} + \dfrac{a+b}{a-b}$ **86.** $\dfrac{1}{a^2-b^2} - \dfrac{1}{a^2+b^2}$

ADDITION AND SUBTRACTION OF FUNCTIONS

Exercises 87–90: Find $(f+g)(x)$ *and* $(f-g)(x)$.

87. $f(x) = \dfrac{1}{x+1}, g(x) = \dfrac{x}{x+1}$

88. $f(x) = \dfrac{1}{2x}, g(x) = \dfrac{3}{4x}$

89. $f(x) = \dfrac{1}{x+2}, g(x) = \dfrac{1}{x-2}$

90. $f(x) = \dfrac{1}{x+1}, g(x) = \dfrac{1}{x}$

APPLICATIONS

91. *Average Cost* The average cost per item in dollars to make x video games is given by

$$M(x) = \frac{5x + 1,000,000}{x},$$

and the average cost per item in dollars to package the same video game is given by

$$P(x) = \frac{2x + 500,000}{x}.$$

Write a function $C(x)$ that gives the total cost per item of making and packaging x video games.

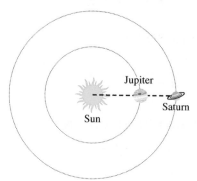

92. *Breaking Even* Use the result from Exercise 91 to determine the number of video games the company must sell to break even, if it charges $37 per game.

93. *Planet Alignment* Suppose that Saturn and Jupiter are in alignment with respect to the sun. If Jupiter orbits the sun every 12 years and Saturn orbits the sun every 30 years, how many years will it be before these two planets are back in the same location with the same alignment again?

NOT TO SCALE

94. *Working Shifts* Two friends work part-time at a store. The first person works every sixth day and the second person works every tenth day. If they are both working today, how many days pass before they both work on the same day again?

95. *Electrical Resistance* (Refer to Example 8.) A 150-watt light bulb with a resistance of 80 ohms and a 40-watt light bulb with a resistance of 300 ohms are wired in parallel. Find the combined resistance.

96. *Electrical Resistance* Solve the formula

$$\frac{1}{R} = \frac{1}{R_1} + \frac{1}{R_2}$$

for R. Use your formula to solve Exercise 95.

97. *Photography* A lens in a camera has a focal length, which is important in focusing the camera. If an object is at distance D from a lens that has a focal length F, then to be in focus the distance S between the lens and the film should satisfy the equation

$$\frac{1}{S} = \frac{1}{F} - \frac{1}{D}.$$

(See the accompanying figure.) If the focal length is $F = 0.1$ foot and the object is $D = 10$ feet from the camera, find S.

Lens   Film

98. *Photography* (Continuation of Exercise 97.) Suppose that the object is closer to the lens than the focal length of the lens. That is, suppose $D < F$. According to the formula, is it possible to focus the image on the film? Explain your reasoning.

99. *Intensity of a Light Bulb* The intensity of a light bulb at a point varies according to its distance from the light bulb. The expression $\frac{8}{d^2}$ approximates the intensity of a 100-watt light bulb in watts per square meter (W/m^2) at a distance of d meters. Calculate the combined intensity at a point d meters from two 100-watt light bulbs.

100. *Intensity of a Light Bulb* (Refer to the preceding exercise.) Suppose that one 100-watt light bulb is at a distance d and another 100-watt light bulb is at a distance $\frac{1}{2}d$ from a point. Write an expression for the combined intensity of the two light bulbs.

WRITING ABOUT MATHEMATICS

101. A student does the following to add two rational expressions. Explain the error that the student is making and how it can be corrected.

$$\frac{x}{x + 1} + \frac{6x}{x} \stackrel{?}{=} \frac{7x}{2x + 1}$$

102. Explain in words how to subtract two rational expressions with like denominators.

4.4 Rational Equations

Solving Rational Equations • Solving an Equation for a Variable

A LOOK INTO MATH ▶ Although thousands of mobile phone applications are being written each year, most users who download these applications use them only once. For example, only about 25% of people who downloaded an application are still using it on the second day. This aspect of mobile phone applications can be modeled by a rational function. See Example 4.

Solving Rational Equations

A rational expression is a ratio of two polynomials. In Sections 4.2 and 4.3, we *simplified* and *evaluated* rational expressions. Unlike a rational *expression*, a rational *equation* always contains an equals sign, and we *solve* this equation for values of the variables that make the equation a true statement. One way to solve a rational equation is to *clear fractions* by multiplying each side of the equation by the least common denominator (LCD). For example, to solve

$$\frac{1}{2x} + \frac{2}{3} = \frac{5}{2x}$$

multiply each side (or each term) by the LCD (LCM of 3 and $2x$), which is $6x$.

$$6x\left(\frac{1}{2x} + \frac{2}{3}\right) = 6x\left(\frac{5}{2x}\right) \qquad \text{Multiply each side by } 6x.$$

$$\frac{6x}{2x} + \frac{12x}{3} = \frac{30x}{2x} \qquad \text{Distributive property}$$

$$3 + 4x = 15 \qquad \text{Simplify.}$$

$$4x = 12 \qquad \text{Subtract 3 from each side.}$$

$$x = 3 \qquad \text{Divide each side by 4.}$$

Check this answer to verify that 3 is indeed a solution. *When solving a rational equation, always check your answer.* If one of your *possible answers* makes the denominator of an expression in the given equation equal to 0, it cannot be a solution.

EXAMPLE 1 | **Solving rational equations**

Solve each equation and check your answer.

(a) $\dfrac{x+1}{2x} - \dfrac{x-1}{4x} = \dfrac{1}{3}$ **(b)** $\dfrac{3}{x-2} + \dfrac{5}{x+2} = \dfrac{12}{x^2-4}$

Solution

(a) Note that the left side of the equation is undefined when $x = 0$. Thus 0 cannot be a solution. Start by determining the LCD, which is $12x$.

$$12x\left(\frac{x+1}{2x} - \frac{x-1}{4x}\right) = 12x\left(\frac{1}{3}\right) \qquad \text{Multiply each side by } 12x.$$

$$\frac{12x(x+1)}{2x} - \frac{12x(x-1)}{4x} = \frac{12x}{3} \qquad \text{Distributive property}$$

$$6(x+1) - 3(x-1) = 4x \qquad \text{Simplify.}$$

$$6x + 6 - 3x + 3 = 4x \qquad \text{Distributive property}$$

$$3x + 9 = 4x \qquad \text{Combine like terms.}$$

$$x = 9 \qquad \text{Solve for } x.$$

Check:

$$\frac{9+1}{2(9)} - \frac{9-1}{4(9)} \overset{?}{=} \frac{1}{3}$$ Let $x = 9$ in $\frac{x+1}{2x} - \frac{x-1}{4x} = \frac{1}{3}$.

$$\frac{10}{18} - \frac{8}{36} \overset{?}{=} \frac{1}{3}$$ Simplify.

$$\frac{1}{3} = \frac{1}{3} \checkmark$$ It checks.

(b) Note that both sides of $\frac{3}{x-2} + \frac{5}{x+2} = \frac{12}{x^2-4}$ are undefined when $x = 2$ or $x = -2$. Thus neither 2 nor -2 can be a solution. The LCD is $x^2 - 4 = (x-2)(x+2)$.

$$\frac{3(x-2)(x+2)}{x-2} + \frac{5(x-2)(x+2)}{x+2} = \frac{12(x^2-4)}{x^2-4}$$ Multiply each term by the LCD.

$$3(x+2) + 5(x-2) = 12$$ Simplify.

$$3x + 6 + 5x - 10 = 12$$ Distributive property

$$8x - 4 = 12$$ Combine like terms.

$$8x = 16$$ Add 4.

$$x = 2$$ Divide by 8.

Check: We already noted that 2 cannot be a solution. However, checking this answer gives the following result.

$$\frac{3}{2-2} + \frac{5}{2+2} \overset{?}{=} \frac{12}{2^2-4}$$ Let $x = 2$ in $\frac{3}{x-2} + \frac{5}{x+2} = \frac{12}{x^2-4}$.

$$\frac{3}{0} + \frac{5}{4} \overset{?}{=} \frac{12}{0} \quad \textbf{X}$$ Simplify fractions.

Both sides are undefined because division by 0 is not possible. There are no solutions.

Now Try Exercises 31, 39

The next example illustrates how to solve a rational equation graphically. Because graphical solutions are only estimates, be sure to check them by substituting observed values in the given equation.

READING CHECK

What is a good first step when solving a rational equation?

EXAMPLE 2

Solving a rational equation graphically

Solve the equation $\frac{4}{x-1} = 2x$ graphically. Check your results.

Solution
Start by graphing $y_1 = \frac{4}{x-1}$ and $y_2 = 2x$. The graph of y_2 is a line with slope 2 passing through the origin. To help graph y_1 make a table of values or use a graphing calculator. The two graphs intersect when $x = -1$ and $x = 2$, as shown in Figure 4.11.

Figure 4.11

Check:

$$\frac{4}{-1-1} \overset{?}{=} 2(-1)$$ Let $x = -1$.

$$-2 = -2 \checkmark$$ It checks.

$$\frac{4}{2-1} \overset{?}{=} 2(2)$$ Let $x = 2$.

$$4 = 4 \checkmark$$ It checks.

Now Try Exercises 53, 57

The next example illustrates how to solve rational equations and support the results with a graphing calculator.

Solving rational equations

Solve each equation. Support your results either graphically or numerically.

(a) $\dfrac{1}{2} + \dfrac{x}{3} = \dfrac{x}{5}$ **(b)** $\dfrac{3}{x+3} - 2 = \dfrac{x}{x+3}$ **(c)** $\dfrac{3}{x-2} = \dfrac{5}{x+2}$

Solution

(a) The LCD is the product of 2, 3, and 5, which is **30**.

$$30 \cdot \left(\dfrac{1}{2} + \dfrac{x}{3}\right) = \dfrac{x}{5} \cdot 30 \qquad \text{Multiply by the LCD.}$$

$$\dfrac{30}{2} + \dfrac{30x}{3} = \dfrac{30x}{5} \qquad \text{Distributive property}$$

$$15 + 10x = 6x \qquad \text{Simplify.}$$

$$4x = -15 \qquad \text{Subtract } 6x \text{ and } 15.$$

$$x = -\dfrac{15}{4} \qquad \text{Solve.}$$

This result can be supported graphically by letting $y_1 = \frac{1}{2} + \frac{x}{3}$ and $y_2 = \frac{x}{5}$. Their graphs intersect at the point $(-3.75, -0.75)$, as shown in Figure 4.12. Therefore the solution to this equation is -3.75, or $-\frac{15}{4}$.

(b) Multiply each side by the LCD, which is $x + 3$.

$$(x+3) \cdot \left(\dfrac{3}{x+3} - 2\right) = \dfrac{x}{x+3} \cdot (x+3) \qquad \text{Multiply by the LCD.}$$

$$3 - 2(x+3) = x \qquad \text{Distributive property}$$

$$3 - 2x - 6 = x \qquad \text{Distributive property}$$

$$-3 = 3x \qquad \text{Add } 2x \text{ to each side.}$$

$$x = -1 \qquad \text{Divide by 3; rewrite.}$$

Figure 4.13 supports the finding that -1 is a solution by showing that the graphs of the equations $y_1 = \frac{3}{x+3} - 2$, and $y_2 = \frac{x}{x+3}$ intersect at $(-1, -0.5)$.

NOTE: Because graphs of rational expressions are often nonlinear, it may be difficult to locate graphical solutions.

(c) Multiply each side by the LCD, which is $(x-2)(x+2)$.

$$(x-2)(x+2) \cdot \dfrac{3}{x-2} = \dfrac{5}{x+2} \cdot (x-2)(x+2) \qquad \text{Multiply by the LCD.}$$

$$\dfrac{3(x-2)(x+2)}{x-2} = \dfrac{5(x-2)(x+2)}{x+2} \qquad \text{Multiply expressions.}$$

$$3(x+2) = 5(x-2) \qquad \text{Simplify.}$$

$$3x + 6 = 5x - 10 \qquad \text{Distributive property}$$

$$16 = 2x \qquad \text{Add 10 and subtract } 3x.$$

$$x = 8 \qquad \text{Divide by 2; rewrite.}$$

To support this result numerically, let $y_1 = \frac{3}{x-2}$ and $y_2 = \frac{5}{x+2}$. The table in Figure 4.14 shows that $y_1 = y_2 = 0.5$ when $x = 8$. The solution is 8.

Now Try Exercises 67, 69

[−9, 9, 1] by [−6, 6, 1]

Figure 4.12

[−9.4, 9.4, 1] by [−6.2, 6.2, 1]

Figure 4.13

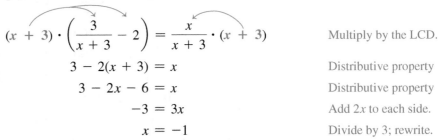

X	Y₁	Y₂
5	1	.71429
6	.75	.625
7	.6	.55556
8	.5	.5
9	.42857	.45455
10	.375	.41667
11	.33333	.38462

X=8

Figure 4.14

STUDY TIP

If you use a graphing calculator, the Technology Note will help you enter rational expressions correctly.

TECHNOLOGY NOTE

Entering Rational Expressions
When entering a rational expression, use parentheses around the numerator and denominator, as in the following example. Enter

$$y = \frac{x+1}{2x-1} \quad \text{as} \quad Y_1 = (X+1)/(2X-1).$$

Sometimes solving a rational equation results in the need to solve a quadratic equation, which is demonstrated in the next application.

EXAMPLE 4 **Modeling mobile phone applications**

The rational function $f(x) = \frac{100}{x^2}$, $1 \le x \le 10$, approximates the percentage of people who are still using a mobile phone application after x days. (Refer to A Look Into Math at the beginning of this section.) In this formula, the application is downloaded and first used on day 1. On what day are only 4% of people still using a typical mobile phone application?

Solution
We must solve the rational equation $\frac{100}{x^2} = 4$.

$$\frac{100}{x^2} = 4 \qquad \text{Equation to be solved}$$

$$x^2 \cdot \frac{100}{x^2} = 4 \cdot x^2 \qquad \text{Multiply each side by } x^2.$$

$$100 = 4x^2 \qquad \text{Simplify.}$$

$$4x^2 - 100 = 0 \qquad \text{Rewrite equation.}$$

$$(2x - 10)(2x + 10) = 0 \qquad \text{Difference of squares}$$

$$2x - 10 = 0 \quad \text{or} \quad 2x + 10 = 0 \qquad \text{Zero-product property}$$

$$x = 5 \quad \text{or} \quad x = -5 \qquad \text{Solve.}$$

Since we do not allow a negative number of days, the only solution is 5. Thus, after 5 days about 4% of people are still using a typical mobile phone application. (Check this.)

Now Try Exercise 93

EXAMPLE 5 **Solving rational equations**

Solve the equation.

(a) $\dfrac{1}{x} + \dfrac{1}{x^2} = \dfrac{3}{4}$ **(b)** $\dfrac{2x}{x+2} + \dfrac{3x}{x-1} = 7$

Solution
(a) The LCD is $4x^2$. Note that 0 cannot be a solution.

$$4x^2 \cdot \left(\frac{1}{x} + \frac{1}{x^2}\right) = \frac{3}{4} \cdot 4x^2 \qquad \text{Multiply by } 4x^2.$$

$$\frac{4x^2}{x} + \frac{4x^2}{x^2} = \frac{12x^2}{4} \qquad \text{Distributive property}$$

$$4x + 4 = 3x^2 \qquad \text{Simplify.}$$

$$0 = 3x^2 - 4x - 4 \qquad \text{Subtract } 4x \text{ and } 4.$$

$$0 = (3x + 2)(x - 2) \qquad \text{Factor.}$$

$$x = -\frac{2}{3} \quad \text{or} \quad x = 2 \qquad \text{Solve.}$$

Both solutions check.

(b) The LCD is $(x + 2)(x - 1)$. Note that -2 and 1 cannot be solutions.

$$(x + 2)(x - 1)\left(\frac{2x}{x + 2} + \frac{3x}{x - 1}\right) = 7(x + 2)(x - 1) \quad \text{Multiply by the LCD.}$$

$$\frac{2x(x + 2)(x - 1)}{x + 2} + \frac{3x(x + 2)(x - 1)}{x - 1} = 7(x + 2)(x - 1) \quad \text{Distributive property}$$

$$2x(x - 1) + 3x(x + 2) = 7(x + 2)(x - 1) \quad \text{Simplify.}$$

$$2x^2 - 2x + 3x^2 + 6x = 7(x^2 + x - 2) \quad \text{Multiply.}$$

$$5x^2 + 4x = 7x^2 + 7x - 14 \quad \text{Simplify.}$$

$$0 = 2x^2 + 3x - 14 \quad \text{Subtract } 5x^2 \text{ and } 4x.$$

$$0 = (2x + 7)(x - 2) \quad \text{Factor.}$$

$$x = -\frac{7}{2} \quad \text{or} \quad x = 2 \quad \text{Solve.}$$

Both solutions check.

Now Try Exercises 35, 41

▶ **REAL-WORLD CONNECTION** A customer often has to wait to check out at a store, and a commuter often has to wait in a traffic jam. During a lifetime, a typical person spends thousands of hours waiting in line. Rational equations are frequently used to estimate the time spent waiting in line whenever arrivals are random. This concept is illustrated in the next example.

EXAMPLE 6 **Modeling waiting time**

Suppose that cars are arriving randomly at a construction zone and that the flag person can instruct x drivers per minute. If cars arrive at an average rate of 7 cars per minute, the average time T in minutes for each driver to wait and talk to the flag person is

$$T(x) = \frac{1}{x - 7},$$

where $x > 7$. How many drivers per minute should the flag person be able to instruct to keep the average wait to 1 minute? (*Source:* N. Garber.)

Solution
We must determine x such that $\frac{1}{x - 7} = 1$.

$$\frac{1}{x - 7} = 1 \quad \text{Equation to be solved}$$

$$(x - 7) \cdot \frac{1}{x - 7} = 1 \cdot (x - 7) \quad \text{Multiply by the LCD.}$$

$$1 = x - 7 \quad \text{Simplify.}$$

$$8 = x \quad \text{Add 7 to each side.}$$

The flag person should be able to instruct 8 drivers per minute to limit the average wait to 1 minute.

Now Try Exercise 87(a)

Rational equations occur in applications involving time and rate, as demonstrated in the next example.

EXAMPLE 7 **Determining the time required to empty a pool**

A pump can empty a swimming pool in 50 hours. To speed up the process, a second pump that can empty the pool in 80 hours is used. How long will it take for both pumps working together to empty the pool?

Solution

Because the first pump can empty the entire pool in 50 hours, it can empty $\frac{1}{50}$ of the pool in 1 hour, $\frac{2}{50}$ of the pool in 2 hours, $\frac{3}{50}$ of the pool in 3 hours, and in general, it can empty $\frac{t}{50}$ of the pool in t hours. That is, the amount of water pumped equals the rate $\frac{1}{50}$ times the time t. The second pump can empty the pool in 80 hours, so (using similar reasoning) it can empty $\frac{t}{80}$ of the pool in t hours.

Together the pumps can empty

$$\frac{t}{50} + \frac{t}{80}$$

of the pool in t hours. The job will be complete when the fraction of the pool that is empty equals 1. Thus we must solve the equation

$$\frac{t}{50} + \frac{t}{80} = 1.$$

To clear fractions we can multiply each side by **(50)(80)**. (We could also use the LCD of 400.)

$$(50)(80)\left(\frac{t}{50} + \frac{t}{80}\right) = 1(50)(80) \qquad \text{Multiply by common denominator.}$$

$$\frac{50 \cdot 80 \cdot t}{50} + \frac{50 \cdot 80 \cdot t}{80} = 4000 \qquad \text{Distributive property}$$

$$80t + 50t = 4000 \qquad \text{Simplify.}$$

$$130t = 4000 \qquad \text{Combine like terms.}$$

$$t = \frac{4000}{130} \approx 30.8 \text{ hours} \qquad \text{Solve.}$$

The two pumps can empty the pool in about 30.8 hours.

▌ Now Try Exercise 95

CRITICAL THINKING

A bicyclist rides uphill at 6 miles per hour for 1 mile and then rides downhill at 12 miles per hour for 1 mile. What is the average speed of the bicyclist?

▶ **REAL-WORLD CONNECTION** If a person drives a car 60 miles per hour for 4 hours, the total distance d traveled is

$$d = 60 \cdot 4 = 240 \text{ miles.}$$

That is, distance equals the product of the rate (speed) and the elapsed time. This may be written as $d = rt$ and expressed verbally as "distance equals rate times time." This formula is used in Example 8.

EXAMPLE 8 **Solving an application**

The winner of a 3-mile race finishes 3 minutes ahead of another runner. If the winner runs 2 miles per hour faster than the slower runner, find the average speed of each runner.

Solution

Let x be the speed of the slower runner. Then $x + 2$ represents the speed of the winner. See Figure 4.15. To determine the time for each runner to finish the race, divide each side of $d = rt$ by r to obtain

$$t = \frac{d}{r}.$$

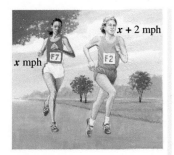

Figure 4.15

The slower runner runs 3 miles at x miles per hour, so the time is $\frac{3}{x}$; the winner runs 3 miles at $x + 2$ miles per hour, so the winning time is $\frac{3}{x + 2}$. We summarize this in Table 4.3.

TABLE 4.3

	Distance (mi)	Rate (mi/hr)	Time (hr)
Winning Runner	3	$x + 2$	$\frac{3}{x + 2}$
Slower Runner	3	x	$\frac{3}{x}$

If you add 3 minutes (or, equivalently, $\frac{3}{60} = \frac{1}{20}$ hour) to the winner's time, it equals the slower runner's time, or

$$\frac{3}{x + 2} + \frac{1}{20} = \frac{3}{x}.$$

NOTE: The runners' speeds are in miles per *hour*, so you need to keep time in hours.

Multiply each side by the LCD, which is $20x(x + 2)$.

$$20x(x + 2)\left(\frac{3}{x + 2} + \frac{1}{20}\right) = 20x(x + 2)\left(\frac{3}{x}\right) \qquad \text{Multiply by the LCD.}$$

$$60x + x(x + 2) = 60(x + 2) \qquad \text{Distributive property}$$

$$60x + x^2 + 2x = 60x + 120 \qquad \text{Distributive property}$$

$$x^2 + 2x - 120 = 0 \qquad \text{Rewrite the equation.}$$

$$(x + 12)(x - 10) = 0 \qquad \text{Factor.}$$

$$x = -12 \quad \text{or} \quad x = 10 \qquad \text{Solve.}$$

The only valid solution is 10 because a running speed cannot be negative. Thus the slower runner is running at 10 miles per hour, and the faster runner is running at 12 miles per hour.

Now Try Exercise 97

Solving an Equation for a Variable

▶ **REAL-WORLD CONNECTION** Sometimes in science and other disciplines, it is necessary to solve a formula for a variable. These formulas are often rational equations. This technique is demonstrated in the next two examples.

EXAMPLE 9   **Solving an equation for a variable**

Solve the equation $P = \frac{nrT}{V}$ for V. (This formula is used to calculate the pressure of a gas.)

Solution
Start by multiplying each side of the equation by V.

$$V \cdot P = V\left(\frac{nrT}{V}\right) \qquad \text{Multiply by } V.$$

$$PV = nrT \qquad \text{Simplify.}$$

$$\frac{PV}{P} = \frac{nrT}{P} \qquad \text{Divide each side by } P.$$

$$V = \frac{nrT}{P} \qquad \text{Simplify.}$$

Now Try Exercise 73

EXAMPLE 10 **Solving an equation involving electricity**

Solve the equation $\dfrac{1}{R} = \dfrac{1}{R_1} + \dfrac{1}{R_2}$ for R_2.

Solution

Start by multiplying each side of the equation by the LCD: RR_1R_2.

$$(RR_1R_2)\dfrac{1}{R} = (RR_1R_2)\left(\dfrac{1}{R_1} + \dfrac{1}{R_2}\right) \quad \text{Multiply by the LCD.}$$

$$R_1R_2 = RR_2 + RR_1 \quad \text{Distributive property}$$

$$R_1R_2 - RR_2 = RR_1 \quad \text{Subtract } RR_2.$$

$$R_2(R_1 - R) = RR_1 \quad \text{Factor out } R_2.$$

$$R_2 = \dfrac{RR_1}{R_1 - R} \quad \text{Divide each side by } R_1 - R.$$

■ **Now Try Exercise 79**

4.4   Putting It All Together

CONCEPT	EXPLANATION	EXAMPLE
Rational Equations	To solve a rational equation, first multiply each side of the equation by the LCD. Then solve the resulting polynomial equation. Be sure to check your answer(s). The LCD is the LCM of the denominators.	Multiply each term by $4x^2$. $\dfrac{1}{4x} + \dfrac{2}{x^2} = \dfrac{1}{x}$ $\dfrac{4x^2}{4x} + \dfrac{8x^2}{x^2} = \dfrac{4x^2}{x}$ $x + 8 = 4x$ $8 = 3x$ $x = \dfrac{8}{3}$

The following example illustrates how to solve the rational equation $\frac{2}{x} + 2 = 3$ symbolically, graphically, and numerically with the aid of a graphing calculator, where we let $y_1 = \frac{2}{x} + 2$ and $y_2 = 3$.

Symbolic Solution

$$\dfrac{2}{x} + 2 = 3$$

$$\dfrac{2}{x} = 1$$

$$2 = x$$

The solution is **2**.

Numerical Solution

$y_1 = 3$ when $x = 2$.

Graphical Solution

The graphs intersect at (**2, 3**).

MyMathLab PRACTICE WATCH DOWNLOAD READ REVIEW

CONCEPTS AND VOCABULARY

1. When solving the equation $\frac{4}{x+2} = 2$, what is a good first step?

2. In general, what is a good first step when solving a rational equation?

3. If $\frac{1}{x} = 2$, then $x = $ _____.

4. If $\frac{a}{b} = c$, then $a = $ _____.

5. To clear an equation of fractions, multiply each side of the equation by the _____.

6. To solve a rational equation graphically, graph each side of the equation and determine x-coordinates of the point(s) where the graphs _____.

7. (True or False?) A solution to $\frac{x}{x+2} = \frac{2}{2-x}$ is 2.

8. (True or False?) A solution to $\frac{2x}{x-2} + \frac{x}{x+2} = 3$ is -6.

SOLVING RATIONAL EQUATIONS

Exercises 9–14: Find the LCD.

9. $\frac{1}{x}, \frac{1}{5}$

10. $\frac{1}{x-1}, \frac{1}{x+5}$

11. $\frac{1}{x-1}, \frac{1}{x^2-1}$

12. $\frac{1}{x^2-x}, \frac{1}{2x}$

13. $\frac{3}{2}, \frac{x}{2x+1}, \frac{x}{2x-4}$

14. $\frac{1}{x}, \frac{1}{x^2-4x}, \frac{1}{2x}$

Exercises 15–48: Solve. Check your result.

15. $\frac{x}{3} + \frac{1}{2} = \frac{5}{6}$

16. $\frac{7}{8} - \frac{x}{4} = -\frac{11}{8}$

17. $\frac{2}{x} - \frac{7}{3} = -\frac{29}{15}$

18. $\frac{1}{3x} + \frac{1}{x} = \frac{4}{15}$

19. $\frac{x}{x-1} = \frac{4}{3}$

20. $\frac{4}{5x} = -\frac{1}{x+1}$

21. $\frac{1}{2x} - \frac{5}{3x} = 1$

22. $\frac{3}{4x} + \frac{5}{6x} = -\frac{19}{12}$

23. $\frac{1}{x+1} - 1 = \frac{3}{x+1}$

24. $\frac{2}{x-2} + 2 = \frac{4}{x-2}$

25. $\frac{1}{x-3} + \frac{x}{x-3} = \frac{2x}{x-3}$

26. $\frac{6}{x+2} + \frac{3x}{x+2} = \frac{3}{x+2}$

27. $\frac{3}{x-1} = \frac{6}{x+4}$

28. $\frac{1}{x+5} = \frac{2}{2x+1}$

29. $\frac{6}{3z+4} = \frac{4}{2z-5}$

30. $\frac{2}{z-1} - \frac{5}{z+1} = \frac{4}{z^2-1}$

31. $\frac{5}{t-1} + \frac{2}{t+2} = \frac{15}{t^2+t-2}$

32. $\frac{3}{5t} - \frac{1}{t+1} = \frac{6}{5t^2+5t}$

33. $\frac{1}{3n} - 2 = \frac{1}{2n}$

34. $\frac{4}{n} - 3 = \frac{1}{3n}$

35. $\frac{1}{x} + \frac{1}{x^2} = 2$

36. $\frac{1}{x} - \frac{1}{x+1} = \frac{1}{56}$

37. $\frac{x}{x+2} = \frac{4}{x-3}$

38. $\frac{2x}{1-x} - \frac{1}{x} = 0$

39. $\frac{2w+1}{3w} - \frac{4w-3}{w} = 0$

40. $\frac{1}{2w} - \frac{2}{1-w} = -\frac{3}{2}$

41. $\frac{3}{2y} + \frac{2y}{y-4} = -\frac{11}{2}$

42. $\frac{3}{y-2} + \frac{6y}{y+1} = 2$

43. $\frac{1}{(x-1)^2} + \frac{3}{x^2-1} = \frac{5}{x^2-1}$

44. $\frac{1}{x^2-4} + \frac{1}{(x-2)^2} = \frac{2}{(x+2)^2}$

45. $\frac{x^2+x-2}{x-2} - \frac{4}{x-2} = 0$

46. $\frac{x^2-4x-5}{x-1} + \frac{8}{x-1} = 0$

47. $\frac{4}{x+3} - \frac{x}{3-x} = \frac{18}{x^2-9}$

48. $\frac{12}{x^2-9} + \frac{2}{x+3} = \frac{x}{3-x}$

Exercises 49 and 50: Solve $f(x) = 0$ for the given $f(x)$.

49. $f(x) = \dfrac{1}{x} - 4x$ **50.** $f(x) = \dfrac{2 - x}{x} + 2$

Exercises 51 and 52: **Thinking Generally** *Solve for x.*

51. $\dfrac{a}{x} - \dfrac{b}{x} = c$ **52.** $\dfrac{ab}{x} - c = \dfrac{1}{x}$

Exercises 53–56: Use the graph to solve the rational equation. Then check your answer.

53. $\dfrac{2}{x} + 1 = 3$ **54.** $\dfrac{1}{x - 1} = \dfrac{2}{x}$

55. $\dfrac{3}{x^2 - 1} = \dfrac{1}{2}x$ **56.** $\dfrac{1}{x^2} = -x$

Exercises 57–66: Solve the rational equation graphically. Approximate your answer(s) to the nearest hundredth when appropriate.

57. $\dfrac{1}{x - 1} = \dfrac{1}{2}$ **58.** $\dfrac{1}{x + 1} = 2$

59. $\dfrac{3}{x + 2} = x$ **60.** $\dfrac{3}{x - 2} = x$

61. $\dfrac{1}{x - 2} = 2$ **62.** $\dfrac{2x}{x + 1} = 3$

63. $\dfrac{1}{x} + \dfrac{1}{x^2} = \dfrac{15}{4}$ **64.** $\dfrac{1}{x} + \dfrac{1}{2x} = 2x$

65. $\dfrac{1}{x + 2} - \dfrac{1}{x - 2} = \dfrac{4}{3}$

66. $\dfrac{x}{2x + 4} - \dfrac{2x}{x^2 - 4} = 2.7$

USING MORE THAN ONE METHOD

*Exercises 67–70: Solve the equation (**a**) symbolically, (**b**) graphically, and (**c**) numerically.*

67. $\dfrac{1}{x} + \dfrac{2}{3} = 1$ **68.** $\dfrac{1}{x} - \dfrac{1}{x^2} = -2$

69. $\dfrac{1}{x} + \dfrac{1}{x + 2} = \dfrac{4}{3}$

70. $\dfrac{1}{x - 2} + \dfrac{1}{x + 2} = -\dfrac{2}{3}$

Exercises 71 and 72: Solve the equation graphically to the nearest hundredth.

71. $\dfrac{x}{x^2 - 1} - \dfrac{3}{x + 2} = 2$

72. $\dfrac{2.2}{x - 0.1} + \dfrac{x}{0.4x - 1} = 1$

SOLVING AN EQUATION FOR A VARIABLE

Exercises 73–86: Solve for the specified variable.

73. $t = \dfrac{d}{r}$ for r **74.** $r = \dfrac{C}{2\pi}$ for C

75. $h = \dfrac{2A}{b}$ for b **76.** $P = VT$ for T

77. $\dfrac{1}{2a} = \dfrac{1}{b}$ for a **78.** $\dfrac{a}{b} = \dfrac{c}{d}$ for d

79. $\dfrac{1}{R} = \dfrac{1}{R_1} + \dfrac{1}{R_2}$ for R_1 **80.** $S = \dfrac{5}{8H}$ for H

81. $T = \dfrac{1}{15 - x}$ for x **82.** $h = \dfrac{V}{\pi r^2}$ for V

83. $\dfrac{1}{r} = \dfrac{1}{t + 1}$ for t **84.** $R = \dfrac{R_1 R_2}{R_1 + R_2}$ for R_2

85. $\dfrac{1}{r} = \dfrac{a}{a + b}$ for b **86.** $\dfrac{1}{t + 1} = \dfrac{a}{a - b}$ for b

APPLICATIONS

87. *Waiting in Traffic* Suppose that cars are arriving randomly at a construction zone and the flag person can instruct x drivers per hour. If cars arrive at an average rate of 80 cars per hour, the average time T in minutes for each driver to wait and talk to the flag person is given by the formula

$$T(x) = \dfrac{1}{x - 80},$$

where $x > 80$. (*Source:* N. Garber.)

(a) How many drivers per hour should the flag person be able to instruct to keep the average wait to 0.5 minute?

(b) What happens to T if x is only slightly more than 80?

88. *Waiting in Line* At a parking lot, the attendant can wait on 60 people per hour. If people arrive randomly at an average rate of x cars per hour, the average number of cars N waiting to exit the lot is given by

$$N(x) = \frac{x^2}{3600 - 60x},$$

where $x < 60$. (*Source:* N. Garber.)

(a) Approximate x when $N(x) = 8$.

(b) Interpret your answer.

89. *Mowing the Lawn* Suppose that a person with a push mower can mow a large lawn in 5 hours, whereas the same lawn can be mowed with a riding mower in 2 hours.

(a) Write an equation whose solution gives the time needed to mow the lawn if both mowers are used at the same time.

(b) Solve the equation in part (a) symbolically.

(c) Solve the equation in part (a) either graphically or numerically.

90. *Working Together* It takes a more experienced person 1 hour less to complete a task than it does a less experienced person. If they work together, they can complete the task in 1.2 hours. How long does it take each person to complete the task working alone?

91. *Finding Glitches in New Products* Before a new product such as a mobile phone is released, there is usually a time period when people test it to find any problems. After several people have tested a product, most problems are found and fixed. The rational function

$$f(x) = \frac{100x}{x + 1}, \quad 0 \le x \le 20$$

approximates the percentage of the problems that are found after x testers have used a new product.

(a) Calculate $f(3)$. Interpret your answer.

(b) How many testers are necessary to find 95% of glitches?

(c) Graph $y = f(x)$. Interpret the graph for large values of x.

92. *Cost–Benefit Function* A cost–benefit function C computes the cost in millions of dollars to implement a city recycling project aiming at getting x percent of its citizens to participate, where

$$C(x) = \frac{2x}{100 - x}, \quad 0 \le x < 100.$$

(a) Evaluate $C(90)$ and interpret the result.

(b) Evaluate $C(95) - C(90)$. Comment about the additional cost to get an extra 5% participation.

(c) Graph $y = C(x)$. Use the graph to explain why expecting 100% participation is not practical.

(d) If the city has $8 million to spend, what participation rate can be expected?

93. *Economics of the NFL Draft* The top picks in the NFL draft are often paid high salaries. However, compared to the top draft picks, lower picks often receive considerably lower salaries. The following function S approximates the percentage of salary that draft pick x receives compared to the number one draft pick's salary.

$$S(x) = \frac{500}{x + 4}$$

(a) Evaluate $S(36)$ and interpret your answer.

(b) Determine the pick that receives 20% of the number one pick's salary.

94. *Cost of Making Cookies* Because of startup expenses, suppose that it costs $100 to make the first specialty cookie and $1 for each cookie thereafter. The average cost for making x cookies is given by

$$C(x) = \frac{x + 99}{x}.$$

(a) What is the average cost to make 10 cookies?

(b) How many cookies should be made to have an average cost of $1.19?

(c) What happens to the average cost as the number of cookies made becomes very large?

95. *Pumping Water* (Refer to Example 7.) Suppose that a large pump can empty a swimming pool in 40 hours and that a small pump can empty the same pool in 70 hours.

(a) Write an equation whose solution gives the time needed for both pumps to empty the pool.

(b) Solve the equation in part (a) symbolically.

(c) Solve the equation in part (a) either graphically or numerically.

96. *Filling a Water Tank* A large pump can fill a 10,000-gallon tank 5 hours faster than a small pump. The large pump outputs water 100 gallons per hour faster than the small pump. Find the number of gallons pumped in 1 hour by each pump.

97. *Running a Race* (Refer to Example 8.) The winner of a 5-mile race finishes 7.5 minutes ahead of the second-place runner. On average, the winner ran 2 miles per hour faster than the second-place runner. Find the average running speed for each runner.

98. *Waiting in Line* If a clerk can wait on 30 people per hour and people arrive randomly at x people per hour, then the average amount of time spent waiting and checking out, *in hours,* is given by

$$T(x) = \frac{1}{30 - x}.$$

If the average wait is 3 minutes, how many people are arriving per hour, on average?

99. *Speed of a Current* In still water a tugboat can travel 15 miles per hour. It travels 36 miles upstream and then 36 miles downstream in a total time of 5 hours. Find the speed of the current.

100. *Wind Speed* Without any wind an airplane flies at 200 miles per hour. The plane travels 800 miles into the wind and then returns with the wind in a total time of 8 hours and 20 minutes. Find the average speed of the wind.

101. *Speed of an Airplane* When there is a 50-mile-per-hour wind, an airplane can fly 675 miles with the wind in the same time that it can fly 450 miles against the wind. Find the speed of the plane when there is no wind.

102. *Waiting in Line* If a ticket agent can wait on 25 people per hour and people are arriving randomly at an average rate of x people per hour, the average time T in hours for people waiting in line *and* paying the agent is

$$T(x) = \frac{1}{25 - x},$$

where $x < 25$. (*Source:* N. Garber.)
(a) Solve the equation $T(x) = 5$ symbolically and interpret the result.
(b) Solve part (a) either graphically or numerically.

103. *Working Alone* It takes one employee 3 hours longer to mow a football field than it does a more experienced employee. Together they can mow the grass in 2 hours. How long does it take for each person to mow the football field working alone?

104. *Painting a House* It takes a less experienced painter 20 hours longer to paint a house than it does a more experienced painter. Together they can paint the house in 24 hours. How long does it take for each painter to paint the house working alone?

105. *Walking Speed* One person can walk 1 mile per hour faster than another person. The faster person can walk 12 miles in the time it takes the slower person to walk 9 miles. What is the walking speed of each person?

106. *Freeway Speed* On a freeway, a car passes another car that is traveling in the same direction but is going 5 miles per hour slower. The faster car travels 340 miles in the time it takes the slower car to travel 315 miles. What is the speed of each car?

107. *Emptying a Pool* An inlet pipe can fill a pool in 60 hours, whereas an outlet pipe can empty the pool in 40 hours. If both pipes are left open, how long will it take to empty the pool if the pool is full initially?

108. *Emptying a Boat* A small leak will fill an empty boat in 5 hours. The boat's bilge pump will empty a full boat in 3 hours. If the boat were half full and leaking, how long would it take the pump to empty the boat?

Exercises 109 and 110: Graphical Interpretation Use the graph of the rational function f to decide if there is a solution to the given equation. If there is a solution, discuss its value.

109. $f(x) = 100$ **110.** $f(x) = -100$

WRITING ABOUT MATHEMATICS

111. A student does the following to solve a rational equation. Is the work correct? Explain any errors and how you might correct them.

$$\frac{1}{x + 1} + \frac{2}{x - 1} = -1$$

$$(x - 1) + 2(x + 1) \overset{?}{=} -1$$

$$3x + 1 \overset{?}{=} -1$$

$$x \overset{?}{=} -\frac{2}{3}$$

112. Explain the difference between simplifying the rational expression $\frac{x + 1}{x^2 - 1}$ and solving the rational equation $\frac{x + 1}{x^2 - 1} = \frac{1}{2}$.

Checking Basic Concepts

1. Simplify each expression.

   (a) $\dfrac{x}{x^2 - 1} + \dfrac{1}{x^2 - 1}$

   (b) $\dfrac{1}{x - 2} - \dfrac{3}{x}$

   (c) $\dfrac{1}{x(x - 1)} + \dfrac{1}{x^2 - 1} - \dfrac{2}{x(x + 1)}$

2. Solve each equation.

   (a) $\dfrac{6}{x} - \dfrac{1}{2} = 1$ (b) $\dfrac{3}{2x - 1} = \dfrac{2}{x + 1}$

   (c) $\dfrac{2}{x - 1} + \dfrac{3}{x + 2} = \dfrac{x}{x^2 + x - 2}$

3. If a gas pump can fill a 200-gallon tank in 12 minutes and a smaller gas pump can fill the same tank in 28 minutes, how long will it take for the pumps to fill the tank together?

4. Solve $\dfrac{1}{S} = \dfrac{1}{F} - \dfrac{1}{D}$ for S.

4.5   Complex Fractions

Basic Concepts • Simplifying Complex Fractions

A LOOK INTO MATH ▶ If two and a half pizzas are cut into fourths, then there are 10 pieces of pizza. This problem can be written as

$$\frac{2 + \dfrac{1}{2}}{\dfrac{1}{4}} = 10.$$

The expression on the left side of the equation is called a *complex fraction*. Typically, we want to simplify a complex fraction to a fraction with the standard form $\frac{a}{b}$. In this section we discuss how to simplify complex fractions.

NEW VOCABULARY

☐ Complex fraction

Basic Concepts

A **complex fraction** is a rational expression that contains fractions in its numerator, denominator, or both. Examples of complex fractions include

$$\frac{1 + \dfrac{1}{x}}{1 - \dfrac{1}{x}}, \quad \frac{2x}{\dfrac{4}{x} + \dfrac{3}{y}}, \quad \text{and} \quad \frac{\dfrac{a}{3} + \dfrac{a}{4}}{a - \dfrac{1}{a - 1}}. \quad \text{Complex fractions}$$

Complex fractions involve division of fractions. When dividing two fractions, we can multiply the first fraction by the reciprocal of the second fraction.

> **SIMPLIFYING COMPLEX FRACTIONS**
>
> For any real numbers a, b, c, and d,
>
> $$\frac{\dfrac{a}{b}}{\dfrac{c}{d}} = \frac{a}{b} \cdot \frac{d}{c},$$
>
> where b, c, and d are not zero.

EXAMPLE 1   **Simplifying basic types of complex fractions**

Simplify.

(a) $\dfrac{\dfrac{7}{8}}{\dfrac{3}{4}}$ (b) $\dfrac{\dfrac{a}{4b}}{\dfrac{a}{6b^2}}$ (c) $\dfrac{2 + \dfrac{1}{2}}{\dfrac{1}{4}}$

Solution

(a) Rather than dividing $\frac{7}{8}$ by $\frac{3}{4}$, multiply $\frac{7}{8}$ by $\frac{4}{3}$.

$$\frac{\dfrac{7}{8}}{\dfrac{3}{4}} = \frac{7}{8} \cdot \frac{4}{3} \qquad \text{"Invert and multiply."}$$

$$= \frac{7}{6} \qquad \text{Multiply and simplify.}$$

(b) Rather than dividing $\frac{a}{4b}$ by $\frac{a}{6b^2}$, multiply $\frac{a}{4b}$ by $\frac{6b^2}{a}$.

$$\frac{\dfrac{a}{4b}}{\dfrac{a}{6b^2}} = \frac{a}{4b} \cdot \frac{6b^2}{a} \qquad \text{"Invert and multiply."}$$

$$= \frac{6ab^2}{4ab} \qquad \text{Multiply fractions.}$$

$$= \frac{3b}{2} \qquad \text{Simplify.}$$

(c) Start by writing $2 + \frac{1}{2}$ as one fraction.

READING CHECK

What does the phrase "invert and multiply" mean?

$$\frac{2 + \dfrac{1}{2}}{\dfrac{1}{4}} = \frac{\dfrac{5}{2}}{\dfrac{1}{4}} \qquad \text{Write numerator as an improper fraction.}$$

$$= \frac{5}{2} \cdot \frac{4}{1} \qquad \text{"Invert and multiply."}$$

$$= 10 \qquad \text{Simplify.}$$

Now Try Exercises 7, 11, 13

Simplifying Complex Fractions

There are two basic strategies for simplifying a complex fraction. The first is to simplify both the numerator and the denominator and then divide the resulting fractions as was done in Example 1(c). The second is to multiply the numerator and denominator by the least common denominator of the fractions in the numerator and denominator.

SIMPLIFYING THE NUMERATOR AND DENOMINATOR The next example illustrates the method whereby the numerator and denominator are simplified first.

EXAMPLE 2 **Simplifying complex fractions**

Simplify. Leave your answer in factored form when appropriate.

(a) $\dfrac{1 + \dfrac{1}{x}}{1 - \dfrac{1}{x}}$ (b) $\dfrac{2t - \dfrac{1}{2t}}{2t + \dfrac{1}{2t}}$ (c) $\dfrac{\dfrac{1}{z+1} - \dfrac{1}{z-1}}{\dfrac{2}{z+2} - \dfrac{2}{z-2}}$

Solution
(a) First, simplify the numerator by writing it as one term. The LCD is x.

$$1 + \frac{1}{x} = \frac{x}{x} + \frac{1}{x} = \frac{x+1}{x}$$

Second, simplify the denominator by writing it as one term.

$$1 - \frac{1}{x} = \frac{x}{x} - \frac{1}{x} = \frac{x-1}{x}$$

Finally, simplify the complex fraction.

$$\frac{1 + \dfrac{1}{x}}{1 - \dfrac{1}{x}} = \frac{\dfrac{x+1}{x}}{\dfrac{x-1}{x}} \qquad \text{Simplify.}$$

$$= \frac{x+1}{x} \cdot \frac{x}{x-1} \qquad \text{"Invert and multiply."}$$

$$= \frac{x+1}{x-1} \qquad \text{Multiply and simplify.}$$

(b) Combine the terms in the numerator and in the denominator. The LCD is $2t$.

$$\frac{2t - \dfrac{1}{2t}}{2t + \dfrac{1}{2t}} = \frac{\dfrac{4t^2}{2t} - \dfrac{1}{2t}}{\dfrac{4t^2}{2t} + \dfrac{1}{2t}} \qquad \text{Write with the LCD.}$$

$$= \frac{\dfrac{4t^2 - 1}{2t}}{\dfrac{4t^2 + 1}{2t}} \qquad \text{Combine terms.}$$

$$= \frac{4t^2 - 1}{2t} \cdot \frac{2t}{4t^2 + 1} \qquad \text{"Invert and multiply."}$$

$$= \frac{4t^2 - 1}{4t^2 + 1} \qquad \text{Multiply and simplify.}$$

(c) The LCD is $(z + 1)(z - 1)$ for the numerator and $(z + 2)(z - 2)$ for the denominator.

$$\dfrac{\dfrac{1}{z + 1} - \dfrac{1}{z - 1}}{\dfrac{2}{z + 2} - \dfrac{2}{z - 2}} = \dfrac{\dfrac{z - 1}{(z + 1)(z - 1)} - \dfrac{z + 1}{(z + 1)(z - 1)}}{\dfrac{2(z - 2)}{(z + 2)(z - 2)} - \dfrac{2(z + 2)}{(z + 2)(z - 2)}}$$

$$= \dfrac{\dfrac{-2}{(z + 1)(z - 1)}}{\dfrac{-8}{(z + 2)(z - 2)}}$$

$$= \dfrac{-2}{(z + 1)(z - 1)} \cdot \dfrac{(z + 2)(z - 2)}{-8}$$

$$= \dfrac{(z + 2)(z - 2)}{4(z + 1)(z - 1)}$$

▌ Now Try Exercises **27, 29, 31**

MULTIPLYING BY THE LEAST COMMON DENOMINATOR A second strategy for simplifying a complex fraction is to multiply by **1** in the form $\frac{\text{LCD}}{\text{LCD}}$. To do this, we multiply the numerator and denominator by the LCD of the fractions in the numerator *and* denominator. For example, the LCD for the complex fraction

$$\dfrac{1 - \dfrac{1}{x}}{1 + \dfrac{1}{2x}}$$

is $2x$. To simplify, multiply the complex fraction by **1**, expressed in the form $\frac{2x}{2x}$.

$$\dfrac{\left(1 - \dfrac{1}{x}\right) \cdot 2x}{\left(1 + \dfrac{1}{2x}\right) \cdot 2x} = \dfrac{2x - \dfrac{2x}{x}}{2x + \dfrac{2x}{2x}} \qquad \text{Distributive property}$$

$$= \dfrac{2x - 2}{2x + 1} \qquad \text{Simplify fractions.}$$

In the next example we use this method to simplify other complex fractions.

CRITICAL THINKING

Does the expression $\dfrac{\dfrac{x}{y}}{2 + \dfrac{x}{y}}$ equal $\frac{1}{3}$? Explain.

Does the expression $\dfrac{2 + \dfrac{x}{y}}{\dfrac{x}{y}}$ equal 3? Explain.

EXAMPLE 3 **Simplifying complex fractions**

Simplify.

(a) $\dfrac{1 + \dfrac{1}{x}}{1 + \dfrac{1}{y}}$ **(b)** $\dfrac{\dfrac{1}{x} - \dfrac{1}{y}}{x - y}$ **(c)** $\dfrac{\dfrac{3}{x - 1} - \dfrac{2}{x}}{\dfrac{1}{x - 1} + \dfrac{3}{x}}$ **(d)** $\dfrac{n^{-2} + m^{-2}}{1 + (nm)^{-2}}$

Solution

(a) The LCD for the numerator *and* the denominator is xy.

$$\frac{1 + \dfrac{1}{x}}{1 + \dfrac{1}{y}} = \frac{\left(1 + \dfrac{1}{x}\right) \cdot xy}{\left(1 + \dfrac{1}{y}\right) \cdot xy} \qquad \text{Multiply the numerator and the denominator by the LCD.}$$

$$= \frac{xy + y}{xy + x} \qquad \text{Distributive property}$$

(b) The LCD is xy. Multiply the given expression by $\dfrac{xy}{xy}$.

$$\frac{\left(\dfrac{1}{x} - \dfrac{1}{y}\right) \cdot xy}{(x - y) \cdot xy} = \frac{\dfrac{xy}{x} - \dfrac{xy}{y}}{xy(x - y)} \qquad \text{Distributive and commutative properties}$$

$$= \frac{y - x}{xy(x - y)} \qquad \text{Simplify fractions in numerator.}$$

$$= \frac{-1(x - y)}{xy(x - y)} \qquad \text{Factor out } -1; \text{ rewrite numerator.}$$

$$= -\frac{1}{xy} \qquad \text{Simplify.}$$

(c) The LCD is $x(x - 1)$. Multiply the given expression by $\dfrac{x(x - 1)}{x(x - 1)}$.

$$\frac{\left(\dfrac{3}{x - 1} - \dfrac{2}{x}\right) \cdot x(x - 1)}{\left(\dfrac{1}{x - 1} + \dfrac{3}{x}\right) \cdot x(x - 1)} = \frac{\dfrac{3x(x - 1)}{x - 1} - \dfrac{2x(x - 1)}{x}}{\dfrac{x(x - 1)}{x - 1} + \dfrac{3x(x - 1)}{x}} \qquad \text{Distributive property}$$

$$= \frac{3x - 2(x - 1)}{x + 3(x - 1)} \qquad \text{Simplify.}$$

$$= \frac{3x - 2x + 2}{x + 3x - 3} \qquad \text{Distributive property}$$

$$= \frac{x + 2}{4x - 3} \qquad \text{Combine like terms.}$$

(d) Start by rewriting the ratio with positive exponents.

$$\frac{n^{-2} + m^{-2}}{1 + (nm)^{-2}} = \frac{\dfrac{1}{n^2} + \dfrac{1}{m^2}}{1 + \dfrac{1}{n^2 m^2}}$$

The LCD for the numerator *and* the denominator is $n^2 m^2$.

$$\frac{\dfrac{1}{n^2} + \dfrac{1}{m^2}}{1 + \dfrac{1}{n^2 m^2}} = \frac{\left(\dfrac{1}{n^2} + \dfrac{1}{m^2}\right) \cdot n^2 m^2}{\left(1 + \dfrac{1}{n^2 m^2}\right) \cdot n^2 m^2} \qquad \text{Multiply by LCD.}$$

$$= \frac{m^2 + n^2}{n^2 m^2 + 1} \qquad \text{Distributive property}$$

Now Try Exercises 25, 37, 39, 43

4.5   Putting It All Together

CONCEPT	EXPLANATION	EXAMPLES
Complex Fraction	A rational expression that contains fractions in its numerator, denominator, or both	$\dfrac{\dfrac{1}{x}+\dfrac{1}{2x+1}}{1-\dfrac{1}{2x+1}}$ and $\dfrac{\dfrac{a}{2b}-\dfrac{b}{2a}}{\dfrac{a}{2b}+\dfrac{b}{2a}}$
Simplifying Basic Complex Fractions	$\dfrac{\dfrac{a}{b}}{\dfrac{c}{d}}=\dfrac{a}{b}\cdot\dfrac{d}{c}$ $b, c,$ and d not zero	$\dfrac{\dfrac{2y}{z}}{\dfrac{y}{z-1}}=\dfrac{2y}{z}\cdot\dfrac{z-1}{y}=\dfrac{2(z-1)}{z}$
Method I: Simplifying the Numerator and Denominator First and then Dividing	Combine the terms in the numerator, combine the terms in the denominator, and then invert and multiply.	$\dfrac{\dfrac{1}{2b}+\dfrac{1}{2a}}{\dfrac{1}{2b}-\dfrac{1}{2a}}=\dfrac{\dfrac{a+b}{2ab}}{\dfrac{a-b}{2ab}}$ $=\dfrac{a+b}{2ab}\cdot\dfrac{2ab}{a-b}$ $=\dfrac{a+b}{a-b}$
Method II: Multiplying the Numerator and Denominator by the LCD	Start by multiplying the numerator and denominator by the LCD of the numerator *and* the denominator.	$\dfrac{\dfrac{1}{2b}+\dfrac{1}{2a}}{\dfrac{1}{2b}-\dfrac{1}{2a}}=\dfrac{\left(\dfrac{1}{2b}+\dfrac{1}{2a}\right)\cdot 2ab}{\left(\dfrac{1}{2b}-\dfrac{1}{2a}\right)\cdot 2ab}$ $=\dfrac{a+b}{a-b}$ Note that the LCD is $2ab$.

4.5   Exercises

MyMathLab   Math XL PRACTICE   WATCH   DOWNLOAD   READ   REVIEW

CONCEPTS AND VOCABULARY

1. $\dfrac{\dfrac{5}{7}}{\dfrac{3}{11}}=$ _____.

2. $\dfrac{\dfrac{a}{b}}{\dfrac{c}{d}}=$ _____.

3. What is a good first step when simplifying

$$\dfrac{2+\dfrac{1}{x-1}}{2-\dfrac{1}{x-1}}?$$

4. Explain what a complex fraction is.

5. Write the phrase "the quantity z plus three-fourths divided by the quantity z minus three-fourths" as a complex fraction.

6. Write the expression $\frac{a}{b} \div \frac{a-b}{a+b}$ as a complex fraction.

SIMPLIFYING COMPLEX FRACTIONS

Exercises 7–48: Simplify the complex fraction. Leave your answer in factored form when appropriate.

7. $\dfrac{\dfrac{1}{5}}{\dfrac{4}{7}}$

8. $\dfrac{\dfrac{3}{7}}{\dfrac{2}{9}}$

9. $\dfrac{1 + \dfrac{1}{3}}{1 - \dfrac{1}{3}}$

10. $\dfrac{\dfrac{1}{2} - 3}{\dfrac{1}{2} + 3}$

11. $\dfrac{2 + \dfrac{2}{3}}{2 - \dfrac{1}{4}}$

12. $\dfrac{\dfrac{1}{2} + \dfrac{3}{4}}{\dfrac{1}{2} - \dfrac{3}{4}}$

13. $\dfrac{\dfrac{a}{b}}{\dfrac{3a}{2b^2}}$

14. $\dfrac{\dfrac{7}{y}}{\dfrac{14}{y}}$

15. $\dfrac{\dfrac{x}{2y}}{\dfrac{2x}{3y}}$

16. $\dfrac{\dfrac{ab^2}{2c}}{\dfrac{a}{4bc}}$

17. $\dfrac{\dfrac{8}{n+1}}{\dfrac{4}{n-1}}$

18. $\dfrac{\dfrac{n}{m-2}}{\dfrac{3n}{m-2}}$

19. $\dfrac{\dfrac{2k+3}{k}}{\dfrac{k-4}{k}}$

20. $\dfrac{\dfrac{2k}{k-7}}{\dfrac{1}{(k-7)^2}}$

21. $\dfrac{\dfrac{3}{z^2-4}}{\dfrac{z}{z^2-4}}$

22. $\dfrac{\dfrac{z}{(z-2)^2}}{\dfrac{2z}{z^2-4}}$

23. $\dfrac{\dfrac{x}{x^2-16}}{\dfrac{1}{x-4}}$

24. $\dfrac{\dfrac{4y}{x-y}}{\dfrac{1}{x^2-y^2}}$

25. $\dfrac{1 + \dfrac{1}{x}}{x+1}$

26. $\dfrac{2-x}{\dfrac{1}{x} - \dfrac{1}{2}}$

27. $\dfrac{\dfrac{1}{x-3}}{\dfrac{1}{x} - \dfrac{3}{x-3}}$

28. $\dfrac{5 + \dfrac{1}{x-1}}{\dfrac{1}{x-1} - \dfrac{1}{4}}$

29. $\dfrac{\dfrac{1}{x} + \dfrac{2}{x^2}}{\dfrac{3}{x} - \dfrac{1}{x^2}}$

30. $\dfrac{\dfrac{1}{x-1} + \dfrac{2}{x}}{2 - \dfrac{1}{x}}$

31. $\dfrac{\dfrac{1}{x+3} + \dfrac{2}{x-3}}{2 - \dfrac{1}{x-3}}$

32. $\dfrac{\dfrac{1}{x} + \dfrac{2}{x}}{\dfrac{1}{x-1} + \dfrac{x}{2}}$

33. $\dfrac{\dfrac{4}{x-5}}{\dfrac{1}{x+5} + \dfrac{1}{x}}$

34. $\dfrac{\dfrac{1}{x-4} + \dfrac{1}{x-4}}{1 - \dfrac{1}{x+4}}$

35. $\dfrac{\dfrac{1}{p^2q} + \dfrac{1}{pq^2}}{\dfrac{1}{p^2q} - \dfrac{1}{pq^2}}$

36. $\dfrac{\dfrac{1}{p-1}}{\dfrac{1}{p-1} + 2}$

37. $\dfrac{\dfrac{1}{a} + \dfrac{1}{b}}{\dfrac{1}{b} - \dfrac{1}{a}}$

38. $\dfrac{\dfrac{1}{a} + \dfrac{1}{b} + \dfrac{1}{c}}{\dfrac{1}{ab} + \dfrac{1}{bc}}$

39. $\dfrac{\dfrac{1}{x} + \dfrac{1}{x+1}}{\dfrac{2}{x+1} - \dfrac{1}{x+1}}$

40. $\dfrac{\dfrac{2}{x-1} - 4}{\dfrac{1}{x-1} + \dfrac{1}{x-2}}$

41. $\dfrac{3^{-1} - 4^{-1}}{5^{-1} + 4^{-1}}$

42. $\dfrac{1 + 2^{-3}}{2^{-3} - 1}$

43. $\dfrac{m^{-1} - 2n^{-2}}{1 + (mn)^{-2}}$

44. $\dfrac{1 + p^{-2}}{1 - p^{-2}}$

45. $\dfrac{1 - (2n + 1)^{-1}}{1 + (2n + 1)^{-1}}$

46. $\dfrac{(a + b)^{-1} - (a - b)^{-1}}{1 + (a - b)^{-1}}$

47. $\dfrac{\dfrac{x}{x^2 - 4} - \dfrac{1}{x^2 - 4}}{\dfrac{1}{x + 4}}$

48. $\dfrac{\dfrac{1}{x^2 + 2x + 1} - \dfrac{1}{x^2 - 2x + 1}}{(x + 1)(x - 1)}$

APPLICATIONS

49. *Annuity* If P dollars are deposited every month in an account paying an annual interest rate r expressed as a decimal, then the amount A in the account after 2 years can be approximated by

$$\left(P\left(1 + \dfrac{r}{12}\right)^{24} - P\right) \div \dfrac{r}{12}.$$

Write this expression as a complex fraction.

50. *Annuity* (Continuation of the preceding exercise.) Use a calculator to evaluate the expression when $r = 0.06$ (6%) and $P = \$250$. Interpret the result.

51. *Resistance in Electricity* Light bulbs are often wired so that electricity can flow through either bulb as illustrated in the accompanying figure.

In this way, if one bulb burns out, the other bulb still works. If two light bulbs have resistances R_1 and R_2, then their combined resistance R is given by the complex fraction

$$R = \dfrac{1}{\dfrac{1}{R_1} + \dfrac{1}{R_2}}.$$

Simplify this formula.

52. *Resistance in Electricity* (Refer to the preceding exercise.) Evaluate the formula

$$R = \dfrac{1}{\dfrac{1}{R_1} + \dfrac{1}{R_2}}$$

when $R_1 = 75$ ohms and $R_2 = 100$ ohms.

53. *The Power of Practice* If a person practices doing a task, he or she usually gets faster at completing the task. This observation can be modeled by

$$T(x) = \dfrac{10}{\frac{1}{10}x + \frac{9}{10}},$$

where $T(x)$ gives the time in seconds to perform a simple task after practicing x times.
(a) Evaluate $T(11)$ and interpret the result.
(b) Rewrite $T(x)$ as a fraction in standard form $\frac{a}{b}$, without using decimals.

54. *Doppler Effect* Have you ever noticed how a siren sounds higher when it is approaching you and then its pitch drops when it passes you? This observation, called the Doppler effect, is described by the following equation.

$$F = \dfrac{f}{1 - \frac{v}{c}}$$

Simplify the complex fraction on the right side of the equation.

WRITING ABOUT MATHEMATICS

55. Describe a method to simplify a complex fraction.

56. A student simplifies a complex fraction as follows. Explain what the student's mistake is and how to work it correctly.

$$\dfrac{\dfrac{1}{x} + \dfrac{1}{y}}{\dfrac{1}{x} + \dfrac{1}{y}} \overset{?}{=} \dfrac{\dfrac{1}{x}}{\dfrac{1}{x}} + \dfrac{\dfrac{1}{y}}{\dfrac{1}{y}} \overset{?}{=} 1 + 1 = 2$$

Modeling with Proportions and Variation

Proportions • Direct Variation • Inverse Variation • Joint Variation

A LOOK INTO MATH ▶

Proportions are used frequently to solve problems. The following are examples.

- If someone earns $100 per day, that person can earn $500 in 5 days.
- If 1 out of 3 adults believes in ghosts, 77 million out of 231 million adults believe in ghosts.
- If a person walks a mile in 16 minutes, that person can walk a half mile in 8 minutes.

Many applications involve proportions or variation. In this section we discuss some of them.

NEW VOCABULARY

- ☐ Proportion
- ☐ Similar figures
- ☐ Similar triangles
- ☐ Directly proportional
- ☐ Varies directly
- ☐ Constant of proportionality
- ☐ Constant of variation
- ☐ Inversely proportional
- ☐ Varies inversely
- ☐ Varies jointly

Proportions

▶ **REAL-WORLD CONNECTION** A 650-megabyte compact disc (CD) can store about 74 minutes of music. Suppose that we have already selected some music to record on the CD and 256 megabytes are still available. Using proportions we can determine how many more minutes of music could be recorded. A **proportion** is a statement (equation) that two ratios (fractions) are equal.

Let x be the number of minutes available on the CD. Then **74** minutes *are to* **650** megabytes *as* x minutes *are to* **256** megabytes, which can be written as the proportion

$$\frac{74}{650} = \frac{x}{256}. \qquad \frac{\text{Minutes}}{\text{Megabytes}} = \frac{\text{Minutes}}{\text{Megabytes}}$$

Solving this equation for x gives

$$x = \frac{74 \cdot 256}{650} \approx 29.1 \text{ minutes.} \qquad \text{Multiply by 256; simplify.}$$

About 29 minutes are still available on the CD.

MAKING CONNECTIONS

Proportions and Fractional Parts

We could have solved the preceding problem by noting that the fraction of the CD still available for recording music is $\frac{256}{650}$. So $\frac{256}{650}$ of 74 minutes equals

$$\frac{256}{650} \cdot 74 \approx 29.1 \text{ minutes.}$$

The following property is a convenient way to solve proportions:

$$\frac{a}{b} = \frac{c}{d} \quad \text{is equivalent to} \quad ad = bc,$$

provided $b \neq 0$ and $d \neq 0$. This is a result of multiplying each side of the equation by a common denominator bd, and is sometimes referred to as *clearing fractions*.

$$bd \cdot \frac{a}{b} = \frac{c}{d} \cdot bd \qquad \text{Multiply by } bd.$$

$$\frac{bda}{b} = \frac{cbd}{d} \qquad \text{Property of multiplying fractions}$$

$$ad = bc \qquad \text{Simplify.}$$

For example, the proportion

is equivalent to

$$6x = 5 \cdot 8 \quad \text{or} \quad x = \frac{40}{6} = \frac{20}{3}.$$

READING CHECK

Explain how to solve the proportion $\frac{4}{x} = \frac{6}{7}$. Solve the equation for x.

▶ **REAL-WORLD CONNECTION** Flooding in Fargo, North Dakota, has been an annual problem in recent years. With snow drifts reaching 10 to 15 feet high in some areas, an accurate estimate of the water content in the snow is essential for predicting spring flood levels. In the next example we estimate the water content in snow.

EXAMPLE 1 **Calculating the water content in snow**

Six inches of light, fluffy snow is equivalent to about half an inch of rain in terms of water content. If 21 inches of such snow fall, use proportions to estimate the water content.

Solution

Let x be the equivalent amount of rain. Then 6 inches of snow is to $\frac{1}{2}$ inch of rain as 21 inches of snow is to x inches of rain, which can be written as the proportion

$$\frac{6}{\frac{1}{2}} = \frac{21}{x}. \qquad \frac{\text{Snow}}{\text{Rain}} = \frac{\text{Snow}}{\text{Rain}}$$

Solving this equation gives

$$6x = \frac{21}{2} \quad \text{or} \quad x = \frac{21}{12} = 1.75.$$

Thus 21 inches of light, fluffy snow is equivalent to about 1.75 inches of rain.

▮ Now Try Exercise 67

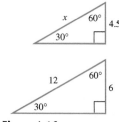

Figure 4.16

▶ **REAL-WORLD CONNECTION** Proportions frequently occur in geometry when we work with **similar figures**. Two triangles are similar if the measures of their corresponding angles are equal. Corresponding sides of **similar triangles** are proportional. Figure 4.16 shows two right triangles that are similar because each has angles of 30°, 60°, and 90°.

We can find the length of side x by using proportions. Side x *is to* 12 *as* 4.5 *is to* 6, which can be written as the proportion

$$\frac{x}{12} = \frac{4.5}{6}. \qquad \frac{\text{Hypotenuse}}{\text{Hypotenuse}} = \frac{\text{Shorter leg}}{\text{Shorter leg}}$$

Solving yields the equation

$$6x = 4.5(12) \qquad \text{Clear fractions.}$$
$$x = 9. \qquad \text{Divide by 6.}$$

EXAMPLE 2 | **Calculating the height of a tree**

A 6-foot-tall person casts a 4-foot-long shadow. If a nearby tree casts a 44-foot-long shadow, estimate the height of the tree. See Figure 4.17.

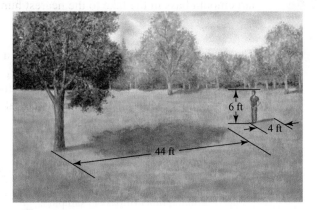

Figure 4.17

Solution

The triangles in Figure 4.18 are similar because the measures of corresponding angles are equal. Therefore corresponding sides are proportional. Let h be the height of the tree.

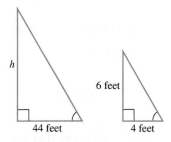

Figure 4.18

$$\frac{h}{6} = \frac{44}{4} \qquad \frac{\text{Height}}{\text{Height}} = \frac{\text{Shadow length}}{\text{Shadow length}}$$

$$4h = 6(44) \qquad \text{Clear fractions.}$$

$$h = \frac{6(44)}{4} \qquad \text{Divide by 4.}$$

$$h = 66 \qquad \text{Simplify.}$$

The tree is 66 feet tall.

▌ Now Try Exercise 65

▶ **REAL-WORLD CONNECTION** Surveys are based on the concept of proportions and are used in a wide variety of areas because it is usually impossible to ask *every* individual the same question. For example, in 2011 Nielsen polled 2131 people about what 4G meant. At that time, only 482 people knew that 4G meant superfast wireless. By using proportions, we might conclude that only about 52 million out of 231 million adults in the United States knew what 4G meant. See Exercise 70.

Biologists also use proportions to determine fish populations in a lake. They tag a small number of a particular species of fish and then release them. It is assumed that over time these tagged fish will distribute themselves evenly throughout the lake. Later, a sample of fish is taken and the number of tagged fish is compared to the total number of fish in the sample. These numbers can be used to estimate the population of a particular species of fish in the lake. (*Source:* Minnesota Department of Natural Resources.)

EXAMPLE 3   **Estimating fish population**

In May, 500 tagged largemouth bass are released into a lake. Later in the summer, a sample of 194 largemouth bass from the lake contains 28 tagged fish. Estimate the population of largemouth bass in the lake to the nearest hundred.

Solution

The sample contains 28 tagged bass out of a total of 194 bass. The ratio of tagged bass to the total number of bass in this sample is $\frac{28}{194}$. Let B be the total number of largemouth bass in the lake. Then the ratio of tagged bass to the total number of bass in the lake is $\frac{500}{B}$. If the bass are evenly distributed throughout the lake, then these two ratios are equal and form the following proportion.

Tagged bass in sample   Total number of tagged bass

$$\frac{28}{194} = \frac{500}{B}$$

Total number of bass in sample   Total number of bass in the lake

To solve this proportion we clear fractions to obtain the following equation.

$$28B = 194 \cdot 500 \qquad \text{Clear fractions.}$$

$$B = \frac{194 \cdot 500}{28} \approx 3464 \qquad \text{Divide by 28 and approximate.}$$

To the nearest hundred there are approximately 3500 largemouth bass in the lake.

Now Try Exercise 71

Direct Variation

▶ **REAL-WORLD CONNECTION** If your wage is $9 per hour, the amount you earn is proportional to the number of hours that you work. If you work H hours, your total pay P satisfies the equation

$$\frac{P}{H} = \frac{9}{1}, \qquad \frac{\text{Pay}}{\text{Hours}}$$

or, equivalently,

$$P = 9H.$$

We say that your pay P is *directly proportional* to the number of hours H worked, and the *constant of proportionality* is 9.

Direct Variation

y

$y = kx, k > 0$

x

Figure 4.19

DIRECT VARIATION

Let x and y denote two quantities. Then y is **directly proportional** to x, or y **varies directly** with x, if there is a nonzero number k such that

$$y = kx.$$

The number k is called the **constant of proportionality**, or the **constant of variation**.

The graph of $y = kx$ for $x > 0$ is a line passing through the origin, as illustrated in Figure 4.19. Sometimes data in a scatterplot indicate that two quantities are directly proportional. The constant of proportionality k corresponds to the *slope m* of the line in Figure 4.19.

EXAMPLE 4   **Modeling college tuition**

Table 4.4 lists the tuition for taking various numbers of credits.

TABLE 4.4

Credits	3	5	8	11	17
Tuition	$189	$315	$504	$693	$1071

(a) A scatterplot of the data is shown in Figure 4.20. Could the data be modeled using a line?

Figure 4.20

(b) Explain why tuition is directly proportional to the number of credits taken.
(c) Find the constant of proportionality. Interpret your result.
(d) Predict the cost of taking 15 credits.

Solution
(a) The data are linear and suggest a line passing through the origin.
(b) Because the data can be modeled by a line passing through the origin, tuition is directly proportional to the number of credits taken. Hence doubling the credits will double the tuition and tripling the credits will triple the tuition. Zero credits cost $0.
(c) The slope of the line equals the constant of proportionality k. If we use the first and last data points $(3, 189)$ and $(17, 1071)$, the slope is

$$k = \frac{1071 - 189}{17 - 3} = 63.$$

That is, tuition is $63 per credit. If we graph the line $y = 63x$, it models the data as shown in Figure 4.21. This graph can also be created with a graphing calculator.

READING CHECK

If y varies directly with x, what happens to y if x triples?

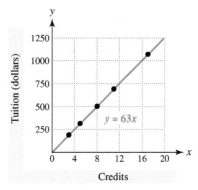

Figure 4.21

(d) If y represents tuition and x represents the credits taken, 15 credits would cost

$$y = 63(15) = \$945.$$

Now Try Exercise 81

MAKING CONNECTIONS

Ratios and the Constant of Proportionality

The constant of proportionality in Example 4 can also be found by calculating the ratios $\frac{y}{x}$, where y is the tuition and x is the credits taken. Note that each ratio in the table equals 63 because the equation $y = 63x$ is equivalent to the equation $\frac{y}{x} = 63$.

x	3	5	8	11	17
y	189	315	504	693	1071
$\frac{y}{x}$	63	63	63	63	63

← Ratios are constant for direct variation.

STEPS FOR SOLVING A VARIATION PROBLEM The following four-step process can be helpful when solving a variation application. This process is used to solve Example 5 and can also be used to solve other types of variation problems.

STUDY TIP

These steps can be helpful in solving any type of variation problem.

SOLVING A VARIATION APPLICATION

When solving a variation problem, the following steps can be used.

STEP 1: Write the general equation for the type of variation problem that you are solving.

STEP 2: Substitute given values in this equation so the constant of variation k is the only unknown value in the equation. Solve for k.

STEP 3: Substitute the value of k in the general equation in Step 1.

STEP 4: Use this equation to find the requested quantity.

▶ **REAL-WORLD CONNECTION** If you have ever dived into deep water, you may have experienced pressure on your eardrums. The water pressure exerted on a diver *varies directly* with the depth, as illustrated in the next example.

EXAMPLE 5 **Modeling pressure on a diver**

At a depth of 18 feet, a diver experiences water pressure equal to 8 pounds per square inch. Find the pressure at 63 feet.

Solution

STEP 1: The general equation for direct variation is $y = kx$, where, in this case, y is the pressure and x is the depth.

STEP 2: Substitute 8 for y and 18 for x in $y = kx$. Solve for k.

$$8 = k(18) \quad y = kx$$

$$\frac{8}{18} = k \qquad \text{Divide each side by 18.}$$

$$k = \frac{4}{9} \qquad \text{Simplify; rewrite equation.}$$

STEP 3: Replace k with $\frac{4}{9}$ in $y = kx$ to obtain $y = \frac{4}{9}x$.

STEP 4: Find the pressure by letting $x = 63$ in $y = \frac{4}{9}x$.

$$y = \frac{4}{9}(63) = 28 \text{ pounds per square inch}$$

Now Try Exercise 83

NOTE: In Example 5 the water depth increased by a factor of $\frac{63}{18} = 3.5$, so with direct variation the pressure also increased by a factor of 3.5, or 3.5(8) = 28 pounds per square inch.

Inverse Variation

▶ **REAL-WORLD CONNECTION** When two quantities vary inversely, an *increase* in one quantity results in a *decrease* in the second quantity. For example, at 25 miles per hour a car travels 100 miles in 4 hours, whereas at 50 miles per hour the car travels 100 miles in 2 hours. Doubling the speed (or rate) decreases the travel time by half. Distance equals rate times time, so $d = rt$. Thus

$$100 = rt, \quad \text{or equivalently,} \quad t = \frac{100}{r}.$$

We say that the time t to travel 100 miles is *inversely proportional* to the speed or rate r. The constant of proportionality or constant of variation is 100 in this example.

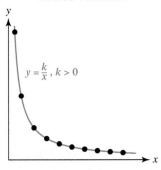

Inverse Variation

$y = \frac{k}{x}, k > 0$

Figure 4.22

> **INVERSE VARIATION**
>
> Let x and y denote two quantities. Then y is **inversely proportional** to x, or y **varies inversely** with x, if there is a nonzero number k such that
>
> $$y = \frac{k}{x}.$$

NOTE: We assume that the constant k is positive.

The data shown in Figure 4.22 represent inverse variation and are modeled by $y = \frac{k}{x}$. Note that as x increases, y decreases.

▶ **REAL-WORLD CONNECTION** A wrench is commonly used to loosen a nut on a bolt. See Figure 4.23. If the nut is difficult to loosen, a wrench with a longer handle is often helpful because a longer wrench requires less force. The length of the wrench and the force needed to loosen a nut on a bolt are *inversely* proportional, as illustrated in the next example.

Figure 4.23

| EXAMPLE 6 | **Loosening a nut on a bolt** |

It takes a force F of 10 pounds to loosen a nut on a bolt with an 8-inch wrench. Find the force necessary to loosen the same nut if a 16-inch wrench is used.

Solution
STEP 1: The equation for inverse variation is $F = \frac{k}{L}$, where L is the length of the wrench.

STEP 2: Substitute 10 for F and 8 for L in $F = \frac{k}{L}$. Solve for k.

$$10 = \frac{k}{8} \qquad\qquad F = \frac{k}{L}$$

$$8 \cdot 10 = \frac{k}{8} \cdot 8 \qquad \text{Multiply each side by 8.}$$

$$80 = k \qquad\qquad \text{Simplify.}$$

STEP 3: Replace k with 80 in $F = \frac{k}{L}$ to obtain $F = \frac{80}{L}$.

STEP 4: Find the necessary force by letting $L = 16$ in $F = \frac{80}{L}$.

$$F = \frac{80}{16} = 5 \text{ pounds}$$

Now Try Exercise 79

READING CHECK

If y varies inversely with x, what happens to y if x doubles?

NOTE: In Example 6 the length of the wrench doubled, so with inverse variation the necessary force was half as much, or $\frac{1}{2}(10) = 5$ pounds.

EXAMPLE 7 **Analyzing data**

Determine whether the data in each table represent direct variation, inverse variation, or neither. For direct and inverse variation, find an equation. Graph the data and equation.

(a)

x	4	5	10	20
y	50	40	20	10

(b)

x	2	5	9	11
y	14	35	63	77

(c)

x	2	4	6	8
y	10	16	24	48

Solution

(a) As x increases, y decreases. With inverse variation $y = \frac{k}{x}$, so $k = xy$. Because $xy = 200$ for each data point, $k = 200$ and the equation $y = \frac{200}{x}$ models the data. The data represent inverse variation. The data and equation are graphed in Figure 4.24(a).

(b) Because $\frac{y}{x} = 7$ for each data point, the equation $y = 7x$ models the data. These data represent direct variation. The data and equation are graphed in Figure 4.24(b).

(c) Neither the product xy nor the ratio $\frac{y}{x}$ is constant for the data in the table. Therefore these data represent neither direct variation nor inverse variation. The data are plotted in Figure 4.24(c). Note that the data values increase and are nonlinear.

Figure 4.24

Now Try Exercises 49, 51, 53

Joint Variation

▶ **REAL-WORLD CONNECTION** In many applications a quantity depends on more than one variable. In *joint variation* a quantity varies with the product of more than one variable. For example, the formula for the area A of a rectangle is given by

$$A = WL,$$

where W and L are the width and length, respectively. Thus the area of a rectangle varies jointly with the width and length.

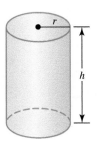

Figure 4.25 $V = \pi r^2 h$

JOINT VARIATION

Let x, y, and z denote three quantities. Then z **varies jointly** with x and y if there is a nonzero number k such that

$$z = kxy.$$

Sometimes joint variation can involve a power of a variable. For example, the volume V of a cylinder is given by $V = \pi r^2 h$, where r is its radius and h is its height, as illustrated in Figure 4.25. In this case we say that the volume varies jointly with the height and the *square* of the radius. The constant of variation is $k = \pi$.

EXAMPLE 8 **Finding the strength of a rectangular beam**

Figure 4.26

The strength S of a rectangular beam varies jointly with its width w and the square of its thickness t. See Figure 4.26. If a beam 3 inches wide and 5 inches thick supports 750 pounds, how much can a similar beam 2 inches wide and 6 inches thick support?

Solution
The strength of a beam is modeled by

$$S = kwt^2, \qquad \text{\textit{S} varies jointly with \textit{w} and the square of \textit{t}.}$$

where k is a constant of variation. We can find k by substituting $S = 750$, $w = 3$, and $t = 5$ in the formula.

$$750 = k \cdot 3 \cdot 5^2 \qquad \text{Substitute in } S = kwt^2.$$
$$k = \frac{750}{3 \cdot 5^2} \qquad \text{Solve for } k; \text{ rewrite.}$$
$$= 10 \qquad \text{Simplify.}$$

Thus $S = 10wt^2$ models the strength of this type of beam. When $w = 2$ and $t = 6$, the beam can support

$$S = 10 \cdot 2 \cdot 6^2 = 720 \text{ pounds.}$$

Now Try Exercise 91

CRITICAL THINKING

Compare the increased strength of a beam if the width doubles and if the thickness doubles. What happens to the strength of a beam if both the width and thickness triple?

4.6 **Putting It All Together**

CONCEPT	EXPLANATION	EXAMPLES
Proportion	A statement (equation) that two ratios (fractions) are equal The proportion $\frac{a}{b} = \frac{c}{d}$ can be expressed verbally as "a is to b as c is to d."	10 is to 13 as 32 is to x: $\frac{10}{13} = \frac{32}{x}$. x is to 7 as 2 is to 5: $\frac{x}{7} = \frac{2}{5}$.

continued on next page

continued from previous page

CONCEPT	EXPLANATION	EXAMPLES
Direct Variation	Two quantities x and y vary according to the equation $y = kx$, where k is a nonzero constant of proportionality (or variation). The ratios $\frac{y}{x}$ all equal k.	$y = 3x$ or $\frac{y}{x} = 3$; $k = 3$ <table><tr><td>x</td><td>1</td><td>2</td><td>4</td></tr><tr><td>y</td><td>3</td><td>6</td><td>12</td></tr></table> If x doubles, then y also doubles.
Inverse Variation	Two quantities x and y vary according to the equation $y = \frac{k}{x}$, where k is a nonzero constant of proportionality (or variation). The products xy all equal k.	$y = \frac{2}{x}$ or $xy = 2$; $k = 2$ <table><tr><td>x</td><td>1</td><td>2</td><td>4</td></tr><tr><td>y</td><td>2</td><td>1</td><td>$\frac{1}{2}$</td></tr></table> If x doubles, then y decreases by half.
Joint Variation	Three quantities x, y, and z vary according to the equation $z = kxy$, where k is a constant.	The area A of a triangle varies jointly with b and h according to the equation $A = \frac{1}{2}bh$, where b is its base and h is its height. The constant of variation is $k = \frac{1}{2}$.

4.6   Exercises

MyMathLab | Math XL PRACTICE | WATCH | DOWNLOAD | READ | REVIEW

CONCEPTS AND VOCABULARY

1. What is a proportion?

2. If 5 is to 6 as x is to 7, write a proportion that allows you to find x.

3. Suppose that y is directly proportional to x. If x doubles, what happens to y?

4. Suppose that y is inversely proportional to x. If x doubles, what happens to y?

5. If y varies inversely with x, then xy equals a(n) _____.

6. If y varies directly with x, then $\frac{y}{x}$ equals a(n) _____.

7. If z varies jointly with x and y, then $z = $ _____.

8. If z varies jointly with the square of x and the cube of y, then $z = $ _____.

9. Would a food bill B generally vary directly or vary inversely with the number of people N being fed? Explain your reasoning.

10. Would the time T needed to paint a building vary directly or inversely with the number of painters N working on the job? Explain your reasoning.

PROPORTIONS

Exercises 11–22: Solve the proportion.

11. $\dfrac{x}{14} = \dfrac{5}{7}$

12. $\dfrac{x}{5} = \dfrac{4}{9}$

13. $\dfrac{8}{x} = \dfrac{2}{3}$

14. $\dfrac{5}{11} = \dfrac{9}{x}$

15. $\dfrac{6}{13} = \dfrac{h}{156}$

16. $\dfrac{25}{a} = \dfrac{15}{8}$

17. $\dfrac{7}{4z} = \dfrac{5}{3}$

18. $\dfrac{3}{2} = \dfrac{2x}{9}$

19. $\dfrac{2}{3x + 1} = \dfrac{5}{x}$

20. $\dfrac{7}{x - 1} = -\dfrac{5}{3x}$

21. $\dfrac{4}{x} = \dfrac{x}{9}$

22. $\dfrac{2x}{5} = \dfrac{40}{x}$

Exercises 23–30: Complete the following.
   (a) Write a proportion that models the situation.
   (b) Solve the proportion for x.

23. 7 is to 9 as 10 is to x

24. x is to 11 as 9 is to 2

25. A triangle has sides of 3, 4, and 6. In a similar triangle the shortest side is 5 and the longest side is x.

26. A rectangle has sides of 9 and 14. In a similar rectangle the longer side is 8 and the shorter side is x.

27. If you earn $78 in 6 hours, then you earn x dollars in 8 hours.

28. If 12 gallons of gas contain 1.2 gallons of ethanol, 18 gallons of gas contain x gallons of ethanol.

29. If 2 compact discs can record 120 minutes of music, 5 compact discs can record x minutes.

30. If a gas pump fills a 30-gallon tank in 8 minutes, it can fill a 17-gallon tank in x minutes.

VARIATION

Exercises 31–36: Let y be directly proportional to x.
   (a) Find the constant of proportionality k.
   (b) Use $y = kx$ to find y when $x = 7$.

31. $y = 6$ when $x = 3$ **32.** $y = 7$ when $x = 14$

33. $y = 5$ when $x = 2$ **34.** $y = 11$ when $x = 22$

35. $y = -120$ when $x = 16$

36. $y = -34$ when $x = 17$

Exercises 37–42: Let y be inversely proportional to x.
   (a) Find the constant of proportionality k.
   (b) Use $y = \frac{k}{x}$ to find y when $x = 10$.

37. $y = 5$ when $x = 4$ **38.** $y = 2$ when $x = 30$

39. $y = 100$ when $x = \frac{1}{2}$ **40.** $y = \frac{1}{4}$ when $x = 40$

41. $y = 20$ when $x = 20$ **42.** $y = \frac{45}{4}$ when $x = 8$

Exercises 43–48: Let z vary jointly with x and y.
   (a) Find the constant of variation k.
   (b) Use $z = kxy$ to find z when $x = 5$ and $y = 7$.

43. $z = 6$ when $x = 3$ and $y = 8$

44. $z = 135$ when $x = 2.5$ and $y = 9$

45. $z = 5775$ when $x = 25$ and $y = 21$

46. $z = 1530$ when $x = 22.5$ and $y = 4$

47. $z = 25$ when $x = \frac{1}{2}$ and $y = 5$

48. $z = 12$ when $x = \frac{1}{4}$ and $y = 12$

Exercises 49–56: (Refer to Example 7.)
   (a) Determine whether the data represent direct variation, inverse variation, or neither.
   (b) If the data represent either direct or inverse variation, find an equation that models the data.
   (c) Graph the equation and the data.

49.

x	2	3	4	5
y	3	4.5	6	7.5

50.

x	3	6	9	12
y	12	6	4	3

51.

x	10	20	30	40
y	12	6	5	4

52.

x	4	6	12	20
y	10	20	30	40

53.

x	2	6	10	14
y	105	35	21	15

54.

x	1	5	9	15
y	6	30	54	90

55. Thinking Generally (Do not graph.)

x	−2	−1	1	2
y	$4b$	$2b$	$-2b$	$-4b$

56. Thinking Generally (Do not graph.)

x	$-2a$	$-a$	a	$2a$
y	$-b$	$-2b$	$2b$	b

Exercises 57–62: Use the graph to determine whether the data represent direct variation, inverse variation, or neither. Find the constant of variation whenever possible.

57.

58.

59.

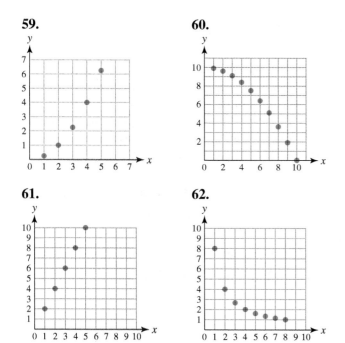

60.

61.

62.

63. Online Exploration Go online and find a study that gives its sample size. Use proportions to generalize the study to the larger U.S. population. You may need to also look up the population of the United States.

64. Online Exploration Go online and find the dimensions of a famous building or structure. Use proportions to draw a view of the structure to scale. Record both the actual dimensions and your scale dimensions.

APPLICATIONS

65. *Height of a Tree* (Refer to Example 2.) A 6-foot-tall person casts a 7-foot shadow, and a nearby tree casts a 27-foot shadow. Estimate the height of the tree.

66. *Recording Music* A 600-megabyte CD can record 68 minutes of music. How many minutes can be recorded on 360 megabytes?

67. *Water Content in Snow* (Refer to Example 1.) Eight inches of heavy, wet snow is equivalent to an inch of rain. Estimate the water content in 11 inches of heavy, wet snow.

68. *Wages* If a person earns \$143 in 11 hours, how much will that person earn in 17 hours?

69. *Buying 4G Phones* In a 2011 Nielsen poll with a sample size of 2131 respondents, 618 were planning to buy a 4G phone in 2011. Of the 231 million adults in the United States, about how many were planning to buy a 4G phone in 2011?

70. *What Does 4G Mean?* In a 2011 Nielsen poll with a sample size of 2131 respondents, only 482 knew that 4G meant superfast wireless. Of the 231 million adults in the United States, about how many knew what 4G meant?

71. *Largemouth Bass Population* (Refer to Example 3.) Three hundred largemouth bass are tagged and released into a lake. Later, a sample of 112 largemouth bass contains 17 tagged bass. Estimate the largemouth bass population to the nearest hundred.

72. *Eagle Population* Twenty-two bald eagles are tagged and released into the wilderness. Later, an observed sample of 56 bald eagles contains 7 eagles that are tagged. Estimate the bald eagle population in this wilderness area.

73. *Braking Distance* The distance d required for a car to stop after the brakes have been applied is directly proportional to the square of the car's speed x. If a car moving at 60 miles per hour requires 300 feet to stop on dry, level pavement, how many feet would be required to stop the car at 30 miles per hour?

74. *Points in Basketball* If a player scores 132 points in 11 games, use proportions to estimate the number of points the player might score in a 20-game season.

75. *Rolling Resistance of Cars* If you were to try to push a car, you would experience *rolling resistance*. This resistance equals the force necessary to keep the car moving slowly in neutral gear. The following table shows the rolling resistance R for passenger cars of different gross weights W. (*Source:* N. Garber and L. Hoel, *Traffic and Highway Engineering.*)

W (pounds)	2000	2500	3000	3500
R (pounds)	24	30	36	42

(a) Find an equation that models the data. Graph the equation with the data.

(b) Find the rolling resistance of a 3200-pound car.

76. *Transportation Costs* The use of a toll bridge varies inversely according to the toll. When the toll is $0.75, 6000 vehicles use the bridge. Estimate the number of users if the toll is $0.40. (*Source:* N. Garber.)

77. *Hooke's Law* The table shows the distance D that a spring stretches when a weight W is hung on it.

W (pounds)	2	6	9	15
D (inches)	1.5	4.5	4.75	11.25

(a) Do the data represent direct or inverse variation? Explain.

(b) Find an equation that models the data.

(c) How far will the spring stretch if an 11-pound weight is hung on it, as depicted in the figure?

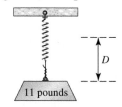

11 pounds

78. *Flow of Water* The gallons of water G flowing in 1 minute through a hose with a cross-sectional area A are shown in the table.

A (square inch)	0.2	0.3	0.4	0.5
G (gallons)	5.4	8.1	10.8	13.5

(a) Do the data represent direct or inverse variation? Explain.

(b) Find an equation that models the data. Graph the equation with the data.

(c) Interpret the constant of variation k.

79. *Tightening Lug Nuts* (Refer to Example 6.) When a tire is mounted on a car, the lug nuts should not be over-tightened. The following table shows the maximum force used with wrenches of different lengths.

L (inches)	8	10	16
F (pounds)	150	120	75

Source: Tires Plus.

(a) Model the data, using the equation $F = \frac{k}{L}$.

(b) How much force should be used with a wrench 20 inches long?

80. *Loosening a Nut on a Bolt* (Refer to Example 6.) It takes a force F of 20 pounds to loosen a nut on a bolt with a wrench having a handle length L of 12 inches. Find the force necessary to loosen the nut if a 10-inch wrench is used.

81. *Cost of Tuition* (Refer to Example 4.) The cost of tuition is directly proportional to the number of credits taken. If 6 credits cost $435, find the cost of 11 credits. What does the constant of proportionality represent?

82. *Diving and Pressure* (Refer to Example 5.) At a depth of 45 feet a diver experiences water pressure equal to 20 pounds per square inch. Find the pressure at 72 feet.

83. *Whales and Diving* (Refer to Example 5.) At a depth of 1800 feet a sperm whale experiences water pressure equal to 800 pounds per square inch. Find the pressure at 2700 feet.

84. *Stretching a Spring* A 10-pound weight causes a spring to stretch 2 inches. Use direct variation to predict how much an 18-pound weight will stretch the same spring.

85. *Air Temperature and Altitude* In the first 6 miles of Earth's atmosphere, air cools as the altitude increases. The following graph shows the temperature change y in degrees Fahrenheit at an altitude of x miles. (*Source:* A. Miller and R. Anthes, *Meteorology.*)

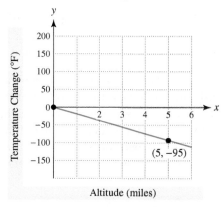

(a) Does this graph represent direct variation or inverse variation?

(b) Find an equation for the line in the graph.

(c) Is the constant of proportionality k positive or negative? Interpret k.

(d) Estimate the temperature change 3.5 miles high.

86. *Ozone and UV Radiation* Depletion of the ozone layer has caused an increase in the amount of UV radiation reaching Earth's surface. An increase in UV radiation is associated with skin cancer. The graph on the next page shows the percentage increase y in UV radiation for a decrease in the ozone layer of x percent. (*Source:* R. Turner, D. Pearce, and I. Bateman, *Environmental Economics.*)

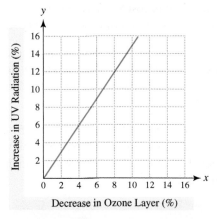

Decrease in Ozone Layer (%)

(a) Does this graph represent direct variation or inverse variation?

(b) Find an equation for the line in the graph.

(c) Estimate the percentage increase in UV radiation if the ozone layer decreases by 7%.

87. *Electrical Resistance* The electrical resistance of a wire is directly proportional to its length. If a 35-foot-long wire has a resistance of 2 ohms, find the resistance of a 25-foot-long wire.

88. *Resistance and Current* The current that flows through an electrical circuit is inversely proportional to the resistance. When the resistance R is 150 ohms, the current I is 0.8 amp. Find the current when the resistance is 40 ohms.

89. *Joint Variation* The variable z varies jointly with the second power of x and the third power of y. Write a formula for z if $z = 31.9$ when $x = 2$ and $y = 2.5$.

90. *Wind Power* The electrical power generated by a windmill varies jointly with the square of the diameter of the area swept out by the blades and the cube of the wind velocity. If a windmill with a 10-foot diameter in a 16-mile-per-hour wind generates 15,392 watts, how much power would be generated if the blades swept out an area 12 feet in diameter and the wind speed was 15 miles per hour?

91. *Strength of a Beam* (Refer to Example 8.) If a wood beam 5 inches wide and 3 inches thick supports 300 pounds, how much can a similar beam 5 inches wide and 2 inches thick support?

92. *Carpeting* The cost of carpet for a rectangular room varies jointly with its width and length. If a room 11 feet wide and 14 feet long costs $539 to carpet, find the cost to carpet a room 17 feet by 19 feet. Interpret the constant of variation k.

93. *Weight on the Moon* The weight of a person on the moon is directly proportional to the weight of the person on Earth. If a 175-pound person weighs 28 pounds on the moon, how much will a 220-pound person weigh on the moon?

94. *Weight Near Earth* The weight W of a person near Earth is inversely proportional to the square of the person's distance d from the *center* of Earth. If a person weighs 200 pounds when $d = 4000$ miles, how much does the same person weigh when $d = 7000$ miles? (*Note:* The radius of Earth is about 4000 miles.)

95. *Ohm's Law* The voltage V in an electrical circuit varies jointly with the amperage I and resistance R. If $V = 220$ when $I = 10$ and $R = 22$, find V when $I = 15$ and $R = 50$.

96. *Revenue* The revenue R from selling x items at price p varies jointly with x and p. If $R = \$24,000$ when $x = 3000$ and $p = \$8$, find the number of items x sold when $R = \$30,000$ and $p = \$6$.

WRITING ABOUT MATHEMATICS

97. Explain in words what it means for a quantity y to be directly proportional to a quantity x.

98. Explain in words what it means for a quantity y to be inversely proportional to a quantity x.

SECTIONS 4.5 AND 4.6   **Checking Basic Concepts**

1. Simplify each complex fraction.

(a) $\dfrac{3 - \dfrac{1}{x^2}}{3 + \dfrac{1}{x^2}}$ (b) $\dfrac{\dfrac{2}{x-1} - \dfrac{2}{x+1}}{\dfrac{4}{x^2-1}}$

2. Suppose that y is directly proportional to x and that $y = 6$ when $x = 8$.

(a) Find the constant of proportionality k.

(b) Use $y = kx$ to find y when $x = 11$.

3. Determine whether the data represent direct variation or inverse variation. Find an equation that models the data.

(a)

x	10	15	25	40
y	4	6	10	16

(b)

x	5	10	15	20
y	24	12	8	6

Division by a Monomial • **Division by a Polynomial** • **Synthetic Division**

A LOOK INTO MATH ▶

Girolamo Cardano (1501–1576)

NEW VOCABULARY

☐ Divisor
☐ Quotient
☐ Remainder
☐ Synthetic division

The study of polynomials has occupied the minds of mathematicians for centuries. During the sixteenth century, Italian mathematicians, such as Cardano, discovered how to solve higher degree polynomial equations. In this section we demonstrate symbolic methods for dividing polynomials. Division is often needed to factor higher degree polynomials and to solve polynomial equations. (*Source:* H. Eves, *An Introduction to the History of Mathematics.*)

Division by a Monomial

To divide a polynomial by a monomial we use the two properties

$$\frac{a + b}{c} = \frac{a}{c} + \frac{b}{c} \quad \text{and} \quad \frac{a - b}{c} = \frac{a}{c} - \frac{b}{c}.$$

For example,

$$\frac{3x^2 + x}{x} = \frac{3x^2}{x} + \frac{x}{x} = 3x + 1. \qquad \text{Divide each term by } x.$$

Factoring and the basic principle of fractions can also be applied to simplify fractions, as follows.

$$\frac{3x^2 + x}{x} = \frac{x(3x + 1)}{x} = 3x + 1$$

When dividing natural numbers, we can check our work by using multiplication. Because

$$\frac{6}{2} = 3,$$

it follows that $2 \cdot 3 = 6$. Similarly, to check whether

$$\frac{3x^2 + x}{x} = 3x + 1,$$

we multiply x and $3x + 1$.

$$\overparen{x(3x + 1)} = x \cdot 3x + x \cdot 1 \qquad \text{Distributive property}$$
$$= 3x^2 + x \; ✓ \qquad \text{It checks.}$$

Graphical support for this division problem is shown in Figures 4.27(a) and 4.27(b), where the graphs of $y_1 = \frac{3x^2 + x}{x}$ and $y_2 = 3x + 1$ appear to be identical. In Figure 4.27(c) numerical support is given, where $y_1 = y_2$ for all x-values except 0. Note that we assumed that $x \neq 0$ in $\frac{3x^2 + x}{x}$ because 0 would result in this expression being undefined.

Graphical and Numerical Support for $\dfrac{3x^2 + x}{x} = 3x + 1$

$[-4.7, 4.7, 1]$ by $[-3.1, 3.1, 1]$

(a)

$[-4.7, 4.7, 1]$ by $[-3.1, 3.1, 1]$

(b)

(c)

Figure 4.27

EXAMPLE 1   **Dividing by a monomial**

Divide and check.

(a) $\dfrac{5x^3 - 15x^2}{15x}$ (b) $\dfrac{4x^2 + 8x - 12}{4x^2}$ (c) $\dfrac{5x^2y + 10xy^2}{5xy}$

Solution

(a) $\dfrac{5x^3 - 15x^2}{15x} = \dfrac{5x^3}{15x} - \dfrac{15x^2}{15x} = \dfrac{x^2}{3} - x$

Check: $15x\left(\dfrac{x^2}{3} - x\right) = \dfrac{15x \cdot x^2}{3} - 15x \cdot x$

$= 5x^3 - 15x^2 \checkmark$

(b) $\dfrac{4x^2 + 8x - 12}{4x^2} = \dfrac{4x^2}{4x^2} + \dfrac{8x}{4x^2} - \dfrac{12}{4x^2} = 1 + \dfrac{2}{x} - \dfrac{3}{x^2}$

Check: $4x^2\left(1 + \dfrac{2}{x} - \dfrac{3}{x^2}\right) = 4x^2 \cdot 1 + \dfrac{4x^2 \cdot 2}{x} - \dfrac{4x^2 \cdot 3}{x^2}$

$= 4x^2 + 8x - 12 \checkmark$

(c) $\dfrac{5x^2y + 10xy^2}{5xy} = \dfrac{5x^2y}{5xy} + \dfrac{10xy^2}{5xy} = x + 2y$

Check: $5xy(x + 2y) = 5xy \cdot x + 5xy \cdot 2y$

$= 5x^2y + 10xy^2 \checkmark$

▌ Now Try Exercises 9, 11, 19

MAKING CONNECTIONS

Division and "Canceling" Incorrectly

When dividing expressions, students commonly "cancel" incorrectly. For example,

$$\dfrac{x - 3x^3}{x} \neq 1 - 3x^3 \quad \text{and} \quad \dfrac{x - 3x^3}{x} \neq -3x^2.$$

Rather, $\dfrac{x - 3x^3}{x} = \dfrac{x}{x} - \dfrac{3x^3}{x} = 1 - 3x^2.$

Divide the monomial into *every* term in the numerator.

Division by a Polynomial

First, we briefly review division of natural numbers.

Quotient $\longrightarrow$ 58 R 1 $\longleftarrow$ Remainder
Divisor $\longrightarrow$ 3)175 $\longleftarrow$ Dividend
$\underline{15}$
25
$\underline{24}$
1

READING CHECK

How do you check a division problem?

Because $3 \cdot 58 + 1 = 175$, the answer checks. The quotient and remainder also can be expressed as $58\frac{1}{3}$. Division of polynomials is similar to long division of natural numbers.

EXAMPLE 2 | **Dividing polynomials**

Divide $4x^2 - 2x + 1$ by $2x + 1$ and check.

Solution

Begin by dividing $2x$ into $4x^2$.

$$
\begin{array}{r}
2x \\
2x + 1{\overline{\smash{\big)}\,4x^2 - 2x + 1}} \\
\underline{4x^2 + 2x} \\
-4x + 1
\end{array}
$$

$\dfrac{4x^2}{2x} = 2x$

$2x(2x + 1) = 4x^2 + 2x$

Subtract $-2x - 2x = -4x$.
Bring down the 1.

Next, divide $2x$ into $-4x$.

$$
\begin{array}{r}
2x - 2 \\
2x + 1{\overline{\smash{\big)}\,4x^2 - 2x + 1}} \\
\underline{4x^2 + 2x} \\
-4x + 1 \\
\underline{-4x - 2} \\
3
\end{array}
$$

$\dfrac{-4x}{2x} = -2$

$-2(2x + 1) = -4x - 2$

Subtract $1 - (-2) = 3$.
Remainder is 3.

The quotient is $2x - 2$ with remainder 3, which can also be written as

$$
2x - 2 + \frac{3}{2x + 1}, \qquad \text{Quotient} + \frac{\text{Remainder}}{\text{Divisor}}
$$

in the same manner as 58 R 1 was expressed earlier as $58\frac{1}{3}$. Polynomial division is checked by multiplying the divisor and the quotient and adding the remainder.

$$
(2x + 1)(2x - 2) + 3 = 4x^2 - 4x + 2x - 2 + 3
$$

$$
 = 4x^2 - 2x + 1 \longleftarrow \text{Dividend } \checkmark
$$

Divisor   Quotient   Remainder

Now Try Exercise 25

EXAMPLE 3 | **Dividing polynomials**

Divide $2x^3 - 5x^2 + 4x - 1$ by $x - 1$.

Solution

Begin by dividing x into $2x^3$.

$$
\begin{array}{r}
2x^2 \\
x - 1{\overline{\smash{\big)}\,2x^3 - 5x^2 + 4x - 1}} \\
\underline{2x^3 - 2x^2} \\
-3x^2 + 4x
\end{array}
$$

$\dfrac{2x^3}{x} = 2x^2$

$2x^2(x - 1) = 2x^3 - 2x^2$

Subtract $-5x^2 - (-2x^2) = -3x^2$.
Bring down $4x$.

Next, divide x into $-3x^2$.

$$
\begin{array}{r}
2x^2 - 3x \\
x - 1{\overline{\smash{\big)}\,2x^3 - 5x^2 + 4x - 1}} \\
\underline{2x^3 - 2x^2} \\
-3x^2 + 4x \\
\underline{-3x^2 + 3x} \\
x - 1
\end{array}
$$

$\dfrac{-3x^2}{x} = -3x$

$-3x(x - 1) = -3x^2 + 3x$

Subtract $4x - 3x = x$.
Bring down -1.

Finally, divide x into x.

$$
\begin{array}{r}
2x^2 - 3x + 1 \\
x - 1{\overline{\smash{\big)}\,2x^3 - 5x^2 + 4x - 1}} \\
\underline{2x^3 - 2x^2} \\
-3x^2 + 4x \\
\underline{-3x^2 + 3x} \\
x - 1 \\
\underline{x - 1} \\
0
\end{array}
$$

$\dfrac{x}{x} = 1$

$1(x - 1) = x - 1$

Subtract. Remainder is 0.

The quotient is $2x^2 - 3x + 1$, and the remainder is 0.

▌ **Now Try Exercise 29**

EXAMPLE 4 **Dividing by a quadratic divisor**

Divide $3x^3 - 2x^2 - 4x + 4$ by $x^2 - 1$.

Solution
Begin by writing $x^2 - 1$ as $x^2 + 0x - 1$.

$$
\begin{array}{r}
3x - 2 \\
x^2 + 0x - 1{\overline{\smash{\big)}\,3x^3 - 2x^2 - 4x + 4}} \\
\underline{3x^3 + 0x^2 - 3x} \\
-2x^2 - x + 4 \\
\underline{-2x^2 - 0x + 2} \\
-x + 2
\end{array}
$$

The quotient is $3x - 2$ with remainder $-x + 2$, or $2 - x$, which can be written as

$$3x - 2 + \frac{2 - x}{x^2 - 1}.$$

▌ **Now Try Exercise 37**

EXAMPLE 5 **Dividing into a polynomial with missing terms**

Divide $2x^3 - 3$ by $x + 1$.

Solution
Begin by writing $2x^3 - 3$ as $2x^3 + 0x^2 + 0x - 3$.

$$
\begin{array}{r}
2x^2 - 2x + 2 \\
x + 1{\overline{\smash{\big)}\,2x^3 + 0x^2 + 0x - 3}} \\
\underline{2x^3 + 2x^2} \\
-2x^2 + 0x \\
\underline{-2x^2 - 2x} \\
2x - 3 \\
\underline{2x + 2} \\
-5
\end{array}
$$

The quotient is $2x^2 - 2x + 2$ with remainder -5, which can be written as

$$2x^2 - 2x + 2 - \frac{5}{x + 1}.$$

▌ **Now Try Exercise 31**

Synthetic Division

A shortcut called **synthetic division** can be used to divide $x - k$, where k is a constant, into a polynomial. For example, to divide $x - 2$ into $3x^3 - 8x^2 + 7x - 6$, we do the following (with the equivalent long division shown at the right).

Synthetic Division

$$
\begin{array}{r|rrrr}
2] & 3 & -8 & 7 & -6 \\
 & & 6 & -4 & 6 \\
\hline
 & 3 & -2 & 3 & 0
\end{array}
$$

Add to find
row 3.

Long Division of Polynomials

$$
\begin{array}{r}
3x^2 - 2x + 3 \\
x - 2 \overline{)3x^3 - 8x^2 + 7x - 6} \\
\underline{3x^3 - 6x^2} \\
-2x^2 + 7x \\
\underline{-2x^2 + 4x} \\
3x - 6 \\
\underline{3x - 6} \\
0
\end{array}
$$

Note that the blue numbers in the expression for long division correspond to the third row in synthetic division. The remainder is 0, which is the last number in the third row. The quotient is $3x^2 - 2x + 3$. Its coefficients are 3, -2, and 3 and are located in the third row. To divide $x - 2$ into $3x^3 - 8x^2 + 7x - 6$ with synthetic division use the following steps.

STEP 1: In the top row write 2 (the value of k) on the left and then write the coefficients of the dividend $3x^3 - 8x^2 + 7x - 6$.

STEP 2: **(a)** Copy the leading coefficient 3 of $3x^3 - 8x^2 + 7x - 6$ into the third row and multiply it by 2 (the value of k). Write the result 6 in the second row below -8. Add -8 and 6 in the second column to obtain the -2 in the third row.

(b) Repeat the process by multiplying -2 by 2 and place the result -4 below 7. Then add 7 and -4 to obtain 3.

(c) Multiply 3 by 2 and place the result 6 below the -6. Adding 6 and -6 gives 0.

STEP 3: The last number in the third row is 0, which is the remainder. The other numbers in the third row are the coefficients of the quotient, which is $3x^2 - 2x + 3$.

EXAMPLE 6 **Performing synthetic division**

Use synthetic division to divide $x^4 - 5x^3 + 9x^2 - 10x + 3$ by $x - 3$.

Solution
Because the divisor is $x - 3$, the value of k is 3.

$$
\begin{array}{r|rrrrr}
3] & 1 & -5 & 9 & -10 & 3 \\
 & & 3 & -6 & 9 & -3 \\
\hline
 & 1 & -2 & 3 & -1 & 0
\end{array}
$$

The quotient is $x^3 - 2x^2 + 3x - 1$ and the remainder is 0. This result is expressed by

$$
\frac{x^4 - 5x^3 + 9x^2 - 10x + 3}{x - 3} = x^3 - 2x^2 + 3x - 1 + \frac{0}{x - 3}, \quad \text{or}
$$

$$
\frac{x^4 - 5x^3 + 9x^2 - 10x + 3}{x - 3} = x^3 - 2x^2 + 3x - 1.
$$

Now Try Exercise 49

MAKING CONNECTIONS

Factors and Remainders

Multiplying the last equation in the solution to Example 6 by $x - 3$ gives

$$x^4 - 5x^3 + 9x^2 - 10x + 3 = (x - 3)(x^3 - 2x^2 + 3x - 1).$$

That is, $x - 3$ is a *factor* of $x^4 - 5x^3 + 9x^2 - 10x + 3$ because the remainder is 0.

This concept is true in general: If a polynomial $p(x)$ is divided by $x - k$ and the remainder is 0, then $x - k$ is a factor of $p(x)$. See Exercises 61 and 62.

EXAMPLE 7 | **Performing synthetic division**

Use synthetic division to divide $2x^3 - x + 5$ by $x + 1$.

Solution

Write $2x^3 - x + 5$ as $2x^3 + 0x^2 - x + 5$. The divisor $x + 1$ can be written as

$$x + 1 = x - (-1),$$

so we let $k = -1$.

$$
\begin{array}{r|rrrr}
-1 & 2 & 0 & -1 & 5 \\
   &   & -2 & 2 & -1 \\
\hline
   & 2 & -2 & 1 & 4
\end{array}
$$

The remainder is 4, and the quotient is $2x^2 - 2x + 1$. This result can also be expressed as

$$\frac{2x^3 - x + 5}{x + 1} = 2x^2 - 2x + 1 + \frac{4}{x + 1}.$$

▌ Now Try Exercise 53

CRITICAL THINKING

Suppose that $p(x)$ is a polynomial and that $(x - k)$ divides into $p(x)$ with remainder 0.

1. Evaluate $p(k)$.
2. Give one x-intercept on the graph of $p(x)$.

4.7 Putting It All Together

TYPE OF DIVISION	EXPLANATION	EXAMPLE
By a Monomial	Use the property $\frac{a \pm b}{c} = \frac{a}{c} \pm \frac{b}{c}$ to divide a polynomial by a monomial. Be sure to divide the denominator into every term of the numerator.	$\dfrac{8a^3 - 4a^2}{2a} = \dfrac{8a^3}{2a} - \dfrac{4a^2}{2a} = 4a^2 - 2a$

TYPE OF DIVISION	EXPLANATION	EXAMPLE
By a Polynomial	Division by a polynomial may be done in a manner similar to long division of natural numbers. See Examples 2–5.	When $2x^2 - 7x + 4$ is divided by $2x - 1$, the quotient is $x - 3$ and the remainder is 1. This result may be expressed as $$\frac{2x^2 - 7x + 4}{2x - 1} = x - 3 + \frac{1}{2x - 1}.$$
Synthetic	Synthetic division is a fast way to divide a polynomial by a divisor in the form $x - k$.	Divide $4x^2 + 7x - 14$ by $x + 3$. $$\begin{array}{r\|rrr} -3 & 4 & 7 & -14 \\ & & -12 & 15 \\ \hline & 4 & -5 & 1 \end{array}$$ The quotient is $4x - 5$ with remainder 1.

4.7 Exercises

CONCEPTS AND VOCABULARY

1. To divide a monomial into a polynomial, divide the monomial into every _____ in the numerator.

2. $\dfrac{a + b}{c} =$ _____.

3. Because $\frac{21}{5} = 4$ with remainder 1, it follows that $21 = $ _____ · _____ + _____.

4. Because $\frac{3x^2 - 11x + 8}{3x - 5} = x - 2$ with remainder -2, $3x^2 - 11x + 8 = ($ ___ $) \cdot ($ ___ $) + ($ ___ $)$.

5. Is it possible to use synthetic division to divide $3x^3 - 2x^2 + x - 3$ by $x^2 - 2x$? Explain.

6. Where is the remainder located when you finish with synthetic division?

DIVISION BY A MONOMIAL

Exercises 7–12: Divide and check. Give graphical or numerical support for your result.

7. $\dfrac{4x - 6}{2}$

8. $\dfrac{4x^2 - 8x + 12}{4}$

9. $\dfrac{6x^3 - 9x}{3x}$

10. $\dfrac{3x^4 + x^2}{6x^2}$

11. $(4x^2 - x + 1) \div 2x^2$

12. $(5x^3 - 4x + 2) \div 20x$

Exercises 13–22: Divide.

13. $\dfrac{9x^2 - 12x - 3}{3}$

14. $\dfrac{10x^3 - 15x^2 + 5x}{5}$

15. $\dfrac{12a^3 - 18a}{6a}$

16. $\dfrac{50x^4 + 25x^2 + 100x}{25x}$

17. $(16x^3 - 24x) \div (12x)$

18. $(2y^4 - 4y^2 + 16) \div (2y^2)$

19. $(a^2b^2 - 4ab + ab^2) \div (ab)$

20. $(10x^3y^2 + 5x^2y^3) \div (5x^2y^2)$

21. $\dfrac{6m^4n^4 + 3m^2n^2 - 12}{3m^2n^2}$

22. $\dfrac{6p^2q^4 - 9p^6q^2}{-3pq}$

DIVISION BY A POLYNOMIAL

Exercises 23–28: Divide and check.

23. $\dfrac{3x^2 - 16x + 21}{x - 3}$

24. $\dfrac{4x^2 - x - 18}{x + 2}$

25. $\dfrac{2x^3 + 3x^2 - 2x - 2}{2x + 3}$

26. $\dfrac{2x^3 - 7x^2 + 8}{x - 2}$

27. $(10x^2 - 5) \div (x - 1)$

28. $(6x^2 - 11x + 4) \div (2x - 3)$

Exercises 29–42: Divide.

29. $\dfrac{4x^3 + 8x^2 - x - 2}{x + 2}$ **30.** $\dfrac{3x^3 - 4x^2 + 3x - 2}{x - 1}$

31. $\dfrac{x^3 + 3x - 4}{x + 4}$ **32.** $\dfrac{2x^3 - x^2 + 5}{x - 2}$

33. $(3x^3 + 8x^2 - 21x + 7) \div (3x - 1)$

34. $(14x^3 + 3x^2 - 9x + 3) \div (7x - 2)$

35. $(2a^4 + 5a^3 - 2a^2 - 5a) \div (2a + 5)$

36. $(4b^4 + 10b^3 - 2b^2 - 3b + 5) \div (2b + 1)$

37. $\dfrac{3x^3 + 4x^2 - 12x - 16}{x^2 - 4}$

38. $\dfrac{2x^4 - x^3 - 5x^2 + 4x - 12}{2x^2 - x + 3}$

39. $\dfrac{x^3 + x^2 - x}{x^2 - 1}$ **40.** $\dfrac{x^3 + x^2 - 6x}{x^2 - 2x}$

41. $(2a^4 - 3a^3 + 14a^2 - 8a + 10) \div (a^2 - a + 5)$

42. $(2z^3 + 3z^2 - 9z - 12) \div (z^2 - 1)$

43. **Thinking Generally** If the divisor is $a - b$, the quotient is $a^2 + ab + b^2$, and the remainder is 1, find the dividend.

44. **Thinking Generally** If the dividend is given by $x^3 + x^2 - 3x - 2$, the quotient is $x^2 - 3$, and the remainder is 1, find the divisor.

SYNTHETIC DIVISION

Exercises 45–56: Use synthetic division to divide.

45. $\dfrac{x^2 + 3x - 1}{x - 1}$ **46.** $\dfrac{2x^2 + x - 1}{x - 3}$

47. $(3x^2 - 22x + 7) \div (x - 7)$

48. $(5x^2 + 29x - 6) \div (x + 6)$

49. $\dfrac{x^3 + 7x^2 + 14x + 8}{x + 4}$ **50.** $\dfrac{2x^3 + 3x^2 + 2x + 4}{x + 1}$

51. $\dfrac{2x^3 + x^2 - 1}{x - 2}$ **52.** $\dfrac{x^3 + x - 2}{x + 3}$

53. $(2x^4 + 3x^2 - 4) \div (x + 2)$

54. $(x^3 - 2x^2 - 2x + 4) \div (x - 4)$

55. $(b^4 - 1) \div (b - 1)$

56. $(a^2 + a) \div (a + 2.5)$

GEOMETRY

57. *Area of a Rectangle* Use the figure to find the length L of the rectangle from its width and area A. Determine the length when $x = 8$ feet.

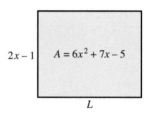

58. *Area of a Rectangle* Use the figure to find the width W of the rectangle from its length and area A. Determine the width when $x = 20$ inches.

59. *Volume of a Box* The volume of a rectangular box is $x^3 + 7x^2 + 14x + 8$. If the width of the box is $x + 1$ and its length is $x + 4$, find the height of the box.

60. *Area of a Triangle* The area A of a triangle is $12x^2 - 5x - 3$. If the height of the triangle is $3x + 1$, find the length of its base.

THEOREMS ABOUT POLYNOMIALS

61. *Remainder Theorem* Divide $p(x)$ by $x - k$ and determine the remainder. Then evaluate $p(k)$.
   (a) $p(x) = x^2 - 3x + 2$ $k = 1$
   (b) $p(x) = 3x^2 + 5x - 2$ $k = -2$
   (c) $p(x) = 3x^3 - 4x^2 - 5x + 3$ $k = 2$
   (d) $p(x) = x^3 - 2x^2 - x + 2$ $k = -1$
   (e) $p(x) = x^4 - 5x^2 - 1$ $k = 3$

62. *Remainder Theorem* Try to generalize the results from Exercise 61. It can be done, and the result is called the **remainder theorem**.

63. *Factor Theorem* Evaluate $p(k)$. Determine whether $x - k$ is a factor of $p(x)$.

(a) $p(x) = x^2 + x - 6$ $k = 2$

(b) $p(x) = x^2 + 4x - 5$ $k = 1$

(c) $p(x) = x^2 + 8x + 11$ $k = -2$

(d) $p(x) = x^3 + x^2 + x + 1$ $k = -1$

(e) $p(x) = x^3 - 3x^2 - x - 3$ $k = 2$

64. *Factor Theorem* Try to generalize the results from Exercise 63. It can be done, and the result is called the **factor theorem**.

WRITING ABOUT MATHEMATICS

65. A student dividing $2x^3 + 5x^2 - 13x + 5$ by $2x - 1$ does the following.

$$\begin{array}{r} 1\rfloor \quad 2 \quad 5 \quad -13 \quad \quad 5 \\ \underline{\quad\quad 2 \quad\quad 7 \quad -6} \\ 2 \quad 7 \quad -6 \quad -1 \end{array}$$

What would you tell the student?

66. If you add, subtract, or multiply two polynomials, is the result a polynomial? If you divide two polynomials, is the result always a polynomial? Explain.

SECTION 4.7   Checking Basic Concepts

1. Divide and simplify.

(a) $\dfrac{2x - x^2}{x^2}$ (b) $\dfrac{6a^2 - 9a + 15}{3a}$

2. Divide $\dfrac{10x^2 - x + 4}{2x + 1}$.

3. Use synthetic division to divide $2x^3 - 5x^2 - 1$ by each expression.

(a) $x - 1$ (b) $x + 2$

CHAPTER 4   Summary

SECTION 4.1 ■ INTRODUCTION TO RATIONAL FUNCTIONS AND EQUATIONS

Rational Functions A rational function is given by $f(x) = \dfrac{p(x)}{q(x)}$, where $p(x)$ and $q(x)$ are polynomials. The domain of f includes all x-values such that $q(x) \neq 0$.

Example: $f(x) = \dfrac{4}{x - 2}$ defines a rational function with domain $\{x \mid x \neq 2\}$.

Graphs of Rational Functions Graphs of rational functions are usually curves. A vertical asymptote typically occurs at an x-value where the denominator equals zero but the numerator does not. The graph of a rational function never crosses a vertical asymptote. Graphing a rational function by hand may require plotting several points on each side of a vertical asymptote.

Example: $f(x) = \dfrac{2x}{x - 2}$

A vertical asymptote occurs at $x = 2$. The graph does not cross this vertical asymptote.

Rational Equations   A rational equation contains one or more rational expressions. To solve a rational equation in the form $\frac{A}{B} = C$, start by multiplying each side of the equation by B to obtain $A = BC$. This step clears fractions from the equation.

Example: To solve $\frac{2x}{x - 3} = 8$, start by multiplying each side by $x - 3$.

$$(x - 3)\frac{2x}{x - 3} = (x - 3)8$$

$$2x = 8x - 24$$

$$x = 4 \qquad\qquad \text{Check your answer.}$$

Operations on Functions   If $f(x)$ and $g(x)$ are both defined, then the sum, difference, product, and quotient of two functions f and g are defined by

$$(f + g)(x) = f(x) + g(x) \qquad\qquad \text{Sum}$$

$$(f - g)(x) = f(x) - g(x) \qquad\qquad \text{Difference}$$

$$(fg)(x) = f(x) \cdot g(x) \qquad\qquad \text{Product}$$

$$\left(\frac{f}{g}\right)(x) = \frac{f(x)}{g(x)}, \text{ where } g(x) \neq 0. \quad \text{Quotient}$$

Example: Let $f(x) = x^2 - 1$ and $g(x) = x^2 + 1$.

$$(f + g)(x) = f(x) + g(x) = (x^2 - 1) + (x^2 + 1) = 2x^2$$

$$(f - g)(x) = f(x) - g(x) = (x^2 - 1) - (x^2 + 1) = -2$$

$$(fg)(x) = f(x) \cdot g(x) = (x^2 - 1)(x^2 + 1) = x^4 - 1$$

$$\left(\frac{f}{g}\right)(x) = \frac{f(x)}{g(x)} = \frac{x^2 - 1}{x^2 + 1}$$

SECTION 4.2 ■ MULTIPLICATION AND DIVISION OF RATIONAL EXPRESSIONS

Simplifying a Rational Expression   To simplify a rational expression, factor the numerator and the denominator. Then apply the following principle.

$$\frac{PR}{QR} = \frac{P}{Q}$$

Example: $\dfrac{x^2 - 1}{x^2 + 2x + 1} = \dfrac{(x - 1)(x + 1)}{(x + 1)(x + 1)} = \dfrac{x - 1}{x + 1}$

Multiplying Rational Expressions   To multiply two rational expressions, multiply numerators and multiply denominators. Simplify the result, if possible.

$$\frac{A}{B} \cdot \frac{C}{D} = \frac{AC}{BD} \qquad B \text{ and } D \text{ not zero}$$

Example: $\dfrac{3}{x - 1} \cdot \dfrac{x - 1}{x + 1} = \dfrac{3(x - 1)}{(x - 1)(x + 1)} = \dfrac{3}{x + 1}$

Dividing Rational Expressions   To divide two rational expressions, multiply by the reciprocal of the divisor. Simplify the result, if possible.

$$\frac{A}{B} \div \frac{C}{D} = \frac{A}{B} \cdot \frac{D}{C} = \frac{AD}{BC} \qquad B, C, \text{ and } D \text{ not zero}$$

Example: $\dfrac{x + 1}{x^2 - 4} \div \dfrac{x + 1}{x - 2} = \dfrac{x + 1}{(x - 2)(x + 2)} \cdot \dfrac{x - 2}{x + 1}$

$$= \frac{(x + 1)(x - 2)}{(x - 2)(x + 2)(x + 1)} = \frac{1}{x + 2}$$

Addition and Subtraction of Rational Expressions with Like Denominators To add (subtract) two rational expressions with like denominators, add (subtract) their numerators. The denominator does not change.

$$\frac{A}{C} + \frac{B}{C} = \frac{A + B}{C} \quad \text{and} \quad \frac{A}{C} - \frac{B}{C} = \frac{A - B}{C}$$

Examples: $\dfrac{2x}{2x + 1} + \dfrac{3x}{2x + 1} = \dfrac{5x}{2x + 1}$ and

$$\frac{x}{x^2 - 1} - \frac{1}{x^2 - 1} = \frac{x - 1}{x^2 - 1} = \frac{x - 1}{(x - 1)(x + 1)} = \frac{1}{x + 1}$$

Finding the Least Common Denominator The least common denominator (LCD) is the least common multiple (LCM) of the denominators.

Example: The LCD for $\frac{1}{x(x + 1)}$ and $\frac{1}{x^2}$ is $x^2(x + 1)$.

Addition and Subtraction of Rational Expressions with Unlike Denominators First write each rational expression with the LCD. Then add or subtract the numerators.

Examples: $\dfrac{2}{x + 1} - \dfrac{1}{x} = \dfrac{2x}{x(x + 1)} - \dfrac{x + 1}{x(x + 1)} = \dfrac{2x - (x + 1)}{x(x + 1)} = \dfrac{x - 1}{x(x + 1)}$

$$\frac{1}{x + 1} + \frac{2}{x - 1} = \frac{1(x - 1)}{(x + 1)(x - 1)} + \frac{2(x + 1)}{(x - 1)(x + 1)} = \frac{3x + 1}{(x - 1)(x + 1)}$$

Solving Rational Equations A first step in solving a rational equation is to multiply each side by the LCD of the rational expressions to clear fractions from the equation. *Be sure to check all answers.*

Example: The LCD for the equation $\frac{2}{x} + 1 = \frac{4 - x}{x}$ is x.

$$\frac{2}{x} + 1 = \frac{4 - x}{x} \qquad \text{Given equation}$$

$$x\left(\frac{2}{x} + 1\right) = \left(\frac{4 - x}{x}\right)x \qquad \text{Multiply by } x.$$

$$2 + x = 4 - x \qquad \text{Clear fractions.}$$

$$2x = 2 \qquad \text{Add } x \text{ and subtract 2.}$$

$$x = 1 \qquad \text{Divide by 2. Check your answer.}$$

Complex Fractions A complex fraction is a rational expression that contains fractions in its numerator, denominator, or both. The following equation can be used to help simplify basic complex fractions.

$$\frac{\dfrac{a}{b}}{\dfrac{c}{d}} = \frac{a}{b} \cdot \frac{d}{c} \qquad \text{"Invert and multiply."}$$

Example: $\dfrac{\dfrac{1 - x}{2}}{\dfrac{4}{1 + x}} = \dfrac{1 - x}{2} \cdot \dfrac{1 + x}{4} = \dfrac{(1 - x)(1 + x)}{(2)(4)} = \dfrac{1 - x^2}{8}$

Simplifying Complex Fractions

Method I: Combine terms in the numerator, combine terms in the denominator, and simplify the resulting expression.

Method II: Multiply the numerator and the denominator by the LCD and simplify the resulting expression.

Example: *Method I:* $\dfrac{2 - \dfrac{1}{b}}{2 + \dfrac{1}{b}} = \dfrac{\dfrac{2b-1}{b}}{\dfrac{2b+1}{b}} = \dfrac{2b-1}{b} \cdot \dfrac{b}{2b+1} = \dfrac{2b-1}{2b+1}$

            Method II: The LCD is b.

$$\dfrac{\left(2 - \dfrac{1}{b}\right)b}{\left(2 + \dfrac{1}{b}\right)b} = \dfrac{2b - \dfrac{b}{b}}{2b + \dfrac{b}{b}} = \dfrac{2b - 1}{2b + 1}$$

SECTION 4.6 ■ MODELING WITH PROPORTIONS AND VARIATION

Proportions   A proportion is a statement (equation) that two ratios (fractions) are equal.

Example: $\frac{5}{x} = \frac{4}{7}$ (in words, 5 *is to x as* 4 *is to* 7.)

Similar Triangles   Two triangles are similar if the measures of their corresponding angles are equal. Corresponding sides of similar triangles are proportional.

Example: A right triangle has legs with lengths 3 and 4. A similar right triangle has a shorter leg with length 6. Its longer leg can be found by solving the proportion $\frac{3}{6} = \frac{4}{x}$, or $x = 8$.

Direct Variation   A quantity y is *directly proportional* to a quantity x, or y *varies directly* with x, if there is a nonzero constant k such that $y = kx$. The number k is called the *constant of proportionality* or the *constant of variation*.

Example: If y varies directly with x, then the ratio $\frac{y}{x}$ always equals k. The following data satisfy $\frac{y}{x} = 4$, so the constant of variation is 4. Thus $y = 4x$.

Direct Variation

x	1	2	3	4
y	4	8	12	16

$\frac{4}{1} = \frac{8}{2} = \frac{12}{3} = \frac{16}{4} = 4$, so $k = 4$.

Inverse Variation   A quantity y is *inversely proportional* to a quantity x, or y *varies inversely* with x, if there is a nonzero constant k such that $y = \frac{k}{x}$. (We assume that $k > 0$.)

Example: If y varies inversely with x, then $xy = k$. The following data satisfy $xy = 12$, so the constant of variation is 12. Thus $y = \frac{12}{x}$.

Inverse Variation

x	1	2	4	6
y	12	6	3	2

$1 \cdot 12 = 2 \cdot 6 = 4 \cdot 3 = 6 \cdot 2 = 12$, so $k = 12$.

Joint Variation   The quantity z *varies jointly* with x and y if $z = kxy$, $k \neq 0$.

Example: The area A of a rectangle varies jointly with the width W and length L because $A = LW$. Note that $k = 1$ in this example.

SECTION 4.7 ▪ DIVISION OF POLYNOMIALS

Division of a Polynomial by a Monomial Divide the monomial in the denominator into *every* term of the numerator.

Example: $\dfrac{4x^4 - 8x^3 + 16x^2}{8x^2} = \dfrac{4x^4}{8x^2} - \dfrac{8x^3}{8x^2} + \dfrac{16x^2}{8x^2} = \dfrac{x^2}{2} - x + 2$

Division of a Polynomial by a Polynomial Division of polynomials is similar to long division of natural numbers.

Example: Divide $2x^3 - 3x + 3$ by $x - 1$. (Be sure to include $0x^2$.)

$$
\begin{array}{r}
2x^2 + 2x - 1 \\
x - 1 \overline{)\,2x^3 + 0x^2 - 3x + 3} \\
\underline{2x^3 - 2x^2} \\
2x^2 - 3x \\
\underline{2x^2 - 2x} \\
-x + 3 \\
\underline{-x + 1} \\
2
\end{array}
$$

The quotient is $2x^2 + 2x - 1$ with remainder 2, which can be written as

$$2x^2 + 2x - 1 + \dfrac{2}{x - 1}.$$

Synthetic Division Synthetic division is a fast way to divide a polynomial by an expression in the form $x - k$, where k is a constant.

Example: Divide $3x^3 + 4x^2 - 7x - 1$ by $x + 2$.

$$
\begin{array}{r|rrrr}
-2 & 3 & 4 & -7 & -1 \\
   &   & -6 & 4 & 6 \\
\hline
   & 3 & -2 & -3 & 5
\end{array}
$$

The quotient is $3x^2 - 2x - 3$ with remainder 5.

CHAPTER 4   Review Exercises

SECTION 4.1

Exercises 1 and 2: Write a symbolic representation (or formula) for the rational function f described.

1. Divide 1 by the quantity x minus 1.

2. Subtract 3 from x and then divide the result by x.

3. Sketch a graph of $f(x) = \frac{1}{2x + 4}$. Show any vertical asymptotes as dashed lines. State the domain of f in set-builder notation.

4. Evaluate $f(x) = \frac{1}{x^2 - 1}$ at $x = 3$. Find any x-values that are not in the domain of f.

Exercises 5 and 6: If possible, evaluate f(x) for each x.

5. $f(x) = \dfrac{3}{x + 2}$ \qquad $x = -3, x = 2$

6. $f(x) = \dfrac{2x}{x^2 - 4}$ \qquad $x = -2, x = 3$

Exercises 7 and 8: Use the graph of f to evaluate the expressions. Give the equation of any vertical asymptotes.

7. $f(0)$ and $f(2)$ **8.** $f(-3)$ and $f(-2)$

Exercises 9–12: Solve. Check your answer.

9. $\dfrac{3-x}{x} = 2$ **10.** $\dfrac{1}{x+3} = \dfrac{1}{5}$

11. $\dfrac{x}{x-2} = \dfrac{2x-2}{x-2}$ **12.** $\dfrac{4}{2-3x} = -1$

13. Use $f(x) = 2x^2 - 3x$ and $g(x) = 2x - 3$ to find each of the following.
     (a) $(f+g)(3)$ **(b)** $(fg)(3)$

14. Use $f(x) = x^2 - 1$ and $g(x) = x - 1$ to find each of the following.
     (a) $(f-g)(x)$ **(b)** $(f/g)(x)$

SECTION 4.2

Exercises 15–20: Simplify the expression.

15. $\dfrac{4a}{6a^4}$ **16.** $\dfrac{(x-3)(x+2)}{(x+1)(x-3)}$

17. $\dfrac{x^2-4}{x-2}$ **18.** $\dfrac{x^2-6x-7}{2x^2-x-3}$

19. $\dfrac{8-x}{x-8}$ **20.** $-\dfrac{3-2x}{2x-3}$

Exercises 21–30: Simplify the expression.

21. $\dfrac{1}{2y} \cdot \dfrac{4y^2}{8}$ **22.** $\dfrac{x+2}{x-5} \cdot \dfrac{x-5}{x+1}$

23. $\dfrac{x^2+1}{x^2-1} \cdot \dfrac{x-1}{x+1}$ **24.** $\dfrac{x^2+2x+1}{x^2-9} \cdot \dfrac{x+3}{x+1}$

25. $\dfrac{1}{3y} \div \dfrac{1}{9y^4}$ **26.** $\dfrac{2x+2}{3x-3} \div \dfrac{x+1}{x-1}$

27. $\dfrac{x^2+2x}{x^2-25} \div \dfrac{x+2}{x+5}$

28. $\dfrac{x^2+2x-15}{x^2+4x+3} \div \dfrac{x-3}{x+1}$

29. $\dfrac{x^2+x-2}{2x^2-7x+3} \cdot \dfrac{x^2-3x}{x^2+2x-3}$

30. $\dfrac{x^2+3x+2}{x^2+7x+12} \div \dfrac{x^2+4x+4}{x^2+4x+3}$

SECTION 4.3

Exercises 31–36: Find the least common multiple.

31. $36, 24, 16$ **32.** $4ab, a^2b$

33. $9x^2y, 6xy^3$ **34.** $(x-1), (x+2)$

35. $x^2-9, x(x+3)$

36. $x^2, x-3, x^2-6x+9$

Exercises 37–50: Simplify.

37. $\dfrac{1}{x+4} + \dfrac{3}{x+4}$ **38.** $\dfrac{2}{x} + \dfrac{x-3}{x}$

39. $\dfrac{1}{x+1} - \dfrac{x}{x+1}$ **40.** $\dfrac{2x}{x-2} - \dfrac{2}{x-2}$

41. $\dfrac{4}{1-t} + \dfrac{t}{t-1}$

42. $\dfrac{2}{y-2} - \dfrac{2}{y+2}$

43. $\dfrac{4b}{a^2c} - \dfrac{3a}{b^2c}$ **44.** $\dfrac{r}{5t^2} + \dfrac{t}{5r^2}$

45. $\dfrac{4}{a^2-b^2} - \dfrac{2}{a+b}$ **46.** $\dfrac{a}{a-b} + \dfrac{b}{a+b}$

47. $\dfrac{1}{x^2-3x+2} + \dfrac{1}{x^2+x-2}$

48. $\dfrac{1}{x^2-5x+6} - \dfrac{1}{x^2+x-6}$

49. $\dfrac{1}{x-2} + \dfrac{2}{x+2} - \dfrac{x}{x-2}$

50. $\dfrac{2x}{2x-1} - \dfrac{3}{2x+1} - \dfrac{1}{2x-1}$

SECTION 4.4

Exercises 51–60: Solve. Check your result.

51. $\dfrac{4}{x} - \dfrac{5}{2x} = \dfrac{1}{2}$ **52.** $\dfrac{1}{x-4} = \dfrac{3}{2x-1}$

53. $\dfrac{2}{x^2} - \dfrac{1}{x} = 1$

54. $\dfrac{1}{x+4} - \dfrac{1}{x} = 1$

55. $\dfrac{1}{x^2-1} - \dfrac{1}{x-1} = \dfrac{2}{3}$

56. $\dfrac{1}{x-3} + \dfrac{1}{x+3} = \dfrac{-5}{x^2-9}$

57. $\dfrac{1}{(x-2)^2} - \dfrac{1}{x^2-4} = \dfrac{2}{(x-2)^2}$

58. $\dfrac{1}{x^2+3x+2} + \dfrac{x}{x+2} = \dfrac{1}{2}$

59. $\dfrac{-3x-3}{x-3} + \dfrac{x^2+x}{x-3} = 7x+7$

60. $\dfrac{1}{x-4} + \dfrac{x}{x+4} = \dfrac{8}{x^2-16}$

Exercises 61 and 62: Use the graph to solve the rational equation. Then check your answer.

61. $\dfrac{1}{x} = \dfrac{2}{x+2}$

62. $\dfrac{3}{x-1} = \dfrac{1}{2}x$

   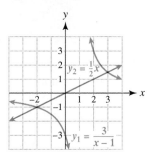

Exercises 63–66: Solve for the specified variable.

63. $m = \dfrac{y_2-y_1}{x_2-x_1}$ for y_2

64. $T = \dfrac{a}{b+2}$ for a

65. $\dfrac{1}{f} = \dfrac{1}{p} + \dfrac{1}{q}$ for p

66. $I = \dfrac{2a+3b}{ab}$ for b

SECTION 4.5

Exercises 67–74: Simplify the complex fraction.

67. $\dfrac{\frac{3}{5}}{\frac{10}{13}}$

68. $\dfrac{\frac{4}{ab}}{\frac{2}{bc}}$

69. $\dfrac{\frac{2n-1}{n}}{\frac{3n}{2n+1}}$

70. $\dfrac{\frac{1}{x-y}}{\frac{1}{x^2-y^2}}$

71. $\dfrac{2+\frac{3}{x}}{2-\frac{3}{x}}$

72. $\dfrac{\frac{1}{x}+\frac{1}{2}}{\frac{1}{4}-\frac{2}{x}}$

73. $\dfrac{\frac{4}{x}+\frac{1}{x-1}}{\frac{1}{x}-\frac{2}{x-1}}$

74. $\dfrac{\frac{1}{x+3}-\frac{1}{x-3}}{\frac{4}{x+3}-\frac{2}{x-3}}$

SECTION 4.6

Exercises 75–78: Solve the proportion.

75. $\dfrac{x}{6} = \dfrac{6}{20}$

76. $\dfrac{11}{x} = \dfrac{5}{7}$

77. $\dfrac{x+1}{5} = \dfrac{x}{3}$

78. $\dfrac{3}{7} = \dfrac{4}{x-1}$

79. If $x+1$ is to 5 as 10 is to 15, use a proportion to find the value of x.

80. A rectangle has sides with lengths 7 and 8. Find the longer side of a similar rectangle whose shorter side has length 11.

81. Suppose that y varies directly with x. If $y = 8$ when $x = 2$, find y when $x = 7$.

82. Suppose that y varies inversely with x. If $y = 5$ when $x = 10$, find y when $x = 25$.

83. Suppose that z varies jointly with x and y. If $z = 483$ when $x = 23$ and $y = 7$, find the constant of variation k.

84. Suppose that z varies jointly with x and the square of y. If $z = 891$ when $x = 22$ and $y = 3$, find z when $x = 10$ and $y = 4$.

Exercises 85 and 86: Use the table to determine whether the data represent direct or inverse variation. Find an equation that models the data.

85.

x	2	4	5	8
y	100	50	40	25

86.

x	3	7	8	11
y	9	21	24	33

Exercises 87 and 88: Decide if the graph represents direct or inverse variation. Find the constant of variation k.

87.

88.

SECTION 4.7

Exercises 89–96: Divide.

89. $\dfrac{10x + 15}{5}$

90. $\dfrac{2x^2 + x}{x}$

91. $(4x^3 - x^2 + 2x) \div (2x^2)$

92. $(4a^3b - 6ab^2) \div (2a^2b^2)$

93. $\dfrac{2x^2 - x - 2}{x + 1}$

94. $(x^3 + x - 1) \div (x + 1)$

95. $(6x^3 - 7x^2 + 5x - 1) \div (3x - 2)$

96. $\dfrac{2x^3 - 9x^2 + 21x - 21}{x^2 - 2}$

Exercises 97 and 98: Use synthetic division to divide.

97. $\dfrac{2x^2 - 11x + 13}{x - 3}$

98. $(3x^3 + 10x^2 - 4x + 19) \div (x + 4)$

APPLICATIONS

99. *Time Spent in Line* Suppose that amusement park attendants can wait on 10 vehicles per minute and vehicles are arriving at the park randomly at an average rate of x vehicles per minute. Then the average time T in minutes spent waiting in line *and* paying the attendant is given by

$$T(x) = \frac{1}{10 - x},$$

where $x < 10$. (*Source:* N. Garber.)
  (a) Construct a table of T, starting at $x = 9$ and incrementing by 0.1.
  (b) What happens to the waiting time as the value of x approaches 10? Interpret this result.

100. *Downhill Highway Grade* The braking distance D in feet for a car traveling downhill at 40 miles per hour on a wet grade x is given by

$$D(x) = \frac{1600}{9.6 - 30x}.$$

(*Source:* N. Garber.)
  (a) In this formula a level road is represented by $x = 0$ and a 10% downhill grade is represented by $x = 0.1$. Evaluate $D(0)$ and $D(0.1)$. How much does the downhill grade add to the braking distance compared to a level road?
  (b) If the braking distance is 200 feet, estimate the downhill grade x.

101. *Number of Cars Waiting* A car wash can clean 15 cars per hour. If cars are arriving randomly at an average rate of x per hour, the average number N of cars waiting in line is given by

$$N(x) = \frac{x^2}{225 - 15x},$$

where $x < 15$. (*Source:* N. Garber.)
  (a) Estimate the average length of a line when 14 cars per hour are arriving.
  (b) A graph of $y = N(x)$ is shown in the figure. Interpret the graph as x increases. Does it agree with your intuition?

102. *Fish Population* Suppose that a fish population P in thousands in a lake after x years is modeled by

$$P(x) = \frac{5}{x^2 + 1}.$$

(a) Evaluate $P(0)$ and interpret the result.

(b) Graph P in $[0, 6, 1]$ by $[0, 6, 1]$.

(c) What happens to the population over this 6-year period?

(d) When was the population 1000?

103. *Working Together* Suppose that two students are working collaboratively to solve a large number of quadratic equations. The first student can solve all the problems in 2 hours, whereas the second student can solve them in 3 hours.

(a) Write an equation whose solution gives the time needed to solve all the problems if the two students work together and share answers.

(b) Solve the equation in part (a) symbolically.

(c) Solve the equation in part (a) either graphically or numerically.

104. *Speed of a Boat* In still water a riverboat can travel 12 miles per hour. It travels 48 miles upstream and then 48 miles downstream in a total time of 9 hours. Find the speed of the current.

105. *Recording Music* A 650-megabyte CD can record 74 minutes of music. Estimate the number of minutes that can be recorded on 387 megabytes.

106. *Height of a Building* A 5-foot-tall person casts a 3-foot-long shadow, while a nearby building casts a 26-foot-long shadow. Find the height of the building.

107. *Light Bulbs* The approximate resistances R for light bulbs of wattage W are measured and recorded in the following table. (*Source:* D. Horn, *Basic Electronics Theory*.)

W (watts)	50	100	200	250
R (ohms)	242	121	60.5	48.4

(a) Make a scatterplot of the data. Do the data represent direct or inverse variation?

(b) Find an equation that models the data. What is the constant of proportionality k?

(c) Find R for a 55-watt light bulb.

108. *Scales* The distance D that the spring in a produce scale stretches is directly proportional to the weight W of the fruits and vegetables placed in the pan.

(a) If 5 pounds of apples stretch the spring 0.3 inch, find an equation that relates D and W. What is the constant of proportionality k?

(b) How far will 7 pounds of oranges stretch the spring?

109. *Air Temperature and Altitude* In the first 30,000 feet of Earth's atmosphere the *change* in air temperature is directly proportional to the altitude. If the temperature is $80°F$ on the ground and $62°F$ 4000 feet above the ground, find the air temperature at 6000 feet. (*Source:* L. Battan, *Weather in Your Life*.)

110. *Skin Cancer and UV Radiation* Depletion of the ozone layer has caused an increase in the amount of UV radiation reaching Earth's surface. The following table shows the estimated percent increase in skin cancer y for an x percent increase in the amount of UV radiation reaching Earth's surface. (*Source:* R. Turner, D. Pearce, and I. Bateman, *Environmental Economics*.)

x (%)	0	1	2	3	4
y (%)	0	3.5	7	10.5	14

(a) Do these data represent direct variation, inverse variation, or neither?

(b) Find an equation that models the data.

(c) Estimate the percent increase in skin cancer if UV radiation increases by 2.3%.

CHAPTER 4 **Test** CHAPTER Test Prep VIDEOS Step-by-step test solutions are found on the Chapter Test Prep Videos available via the Video Resources on DVD, in *MyMathLab*, and on You Tube (search "RockswoldInterAlg" and click on "Channels").

1. Write a symbolic representation (formula) for $f(x)$ that divides x by the quantity x plus 2.

2. Let $f(x) = \frac{1}{4x^2 - 1}$.

(a) Evaluate $f(-2)$.

(b) Write the domain of f in set-builder notation.

3. Graph $y = \frac{1}{x + 2}$. Show any vertical asymptotes as dashed lines.

Exercises 4–6: Simplify the expression.

4. $\dfrac{2a^3}{4a^2}$

5. $\dfrac{1 - 2t}{2t - 1}$

6. $\dfrac{x^2 - 2x - 15}{2x^2 - x - 21}$

Exercises 7–15: Simplify.

7. $\dfrac{x^2 + 4}{x^2 - 4} \cdot \dfrac{x - 2}{x + 2}$

8. $\dfrac{1}{4y^2} \div \dfrac{1}{8y^4}$

9. $\dfrac{x}{x + 5} + \dfrac{1 - x}{x + 5}$

10. $\dfrac{2x}{x - 2} - \dfrac{1}{x + 2}$

11. $\dfrac{a^2}{3b} - \dfrac{2b^3}{5a}$

12. $\dfrac{x}{x - 2} - \dfrac{4}{x^2} - \dfrac{2}{x}$

13. $\dfrac{3 + \frac{3}{x}}{3 - \frac{3}{x}}$

14. $\dfrac{1}{z + 4} - \dfrac{z}{(z + 4)^2}$

15. $\dfrac{\frac{1}{x - 2} + \frac{x}{x - 2}}{\frac{1}{3} - \frac{5}{x - 2}}$

Exercises 16–21: Solve. Check your result.

16. $\dfrac{t}{5t + 1} = \dfrac{2}{7}$

17. $\dfrac{x}{2x - 1} = \dfrac{x + 2}{x + 4}$

18. $\dfrac{x + 4}{2 - x} - \dfrac{2x - 1}{2 - x} = 0$ **19.** $\dfrac{5}{x + 1} = 4$

20. $\dfrac{1}{x + 2} + \dfrac{1}{x - 2} = \dfrac{4}{x^2 - 4}$

21. $\dfrac{1}{x^2 - 4} - \dfrac{1}{x - 2} = \dfrac{1}{x + 2}$

22. Solve $F = \dfrac{Gm}{r^2}$ for m.

 23. Solve the equation $\dfrac{\sqrt{12}}{x^2 + 2} - \dfrac{1.7x}{x - 1.2} = \sqrt{3}$ to the nearest hundredth.

24. Let $f(x) = x - 1$ and $g(x) = x^2 - 2x + 1$. Find $(f - g)(2)$ and $(f/g)(x)$.

25. A triangle has sides with lengths 12, 15, and 20. Find the longest side of a similar triangle with a shortest side of length 7.

26. Suppose that y varies directly with x. If $y = 8$ when $x = 23$, find y when $x = 10$.

27. Use the table to determine whether the data represent direct or inverse variation. Find an equation that models the data.

x	2	4	5	10
y	50	25	20	10

28. Determine whether the data represent direct or inverse variation. Find an equation that models the data.

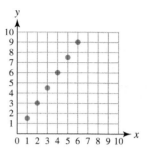

Exercises 29 and 30: Divide.

29. $\dfrac{4a^3 + 10a}{2a}$

30. $\dfrac{3x^3 + 5x^2 - 2}{x + 2}$

31. *Height of a Building* A person 73 inches tall casts a shadow 50 inches long while a nearby building casts a shadow 15 feet long. Find the height of the building.

32. *Time Spent in Line* Suppose that parking lot attendants can wait on 25 vehicles per minute and vehicles are arriving at the lot randomly at an average rate of x vehicles per minute. Then the average time T in minutes spent waiting in line *and* paying the attendant is given by

$$T(x) = \dfrac{1}{25 - x},$$

where $x < 25$. (*Source:* N. Garber.)

 (a) Graph T in $[0, 25, 5]$ by $[0, 2, 0.5]$. Identify any vertical asymptotes.

(b) If the wait is 1 minute, how many vehicles are arriving on average?

33. *Working Together* Suppose that one pump can empty a pool in 24 hours, and a second pump can empty the pool in 30 hours.

(a) Write an equation whose solution gives the time needed for the pumps working together to empty the pool.

(b) Solve the equation in part (a).

34. *Dew Point and Altitude* In the first 30,000 feet of Earth's atmosphere the change in the dew point is directly proportional to the altitude. If the dew point is 50°F on the ground and 39°F 10,000 feet above the ground, find the dew point at 7500 feet. (*Source:* L. Battan, *Weather in Your Life.*)

CHAPTER 4   Extended and Discovery Exercises

OTHER TYPES OF DIRECT VARIATION

Exercises 1–4: Sometimes a quantity y varies directly with a power of x. For example, the area A of a circle varies directly with the second power of the radius r, since $A = \pi r^2$ and π is a constant. Let x and y denote two quantities and n be a positive number. Then y is directly proportional to the nth power of x, or y varies directly with the nth power of x, if there exists a nonzero number k such that

$$y = kx^n.$$

1. Let y be directly proportional to the second power of x. If x doubles, what happens to y?

2. Let y be directly proportional to the $\frac{1}{2}$ power of x. If x quadruples, what happens to y?

3. *Allometric Growth* If x is the weight of a fiddler crab and y is the weight of its claws, then y is directly proportional to the 1.25 power of x; that is, $y = kx^{1.25}$. Suppose that a typical crab with a body weight of 2.1 grams has claws weighing 1.125 grams. (*Source:* D. Brown and P. Rothery, *Models in Biology.*)
   (a) Find the constant of proportionality k. Round your answer to the nearest thousandth.
   (b) Estimate the weight of a fiddler crab with claws weighing 0.8 gram.

4. *Volume* The volume V of a cylinder is directly proportional to the square of its radius r. If a cylinder with a radius of 5 inches has a volume of 150 cubic inches, what is the volume of a cylinder with the same height and a radius of 7 inches?

OTHER TYPES OF INVERSE VARIATION

Exercises 5–8: Sometimes a quantity varies inversely with a power of x. Let x and y denote two quantities and n be a positive number. Then y is inversely proportional to the nth power of x, or y varies inversely with the nth power of x, if there exists a nonzero number k such that

$$y = \frac{k}{x^n}.$$

5. Let y be inversely proportional to the second power of x. If x doubles, what happens to y?

6. Let y be inversely proportional to the third power of x. If x doubles, what happens to y?

7. *Earth's Gravity* The weight W of an object can be modeled by $W = \frac{k}{d^2}$, where d is the distance that the object is from Earth's center and k is a constant. Earth's radius is about 4000 miles.
   (a) Find k for a person who weighs 200 pounds on Earth's surface.
   (b) Graph W in a convenient viewing rectangle. At what distance from Earth's center is this person's weight 50 pounds?
   (c) How far from the center of Earth would an object be if its weight were 1% of its weight on the surface of Earth?

8. *Modeling Brightness* Inverse variation occurs when the intensity of a light is measured. If you increase your distance from a light bulb, the intensity of the light decreases. Intensity I is inversely proportional to the second power of the distance d. The equation $I = \frac{k}{d^2}$ models this phenomenon. The following table gives the intensity of a 100-watt light bulb at various distances. (*Source:* R. Weidner and R. Sells, *Elementary Classical Physics, Vol. 2.*)

d (meters)	0.5	2	3	4
I (watts/square meter)	31.68	1.98	0.88	0.495

   (a) Find the constant of proportionality k.
   (b) Graph I in [0, 5, 1] by [0, 30, 5]. What happens to the intensity as the distances increase?
   (c) If the distance from the light bulb doubles, what happens to the intensity?
   (d) Determine d when $I = 1$ watt per square meter.

CHAPTERS 1–4   Cumulative Review Exercises

Exercises 1 and 2: Evaluate the formula for the given value of the variable.

1. $y = \sqrt{74 + t}$ $t = 7$

2. $r = 16 - w^2$ $w = -4$

3. Classify each number as one or more of the following: natural number, whole number, integer, rational number, or irrational number.

$$-\frac{12}{4}, 0, \sqrt{3}, 1, 2.\overline{11}, \frac{13}{2}$$

4. Select the formula that best models the data.
  a. $y = 2x - 5$ **b.** $y = x - 7$ **c.** $y = 2x + 3$

x	-2	-1	0	1	2
y	-9	-7	-5	-3	-1

Exercises 5 and 6: Simplify the expression. Write the result using positive exponents.

5. $\dfrac{18x^{-2}y^3}{3x^2y^{-3}}$

6. $\left(\dfrac{2c^2}{3d^3}\right)^{-2}$

7. Write 67,300,000,000 in scientific notation.

8. Identify the domain and range of the relation given by $S = \{(-3, 5), (0, 1), (-1, -2), (4, 0)\}$.

Exercises 9 and 10: Evaluate the given formula for $x = -2, -1, 0, 1,$ and 2. Plot the resulting ordered pairs.

9. $y = 3x - 1$

10. $y = \dfrac{4 - x^2}{2}$

11. Sketch the graph of $f(x) = x^2 + 2$ by hand.

12. Find the domain of $f(x) = \dfrac{5}{x - 1}$.

13. Use the table to write the formula for $f(x) = ax + b$.

x	-2	-1	0	1	2
$f(x)$	-5	-3	-1	1	3

14. Sketch a graph of $f(x) = -2$.

15. Find the slope and the y-intercept of the graph of $f(x) = -3x + 2$.

16. Calculate the slope of the line passing through the points $(6, -3)$ and $(2, 9)$.

17. Sketch the graph of a line passing through the point $(3, -1)$ with slope $m = -2$.

18. Use the graph to express the equation of the line in slope–intercept form.

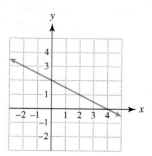

Exercises 19 and 20: Write the slope–intercept form for a line satisfying the given conditions.

19. Parallel to $y = 2x + 3$, passing through $(1, 4)$

20. Perpendicular to $y = \frac{2}{3}x - 2$, passing through $(2, 1)$

Exercises 21 and 22: Solve the equation.

21. $\dfrac{2}{5}(x + 1) - 6 = -4$

22. $\dfrac{1}{4}\left(\dfrac{t - 5}{3}\right) - 6 = \dfrac{2}{3}t - (3t + 7)$

23. Use the graph to solve the equation $y_1 = y_2$.

Exercises 24 and 25: Solve the inequality symbolically. Write the solution set in interval notation.

24. $\dfrac{2x + 3}{4} \le \dfrac{1}{3}$

25. $\dfrac{1}{2}z - 5 > \dfrac{3}{4}z - (2z + 5)$

Exercises 26 and 27: Solve the compound inequality. Graph the solution set on a number line.

26. $-6 \le -\dfrac{2}{3}x - 4 < -2$

27. $3x - 1 \le 5$ or $2x + 5 > 13$

28. Solve the absolute value equation $\left|\frac{1}{3}x + 6\right| = 4$.

Exercises 29 and 30: Solve the absolute value inequality. Write the solution set in interval notation.

29. $|2x - 3| < 11$ **30.** $-3|t - 5| \le -18$

31. Determine which ordered pair is a solution to the system of equations: $(2, -6), (-8, -1)$.
$$x + 2y = -10$$
$$3x - 10y = -14$$

32. Shade the solution set in the xy-plane.
$$x + y < 4$$
$$x - 2y \ge 1$$

Exercises 33 and 34: Solve the system of equations.

33. $\begin{aligned} 2x - 8y &= 5 \\ 4x + 2y &= 1 \end{aligned}$ **34.** $\begin{aligned} 2x - 3y &= 12 \\ -x + 2y &= -6 \end{aligned}$

35. Maximize the objective function R subject to the given constraints.
$$R = 2x + 3y$$
$$2x + y \le 6$$
$$x + 2y \le 6$$
$$x \ge 0, y \ge 0$$

36. Use elimination and substitution to solve the system of linear equations.
$$\begin{aligned} 2x + 3y - z &= 3 \\ 3x - y + 4z &= 10 \\ 2x + y - 2z &= -1 \end{aligned}$$

37. Write the system of linear equations as an augmented matrix. Then use Gauss–Jordan elimination to solve the system. Write the solution as an ordered triple.
$$\begin{aligned} x + y - z &= 4 \\ -x - y - z &= 0 \\ x - 2y + z &= -9 \end{aligned}$$

38. Evaluate $\det A$ if $A = \begin{bmatrix} 4 & -2 \\ 1 & 3 \end{bmatrix}$.

39. Find the area of the triangle by using a determinant. Assume that the units are inches.

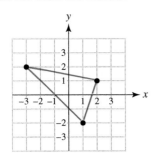

40. Use Cramer's rule to solve the system of equations.
$$\begin{aligned} 6x + 7y &= 8 \\ -8x + 5y &= 18 \end{aligned}$$

Exercises 41 and 42: Multiply the expressions.

41. $3x^2(x^3 + 5x - 2)$ **42.** $(2x - 5)(x + 3)$

43. Use factoring to solve $6x + 3x^2 = 0$.

44. Use grouping to factor $3a^3 - a^2 + 15a - 5$.

Exercises 45–48: Factor completely.

45. $4x^2 + 5x - 6$ **46.** $6x^3 - 9x^2 - 6x$

47. $9a^2 - 4b^2$ **48.** $64t^3 + 27$

Exercises 49 and 50: Solve the equation.

49. $3x^2 - 11x = 4$ **50.** $x^4 - x^3 - 30x^2 = 0$

Exercises 51–54: Simplify the expressions.

51. $\dfrac{x^2 + 3x - 10}{x^2 - 4} \cdot \dfrac{x - 2}{x + 5}$

52. $\dfrac{x^2 + 2x - 24}{x^2 + 3x - 18} \div \dfrac{x + 3}{x^2 - 9}$

53. $\dfrac{2}{t + 2} - \dfrac{t}{t^2 - 4}$ **54.** $\dfrac{4a}{3ab^2} + \dfrac{b}{a^2 c}$

Exercises 55 and 56: Solve. Check your result.

55. $\dfrac{1}{x + 4} + \dfrac{1}{x - 4} = \dfrac{-7}{x^2 - 16}$

56. $\dfrac{1}{y^2 + 3y - 4} - \dfrac{y}{y - 1} = -1$

57. Solve $J = \dfrac{y + z}{z}$ for z.

58. Simplify the complex fraction.
$$\dfrac{\dfrac{4}{x^2} + \dfrac{1}{x}}{\dfrac{4}{x^2} - \dfrac{1}{x}}$$

59. Suppose that y varies inversely with x. If $y = 2$ when $x = 4$, find y when x is 16.

60. Simplify $(x^3 + 2x + 11) \div (x + 2)$.

Exercises 61 and 62: Let $f(x) = x^2 - 3x + 2$ and let $g(x) = x - 2$. Simplify the expression.

61. $(f + g)(3)$ **62.** $(f/g)(x)$

APPLICATIONS

63. *Temperature Scales* The accompanying table shows equivalent temperatures in degrees Fahrenheit and degrees Celsius.

°F	−40	32	59	95	212
°C	−40	0	15	35	100

(a) Plot the data. Let the *x*-axis correspond to the Fahrenheit temperature and the *y*-axis correspond to the Celsius temperature. What type of relation exists between the data?

(b) Find $f(x) = m(x - h) + k$ so that f receives the Fahrenheit temperature as input and outputs the corresponding Celsius temperature.

(c) If the temperature is 104° F, what is the equivalent temperature in degrees Celsius?

64. *Geometry* An isosceles triangle has two shorter sides of the same length and a longer side that is 7 inches longer than half of the length of either of the shorter sides. If the perimeter of the triangle is 22 inches, what are the lengths of the three sides?

65. *Burning Calories* During strenuous exercise, an athlete burns 690 calories per hour on a stair climber and 540 calories per hour on a stationary bicycle. During a 90-minute workout the athlete burns 885 calories. How much time (in hours) is spent on each type of exercise equipment? (*Source: Runner's World.*)

66. *Tickets* The price of admission to a county fair is $2 for children and $5 for adults. If a group of 30 people pays $78 to enter the fairgrounds, find the number of children and the number of adults in the group.

67. *Area of a Rectangle* A rectangle has an area of 165 square feet. Its length is 4 feet more than its width. Find the dimensions of the rectangle.

68. *Flight of a Ball* If a ball is thrown upward with a velocity of 44 feet per second (30 miles per hour), its height *h* in feet above the ground after *t* seconds can be modeled by

$$h(t) = -16t^2 + 44t.$$

(a) Determine when the ball strikes the ground.

(b) When does the ball reach a height of 18 feet?

69. *Working Together* An amateur painter can paint a room in 15 hours. A professional painter can paint the same room in 10 hours.

(a) Write an equation whose solution gives the time to paint the room if the painters work together.

(b) Solve the equation in part (a).

70. *Height of a Tree* A 6-foot-tall person casts a 4-foot-long shadow while a nearby tree casts a 32-foot-long shadow. Find the height of the tree.

5

Radical Expressions and Functions

Bear in mind that the wonderful things you learn in schools are the work of many generations, produced by enthusiastic effort and infinite labor in every country.

—ALBERT EINSTEIN

Throughout history, people have created (or discovered) new numbers. Often these new numbers were met with resistance and regarded as being imaginary or unreal. The number 0 was not invented at the same time as the natural numbers. There was no Roman numeral for 0, which is one reason why our calendar started with A.D. 1 and, as a result, the twenty-first century began in 2001. No doubt there were skeptics during the time of the Roman Empire who questioned why anyone needed a number to represent nothing. Negative numbers also met strong resistance. After all, how could anyone possibly have −6 apples?

In this chapter we describe a new number system called *complex numbers*, which involve square roots of negative numbers. The Italian mathematician Cardano (1501–1576) was one of the first mathematicians to work with complex numbers and called them useless. René Descartes (1596–1650) originated the term *imaginary number*, which is associated with complex numbers. Today complex numbers are used in many applications, such as electricity, fiber optics, and the design of airplanes. We are privileged to study in a period of days what took people centuries to discover.

Source: Historical Topics for the Mathematics Classroom, Thirty-first Yearbook, NCTM.

5.1   Radical Expressions and Functions

Radical Notation • The Square Root Function • The Cube Root Function

Suppose you start a summer painting business, and initially you are the only employee. Because business is good, you hire another employee and productivity goes up, more than enough to pay for the new employee. As time goes on, you hire more employees. Eventually, productivity starts to level off because there are too many employees to keep busy. This situation is common in business and can be modeled by using a function involving a square root. (See Example 12.)

NEW VOCABULARY

☐ Radical sign
☐ Radicand
☐ Radical expression
☐ *n*th root
☐ Index
☐ Odd root
☐ Even root
☐ Principal *n*th root
☐ Square root function
☐ Cube root function

Radical Notation

SQUARE ROOTS Recall the definition of the square root of a number a.

> ### SQUARE ROOT
>
> The number b is a *square root* of a if $b^2 = a$.

EXAMPLE 1 | **Finding square roots**

Find the square roots of 100.

Solution

The square roots of 100 are **10** *and* **−10** because $10^2 = 100$ and $(-10)^2 = 100$.

Now Try Exercise 1

Every positive number a has two square roots: one positive and one negative. Recall that the *positive square root* is called the *principal square root* and is denoted $\sqrt{a}$. The *negative square root* is denoted $-\sqrt{a}$. To identify both square roots, we write $\pm\sqrt{a}$. The symbol $\pm$ is read "plus or minus." The symbol $\sqrt{}$ is called the **radical sign**. The expression under the radical sign is called the **radicand**, and an expression containing a radical sign is called a **radical expression**. Examples of radical expressions include

$$\sqrt{6}, \quad 5 + \sqrt{x + 1}, \quad \text{and} \quad \sqrt{\frac{3x}{2x - 1}}.$$

MAKING CONNECTIONS

Expressions and Equations

Expressions and equations are *different* mathematical concepts. An expression does not contain an equals sign, whereas an equation *always* contains an equals sign. *An equation is a statement that two expressions are equal.* For example,

$$\sqrt{x + 1} \quad \text{and} \quad \sqrt{5 - x} \qquad \text{Expressions}$$

are two different expressions, and

$$\sqrt{x + 1} = \sqrt{5 - x} \qquad \text{Equation}$$

is an equation. We often *solve an equation*, but we *do not solve an expression*. Instead, we *simplify* and *evaluate* expressions.

In the next example we show how to find the principal square root of an expression.

EXAMPLE 2 **Finding principal square roots**

Evaluate each square root.

(a) $\sqrt{25}$ **(b)** $\sqrt{0.49}$ **(c)** $\sqrt{\frac{4}{9}}$ **(d)** $\sqrt{c^2}, c > 0$

Solution

(a) Because $5 \cdot 5 = 25$, the principal, or *positive*, square root of 25 is $\sqrt{25} = 5$.

(b) Because $(0.7)(0.7) = 0.49$, the principal square root of 0.49 is $\sqrt{0.49} = 0.7$.

(c) Because $\frac{2}{3} \cdot \frac{2}{3} = \frac{4}{9}$, the principal square root of $\frac{4}{9}$ is $\sqrt{\frac{4}{9}} = \frac{2}{3}$.

(d) The principal square root of c^2 is $\sqrt{c^2} = c$, as c is positive.

Now Try Exercises 15, 17, 19, 21

The square roots of many real numbers, such as $\sqrt{17}$, $\sqrt{1.2}$, and $\sqrt{\frac{5}{7}}$, cannot be conveniently evaluated (or approximated) by hand. In these cases we sometimes use a calculator to give a decimal *approximation*, as demonstrated in the next example.

EXAMPLE 3 **Approximating a square root**

Approximate $\sqrt{17}$ to the nearest thousandth.

Solution

Figure 5.1 shows that $\sqrt{17} \approx 4.123$, rounded to the nearest thousandth. This result means that $4.123 \times 4.123 \approx 17$.

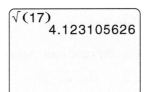

```
√(17)
          4.123105626
```

Figure 5.1

Now Try Exercise 39

SQUARE ROOTS OF NEGATIVE NUMBERS The square root of a *negative* number is *not* a real number. For example, $\sqrt{-4} \neq 2$ because $2 \cdot 2 \neq -4$ and $\sqrt{-4} \neq -2$ because $(-2)(-2) \neq -4$. (Later in this chapter, we will use the complex numbers to identify square roots of negative numbers.)

READING CHECK

Are square roots of negative numbers real numbers? Explain.

▶ **REAL-WORLD CONNECTION** Have you ever noticed that if you climb up a hill or a tower you can see farther to the horizon? This phenomenon can be described by a formula containing a square root, as demonstrated in the next example.

EXAMPLE 4 | **Seeing the horizon**

A formula for calculating the distance d in miles that one can see to the horizon on a clear day is approximated by $d = 1.22\sqrt{x}$, where x is the elevation, in feet, of a person.
(a) Approximate how far a 6-foot-tall person can see to the horizon.
(b) Approximate how far a person can see from an 8000-foot mountain.

Solution
(a) Let $x = 6$ in the formula $d = 1.22\sqrt{x}$.

$$d = 1.22\sqrt{6} \approx 3, \text{ or about 3 miles.}$$

(b) If $x = 8000$, then $d = 1.22\sqrt{8000} \approx 109$, or about 109 miles.

Now Try Exercise 107

CUBE ROOTS The cube root of a number a is denoted $\sqrt[3]{a}$.

CALCULATOR HELP

To calculate a cube root, see Appendix A (page AP-1).

CUBE ROOT

The number b is a *cube root* of a if $b^3 = a$.

Although the square root of a negative number is *not* a real number, the cube root of a negative number is a negative real number. *Every real number has one real cube root.*

EXAMPLE 5 | **Finding cube roots**

Evaluate the cube root. Approximate your answer to the nearest hundredth when appropriate.
(a) $\sqrt[3]{8}$ (b) $\sqrt[3]{-27}$ (c) $\sqrt[3]{\frac{1}{64}}$ (d) $\sqrt[3]{d^6}$ (e) $\sqrt[3]{16}$

Solution
(a) $\sqrt[3]{8} = 2$ because $2^3 = 2 \cdot 2 \cdot 2 = 8$.
(b) $\sqrt[3]{-27} = -3$ because $(-3)^3 = (-3)(-3)(-3) = -27$.
(c) $\sqrt[3]{\frac{1}{64}} = \frac{1}{4}$ because $\left(\frac{1}{4}\right)^3 = \frac{1}{4} \cdot \frac{1}{4} \cdot \frac{1}{4} = \frac{1}{64}$.
(d) $\sqrt[3]{d^6} = d^2$ because $(d^2)^3 = d^2 \cdot d^2 \cdot d^2 = d^{2+2+2} = d^6$.
(e) $\sqrt[3]{16}$ is not an integer. Figure 5.2 shows that $\sqrt[3]{16} \approx 2.52$.

Now Try Exercises 23, 25, 27, 41

```
³√(16)
         2.5198421
```

Figure 5.2

NOTE: $\sqrt[3]{-b} = -\sqrt[3]{b}$ for any real number b. That is, the cube root of a negative is the negative of the cube root. For example, $\sqrt[3]{-8} = -\sqrt[3]{8} = -2$.

Table 5.1 illustrates how to evaluate both square roots and cube roots. If the radical expression is undefined, a dash is used.

TABLE 5.1 Radicals

Expression	$\sqrt{64}$	$-\sqrt{64}$	$\sqrt{-64}$	$\sqrt[3]{64}$	$-\sqrt[3]{64}$	$\sqrt[3]{-64}$
Evaluated	8	-8	—	4	-4	-4

Nth ROOTS We can generalize square roots and cube roots to include *n*th roots of a number *a*. The number *b* is an ***n*th root** of *a* if $b^n = a$, where *n* is a positive integer. For example, $2^5 = 32$, so the 5th root of 32 is 2 and can be written as $\sqrt[5]{32} = 2$.

THE NOTATION $\sqrt[n]{a}$

The equation $\sqrt[n]{a} = b$ means that $b^n = a$, where *n* is a natural number called the **index**. If *n* is odd, we are finding an **odd root** and if *n* is even, we are finding an **even root**.

1. If $a > 0$, then $\sqrt[n]{a}$ is a positive number. $\quad\sqrt[4]{16} = 2$ and is positive.
2. If $a < 0$ and
   (a) *n* is odd, then $\sqrt[n]{a}$ is a negative number. $\quad\sqrt[3]{-8} = -2$ and is negative.
   (b) *n* is even, then $\sqrt[n]{a}$ is *not* a real number. $\quad\sqrt[4]{-8}$ is undefined.

If $a > 0$ and *n* is even, then *a* has two real *n*th roots: one positive and one negative. The positive root is denoted $\sqrt[n]{a}$ and called the **principal *n*th root** of *a*. For example, $(-3)^4 = 81$ *and* $3^4 = 81$, but $\sqrt[4]{81} = 3$ in the same way *principal square roots* are calculated.

EXAMPLE 6 **Finding *n*th roots**

Find each root, if possible.

(a) $\sqrt[4]{16}$ **(b)** $\sqrt[5]{-32}$ **(c)** $\sqrt[4]{-81}$ **(d)** $-\sqrt[4]{81}$

Solution
(a) $\sqrt[4]{16} = 2$ because $2^4 = 2 \cdot 2 \cdot 2 \cdot 2 = 16$.
(b) $\sqrt[5]{-32} = -2$ because $(-2)^5 = (-2)(-2)(-2)(-2)(-2) = -32$.
(c) An *even* root of a *negative* number is *not* a real number.
(d) $-\sqrt[4]{81} = -3$ because $\sqrt[4]{81} = 3$.

Now Try Exercises 33, 35, 37

ABSOLUTE VALUE Consider the calculations

$$\sqrt{3^2} = \sqrt{9} = 3, \quad \sqrt{(-4)^2} = \sqrt{16} = 4, \quad \text{and} \quad \sqrt{(-6)^2} = \sqrt{36} = 6.$$

In general, the expression $\sqrt{x^2}$ equals $|x|$. Graphical support is shown in Figure 5.3, where the graphs of $Y_1 = \sqrt{(X^2)}$ and $Y_2 = \text{abs}(X)$ appear to be identical.

CRITICAL THINKING

Evaluate $\sqrt[6]{(-2)^6}$ and $\sqrt[3]{(-2)^3}$. Now simplify $\sqrt[n]{x^n}$ when *n* is even and when *n* is odd.

[−6, 6, 1] by [−4, 4, 1]

(a)

[−6, 6, 1] by [−4, 4, 1]

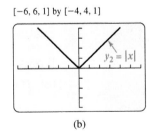

(b)

Figure 5.3

THE EXPRESSION $\sqrt{x^2}$

For every real number *x*, $\sqrt{x^2} = |x|$.

EXAMPLE 7 **Simplifying expressions**

Write each expression in terms of an absolute value.
(a) $\sqrt{(-3)^2}$ (b) $\sqrt{(x+1)^2}$ (c) $\sqrt{z^2 - 4z + 4}$

Solution
(a) $\sqrt{x^2} = |x|$, so $\sqrt{(-3)^2} = |-3|$
(b) $\sqrt{(x+1)^2} = |x+1|$
(c) $\sqrt{z^2 - 4z + 4} = \sqrt{(z-2)^2} = |z-2|$

Now Try Exercises 45, 49, 51

The Square Root Function

The **square root function** is given by $f(x) = \sqrt{x}$. The domain of the square root function is all nonnegative real numbers because we have *not* defined the square root of a negative number. Table 5.2 lists three points that lie on the graph of $f(x) = \sqrt{x}$. In Figure 5.4 these points are plotted and the graph of $y = \sqrt{x}$ has been sketched. The graph does not appear to the left of the origin because $f(x) = \sqrt{x}$ is undefined for negative inputs.

TABLE 5.2

x	$\sqrt{x}$
0	0
1	1
4	2

Square Root Function

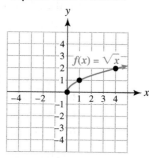

Figure 5.4

TECHNOLOGY NOTE

Square Roots of Negative Numbers
If a table of values for $y_1 = \sqrt{x}$ includes both negative and positive values for x, then many calculators give error messages when x is negative, as shown in the figure in the margin.

X	Y1
-9	ERROR
-4	ERROR
-1	ERROR
0	0
1	1
4	2
9	3

$Y_1 = \sqrt{(X)}$

EXAMPLE 8 **Evaluating functions involving square roots**

If possible, evaluate $f(1)$ and $f(-2)$ for each $f(x)$.
(a) $f(x) = \sqrt{2x - 1}$ (b) $f(x) = \sqrt{4 - x^2}$

Solution
(a) $f(1) = \sqrt{2(1) - 1} = \sqrt{1} = 1$
$f(-2) = \sqrt{2(-2) - 1} = \sqrt{-5}$, which does not equal a real number.
(b) $f(1) = \sqrt{4 - (1)^2} = \sqrt{3}$
$f(-2) = \sqrt{4 - (-2)^2} = \sqrt{0} = 0$

Now Try Exercises 61, 63

▶ **REAL-WORLD CONNECTION** A good punter can kick a football so that the ball has a long *hang time*. Hang time is the length of time that the ball is in the air, and a long hang time gives the kicking team time to run down the field and stop the punt return. By using a function involving a square root, we can estimate hang time.

EXAMPLE 9 **Calculating hang time**

If a football is kicked x feet high, then the time T in seconds that the ball is in the air is given by the function

$$T(x) = \frac{1}{2}\sqrt{x}.$$

(a) Find the hang time if the ball is kicked 50 feet into the air.
(b) Does the hang time double if the ball is kicked 100 feet in the air?

Solution
(a) The hang time is $T(50) = \frac{1}{2}\sqrt{50} \approx 3.5$ seconds.
(b) The hang time is $T(100) = \frac{1}{2}\sqrt{100} = 5$ seconds. The time does *not* double when the height doubles.

Now Try Exercise 105

CRITICAL THINKING

How high would a football have to be kicked to have twice the hang time of a football kicked 50 feet into the air?

EXAMPLE 10 **Finding the domain of a square root function**

Let $f(x) = \sqrt{x - 1}$.
(a) Find the domain of f. Write your answer in interval notation.
(b) Graph $y = f(x)$ and compare it to the graph of $y = \sqrt{x}$.

Solution
(a) For $f(x)$ to be defined, $x - 1$ cannot be negative. Thus valid inputs for x must satisfy

$$x - 1 \geq 0 \quad \text{or} \quad x \geq 1.$$

The domain is $[1, \infty)$.
(b) Table 5.3 lists points that lie on the graph of $y = \sqrt{x - 1}$. Note in Figure 5.5 that the graph appears only when $x \geq 1$. This graph is similar to $y = \sqrt{x}$ (see Figure 5.4) except that it is shifted one unit to the right.

TABLE 5.3

x	$\sqrt{x - 1}$
1	0
2	1
5	2

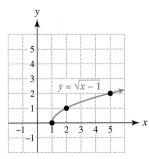

Figure 5.5

Now Try Exercises 75, 89

EXAMPLE 11

Finding the domains of square root functions

Find the domain of each function. Write your answer in interval notation.

(a) $f(x) = \sqrt{4 - 2x}$ (b) $g(x) = \sqrt{x^2 + 1}$

Solution

(a) To determine when $f(x) = \sqrt{4 - 2x}$ is defined, we must solve $4 - 2x \geq 0$.

$$4 - 2x \geq 0 \qquad \text{Inequality to be solved}$$
$$4 \geq 2x \qquad \text{Add } 2x \text{ to each side.}$$
$$2 \geq x \qquad \text{Divide each side by 2.}$$

The domain is $(-\infty, 2]$.

(b) Regardless of the value of x in $g(x) = \sqrt{x^2 + 1}$, the expression $x^2 + 1$ is always positive because $x^2 \geq 0$. Thus $g(x)$ is defined for all real numbers, and its domain is $(-\infty, \infty)$.

Now Try Exercises 83, 85

MAKING CONNECTIONS

Domains of Functions and Their Graphs

In Example 11, the domains of f and g were found *symbolically*. Notice that the graph of f does not appear to the right of $x = 2$ because the domain of f is $(-\infty, 2]$, whereas the graph of g appears for all values of x because the domain of g is $(-\infty, \infty)$.

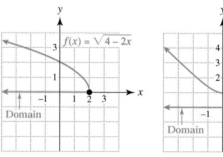

▶ **REAL-WORLD CONNECTION** (Refer to A Look Into Math at the beginning of this section.) In the next example, we analyze the benefit of adding employees to a small business.

EXAMPLE 12

Increasing productivity with more employees

The function $R(x) = 108\sqrt{x}$ gives the total revenue per year in thousands of dollars generated by a small business having x employees. A graph of $y = R(x)$ is shown in Figure 5.6.

Revenue as a Function of Employees

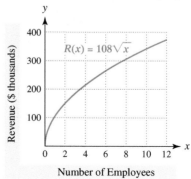

Figure 5.6

(a) Approximate values for $R(4)$, $R(8)$, and $R(12)$ by using both the formula and the graph.

(b) Evaluate $R(12) - R(8)$ and $R(8) - R(4)$ using the formula. Interpret your answer.

Solution

(a) $R(4) = 108\sqrt{4} = \$216$ thousand, $R(8) = 108\sqrt{8} \approx \$305$ thousand, and finally $R(12) = 108\sqrt{12} \approx \$374$ thousand.

We can graphically evaluate $R(4) \approx \$215$ thousand, $R(8) \approx \$305$ thousand, and $R(12) \approx \$375$ thousand, as shown in Figure 5.7.

Revenue as a Function of Employees

Figure 5.7

(b) $R(8) - R(4) \approx 305 - 216 = \$89$ thousand

$R(12) - R(8) \approx 374 - 305 = \$69$ thousand

There is more revenue gained from 4 to 8 employees than there is from 8 to 12 employees. Because the graph of $R(x) = 108\sqrt{x}$ starts to level off, there is a limited benefit to adding employees.

▌ Now Try Exercise 109

The Cube Root Function

Cube Root Function

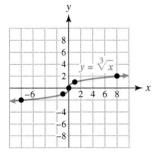

Figure 5.8

We can define the **cube root function** by $f(x) = \sqrt[3]{x}$. Cube roots are defined for both positive and negative numbers, so *the domain of the cube root function includes all real numbers*. Table 5.4 lists points that lie on the graph of the cube root function. Figure 5.8 shows a graph of $y = \sqrt[3]{x}$.

TABLE 5.4 Cube Root Function

x	-27	-8	-1	0	1	8	27
$\sqrt[3]{x}$	-3	-2	-1	0	1	2	3

MAKING CONNECTIONS

Domains of the Square Root and Cube Root Functions

$f(x) = \sqrt{x}$ equals a real number for any nonnegative x. Thus $D = [0, \infty)$.

$f(x) = \sqrt[3]{x}$ equals a real number for any x. Thus $D = (-\infty, \infty)$.

Examples: $\sqrt{4} = 2$ but $\sqrt{-4}$ is *not* a real number. $\sqrt[3]{8} = 2$ and $\sqrt[3]{-8} = -2$.

EXAMPLE 13 | **Evaluating functions involving cube roots**

Evaluate $f(1)$ and $f(-3)$ for each $f(x)$.

(a) $f(x) = \sqrt[3]{x^2 - 1}$ (b) $f(x) = \sqrt[3]{2 - x^2}$

Solution

(a) $f(1) = \sqrt[3]{1^2 - 1} = \sqrt[3]{0} = 0$; $f(-3) = \sqrt[3]{(-3)^2 - 1} = \sqrt[3]{8} = 2$

(b) $f(1) = \sqrt[3]{2 - 1^2} = \sqrt[3]{1} = 1$; $f(-3) = \sqrt[3]{2 - (-3)^2} = \sqrt[3]{-7}$ or $-\sqrt[3]{7}$

▌ Now Try Exercises 65, 69

5.1   Putting It All Together

CONCEPT	EXPLANATION	EXAMPLES
nth Root of a Real Number	An nth root of a real number a is b if $b^n = a$, and the (principal) nth root is denoted $\sqrt[n]{a}$. If $a < 0$ and n is even, $\sqrt[n]{a}$ is not a real number.	The square roots of 25 are 5 and -5. The principal square root is $\sqrt{25} = 5$. $\sqrt[3]{-125} = -5$ because $(-5)^3 = -125$. $\sqrt[4]{-9}$ is not a real number.
Square Root and Cube Root Functions	$f(x) = \sqrt{x}$ and $g(x) = \sqrt[3]{x}$ The cube root function g is defined for all inputs, whereas the square root function f is defined only for nonnegative inputs. **Square Root Function** **Cube Root Function** Domain: $[0, \infty)$ Domain: $(-\infty, \infty)$	$f(64) = \sqrt{64} = 8$ $f(-64) = \sqrt{-64}$ is *not* a real number. $g(64) = \sqrt[3]{64} = 4$ $g(-64) = \sqrt[3]{-64} = -4$

5.1   Exercises

CONCEPTS AND VOCABULARY

1. What are the square roots of 9?

2. What is the principal square root of 9?

3. What is the cube root of 8?

4. Does every real number have a cube root?

5. If $b^n = a$ and $b > 0$, then $\sqrt[n]{a} = $ _____.

6. What is $\sqrt{x^2}$ equal to?

7. Evaluate $\sqrt{-25}$, if possible.

8. Evaluate $\sqrt[3]{-27}$, if possible.

9. Which of the following (a.–d.) equals -4?
a. $\sqrt{16}$ **b.** $\sqrt{-16}$
c. $-\sqrt[3]{16}$ **d.** $\sqrt[3]{-64}$

10. Which of the following (a.–d.) equals $|2x + 1|$?
a. $\sqrt{(2x + 1)^2}$ **b.** $\sqrt[3]{(2x + 1)^3}$
c. $\left(\sqrt{2x + 1}\right)^2$ **d.** $\sqrt{(2x)^2 + 1}$

11. Sketch a graph of the square root function.

12. Sketch a graph of the cube root function.

13. What is the domain of the square root function?

14. What is the domain of the cube root function?

RADICAL EXPRESSIONS

Exercises 15–38: Evaluate the expression by hand, if possible. Variables represent any real number.

15. $\sqrt{9}$ **16.** $\sqrt{121}$

17. $\sqrt{0.36}$ **18.** $\sqrt{0.64}$

19. $\sqrt{\frac{16}{25}}$ **20.** $\sqrt{\frac{9}{49}}$

21. $\sqrt{x^2}, x > 0$ **22.** $\sqrt{(x - 1)^2}, x > 1$

23. $\sqrt[3]{27}$ **24.** $\sqrt[3]{64}$

25. $\sqrt[3]{-64}$ **26.** $-\sqrt[3]{-1}$

27. $\sqrt[3]{\frac{8}{27}}$ **28.** $\sqrt[3]{-\frac{1}{125}}$

29. $-\sqrt[3]{x^9}$ **30.** $\sqrt[3]{(x + 1)^6}$

31. $\sqrt[3]{(2x)^6}$ **32.** $\sqrt[3]{27x^3}$

33. $\sqrt[4]{81}$ **34.** $\sqrt[5]{-1}$

35. $\sqrt[5]{-243}$ **36.** $\sqrt[4]{625}$

37. $\sqrt[4]{-16}$ **38.** $\sqrt[6]{-64}$

Exercises 39–44: Approximate to the nearest hundredth.

39. $-\sqrt{5}$ **40.** $\sqrt{11}$

41. $\sqrt[3]{5}$ **42.** $\sqrt[3]{-13}$

43. $\sqrt[5]{-7}$ **44.** $\sqrt[4]{6}$

Exercises 45–58: Simplify the expression. Assume that all variables are real numbers.

45. $\sqrt{(-4)^2}$ **46.** $\sqrt{9^2}$

47. $\sqrt{y^2}$ **48.** $\sqrt{z^4}$

49. $\sqrt{(x - 5)^2}$ **50.** $\sqrt{(2x - 1)^2}$

51. $\sqrt{x^2 - 2x + 1}$ **52.** $\sqrt{4x^2 + 4x + 1}$

53. $\sqrt[4]{y^4}$ **54.** $\sqrt[4]{x^8 z^4}$

55. $\sqrt[4]{x^{12}}$ **56.** $\sqrt[6]{x^6}$

57. $\sqrt[5]{x^5}$ **58.** $\sqrt[5]{32(x + 4)^5}$

SQUARE AND CUBE ROOT FUNCTIONS

Exercises 59–74: If possible, evaluate the function at the given value(s) of the variable.

59. $f(x) = \sqrt{x - 1}$ $x = 10, 0$

60. $f(x) = \sqrt{4 - 3x}$ $x = -4, 1$

61. $f(x) = \sqrt{3 - 3x}$ $x = -1, 5$

62. $f(x) = \sqrt{x - 5}$ $x = -1, 5$

63. $f(x) = \sqrt{x^2 - x}$ $x = -4, 3$

64. $f(x) = \sqrt{2x^2 - 3}$ $x = -1, 2$

65. $f(x) = \sqrt[3]{x^2 - 8}$ $x = -3, 4$

66. $f(x) = \sqrt[3]{2x^2}$ $x = -2, 2$

67. $f(x) = \sqrt[3]{x - 9}$ $x = 1, 10$

68. $f(x) = \sqrt[3]{5x - 2}$ $x = -5, 2$

69. $f(x) = \sqrt[3]{3 - x^2}$ $x = -2, 3$

70. $f(x) = \sqrt[3]{-1 - x^2}$ $x = 0, 3$

71. $T(h) = \frac{1}{2}\sqrt{h}$ $h = 64$

72. $L(k) = 2\sqrt{k + 2}$ $k = 23$

73. $f(x) = \sqrt{x + 5} + \sqrt{x}$ $x = 4$

74. $f(x) = \dfrac{\sqrt{x - 5} - \sqrt{x}}{2}$ $x = 9$

Exercises 75–88: Find the domain of f. Write your answer in interval notation.

75. $f(x) = \sqrt{x + 2}$ **76.** $f(x) = \sqrt{x - 1}$

77. $f(x) = \sqrt{x - 2}$ **78.** $f(x) = \sqrt{x + 1}$

79. $f(x) = \sqrt{2x - 4}$ **80.** $f(x) = \sqrt{4x + 2}$

81. $f(x) = \sqrt{1 - x}$ **82.** $f(x) = \sqrt{6 - 3x}$

83. $f(x) = \sqrt{8 - 5x}$ **84.** $f(x) = \sqrt{3 - 2x}$

85. $f(x) = \sqrt{3x^2 + 4}$ **86.** $f(x) = \sqrt{1 + 2x^2}$

87. $f(x) = \dfrac{1}{\sqrt{2x + 1}}$ **88.** $f(x) = \dfrac{1}{\sqrt{x - 1}}$

Exercises 89–94: Graph the equation. Compare the graph to either $y = \sqrt{x}$ *or* $y = \sqrt[3]{x}$.

89. $y = \sqrt{x} + 2$ **90.** $y = \sqrt{x} - 1$

91. $y = \sqrt{x+2}$ **92.** $y = \sqrt[3]{x} + 2$

93. $y = \sqrt[3]{x+2}$ **94.** $y = \sqrt[3]{x} - 1$

REPRESENTATIONS OF ROOT FUNCTIONS

Exercises 95–102: Give symbolic, numerical, and graphical representations for the function f.

95. Function *f* takes the square root of *x* and then adds 1 to the result.

96. Function *f* takes the square root of *x* and then subtracts 2 from the result.

97. Function *f* takes the square root of the quantity three times *x*.

98. Function *f* takes the square root of the quantity *x* plus 1.

99. Function *f* takes the cube root of *x* and then multiplies the result by 2.

100. Function *f* takes the cube root of the quantity 4 times *x*.

101. Function *f* takes the cube root of the quantity *x* minus 1.

102. Function *f* takes the cube root of *x* and then adds 1.

AREA OF A TRIANGLE

Exercises 103 and 104: **Heron's Formula** *Suppose the lengths of the sides of a triangle are a, b, and c as illustrated in the figure.*

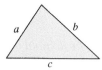

If the **semiperimeter** *(half of the perimeter) of the triangle is* $s = \frac{1}{2}(a + b + c)$*, then the area of the triangle is*

$$A = \sqrt{s(s - a)(s - b)(s - c)}.$$

Find the area A of the triangle with the given sides.

103. $a = 3, b = 4, c = 5$

104. $a = 5, b = 9, c = 10$

APPLICATIONS

105. *Jumping* (Refer to Example 9.) If a person jumps 4 feet off the ground, estimate how long the person is in the air.

106. *Hang Time* (Refer to Example 9.) Find the hang time for a golf ball hit 80 feet into the air.

107. *Distance to the Horizon* (Refer to Example 4.) Use the formula $d = 1.22\sqrt{x}$ to estimate how many miles a person can see from a jet airliner at 10,000 feet.

108. *Distance to the Horizon* (Refer to Example 4.) Use the formula $d = 1.22\sqrt{x}$ to estimate how many miles a 5-foot-tall person can see standing on the deck of a ship that is 50 feet above the ocean.

109. *Increasing Productivity* (Refer to Example 12.) Use $R(x) = 108\sqrt{x}$ to evaluate $R(16) - R(15)$. If the salary for the sixteenth employee is $25,000, is it a good decision to hire the sixteenth employee?

110. *Increasing Productivity* (Refer to Example 12.) Use $R(x) = 108\sqrt{x}$ to evaluate $R(2) - R(1)$. If the salary for the second employee is $25,000, is it a good decision to hire the second employee?

111. *Productivity of Workers* If workers are given more equipment, or *physical capital*, they are often more productive. For example, a carpenter definitely needs a hammer to be productive, but probably does not need 20 hammers. There is a leveling off in a worker's productivity as more is spent on equipment. The function $P(x) = 400\sqrt{x} + 8000$ approximates the worth of the goods produced by a typical U.S. worker in dollars when *x* dollars are spent on equipment per worker.
   (a) Evaluate $P(25,000)$ and interpret the result.
   (b) Sketch a graph of $y = P(x)$.
   (c) Use the graph from (b) and the formula to evaluate $P(50,000) - P(25,000)$ and also to evaluate $P(75,000) - P(50,000)$. Interpret the result.

112. *Design of Open Channels* To protect cities from flooding during heavy rains, open channels are sometimes constructed to handle runoff. The rate R at which water flows through the channel is modeled by $R = k\sqrt{m}$, where m is the slope of the channel and k is a constant determined by the shape of the channel. (*Source:* N. Garber and L. Hoel, *Traffic and Highway Design.*)

    (a) Suppose that a channel has a slope of $m = 0.01$ (or 1%) and a runoff rate of $R = 340$ cubic feet per second (cfs). Find k.

    (b) If the slope of the channel increases to $m = 0.04$ (or 4%), what happens to R? Be specific.

WRITING ABOUT MATHEMATICS

113. Try to calculate $\sqrt{-7}$, $\sqrt[4]{-56}$, and $\sqrt[6]{-10}$ with a calculator. Describe what happens when you evaluate an even root of a negative number. Does the same difficulty occur when you evaluate an odd root of a negative number? Try to evaluate $\sqrt[3]{-7}$, $\sqrt[5]{-56}$, and $\sqrt[7]{-10}$. Explain.

114. Explain the difference between a root and a positive integer power of a number. Give examples.

5.2 Rational Exponents

Basic Concepts • **Properties of Rational Exponents**

A LOOK INTO MATH ▶ In today's society, people are used to having a lot of choices when it comes to online videos. In fact, if the average online video has 1,000,000 viewers, then about 200,000 of them, or 20%, have abandoned the video in 10 seconds or less. This average viewer abandonment rate can be modeled by a new function A, given by

$$A(x) = 7.3x^{7/16},$$

where A computes the percentage of viewers who abandon an online video after x seconds. But what does the exponent $\frac{7}{16}$ mean? To answer this question we need to discuss rational exponents and their properties. See Example 3. (*Source: Business Insider.*)

Basic Concepts

When m and n are integers, the product rule states that $a^m a^n = a^{m+n}$. This rule can be extended to include exponents that are fractions. For example,

$$4^{1/2} \cdot 4^{1/2} = 4^{1/2 + 1/2} = 4^1 = 4.$$

That is, if we multiply the expression $4^{1/2}$ by itself, the result is 4. Because we also know that $\sqrt{4} \cdot \sqrt{4} = 4$, this discussion suggests that $4^{1/2} = \sqrt{4}$ and leads to the following definition.

THE EXPRESSION $a^{1/n}$

If n is an integer greater than 1 and a is a real number, then

$$a^{1/n} = \sqrt[n]{a}. \qquad\qquad 7^{1/5} = \sqrt[5]{7}$$

NOTE: If $a < 0$ and n is an even positive integer, then $a^{1/n}$ is not a real number.

In the next two examples, we show how to interpret rational exponents.

EXAMPLE 1   Interpreting rational exponents

Write each expression in radical notation. Then evaluate the expression and round to the nearest hundredth when appropriate.

(a) $36^{1/2}$ (b) $23^{1/5}$ (c) $x^{1/3}$ (d) $(5x)^{1/2}$

Solution

(a) The exponent $\frac{1}{2}$ indicates a square root. Thus $36^{1/2} = \sqrt{36}$, which evaluates to 6.

(b) The exponent $\frac{1}{5}$ indicates a fifth root. Thus $23^{1/5} = \sqrt[5]{23}$, which is not an integer. Figure 5.9 shows this expression approximated in both exponential and radical notation. In either case $23^{1/5} \approx 1.87$.

(c) The exponent $\frac{1}{3}$ indicates a cube root, so $x^{1/3} = \sqrt[3]{x}$.

(d) The exponent $\frac{1}{2}$ indicates a square root, so $(5x)^{1/2} = \sqrt{5x}$.

Now Try Exercises 37, 45, 59, 63

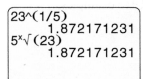

```
23^(1/5)
        1.872171231
5ˣ√(23)
        1.872171231
```

Figure 5.9

CALCULATOR HELP

To calculate other roots, see Appendix A (pages AP-7 and AP-8).

Suppose that we want to define the expression $8^{2/3}$. On the one hand, using properties of exponents we have

$$8^{1/3} \cdot 8^{1/3} = 8^{1/3 + 1/3} = 8^{2/3}.$$

On the other hand, we have

$$8^{1/3} \cdot 8^{1/3} = \sqrt[3]{8} \cdot \sqrt[3]{8} = 2 \cdot 2 = 4.$$

Thus $8^{2/3} = 4$, and that value is obtained whether we interpret $8^{2/3}$ as either

$$8^{2/3} = (8^{1/3})^2 = (\sqrt[3]{8})^2 = 2^2 = 4$$

or

$$8^{2/3} = (8^2)^{1/3} = \sqrt[3]{8^2} = \sqrt[3]{64} = 4.$$

This result suggests the following definition.

STUDY TIP

Be sure that you understand how rational exponents relate to radical notation.

THE EXPRESSION $a^{m/n}$

If m and n are positive integers with $\frac{m}{n}$ in lowest terms, then

$$a^{m/n} = \sqrt[n]{a^m} = (\sqrt[n]{a})^m. \qquad 2^{3/4} = \sqrt[4]{2^3} = (\sqrt[4]{2})^3$$

NOTE: If $a < 0$ and n is an even integer, then $a^{m/n}$ is *not* a real number.

The exponent $\frac{m}{n}$ indicates that we either take the nth root and then calculate the mth power of the result or calculate the mth power and then take the nth root. For example, $4^{3/2}$ means that we can either take the **square root** of 4 and then **cube** the result or we can **cube** 4 and then take the **square root** of the result. In either case the result is the same: $4^{3/2} = 8$. This concept is illustrated in the next example.

EXAMPLE 2   Interpreting rational exponents

Write each expression in radical notation. Evaluate the expression by hand when possible.

(a) $(-27)^{2/3}$ (b) $12^{3/5}$

Solution

(a) The exponent $\frac{2}{3}$ indicates either that we take the **cube root** of -27 and then **square** it or that we **square** -27 and then take the **cube root**. Thus

$$(-27)^{2/3} = (\sqrt[3]{-27})^2 = (-3)^2 = 9$$

or

$$(-27)^{2/3} = \sqrt[3]{(-27)^2} = \sqrt[3]{729} = 9.$$

Same result

(b) The exponent $\frac{3}{5}$ indicates either that we take the **fifth root** of 12 and then **cube** it or that we **cube** 12 and then take the **fifth root**. Thus

$$12^{3/5} = (\sqrt[5]{12})^3 \quad \text{or} \quad 12^{3/5} = \sqrt[5]{12^3}.$$

This result cannot be evaluated by hand.

▌ Now Try Exercises 47, 51

TECHNOLOGY NOTE

Rational Exponents
When evaluating expressions with rational (fractional) exponents, be sure to put parentheses around the fraction. For example, most calculators will evaluate 8^(2/3) and 8^2/3 differently. The accompanying figure shows that evaluating $8^{2/3}$ correctly as 8^(2/3) results in 4 but evaluating $8^{2/3}$ incorrectly as 8^2/3 results in $\frac{8^2}{3} = 21.\overline{3}$.

Correct ⟶ | 8^(2/3)
| | 4
Incorrect ⟶ | 8^2/3
| | 21.33333333

▶ **REAL-WORLD CONNECTION** In the next example, we evaluate the function A presented in A Look Into Math at the beginning of this section. This function calculates the average viewer abandonment rate for online videos.

EXAMPLE 3 **Calculating abandonment rates for online videos**

The function A, given by $A(x) = 7.3x^{7/16}$, computes the percentage of viewers who abandon an online video after x seconds.
(a) Find $A(10)$ and $A(90)$. Interpret your answers.
(b) Use radical notation to write $A(x)$.

Solution

7.3*10^(7/16)
          19.99046333
7.3*90^(7/16)
          52.27619364

Figure 5.10

(a) To approximate these expressions we will use a calculator, as shown in Figure 5.10.

$$A(10) = 7.3(10)^{7/16} \approx 20\%$$
$$A(90) = 7.3(90)^{7/16} \approx 52\%$$

After **10** seconds about **20%** of the viewers have abandoned the online video, and after **90** seconds over half, or **52%**, of the viewers have abandoned the online video.

(b) The exponent $\frac{7}{16}$ means we raise x to the **seventh** power and then take the **sixteenth** root. That is, $A(x) = 7.3\sqrt[16]{x^7}$.

▌ Now Try Exercise 99

From properties of exponents we know that $a^{-n} = \frac{1}{a^n}$, where n is a positive integer. We now define this property for negative rational exponents.

THE EXPRESSION $a^{-m/n}$

If m and n are positive integers with $\frac{m}{n}$ in lowest terms, then

$$a^{-m/n} = \frac{1}{a^{m/n}}, \qquad a \neq 0.$$

$$2^{-3/4} = \frac{1}{2^{3/4}}$$

Examples of changing rational exponents to radical expressions are shown in Table 5.5.

TABLE 5.5 Converting Forms

Expression	$a^{3/4}$	$5^{1/7}$	$x^{-5/3}$
Radical Form	$\sqrt[4]{a^3}$	$\sqrt[7]{5}$	$\frac{1}{\sqrt[3]{x^5}}$

EXAMPLE 4 Interpreting negative rational exponents

Write each expression in radical notation and then evaluate.
(a) $64^{-1/3}$ **(b)** $81^{-3/4}$

Solution

(a) $64^{-1/3} = \dfrac{1}{64^{1/3}} = \dfrac{1}{\sqrt[3]{64}} = \dfrac{1}{4}$.

(b) $81^{-3/4} = \dfrac{1}{81^{3/4}} = \dfrac{1}{(\sqrt[4]{81})^3} = \dfrac{1}{3^3} = \dfrac{1}{27}$.

Now Try Exercises 53, 55

EXAMPLE 5 Converting to rational exponents

Use rational exponents to write each radical expression.
(a) $\sqrt[5]{x^4}$ **(b)** $\dfrac{1}{\sqrt{b^5}}$ **(c)** $\sqrt[3]{(x-1)^2}$ **(d)** $\sqrt[3]{a^2 + b^2}$

Solution
(a) $\sqrt[5]{x^4} = x^{4/5}$

(b) $\dfrac{1}{\sqrt{b^5}} = b^{-5/2}$

(c) $\sqrt[3]{(x-1)^2} = (x-1)^{2/3}$

(d) $\sqrt[3]{a^2 + b^2} = (a^2 + b^2)^{1/3}$ Note that $\sqrt[3]{a^2 + b^2} \neq a^{2/3} + b^{2/3}$.

Now Try Exercises 27, 29, 33, 35

▶ **REAL-WORLD CONNECTION** In the next example, we use a formula from biology that involves a rational exponent.

EXAMPLE 6   **Analyzing stepping frequency**

When smaller (four-legged) animals walk, they tend to take faster, shorter steps, whereas larger animals tend to take slower, longer steps. If an animal is h feet high at the shoulder, then the number N of steps per second that the animal takes *while walking* can be estimated by $N(h) = 1.6h^{-1/2}$.   (*Source:* C. Pennycuick, *Newton Rules Biology.*)
(a) Use radical notation to write $N(h)$.
(b) Estimate the stepping frequency for an adult African elephant that is 10 feet high at the shoulders and a baby elephant that is only 33 inches high.

Solution
(a) We can rewrite the formula as $N(h) = \dfrac{1.6}{\sqrt{h}}$.
(b) We can evaluate N as follows. Note that 33 inches is $\dfrac{33}{12} = 2.75$ feet.

$$N(10) = \frac{1.6}{\sqrt{10}} \approx 0.51 \quad \text{and} \quad N(2.75) = \frac{1.6}{\sqrt{2.75}} \approx 0.96$$

While walking, the adult elephant takes about 1 step every 2 seconds, and the baby elephant takes about 1 step every second.

▌ Now Try Exercise 101

Properties of Rational Exponents

Any rational number can be written as a ratio of two integers. That is, if p is a rational number, then $p = \frac{m}{n}$, where m and n are integers. Properties for integer exponents also apply to rational exponents, with one exception. If n is even in the expression $a^{m/n}$ and $\frac{m}{n}$ is written in lowest terms, then a must be nonnegative for the result to be a real number.

For example, the expression $(-8)^{3/2}$ is not a real number because -8 is negative and 2 is even. That is, $(-8)^{3/2} = (\sqrt{-8})^3$, which is undefined because the square root of a negative number is not a real number.

PROPERTIES OF EXPONENTS

Let p and q be rational numbers written in lowest terms. For all real numbers a and b for which the expressions are real numbers, the following properties hold.

1. $a^p \cdot a^q = a^{p+q}$ Product rule for exponents $3^{1/7} \cdot 3^{2/7} = 3^{3/7}$

2. $a^{-p} = \dfrac{1}{a^p}, \; \dfrac{1}{a^{-p}} = a^p$ Negative exponents $7^{-1/4} = \dfrac{1}{7^{1/4}}, \; \dfrac{1}{7^{-1/4}} = 7^{1/4}$

3. $\left(\dfrac{a}{b}\right)^{-p} = \left(\dfrac{b}{a}\right)^{p}$ Negative exponents for quotients $\left(\dfrac{3}{7}\right)^{-1/3} = \left(\dfrac{7}{3}\right)^{1/3}$

4. $\dfrac{a^p}{a^q} = a^{p-q}$ Quotient rule for exponents $\dfrac{5^{4/7}}{5^{1/7}} = 5^{3/7}$

5. $(a^p)^q = a^{pq}$ Power rule for exponents $(2^{1/3})^{1/2} = 2^{1/6}$

6. $(ab)^p = a^p b^p$ Power rule for products $(5x)^{2/3} = 5^{2/3} x^{2/3}$

7. $\left(\dfrac{a}{b}\right)^p = \dfrac{a^p}{b^p}$ Power rule for quotients $\left(\dfrac{5}{3}\right)^{3/4} = \dfrac{5^{3/4}}{3^{3/4}}$

In the next two examples, we apply these properties.

EXAMPLE 7 **Applying properties of exponents**

Write each expression using rational exponents and simplify. Write the answer with a positive exponent. Assume that all variables are positive numbers.

(a) $\sqrt{x} \cdot \sqrt[3]{x}$ **(b)** $\sqrt[3]{27x^2}$ **(c)** $\dfrac{\sqrt[4]{16x}}{\sqrt[3]{x}}$ **(d)** $\left(\dfrac{x^2}{81}\right)^{-1/2}$

Solution

(a) $\sqrt{x} \cdot \sqrt[3]{x} = x^{1/2} \cdot x^{1/3}$ Use rational exponents.

$= x^{1/2 + 1/3}$ Product rule for exponents

$= x^{5/6}$ Simplify: $\frac{1}{2} + \frac{1}{3} = \frac{3}{6} + \frac{2}{6} = \frac{5}{6}$.

(b) $\sqrt[3]{27x^2} = (27x^2)^{1/3}$ Use rational exponents.

$= 27^{1/3}(x^2)^{1/3}$ Power rule for products

$= 3x^{2/3}$ Simplify; power rule for exponents.

(c) $\dfrac{\sqrt[4]{16x}}{\sqrt[3]{x}} = \dfrac{(16x)^{1/4}}{x^{1/3}}$ Use rational exponents.

$= \dfrac{16^{1/4}x^{1/4}}{x^{1/3}}$ Power rule for products

$= 16^{1/4}x^{1/4 - 1/3}$ Quotient rule for exponents

$= 2x^{-1/12}$ Simplify: $\frac{1}{4} - \frac{1}{3} = \frac{3}{12} - \frac{4}{12} = -\frac{1}{12}$.

$= \dfrac{2}{x^{1/12}}$ Negative exponents

(d) $\left(\dfrac{x^2}{81}\right)^{-1/2} = \left(\dfrac{81}{x^2}\right)^{1/2}$ Negative exponents for quotients

$= \dfrac{(81)^{1/2}}{(x^2)^{1/2}}$ Power rule for quotients

$= \dfrac{9}{x}$ Simplify; power rule for exponents.

Now Try Exercises 77, 83, 91, 97

EXAMPLE 8 **Applying properties of exponents**

Write each expression with positive rational exponents and simplify, if possible.

(a) $\sqrt[3]{\sqrt{x + 1}}$ **(b)** $\sqrt[5]{c^{15}}$ **(c)** $\dfrac{y^{-1/2}}{x^{-1/3}}$ **(d)** $\sqrt{x}(\sqrt{x} - 1)$

Solution

(a) $\sqrt[3]{\sqrt{x + 1}} = \left((x + 1)^{1/2}\right)^{1/3} = (x + 1)^{1/6}$

(b) $\sqrt[5]{c^{15}} = c^{15/5} = c^3$

(c) $\dfrac{y^{-1/2}}{x^{-1/3}} = \dfrac{x^{1/3}}{y^{1/2}}$

(d) $\sqrt{x}(\sqrt{x} - 1) = x^{1/2}(x^{1/2} - 1) = x^{1/2}x^{1/2} - x^{1/2} = x - x^{1/2}$

Now Try Exercises 85, 89, 95

5.2 Putting It All Together

CONCEPT	EXPLANATION	EXAMPLES
Rational Exponents	If m and n are positive integers with $\frac{m}{n}$ in lowest terms, $$a^{m/n} = \sqrt[n]{a^m} = \left(\sqrt[n]{a}\right)^m.$$ If $a < 0$ and n is even, $a^{m/n}$ is not a real number.	$8^{4/3} = \left(\sqrt[3]{8}\right)^4 = 2^4 = 16$ $(-27)^{3/4} = \left(\sqrt[4]{-27}\right)^3$ is *not* a real number.
Properties of Exponents	Let p and q be rational numbers. **1.** $a^p \cdot a^q = a^{p+q}$ **2.** $a^{-p} = \dfrac{1}{a^p}, \ \dfrac{1}{a^{-p}} = a^p$ **3.** $\left(\dfrac{a}{b}\right)^{-p} = \left(\dfrac{b}{a}\right)^p$ **4.** $\dfrac{a^p}{a^q} = a^{p-q}$ **5.** $(a^p)^q = a^{pq}$ **6.** $(ab)^p = a^p b^p$ **7.** $\left(\dfrac{a}{b}\right)^p = \dfrac{a^p}{b^p}$	**1.** $2^{1/3} \cdot 2^{2/3} = 2^{1/3+2/3} = 2^1 = 2$ **2.** $2^{-1/2} = \dfrac{1}{2^{1/2}}, \ \dfrac{1}{3^{-1/4}} = 3^{1/4}$ **3.** $\left(\dfrac{3}{4}\right)^{-4/5} = \left(\dfrac{4}{3}\right)^{4/5}$ **4.** $\dfrac{7^{2/3}}{7^{1/3}} = 7^{2/3-1/3} = 7^{1/3}$ **5.** $\left(8^{2/3}\right)^{1/2} = 8^{(2/3)\cdot(1/2)} = 8^{1/3} = 2$ **6.** $(2x)^{1/3} = 2^{1/3} x^{1/3}$ **7.** $\left(\dfrac{x}{y}\right)^{1/6} = \dfrac{x^{1/6}}{y^{1/6}}$

5.2 Exercises

MyMathLab Math XL PRACTICE   WATCH   DOWNLOAD   READ   REVIEW

CONCEPTS AND VOCABULARY

1. Simplify $4^{1/2}$.

2. Simplify $8^{1/3}$.

3. Simplify $4^{-1/2}$.

4. Simplify $8^{-1/3}$.

5. Use a rational exponent to write $\sqrt{x}$.

6. Use a rational exponent to write $\sqrt[3]{a^4}$.

7. Write $a^{1/n}$ in radical notation.

8. Write $a^{m/n}$ in radical notation.

Exercises 9–16: Match the given expression to the expression (a.–h.) that it equals.

9. $\sqrt{x^3}$

10. $\sqrt[3]{8^2}$

11. $25^{-1/2}$

12. $27^{-2/3}$

13. $x^{1/5}$

14. $(x^{1/3})^2$

15. $\sqrt{x} \cdot \sqrt[3]{x}$

16. $\dfrac{x^{1/2}}{x^{1/3}}$

a. $\sqrt[6]{x^5}$

b. $\sqrt[6]{x}$

c. $x^{3/2}$

d. $\sqrt[5]{x}$

e. $\sqrt[3]{x^2}$

f. 4

g. $\frac{1}{5}$

h. $\frac{1}{9}$

CONVERTING FORMS

Exercises 17–26: Use radical notation to write each expression.

17. $7^{1/2}$

18. $10^{1/2}$

19. $a^{1/3}$

20. $y^{1/4}$

21. $x^{5/6}$ **22.** $x^{3/2}$

23. $(x + 5)^{1/2}$ **24.** $(x + y)^{2/3}$

25. $b^{-2/3}$ **26.** $b^{-3/4}$

Exercise 27–36: Use rational exponents to write each expression.

27. $\sqrt{t}$ **28.** $\sqrt[3]{t}$

29. $\sqrt[3]{(x + 1)}$ **30.** $\sqrt{y - 3}$

31. $\dfrac{1}{\sqrt{x + 1}}$ **32.** $\dfrac{1}{\sqrt[3]{x - 3}}$

33. $\sqrt{a^2 - b^2}$ **34.** $\sqrt[3]{a^3 + b^3}$

35. $\dfrac{1}{\sqrt[3]{x^7}}$ **36.** $\dfrac{1}{\sqrt[3]{y^4}}$

RATIONAL EXPONENTS

Exercises 37–44: Approximate to the nearest hundredth.

37. $16^{1/5}$ **38.** $7^{1/4}$

39. $5^{1/3}$ **40.** $11^{1/2}$

41. $9^{3/5}$ **42.** $13^{5/4}$

43. $4^{-3/7}$ **44.** $2^{-3/4}$

Exercises 45–64: Write each expression in radical notation. Evaluate the expression by hand when possible.

45. $9^{1/2}$ **46.** $100^{1/2}$

47. $8^{1/3}$ **48.** $(-8)^{1/3}$

49. $\left(\frac{4}{9}\right)^{1/2}$ **50.** $\left(\frac{64}{27}\right)^{1/3}$

51. $(-8)^{2/3}$ **52.** $(16)^{3/2}$

53. $\left(\frac{1}{8}\right)^{-1/3}$ **54.** $\left(\frac{1}{81}\right)^{-1/4}$

55. $16^{-3/4}$ **56.** $(32)^{-2/5}$

57. $(4^{1/2})^{-3}$ **58.** $(8^{1/3})^{-2}$

59. $z^{1/4}$ **60.** $b^{1/3}$

61. $y^{-2/5}$ **62.** $z^{-3/4}$

63. $(3x)^{1/3}$ **64.** $(5x)^{1/2}$

Exercises 65–72: Use a positive rational exponent to write the expression.

65. $\sqrt{y}$ **66.** $\sqrt{z + 1}$

67. $\sqrt{x} \cdot \sqrt{x}$ **68.** $\sqrt[3]{x} \cdot \sqrt[3]{x}$

69. $\sqrt[3]{8x^2}$ **70.** $\sqrt[3]{27z}$

71. $\dfrac{\sqrt{49x}}{\sqrt[3]{x^2}}$ **72.** $\dfrac{\sqrt[3]{8x}}{\sqrt[4]{x^3}}$

Exercises 73 and 74: **Thinking Generally** *Simplify the expression. Assume that a and b are positive integers.*

73. $(b^{1/a}b^{2/a})^a$ **74.** $b^{(b-1)/b} \cdot \sqrt[b]{b}$

Exercises 75–98: Use positive rational exponents to simplify the expression. Assume that all variables are positive.

75. $(x^2)^{3/2}$ **76.** $(y^4)^{1/2}$

77. $\sqrt[3]{x^3 y^6}$ **78.** $\sqrt{16x^4}$

79. $\sqrt{y^3} \cdot \sqrt[3]{y^2}$ **80.** $\left(\dfrac{x^6}{81}\right)^{1/4}$

81. $\left(\dfrac{x^6}{27}\right)^{2/3}$ **82.** $\left(\dfrac{1}{x^8}\right)^{-1/4}$

83. $\left(\dfrac{x^2}{y^6}\right)^{-1/2}$ **84.** $\dfrac{\sqrt{x}}{\sqrt[3]{27x^6}}$

85. $\sqrt{\sqrt{y}}$ **86.** $\sqrt{\sqrt[3]{(3x)^2}}$

87. $(a^{-1/2})^{4/3}$ **88.** $(x^{-3/2})^{2/3}$

89. $\dfrac{(k^{1/2})^{-3}}{(k^2)^{1/4}}$ **90.** $\dfrac{(b^{3/4})^4}{(b^{4/5})^{-5}}$

91. $\sqrt{b} \cdot \sqrt[4]{b}$ **92.** $\sqrt[3]{t} \cdot \sqrt[5]{t}$

93. $p^{1/2}(p^{3/2} + p^{1/2})$ **94.** $d^{3/4}(d^{1/4} - d^{-1/4})$

95. $\sqrt[3]{x}(\sqrt{x} - \sqrt[3]{x^2})$ **96.** $\frac{1}{2}\sqrt{x}(\sqrt{x} + \sqrt[4]{x^2})$

97. $\dfrac{\sqrt[3]{27x}}{\sqrt{x}}$ **98.** $\dfrac{\sqrt[5]{32x^2}}{\sqrt[3]{8x}}$

APPLICATIONS

99. *Online Videos* (Refer to Example 3.) The function given by $A(x) = 7.3x^{7/16}$ computes the percentage of viewers who abandon an online video after x seconds for $0 \le x \le 120$.
 (a) Make a table of values for $x = 0, 20, 40, 60,$ and 80. Round values to the nearest percent.
 (b) Interpret the table in terms of how people watch online videos.

100. *Online Videos* (Refer to Example 3.) Suppose that the function given by $A(x) = 7.3x^{4/3}$ computes the percentage of viewers who abandon an online video after x seconds. Evaluate $A(10)$. Is this function realistic?

101. *Animal Stepping Frequency* (Refer to Example 6.) Use the formula $N(h) = 1.6h^{-1/2}$ to estimate the stepping frequency of a dog that is 2.5 feet high at the shoulders. (*Source:* C. Pennycuick.)

102. *Animal Pulse Rate* According to one model, an animal's heart rate varies according to its weight. The formula $N(w) = 885w^{-1/2}$ gives an estimate for the average number N of beats per minute for an animal that weighs w pounds. Use the formula to estimate the heart rate for a horse that weighs 800 pounds. (*Source:* C. Pennycuick.)

103. *Bird Wings* Heavier birds tend to have larger wings than lighter birds do. For some birds the relationship between the surface area A of the bird's wings in square inches and its weight W in pounds can be modeled by $A = 100\sqrt[3]{W^2}$. (*Source:* C. Pennycuick, *Newton Rules Biology.*)
(a) Find the area of the wings when the weight is 8 pounds.
(b) Write this formula with rational exponents.

104. *Planet Orbits and Distance* Johannes Kepler (1571–1630) discovered a relationship between a planet's distance D from the sun and the time T it takes to orbit the sun. This formula is $T = \sqrt{D^3}$, where T is in Earth years and $D = 1$ corresponds to the distance between Earth and the sun, or 93,000,000 miles.
(a) The planet Neptune is 30 times farther from the sun than Earth ($D = 30$). Estimate the number of years required for Neptune to orbit the sun.
(b) Write this formula with rational exponents.

105. *Baby's Head Size* If a female baby's head circumference is 32.5 centimeters at birth, then the function given by $H(x) = 35.2x^{3/40}$ gives the infant's head circumference at x months for $1 \le x \le 36$.
(a) Evaluate $H(12)$ and $H(24)$.
(b) Does an infant's head circumference increase the most in the first year or the second year?

106. *Musical Tones* One octave on a piano contains 12 keys (including both the black and white keys). The frequency of each successive key increases by a factor of $2^{1/12}$. For example, middle C is two keys below the first D above it. Therefore the frequency of this D is
$$2^{1/12} \cdot 2^{1/12} = 2^{1/6} \approx 1.12$$
times the frequency of middle C.
(a) If two tones are one octave apart, how do their frequencies compare?
(b) The A tone below middle C on a piano has a frequency of 220 cycles per second. Middle C is 3 keys above this A note. Estimate the frequency of middle C.

107. Online Exploration Go online and look up the shoulder height of three animals of different sizes. Use the formula in Exercise 101 to calculate their stepping frequencies while walking.

108. Online Exploration Go online and look up the weight of three animals of different sizes. Use the formula in Exercise 102 to calculate their heart rates.

WRITING ABOUT MATHEMATICS

109. Explain the meaning of the rational exponent in $x^{3/5}$.

110. Explain the meaning of each expression: $\sqrt[3]{x^5}$ and $(\sqrt[3]{x})^5$. Are these two expressions equal?

Checking Basic Concepts

1. Find the following.
   (a) The square roots of 49
   (b) The principal square root of 49

2. Evaluate.
   (a) $\sqrt[3]{-8}$ **(b)** $-\sqrt[4]{81}$

3. Write the expression in radical notation.
   (a) $x^{3/2}$ **(b)** $x^{2/3}$ **(c)** $x^{-2/5}$

4. Simplify $\sqrt{(x-1)^2}$ for any real number x.

5. Evaluate each function at the given value of x.
   (a) $f(x) = \sqrt{x}$, $x = 9$
   (b) $g(x) = \sqrt[3]{x}$, $x = 125$
   (c) $h(x) = x^{7/12}$, $x = \frac{12}{7}$

5.3 Simplifying Radical Expressions

Product Rule for Radical Expressions • Quotient Rule for Radical Expressions

A LOOK INTO MATH ▶

When a car stops suddenly, it often leaves skid marks. If the car is involved in an accident, authorities often measure the length of the skid marks M and use this information to determine the minimum speed S of the car. One formula that is sometimes used when the road surface is both wet and level is given by $S = \sqrt{9M}$. In Example 4 we simplify this radical expression and estimate the speed of a car based on the length of its skid marks.

Product Rule for Radical Expressions

Consider the following examples of multiplying radical expressions. The equations

$$\sqrt{4} \cdot \sqrt{25} = 2 \cdot 5 = 10 \quad \text{and} \quad \sqrt{4 \cdot 25} = \sqrt{100} = 10$$

NEW VOCABULARY

☐ Perfect nth power
☐ Perfect square
☐ Perfect cube

imply that

$$\sqrt{4} \cdot \sqrt{25} = \sqrt{4 \cdot 25} \quad \text{(see Figure 5.11(a)).}$$

Similarly, the equations

$$\sqrt[3]{8} \cdot \sqrt[3]{27} = 2 \cdot 3 = 6 \quad \text{and} \quad \sqrt[3]{8 \cdot 27} = \sqrt[3]{216} = 6$$

imply that

$$\sqrt[3]{8} \cdot \sqrt[3]{27} = \sqrt[3]{8 \cdot 27} \quad \text{(see Figure 5.11(b)).}$$

(a)	(b)

Figure 5.11

These examples suggest that *the product of the roots is equal to the root of the product.*

PRODUCT RULE FOR RADICAL EXPRESSIONS

Let a and b be real numbers, where $\sqrt[n]{a}$ and $\sqrt[n]{b}$ are both defined. Then

$$\sqrt[n]{a} \cdot \sqrt[n]{b} = \sqrt[n]{a \cdot b}.$$

$$\sqrt[4]{2} \cdot \sqrt[4]{8} = \sqrt[4]{2 \cdot 8}$$

NOTE: The product rule works only when the radicals have the *same index*. For example, the product $\sqrt{2} \cdot \sqrt[3]{4}$ cannot be simplified because the indexes are 2 and 3. (However, by using rational exponents, we can simplify this product. See Example 6(b).)

We apply the product rule in the next two examples.

EXAMPLE 1 **Multiplying radical expressions**

Multiply each radical expression.

(a) $\sqrt{5} \cdot \sqrt{20}$ **(b)** $\sqrt[3]{-3} \cdot \sqrt[3]{9}$ **(c)** $\sqrt[4]{\frac{1}{3}} \cdot \sqrt[4]{\frac{1}{9}} \cdot \sqrt[4]{\frac{1}{3}}$

Solution

(a) $\sqrt{5} \cdot \sqrt{20} = \sqrt{5 \cdot 20} = \sqrt{100} = 10$

(b) $\sqrt[3]{-3} \cdot \sqrt[3]{9} = \sqrt[3]{-3 \cdot 9} = \sqrt[3]{-27} = -3$

(c) The product rule can also be applied to three or more factors. Thus

$$\sqrt[4]{\frac{1}{3}} \cdot \sqrt[4]{\frac{1}{9}} \cdot \sqrt[4]{\frac{1}{3}} = \sqrt[4]{\frac{1}{3} \cdot \frac{1}{9} \cdot \frac{1}{3}} = \sqrt[4]{\frac{1}{81}} = \frac{1}{3},$$

because $\frac{1}{3} \cdot \frac{1}{3} \cdot \frac{1}{3} \cdot \frac{1}{3} = \frac{1}{81}$.

Now Try Exercises 13, 15, 21

EXAMPLE 2 **Multiplying radical expressions containing variables**

Multiply each radical expression. Assume that all variables are positive.

(a) $\sqrt{x} \cdot \sqrt{x^3}$ **(b)** $\sqrt[3]{2a} \cdot \sqrt[3]{5a}$ **(c)** $\sqrt{11} \cdot \sqrt{xy}$ **(d)** $\sqrt[5]{\frac{2x}{y}} \cdot \sqrt[5]{\frac{16y}{x}}$

Solution

(a) $\sqrt{x} \cdot \sqrt{x^3} = \sqrt{x \cdot x^3} = \sqrt{x^4} = x^2$

(b) $\sqrt[3]{2a} \cdot \sqrt[3]{5a} = \sqrt[3]{2a \cdot 5a} = \sqrt[3]{10a^2}$

(c) $\sqrt{11} \cdot \sqrt{xy} = \sqrt{11xy}$

(d) $\sqrt[5]{\frac{2x}{y}} \cdot \sqrt[5]{\frac{16y}{x}} = \sqrt[5]{\frac{2x}{y} \cdot \frac{16y}{x}}$ Product rule

$\qquad = \sqrt[5]{\frac{32xy}{xy}}$ Multiply fractions.

$\qquad = \sqrt[5]{32}$ Simplify.

$\qquad = 2$ $2^5 = 32$

Now Try Exercises 23, 51, 57, 61

An integer a is a **perfect nth power** if there exists an integer b such that $b^n = a$. Thus 36 is a **perfect square** because $6^2 = 36$. Similarly, 8 is a **perfect cube** because $2^3 = 8$, and 81 is a *perfect fourth power* because $3^4 = 81$. Table 5.6 lists examples of perfect squares and perfect cubes.

TABLE 5.6

Perfect Squares	1	4	9	16	25	36
Perfect Cubes	1	8	27	64	125	216

To simplify a square root, we sometimes need to recognize the *largest* perfect square factor of the radicand. For example, 50 has several factors.

$$1, \ 2, \ 5, \ 10, \ 25, \ 50 \quad \text{Factors of 50}$$

From Table 5.6, the perfect square factors of 50 are **1** and **25**. The *largest* perfect square factor of 50 is **25**.

The product rule for radicals can be used to simplify radical expressions. For example, because the largest perfect square factor of 50 is 25, the expression $\sqrt{50}$ can be simplified as

$$\sqrt{50} = \sqrt{25 \cdot 2} = \sqrt{25} \cdot \sqrt{2} = 5\sqrt{2}.$$

This procedure is generalized as follows.

READING CHECK

Explain how to simplify $\sqrt{40}$.

SIMPLIFYING RADICALS (nth ROOTS)

STEP 1: Determine the largest perfect nth power factor of the radicand.

STEP 2: Use the product rule to factor out and simplify this perfect nth power.

> **EXAMPLE 3** ▌ **Simplifying radical expressions**

Simplify each expression.
(a) $\sqrt{300}$ **(b)** $\sqrt[3]{16}$ **(c)** $\sqrt{54}$ **(d)** $\sqrt[4]{512}$

Solution
(a) First note that $300 = 100 \cdot 3$ and that 100 is the largest perfect square factor of 300.

$$\sqrt{300} = \sqrt{100 \cdot 3} = \sqrt{100} \cdot \sqrt{3} = 10\sqrt{3}$$

(b) The largest perfect cube factor of 16 is 8. (See Table 5.6.) Thus

$$\sqrt[3]{16} = \sqrt[3]{8} \cdot \sqrt[3]{2} = 2\sqrt[3]{2}.$$

(c) $\sqrt{54} = \sqrt{9} \cdot \sqrt{6} = 3\sqrt{6}$

(d) $\sqrt[4]{512} = \sqrt[4]{256} \cdot \sqrt[4]{2} = 4\sqrt[4]{2}$ because $4^4 = 256$.

▌ Now Try Exercises 73, 75, 77, 79

▶ **REAL-WORLD CONNECTION** In A Look Into Math at the beginning of this section, we discussed a formula for estimating the minimum speed of a car by using its skid marks. In the next example, we simplify and use this formula.

EXAMPLE 4   **Calculating minimum speed**

A car is in an accident and leaves skid marks on wet, level pavement that are 121 feet long. The formula $S = \sqrt{9M}$ calculates the minimum speed S in miles per hour for skid marks M feet long.
(a) Simplify this formula.
(b) Determine the minimum speed of the car.

Solution
(a) Because 9 is a perfect square, we can factor it out.

$$\sqrt{9M} = \sqrt{9} \cdot \sqrt{M} = 3\sqrt{M}$$

Thus $S = 3\sqrt{M}$.
(b) $S = 3\sqrt{121} = 3 \cdot 11 = 33$ miles per hour.

▍ Now Try Exercise 111

NOTE: To simplify a cube root of a negative number we factor out the negative of the largest perfect cube factor. For example, $-16 = -8 \cdot 2$, so $\sqrt[3]{-16} = \sqrt[3]{-8} \cdot \sqrt[3]{2} = -2\sqrt[3]{2}$. This procedure can be used with any odd root of a negative number. (See Example 5(c).)

EXAMPLE 5   **Simplifying radical expressions**

Simplify each expression. Assume that all variables are positive.
(a) $\sqrt{25x^4}$ **(b)** $\sqrt{32n^3}$ **(c)** $\sqrt[3]{-16x^3y^5}$ **(d)** $\sqrt[3]{2a} \cdot \sqrt[3]{4a^2b}$

Solution
(a) $\sqrt{25x^4} = 5x^2$ Perfect square: $(5x^2)^2 = 25x^4$

(b) $\sqrt{32n^3} = \sqrt{(16n^2)2n}$ $16n^2$ is the largest perfect square factor.

$\qquad\qquad = \sqrt{16n^2} \cdot \sqrt{2n}$ Product rule

$\qquad\qquad = 4n\sqrt{2n}$ $(4n)^2 = 16n^2$

(c) $\sqrt[3]{-16x^3y^5} = \sqrt[3]{(-8x^3y^3)2y^2}$ $8x^3y^3$ is the largest perfect cube factor.

$\qquad\qquad = \sqrt[3]{-8x^3y^3} \cdot \sqrt[3]{2y^2}$ Product rule

$\qquad\qquad = -2xy\sqrt[3]{2y^2}$ $(-2xy)^3 = -8x^3y^3$

(d) $\sqrt[3]{2a} \cdot \sqrt[3]{4a^2b} = \sqrt[3]{(2a)(4a^2b)}$ Product rule

$\qquad\qquad = \sqrt[3]{(8a^3)b}$ $8a^3$ is the largest perfect cube factor.

$\qquad\qquad = \sqrt[3]{8a^3} \cdot \sqrt[3]{b}$ Product rule

$\qquad\qquad = 2a\sqrt[3]{b}$ $(2a)^3 = 8a^3$

▍ Now Try Exercises 45, 85, 89, 91

The product rule for radical expressions cannot be used if the radicals do not have the same indexes. In this case we use rational exponents, as illustrated in the next example.

EXAMPLE 6 **Multiplying radicals with different indexes**

Simplify each expression. Write your answer in radical notation.

(a) $\sqrt{5} \cdot \sqrt[4]{5}$ (b) $\sqrt{2} \cdot \sqrt[3]{4}$ (c) $\sqrt[3]{x} \cdot \sqrt[4]{x}$

Solution

(a) Because $\sqrt{5} = 5^{1/2}$ and $\sqrt[4]{5} = 5^{1/4}$,

$$\sqrt{5} \cdot \sqrt[4]{5} = 5^{1/2} \cdot 5^{1/4} = 5^{1/2+1/4} = 5^{3/4}.$$

In radical notation, $5^{3/4} = \sqrt[4]{5^3} = \sqrt[4]{125}$.

(b) Because $\sqrt[3]{4} = \sqrt[3]{2^2} = 2^{2/3}$,

$$\sqrt{2} \cdot \sqrt[3]{4} = 2^{1/2} \cdot 2^{2/3} = 2^{1/2+2/3} = 2^{7/6}.$$

In radical notation, $2^{7/6} = \sqrt[6]{2^7} = \sqrt[6]{2^6 \cdot 2^1} = \sqrt[6]{2^6} \cdot \sqrt[6]{2} = 2\sqrt[6]{2}$.

(c) $\sqrt[3]{x} \cdot \sqrt[4]{x} = x^{1/3} \cdot x^{1/4} = x^{7/12} = \sqrt[12]{x^7}$

Now Try Exercises 101, 103, 107

Quotient Rule for Radical Expressions

Consider the following examples of dividing radical expressions. The equations

$$\sqrt{\frac{4}{9}} = \sqrt{\frac{2}{3} \cdot \frac{2}{3}} = \frac{2}{3} \quad \text{and} \quad \frac{\sqrt{4}}{\sqrt{9}} = \frac{2}{3}$$

imply that

$$\sqrt{\frac{4}{9}} = \frac{\sqrt{4}}{\sqrt{9}} \quad \text{(see Figure 5.12)}.$$

These examples suggest that *the root of a quotient is equal to the quotient of the roots.*

$\sqrt{(4/9)} \blacktriangleright \text{Frac}$
$\quad\quad\quad\quad 2/3$
$\sqrt{(4)}/\sqrt{(9)} \blacktriangleright \text{Frac}$
$\quad\quad\quad\quad 2/3$

Figure 5.12

CALCULATOR HELP

To use the Frac feature, see Appendix A (pages AP-1 and AP-2).

QUOTIENT RULE FOR RADICAL EXPRESSIONS

Let a and b be real numbers, where $\sqrt[n]{a}$ and $\sqrt[n]{b}$ are both defined and $b \neq 0$. Then

$$\sqrt[n]{\frac{a}{b}} = \frac{\sqrt[n]{a}}{\sqrt[n]{b}}.$$

$$\sqrt[3]{\frac{23}{5}} = \frac{\sqrt[3]{23}}{\sqrt[3]{5}}$$

EXAMPLE 7 **Simplifying quotients**

Simplify each radical expression. Assume that all variables are positive.

(a) $\sqrt[3]{\frac{5}{8}}$ (b) $\sqrt[4]{\frac{x}{16}}$ (c) $\sqrt{\frac{16}{y^2}}$

Solution

(a) $\sqrt[3]{\frac{5}{8}} = \frac{\sqrt[3]{5}}{\sqrt[3]{8}} = \frac{\sqrt[3]{5}}{2}$ (b) $\sqrt[4]{\frac{x}{16}} = \frac{\sqrt[4]{x}}{\sqrt[4]{16}} = \frac{\sqrt[4]{x}}{2}$

(c) $\sqrt{\frac{16}{y^2}} = \frac{\sqrt{16}}{\sqrt{y^2}} = \frac{4}{y}$ because $y > 0$.

Now Try Exercises 25, 27, 29

EXAMPLE 8 | **Simplifying quotients**

Simplify each radical expression. Assume that all variables are positive.

(a) $\dfrac{\sqrt{40}}{\sqrt{10}}$ (b) $\dfrac{\sqrt[3]{2}}{\sqrt[3]{16}}$ (c) $\dfrac{\sqrt{x^2 y}}{\sqrt{y}}$

Solution

(a) $\dfrac{\sqrt{40}}{\sqrt{10}} = \sqrt{\dfrac{40}{10}} = \sqrt{4} = 2$

(b) $\dfrac{\sqrt[3]{2}}{\sqrt[3]{16}} = \sqrt[3]{\dfrac{2}{16}} = \sqrt[3]{\dfrac{1}{8}} = \dfrac{1}{2}$ because $\dfrac{1}{2} \cdot \dfrac{1}{2} \cdot \dfrac{1}{2} = \dfrac{1}{8}.$

(c) $\dfrac{\sqrt{x^2 y}}{\sqrt{y}} = \sqrt{\dfrac{x^2 y}{y}} = \sqrt{x^2} = x$ because $x > 0.$

▪ **Now Try Exercises 33, 39, 41**

MAKING CONNECTIONS

Rules for Radical Expressions and Rational Exponents

The rules for radical expressions are a result of the properties of rational exponents.

$$\sqrt[n]{a \cdot b} = \sqrt[n]{a} \cdot \sqrt[n]{b} \quad \text{is equivalent to} \quad (a \cdot b)^{1/n} = a^{1/n} \cdot b^{1/n}.$$

$$\sqrt[n]{\dfrac{a}{b}} = \dfrac{\sqrt[n]{a}}{\sqrt[n]{b}} \quad \text{is equivalent to} \quad \left(\dfrac{a}{b}\right)^{1/n} = \dfrac{a^{1/n}}{b^{1/n}}.$$

READING CHECK

Use rational exponents to explain why $\sqrt[3]{x} \cdot \sqrt[3]{x} \cdot \sqrt[3]{x} = x.$

EXAMPLE 9 | **Simplifying radical expressions**

Simplify each radical expression. Assume that all variables are positive.

(a) $\sqrt[4]{\dfrac{16x^3}{y^4}}$ (b) $\sqrt{\dfrac{5a^2}{8}} \cdot \sqrt{\dfrac{5a^3}{2}}$

Solution

(a) To simplify this expression, we first use the quotient rule for radical expressions and then apply the product rule for radical expressions.

$$\sqrt[4]{\dfrac{16x^3}{y^4}} = \dfrac{\sqrt[4]{16x^3}}{\sqrt[4]{y^4}} \qquad \text{Quotient rule}$$

$$= \dfrac{\sqrt[4]{16}\,\sqrt[4]{x^3}}{\sqrt[4]{y^4}} \qquad \text{Product rule}$$

$$= \dfrac{2\sqrt[4]{x^3}}{y} \qquad \text{Evaluate 4th roots.}$$

(b) To simplify this expression, we use both the product and quotient rules.

$$\sqrt{\frac{5a^2}{8}} \cdot \sqrt{\frac{5a^3}{2}} = \sqrt{\frac{5a^2 \cdot 5a^3}{8 \cdot 2}} \qquad \text{Product rule}$$

$$= \sqrt{\frac{25a^5}{16}} \qquad \text{Multiply.}$$

$$= \frac{\sqrt{25a^5}}{\sqrt{16}} \qquad \text{Quotient rule}$$

$$= \frac{\sqrt{25a^4 \cdot a}}{\sqrt{16}} \qquad \text{Factor out largest perfect square.}$$

$$= \frac{\sqrt{25a^4} \cdot \sqrt{a}}{\sqrt{16}} \qquad \text{Product rule}$$

$$= \frac{5a^2\sqrt{a}}{4} \qquad (5a^2)^2 = 25a^4$$

█ Now Try Exercises 95, 97

EXAMPLE 10   **Simplifying products and quotients of roots**

Simplify each expression. Assume all radicands are positive.

(a) $\sqrt{x-3} \cdot \sqrt{x+3}$ **(b)** $\dfrac{\sqrt[3]{x^2+3x+2}}{\sqrt[3]{x+1}}$

Solution

(a) Start by applying the product rule for radical expressions.

$$\sqrt{x-3} \cdot \sqrt{x+3} = \sqrt{(x-3)(x+3)} \qquad \text{Product rule}$$

$$= \sqrt{x^2-9} \qquad \text{Multiply binomials.}$$

NOTE: The expression $\sqrt{x^2-9}$ does *not* simplify further. It is important to realize that

$$\sqrt{x^2-9} \neq \sqrt{x^2} - \sqrt{9} = x-3.$$

For example, $\sqrt{5^2-3^2} = \sqrt{16} = 4$, but $\sqrt{5^2} - \sqrt{3^2} = 5-3 = 2$.

(b) Start by applying the quotient rule for radical expressions.

$$\frac{\sqrt[3]{x^2+3x+2}}{\sqrt[3]{x+1}} = \sqrt[3]{\frac{x^2+3x+2}{x+1}} \qquad \text{Quotient rule}$$

$$= \sqrt[3]{\frac{(x+1)(x+2)}{x+1}} \qquad \text{Factor trinomial.}$$

$$= \sqrt[3]{x+2} \qquad \text{Simplify quotient.}$$

█ Now Try Exercises 63, 67

5.3 Putting It All Together

CONCEPT	EXPLANATION	EXAMPLES
Product Rule for Radical Expressions	Let a and b be real numbers, where $\sqrt[n]{a}$ and $\sqrt[n]{b}$ are both defined. Then $$\sqrt[n]{a} \cdot \sqrt[n]{b} = \sqrt[n]{a \cdot b}.$$	$$\sqrt{2} \cdot \sqrt{32} = \sqrt{64} = 8$$ $$\sqrt{500} = \sqrt{100} \cdot \sqrt{5} = 10\sqrt{5}$$
Simplifying Radicals (nth roots)	**STEP 1:** Find the largest perfect nth power factor of the radicand. **STEP 2:** Factor out and simplify this perfect nth power.	$$\sqrt{12} = \sqrt{4 \cdot 3} = \sqrt{4} \cdot \sqrt{3} = 2\sqrt{3}$$ $$\sqrt[3]{81} = \sqrt[3]{27 \cdot 3} = \sqrt[3]{27} \cdot \sqrt[3]{3} = 3\sqrt[3]{3}$$ $$\sqrt[4]{x^5} = \sqrt[4]{x^4 \cdot x} = \sqrt[4]{x^4} \cdot \sqrt[4]{x} = x\sqrt[4]{x},$$ provided $x \geq 0$.
Quotient Rule for Radical Expressions	Let a and b be real numbers, where $\sqrt[n]{a}$ and $\sqrt[n]{b}$ are both defined and $b \neq 0$. Then $$\sqrt[n]{\frac{a}{b}} = \frac{\sqrt[n]{a}}{\sqrt[n]{b}}.$$	$$\frac{\sqrt{60}}{\sqrt{15}} = \sqrt{\frac{60}{15}} = \sqrt{4} = 2$$ $$\sqrt[3]{\frac{x^2}{-27}} = \frac{\sqrt[3]{x^2}}{\sqrt[3]{-27}} = \frac{\sqrt[3]{x^2}}{-3} = -\frac{\sqrt[3]{x^2}}{3}$$

5.3 Exercises

MyMathLab · Math XL PRACTICE · WATCH · DOWNLOAD · READ · REVIEW

CONCEPTS AND VOCABULARY

1. Does $\sqrt{2} \cdot \sqrt{3}$ equal $\sqrt{6}$?

2. Does $\sqrt{5} \cdot \sqrt[3]{5}$ equal 5?

3. $\sqrt[3]{a} \cdot \sqrt[3]{b} = $ _____

4. $\dfrac{\sqrt{a}}{\sqrt{b}} = \sqrt{?}$

5. $\dfrac{\sqrt[n]{a}}{\sqrt[n]{b}} = \sqrt[n]{?}$

6. $\dfrac{\sqrt{3}}{\sqrt{27}} = $ _____

7. Does $\sqrt{50} = \sqrt{25} + \sqrt{25}$?

8. Does $\sqrt{50} = 5\sqrt{2}$?

9. Is $\sqrt[3]{3}$ equal to 1? Explain.

10. Is 64 a perfect cube? Explain.

MULTIPLYING AND DIVIDING

Exercises 11–62: Simplify the expression. Assume that all variables are positive.

11. $\sqrt{3} \cdot \sqrt{3}$

12. $\sqrt{2} \cdot \sqrt{18}$

13. $\sqrt{2} \cdot \sqrt{50}$

14. $\sqrt[3]{-2} \cdot \sqrt[3]{-4}$

15. $\sqrt[3]{4} \cdot \sqrt[3]{16}$

16. $\sqrt[3]{x} \cdot \sqrt[3]{x^2}$

17. $\sqrt{\dfrac{9}{25}}$

18. $\sqrt[3]{\dfrac{x}{8}}$

19. $\sqrt{\dfrac{1}{2}} \cdot \sqrt{\dfrac{1}{8}}$

20. $\sqrt{\dfrac{5}{3}} \cdot \sqrt{\dfrac{1}{3}}$

21. $\sqrt[3]{\dfrac{2}{3}} \cdot \sqrt[3]{\dfrac{4}{3}} \cdot \sqrt[3]{\dfrac{1}{3}}$

22. $\sqrt[4]{\dfrac{8}{3}} \cdot \sqrt[4]{\dfrac{4}{9}} \cdot \sqrt[4]{\dfrac{8}{3}}$

23. $\sqrt{x^3} \cdot \sqrt{x^3}$

24. $\sqrt{z} \cdot \sqrt{z^7}$

25. $\sqrt[3]{\dfrac{7}{27}}$

26. $\sqrt[3]{\dfrac{9}{64}}$

27. $\sqrt[4]{\dfrac{x}{81}}$

28. $\sqrt[4]{\dfrac{16x}{81}}$

29. $\sqrt{\dfrac{9}{z^2}}$

30. $\sqrt{\dfrac{x^2}{81}}$

31. $\sqrt{\dfrac{x}{2}} \cdot \sqrt{\dfrac{x}{8}}$

32. $\sqrt{\dfrac{4}{y}} \cdot \sqrt{\dfrac{y}{5}}$

33. $\dfrac{\sqrt{45}}{\sqrt{5}}$

34. $\dfrac{\sqrt{7}}{\sqrt{28}}$

35. $\sqrt[3]{-4} \cdot \sqrt[3]{-16}$

36. $\sqrt[3]{9} \cdot \sqrt[3]{3}$

37. $\sqrt[4]{9} \cdot \sqrt[4]{9}$

38. $\sqrt[5]{16} \cdot \sqrt[5]{-2}$

39. $\dfrac{\sqrt[5]{64}}{\sqrt[5]{-2}}$

40. $\dfrac{\sqrt[4]{324}}{\sqrt[4]{4}}$

41. $\dfrac{\sqrt{a^2 b}}{\sqrt{b}}$

42. $\dfrac{\sqrt{4xy^2}}{\sqrt{x}}$

43. $\dfrac{\sqrt[3]{54}}{\sqrt[3]{2}}$

44. $\dfrac{\sqrt[3]{x^3 y^7}}{\sqrt[3]{y^4}}$

45. $\sqrt{4x^4}$

46. $\sqrt[3]{-8y^3}$

47. $\sqrt[3]{-5a^6}$

48. $\sqrt{9x^2y}$

49. $\sqrt[4]{16x^4y}$

50. $\sqrt[3]{8xy^3}$

51. $\sqrt{3x} \cdot \sqrt{12x}$

52. $\sqrt{6x^5} \cdot \sqrt{6x}$

53. $\sqrt[3]{8x^6y^3z^9}$

54. $\sqrt{16x^4y^6}$

55. $\sqrt[4]{\dfrac{3}{4}} \cdot \sqrt[4]{\dfrac{27}{4}}$

56. $\sqrt[5]{\dfrac{4}{-9}} \cdot \sqrt[5]{\dfrac{8}{-27}}$

57. $\sqrt[3]{12} \cdot \sqrt[3]{ab}$

58. $\sqrt{5x} \cdot \sqrt{5z}$

59. $\sqrt[4]{25z} \cdot \sqrt[4]{25z}$

60. $\sqrt[5]{3z^2} \cdot \sqrt[5]{7z}$

61. $\sqrt[5]{\dfrac{7a}{b^2}} \cdot \sqrt[5]{\dfrac{b^2}{7a^6}}$

62. $\sqrt[3]{\dfrac{8m}{n}} \cdot \sqrt[3]{\dfrac{n^4}{m^2}}$

Exercises 63–68: Use properties of polynomials to simplify the expression. Assume all radicands are positive.

63. $\sqrt{x+4} \cdot \sqrt{x-4}$

64. $\sqrt[3]{x-1} \cdot \sqrt[3]{x^2+x+1}$

65. $\sqrt[3]{a+1} \cdot \sqrt[3]{a^2-a+1}$

66. $\sqrt{b-1} \cdot \sqrt{b+1}$

67. $\dfrac{\sqrt{x^2+2x+1}}{\sqrt{x+1}}$

68. $\dfrac{\sqrt{x^2-4x+4}}{\sqrt{x-2}}$

Exercises 69–74: Complete the equation.

69. $\sqrt{500} = $ _____ $\sqrt{5}$

70. $\sqrt{28} = $ _____ $\sqrt{7}$

71. $\sqrt{8} = $ _____ $\sqrt{2}$

72. $\sqrt{99} = $ _____ $\sqrt{11}$

73. $\sqrt{45} = $ _____ $\sqrt{5}$

74. $\sqrt{243} = $ _____ $\sqrt{3}$

Exercises 75–98: Simplify the radical expression by factoring out the largest perfect nth power. Assume that all variables are positive.

75. $\sqrt{200}$

76. $\sqrt{72}$

77. $\sqrt[3]{81}$

78. $\sqrt[3]{256}$

79. $\sqrt[4]{64}$

80. $\sqrt[5]{27 \cdot 81}$

81. $\sqrt[5]{-64}$

82. $\sqrt[3]{-81}$

83. $\sqrt{b^5}$

84. $\sqrt{t^3}$

85. $\sqrt{8n^3}$

86. $\sqrt{32a^2}$

87. $\sqrt{12a^2b^5}$

88. $\sqrt{20a^3b^2}$

89. $\sqrt[3]{-125x^4y^5}$

90. $\sqrt[3]{-81a^5b^2}$

91. $\sqrt[3]{5t} \cdot \sqrt[3]{125t}$

92. $\sqrt[4]{4bc^3} \cdot \sqrt[4]{64ab^3c^2}$

93. $\sqrt[4]{\dfrac{9t^5}{r^8}} \cdot \sqrt[4]{\dfrac{9r}{5t}}$

94. $\sqrt[5]{\dfrac{4t^6}{r}} \cdot \sqrt[5]{\dfrac{8t}{r^6}}$

95. $\sqrt[3]{\dfrac{27x^2}{y^3}}$

96. $\sqrt[4]{\dfrac{32x^8}{z^4}}$

97. $\sqrt{\dfrac{7a^2}{27}} \cdot \sqrt{\dfrac{7a}{3}}$

98. $\sqrt{\dfrac{8a}{125}} \cdot \sqrt{\dfrac{2a}{5}}$

Exercises 99 and 100: **Thinking Generally** *Let m and n be positive integers and assume each expression exists.*

99. Simplify $\left(\sqrt[mn]{a^m b^m}\right)^n$ so that it equals ab.

100. Simplify $\left(\sqrt[mn]{a^n b^m}\right) \cdot \left(\sqrt[mn]{a^m b^m}\right)$ so that it equals $\sqrt[m]{ab} \cdot \sqrt[n]{ab}$.

Exercises 101–110: Simplify the expression. Let all variables be positive and write your answer in radical notation.

101. $\sqrt{3} \cdot \sqrt[3]{3}$

102. $\sqrt{5} \cdot \sqrt[3]{5}$

103. $\sqrt[4]{8} \cdot \sqrt[3]{4}$

104. $\sqrt[5]{16} \cdot \sqrt{2}$

105. $\sqrt[4]{27} \cdot \sqrt[3]{9} \cdot \sqrt{3}$

106. $\sqrt[5]{16} \cdot \sqrt[3]{16}$

107. $\sqrt[4]{x^3} \cdot \sqrt[3]{x}$

108. $\sqrt[4]{x^3} \cdot \sqrt{x}$

109. $\sqrt[4]{rt} \cdot \sqrt[3]{r^2t}$

110. $\sqrt[3]{a^3b^2} \cdot \sqrt{a^2b}$

APPLICATIONS

111. *Minimum Speed* (Refer to Example 4.) If the pavement is dry cement, then $S = \sqrt{25M}$ is an estimate for a car's speed S in miles per hour when it leaves skid marks M feet long.
(a) Simplify this formula.
(b) Determine the minimum speed of the car if the skid marks are 100 feet.

112. *Minimum Speed* (Refer to Example 4.) If the road surface is gravel, then $S = \sqrt{15M}$ is an estimate for a car's speed S in miles per hour when it leaves skid marks M feet long in the gravel. Determine the minimum speed of the car if the skid marks are 30 feet.

WRITING ABOUT MATHEMATICS

113. Explain what it means for a positive integer to be a *perfect square* or a *perfect cube*. List the positive integers that are perfect squares and less than 101. List the positive integers that are perfect cubes and less than 220.

114. Explain how the product and quotient rules for radical expressions are the result of properties of rational exponents.

Group Activity   Working with Real Data

Directions: Form a group of 2 to 4 people. Select someone to record the group's responses for this activity. All members of the group should work cooperatively to answer the questions. If your instructor asks for your results, each member of the group should be prepared to respond.

Designing a Paper Cup A paper drinking cup is being designed in the shape shown in the accompanying figure. The amount of paper needed to manufacture the cup is determined by the surface area S of the cup, which is given by

$$S = \pi r \sqrt{r^2 + h^2},$$

where r is the radius and h is the height.

(a) Approximate S to the nearest hundredth when $r = 1.5$ inches and $h = 4$ inches.
(b) Could the formula for S be simplified as follows?

$$\pi r \sqrt{r^2 + h^2} \overset{?}{=} \pi r (\sqrt{r^2} + \sqrt{h^2})$$
$$\overset{?}{=} \pi r (r + h)$$

Try evaluating this second formula with $r = 1.5$ inches and $h = 4$ inches. Is your answer the same as in part (a)? Explain.
(c) Discuss why evaluating real-world formulas correctly is important.
(d) In general, does $\sqrt{a + b}$ equal $\sqrt{a} + \sqrt{b}$? Justify your answer by completing the following table. Approximate answers to the nearest hundredth when appropriate.

a	b	$\sqrt{a + b}$	$\sqrt{a} + \sqrt{b}$
0	4		
4	0		
5	4		
9	7		
4	16		
25	100		

5.4   Operations on Radical Expressions

Addition and Subtraction • Multiplication • Rationalizing the Denominator

A LOOK INTO MATH ▶ Our productivity as a nation has increased significantly during the past 70 years because of new technology. For example, if a typical business bought $10,000 in equipment per worker in 2005, it would have generated about $48,000 per worker in revenue. This same investment by a business in 1935 would have generated only $23,000 in revenue (adjusted to 2005 dollars). This situation can be described by the following two functions.

$$N(x) = 400\sqrt{x} + 8000 \quad \text{and} \quad O(x) = 195\sqrt{x} + 3500$$
2005 technology (new)   1935 technology (old)

What does the difference of these two functions represent? In this section we learn how to subtract expressions that contain radicals. See Example 7.

NEW VOCABULARY

☐ Like radicals
☐ Rationalizing the denominator
☐ Conjugate

Addition and Subtraction

We can add $2x^2$ and $5x^2$ to obtain $7x^2$ because they are *like* terms. That is,

$$2x^2 + 5x^2 = (2 + 5)x^2 = 7x^2. \quad \text{Like terms}$$

We can also add and subtract *like radicals*. **Like radicals** *have the same index and the same radicand*. For example, we can add $3\sqrt{2}$ and $5\sqrt{2}$ because they are like radicals.

$$3\sqrt{2} + 5\sqrt{2} = (3 + 5)\sqrt{2} = 8\sqrt{2} \quad \text{Like radicals}$$

EXAMPLE 1 **Adding like radicals**

If possible, add the expressions and simplify.

(a) $10\sqrt{11} + 4\sqrt{11}$ **(b)** $5\sqrt[3]{6} + \sqrt[3]{6}$

(c) $4 + 5\sqrt{3}$ **(d)** $\sqrt{7} + \sqrt{11}$

Solution

(a) These terms are like radicals because they have the same index, 2, and the same radicand, 11.

$$10\sqrt{11} + 4\sqrt{11} = (10 + 4)\sqrt{11} = 14\sqrt{11}$$

(b) These terms are like radicals because they have the same index, 3, and the same radicand, 6. Note that the coefficient on the second term is understood to be 1.

$$5\sqrt[3]{6} + 1\sqrt[3]{6} = (5 + 1)\sqrt[3]{6} = 6\sqrt[3]{6}$$

(c) The expression $4 + 5\sqrt{3}$ can be written as $4\sqrt{1} + 5\sqrt{3}$. These terms cannot be added because they are not like radicals.

NOTE: $4 + 5\sqrt{3} \neq 9\sqrt{3}$ because multiplication is performed before addition.

(d) The expression $\sqrt{7} + \sqrt{11}$ contains unlike radicals that *cannot* be added.

Now Try Exercises 19, 21, 23, 25

Sometimes two radical expressions that are not alike can be added by changing them to like radicals. For example, $\sqrt{20}$ and $\sqrt{5}$ are unlike radicals. However,

because $\qquad \sqrt{20} = \sqrt{4 \cdot 5} = \sqrt{4} \cdot \sqrt{5} = 2\sqrt{5},$

we have $\qquad \sqrt{20} + \sqrt{5} = 2\sqrt{5} + 1\sqrt{5} = 3\sqrt{5}.$

We cannot combine $x + x^2$ because they are unlike terms. Similarly, we cannot combine $\sqrt{2} + \sqrt{5}$ because they are unlike radicals. When combining radicals, the first step is to see if we can write pairs of terms as like radicals, as demonstrated in the next example.

EXAMPLE 2 **Finding like radicals**

Write each pair of terms as like radicals, if possible.

(a) $\sqrt{45}, \sqrt{20}$ **(b)** $\sqrt{27}, \sqrt{5}$ **(c)** $5\sqrt[3]{16}, 4\sqrt[3]{54}$

Solution

(a) The expressions $\sqrt{45}$ and $\sqrt{20}$ are unlike radicals. However, they can be changed to like radicals, as follows.

$$\sqrt{45} = \sqrt{9 \cdot 5} = \sqrt{9} \cdot \sqrt{5} = 3\sqrt{5} \quad \text{and}$$

$$\sqrt{20} = \sqrt{4 \cdot 5} = \sqrt{4} \cdot \sqrt{5} = 2\sqrt{5}$$

The expressions $3\sqrt{5}$ and $2\sqrt{5}$ are like radicals.

READING CHECK

What are like radicals?

(b) Because $\sqrt{27} = \sqrt{9 \cdot 3} = \sqrt{9} \cdot \sqrt{3} = 3\sqrt{3}$, the given expressions $\sqrt{27}$ and $\sqrt{5}$ are unlike radicals and cannot be written as like radicals.

(c) $5\sqrt[3]{16} = 5\sqrt[3]{8 \cdot 2} = 5\sqrt[3]{8} \cdot \sqrt[3]{2} = 5 \cdot 2 \cdot \sqrt[3]{2} = 10\sqrt[3]{2}$ and

$4\sqrt[3]{54} = 4\sqrt[3]{27 \cdot 2} = 4\sqrt[3]{27} \cdot \sqrt[3]{2} = 4 \cdot 3 \cdot \sqrt[3]{2} = 12\sqrt[3]{2}$

The expressions $10\sqrt[3]{2}$ and $12\sqrt[3]{2}$ are like radicals.

▌ Now Try Exercises 9, 11, 13

We use these techniques to add radical expressions in the next two examples.

EXAMPLE 3 **Adding radical expressions**

Add the expressions and simplify.

(a) $\sqrt{12} + 7\sqrt{3}$ **(b)** $\sqrt[3]{16} + \sqrt[3]{2}$ **(c)** $3\sqrt{2} + \sqrt{8} + \sqrt{18}$

Solution

(a)
$$
\begin{aligned}
\sqrt{12} + 7\sqrt{3} &= \sqrt{4 \cdot 3} + 7\sqrt{3} \\
&= \sqrt{4} \cdot \sqrt{3} + 7\sqrt{3} \\
&= 2\sqrt{3} + 7\sqrt{3} \\
&= 9\sqrt{3}
\end{aligned}
$$

(b)
$$
\begin{aligned}
\sqrt[3]{16} + \sqrt[3]{2} &= \sqrt[3]{8 \cdot 2} + \sqrt[3]{2} \\
&= \sqrt[3]{8} \cdot \sqrt[3]{2} + \sqrt[3]{2} \\
&= 2\sqrt[3]{2} + 1\sqrt[3]{2} \\
&= 3\sqrt[3]{2}
\end{aligned}
$$

(c)
$$
\begin{aligned}
3\sqrt{2} + \sqrt{8} + \sqrt{18} &= 3\sqrt{2} + \sqrt{4 \cdot 2} + \sqrt{9 \cdot 2} \\
&= 3\sqrt{2} + \sqrt{4} \cdot \sqrt{2} + \sqrt{9} \cdot \sqrt{2} \\
&= 3\sqrt{2} + 2\sqrt{2} + 3\sqrt{2} \\
&= 8\sqrt{2}
\end{aligned}
$$

▌ Now Try Exercises 29, 31, 43

EXAMPLE 4 **Adding radical expressions**

Add the expressions and simplify. Assume that all variables are positive.

(a) $\sqrt[4]{32} + 3\sqrt[4]{2}$ **(b)** $-2\sqrt{4x} + \sqrt{x}$ **(c)** $3\sqrt{3k} + 5\sqrt{12k} + 9\sqrt{48k}$

Solution

(a) Because $\sqrt[4]{32} = \sqrt[4]{16 \cdot 2} = \sqrt[4]{16} \cdot \sqrt[4]{2} = 2\sqrt[4]{2}$, we can add and simplify as follows.

$$\sqrt[4]{32} + 3\sqrt[4]{2} = 2\sqrt[4]{2} + 3\sqrt[4]{2} = 5\sqrt[4]{2}$$

(b) Note that $\sqrt{4x} = \sqrt{4} \cdot \sqrt{x} = 2\sqrt{x}$.

$$-2\sqrt{4x} + \sqrt{x} = -2(2\sqrt{x}) + \sqrt{x} = -4\sqrt{x} + 1\sqrt{x} = -3\sqrt{x}$$

(c) Note that $\sqrt{12k} = \sqrt{4} \cdot \sqrt{3k} = 2\sqrt{3k}$ and that $\sqrt{48k} = \sqrt{16} \cdot \sqrt{3k} = 4\sqrt{3k}$.

$$
\begin{aligned}
3\sqrt{3k} + 5\sqrt{12k} + 9\sqrt{48k} &= 3\sqrt{3k} + 5(2\sqrt{3k}) + 9(4\sqrt{3k}) \\
&= (3 + 10 + 36)\sqrt{3k} \\
&= 49\sqrt{3k}
\end{aligned}
$$

▌ Now Try Exercises 45, 47, 49

Subtraction of radical expressions is similar to addition, as illustrated in the next three examples.

EXAMPLE 5 **Subtracting like radicals**

Simplify the expressions.

(a) $5\sqrt{7} - 3\sqrt{7}$ **(b)** $8\sqrt[3]{5} - 3\sqrt[3]{5} + \sqrt[3]{11}$ **(c)** $5\sqrt{z} + \sqrt[3]{z} - 2\sqrt{z}$

Solution

(a) $\qquad 5\sqrt{7} - 3\sqrt{7} = (5 - 3)\sqrt{7} = 2\sqrt{7}$

(b) $8\sqrt[3]{5} - 3\sqrt[3]{5} + \sqrt[3]{11} = (8 - 3)\sqrt[3]{5} + \sqrt[3]{11} = 5\sqrt[3]{5} + \sqrt[3]{11}$

(c) $\quad 5\sqrt{z} + \sqrt[3]{z} - 2\sqrt{z} = 5\sqrt{z} - 2\sqrt{z} + \sqrt[3]{z}$ \qquad Commutative property

$\qquad\qquad\qquad\qquad = (5 - 2)\sqrt{z} + \sqrt[3]{z}$ \qquad Distributive property

$\qquad\qquad\qquad\qquad = 3\sqrt{z} + \sqrt[3]{z}$ \qquad Subtract.

NOTE: We cannot combine $3\sqrt{z} + \sqrt[3]{z}$ because their indexes are different. That is, one term is a square root and the other is a cube root.

▌ Now Try Exercises 33, 35, 39

EXAMPLE 6 **Subtracting radical expressions**

Subtract and simplify. Assume that all variables are positive.

(a) $3\sqrt[3]{xy^2} - 2\sqrt[3]{xy^2}$ **(b)** $\sqrt{16x^3} - \sqrt{x^3}$ **(c)** $\sqrt[3]{\dfrac{5x}{27}} - \dfrac{\sqrt[3]{5x}}{6}$

Solution

(a) $3\sqrt[3]{xy^2} - 2\sqrt[3]{xy^2} = (3 - 2)\sqrt[3]{xy^2} = \sqrt[3]{xy^2}$

(b) $\quad \sqrt{16x^3} - \sqrt{x^3} = \sqrt{16x^2} \cdot \sqrt{x} - \sqrt{x^2} \cdot \sqrt{x}$ \qquad Factor out perfect squares.

$\qquad\qquad\qquad\quad = 4x\sqrt{x} - x\sqrt{x}$ \qquad Simplify.

$\qquad\qquad\qquad\quad = (4x - x)\sqrt{x}$ \qquad Distributive property

$\qquad\qquad\qquad\quad = 3x\sqrt{x}$ \qquad Subtract.

(c) $\quad \sqrt[3]{\dfrac{5x}{27}} - \dfrac{\sqrt[3]{5x}}{6} = \dfrac{\sqrt[3]{5x}}{\sqrt[3]{27}} - \dfrac{\sqrt[3]{5x}}{6}$ \qquad Quotient rule for radical expressions

$\qquad\qquad\qquad\qquad = \dfrac{\sqrt[3]{5x}}{3} - \dfrac{\sqrt[3]{5x}}{6}$ \qquad Evaluate $\sqrt[3]{27} = 3$.

$\qquad\qquad\qquad\qquad = \dfrac{2\sqrt[3]{5x}}{6} - \dfrac{\sqrt[3]{5x}}{6}$ \qquad Find a common denominator.

$\qquad\qquad\qquad\qquad = \dfrac{2\sqrt[3]{5x} - \sqrt[3]{5x}}{6}$ \qquad Subtract numerators.

$\qquad\qquad\qquad\qquad = \dfrac{\sqrt[3]{5x}}{6}$ \qquad Simplify.

▌ Now Try Exercises 55, 63, 65

▶ **REAL-WORLD CONNECTION** In A Look Into Math at the beginning of this section, we discussed how functions with radicals could describe an increase in productivity due to technology. In the next example, we calculate the difference of these two functions and interpret the result.

EXAMPLE 7   **Increasing productivity with new technology**

The functions given by

$$N(x) = 400\sqrt{x} + 8000 \quad \text{and} \quad O(x) = 195\sqrt{x} + 3500$$

2005 technology (new)   1935 technology (old)

approximate the increase in revenue resulting from investing x dollars in equipment (per worker).
(a) Find their difference $D(x) = N(x) - O(x)$. Simplify your answer.
(b) Evaluate $D(40{,}000)$ and interpret the result.

Solution
(a) $D(x) = N(x) - O(x)$

$\qquad = (400\sqrt{x} + 8000) - (195\sqrt{x} + 3500)$ Substitute.

$\qquad = 400\sqrt{x} - 195\sqrt{x} + 8000 - 3500$ Rewrite terms.

$\qquad = (400 - 195)\sqrt{x} + 4500$ Distributive property

$\qquad = 205\sqrt{x} + 4500$ Simplify.

The difference is given by $D(x) = 205\sqrt{x} + 4500$.
(b) $D(40{,}000) = 205\sqrt{40{,}000} + 4500 = \$45{,}500$. An investment of \$40,000 per worker resulted in \$45,500 *more* revenue per worker in 2005 than in 1935 (adjusted to 2005 dollars).

Now Try Exercise 81

EXAMPLE 8   **Subtracting radical expressions**

Subtract and simplify. Assume that all variables are positive.

(a) $\dfrac{5\sqrt{2}}{3} - \dfrac{2\sqrt{2}}{4}$ **(b)** $\sqrt[4]{81a^5b^6} - \sqrt[4]{16ab^2}$ **(c)** $3\sqrt[3]{\dfrac{n^5}{27}} - 2\sqrt[3]{n^2}$

Solution

(a) $\dfrac{5\sqrt{2}}{3} - \dfrac{2\sqrt{2}}{4} = \dfrac{5\sqrt{2}}{3}\cdot\dfrac{4}{4} - \dfrac{2\sqrt{2}}{4}\cdot\dfrac{3}{3}$ LCD is 12.

$\qquad = \dfrac{20\sqrt{2}}{12} - \dfrac{6\sqrt{2}}{12}$ Multiply fractions.

$\qquad = \dfrac{14\sqrt{2}}{12}$ Subtract numerators.

$\qquad = \dfrac{7\sqrt{2}}{6}$ Simplify.

(b) $\sqrt[4]{81a^5b^6} - \sqrt[4]{16ab^2} = \sqrt[4]{81a^4b^4}\cdot\sqrt[4]{ab^2} - \sqrt[4]{16}\cdot\sqrt[4]{ab^2}$ Factor out perfect powers.

$\qquad = 3ab\sqrt[4]{ab^2} - 2\sqrt[4]{ab^2}$ Simplify.

$\qquad = (3ab - 2)\sqrt[4]{ab^2}$ Distributive property

(c) $3\sqrt[3]{\dfrac{n^5}{27}} - 2\sqrt[3]{n^2} = 3\sqrt[3]{\dfrac{n^3}{27}} \cdot \sqrt[3]{n^2} - 2\sqrt[3]{n^2}$ Factor out perfect cube.

$\qquad\qquad\qquad = \dfrac{3\sqrt[3]{n^3}}{\sqrt[3]{27}} \cdot \sqrt[3]{n^2} - 2\sqrt[3]{n^2}$ Quotient rule

$\qquad\qquad\qquad = n\sqrt[3]{n^2} - 2\sqrt[3]{n^2}$ Simplify: $\sqrt[3]{n^3} = n$ and $\sqrt[3]{27} = 3$.

$\qquad\qquad\qquad = (n - 2)\sqrt[3]{n^2}$ Distributive property

▮ **Now Try Exercises 69, 77, 79**

Radicals often occur in geometry. In the next example, we find the perimeter of a triangle by adding radical expressions.

EXAMPLE 9   **Finding the perimeter of a triangle**

√50 feet

√18 feet

√32 feet

Figure 5.13

Find the *exact* perimeter of the right triangle shown in Figure 5.13. Then approximate your answer to the nearest hundredth of a foot.

Solution

The sum of the lengths of the sides of the triangle is

$$\sqrt{18} + \sqrt{32} + \sqrt{50} = 3\sqrt{2} + 4\sqrt{2} + 5\sqrt{2} = 12\sqrt{2}.$$

The perimeter is $12\sqrt{2} \approx 16.97$ feet.

▮ **Now Try Exercise 125**

Multiplication

Some types of radical expressions can be multiplied like binomials. For example, because

$$(x + 1)(x + 2) = x^2 + 3x + 2,$$

we have $(\sqrt{x} + 1)(\sqrt{x} + 2) = (\sqrt{x})^2 + 2\sqrt{x} + 1\sqrt{x} + 2 = x + 3\sqrt{x} + 2,$

provided that $x \geq 0$. The next example demonstrates this technique.

EXAMPLE 10   **Multiplying radical expressions**

Multiply and simplify.
(a) $(\sqrt{b} - 4)(\sqrt{b} + 5)$ **(b)** $(4 + \sqrt{3})(4 - \sqrt{3})$

Solution

(a) This expression can be multiplied and then simplified.

$$(\sqrt{b} - 4)(\sqrt{b} + 5) = \sqrt{b} \cdot \sqrt{b} + 5\sqrt{b} - 4\sqrt{b} - 4 \cdot 5$$

$$= b + \sqrt{b} - 20$$

Compare this product with $(b - 4)(b + 5) = b^2 + b - 20$.

(b) This expression is in the form $(a + b)(a - b)$, which equals $a^2 - b^2$.

$$(4 + \sqrt{3})(4 - \sqrt{3}) = (4)^2 - (\sqrt{3})^2 \qquad a = 4, b = \sqrt{3}$$
$$= 16 - 3$$
$$= 13$$

▌ Now Try Exercises 85, 87

NOTE: Example 10(b) illustrates a special case for multiplying radicals. In general,

$$(\sqrt{a} + \sqrt{b})(\sqrt{a} - \sqrt{b}) = (\sqrt{a})^2 - (\sqrt{b})^2 = a - b,$$

provided a and b are nonnegative.

Rationalizing the Denominator

In mathematics it is common to write expressions without radicals in the denominator. Quotients containing radical expressions in the numerator or denominator can appear to be different but actually be equal. For example, $\frac{1}{\sqrt{3}}$ and $\frac{\sqrt{3}}{3}$ represent the same real number even though they look as though they are unequal. To show that they are equal, we multiply the first quotient by 1 in the form $\frac{\sqrt{3}}{\sqrt{3}}$.

$$\frac{1}{\sqrt{3}} \cdot \frac{\sqrt{3}}{\sqrt{3}} = \frac{1 \cdot \sqrt{3}}{\sqrt{3} \cdot \sqrt{3}} = \frac{\sqrt{3}}{3}$$

If the denominator of a quotient contains only one term with one square root, then we can rationalize the denominator by multiplying the numerator and denominator by this square root. For example, the denominator of $\frac{1}{\sqrt{3}}$ contains one term, which is $\sqrt{3}$. Therefore, we multiplied $\frac{1}{\sqrt{3}}$ by $\frac{\sqrt{3}}{\sqrt{3}}$ to rationalize the denominator.

NOTE: $\sqrt{b} \cdot \sqrt{b} = \sqrt{b^2} = b$ for any *positive* number b.

One way to *standardize* radical expressions is to remove any radical expressions from the denominator. This process is called **rationalizing the denominator**. Exercise 133 suggests one reason why people rationalized denominators before calculators were invented. The next example demonstrates how to rationalize the denominator of several quotients.

EXAMPLE 11   **Rationalizing the denominator**

Rationalize each denominator. Assume that all variables are positive.

(a) $\dfrac{1}{\sqrt{2}}$ **(b)** $\dfrac{3}{5\sqrt{3}}$ **(c)** $\sqrt{\dfrac{x}{24}}$ **(d)** $\dfrac{xy}{\sqrt{y^3}}$

Solution

(a) We start by multiplying this expression by 1 in the form $\frac{\sqrt{2}}{\sqrt{2}}$.

$$\frac{1}{\sqrt{2}} \cdot \frac{\sqrt{2}}{\sqrt{2}} = \frac{\sqrt{2}}{\sqrt{4}} = \frac{\sqrt{2}}{2}$$

Note that the expression $\frac{\sqrt{2}}{2}$ does not have a radical in the denominator.

(b) We multiply $\dfrac{3}{5\sqrt{3}}$ by 1 in the form $\dfrac{\sqrt{3}}{\sqrt{3}}$.

$$\frac{3}{5\sqrt{3}} \cdot \frac{\sqrt{3}}{\sqrt{3}} = \frac{3\sqrt{3}}{5\sqrt{9}} = \frac{3\sqrt{3}}{5\cdot 3} = \frac{\sqrt{3}}{5}$$

(c) Because $\sqrt{24} = \sqrt{4}\cdot\sqrt{6} = 2\sqrt{6}$, we start by simplifying $\sqrt{\dfrac{x}{24}}$.

$$\sqrt{\frac{x}{24}} = \frac{\sqrt{x}}{\sqrt{24}} = \frac{\sqrt{x}}{2\sqrt{6}}$$

To rationalize the denominator we multiply this expression by 1 in the form $\dfrac{\sqrt{6}}{\sqrt{6}}$.

$$\frac{\sqrt{x}}{2\sqrt{6}} = \frac{\sqrt{x}}{2\sqrt{6}}\cdot\frac{\sqrt{6}}{\sqrt{6}} = \frac{\sqrt{6x}}{12}$$

(d) Because $\sqrt{y^3} = \sqrt{y^2}\cdot\sqrt{y} = y\sqrt{y}$, we start by simplifying $\dfrac{xy}{\sqrt{y^3}}$.

$$\frac{xy}{\sqrt{y^3}} = \frac{xy}{y\sqrt{y}} = \frac{x}{\sqrt{y}}$$

To rationalize the denominator we multiply by 1 in the form $\dfrac{\sqrt{y}}{\sqrt{y}}$.

$$\frac{x}{\sqrt{y}}\cdot\frac{\sqrt{y}}{\sqrt{y}} = \frac{x\sqrt{y}}{y}$$

Now Try Exercises 97, 101, 103, 105

EXAMPLE 12 **Rationalizing a denominator in geometry**

A square with a diagonal of length x has sides of length $\dfrac{x}{\sqrt{2}}$. Find the perimeter and rationalize the denominator. See Figure 5.14.

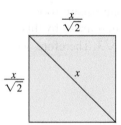

Figure 5.14

Solution
The perimeter is 4 times the length of one side.

$$4\cdot\frac{x}{\sqrt{2}} = \frac{4x}{\sqrt{2}}$$

To rationalize the denominator we multiply the ratio by 1 in the form $\dfrac{\sqrt{2}}{\sqrt{2}}$.

$$\frac{4x}{\sqrt{2}}\cdot\frac{\sqrt{2}}{\sqrt{2}} = \frac{4x\sqrt{2}}{2} = 2x\sqrt{2}$$

The perimeter is $2x\sqrt{2}$.

Now Try Exercise 127

When the denominator is either a sum or difference containing a square root, we rationalize the denominator by multiplying the numerator and denominator by the *conjugate* of the denominator. In this case, the **conjugate** of the denominator is found by changing a $+$ sign to a $-$ sign or vice versa. Table 5.7 lists examples of conjugates.

TABLE 5.7

Expression	$1 + \sqrt{2}$	$\sqrt{3} - 2$	$\sqrt{x} + 7$	$\sqrt{a} - \sqrt{b}$
Conjugate	$1 - \sqrt{2}$	$\sqrt{3} + 2$	$\sqrt{x} - 7$	$\sqrt{a} + \sqrt{b}$

In the next two examples we use this method to rationalize a denominator.

EXAMPLE 13 **Using a conjugate to rationalize the denominator**

Rationalize the denominator of $\dfrac{1}{1 + \sqrt{2}}$.

Solution

From Table 5.7, the conjugate of $1 + \sqrt{2}$ is $\mathbf{1 - \sqrt{2}}$.

$$\frac{1}{1 + \sqrt{2}} = \frac{1}{1 + \sqrt{2}} \cdot \frac{(1 - \sqrt{2})}{(1 - \sqrt{2})} \qquad \text{Multiply numerator and denominator by the conjugate.}$$

$$= \frac{1 - \sqrt{2}}{(1)^2 - (\sqrt{2})^2} \qquad (a + b)(a - b) = a^2 - b^2$$

$$= \frac{1 - \sqrt{2}}{1 - 2} \qquad \text{Simplify.}$$

$$= \frac{1 - \sqrt{2}}{-1} \qquad \text{Subtract.}$$

$$= \frac{1}{-1} - \frac{\sqrt{2}}{-1} \qquad \frac{a - b}{c} = \frac{a}{c} - \frac{b}{c}$$

$$= -1 + \sqrt{2} \qquad \text{Simplify.}$$

READING CHECK

How do you rationalize a denominator?

▌ **Now Try Exercise 107**

EXAMPLE 14 **Rationalizing the denominator**

Rationalize the denominator.

(a) $\dfrac{3 + \sqrt{5}}{2 - \sqrt{5}}$ **(b)** $\dfrac{\sqrt{x}}{\sqrt{x} - 2}$

Solution

(a) The conjugate of the denominator is $2 + \sqrt{5}$.

$$\frac{3 + \sqrt{5}}{2 - \sqrt{5}} = \frac{(3 + \sqrt{5})}{(2 - \sqrt{5})} \cdot \frac{(2 + \sqrt{5})}{(2 + \sqrt{5})} \qquad \text{Multiply by 1.}$$

$$= \frac{6 + 3\sqrt{5} + 2\sqrt{5} + (\sqrt{5})^2}{(2)^2 - (\sqrt{5})^2} \qquad \text{Multiply.}$$

$$= \frac{11 + 5\sqrt{5}}{4 - 5} \qquad \text{Combine terms.}$$

$$= -11 - 5\sqrt{5} \qquad \text{Simplify.}$$

(b) The conjugate of the denominator is $\sqrt{x} + 2$.

$$\frac{\sqrt{x}}{\sqrt{x} - 2} = \frac{\sqrt{x}}{(\sqrt{x} - 2)} \cdot \frac{(\sqrt{x} + 2)}{(\sqrt{x} + 2)} \qquad \text{Multiply by 1.}$$

$$= \frac{x + 2\sqrt{x}}{x - 4} \qquad \text{Multiply.}$$

▌ **Now Try Exercises 111, 115**

EXAMPLE 15 **Rationalizing a denominator having a cube root**

Rationalize the denominator of $\dfrac{5}{\sqrt[3]{x}}$.

Solution

The expression $\dfrac{5}{\sqrt[3]{x}}$ is equal to $\dfrac{5}{x^{1/3}}$. To rationalize the denominator, $x^{1/3}$, we can multiply it by $x^{2/3}$ because $x^{1/3} \cdot x^{2/3} = x^{1/3+2/3} = x^1$.

$$\dfrac{5}{x^{1/3}} = \dfrac{5}{x^{1/3}} \cdot \dfrac{x^{2/3}}{x^{2/3}} \qquad \text{Multiply by 1.}$$

$$= \dfrac{5x^{2/3}}{x^{1/3+2/3}} \qquad \text{Product rule}$$

$$= \dfrac{5\sqrt[3]{x^2}}{x} \qquad \text{Add; write in radical notation.}$$

Now Try Exercise 121

5.4 Putting It All Together

CONCEPT	EXPLANATION	EXAMPLES
Like Radicals	Like radicals have the same index and the same radicand.	$7\sqrt{5}$ and $3\sqrt{5}$ are like radicals. $5\sqrt[3]{ab}$ and $\sqrt[3]{ab}$ are like radicals. $\sqrt[3]{5}$ and $\sqrt[3]{4}$ are unlike radicals. $\sqrt[3]{7}$ and $\sqrt{7}$ are unlike radicals.
Adding and Subtracting Radical Expressions	Combine like radicals when adding or subtracting. We cannot combine unlike radicals such as $\sqrt{2}$ and $\sqrt{5}$. But sometimes we can rewrite radicals and then combine.	$6\sqrt{13} + \sqrt{13} = (6+1)\sqrt{13} = 7\sqrt{13}$ $\begin{aligned}\sqrt{40} - \sqrt{10} &= \sqrt{4} \cdot \sqrt{10} - \sqrt{10} \\ &= 2\sqrt{10} - \sqrt{10} \\ &= \sqrt{10}\end{aligned}$
Multiplying Radical Expressions	Radical expressions can sometimes be multiplied like binomials.	$(\sqrt{a} - 5)(\sqrt{a} + 5) = a - 25$ and $(\sqrt{x} - 3)(\sqrt{x} + 1) = x - 2\sqrt{x} - 3$
Conjugate	The conjugate is found by changing a $+$ sign to a $-$ sign or vice versa.	*Expression* $\qquad$ *Conjugate* $\sqrt{x} + 7 \qquad\qquad \sqrt{x} - 7$ $\sqrt{a} - 2\sqrt{b} \qquad \sqrt{a} + 2\sqrt{b}$
Rationalizing a Denominator Having One Term	Write the quotient without a radical expression in the denominator.	To rationalize $\dfrac{5}{\sqrt{7}}$, multiply the expression by 1 in the form $\dfrac{\sqrt{7}}{\sqrt{7}}$. $\dfrac{5}{\sqrt{7}} \cdot \dfrac{\sqrt{7}}{\sqrt{7}} = \dfrac{5\sqrt{7}}{\sqrt{49}} = \dfrac{5\sqrt{7}}{7}$
Rationalizing a Denominator Having Two Terms	Multiply the numerator and denominator by the conjugate of the denominator.	$\dfrac{1}{2 - \sqrt{3}} = \dfrac{1}{2 - \sqrt{3}} \cdot \dfrac{(2 + \sqrt{3})}{(2 + \sqrt{3})}$ $= \dfrac{2 + \sqrt{3}}{4 - 3} = 2 + \sqrt{3}$

5.4   Exercises

MyMathLab | Math XL PRACTICE | WATCH | DOWNLOAD | READ | REVIEW

CONCEPTS AND VOCABULARY

1. $\sqrt{a} + \sqrt{a} = $ _____

2. $\sqrt[3]{b} + \sqrt[3]{b} + \sqrt[3]{b} = $ _____

3. You cannot simplify $\sqrt[3]{4} + \sqrt[3]{7}$ because they are not _____ radicals.

4. Can you simplify $4\sqrt{15} - 3\sqrt{15}$? Explain.

5. Does $6 + 3\sqrt{5}$ equal $9\sqrt{5}$?

6. To rationalize the denominator of $\frac{2}{\sqrt{7}}$, multiply this expression by _____.

7. What is the conjugate of $\sqrt{t} - 5$?

8. To rationalize the denominator of $\frac{1}{5 - \sqrt{2}}$, multiply this expression by _____.

LIKE RADICALS

Exercises 9–18: (Refer to Example 2.) Write the terms as like radicals, if possible. Assume that all variables are positive.

9. $\sqrt{12}, \sqrt{24}$

10. $\sqrt{18}, \sqrt{27}$

11. $\sqrt{7}, \sqrt{28}, \sqrt{63}$

12. $\sqrt{200}, \sqrt{300}, \sqrt{500}$

13. $\sqrt[3]{16}, \sqrt[3]{-54}$

14. $\sqrt[3]{80}, \sqrt[3]{10}$

15. $\sqrt{x^2 y}, \sqrt{4y^2}$

16. $\sqrt{x^5 y^3}, \sqrt{9xy}$

17. $\sqrt[3]{8xy}, \sqrt[3]{x^4 y^4}$

18. $\sqrt[3]{64x^4}, \sqrt[3]{-8x}$

ADDITION AND SUBTRACTION OF RADICALS

Exercises 19–80: If possible, simplify the expression. Assume that all variables are positive.

19. $2\sqrt{3} + 7\sqrt{3}$

20. $8\sqrt{7} + 2\sqrt{7}$

21. $4\sqrt[3]{5} + 2\sqrt[3]{5}$

22. $\sqrt[3]{13} + 3\sqrt[3]{13}$

23. $7 + 4\sqrt{7}$

24. $8 - 4\sqrt{3}$

25. $2\sqrt{3} + 3\sqrt{2}$

26. $\sqrt{6} + \sqrt{17}$

27. $\sqrt{3} + \sqrt[3]{3}$

28. $\sqrt{6} + \sqrt[4]{6}$

29. $\sqrt[3]{16} + 3\sqrt[3]{2}$

30. $\sqrt[3]{24} + \sqrt[3]{81}$

31. $\sqrt{2} + \sqrt{18} + \sqrt{32}$

32. $2\sqrt{3} + \sqrt{12} + \sqrt{27}$

33. $11\sqrt{11} - 5\sqrt{11}$

34. $9\sqrt{5} + \sqrt{2} - \sqrt{5}$

35. $\sqrt{x} + \sqrt{x} - \sqrt{y}$

36. $\sqrt{xy^2} - \sqrt{x}$

37. $\sqrt[3]{z} + \sqrt[3]{z}$

38. $\sqrt[3]{y} - \sqrt[3]{y}$

39. $2\sqrt[3]{6} - 7\sqrt[3]{6}$

40. $18\sqrt[3]{3} + 3\sqrt[3]{3}$

41. $\sqrt[3]{y^6} - \sqrt[3]{y^3}$

42. $2\sqrt{20} + 7\sqrt{5} + 3\sqrt{2}$

43. $3\sqrt{28} + 3\sqrt{7}$

44. $9\sqrt{18} - 2\sqrt{8}$

45. $\sqrt[4]{48} + 4\sqrt[4]{3}$

46. $\sqrt[4]{32} + \sqrt[4]{16}$

47. $\sqrt{9x} + \sqrt{16x}$

48. $-3\sqrt{x} + 5\sqrt{x}$

49. $3\sqrt{2k} + \sqrt{8k} + \sqrt{18k}$

50. $3\sqrt{k} + 2\sqrt{4k} + \sqrt{9k}$

51. $\sqrt{44} - 4\sqrt{11}$

52. $\sqrt[4]{5} + 2\sqrt[4]{5}$

53. $2\sqrt[3]{16} + \sqrt[3]{2} - \sqrt{2}$

54. $5\sqrt[3]{x} - 3\sqrt[3]{x}$

55. $\sqrt[3]{xy} - 2\sqrt[3]{xy}$

56. $3\sqrt{x^3} - \sqrt{x}$

57. $\sqrt{4x + 8} + \sqrt{x + 2}$

58. $\sqrt{2a + 1} + \sqrt{8a + 4}$

59. $\sqrt{9x + 18} - \sqrt{4x + 8}$

60. $\sqrt{25x - 25} - \sqrt{4x - 4}$

61. $\sqrt{x^3 + x^2} - \sqrt{x + 1}, x \geq 0$

62. $\sqrt{x^3 - x^2} - \sqrt{4x - 4}, x \geq 1$

63. $\sqrt{25x^3} - \sqrt{x^3}$

64. $\sqrt{36x^5} - \sqrt{25x^5}$

65. $\sqrt[3]{\dfrac{7x}{8}} - \dfrac{\sqrt[3]{7x}}{3}$

66. $\sqrt[3]{\dfrac{8x^2}{27}} - \sqrt[3]{\dfrac{x^2}{8}}$

67. $\dfrac{4\sqrt{3}}{3} + \dfrac{\sqrt{3}}{6}$

68. $\dfrac{8\sqrt{5}}{7} + \dfrac{4\sqrt{5}}{2}$

69. $\dfrac{15\sqrt{8}}{4} - \dfrac{2\sqrt{2}}{5}$

70. $\dfrac{23\sqrt{11}}{2} - \dfrac{\sqrt{44}}{8}$

71. $2\sqrt[4]{64} - \sqrt[4]{324} + \sqrt[4]{4}$

72. $2\sqrt[3]{16} - 5\sqrt[3]{54} + 10\sqrt[3]{2}$

73. $5\sqrt[4]{x^5} - \sqrt[4]{x}$

74. $20\sqrt[3]{b^4} - 4\sqrt[3]{b}$

75. $\sqrt{64x^3} - \sqrt{x} + 3\sqrt{x}$

76. $2\sqrt{3z} + 3\sqrt{12z} + 3\sqrt{48z}$

77. $\sqrt[4]{81a^5 b^5} - \sqrt[4]{ab}$

78. $\sqrt[4]{xy^5} - \sqrt[4]{x^5 y}$

79. $5\sqrt[3]{\dfrac{n^4}{125}} - 2\sqrt[3]{n}$

80. $\sqrt[3]{\dfrac{8x}{27}} - \dfrac{2\sqrt[3]{x}}{3}$

OPERATIONS ON FUNCTIONS

Exercises 81–84: Find $(f + g)(x)$ and $(f - g)(x)$.

81. $f(x) = 5\sqrt{x} - 2$, $g(x) = -2\sqrt{x} + 3$

82. $f(x) = 3\sqrt{4x - 4}$, $g(x) = 5\sqrt{x - 1}$

83. $f(x) = \sqrt[3]{8x} + 1$, $g(x) = 2\sqrt[3]{x} - 1$

84. $f(x) = \sqrt[3]{27x}$, $g(x) = \sqrt[3]{64x}$

MULTIPLYING BINOMIALS CONTAINING RADICALS

Exercises 85–96: Multiply and simplify.

85. $(\sqrt{x} - 3)(\sqrt{x} + 2)$ **86.** $(2\sqrt{x} + 1)(\sqrt{x} + 4)$

87. $(3 + \sqrt{7})(3 - \sqrt{7})$ **88.** $(5 - \sqrt{5})(5 + \sqrt{5})$

89. $(11 - \sqrt{2})(11 + \sqrt{2})$

90. $(6 + \sqrt{3})(6 - \sqrt{3})$

91. $(\sqrt{x} + 8)(\sqrt{x} - 8)$

92. $(\sqrt{ab} - 3)(\sqrt{ab} + 3)$

93. $(\sqrt{ab} - \sqrt{c})(\sqrt{ab} + \sqrt{c})$

94. $(\sqrt{2x} + \sqrt{3y})(\sqrt{2x} - \sqrt{3y})$

95. $(\sqrt{x} - 7)(\sqrt{x} + 8)$

96. $(\sqrt{ab} - 1)(\sqrt{ab} - 2)$

RATIONALIZING THE DENOMINATOR

Exercises 97–124: Rationalize the denominator.

97. $\frac{1}{\sqrt{7}}$

98. $\frac{1}{\sqrt{23}}$

99. $\frac{4}{\sqrt{3}}$

100. $\frac{8}{\sqrt{2}}$

101. $\frac{5}{3\sqrt{5}}$

102. $\frac{6}{11\sqrt{3}}$

103. $\sqrt{\frac{b}{12}}$

104. $\sqrt{\frac{5b}{72}}$

105. $\frac{rt}{2\sqrt{r^3}}$

106. $\frac{m^2 n}{2\sqrt{m^5}}$

107. $\frac{1}{3 - \sqrt{2}}$

108. $\frac{1}{\sqrt{3} - 2}$

109. $\frac{\sqrt{2}}{\sqrt{5} + 2}$

110. $\frac{\sqrt{3}}{\sqrt{3} + 2}$

111. $\frac{\sqrt{7} - 2}{\sqrt{7} + 2}$

112. $\frac{\sqrt{3} - 1}{\sqrt{3} + 1}$

113. $\frac{1}{\sqrt{7} - \sqrt{6}}$

114. $\frac{1}{\sqrt{8} - \sqrt{7}}$

115. $\frac{\sqrt{z}}{\sqrt{z} - 3}$

116. $\frac{2\sqrt{z}}{2 - \sqrt{z}}$

117. $\frac{\sqrt{a} + \sqrt{b}}{\sqrt{a} - \sqrt{b}}$

118. $\frac{\sqrt{x} - 2\sqrt{y}}{\sqrt{x} + 2\sqrt{y}}$

119. $\frac{1}{\sqrt{x + 1} - \sqrt{x}}$

120. $\frac{1}{\sqrt{a + 1} + \sqrt{a}}$

121. $\frac{3}{\sqrt[3]{x}}$

122. $\frac{6}{5\sqrt[3]{x}}$

123. $\frac{1}{\sqrt[3]{x^2}}$

124. $\frac{2}{\sqrt[3]{(x - 2)^2}}$

GEOMETRY

125. *Perimeter* (Refer to Example 9.) Find the exact perimeter of the right triangle. Then approximate your answer.

126. *Perimeter* Find the exact perimeter of the rectangle. Then approximate your answer.

127. *Geometry* (Refer to Example 12.) A square has a diagonal with length $\sqrt{3}$. Find the perimeter and rationalize the denominator.

128. *Geometry* A rectangle has sides of length $\sqrt{8}$ and $\sqrt{32}$. Find the perimeter of the rectangle.

129. *Geometry* (Refer to Example 12.) A square has a diagonal that is 60 feet long. Find the exact perimeter of the rectangle and simplify your answer.

130. *Geometry* A square has a diagonal that is 10 feet long. Find the exact perimeter of the rectangle and simplify your answer.

131. *Geometry* A square has an area of x square feet. Find the length of the diagonal of the square.

132. *Geometry* A square has an area of 16 square feet. Find the length of the diagonal of the square.

WRITING ABOUT MATHEMATICS

133. Suppose that a student knows that $\sqrt{3} \approx 1.73205$ and does not have a calculator. Which of the following expressions would be easier to evaluate by hand? Why?

$$\frac{1}{\sqrt{3}} \quad \text{or} \quad \frac{\sqrt{3}}{3}$$

134. A student simplifies an expression *incorrectly:*

$$\sqrt{8} + \sqrt[3]{16} \overset{?}{=} \sqrt{4 \cdot 2} + \sqrt[3]{8 \cdot 2}$$
$$\overset{?}{=} \sqrt{4} \cdot \sqrt{2} + \sqrt[3]{8} \cdot \sqrt[3]{2}$$
$$\overset{?}{=} 2\sqrt{2} + 2\sqrt[3]{2}$$
$$\overset{?}{=} 4\sqrt{4}$$
$$\overset{?}{=} 8.$$

Explain any errors that the student made. What would you do differently?

SECTIONS 5.3 and 5.4 | **Checking Basic Concepts**

1. Simplify each expression. Assume that all variables are positive.
 (a) $(64^{-3/2})^{1/3}$ **(b)** $\sqrt{5} \cdot \sqrt{20}$

 (c) $\sqrt[3]{-8x^4 y}$ **(d)** $\sqrt{\dfrac{4b}{5}} \cdot \sqrt{\dfrac{4b^3}{5}}$

2. Simplify $\sqrt[3]{7} \cdot \sqrt[3]{7}$

3. Simplify each expression.
 (a) $\sqrt{3} \cdot \sqrt{12}$ **(b)** $\dfrac{\sqrt[3]{81}}{\sqrt[3]{3}}$

 (c) $\sqrt{36x^6}, x > 0$

4. Simplify each expression.
 (a) $5\sqrt{6} + 2\sqrt{6} + \sqrt{7}$
 (b) $8\sqrt[3]{x} - 3\sqrt[3]{x}$
 (c) $\sqrt{9x} - \sqrt{4x}$

5. Simplify each expression.
 (a) $\sqrt[3]{xy^4} - \sqrt[3]{x^4 y}$
 (b) $(4 - \sqrt{2})(4 + \sqrt{2})$

6. Rationalize the denominator of $\dfrac{6}{2\sqrt{6}}$.

7. Rationalize the denominator of $\dfrac{2}{\sqrt{5} - 1}$.

5.5 More Radical Functions

Root Functions • Power Functions • Modeling with Power Functions (Optional)

A LOOK INTO MATH ▶ Radical expressions often occur in biology. In Example 5, we discuss how heavier birds tend to have larger wings. This relationship between weight and wing size can be modeled by a radical function. Another application of radical functions in biology is discussed in Example 3, where a function is used to predict the surface area of a person, given their weight.

Root Functions

NEW VOCABULARY

☐ Root function
☐ Power function

Earlier in this chapter we discussed the square root and cube root functions. There are also functions for higher roots. Figures 5.15–5.18 on the next page show graphs of four common root functions. Note that the higher the root, the more slowly the graph increases for $x \geq 1$. Also, note that the domains for functions of even roots include only the nonnegative real numbers, whereas the domains of functions of odd roots include all real numbers.

Square Root Function

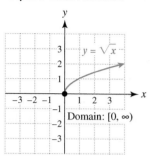

Figure 5.15

Cube Root Function

Figure 5.16

Fourth Root Function

Figure 5.17

Fifth Root Function

Figure 5.18

EXAMPLE 1 **Evaluating root functions**

If possible, evaluate each root function f at the given x-values.
(a) $f(x) = \sqrt{x + 1}$, $x = -5, x = 3$

(b) $f(x) = \sqrt[3]{1 - x}$, $x = -7, x = 28$

(c) $f(x) = \sqrt[4]{x - 7}$, $x = 5, x = 88$

(d) $f(x) = \sqrt[5]{x}$, $x = -1, x = 32$

Solution
(a) $f(-5) = \sqrt{-5 + 1} = \sqrt{-4}$, which is *not* a real number.
$f(3) = \sqrt{3 + 1} = \sqrt{4} = 2$ because $2^2 = 4$.

(b) $f(-7) = \sqrt[3]{1 - (-7)} = \sqrt[3]{8} = 2$ because $2^3 = 8$.
$f(28) = \sqrt[3]{1 - 28} = \sqrt[3]{-27} = -3$ because $(-3)^3 = -27$.

(c) $f(5) = \sqrt[4]{5 - 7} = \sqrt[4]{-2}$, which is not a real number.
$f(88) = \sqrt[4]{88 - 7} = \sqrt[4]{81} = 3$ because $3^4 = 81$.

(d) $f(-1) = \sqrt[5]{-1} = -1$ because $(-1)^5 = -1$.
$f(32) = \sqrt[5]{32} = 2$ because $2^5 = 32$.

Now Try Exercises 9, 11, 13, 15

Power Functions

Power functions are a generalization of root functions. Examples of power functions include

$$f(x) = x^{1/2}, \quad g(x) = x^{2/3}, \quad \text{and} \quad h(x) = x^{-3/5}.$$

The exponent for a power function is frequently a rational number p, written in lowest terms. That is, we usually write $f(x) = x^{1/2}$, rather than $f(x) = x^{3/6}$. The power function $f(x) = x^{m/n}$ can also be written as $f(x) = \sqrt[n]{x^m}$. A power function f is defined for all real numbers when n is odd and defined for only nonnegative numbers when n is even.

POWER FUNCTION

If a function f can be represented by

$$f(x) = x^p,$$

where p is a rational number, then f is a **power function**. If $p = \frac{1}{n}$, where $n \geq 2$ is an integer, then f is also a **root function**, which is given by

$$f(x) = \sqrt[n]{x}.$$

EXAMPLE 2   **Evaluating power functions**

If possible, evaluate $f(x)$ at the given value of x.
(a) $f(x) = x^{0.75}$ at $x = 16$ **(b)** $f(x) = x^{1/4}$ at $x = -81$

Solution
(a) $0.75 = \frac{3}{4}$, so $f(x) = x^{3/4}$. Thus $f(16) = 16^{3/4} = (16^{1/4})^3 = 2^3 = 8$.

  NOTE: $16^{1/4} = \sqrt[4]{16} = 2$.

(b) $f(-81) = (-81)^{1/4} = \sqrt[4]{-81}$, which is undefined. There is no real number a such that $a^4 = -81$ because a^4 is never negative.

▌ Now Try Exercises 23, 27

▶ **REAL-WORLD CONNECTION** The surface area of the skin covering the human body is influenced by both the height and weight of a person. A taller person tends to have a larger surface area, as does a heavier person. See Extended and Discovery Exercise 2 at the end of this chapter. In the next example, we use a power function from biology to model this situation.

EXAMPLE 3   **Modeling surface area of the human body**

The surface area of a person who is 66 inches tall and weighs w pounds can be estimated by $S(w) = 327w^{0.425}$, where S is in square inches. (*Source:* H. Lancaster, *Quantitative Methods in Biological and Medical Sciences.*)
(a) Find S if this person weighs 130 pounds.
(b) If the person gains 20 pounds, by how much does the person's surface area increase?
(c) A graph of $y = S(w)$ is shown in Figure 5.19. Suppose that a person's weight is more than 50 pounds and it doubles. Use the graph to determine if the person's surface area also doubles.

Surface Area of Human Body

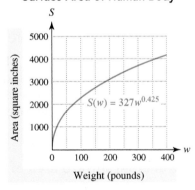

Figure 5.19

Solution
(a) $S(130) = 327(130)^{0.425} \approx 2588$ square inches
(b) Because $S(150) = 327(150)^{0.425} \approx 2750$ square inches, the surface area of the person increases by about $2750 - 2588 = 162$ square inches.
(c) For $w \geq 50$ the graph increases more slowly. This means that the person's surface area (S-values) will not double even if his or her weight doubles (w-values). For example, $A(100) \approx 2300$ square inches and $A(200) \approx 3100$ square inches. The surface area did not double.

▌ Now Try Exercise 51

In the next example, we investigate the graph of $y = x^p$ for different values of p.

EXAMPLE 4   **Graphing power functions**

The graphs of three power functions,

$$f(x) = x^{1/3}, \quad g(x) = x^{0.75}, \quad \text{and} \quad h(x) = x^{1.4},$$

are shown in Figure 5.20, where the two decimal exponents have been written as fractions. Discuss how the value of p affects the graph of $y = x^p$ when $x > 1$ and when $0 < x < 1$.

Power Functions

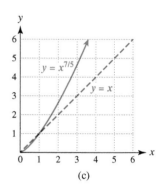

(a)   (b)   (c)

Figure 5.20

Solution

The graphs of these power functions have the following characteristics.
1. If $x > 1$, then $x^{1/3} < x^{3/4} < x^{7/5}$. Larger exponents result in graphs that increase (rise) *faster* for $x > 1$.
2. If $0 < x < 1$, then $x^{7/5} < x^{3/4} < x^{1/3}$. Smaller exponents result in graphs that have larger y-values for $0 < x < 1$.
3. All graphs pass through the points $(0, 0)$ and $(1, 1)$.

Now Try Exercise 35

Modeling with Power Functions (Optional)

▶ **REAL-WORLD CONNECTION** Allometry is the study of the relative sizes of different characteristics of an organism. For example, the weight of a bird is related to the surface area of its wings; heavier birds tend to have larger wings. Allometric relations are often modeled with $f(x) = kx^p$, where k and p are constants. (*Source:* C. Pennycuick, *Newton Rules Biology.*)

EXAMPLE 5   **Modeling surface area of wings**

Weights w of various birds and the corresponding surface area of their wings A are shown in Table 5.8.

TABLE 5.8 **Weight and Wing Size**

w (kilograms)	0.5	2.0	3.5	5.0
A (square meters)	0.069	0.175	0.254	0.325

(a) Make a scatterplot of the data. Discuss any trends in the data.
(b) Biologists modeled the data with $A(w) = kw^{2/3}$, where k is a constant. Find k.
(c) Graph A and the data in the same viewing rectangle.
(d) Estimate the area of the wings of a 3-kilogram bird.

CALCULATOR HELP

To make a scatterplot, see Appendix A (pages AP-3 and AP-4).

[0, 6, 1] by [0, 0.4, 0.1]

(a)

[0, 6, 1] by [0, 0.4, 0.1]

$y_1 = 0.11x^{2/3}$

(b)

Figure 5.21

Solution

(a) A scatterplot of the data is shown in Figure 5.21(a). As the weight of a bird increases so does the surface area of its wings.

(b) To determine k, substitute one of the data points into $A(w)$. We use $(2.0, 0.175)$.

$$A(w) = kw^{2/3} \quad \text{Given formula}$$

$$0.175 = k(2)^{2/3} \quad \begin{array}{l}\text{Let } w = 2 \text{ and } A(w) = 0.175\\ \text{(any data point could be used).}\end{array}$$

$$k = \frac{0.175}{2^{2/3}} \quad \text{Solve for } k\text{; rewrite equation.}$$

$$k \approx 0.11 \quad \text{Approximate } k.$$

Thus $A(w) = 0.11w^{2/3}$.

(c) The data and graph of $Y_1 = 0.11X^{\wedge}(2/3)$ are shown in Figure 5.21(b). Note that the graph appears to pass through each data point.

(d) $A(3) = 0.11(3)^{2/3} \approx 0.23$ square meter

▌ **Now Try Exercise 59**

5.5 Putting It All Together

FUNCTION	EXPLANATION
Root	$f(x) = \sqrt[3]{x}$, $g(x) = \sqrt[4]{x}$, and $h(x) = \sqrt[5]{x}$ Odd root functions are defined for all real numbers, and even root functions are defined for nonnegative real numbers.
Power	$f(x) = x^p$, where p is a rational number, is a power function. If $p = \frac{1}{n}$, where $n \geq 2$ is an integer, f is also a root function, given by $f(x) = \sqrt[n]{x}$. ***Examples:*** $f(x) = x^{5/3}$ Power function $g(x) = x^{1/4} = \sqrt[4]{x}$ Root and power function

5.5 Exercises

CONCEPTS AND VOCABULARY

1. Sketch a graph of $y = x^{1/2}$.

2. Sketch a graph of $y = x^{1/3}$.

3. What is the domain of $f(x) = x^{1/2}$?

4. What is the domain of $f(x) = x^{1/3}$?

5. Give a symbolic representation for a power function.

6. Give a symbolic representation for a root function.

7. What is the domain of $f(x) = \sqrt[4]{x}$?

8. What is the domain of $f(x) = \sqrt[5]{x}$?

ROOT FUNCTIONS

Exercises 9–16: If possible, evaluate each root function f at the given x-values. When the result is not an integer, approximate it to the nearest hundredth.

9. $f(x) = \sqrt{x^2 - 1}$, $x = -2, x = 0$

10. $f(x) = \sqrt{2x - 5}$, $x = 0, x = 3$

11. $f(x) = \sqrt[4]{1 - x}$, $\quad x = -5$, $\quad x = 2$

12. $f(x) = \sqrt[4]{x + 1}$, $\quad x = -15$, $x = 15$

13. $f(x) = \sqrt[5]{4 - 3x}$, $\quad x = -3$, $\quad x = 1$

14. $f(x) = \sqrt[5]{1 - x^2}$, $\quad x = 3$, $\quad x = 1$

15. $f(x) = \sqrt[3]{1 - x}$, $\quad x = -5$, $\quad x = 2$

16. $f(x) = \sqrt[3]{(x + 1)^2}$, $x = -2$, $\quad x = 7$

POWER FUNCTIONS

Exercises 17–22: Use radical notation to write f(x).

17. $f(x) = x^{1/2}$ **18.** $f(x) = x^{1/3}$

19. $f(x) = x^{2/3}$ **20.** $f(x) = x^{3/4}$

21. $f(x) = x^{-1/5}$ **22.** $f(x) = x^{-2/5}$

Exercises 23–30: If possible, evaluate f(x) at the given values of x. When appropriate, approximate the answer to the nearest hundredth.

23. $f(x) = x^{5/2}$ $\quad x = 4, x = 5$

24. $f(x) = x^{-3/4}$ $\quad x = 1, x = 3$

25. $f(x) = x^{-7/5}$ $\quad x = -32, x = 10$

26. $f(x) = x^{4/3}$ $\quad x = -8, x = 27$

27. $f(x) = x^{1/4}$ $\quad x = 256, x = -10$

28. $f(x) = x^{3/4}$ $\quad x = 16, x = -1$

29. $f(x) = x^{2/5}$ $\quad x = 32, x = -32$

30. $f(x) = x^{5/6}$ $\quad x = -5, x = 64$

Exercises 31–34: Graph y = f (x). Write the domain of f in interval notation.

31. $f(x) = x^{1/4}$ **32.** $f(x) = x^{1/5}$

33. $f(x) = x^{2/3}$ **34.** $f(x) = (x + 1)^{1/4}$

Exercises 35–38: Graph f and g in the window [0, 6, 1] by [0, 6, 1]. Which function is greater when x > 1?

35. $f(x) = x^{1/5}$, $g(x) = x^{1/3}$

36. $f(x) = x^{4/5}$, $g(x) = x^{5/4}$

37. $f(x) = x^{1.2}$, $g(x) = x^{0.45}$

38. $f(x) = x^{-1.4}$, $g(x) = x^{1.4}$

Exercises 39 and 40: Thinking Generally *Let* $0 < q < p$, *where p and q are rational numbers.*

39. For $x > 1$, is $x^p > x^q$ or $x^p < x^q$?

40. For $0 < x < 1$, is $x^p > x^q$ or $x^p < x^q$?

Exercises 41 and 42: Operations on Functions For the given f(x) and g(x), evaluate each expression.

   (a) $(f + g)(2)$ **(b)** $(f - g)(x)$
   (c) $(fg)(x)$ **(d)** $(f/g)(x)$

41. $f(x) = \sqrt{8x}$, $g(x) = \sqrt{2x}$

42. $f(x) = \sqrt{9x + 18}$, $g(x) = \sqrt{4x + 8}$

Exercises 43–46: Graphical Interpretation Match the situation with the graph of the power function (a.–d.) that models it best.

43. Amount of water in a barrel that is initially full and has a hole near the bottom

44. The average weight of a type of bird as its wing span increases (*Hint:* The exponent is greater than 1.)

45. Money made after *x* hours by a person who works for a fixed hourly wage

46. Rapid growth of an insect population that eventually slows down

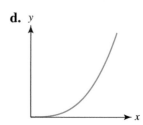

Exercises 47–50 Graphical Recognition Match the equation with its graph (a.–d.). Do not use a calculator.

47. $y = x^{7/4}$ **48.** $y = x^{4/3}$

49. $y = x^{1/3}$ **50.** $y = x^{1/2}$

c. 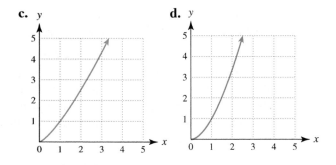 **d.**

APPLICATIONS

Exercises 51 and 52: Surface Area (Refer to Example 3.) The surface area of the skin of a person who is 70 inches tall and weighs w pounds can be estimated by $S(w) = 342w^{0.425}$, *where S is in square inches. Evaluate each of the following.*

51. $S(150)$

52. $S(200)$

Exercises 53–56 Learning Curves The graph shows the percentage P of times that individuals completed a simple task correctly after practicing it x times.

53. If a group of people does 10 practice trials each, what percentage of the time is the task done correctly?

54. How many trials need to be performed to reach 50% accuracy?

55. If a person doubles the number of practice trials, does the accuracy always double? Explain.

56. What happens to a person's accuracy after a large number of trials?

57. *Aging More Slowly* In his theory of relativity, Albert Einstein showed that if a person travels at nearly the speed of light, then time slows down significantly. Suppose that there are twins; one remains on Earth and the other leaves in a very fast spaceship having velocity v. If the twin on Earth ages T_0 years, then according to Einstein the twin in the spaceship ages T years, where

$$T(v) = T_0\sqrt{1 - (v/c)^2}.$$

In this formula c represents the speed of light, which is 186,000 miles per second.
(a) Evaluate T when $v = 0.8c$ (eight-tenths the speed of light) and $T_0 = 10$ years. (*Hint:* Simplify $\frac{v}{c}$ without using 186,000 miles per second.)
(b) Interpret your result.

58. *Increasing Your Weight* (Refer to Exercise 57.) Albert Einstein also showed that the weight (mass) of an object increases when traveling near the speed of light. If a person's weight on Earth is W_0, then the same person's weight W in a spaceship traveling at velocity v is

$$W(v) = \frac{W_0}{\sqrt{1 - (v/c)^2}}.$$

(a) Evaluate W when $v = 0.6c$ (six-tenths the speed of light) and $W_0 = 220$ pounds (100 kilograms).
(b) Interpret your result.

 59. *Modeling Wing Size* (Refer to Example 5.) The surface area of wings for a species of bird with weight w is shown in the table.

w (kilograms)	2	3	4
A (square meters)	0.254	0.333	0.403

(a) Make a scatterplot of the data.
(b) The data can be modeled with $A(w) = kw^{2/3}$. Find k.
(c) Graph A and the data in the same viewing rectangle. Does the graph of A pass through the data points?
(d) Estimate the area of the wings of a 2.5-kilogram bird.

 60. *Pulse Rate in Animals* The following table lists typical pulse rates R in beats per minute (bpm) for animals with various weights W in pounds.
(*Source:* C. Pennycuick.)

W (pounds)	20	150	500	1500
R (beats per minute)	198	72	40	23

(a) Describe what happens to the pulse rate as the weight of the animal increases.
(b) Plot the data in [0, 1600, 400] by [0, 220, 20].
(c) If $R = kW^{-1/2}$, find k.
(d) Find R when $W = 700$, and interpret the result.

61. *Modeling Wing Span* (Refer to Example 5.) Biologists have found that the weight W of a bird and the length L of its wing span are related by $L = kW^{1/3}$, where k is a constant. The following table lists L and W for one species of bird. (*Source:* C. Pennycuick.)

W (kilograms)	0.1	0.4	0.8	1.1
L (meters)	0.422	0.670	0.844	0.938

(a) Use the data to approximate the value of k.

(b) Graph L and the data in the same viewing rectangle. What happens to L as W increases?

(c) Find the wing span of a 0.7-kilogram bird.

(d) Find L when $W = 0.65$, and interpret the result.

62. *Orbits and Distances* The time T in years for a planet to orbit the sun is given by $T = D^{3/2}$, where D is the planet's distance from the sun and $D = 1$ corresponds to Earth's distance from the sun. If a planet is twice the distance from the sun as Earth, does the time to orbit the sun also double?

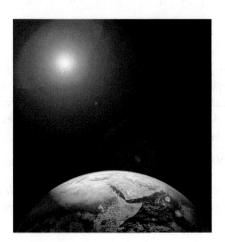

WRITING ABOUT MATHEMATICS

63. Explain why a root function is an example of a power function.

64. Discuss the shape of the graph of $y = x^p$ as p increases. Assume that p is a positive rational number and that x is a positive real number.

Group Activity   Working with Real Data

Directions: Form a group of 2 to 4 people. Select someone to record the group's responses for this activity. All members of the group should work cooperatively to answer the questions. If your instructor asks for your results, each member of the group should be prepared to respond.

Simple Pendulum Gravity is responsible for an object falling toward Earth. The farther the object falls, the faster it is moving when it hits the ground. For each second that an object falls, its speed increases by a constant amount, called the *acceleration due to gravity*, denoted g. One way to calculate the value of g is to use a simple pendulum. See the accompanying figure.

The time T for a pendulum to swing back and forth once is called its *period* and is given by

$$T = 2\pi\sqrt{\frac{L}{g}},$$

where L equals the length of the pendulum. The table lists the periods of pendulums with different lengths.

L (feet)	0.5	1.0	1.5
T (seconds)	0.78	1.11	1.36

(a) Solve the formula for g.

(b) Use the table to determine the value of g. (*Note:* The units for g are feet per second per second.)

(c) Interpret your result.

5.6 Equations Involving Radical Expressions

Solving Radical Equations ● The Distance Formula ● Solving the Equation $x^n = k$

A LOOK INTO MATH ▶

In a fast-paced society, people do not spend time watching videos that they find boring. For example, earlier in this chapter we learned how the function

$$A(x) = 7.3\sqrt[16]{x^7}$$

computes the percentage of viewers who abandon an online video after x seconds. If we want to find the number of seconds that it takes for **50%** of viewers to abandon a typical online video, we could *solve* the *radical equation*

$$7.3\sqrt[16]{x^7} = 50$$

(See Exercise 119.) In this section we discuss how to solve radical equations and equations with rational exponents.

Solving Radical Equations

NEW VOCABULARY

☐ Extraneous solutions
☐ Pythagorean theorem
☐ Distance

Many times, equations contain either radical expressions or rational exponents. Examples include

$$\sqrt{x} = 6, \quad 5x^{1/2} = 1, \quad \text{and} \quad \sqrt[3]{x-1} = 3. \quad \text{Radical equations}$$

One strategy for solving an equation containing a square root is to isolate the square root (if necessary) and then square each side of the equation. This technique is an example of the *power rule for solving equations.*

POWER RULE FOR SOLVING EQUATIONS

If each side of an equation is raised to the same positive integer power, then any solutions to the given equation are among the solutions to the new equation. That is, the solutions to the equation $a = b$ are among the solutions to $a^n = b^n$.

NOTE: After applying the power rule, the new equation can have solutions that do not satisfy the given equation, which are sometimes called **extraneous solutions**. We must *always* check our answers in the *given* equation after applying the power rule.

READING CHECK

When you apply the power rule to solve an equation, what must you do with your solutions? Why?

We illustrate the power rule in the next example.

EXAMPLE 1 **Solving a radical equation symbolically**

Solve $\sqrt{2x - 1} = 3$. Check your solution.

Solution

Begin by squaring each side of the equation. That is, apply the power rule with $n = 2$.

$$\sqrt{2x - 1} = 3 \qquad \text{Given equation}$$
$$(\sqrt{2x - 1})^2 = 3^2 \qquad \text{Square each side.}$$
$$2x - 1 = 9 \qquad \text{Simplify.}$$
$$2x = 10 \qquad \text{Add 1.}$$
$$x = 5 \qquad \text{Divide by 2.}$$

To check this answer we substitute $x = 5$ in the given equation.

$$\sqrt{2(5) - 1} \overset{?}{=} 3$$
$$3 = 3 \checkmark \quad \text{It checks.}$$

Now Try Exercise 21

NOTE: To simplify $(\sqrt{2x - 1})^2$ in Example 1, we used the fact that

$$\left(\sqrt{a}\right)^2 = \sqrt{a} \cdot \sqrt{a} = a.$$

The following steps can be used to solve a radical equation.

SOLVING A RADICAL EQUATION

STEP 1: Isolate a radical term on one side of the equation.

STEP 2: Apply the power rule by raising each side of the equation to the power equal to the index of the isolated radical term.

STEP 3: Solve the equation. If it still contains a radical, repeat Steps 1 and 2.

STEP 4: Check your answers by substituting each result in the *given* equation.

NOTE: In earlier sections, we *simplified expressions*. In this section, we *solve equations*. Equations contain equals signs and when we solve an equation, we try to find values of the variable that make the equation a true statement.

In the next example, we apply these steps to a radical equation.

EXAMPLE 2 **Isolating the radical term**

Solve $\sqrt{4 - x} + 5 = 8$.

Solution

STEP 1: To isolate the radical term, we subtract 5 from each side of the equation.

$$\sqrt{4 - x} + 5 = 8 \qquad \text{Given equation}$$
$$\sqrt{4 - x} = 3 \qquad \text{Subtract 5.}$$

STEP 2: The isolated term involves a square root, so we must **square** each side.

$$(\sqrt{4-x})^2 = (3)^2 \qquad \text{Square each side.}$$

STEP 3: Next we solve the resulting equation. (It is not necessary to repeat Steps 1 and 2 because the resulting equation does not contain any radical expressions.)

$$\begin{aligned} 4 - x &= 9 & \text{Simplify.} \\ -x &= 5 & \text{Subtract 4.} \\ x &= -5 & \text{Multiply by } -1. \end{aligned}$$

STEP 4: To check this answer we substitute $x = -5$ in the given equation.

$$\begin{aligned} \sqrt{4 - (-5)} + 5 &\stackrel{?}{=} 8 \\ \sqrt{9} + 5 &\stackrel{?}{=} 8 \\ 8 &= 8 \checkmark \quad \text{It checks.} \end{aligned}$$

▌ Now Try Exercise 23

The next example shows that we must check our answers to identify extraneous solutions when squaring each side of an equation.

EXAMPLE 3 ▌ **Solving a radical equation**

Solve $\sqrt{3x + 3} = 2x - 1$. Check your results and then solve the equation graphically.

Solution
Symbolic Solution Begin by squaring each side of the equation.

$$\begin{aligned} \sqrt{3x + 3} &= 2x - 1 & \text{Given equation} \\ (\sqrt{3x + 3})^2 &= (2x - 1)^2 & \text{Square each side.} \\ 3x + 3 &= 4x^2 - 4x + 1 & \text{Multiply.} \\ 0 &= 4x^2 - 7x - 2 & \text{Subtract } 3x + 3. \\ 0 &= (4x + 1)(x - 2) & \text{Factor.} \\ x &= -\frac{1}{4} \quad \text{or} \quad x = 2 & \text{Solve for } x. \end{aligned}$$

To check these values substitute $x = -\frac{1}{4}$ and $x = 2$ in the given equation.

$$\begin{aligned} \sqrt{3\left(-\frac{1}{4}\right) + 3} &\stackrel{?}{=} 2\left(-\frac{1}{4}\right) - 1 \\ \sqrt{2.25} &\stackrel{?}{=} -1.5 \\ 1.5 &\neq -1.5 \text{ ✗} \qquad \text{It does not check.} \end{aligned}$$

Thus $-\frac{1}{4}$ is an *extraneous solution*. Next substitute $x = 2$ in the given equation.

$$\begin{aligned} \sqrt{3 \cdot 2 + 3} &\stackrel{?}{=} 2 \cdot 2 - 1 \\ \sqrt{9} &\stackrel{?}{=} 3 \\ 3 &= 3 \checkmark \qquad \text{It checks.} \end{aligned}$$

The only solution is 2. Next we check with a graphical solution.

Figure 5.22

CALCULATOR HELP

To find a point of intersection, see Appendix A (page AP-6).

Graphical Solution The solution **2** to the equation $\sqrt{3x + 3} = 2x - 1$ is supported graphically in Figure 5.22, where the graphs of $y_1 = \sqrt{3x + 3}$ and $y_2 = 2x - 1$ intersect at the point (**2**, 3). *Note that the graphical solution does not give an extraneous solution.*

Now Try Exercises 27, 79(a), (b)

Example 3 demonstrates that *checking a solution is essential when you are squaring each side of an equation.* Squaring may introduce extraneous solutions, which are solutions to the resulting equation but are not solutions to the given equation.

CRITICAL THINKING

Will a numerical solution give extraneous solutions?

When an equation contains two or more terms with square roots, it may be necessary to square each side of the equation more than once. In these situations, isolate one of the square roots and then square each side of the equation. If a radical term remains after simplifying, repeat these steps. We apply this technique in the next example.

EXAMPLE 4 **Squaring twice**

Solve $\sqrt{2x} - 1 = \sqrt{x + 1}$.

Solution
Begin by squaring each side of the equation.

$$\sqrt{2x} - 1 = \sqrt{x + 1} \qquad \text{Given equation}$$

$$(\sqrt{2x} - 1)^2 = (\sqrt{x + 1})^2 \qquad \text{Square each side.}$$

$$(\sqrt{2x})^2 - 2(\sqrt{2x})(1) + 1^2 = x + 1 \qquad (a - b)^2 = a^2 - 2ab + b^2$$

$$2x - 2\sqrt{2x} + 1 = x + 1 \qquad \text{Simplify.}$$

$$2x - 2\sqrt{2x} = x \qquad \text{Subtract 1.}$$

$$x = 2\sqrt{2x} \qquad \text{Subtract } x \text{ and add } 2\sqrt{2x}.$$

$$x^2 = 4(2x) \qquad \text{Square each side again.}$$

$$x^2 - 8x = 0 \qquad \text{Subtract } 8x.$$

$$x(x - 8) = 0 \qquad \text{Factor.}$$

$$x = 0 \quad \text{or} \quad x = 8 \qquad \text{Solve.}$$

To check these answers substitute $x = 0$ and $x = 8$ in the given equation.

$$\sqrt{2 \cdot 0} - 1 \overset{?}{=} \sqrt{0 + 1} \qquad\qquad \sqrt{2 \cdot 8} - 1 \overset{?}{=} \sqrt{8 + 1}$$

$$-1 \neq 1 \; ✗ \quad \text{It does not check.} \qquad\qquad 3 = 3 \; ✓ \quad \text{It checks.}$$

The only solution is 8.

Now Try Exercise 43

In the next example we apply the power rule to an equation that contains a cube root.

EXAMPLE 5 | **Solving an equation containing a cube root**

Solve $\sqrt[3]{4x - 7} = 4$.

Solution

STEP 1: The cube root term is already isolated, so we proceed to Step 2.

STEP 2: Because the index is 3, we **cube** each side of the equation.

$$\sqrt[3]{4x - 7} = 4 \qquad \text{Given equation}$$
$$(\sqrt[3]{4x - 7})^3 = (4)^3 \qquad \text{Cube each side.}$$

STEP 3: We solve the resulting equation.

$$4x - 7 = 64 \qquad \text{Simplify.}$$
$$4x = 71 \qquad \text{Add 7 to each side.}$$
$$x = \frac{71}{4} \qquad \text{Divide each side by 4.}$$

STEP 4: To check this answer we substitute $x = \frac{71}{4}$ in the given equation.

$$\sqrt[3]{4\left(\frac{71}{4}\right) - 7} \stackrel{?}{=} 4$$
$$\sqrt[3]{64} \stackrel{?}{=} 4$$
$$4 = 4 \checkmark \quad \text{It checks.}$$

▌ Now Try Exercise 31

▶ **REAL-WORLD CONNECTION** Larger birds tend to have larger wings. This relationship can sometimes be modeled by $A(W) = 100\sqrt[3]{W^2}$, where W is the weight in pounds of the bird and A is the area of the wings in square inches. In the next example, we use the formula to determine the weight of a bird that has wings with a surface area of 600 square inches. (*Source:* C. Pennycuick, *Newton Rules Biology.*)

EXAMPLE 6 | **Finding the weight of a bird**

Solve the equation $600 = 100\sqrt[3]{W^2}$ to determine the weight in pounds of a bird having wings with an area of 600 square inches.

Solution

Begin by dividing each side of the equation $600 = 100\sqrt[3]{W^2}$ by 100 to isolate the radical term on the right side of the equation.

$$\frac{600}{100} = \sqrt[3]{W^2} \qquad \text{Divide each side by 100.}$$
$$(6)^3 = (\sqrt[3]{W^2})^3 \qquad \text{Cube each side.}$$
$$216 = W^2 \qquad \text{Simplify.}$$
$$\sqrt{216} = W \qquad \text{Take principal square root, } W > 0.$$
$$W \approx 14.7 \qquad \text{Approximate.}$$

The weight of the bird is approximately 14.7 pounds.

▌ Now Try Exercise 117

TECHNOLOGY NOTE

Graphing Radical Expressions

The equation in Example 6 can be solved graphically. Sometimes it is more convenient to use rational exponents than radical notation. Thus $y = 100\sqrt[3]{W^2}$ can be entered as $Y_1 = 100X^{(2/3)}$. (Be sure to include parentheses around the 2/3.) The accompanying figure shows y_1 intersecting the line $y_2 = 600$ near the point (14.7, 600), which supports our symbolic result.

$[0, 20, 5]$ by $[0, 800, 100]$

In the next example we solve an equation that would be difficult to solve symbolically, but an *approximate* solution can be found graphically.

EXAMPLE 7

Solving an equation with rational exponents graphically

Solve $x^{2/3} = 3 - x^2$ graphically.

Solution

Graph $Y_1 = X^{(2/3)}$ and $Y_2 = 3 - X^2$. The graphs intersect near $(-1.34, 1.21)$ and $(1.34, 1.21)$, as shown in Figure 5.23. Thus the solutions are given by $x \approx \pm 1.34$.

$[-6, 6, 1]$ by $[-4, 4, 1]$ $[-6, 6, 1]$ by $[-4, 4, 1]$

(a)   (b)

Figure 5.23

Now Try Exercise 73

The Distance Formula

▶ **REAL-WORLD CONNECTION** One of the most famous theorems in mathematics is the **Pythagorean theorem**. It states that if a right triangle has legs a and b with hypotenuse c (see Figure 5.24), then

$$a^2 + b^2 = c^2. \quad \text{Pythagorean Theorem}$$

$a^2 + b^2 = c^2$

Figure 5.24

For example, if the legs of a right triangle are $a = 3$ and $b = 4$, the hypotenuse is $c = 5$ because $3^2 + 4^2 = 5^2$. Also, if the sides of a triangle satisfy $a^2 + b^2 = c^2$, it is a right triangle.

EXAMPLE 8

Applying the Pythagorean theorem

A rectangular television screen has a width of 20 inches and a height of 15 inches. Find the diagonal of the television. Why is it called a 25-inch television?

Figure 5.25

Solution

In Figure 5.25, let $a = 20$ and $b = 15$. Then the diagonal of the television corresponds to the hypotenuse of a right triangle with legs of 20 inches and 15 inches.

$$
\begin{aligned}
c^2 &= a^2 + b^2 && \text{Pythagorean theorem} \\
c &= \sqrt{a^2 + b^2} && \text{Take the principal square root, } c > 0. \\
c &= \sqrt{20^2 + 15^2} && \text{Substitute } a = 20 \text{ and } b = 15. \\
c &= 25 && \text{Simplify.}
\end{aligned}
$$

A 25-inch television has a diagonal of 25 inches.

▌ **Now Try Exercise 125**

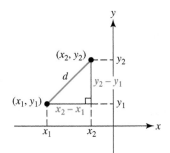

Figure 5.26

The Pythagorean theorem can be used to determine the distance between two points. Suppose that a line segment has endpoints (x_1, y_1) and (x_2, y_2), as illustrated in Figure 5.26. The lengths of the legs of the right triangle are $x_2 - x_1$ and $y_2 - y_1$. The distance d is the hypotenuse of a right triangle. Applying the Pythagorean theorem, we have

$$
d^2 = (x_2 - x_1)^2 + (y_2 - y_1)^2.
$$

Distance is nonnegative, so we let d be the principal square root and obtain

$$
d = \sqrt{(x_2 - x_1)^2 + (y_2 - y_1)^2}.
$$

DISTANCE FORMULA

The **distance** d between the points (x_1, y_1) and (x_2, y_2) in the xy-plane is

$$
d = \sqrt{(x_2 - x_1)^2 + (y_2 - y_1)^2}.
$$

EXAMPLE 9   **Finding distance between points**

Find the distance between the points $(-2, 3)$ and $(1, -4)$.

Solution

Start by letting $(x_1, y_1) = (-2, 3)$ and $(x_2, y_2) = (1, -4)$. Then substitute these values into the distance formula.

$$
\begin{aligned}
d &= \sqrt{(x_2 - x_1)^2 + (y_2 - y_1)^2} && \text{Distance formula} \\
&= \sqrt{(1 - (-2))^2 + (-4 - 3)^2} && \text{Substitute.} \\
&= \sqrt{9 + 49} && \text{Simplify.} \\
&= \sqrt{58} && \text{Add.} \\
&\approx 7.62 && \text{Approximate.}
\end{aligned}
$$

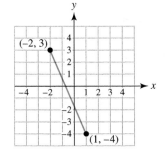

Figure 5.27

The distance between the points, as shown in Figure 5.27, is exactly $\sqrt{58}$ units, or about 5.62 units. Note that we would obtain the same result if we let $(x_1, y_1) = (1, -4)$ and $(x_2, y_2) = (-2, 3)$.

▌ **Now Try Exercise 109**

NOTE: In Example 9, $\sqrt{9 + 49} \neq \sqrt{9} + \sqrt{49} = 3 + 7 = 10$. In general, for any a and b, $\sqrt{a^2 + b^2} \neq a + b$.

Solving the Equation $x^n = k$

The equation $x^n = k$, where n is a *positive integer*, can be solved by taking the nth root of each side of the equation. The following technique allows us to find all *real* solutions to this equation.

SOLVING THE EQUATION $x^n = k$

Take the nth root of each side of $x^n = k$ to obtain $\sqrt[n]{x^n} = \sqrt[n]{k}$.
1. If n is odd, then $\sqrt[n]{x^n} = x$ and the equation becomes $x = \sqrt[n]{k}$.
2. If n is *even* and $k > 0$, then $\sqrt[n]{x^n} = |x|$ and the equation becomes $|x| = \sqrt[n]{k}$. (If $k < 0$, there are no real solutions.)

To understand this technique better, consider the following examples. First let $x^3 = 8$, so that n is odd. Taking the cube root of each side gives

$$\sqrt[3]{x^3} = \sqrt[3]{8}, \text{ which is equivalent to } x = \sqrt[3]{8}, \text{ or } x = 2.$$

Next let $x^2 = 4$, so that n is even. Taking the square root of each side gives

$$\sqrt{x^2} = \sqrt{4}, \text{ which is equivalent to } |x| = \sqrt{4}, \text{ or } |x| = 2.$$

The solutions to $|x| = 2$ are -2 or 2, which can be written as ± 2.

EXAMPLE 10 **Solving the equation $x^n = k$**

Solve each equation.
(a) $x^3 = -64$ **(b)** $x^2 = 12$ **(c)** $2(x - 1)^4 = 32$

Solution
(a) Taking the cube root of each side of $x^3 = -64$ gives

$$\sqrt[3]{x^3} = \sqrt[3]{-64} \text{ or } x = -4.$$

(b) Taking the square root of each side of $x^2 = 12$ gives

$$\sqrt{x^2} = \sqrt{12} \text{ or } |x| = \sqrt{12}.$$

The equation $|x| = \sqrt{12}$ is equivalent to $x = \pm\sqrt{12}$.
(c) First divide each side of $2(x - 1)^4 = 32$ by 2 to isolate the power of $x - 1$.

$$(x - 1)^4 = 16 \qquad \text{Divide each side by 2.}$$

$$\sqrt[4]{(x - 1)^4} = \sqrt[4]{16} \qquad \text{Take the 4th root of each side.}$$

$$|x - 1| = 2 \qquad \text{Simplify: } \sqrt[n]{y^4} = |y|.$$

$$x - 1 = -2 \text{ or } x - 1 = 2 \qquad \text{Solve the absolute value equation.}$$

$$x = -1 \text{ or } x = 3 \qquad \text{Add 1 to each side.}$$

Now Try Exercises 47, 55, 67

▶ **REAL-WORLD CONNECTION** In some parts of the United States, wind power is used to generate electricity. Suppose that the diameter of the circular path created by the blades of a wind-powered generator is 8 feet. Then the wattage W generated by a wind velocity of v miles per hour is modeled by

$$W(v) = 2.4v^3.$$

If the wind blows at 10 miles per hour, the generator can produce about

$$W(10) = 2.4 \cdot 10^3 = 2400 \text{ watts}.$$

(*Source: Conquering the Sciences, Sharp Electronics.*)

EXAMPLE 11   **Modeling a wind generator**

The formula $W(v) = 2.4v^3$ is used to calculate the watts generated when there is a wind velocity of v miles per hour.
(a) Find a function f that calculates the wind velocity when W watts are being produced.
(b) If the wattage doubles, has the wind velocity also doubled? Explain.

Solution
(a) Given W we need a formula to find v, so solve $W = 2.4v^3$ for v.

$$W = 2.4v^3 \qquad \text{Given formula}$$

$$\frac{W}{2.4} = v^3 \qquad \text{Divide by 2.4.}$$

$$\sqrt[3]{\frac{W}{2.4}} = \sqrt[3]{v^3} \qquad \text{Take the cube root of each side.}$$

$$v = \sqrt[3]{\frac{W}{2.4}} \qquad \text{Simplify and rewrite equation.}$$

Thus $f(W) = \sqrt[3]{\frac{W}{2.4}}$.
(b) Suppose that the power generated is 1000 watts. Then the wind speed is

$$f(1000) = \sqrt[3]{\frac{1000}{2.4}} \approx 7.5 \text{ miles per hour.}$$

If the power doubles to 2000 watts, then the wind speed is

$$f(2000) = \sqrt[3]{\frac{2000}{2.4}} \approx 9.4 \text{ miles per hour.}$$

Thus for the wattage to double, the wind speed does not need to double.

Now Try Exercise 133

5.6   Putting It All Together

CONCEPT	DESCRIPTION	EXAMPLE
Power Rule for Solving Equations	If each side of an equation is raised to the same positive integer power, any solutions to the given equation are among the solutions to the new equation.	$\sqrt{2x} = x$ $2x = x^2$ Square each side. $x^2 - 2x = 0$ Rewrite equation. $x = 0$ or $x = 2$ Factor and solve. *Be sure to check any solutions.*

continued on next page

continued from previous page

CONCEPT	DESCRIPTION	EXAMPLE
Pythagorean Theorem	If c is the hypotenuse of a right triangle and a and b are its legs, then $a^2 + b^2 = c^2$. (triangle with legs a, b and hypotenuse c)	If the sides of the right triangle are $a = 5, b = 12$, and $c = 13$, then they satisfy $a^2 + b^2 = c^2$ or $5^2 + 12^2 = 13^2$.
Distance Formula	The distance d between the points (x_1, y_1) and (x_2, y_2) is $$d = \sqrt{(x_2 - x_1)^2 + (y_2 - y_1)^2}.$$	The distance between the points $(2, 3)$ and $(-3, 4)$ is $$d = \sqrt{(-3 - 2)^2 + (4 - 3)^2}$$ $$= \sqrt{(-5)^2 + (1)^2} = \sqrt{26}.$$
Solving the Equation $x^n = k$, Where n Is a Positive Integer	Take the nth root of each side to obtain $\sqrt[n]{x^n} = \sqrt[n]{k}$. Then, **1.** $x = \sqrt[n]{k}$, if n is odd. **2.** $x = \pm\sqrt[n]{k}$, if n is even and $k \geq 0$.	**1.** n odd: If $x^5 = 32$, then $x = \sqrt[5]{32} = 2$. **2.** n even: If $x^4 = 81$, then $x = \pm\sqrt[4]{81} = \pm 3$.

Equations involving radical expressions can be solved symbolically, numerically, and graphically. All symbolic solutions must be checked; *numerical and graphical methods do not give extraneous solutions.* These concepts are illustrated for the equation $\sqrt{x + 2} = x$, where $y_1 = \sqrt{x + 2}$ and $y_2 = x$.

Symbolic Solution

$$\sqrt{x + 2} = x$$
$$x + 2 = x^2$$
$$x^2 - x - 2 = 0$$
$$(x - 2)(x + 1) = 0$$
$$x = 2 \quad \text{or} \quad x = -1$$

Check: $\sqrt{2 + 2} = 2$ ✓
$\sqrt{-1 + 2} \neq -1$ ✗

The only solution is 2.

Numerical Solution

X	Y₁	Y₂
-2	0	-2
-1	1	-1
0	1.4142	0
1	1.7321	1
2		2
3	2.2361	3
4	2.4495	4

X=2

$y_1 = y_2$ when $x = 2$, so 2 is a solution. Note that -1 is *not* a solution.

Graphical Solution

$[-4.7, 4.7, 1]$ by $[-3.1, 3.1, 1]$

(graph with $y_1 = \sqrt{x + 2}$ and $y_2 = x$; Intersection X=2, Y=2)

The graphs intersect at $(2, 2)$. Note that there is no point of intersection when $x = -1$.

5.6   Exercises

MyMathLab
PRACTICE   WATCH   DOWNLOAD   READ   REVIEW

CONCEPTS AND VOCABULARY

1. What is a good first step for solving $\sqrt{4x - 1} = 5$?

2. What is a good first step for solving $\sqrt[3]{x + 1} = 6$?

3. Can an equation involving rational exponents have more than one solution?

4. When you square each side of an equation to solve for an unknown, what must you do with any answers?

5. What is the Pythagorean theorem used for?

6. If the legs of a right triangle are 3 and 4, what is the length of the hypotenuse?

7. What formula can you use to find the distance d between two points?

8. Write the equation $\sqrt{x} + \sqrt[4]{x^3} = 2$ with rational exponents.

SIMPLIFYING RADICALS

Exercises 9–16: Simplify. Assume radicands of square roots are positive.

9. $\sqrt{2} \cdot \sqrt{2}$

10. $\sqrt{5} \cdot \sqrt{5}$

11. $\sqrt{x} \cdot \sqrt{x}$

12. $\sqrt{2x} \cdot \sqrt{2x}$

13. $(\sqrt{2x+1})^2$

14. $(\sqrt{7x})^2$

15. $(\sqrt[3]{5x^2})^3$

16. $(\sqrt[3]{2x-5})^3$

SYMBOLIC SOLUTIONS

Exercises 17–46: Solve the equation symbolically. Check your results.

17. $\sqrt{x} = 8$

18. $\sqrt{3z} = 6$

19. $\sqrt[4]{x} = 3$

20. $\sqrt[3]{x-4} = 2$

21. $\sqrt{2t+4} = 4$

22. $\sqrt{y+4} = 3$

23. $\sqrt{x+1} - 3 = 4$

24. $\sqrt{2x+5} + 2 = 5$

25. $2\sqrt{x-2} + 1 = 5$

26. $-\sqrt{x+7} - 1 = -7$

27. $\sqrt{x+6} = x$

28. $\sqrt{z+6} = z$

29. $\sqrt[3]{x} = 3$

30. $\sqrt[3]{x+10} = 4$

31. $\sqrt[3]{2z-4} = -2$

32. $\sqrt[3]{z-1} = -3$

33. $\sqrt[4]{t+1} = 2$

34. $\sqrt[4]{5t} = 5$

35. $\sqrt{5z-1} = \sqrt{z+1}$

36. $y = \sqrt{y+1} + 1$

37. $\sqrt{1-x} = 1 - x$

38. $\sqrt[3]{4x} = x$

39. $\sqrt{b^2 - 4} = b - 2$

40. $\sqrt{b^2 - 2b + 1} = b$

41. $\sqrt{1 - 2x} = x + 7$

42. $\sqrt{4 - y} = y - 2$

43. $\sqrt{x} = \sqrt{x-5} + 1$

44. $\sqrt{x-1} = \sqrt{x+4} - 1$

45. $\sqrt{2t-2} + \sqrt{t} = 7$

46. $\sqrt{x+1} - \sqrt{x-6} = 1$

SOLVING THE EQUATION $x^n = k$

Exercises 47–68: (Refer to Example 10.) Solve.

47. $x^2 = 49$

48. $x^2 = 9$

49. $2z^2 = 200$

50. $3z^2 = 48$

51. $(t+1)^2 = 16$

52. $(t-5)^2 = 81$

53. $(4-2x)^2 = 100$

54. $(3x-6)^2 = 25$

55. $b^3 = 64$

56. $a^3 = 1000$

57. $2t^3 = -128$

58. $3t^3 = -81$

59. $(x+1)^3 = 8$

60. $(4-x)^3 = -1$

61. $(2-5z)^3 = -125$

62. $(2x+4)^3 = 125$

63. $x^4 = 16$

64. $x^4 = 7$

65. $x^5 = 12$

66. $x^5 = -32$

67. $2(x+2)^4 = 162$

68. $\frac{1}{2}(x-1)^5 = 16$

GRAPHICAL SOLUTIONS

Exercises 69–78: Solve graphically. Approximate solutions to the nearest hundredth when appropriate.

69. $\sqrt[3]{x+5} = 2$

70. $\sqrt[3]{x} + \sqrt{x} = 3.43$

71. $\sqrt{2x-3} = \sqrt{x} - \frac{1}{2}$

72. $x^{4/3} - 1 = 2$

73. $x^{5/3} = 2 - 3x^2$

74. $x^{3/2} = \sqrt{x+2} - 2$

75. $z^{1/3} - 1 = 2 - z$

76. $z^{3/2} - 2z^{1/2} - 1 = 0$

77. $\sqrt{y+2} + \sqrt{3y+2} = 2$

78. $\sqrt{x+1} - \sqrt{x-1} = 4$

USING MORE THAN ONE METHOD

Exercises 79–82: Solve the equation
   (a) *symbolically,*
   (b) *graphically, and*
   (c) *numerically.*

79. $2\sqrt{x} = 8$

80. $\sqrt[3]{5-x} = 2$

81. $\sqrt{6z-2} = 8$

82. $\sqrt{y+4} = \dfrac{y}{3}$

SOLVING AN EQUATION FOR A VARIABLE

Exercises 83–86: Solve for the indicated variable.

83. $T = 2\pi\sqrt{\dfrac{L}{32}}$ for L

84. $Z = \sqrt{L^2 + R^2}$ for R

85. $r = \sqrt{\dfrac{A}{\pi}}$ for A

86. $F = \dfrac{1}{2\pi\sqrt{LC}}$ for C

PYTHAGOREAN THEOREM

Exercises 87–94: If the sides of a triangle are a, b, and c and they satisfy $a^2 + b^2 = c^2$, the triangle is a right triangle. Determine whether the triangle with the given sides is a right triangle.

87. $a = 6$ $b = 8$ $c = 10$

88. $a = 5$ $b = 12$ $c = 13$

89. $a = \sqrt{5}$ $\quad b = \sqrt{9}$ $\quad c = \sqrt{14}$

90. $a = 4$ $\quad b = 5$ $\quad c = 7$

91. $a = 7$ $\quad b = 24$ $\quad c = 25$

92. $a = 1$ $\quad b = \sqrt{3}$ $\quad c = 2$

93. $a = 8$ $\quad b = 8$ $\quad c = 16$

94. $a = 11$ $\quad b = 60$ $\quad c = 61$

Exercises 95–98: Find the length of the missing side in the right triangle.

95.

96.

97.

98.
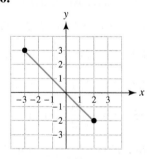

Exercises 99–104: A right triangle has legs a and b with hypotenuse c. Find the length of the missing side.

99. $a = 3, b = 4$

100. $a = 4, b = 7$

101. $a = \sqrt{3}, c = 8$

102. $a = \sqrt{6}, c = \sqrt{10}$

103. $b = 48, c = 50$

104. $b = 10, c = 26$

DISTANCE FORMULA

Exercises 105–108: Find the length of the line segment.

105.

106.

107.

108.
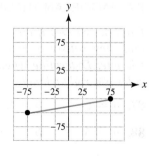

Exercises 109–112: Find the distance between the points.

109. $(-1, 2), (4, 10)$ $\qquad$ **110.** $(5, -40), (-6, 20)$

111. $(0, -3), (4, 0)$ $\qquad$ **112.** $(3, 9), (-4, 2)$

Exercises 113–116: Find x if the distance between the points is d. Assume that $x \geq 0$.

113. $(x, 3), (0, 6)$ $\qquad d = 5$

114. $(x, -1), (6, 11)$ $\quad d = 13$

115. $(x, -5), (62, 6)$ $\quad d = 61$

116. $(x, 3), (12, -4)$ $\quad d = 25$

APPLICATIONS

Exercises 117 and 118: Weight of a Bird (Refer to Example 6.) Estimate the weight W of a bird having wings of area A. Let $A = 100\sqrt[3]{W^2}$.

117. $A = 400$ square inches

118. $A = 1000$ square inches

Exercises 119 and 120: Abandonment Rate (Refer to A Look Into Math for this section.) Use $A(x) = 7.3\sqrt[16]{x^7}$ to find the average number of seconds x that it takes for A percent of the viewers to abandon an online movie.

119. $A = 50$ $\qquad$ **120.** $A = 20$

Exercises 121–124: Distance to the Horizon Because of Earth's curvature, a person can see a limited distance to the horizon. The higher the location of the person, the farther that person can see. The distance D in miles to the horizon can be estimated by $D(h) = 1.22\sqrt{h}$, where h is the height of the person above the ground in feet.

121. Find D for a 6-foot-tall person standing on level ground.

122. Find D for a person on top of Mount Everest with a height of 29,028 feet.

123. What height allows a person to see 20 miles?

124. How high does a plane need to fly for the pilot to be able to see 100 miles?

125. *Diagonal of a Television* (Refer to Example 8.) A rectangular television screen is 11.4 inches by 15.2 inches. Find the diagonal of the television screen.

126. *Dimensions of a Television* The height of a television with a 13-inch diagonal is $\frac{3}{4}$ of its width. Find the width and height of the television set.

127. *DVD and Picture Dimensions* If the picture shown on a television set is h units high and w units wide, the *aspect ratio* of the picture is $\frac{w}{h}$ (see the accompanying figure). Digital video discs support the newer aspect ratio of $\frac{16}{9}$ rather than the older ratio of $\frac{4}{3}$. If the width of a picture with an aspect ratio of $\frac{16}{9}$ is 29 inches, approximate the height and diagonal of the rectangular picture. (*Source:* J. Taylor, *DVD Demystified.*)

128. *Flood Control* The spillway capacity of a dam is important in flood control. Spillway capacity Q in cubic feet of water per second flowing over the spillway depends on the width W and the depth D of the spillway, as illustrated in the accompanying figure. If W and D are measured in feet, capacity can be modeled by $Q = 3.32WD^{3/2}$. (*Source:* D. Callas, Project Director, *Snapshots of Applications in Mathematics.*)
  (a) Find the capacity of a spillway with $W = 20$ feet and $D = 5$ feet.
  (b) A spillway with a width of 30 feet is to have a capacity of $Q = 2690$ cubic feet per second. Estimate to the nearest foot the appropriate depth of the spillway.

129. *Sky Diving* When sky divers initially fall from an airplane, their velocity v in miles per hour after free falling d feet can be approximated by $v = \frac{60}{11}\sqrt{d}$. (Because of air resistance, they will eventually reach a terminal velocity.) How far do sky divers need to fall to attain the following velocities? (These values for d represent minimum distances.)
  (a) 60 miles per hour   **(b)** 100 miles per hour

130. *Guy Wire* A guy wire attached to the top of a 30-foot-long pole is anchored 10 feet from the base of the pole, as illustrated in the figure. Find the length of the guy wire to the nearest tenth of a foot.

131. *Skid Marks* Vehicles involved in accidents often leave skid marks, which can be used to determine how fast a vehicle was traveling. To determine this speed, officials often use a test vehicle to compare skid marks on the same section of road. Suppose that a vehicle in a crash left skid marks D feet long and that a test vehicle traveling at v miles per hour leaves skid marks d feet long. Then the speed V of the vehicle involved in the crash is given by

$$V = v\sqrt{\frac{D}{d}}.$$

(*Source:* N. Garber and L. Hoel, *Traffic and Highway Engineering.*)
  (a) Find V if $v = 30$ mph, $D = 285$ feet, and $d = 178$ feet. Interpret your result.
  (b) A test vehicle traveling at 45 mph leaves skid marks 255 feet long. How long would the skid marks be for a vehicle traveling 60 miles per hour?

132. *Highway Curves* If a circular highway curve without any banking has a radius of R feet, the speed limit L in miles per hour for the curve is $L = 1.5\sqrt{R}$. (*Source:* N. Garber.)
  (a) Find the speed limit for a curve having a radius of 400 feet.
  (b) If the radius of a curve doubles, what happens to the speed limit?
  (c) A curve with a 40-mile-per-hour speed limit is being designed. What should be its radius?

133. *Wind Power* (Refer to Example 11.) If a wind-powered generator has blades that create a circular path with a diameter of 10 feet, then the wattage W generated by a wind velocity of v miles per hour is modeled by $W(v) = 3.8v^3$.
  (a) If the wind velocity doubles, what happens to the wattage generated?
  (b) Solve $W = 3.8v^3$ for v.
  (c) If the wind generator is producing 30,400 watts, find the wind speed.

134. *Height and Weight* Suppose that the weight of a person is directly proportional to the cube of the person's height. If one person weighs twice as much as a (similarly proportioned) second person, by what factor is the heavier person's height greater than the shorter person's height?

135. *45°–45° Right Triangle* Suppose that the legs of a right triangle with angles of 45° and 45° both have length a, as depicted in the accompanying figure. Find the length of the hypotenuse.

136. *30°–60° Right Triangle* In a right triangle with angles of 30° and 60°, the shortest side is half the length of the hypotenuse (see the accompanying figure). If the hypotenuse has length c, find the length of the other two sides, a and b, in terms of c.

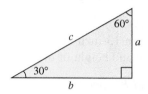

WRITING ABOUT MATHEMATICS

137. A student solves an equation *incorrectly* as follows.

$$\sqrt{3 - x} = \sqrt{x} - 1$$
$$(\sqrt{3 - x})^2 \overset{?}{=} (\sqrt{x})^2 - (1)^2$$
$$3 - x \overset{?}{=} x - 1$$
$$-2x \overset{?}{=} -4$$
$$x \overset{?}{=} 2$$

  (a) How could you convince the student that the answer is wrong?
  (b) Discuss where any errors were made.

138. When each side of an equation is squared, you must check your results. Explain why.

Checking Basic Concepts

1. Sketch a graph of each function and then evaluate $f(-1)$, if possible.
  (a) $f(x) = \sqrt{x}$
  (b) $f(x) = \sqrt[3]{x}$
  (c) $f(x) = \sqrt{x^2}$

2. Evaluate $f(x) = 0.2x^{2/3}$ when $x = 64$.

3. Find the domain of $f(x) = \sqrt{x - 4}$. Write your answer in interval notation.

4. Solve each equation. Check your answers.
  (a) $\sqrt{2x - 4} = 2$
  (b) $\sqrt[3]{x - 1} = 3$
  (c) $\sqrt{3x} = 1 + \sqrt{x + 1}$

5. Find the distance between $(-3, 5)$ and $(2, -7)$.

6. A 16-inch diagonal television set has a rectangular picture with a width of 12.8 inches. Find the height of the picture.

7. Solve $(x + 1)^4 = 16$.

5.7 Complex Numbers

Basic Concepts • Addition, Subtraction, and Multiplication • Powers of *i* • Complex Conjugates and Division

A LOOK INTO MATH ▶

Mathematics is both applied and theoretical. A common misconception is that abstract or theoretical mathematics is unimportant in today's world. Many new ideas with great practical importance were first developed as abstract concepts with no particular application in mind. For example, complex numbers, which are related to square roots of negative numbers, started as an abstract concept to solve equations. Today, complex numbers are used in many sophisticated applications, such as the design of electrical circuits, ships, and airplanes. The *fractal image* shown to the left would not have been discovered without complex numbers.

NEW VOCABULARY

☐ Imaginary unit
☐ Complex number
☐ Standard form
☐ Real part
☐ Imaginary part
☐ Imaginary number
☐ Pure imaginary number
☐ Complex conjugate

Basic Concepts

A graph of $y = x^2 + 1$ is shown in Figure 5.28. There are no *x*-intercepts, so the quadratic equation $x^2 + 1 = 0$ has no real number solutions.

If we try to solve $x^2 + 1 = 0$ by subtracting 1 from each side, the result is $x^2 = -1$. Because $x^2 \geq 0$ for any real number *x*, there are no real solutions. However, mathematicians have invented (or discovered) solutions.

$$x^2 = -1$$
$$x = \pm\sqrt{-1} \quad \text{Solve for } x.$$

We now define a number called the **imaginary unit**, denoted *i*.

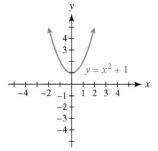

Figure 5.28

PROPERTIES OF THE IMAGINARY UNIT *i*

$$i = \sqrt{-1} \quad \text{and} \quad i^2 = -1$$

By creating the number *i*, the solutions to the equation $x^2 + 1 = 0$ are *i* and $-i$. Using the real numbers and the imaginary unit *i*, we can define a new set of numbers called the *complex numbers*. A **complex number** can be written in **standard form**, as $a + bi$, where *a* and *b* are real numbers. The **real part** is *a* and the **imaginary part** is *b*. Every real number *a* is also a complex number because it can be written $a + 0i$. A complex number $a + bi$ with $b \neq 0$ is an **imaginary number**. A complex number $a + bi$ with $a = 0$ and $b \neq 0$ is sometimes called a **pure imaginary number**. Examples of pure imaginary numbers include $4i$ and $-2i$. Table 5.9 lists several complex numbers with their real and imaginary parts.

TABLE 5.9

Complex Number: $a + bi$	$-3 + 2i$	5	$-3i$	$-1 + 7i$	$-5 - 2i$	$4 + 6i$
Real Part: a	-3	5	0	-1	-5	4
Imaginary Part: b	2	0	-3	7	-2	6

Figure 5.29 on the next page shows how different sets of numbers are related. Note that *the set of complex numbers contains the set of real numbers.*

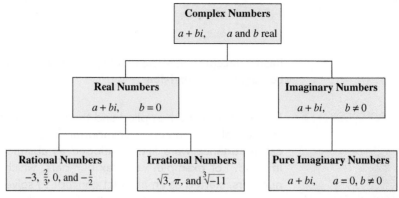

Figure 5.29

Using the imaginary unit i, we may write the square root of a negative number as a complex number. For example, $\sqrt{-2} = i\sqrt{2}$, and $\sqrt{-4} = i\sqrt{4} = 2i$. This method is summarized as follows.

CALCULATOR HELP

To set your calculator in $a + bi$ mode, see Appendix A (page AP-7).

> **THE EXPRESSION $\sqrt{-a}$**
>
> If $a > 0$, then $\sqrt{-a} = i\sqrt{a}$.

NOTE: Although it is standard for a complex number to be expressed as $a + bi$, we often write $\sqrt{2}i$ as $i\sqrt{2}$ so that it is clear that i is not under the square root. Similarly $\frac{1}{2}\sqrt{2}i$ is sometimes written as $\frac{1}{2}i\sqrt{2}$ or $\frac{i\sqrt{2}}{2}$.

EXAMPLE 1 **Writing the square root of a negative number**

Write each square root using the imaginary unit i.
(a) $\sqrt{-25}$ **(b)** $\sqrt{-7}$ **(c)** $\sqrt{-20}$

Solution
(a) $\sqrt{-25} = i\sqrt{25} = 5i$
(b) $\sqrt{-7} = i\sqrt{7}$
(c) $\sqrt{-20} = i\sqrt{20} = i\sqrt{4}\sqrt{5} = 2i\sqrt{5}$

Now Try Exercises 13, 15, 19

Addition, Subtraction, and Multiplication

Addition can be defined for complex numbers in a manner similar to how we add binomials. For example,

$$(-3 + 2x) + (2 - x) = (-3 + 2) + (2x - x) = -1 + x.$$

ADDITION AND SUBTRACTION To add the complex numbers $(-3 + 2i)$ and $(2 - i)$, add the real parts and then add the imaginary parts.

$$(-3 + 2i) + (2 - i) = (-3 + 2) + (2i - i)$$
$$= (-3 + 2) + (2 - 1)i$$
$$= -1 + i$$

This same process works for subtraction.

$$(6 - 3i) - (2 + 5i) = (6 - 2) + (-3i - 5i)$$
$$= (6 - 2) + (-3 - 5)i$$
$$= 4 - 8i$$

This method is summarized as follows.

SUM OR DIFFERENCE OF COMPLEX NUMBERS

Let $a + bi$ and $c + di$ be two complex numbers. Then

$$(a + bi) + (c + di) = (a + c) + (b + d)i \quad \text{Sum}$$

and $\quad (a + bi) - (c + di) = (a - c) + (b - d)i. \quad \text{Difference}$

READING CHECK

How do you add and subtract complex numbers?

EXAMPLE 2 **Adding and subtracting complex numbers**

Write each sum or difference in standard form.
(a) $(-7 + 2i) + (3 - 4i)$ **(b)** $3i - (5 - i)$

Solution
(a) $(-7 + 2i) + (3 - 4i) = (-7 + 3) + (2 - 4)i = -4 - 2i$
(b) $3i - (5 - i) = 3i - 5 + i = -5 + (3 + 1)i = -5 + 4i$

Now Try Exercises 23, 29

TECHNOLOGY NOTE

CALCULATOR HELP

To access the imaginary unit i, see Appendix A (page AP-7).

Complex Numbers
Many calculators can perform arithmetic with complex numbers. The figure shows a calculator display for the results in Example 2.

```
(-7+2i)+(3-4i)
              -4-2i
3i-(5-i)
              -5+4i
```

MULTIPLICATION We multiply two complex numbers in the same way that we multiply binomials and then we apply the property $i^2 = -1$. For example,

$$(2 - 3x)(1 + 4x) = 2 + 8x - 3x - 12x^2 = 2 + 5x - 12x^2.$$

In the next example we find the product of $2 - 3i$ and $1 + 4i$ in a similar manner.

EXAMPLE 3   **Multiplying complex numbers**

Write each product in standard form.
(a) $(2 - 3i)(1 + 4i)$ **(b)** $(5 - 2i)(5 + 2i)$

Solution
(a) Multiply the complex numbers like binomials.

$$(2 - 3i)(1 + 4i) = (2)(1) + (2)(4i) - (3i)(1) - (3i)(4i)$$
$$= 2 + 8i - 3i - 12i^2$$
$$= 2 + 5i - 12(-1) \qquad i^2 = -1$$
$$= 14 + 5i$$

(b)
$$(5 - 2i)(5 + 2i) = (5)(5) + (5)(2i) - (2i)(5) - (2i)(2i)$$
$$= 25 + 10i - 10i - 4i^2$$
$$= 25 - 4(-1) \qquad i^2 = -1$$
$$= 29$$

These results are supported in Figure 5.30.

$(2-3i)(1+4i)$
$\qquad\qquad 14+5i$
$(5-2i)(5+2i)$
$\qquad\qquad 29$

Figure 5.30

Now Try Exercises 31, 35

Powers of i

An interesting pattern appears when powers of i are calculated.

$$i^1 = i$$
$$i^2 = -1$$
$$i^3 = i^2 \cdot i = -1 \cdot i = -i$$
$$i^4 = i^2 \cdot i^2 = (-1)(-1) = 1$$
$$i^5 = i^4 \cdot i = (1)i = i$$
$$i^6 = i^4 \cdot i^2 = (1)(-1) = -1$$
$$i^7 = i^4 \cdot i^3 = (1)(-i) = -i$$
$$i^8 = i^4 \cdot i^4 = (1)(1) = 1$$

The powers of i cycle with the pattern i, -1, $-i$, and $\mathbf{1}$. These examples suggest the following method for calculating powers of i.

> **POWERS OF i**
>
> The value of i^n can be found by dividing n (a positive integer) by 4. If the remainder is r, then
>
> $$i^n = i^r.$$
>
> Note that $i^0 = 1$, $i^1 = i$, $i^2 = -1$, and $i^3 = -i$.

EXAMPLE 4   **Calculating powers of i**

Evaluate each expression.
(a) i^9 **(b)** i^{19} **(c)** i^{40}

Solution
(a) When 9 is divided by 4, the result is 2 with remainder 1. Thus $i^9 = i^1 = i$.
(b) When 19 is divided by 4, the result is 4 with remainder 3. Thus $i^{19} = i^3 = -i$.
(c) When 40 is divided by 4, the result is 10 with remainder 0. Thus $i^{40} = i^0 = 1$.

Now Try Exercises 49, 51, 55

Complex Conjugates and Division

The **complex conjugate** of $a + bi$ is $a - bi$. To find the conjugate, we change the sign of the imaginary part b. Table 5.10 contains some complex numbers and their conjugates.

TABLE 5.10   **Complex Conjugates**

Number	$2 + 5i$	$6 - 3i$	$-2 + 7i$	$-1 - i$	5	$-5i$
Conjugate	$2 - 5i$	$6 + 3i$	$-2 - 7i$	$-1 + i$	5	$5i$

EXAMPLE 5   **Finding complex conjugates**

Find the complex conjugate of each number.
(a) $5 + 3i$ **(b)** $-2 - i$ **(c)** $-4i$ **(d)** -6

Solution
(a) The conjugate is found by changing the imaginary part of $5 + 3i$ to its opposite. The conjugate is $5 - 3i$.
(b) The conjugate is $-2 + i$.
(c) $-4i$ can be written as $0 - 4i$. The conjugate is $0 + 4i$, or $4i$.
(d) -6 can be written as $-6 + 0i$. The conjugate is $-6 - 0i$, or -6. The conjugate of a real number is simply the same real number.

Now Try Exercises 57, 59, 61, 63

NOTE: The product of a complex number and its conjugate is a real number. That is,

$$(a + bi)(a - bi) = a^2 + b^2.$$

For example, $(3 + 4i)(3 - 4i) = 3^2 + 4^2 = 25$, which is a real number.

This property of complex conjugates is used to divide two complex numbers. To convert the quotient $\frac{2 + 3i}{3 - i}$ into standard form $a + bi$, we multiply the numerator and the denominator by the complex conjugate of the *denominator*, which is $3 + i$. The next example illustrates this method.

EXAMPLE 6 **Dividing complex numbers**

Write each quotient in standard form.

(a) $\dfrac{2 + 3i}{3 - i}$ (b) $\dfrac{4}{2i}$

Solution

(a) Multiply the numerator and denominator by $3 + i$.

$$\dfrac{2 + 3i}{3 - i} = \dfrac{(2 + 3i)(3 + i)}{(3 - i)(3 + i)} \qquad \text{Multiply by 1.}$$

$$= \dfrac{2(3) + (2)(i) + (3i)(3) + (3i)(i)}{(3)(3) + (3)(i) - (i)(3) - (i)(i)} \qquad \text{Multiply.}$$

$$= \dfrac{6 + 2i + 9i + 3i^2}{9 + 3i - 3i - i^2} \qquad \text{Simplify.}$$

$$= \dfrac{6 + 11i + 3(-1)}{9 - (-1)} \qquad i^2 = -1$$

$$= \dfrac{3 + 11i}{10} \qquad \text{Simplify.}$$

$$= \dfrac{3}{10} + \dfrac{11}{10}i \qquad \dfrac{a + bi}{c} = \dfrac{a}{c} + \dfrac{b}{c}i$$

(b) Multiply the numerator and denominator by $-2i$.

$$\dfrac{4}{2i} = \dfrac{(4)(-2i)}{(2i)(-2i)} \qquad \text{Multiply by 1.}$$

$$= \dfrac{-8i}{-4i^2} \qquad \text{Simplify.}$$

$$= \dfrac{-8i}{-4(-1)} \qquad i^2 = -1$$

$$= \dfrac{-8i}{4} \qquad \text{Simplify.}$$

$$= -2i \qquad \text{Divide.}$$

```
(2+3i)/(3-i)▶Fra
c
        3/10+11/10i
4/(2i)
            -2i
```

Figure 5.31

These results are supported in Figure 5.31.

Now Try Exercises 71, 73

5.7 Putting It All Together

CONCEPT	EXPLANATION	EXAMPLES
Complex Numbers	A complex number can be expressed as $a + bi$, where a and b are real numbers.	The real part of $5 - 3i$ is 5 and the imaginary part is -3.
	The imaginary unit i satisfies $i = \sqrt{-1}$ and $i^2 = -1$. As a result, we can write $\sqrt{-a} = i\sqrt{a}$ if $a > 0$.	$\sqrt{-13} = i\sqrt{13}$ and $\sqrt{-9} = 3i$

CONCEPT	EXPLANATION	EXAMPLES
Addition, Subtraction, and Multiplication	To add (subtract) complex numbers, add (subtract) the real parts and then add (subtract) the imaginary parts.	$(3 + 6i) + (-1 + 2i)$ Sum $= (3 + -1) + (6 + 2)i$ $= 2 + 8i$ $(2 - 5i) - (1 + 4i)$ Difference $= (2 - 1) + (-5 - 4)i$ $= 1 - 9i$
	Multiply complex numbers in a manner similar to the way *FOIL* is used to multiply binomials. Then apply the property $i^2 = -1$.	$(-1 + 2i)(3 + i)$ Product $= (-1)(3) + (-1)(i) + (2i)(3) + (2i)(i)$ $= -3 - i + 6i + 2i^2$ $= -3 + 5i + 2(-1)$ $= -5 + 5i$
Complex Conjugates	The conjugate of $a + bi$ is $a - bi$.	The conjugate of $3 - 5i$ is $3 + 5i$. The conjugate of $2i$ is $-2i$.
Division	To simplify a quotient, multiply the numerator and denominator by the complex conjugate of the *denominator*. Then simplify the expression and write it in standard form as $a + bi$.	$\dfrac{10}{1 + 2i} = \dfrac{10(1 - 2i)}{(1 + 2i)(1 - 2i)}$ Quotient $= \dfrac{10 - 20i}{5}$ $= 2 - 4i$

5.7   Exercises

MyMathLab   Math XL PRACTICE   WATCH   DOWNLOAD   READ   REVIEW

CONCEPTS AND VOCABULARY

1. Give an example of a complex number that is not a real number.

2. Can you give an example of a real number that is not a complex number? Explain.

3. $\sqrt{-1} =$ _____

4. $i^2 =$ _____

5. $\sqrt{-a} =$ _____, if $a > 0$.

6. The complex conjugate of $10 + 7i$ is _____.

7. The standard form for a complex number is _____.

8. Write $\dfrac{2 + 4i}{2}$ in standard form.

9. The real part of $4 - 5i$ is _____.

10. The imaginary part of $4 - 5i$ is _____.

11. The imaginary part of -7 is _____.

12. The number $7i$ is a(n) _____ imaginary number.

COMPLEX NUMBERS

Exercises 13–22: Use i to write the expression.

13. $\sqrt{-5}$

14. $\sqrt{-21}$

15. $\sqrt{-100}$

16. $\sqrt{-49}$

17. $\sqrt{-144}$

18. $\sqrt{-64}$

19. $\sqrt{-12}$

20. $\sqrt{-8}$

21. $\sqrt{-18}$

22. $\sqrt{-48}$

Exercises 23–46: Write the expression in standard form.

23. $(5 + 3i) + (-2 - 3i)$

24. $(1 - i) + (5 - 7i)$

25. $2i + (-8 + 5i)$

26. $-3i + 5i$

27. $(2 - 7i) - (1 + 2i)$

28. $(1 + 8i) - (3 + 9i)$ **29.** $5i - (10 - 2i)$

30. $-3(4 - 3i)$

31. $(3 + 2i)(-1 + 5i)$

32. $(1 + i) - (1 - i)$ **33.** $4(5 - 3i)$

34. $(1 + 2i)(-6 - i)$ **35.** $(5 + 4i)(5 - 4i)$

36. $(3 + 5i)(3 - 5i)$ **37.** $(-4i)(5i)$

38. $(-6i)(-4i)$

39. $3i + (2 - 3i) - (1 - 5i)$

40. $4 - (5 - 7i) + (3 + 7i)$

41. $(2 + i)^2$ **42.** $(-1 + 2i)^2$

43. $2i(-3 + i)$ **44.** $5i(1 - 9i)$

45. $i(1 + i)^2$ **46.** $2i(1 - i)^2$

Exercises 47 and 48: Thinking Generally *Write in standard form.*

47. $(a + 3bi)(a - 3bi)$ **48.** $(a + bi) - (a - bi)$

Exercises 49–56: (Refer to Example 4.) Simplify.

49. i^{11} **50.** i^{50}

51. i^{21} **52.** i^{103}

53. i^{58} **54.** i^{61}

55. i^{64} **56.** i^{28}

Exercises 57–64: Write the complex conjugate.

57. $3 + 4i$ **58.** $1 - 4i$

59. $-6i$ **60.** -10

61. $5 - 4i$ **62.** $7 + 2i$

63. -1 **64.** $19i$

Exercises 65–78: Write the expression in standard form.

65. $\dfrac{2}{1 + i}$ **66.** $\dfrac{-6}{2 - i}$

67. $\dfrac{3i}{5 - 2i}$ **68.** $\dfrac{-8}{2i}$

69. $\dfrac{8 + 9i}{5 + 2i}$ **70.** $\dfrac{3 - 2i}{1 + 4i}$

71. $\dfrac{5 + 7i}{1 - i}$ **72.** $\dfrac{-7 + 4i}{3 - 2i}$

73. $\dfrac{2 - i}{i}$ **74.** $\dfrac{3 + 2i}{-i}$

75. $\dfrac{1}{i} + \dfrac{1}{2i}$ **76.** $\dfrac{3}{4i} + \dfrac{2}{i}$

77. $\dfrac{1}{-1 + i} - \dfrac{2}{i}$ **78.** $-\dfrac{3}{2i} - \dfrac{2}{1 + i}$

APPLICATIONS

Exercises 79 and 80: Corrosion in Airplanes Corrosion in the metal surface of an airplane can be difficult to detect visually. One test used to locate it involves passing an alternating current through a small area on the plane's surface. If the current varies from one region to another, it may indicate that corrosion is occurring. The impedance Z (or opposition to the flow of electricity) of the metal is related to the voltage V and current I by the equation $Z = \frac{V}{I}$, where Z, V, and I are complex numbers. Calculate Z for the given values of V and I. (**Source:** Society for Industrial and Applied Mathematics.)

79. $V = 40 + 70i, I = 2 + 3i$

80. $V = 10 + 20i, I = 3 + 7i$

81. Online Exploration We graph real numbers on a number line. Can we graph complex numbers on a number line? Go online and find out how to graph complex numbers.

82. Online Exploration Go online and find out how to calculate the absolute value of a complex number. If a complex number is graphed, what does the absolute value tell us?

WRITING ABOUT MATHEMATICS

83. A student multiplies $(2 + 3i)(4 - 5i)$ *incorrectly* to obtain $8 - 15i$. What is the student's mistake?

84. A student divides the ratio $\frac{6 - 10i}{3 + 2i}$ *incorrectly* to obtain $2 - 5i$. What is the student's mistake?

SECTION 5.7

Checking Basic Concepts

1. Use i to write each expression.

(a) $\sqrt{-64}$

(b) $\sqrt{-17}$

2. Simplify each expression.

(a) $(2 - 3i) + (1 - i)$

(b) $4i - (2 + i)$

(c) $(3 - 2i)(1 + i)$

(d) $\dfrac{3}{2 - 2i}$

CHAPTER 5 Summary

SECTION 5.1 ■ RADICAL EXPRESSIONS AND FUNCTIONS

Radicals and Radical Notation

Square Root	b is a square root of a if $b^2 = a$.
Principal Square Root	$\sqrt{a} = b$ if $b^2 = a$ and $b \geq 0$.

Examples: $\sqrt{16} = 4$, $-\sqrt{9} = -3$,

and $\pm\sqrt{36} = \pm 6$

Cube Root b is a cube root of a if $b^3 = a$.

Examples: $\sqrt[3]{27} = 3$, $\sqrt[3]{-8} = -2$

nth Root b is an nth root of a if $b^n = a$.

Example: $\sqrt[4]{16} = 2$ because $2^4 = 16$.

NOTE: An *even* root of a *negative* number is not a real number. Also, $\sqrt[n]{a}$ denotes the *principal* nth root.

Absolute Value   The expressions $|x|$ and $\sqrt{x^2}$ are equivalent.

Example: $\sqrt{(x + y)^2} = |x + y|$

The Square Root Function   The square root function is denoted $f(x) = \sqrt{x}$. Its domain is $\{x \mid x \geq 0\}$ and its graph is shown in the figure.

The Cube Root Function The cube root function is denoted $f(x) = \sqrt[3]{x}$. Its domain is all real numbers and its graph is shown in the figure.

The Expression $a^{1/n}$

$a^{1/n} = \sqrt[n]{a}$ if n is an integer greater than 1.

Examples: $5^{1/2} = \sqrt{5}$ and $64^{1/3} = \sqrt[3]{64} = 4$

The Expression $a^{m/n}$

$a^{m/n} = \sqrt[n]{a^m}$ or $a^{m/n} = (\sqrt[n]{a})^m$

Examples: $8^{2/3} = \sqrt[3]{8^2} = \sqrt[3]{64} = 4$ and

$8^{2/3} = (\sqrt[3]{8})^2 = (2)^2 = 4$

Properties of Exponents

Product Rule $a^p a^q = a^{p+q}$

Negative Exponents $a^{-p} = \dfrac{1}{a^p},\ \dfrac{1}{a^{-p}} = a^p$

Negative Exponents for Quotients $\left(\dfrac{a}{b}\right)^{-p} = \left(\dfrac{b}{a}\right)^p$

Quotient Rule for Exponents $\dfrac{a^p}{a^q} = a^{p-q}$

Power Rule for Exponents $(a^p)^q = a^{pq}$

Power Rule for Products $(ab)^p = a^p b^p$

Power Rule for Quotients $\left(\dfrac{a}{b}\right)^p = \dfrac{a^p}{b^p}$

Product Rule for Radical Expressions Provided each expression is defined,

$$\sqrt[n]{a} \cdot \sqrt[n]{b} = \sqrt[n]{a \cdot b}.$$

Example: $\sqrt[3]{3} \cdot \sqrt[3]{9} = \sqrt[3]{27} = 3$

Perfect nth Power An integer a is a perfect nth power if $b^n = a$ for some integer b.

Examples: 25 is a perfect square, 8 is a perfect cube, and 16 is a perfect fourth power.

Simplifying Radicals (nth roots)

STEP 1: Determine the largest perfect nth power factor of the radicand.

STEP 2: Use the product rule to factor out and simplify this perfect nth power.

Examples: $\sqrt{32} = \sqrt{16 \cdot 2} = \sqrt{16} \cdot \sqrt{2} = 4\sqrt{2}$

$\sqrt[3]{32} = \sqrt[3]{8 \cdot 4} = \sqrt[3]{8} \cdot \sqrt[3]{4} = 2\sqrt[3]{4}$

Quotient Rule for Radical Expressions Provided each expression is defined,

$$\sqrt[n]{\frac{a}{b}} = \frac{\sqrt[n]{a}}{\sqrt[n]{b}}.$$

Example: $\dfrac{\sqrt[3]{24}}{\sqrt[3]{3}} = \sqrt[3]{\dfrac{24}{3}} = \sqrt[3]{8} = 2$

SECTION 5.4 ■ OPERATIONS ON RADICAL EXPRESSIONS

Addition and Subtraction Combine like radicals.

Examples: $2\sqrt[3]{4} + 3\sqrt[3]{4} = 5\sqrt[3]{4}$ and $\sqrt{5} - 2\sqrt{5} = -\sqrt{5}$

Multiplication Sometimes radical expressions can be multiplied like binomials.

Examples: $(4 - \sqrt{2})(2 + \sqrt{2}) = 8 + 4\sqrt{2} - 2\sqrt{2} - 2 = 6 + 2\sqrt{2}$

$(5 - \sqrt{3})(5 + \sqrt{3}) = (5)^2 - (\sqrt{3})^2 = 25 - 3 = 22$ because

$(a - b)(a + b) = a^2 - b^2.$

Rationalizing the Denominator One technique is to multiply the numerator and denominator by the conjugate of the denominator if the denominator is a binomial containing one or more square roots.

Examples: $\dfrac{1}{4 + \sqrt{2}} = \dfrac{1}{(4 + \sqrt{2})} \cdot \dfrac{(4 - \sqrt{2})}{(4 - \sqrt{2})} = \dfrac{4 - \sqrt{2}}{(4)^2 - (\sqrt{2})^2} = \dfrac{4 - \sqrt{2}}{14}$

$\dfrac{4}{\sqrt{7}} = \dfrac{4}{\sqrt{7}} \cdot \dfrac{\sqrt{7}}{\sqrt{7}} = \dfrac{4\sqrt{7}}{7}$

SECTION 5.5 ■ MORE RADICAL FUNCTIONS

Root Functions $f(x) = x^{1/n} = \sqrt[n]{x}$

Odd root functions are defined for all real numbers, and even root functions are defined for non-negative real numbers.

Examples: $f(x) = x^{1/3} = \sqrt[3]{x}$, $g(x) = x^{1/4} = \sqrt[4]{x}$,   and $h(x) = x^{1/5} = \sqrt[5]{x}$

Power Functions If a function can be defined by $f(x) = x^p$, where p is a rational number, then it is a power function.

Examples: $f(x) = x^{4/5}$ and $g(x) = x^{2.3}$

SECTION 5.6 ■ EQUATIONS INVOLVING RADICAL EXPRESSIONS

Power Rule for Solving Radical Equations The solutions to $a = b$ are among the solutions to $a^n = b^n$, where n is a positive integer.

Example: The solutions to the equation $\sqrt{3x + 3} = 2x - 1$ are among the solutions to the equation $3x + 3 = (2x - 1)^2$.

Solving Radical Equations

STEP 1: Isolate a radical term on one side of the equation.

STEP 2: Apply the power rule by raising each side of the equation to the power equal to the index of the isolated radical term.

STEP 3: Solve the equation. If it still contains a radical, repeat Steps 1 and 2.

STEP 4: Check your answers by substituting each result in the *given* equation.

Example: To isolate the radical in $\sqrt{x + 1} + 4 = 6$ subtract 4 from each side to obtain $\sqrt{x + 1} = 2$. Next square each side, which gives $x + 1 = 4$ or $x = 3$. Checking verifies that 3 is a solution.

Pythagorean Theorem If a right triangle has legs a and b with hypotenuse c, then

$$a^2 + b^2 = c^2.$$

Example: If a right triangle has legs 8 and 15, then the hypotenuse equals

$$c = \sqrt{8^2 + 15^2} = \sqrt{289} = 17.$$

The Distance Formula The distance d between (x_1, y_1) and (x_2, y_2) is

$$d = \sqrt{(x_2 - x_1)^2 + (y_2 - y_1)^2}.$$

Example: The distance between $(-1, 3)$ and $(4, 5)$ is

$$d = \sqrt{\left(4 - (-1)\right)^2 + (5 - 3)^2} = \sqrt{25 + 4} = \sqrt{29}.$$

Solving the Equation $x^n = k$ Let n be a positive integer.
Take the nth root of each side of $x^n = k$ to obtain $\sqrt[n]{x^n} = \sqrt[n]{k}$.

1. If n is *odd*, then $\sqrt[n]{x^n} = x$ and the equation becomes $x = \sqrt[n]{k}$.
2. If n is *even* and $k \geq 0$, then $\sqrt[n]{x^n} = |x|$ and the equation becomes $|x| = \sqrt[n]{k}$.

Examples: $x^3 = -27$ implies that $x = \sqrt[3]{-27} = -3$.
$x^4 = 81$ implies that $|x| = \sqrt[4]{81} = 3$ or $x = \pm 3$.

SECTION 5.7 ■ COMPLEX NUMBERS

Complex Numbers

Imaginary Unit	$i = \sqrt{-1}$ and $i^2 = -1$
Standard Form	$a + bi$, where a and b are real numbers
	Examples: $4 + 3i$, $5 - 6i$, 8, and $-2i$
Real Part	The real part of $a + bi$ is a.
	Example: The real part of $3 - 2i$ is 3.
Imaginary Part	The imaginary part of $a + bi$ is b.
	Example: The imaginary part of $2 - i$ is -1.
Arithmetic Operations	Arithmetic operations are similar to arithmetic operations on binomials.

Examples:

$(2 + 2i) + (3 - i) = 5 + i$ Sum

$(1 - i) - (1 - 2i) = i$ Difference

$(1 - i)(1 + i) = 1^2 - i^2 = 1 - (-1) = 2$ Product

$\dfrac{2}{1 - i} = \dfrac{2}{1 - i} \cdot \dfrac{1 + i}{1 + i} = \dfrac{2 + 2i}{2} = 1 + i$ Quotient

Powers of i   The value of i^n equals i^r, where r is the remainder when n is divided by 4. Note that $i^0 = 1$, $i^1 = i$, $i^2 = -1$, and $i^3 = -i$.

Example: $i^{21} = i^1 = i$ because when 21 is divided by 4 the remainder is 1.

CHAPTER 5   Review Exercises

SECTION 5.1

Exercises 1–12: Simplify the expression.

1. $\sqrt{4}$

2. $\sqrt{36}$

3. $\sqrt{9x^2}$

4. $\sqrt{(x-1)^2}$

5. $\sqrt[3]{-64}$

6. $\sqrt[3]{-125}$

7. $\sqrt[3]{x^6}$

8. $\sqrt[3]{27x^3}$

9. $\sqrt[4]{16}$

10. $\sqrt[5]{-1}$

11. $\sqrt[4]{x^8}$

12. $\sqrt[5]{(x+1)^5}$

SECTION 5.2

Exercises 13–16: Write the expression in radical notation.

13. $14^{1/2}$

14. $(-5)^{1/3}$

15. $\left(\dfrac{x}{y}\right)^{3/2}$

16. $(xy)^{-2/3}$

Exercises 17–20: Evaluate the expression.

17. $(-27)^{2/3}$

18. $16^{1/4}$

19. $16^{3/2}$

20. $81^{3/4}$

Exercises 21–24: Simplify the expression. Assume that all variables are positive.

21. $(z^3)^{2/3}$

22. $(x^2y^4)^{1/2}$

23. $\left(\dfrac{x^2}{y^6}\right)^{3/2}$

24. $\left(\dfrac{x^3}{y^6}\right)^{-1/3}$

SECTION 5.3

Exercises 25–40: Simplify the expression. Assume that all variables are positive.

25. $\sqrt{2}\cdot\sqrt{32}$

26. $\sqrt[3]{-4}\cdot\sqrt[3]{2}$

27. $\sqrt[3]{x^4}\cdot\sqrt[3]{x^2}$

28. $\dfrac{\sqrt{80}}{\sqrt{20}}$

29. $\sqrt[3]{-\dfrac{x}{8}}$

30. $\sqrt{\dfrac{1}{3}}\cdot\sqrt{\dfrac{1}{3}}$

31. $\sqrt{48}$

32. $\sqrt{54}$

33. $\sqrt[3]{\dfrac{3}{x}}\cdot\sqrt[3]{\dfrac{9}{x^2}}$

34. $\sqrt{32a^3b^2}$

35. $\sqrt{3xy}\cdot\sqrt{27xy}$

36. $\sqrt[3]{-25z^2}\cdot\sqrt[3]{-5z^2}$

37. $\sqrt{x^2+2x+1}$

38. $\sqrt[4]{\dfrac{2a^2}{b}}\cdot\sqrt[4]{\dfrac{8a^3}{b^3}}$

39. $2\sqrt{x}\cdot\sqrt[3]{x}$

40. $\sqrt[3]{rt}\cdot\sqrt[4]{r^2t^4}$

SECTION 5.4

Exercises 41–50: Simplify the expression. Assume that all variables are positive.

41. $3\sqrt{3}+\sqrt{3}$

42. $\sqrt[3]{x}+2\sqrt[3]{x}$

43. $3\sqrt[3]{5}-6\sqrt[3]{5}$

44. $\sqrt[4]{y}-2\sqrt[4]{y}$

45. $2\sqrt{12}+7\sqrt{3}$

46. $3\sqrt{18}-2\sqrt{2}$

47. $7\sqrt[3]{16}-\sqrt[3]{2}$

48. $\sqrt{4x+4}+\sqrt{x+1}$

49. $\sqrt{4x^3}-\sqrt{x}$

50. $\sqrt[3]{ab^4}+2\sqrt[3]{a^4b}$

Exercises 51–56: Multiply and simplify.

51. $(1+\sqrt{2})(3+\sqrt{2})$

52. $(7-\sqrt{5})(1+\sqrt{3})$

53. $(3+\sqrt{6})(3-\sqrt{6})$

54. $(10-\sqrt{5})(10+\sqrt{5})$

55. $(\sqrt{a}+\sqrt{2b})(\sqrt{a}-\sqrt{2b})$

56. $(\sqrt{xy}-1)(\sqrt{xy}+2)$

Exercises 57–62: Rationalize the denominator.

57. $\dfrac{4}{\sqrt{5}}$

58. $\dfrac{r}{2\sqrt{t}}$

59. $\dfrac{1}{\sqrt{2}+3}$

60. $\dfrac{2}{5-\sqrt{7}}$

61. $\dfrac{1}{\sqrt{8}-\sqrt{7}}$

62. $\dfrac{\sqrt{a}-\sqrt{b}}{\sqrt{a}+\sqrt{b}}$

SECTION 5.5

Exercises 63 and 64: Graph the equation.

63. $y=\sqrt[4]{x}$

64. $y=\sqrt[3]{x}$

Exercises 65 and 66: Write f(x) in radical notation and evaluate f(4).

65. $f(x)=x^{1/2}$

66. $f(x)=x^{2/7}$

Exercises 67 and 68: Graph the equation. Compare the graph to either $y=\sqrt{x}$ or $y=\sqrt[3]{x}$.

67. $y=\sqrt{x}-2$

68. $y=\sqrt[3]{x-1}$

Exercises 69–72: Find the domain of f. Write your answer in interval notation.

69. $f(x) = \sqrt{x - 1}$

70. $f(x) = \sqrt{6 - 2x}$

71. $f(x) = \sqrt{x^2 + 1}$

72. $f(x) = \dfrac{1}{\sqrt{x + 2}}$

SECTION 5.6

Exercises 73–78: Solve. Check your answer.

73. $\sqrt{x + 2} = x$

74. $\sqrt{2x - 1} = \sqrt{x + 3}$

75. $\sqrt[3]{x - 1} = 2$

76. $\sqrt[3]{3x} = 3$

77. $\sqrt{2x} = x - 4$

78. $\sqrt{x} + 1 = \sqrt{x + 2}$

Exercises 79 and 80: Solve graphically. Approximate solutions to the nearest hundredth when appropriate.

79. $\sqrt[3]{2x - 1} = 2$

80. $x^{2/3} = 3 - x$

Exercises 81 and 82: A right triangle has legs a and b with hypotenuse c. Find the length of the missing side.

81. $a = 4, b = 7$

82. $a = 5, c = 8$

Exercises 83 and 84: Find the exact distance between the given points.

83. $(-2, 3), (2, -2)$

84. $(2, -3), (-4, 1)$

Exercises 85–94: Solve.

85. $x^2 = 121$

86. $2z^2 = 32$

87. $(x - 1)^2 = 16$

88. $x^3 = 64$

89. $(x - 1)^3 = 8$

90. $(2x - 1)^3 = 27$

91. $x^4 = 256$

92. $x^5 = -1$

93. $(x - 3)^5 = -32$

94. $3(x + 1)^4 = 3$

SECTION 5.7

Exercises 95–100: Write the complex expression in standard form.

95. $(1 - 2i) + (-3 + 2i)$

96. $(1 + 3i) - (3 - i)$

97. $(1 - i)(2 + 3i)$

98. $\dfrac{3 + i}{1 - i}$

99. $\dfrac{i(4 + i)}{2 - 3i}$

100. $(1 - i)^2(1 + i)$

APPLICATIONS

101. *Hang Time* A football is punted and has a hang time T of 4.6 seconds. Use the formula $T(h) = \frac{1}{2}\sqrt{h}$ to estimate to the nearest foot the height h to which it was kicked.

102. *Baseball Diamond* The four bases of a baseball diamond form a square that is 90 feet on a side. Find the distance from home plate to second base.

103. *Falling Time* The time T in seconds for an object to fall from a height of h feet is given by $T = \frac{1}{4}\sqrt{h}$. If a person steps off a 10-foot-high board into a swimming pool, how long is the person in the air?

104. *Geometry* A cube has sides of length $\sqrt{5}$.
(a) Find the area of one side of the cube.
(b) Find the volume of the cube.
(c) Find the length of the diagonal of one of the sides.
(d) Find the distance from A to B in the figure.

105. *Pendulum* The time required for a pendulum to swing back and forth is called its *period* (see the figure). The period T of a pendulum does not depend on its weight, only on its length L and gravity. It is given by $T = 2\pi\sqrt{\frac{L}{32.2}}$, where T is in seconds and L is in feet. Estimate the length of a pendulum with a period of 1 second.

106. *Pendulum* (Refer to Exercise 105.) If a pendulum were on the moon, its period could be calculated by $T = 2\pi\sqrt{\frac{L}{5.1}}$. Estimate the length of a pendulum with a period of 1 second on the moon. Compare your answer to that for Exercise 105.

107. *Population Growth* In 1790 the population of the United States was 4 million, and by 2000 it had grown to 281 million. The *average* annual percentage growth in the population r (expressed as a decimal) can be determined by the polynomial equation $281 = 4(1 + r)^{210}$. Solve this equation for r and interpret the result.

108. *Highway Curves* If a circular highway curve is banked with a slope of $m = \frac{1}{10}$ (see the accompanying figure) and has a radius of R feet, then the speed limit L in miles per hour for the curve is given by

$$L = \sqrt{3.75R}.$$

(*Source:* N. Garber and L. Hoel, *Traffic and Highway Engineering.*)

(a) Find the speed limit if R is 500 feet.

(b) With no banking, the speed limit is given by $L = 1.5\sqrt{R}$. Find the speed limit for a curve with no banking and a radius of 500 feet. How does banking affect the speed limit? Does this result agree with your intuition?

109. *Geometry* Find the length of a side of a square if the square has an area of 7 square feet.

CHAPTER 5   Test

Step-by-step test solutions are found on the Chapter Test Prep Videos available via the Video Resources on DVD, in *MyMathLab*, and on YouTube (search "RockswoldInterAlg" and click on "Channels").

Exercises 1–6: Simplify the expression.

1. $\sqrt[3]{-27}$

2. $\sqrt{(z + 1)^2}$

3. $\sqrt{25x^4}$

4. $\sqrt[3]{8z^6}$

5. $\sqrt[4]{16x^4y^5}$; $x > 0, y > 0$

6. $(\sqrt{3} - \sqrt{2})(\sqrt{3} + \sqrt{2})$

Exercises 7 and 8: Write the expression in radical notation.

7. $7^{2/5}$

8. $\left(\dfrac{x}{y}\right)^{-2/3}$

Exercises 9 and 10: Evaluate the expression by hand.

9. $(-8)^{4/3}$

10. $36^{-3/2}$

Exercises 11 and 12: Use rational exponents to write the expression.

11. $\sqrt[3]{x^4}$

12. $\sqrt{x} \cdot \sqrt[5]{x}$

13. Find the domain of $f(x) = \sqrt{4 - x}$. Write your answer in interval notation.

14. Sketch a graph of $y = \sqrt{x + 3}$.

Exercises 15–22: Simplify the expression. Assume that all variables are positive.

15. $(2z^{1/2})^3$

16. $\left(\dfrac{y^2}{z^3}\right)^{-1/3}$

17. $\sqrt{3} \cdot \sqrt{27}$

18. $\dfrac{\sqrt{y^3}}{\sqrt{4y}}$

19. $7\sqrt{7} - 3\sqrt{7} + \sqrt{5}$

20. $7\sqrt[3]{x} - \sqrt[3]{x}$

21. $4\sqrt{18} + \sqrt{8}$

22. $\dfrac{\sqrt[3]{32}}{\sqrt[3]{4}}$

23. Solve each equation.

(a) $\sqrt{x - 2} = 5$

(b) $\sqrt[3]{x + 1} = 2$

(c) $(x - 1)^3 = 8$

(d) $\sqrt{2x + 2} = x - 11$

24. Rationalize the denominator.

(a) $\dfrac{2}{3\sqrt{7}}$

(b) $\dfrac{1}{1 + \sqrt{5}}$

25. Solve $\sqrt{3x} - x + 1 = \sqrt[3]{x - 1}$ graphically. Round solutions to the nearest hundredth.

26. One leg of a right triangle has length 7 and the hypotenuse has length 13. Find the length of the third side.

27. Find the distance between $(-3, 5)$ and $(-1, 7)$.

Exercises 28–31: Write the complex expression in standard form.

28. $(-5 + i) + (7 - 20i)$

29. $(3i) - (6 - 5i)$

30. $\left(\dfrac{1}{2} - i\right)\left(\dfrac{1}{2} + i\right)$

31. $\dfrac{2i}{5 + 2i}$

32. *Distance to the Horizon* A formula for calculating the distance d in miles that one can see to the horizon on a clear day is approximated by the formula $d = 1.22\sqrt{x}$, where x is the elevation, in feet, of a person.
   (a) If a person climbs a cliff and stops at an elevation of 200 feet, how far can the person see to the horizon?
   (b) How high should the person climb to see 25 miles to the horizon?

33. *Wing Span of a Bird* The wing span L of a bird with weight W can sometimes be modeled by $L = 27.4W^{1/3}$, where L is in inches and W is in pounds. Use this formula to estimate the weight of a bird that has a wing span of 30 inches. (***Source:*** C. Pennycuick, *Newton Rules Biology.*)

CHAPTER 5   Extended and Discovery Exercises

1. *Modeling Wood in a Tree* Forestry services estimate the volume of timber in a given area of forest. To make such estimates, scientists have developed formulas to find the amount of wood contained in a tree with height h in feet and diameter d in inches. One study concluded that the volume V of wood in cubic feet in a tree is given by $V = kh^{1.12}d^{1.98}$, where k is a constant. Note that the diameter is measured 4.5 feet above the ground. (***Source:*** B. Ryan, B. Joiner, and T. Ryan, *Minitab Handbook.*)
   (a) A tree with an 11-inch diameter and a 47-foot height has a volume of 11.4 cubic feet. Approximate the constant k.
   (b) Estimate the volume of wood in the same type of tree with $d = 20$ inches and $h = 105$ feet.

2. *Area of Skin* The surface area of the skin covering the human body is a function of more than one variable. Both height and weight influence the surface area of a person's body. Hence a taller person tends to have a larger surface area, as does a heavier person. A formula to determine the area of a person's skin in square inches is $S = 15.7w^{0.425}h^{0.725}$, where w is weight in pounds and h is height in inches. (***Source:*** H. Lancaster, *Quantitative Methods in Biological and Medical Sciences.*)
   (a) Use S to estimate the area of a person's skin who is 65 inches tall and weighs 154 pounds.
   (b) If a person's weight doubles, what happens to the area of the person's skin? Explain.
   (c) If a person's height doubles, what happens to the area of the person's skin? Explain.

3. *Minimizing Cost* A natural gas line running along a river is to be connected from point A to a cabin on the other bank located at point D, as illustrated in the figure. The width of the river is 500 feet, and the distance from point A to point C is 1000 feet. The cost of running the pipe along the shoreline is \$30 per foot, and the cost of running it underwater is \$50 per foot. The cost of connecting the gas line from A to D is to be minimized.

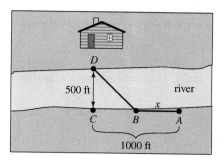

   (a) Write an expression that gives the cost of running the line from A to B if the distance between these points is x feet.
   (b) Find the distance from B to D in terms of x.
   (c) Write an expression that gives the cost of running the line from B to D.
   (d) Use your answer from parts (a) and (c) to write an expression that gives the cost of running the line from A to B to D.
    (e) Graph your expression from part (d) in the window $[0, 1000, 100]$ by $[40000, 60000, 5000]$ to determine the value of x that minimizes the cost of the line going from A to D. What is the minimum cost?

CHAPTERS 1–5 Cumulative Review Exercises

1. Evaluate $S = 4\pi r^2$ when $r = 3$.

2. Identify the domain and range of the relation given by $S = \{(-1, 2), (0, 4), (1, 2)\}$.

3. Simplify each expression. Write the result using positive exponents.

(a) $\left(\dfrac{ab^2}{b^{-1}}\right)^{-3}$ (b) $\dfrac{(x^2y)^3}{x^2(y^2)^{-3}}$

(c) $(rt)^2(r^2t)^3$

4. Write 0.00043 in scientific notation.

5. Find $f(3)$ if $f(x) = \dfrac{x}{x-2}$. What is the domain of f?

6. Find the domain of $f(x) = \sqrt[3]{2x}$.

Exercises 7 and 8: Graph f by hand.

7. $f(x) = 1 - 2x$

8. $f(x) = \sqrt{x+1}$

9. Sketch a graph of $f(x) = x^2 - 4$.
   (a) Identify the domain and range.
   (b) Evaluate $f(-2)$.
   (c) Identify the x-intercepts.
   (d) Solve the equation $f(x) = 0$.

10. Find the slope–intercept form of the line that passes through $(-1, 2)$ and is perpendicular to $y = -2x$.

11. Let f be a linear function. Find a formula for $f(x)$.

x	-2	-1	1	2
$f(x)$	7	4	-2	-5

12. Sketch a graph of a line passing through $(-1, 1)$ with slope $-\frac{1}{2}$.

13. Solve $5x - (3 - x) = \frac{1}{2}x$.

14. Solve $2x - 5 \le 4 - x$.

15. Solve $|x - 2| \le 3$.

16. Solve $-1 \le 1 - 2x \le 6$.

17. Solve each system symbolically, if possible.
   (a) $2x - y = 4$ (b) $3x - 4y = 2$
   $\quad\ x + y = 8$ $\qquad x - \frac{4}{3}y = 1$

18. Shade the solution set in the xy-plane.
$$x + 2y \le 2$$
$$-x + 3y \ge 3$$

19. Solve the system.
$$x + 2y - z = 6$$
$$x - 3y + z = -2$$
$$x + y + z = 6$$

20. Calculate $\det \begin{bmatrix} 4 & 2 & -1 \\ 2 & 1 & 0 \\ 0 & -2 & 1 \end{bmatrix}$.

Exercises 21–24: Multiply the expression.

21. $4x(4 - x^3)$ **22.** $(x - 4)(x + 4)$

23. $(5x + 3)(x - 2)$ **24.** $(4x + 9)^2$

Exercises 25–30: Factor the expression.

25. $9x^2 - 16$ **26.** $x^2 - 4x + 4$

27. $15x^3 - 9x^2$ **28.** $12x^2 - 5x - 3$

29. $r^3 - 1$ **30.** $x^3 - 3x^2 + 5x - 15$

Exercises 31 and 32: Solve each equation.

31. $x^2 - 3x + 2 = 0$ **32.** $x^3 = 4x$

Exercises 33 and 34: Simplify the expression.

33. $\dfrac{x^2 + 3x + 2}{x - 3} \div \dfrac{x + 1}{2x - 6}$

34. $\dfrac{2}{x - 1} + \dfrac{5}{x}$

Exercises 35–42: Simplify the expression. Assume all variables are positive.

35. $\sqrt{36x^2}$ **36.** $\sqrt[3]{64}$

37. $16^{-3/2}$ **38.** $\sqrt[4]{625}$

39. $\sqrt{2x} \cdot \sqrt{8x}$ **40.** $\sqrt{x} \cdot \sqrt[4]{x}$

41. $\dfrac{\sqrt[3]{16x^4}}{\sqrt[3]{2x}}$ **42.** $4\sqrt{12x} - 2\sqrt{3x}$

43. Multiply $(2x + \sqrt{3})(x - \sqrt{3})$.

44. Find the domain of $f(x) = \sqrt{1 - x}$.

45. Graph $f(x) = 3\sqrt[3]{x}$.

46. Find the distance between $(-2, 3)$ and $(1, 2)$.

47. Write $(1 - i)(2 + 3i)$ in standard form.

48. The lengths of the legs of a right triangle are 5 and 12. What is the length of the hypotenuse?

Exercises 49–52: Solve symbolically.

49. $2\sqrt{x + 3} = x$ **50.** $\sqrt[3]{x - 1} = 3$

51. $\sqrt{x} + 4 = 2\sqrt{x + 5}$ **52.** $\frac{1}{3}x^4 = 27$

Exercises 53 and 54: Solve graphically and approximate your answer to the nearest hundredth.

53. $\sqrt[3]{x^2 - 2} + x = \sqrt{x}$ **54.** $x - \sqrt[3]{x} = \sqrt{x + 2}$

APPLICATIONS

55. *Calculating Water Flow* The gallons G of water in a tank after t minutes are given by $G(t) = 300 - 15t$. Interpret the y-intercept and the slope of the graph of G as a rate of change.

56. *Distance* A person jogs away from home at 8 miles per hour for 1 hour, rests in a park for 2 hours, and then walks back home at 4 miles per hour. Sketch a graph that models the distance y that the person is from home after x hours.

57. *Investment* Suppose $2000 is deposited in two accounts paying 5% and 4% annual interest. If the total interest after 1 year is $93, how much is invested at each rate?

58. *Geometry* A rectangular box with a square base has a volume of 256 cubic inches. If its height is 4 inches less than the length of an edge of the base, find the dimensions of the box.

59. *Height of a Building* A 5-foot 3-inch person casts a shadow that is 5.5 feet while a nearby building casts a 32-foot shadow. Find the height of the building.

60. *Angles in a Triangle* The measure of the largest angle in a triangle is 20° less than the sum of the measures of the two smaller angles. The sum of the measures of the two larger angles is 90° greater than the measure of the smaller angle. Find the measure of each angle.

6

Quadratic Functions and Equations

> There is no branch of mathematics, however abstract, which may not some day be applied to the real world.
>
> **—Nikolai Lobachevsky**

W hat size television should you buy? Should you buy a 32-inch screen or a 50-inch screen? According to a home entertainment article in *Money* magazine, the answer depends on how far you sit from your television. The farther you sit from your television, the larger it should be. For example, if you sit only 6 feet from the screen, then a 32-inch television would be adequate; if you sit 10 feet from the screen, then a 50-inch television is more appropriate.

We can use a *quadratic function* to calculate the size S of the television screen needed for a person who sits x feet from the screen. You might want to use S to determine the size of screen that is recommended for you. (See Exercises 97 and 98 in Section 6.1.) Quadratic functions are a special type of polynomial function that occur frequently in applications involving economics, road construction, falling objects, geometry, and modeling real-world data. In this chapter we discuss quadratic functions and equations.

Source: Money, January 2007, p. 107; hdguru.com.

415

6.1 Quadratic Functions and Their Graphs

Graphs of Quadratic Functions ● Min–Max Applications ● Basic Transformations of $y = ax^2$ ● Transformations of $y = ax^2 + bx + c$ (Optional)

A LOOK INTO MATH ▶ Suppose that a hotel is considering giving a group discount on room rates. The regular price is $80, but for each room rented the price decreases by $2. On the one hand, if the hotel rents one room, it makes only $78. On the other hand, if the hotel rents 40 rooms, the rooms are all free and the hotel makes nothing. Is there an optimal number of rooms between 1 and 40 that should be rented to maximize the revenue from the group?

In Figure 6.1 the hotel's revenue is graphed. From the graph it is apparent that "peak" revenue occurs when 20 rooms are rented. Obviously, this graph is not described by a linear function; rather, in Example 7 we see that it is described by a *quadratic function*.

NEW VOCABULARY

☐ Quadratic function
☐ Vertex
☐ Axis of symmetry
☐ Reflection
☐ Vertical shift

Hotel Revenue

Figure 6.1

Graphs of Quadratic Functions

In Chapter 3 we discussed how a quadratic function could be represented by a polynomial of degree 2. We now give an alternative definition of a quadratic function.

QUADRATIC FUNCTION

A **quadratic function** can be written in the form

$$f(x) = ax^2 + bx + c,$$

where a, b, and c are constants with $a \neq 0$.

NOTE: The domain of a quadratic function is all real numbers.

The graph of *any* quadratic function is a *parabola*. Recall that a parabola is a ∪-shaped graph that opens either upward or downward. The graph of the simple quadratic function $y = x^2$ is a parabola that opens upward, with its *vertex* located at the origin, as shown in Figure 6.2(a). The **vertex** is the *lowest* point on the graph of a parabola that opens upward and the *highest* point on the graph of a parabola that opens downward. A parabola opening downward is shown in Figure 6.2(b). Its vertex is the point $(0, 2)$ and is the highest point on the graph. If we were to fold the xy-plane along the y-axis, or the line $x = 0$, the left and right sides of the graph would match. That is, the graph is symmetric with respect to the line $x = 0$. In this case the line $x = 0$ is the **axis of symmetry** for the graph. Figure 6.2(c) shows a parabola that opens upward with vertex $(2, -1)$ and axis of symmetry $x = 2$.

READING CHECK

How can you identify the vertex and the axis of symmetry on the graph of a parabola?

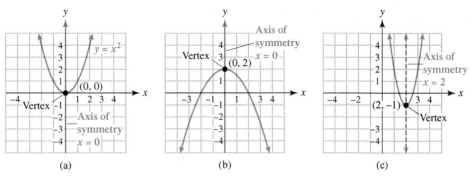

Figure 6.2

EXAMPLE 1 **Identifying the vertex and the axis of symmetry**

Use the graph of the quadratic function to identify the vertex, the axis of symmetry, and whether the parabola opens upward or downward.

(a)

Figure 6.3

(b)

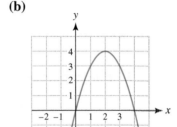

Figure 6.4

Solution

(a) The vertex is the lowest point on the graph shown in Figure 6.3, and its coordinates are $(1, -3)$. The axis of symmetry is the vertical line passing through the vertex, so its equation is $x = 1$. The parabola opens upward.

(b) The vertex is the highest point on the graph shown in Figure 6.4, and its coordinates are $(2, 4)$. The axis of symmetry is the vertical line passing through the vertex, so its equation is $x = 2$. The parabola opens downward.

Now Try Exercises 29, 31

THE VERTEX FORMULA In order to graph a parabola by hand, it is helpful to know the location of the vertex. The following formula can be used to find the coordinates of the vertex for *any* parabola. This formula is derived by *completing the square*, a technique discussed later in the next section.

READING CHECK

How do you use the vertex formula to find the coordinates of the vertex?

VERTEX FORMULA

The x-coordinate of the vertex of the graph of $y = ax^2 + bx + c$, $a \neq 0$, is given by

$$x = -\frac{b}{2a}.$$

To find the y-coordinate of the vertex, substitute this x-value in $y = ax^2 + bx + c$.

NOTE: The equation of the axis of symmetry for $f(x) = ax^2 + bx + c$ is $x = -\frac{b}{2a}$, and the vertex is the point $\left(-\frac{b}{2a}, f\left(-\frac{b}{2a}\right)\right)$.

EXAMPLE 2 | **Finding the vertex of a parabola**

Find the vertex for the graph of $f(x) = 2x^2 - 4x + 1$. Support your answer graphically.

Solution

For $f(x) = 2x^2 - 4x + 1$, $a = 2$ and $b = -4$. The x-coordinate of the vertex is

$$x = -\frac{b}{2a} = -\frac{(-4)}{2(2)} = 1. \qquad \text{x-coordinate of vertex}$$

To find the y-coordinate of the vertex, substitute $x = 1$ in the given formula.

$$f(1) = 2(1)^2 - 4(1) + 1 = \mathbf{-1} \qquad \text{y-coordinate of vertex}$$

Thus the vertex is located at $(1, -1)$, which is supported by Figure 6.5.

[-4.7, 4.7, 1] by [-3.1, 3.1, 1]

Figure 6.5

Now Try Exercise 15

GRAPHING QUADRATIC FUNCTIONS One way to graph a quadratic function without a graphing calculator is to first apply the vertex formula. After the vertex is located, a table of values can be made to locate points on either side of the vertex. This technique is used in the next example to graph three quadratic functions.

EXAMPLE 3 | **Graphing quadratic functions**

Identify the vertex and axis of symmetry on the graph of $y = f(x)$. Graph $y = f(x)$.
(a) $f(x) = x^2 - 1$ **(b)** $f(x) = -(x + 1)^2$ **(c)** $f(x) = x^2 + 4x + 3$

Solution
(a) Begin by applying the vertex formula with $a = 1$ and $b = 0$ to locate the vertex.

$$x = -\frac{b}{2a} = -\frac{0}{2(1)} = 0 \qquad \text{x-coordinate of vertex}$$

The y-coordinate of the vertex is found by evaluating $f(0)$.

$$y = f(0) = 0^2 - 1 = \mathbf{-1} \qquad \text{y-coordinate of vertex}$$

Thus the coordinates of the vertex are $(0, -1)$. Table 6.1 is made by finding points on either side of the vertex. Plotting these points and connecting a smooth ∪-shaped graph results in Figure 6.6. The axis of symmetry is the vertical line passing through the vertex, so its equation is $x = 0$.

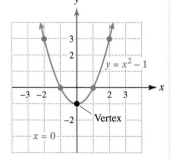

Figure 6.6

TABLE 6.1

	x	$y = x^2 - 1$	
	-2	3	←
	-1	0	←
Vertex →	0	-1	←Equal
	1	0	←
	2	3	←

(b) Before we can apply the vertex formula, we need to determine values for a and b by multiplying the expression for $f(x) = -(x + 1)^2$.

$$-(x + 1)^2 = -(x^2 + 2x + 1) \qquad \text{Multiply.}$$
$$= -x^2 - 2x - 1 \qquad \text{Distribute the negative sign.}$$

Substitute $a = -1$ and $b = -2$ into the vertex formula.

$$x = -\frac{b}{2a} = -\frac{(-2)}{2(-1)} = -1 \qquad \text{x-coordinate of vertex}$$

The y-coordinate of the vertex is found by evaluating $f(-1)$.

$$y = f(-1) = -(-1 + 1)^2 = \mathbf{0} \qquad \text{y-coordinate of vertex}$$

Thus the coordinates of the vertex are $(-1, \mathbf{0})$. Table 6.2 is made by finding points on either side of the vertex. Plotting these points and connecting a smooth ∩-shaped graph results in Figure 6.7. The axis of symmetry is the vertical line passing through the vertex, so its equation is $x = -1$.

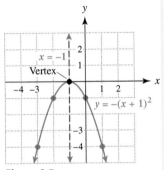

Figure 6.7

TABLE 6.2

	x	$y = -(x + 1)^2$	
	-3	-4	
	-2	-1	
Vertex →	-1	$\mathbf{0}$	Equal
	0	-1	
	1	-4	

(c) The graph of $f(x) = x^2 + 4x + 3$ can be found in a manner similar to that used for the graphs in (a) and (b). See Table 6.3 and Figure 6.8. With $a = 1$ and $b = 4$, the vertex formula can be used to show that the vertex is located at $(-2, -1)$. The equation of the axis of symmetry is $x = -2$.

TABLE 6.3

	x	$y = x^2 + 4x + 3$	
	-5	8	
	-4	3	
	-3	0	
Vertex →	-2	$\mathbf{-1}$	Equal
	-1	0	
	0	3	
	1	8	

Figure 6.8

Now Try Exercises 35, 41, 43

STUDY TIP

The vertex formula is important to memorize because it is often used when graphing parabolas.

Min–Max Applications

▶ **REAL-WORLD CONNECTION** Have you ever noticed that the first piece of pizza tastes really great and gives a person a lot of satisfaction? The second piece may be almost as good. After a few more pieces, there is often a point where the satisfaction starts to level off, and it can even go down as a person starts to eat too much. Eventually, if a person overeats, he or she might regret eating any pizza at all.

In Figure 6.9 a parabola models the total satisfaction received from eating x slices of pizza. Notice that the satisfaction level increases and then decreases. Although maximum satisfaction would vary with the individual, it always occurs at the vertex. (This is a seemingly simple model, but it is nonetheless used frequently in economics to describe consumer satisfaction from buying x identical items.)

Figure 6.9

EXAMPLE 4 Finding maximum satisfaction from pizza

The graph of $S(x) = -6.25x^2 + 50x$ is shown in Figure 6.9. Use the vertex formula to determine the number of slices of pizza that give maximum satisfaction. Does this maximum agree with what is shown in the graph of $y = S(x)$?

Solution
The parabola in Figure 6.9 opens downward, so the greatest y-value occurs at the vertex. To find the x-coordinate of the vertex, we can apply the vertex formula. Substitute $a = -6.25$ and $b = 50$ into the vertex formula.

$$x = -\frac{b}{2a} = -\frac{50}{2(-6.25)} = 4 \qquad \text{\textit{x}-coordinate of vertex}$$

Maximum satisfaction on a scale of 1 to 100 occurs when **4** slices of pizza are eaten, which agrees with Figure 6.9. (This number obviously varies from individual to individual.)

▌ Now Try Exercise 81

READING CHECK

How do you determine if a parabola has a maximum y-value or a minimum y-value?

FINDING MIN–MAX The graph in Figure 6.9 is a parabola that opens downward and whose maximum y-value of 100 occurs at the vertex. When a quadratic function f is used to model real data, the y-coordinate of the vertex represents either a maximum value of $f(x)$ or a minimum value of $f(x)$. For example, Figure 6.10(a) shows a parabola that opens upward. The minimum y-value on this graph is **1** and occurs at the vertex $(2, 1)$. Similarly, Figure 6.10(b) shows a parabola that opens downward. The maximum y-value on this graph is **3** and occurs at the vertex $(-3, 3)$.

Minimum: 1

Maximum: 3

(a)   (b)

Figure 6.10

Figure 6.11

EXAMPLE 5 **Finding a minimum *y*-value**

Find the minimum *y*-value on the graph of $f(x) = x^2 - 4x + 3$.

Solution

To locate the minimum *y*-value on a parabola, first apply the vertex formula with $a = 1$ and $b = -4$ to find the *x*-coordinate of the vertex.

$$x = -\frac{b}{2a} = -\frac{(-4)}{2(1)} = 2 \qquad \textit{x-coordinate of vertex}$$

The minimum *y*-value on the graph is found by evaluating $f(2)$.

$$y = f(2) = 2^2 - 4(2) + 3 = -1 \quad \textit{y-coordinate of vertex}$$

Thus the minimum *y*-coordinate on the graph of $y = f(x)$ is -1. This result is supported by Figure 6.11.

▌ **Now Try Exercise 53**

▶ **REAL-WORLD CONNECTION** In the next example, we demonstrate finding a maximum height reached by a baseball.

EXAMPLE 6 **Finding maximum height**

A baseball is hit into the air, and its height *h* in feet after *t* seconds can be calculated by $h(t) = -16t^2 + 96t + 3$.
(a) What is the height of the baseball when it is hit?
(b) Determine the maximum height of the baseball.

Solution
(a) The baseball is hit when $t = 0$, so $h(0) = -16(0)^2 + 96(0) + 3 = 3$ feet.
(b) The graph of *h* opens downward because $a = -16 < 0$. Thus the maximum height of the baseball occurs at the vertex. To find the vertex, we apply the vertex formula with $a = -16$ and $b = 96$ because $h(t) = -16t^2 + 96t + 3$.

$$t = -\frac{b}{2a} = -\frac{96}{2(-16)} = 3 \text{ seconds}$$

The maximum height of the baseball occurs at $t = 3$ seconds and is

$$h(3) = -16(3)^2 + 96(3) + 3 = 147 \text{ feet.}$$

▌ **Now Try Exercise 87**

▶ **REAL-WORLD CONNECTION** In the next example, we answer the question presented in A Look Into Math for this section.

EXAMPLE 7 **Maximizing revenue**

A hotel is considering giving the following group discount on room rates. The regular price for a room is $80, but for each room rented the price decreases by $2. A graph of the revenue received from renting x rooms is shown in Figure 6.12.
(a) Interpret the graph.
(b) What is the maximum revenue? How many rooms should be rented to receive the maximum revenue?
(c) Write a formula for $f(x)$ whose graph is shown in Figure 6.12.
(d) Use $f(x)$ to determine symbolically the maximum revenue and the number of rooms that should be rented.

Figure 6.12

TECHNOLOGY NOTE

Locating a Vertex
Graphing calculators can locate a vertex with the MAXIMUM or MINIMUM utility. The maximum in Example 7 is found in the figure.

Solution
(a) The revenue increases at first, reaches a maximum (which corresponds to the vertex), and then decreases.
(b) In Figure 6.12 the vertex is $(20, 800)$. Thus the maximum revenue of **$800** occurs when **20** rooms are rented.
(c) If x rooms are rented, the price for each room is $80 - 2x$. The revenue equals the number of rooms rented times the price of each room. Thus $f(x) = x(80 - 2x)$.
(d) First, multiply $x(80 - 2x)$ to obtain $80x - 2x^2$ and then let $f(x) = -2x^2 + 80x$. The x-coordinate of the vertex is

$$ x = -\frac{b}{2a} = -\frac{80}{2(-2)} = 20. $$

The y-coordinate is $f(20) = -2(20)^2 + 80(20) = 800$. These calculations verify our results in part (b).

Now Try Exercise 91

CALCULATOR HELP

To find a minimum or maximum, see Appendix A (page AP-11).

Basic Transformations of $y = ax^2$

THE GRAPH OF $y = ax^2$, $a > 0$ First, graph $y_1 = \frac{1}{2}x^2$, $y_2 = x^2$, and $y_3 = 2x^2$, as shown in Figure 6.13(a). Note that $a = \frac{1}{2}$, $a = 1$, and $a = 2$, respectively, and that as a increases, the resulting parabola becomes narrower. The graph of $y_1 = \frac{1}{2}x^2$ is wider than the graph of $y_2 = x^2$, and the graph of $y_3 = 2x^2$ is narrower than the graph of $y_2 = x^2$. In general, the graph of $y = ax^2$ is wider than the graph of $y = x^2$ when $0 < a < 1$ and narrower than the graph of $y = x^2$ when $a > 1$. When $a > 0$, the graph of $y = ax^2$ opens upward and never lies *below* the x-axis.

THE GRAPH OF $y = ax^2, a < 0$ When $a < 0$, the graph of $y = ax^2$ never lies *above* the x-axis because, for any input x, the product $ax^2 \leq 0$. The graphs of $y_4 = -\frac{1}{2}x^2$, $y_5 = -x^2$, and $y_6 = -2x^2$ are shown in Figure 6.13(b) and open downward. The graph of $y_4 = -\frac{1}{2}x^2$ is wider than the graph of $y_5 = -x^2$ and the graph of $y_6 = -2x^2$ is narrower than the graph of $y_5 = -x^2$.

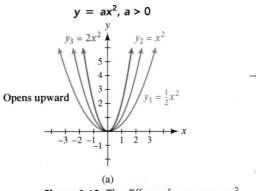

(a)   (b)

Figure 6.13 The Effect of a on $y = ax^2$

THE GRAPH OF $y = ax^2$

The graph of $y = ax^2$ is a parabola with the following characteristics.

1. The vertex is $(0, 0)$, and the axis of symmetry is given by $x = 0$.
2. It opens upward if $a > 0$ and opens downward if $a < 0$.
3. It is wider than the graph of $y = x^2$, if $0 < |a| < 1$. It is narrower than the graph of $y = x^2$, if $|a| > 1$.

Reflection Across the x-Axis

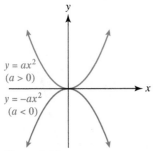

Figure 6.14

REFLECTIONS OF $y = ax^2$ In Figure 6.13 the graph of $y_1 = \frac{1}{2}x^2$ can be *transformed* into the graph of $y_4 = -\frac{1}{2}x^2$ by *reflecting* it across the x-axis. The graph of y_4 is a **reflection** of the graph of y_1 across the x-axis. In general, *the graph of* $y = -ax^2$ *is a reflection of the graph of* $y = ax^2$ *across the x-axis*, as shown in Figure 6.14. That is, if we folded the xy-plane along the x-axis the two graphs would match.

EXAMPLE 8   **Graphing** $y = ax^2$

Compare the graph of $g(x) = -3x^2$ to the graph of $f(x) = x^2$. Then graph both functions on the same coordinate axes.

Solution
Both graphs are parabolas. However, the graph of g opens downward and is narrower than the graph of f. These graphs are shown in Figure 6.15.

Now Try Exercise 67

Figure 6.15

Transformations of $y = ax^2 + bx + c$ (Optional)

The graph of a quadratic function is a parabola, and any quadratic function f can be written as $f(x) = ax^2 + bx + c$, where a, b, and c are constants with $a \neq 0$. As a result, the values of a, b, and c determine both the shape and position of the parabola in the xy-plane. In this subsection, we summarize some of the effects that these constants have on the graph of f.

THE EFFECTS OF a The effects of a on the graph of $y = ax^2$ were already discussed, and these effects can be generalized to include the graph of $y = ax^2 + bx + c$.

1. **Width:** The graph of $f(x) = ax^2 + bx + c$ is wider than the graph of $y = x^2$ if $0 < |a| < 1$ and narrower if $|a| > 1$. See Figures 6.16(a) and (b).
2. **Opening:** The graph of $f(x) = ax^2 + bx + c$ opens upward if $a > 0$ and downward if $a < 0$. See Figure 6.16(c).

The Effects of a on $y = ax^2 + bx + c$

(a)

(b)

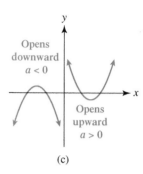
(c)

Figure 6.16

THE EFFECTS OF c The value of c affects the vertical placement of the parabola in the xy-plane. This placement is often called **vertical shift**.

1. **y-Intercept:** Because $f(0) = a(0)^2 + b(0) + c = c$, it follows that the y-intercept for the graph of $y = f(x)$ is c. See Figure 6.17(a).
2. **Vertical Shift:** The graph of $f(x) = ax^2 + bx + c$ is shifted vertically c units compared to the graph of $y = ax^2 + bx$. If $c < 0$, the shift is downward; if $c > 0$, the shift is upward. See Figures 6.17(b) and (c). The parabolas in both figures have identical shapes.

The Effects of c on $y = ax^2 + bx + c$

(a) y-intercept: c

Figure 6.17

(b) Shifted downward: $c < 0$

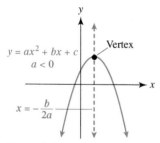
The Combined Effects of a and b

Figure 6.18

(c) Shifted upward: $c > 0$

THE COMBINED EFFECTS OF a AND b The combined values of a and b determine the x-coordinate of the vertex and the equation of the axis of symmetry.

1. **Vertex:** The x-coordinate of the vertex is $-\frac{b}{2a}$.
2. **Axis of Symmetry:** The axis of symmetry is given by $x = -\frac{b}{2a}$.

Figure 6.18 illustrates these concepts.

EXAMPLE 9 **Analyzing the graph of $y = ax^2 + bx + c$**

Let $f(x) = -\frac{1}{2}x^2 + x + \frac{3}{2}$.
(a) Does the graph of f open upward or downward? Is this graph wider or narrower than the graph of $y = x^2$?
(b) Find the axis of symmetry and the vertex.
(c) Find the y-intercept and any x-intercepts.
(d) Sketch a graph of f.

Solution

(a) If $f(x) = -\frac{1}{2}x^2 + x + \frac{3}{2}$, then $a = -\frac{1}{2}, b = 1$, and $c = \frac{3}{2}$. Because $a = -\frac{1}{2} < 0$, the parabola opens downward. Also, because $0 < |a| < 1$, the graph is wider than the graph of $y = x^2$.

(b) The axis of symmetry is $x = -\dfrac{b}{2a} = -\dfrac{1}{2\left(-\frac{1}{2}\right)} = 1$, or $x = 1$. Because

$$f(1) = -\frac{1}{2}(1)^2 + (1) + \frac{3}{2} = -\frac{1}{2} + 1 + \frac{3}{2} = 2,$$

the vertex is $(1, 2)$.

(c) The y-intercept equals c, or $\frac{3}{2}$. To find x-intercepts we let $y = 0$ and solve for x.

$$-\frac{1}{2}x^2 + x + \frac{3}{2} = 0 \quad \text{Equation to be solved}$$

$$x^2 - 2x - 3 = 0 \quad \text{Multiply by } -2; \text{ clear fractions.}$$

$$(x + 1)(x - 3) = 0 \quad \text{Factor.}$$

$$x + 1 = 0 \quad \text{or} \quad x - 3 = 0 \quad \text{Zero-product property}$$

$$x = -1 \quad \text{or} \quad x = 3 \quad \text{Solve.}$$

The x-intercepts are -1 and 3.

(d) Start by plotting the vertex and intercepts, as shown in Figure 6.19. Then sketch a smooth, $\cap$-shaped graph that connects these points.

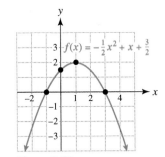

Figure 6.19

Now Try Exercise 75

6.1 Putting It All Together

CONCEPT	EXPLANATION	EXAMPLES
Quadratic Function	Can be written as $f(x) = ax^2 + bx + c, a \neq 0$	$f(x) = x^2 + x - 2$ and $g(x) = -2x^2 + 4 \quad (b = 0)$
Vertex of a Parabola	The x-coordinate of the vertex for the function $f(x) = ax^2 + bx + c$ with $a \neq 0$ is given by $$x = -\frac{b}{2a}.$$ The y-coordinate of the vertex is found by substituting this x-value in the equation. Hence the vertex is $\left(-\frac{b}{2a}, f\left(-\frac{b}{2a}\right)\right)$.	If $f(x) = -2x^2 + 8x - 7$, then $$x = -\frac{8}{2(-2)} = 2$$ and $$f(2) = -2(2)^2 + 8(2) - 7 = 1.$$ The vertex is $(2, 1)$. The graph of f opens downward because $a < 0$.
Graph of a Quadratic Function	Its graph is a parabola that opens upward if $a > 0$ and downward if $a < 0$. The value of $|a|$ affects the width of the parabola. The vertex can be used to determine the maximum or minimum output of a quadratic function.	The graph of $y = -\frac{1}{4}x^2$ opens downward and is wider than the graph of $y = x^2$, as shown in the figure. Each graph has its vertex at $(0, 0)$.

continued on next page

continued from previous page

The following gives symbolic, numerical, and graphical representations for the quadratic function f that *squares the input x and then subtracts 1.*

Symbolic Representation

$$f(x) = x^2 - 1$$

Numerical Representation

	x	$f(x) = x^2 - 1$	
	-2	3	
	-1	0	
Vertex →	0	-1	Equal
	1	0	
	2	3	

Graphical Representation

Axis of symmetry: $x = 0$

$f(x) = x^2 - 1$ Vertex: $(0, -1)$

6.1   Exercises

MyMathLab   Math XL PRACTICE   WATCH   DOWNLOAD   READ   REVIEW

CONCEPTS AND VOCABULARY

1. The graph of a quadratic function is called a(n) _____.

2. If a parabola opens upward, what is the lowest point on the parabola called?

3. If a parabola is symmetric with respect to the y-axis, the y-axis is called the _____.

4. The vertex on the graph of $y = x^2$ is _____.

5. Sketch a parabola that opens downward with a vertex of $(1, 2)$.

6. If $y = ax^2 + bx + c$, the x-coordinate of the vertex is given by $x =$ _____.

7. Compared to the graph of $y = x^2$, the graph of $y = 2x^2$ is (wider/narrower).

8. The graph of $y = -x^2$ is similar to the graph of $y = x^2$ except that it is _____ across the x-axis.

9. Any quadratic function can be written in the form $f(x) =$ _____.

10. If a parabola opens downward, the point with the largest y-value is called the _____.

11. (True or False?) The axis of symmetry for the graph of $y = ax^2 + bx + c$ is given by $x = -\frac{b}{2a}$.

12. (True or False?) If the vertex of a parabola is located at (a, b), then the axis of symmetry is given by $x = b$.

13. (True or False?) If a parabola opens downward and its vertex is (a, b), then the minimum y-value on the parabola is b.

14. (True or False?) The graph of $y = -ax^2$ with $a > 0$ opens downward.

VERTEX FORMULA

Exercises 15–24: Find the vertex of the parabola.

15. $f(x) = x^2 - 4x - 2$

16. $f(x) = 2x^2 + 6x - 3$

17. $f(x) = -\frac{1}{3}x^2 - 2x + 1$

18. $f(x) = 5 - 4x + x^2$

19. $f(x) = 3 - 2x^2$

20. $f(x) = \frac{1}{4}x^2 - 3x - 2$

21. $f(x) = -0.3x^2 + 0.6x + 1.1$

22. $f(x) = 25 - 10x + 20x^2$

23. $f(x) = 6x - x^2$

24. $f(x) = x - \frac{1}{2}x^2$

GRAPHS OF QUADRATIC FUNCTIONS

Exercises 25–28: Use the given graph of f to evaluate the expressions.

25. $f(-2)$ and $f(0)$

26. $f(-2)$ and $f(2)$

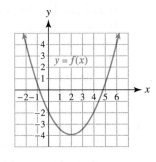

27. $f(-3)$ and $f(1)$

28. $f(-1)$ and $f(2)$

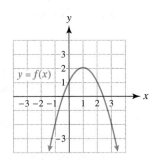

Exercises 29–32: Identify the vertex, axis of symmetry, and whether the parabola opens upward or downward.

29.

30.

31.

32.

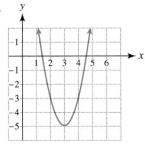

Exercises 33–52: Do the following for the given f(x).
(a) Identify the vertex and axis of symmetry on the graph of $y = f(x)$.
(b) Graph $y = f(x)$.
(c) Evaluate $f(-2)$ and $f(3)$.

33. $f(x) = \frac{1}{2}x^2$

34. $f(x) = -3x^2$

35. $f(x) = x^2 - 2$

36. $f(x) = x^2 - 1$

37. $f(x) = -3x^2 + 1$

38. $f(x) = \frac{1}{2}x^2 + 2$

39. $f(x) = (x - 1)^2$

40. $f(x) = (x + 2)^2$

41. $f(x) = -(x + 2)^2$

42. $f(x) = -(x - 1)^2$

43. $f(x) = x^2 + x - 2$

44. $f(x) = x^2 - 2x + 2$

45. $f(x) = 2x^2 - 3$

46. $f(x) = 1 - 2x^2$

47. $f(x) = 2x - x^2$

48. $f(x) = x^2 + 2x - 8$

49. $f(x) = -2x^2 + 4x - 1$

50. $f(x) = -\frac{1}{2}x^2 + 2x - 3$

51. $f(x) = \frac{1}{4}x^2 - x + 5$

52. $f(x) = 3 - 6x - 4x^2$

MIN–MAX

Exercises 53–58: Find the minimum y-value on the graph of $y = f(x)$.

53. $f(x) = x^2 + 2x - 1$

54. $f(x) = x^2 + 6x + 2$

55. $f(x) = x^2 - 5x$

56. $f(x) = x^2 - 3x$

57. $f(x) = 2x^2 + 2x - 3$

58. $f(x) = 3x^2 - 3x + 7$

Exercises 59–64: Find the maximum y-value on the graph of $y = f(x)$.

59. $f(x) = -x^2 + 2x + 5$

60. $f(x) = -x^2 + 4x - 3$

61. $f(x) = 4x - x^2$

62. $f(x) = 6x - x^2$

63. $f(x) = -2x^2 + x - 5$

64. $f(x) = -5x^2 + 15x - 2$

65. *Numbers* Find two positive numbers whose sum is 20 and whose product is maximum.

66. Thinking Generally Find two positive numbers whose sum is k and whose product is maximum.

TRANSFORMATIONS OF GRAPHS

Exercises 67–74: Graph f(x). Compare the graph of $y = f(x)$ to the graph of $y = x^2$.

67. $f(x) = -x^2$

68. $f(x) = -2x^2$

69. $f(x) = 2x^2$

70. $f(x) = 3x^2$

71. $f(x) = \frac{1}{4}x^2$

72. $f(x) = \frac{1}{2}x^2$

73. $f(x) = -\frac{1}{2}x^2$

74. $f(x) = -\frac{3}{2}x^2$

Exercises 75–80: (Refer to Example 9.) Use the given f(x) to complete the following.

(a) *Does the graph of f open upward or downward? Is this graph wider, narrower, or the same as the graph of $y = x^2$?*

(b) *Find the axis of symmetry and the vertex.*

(c) *Find the y-intercept and any x-intercepts.*

(d) *Sketch a graph of f.*

75. $f(x) = \frac{1}{2}x^2 + x - \frac{3}{2}$ **76.** $f(x) = -x^2 + 4x + 5$

77. $f(x) = 2x - x^2$ **78.** $f(x) = x - 2x^2$

79. $f(x) = 2x^2 + 2x - 4$ **80.** $f(x) = \frac{1}{2}x^2 - \frac{1}{2}x - 1$

APPLICATIONS

Exercises 81 and 82: Eating Pizza (Refer to Example 4.) Let S(x) denote the satisfaction, on a scale from 0 to 100, from eating x pieces of pizza. Find the number of pieces that gives the maximum satisfaction.

81. $S(x) = -\frac{100}{9}x^2 + \frac{200}{3}x$

82. $S(x) = -16x^2 + 80x$

Exercises 83–86: Quadratic Models Match the physical situation with the graph (a.–d.) that models it best.

83. The height y of a stone thrown from ground level after x seconds

84. The number of people attending a popular movie x weeks after its opening

85. The temperature after x hours in a house when the furnace quits and then a repair person fixes it

86. U.S. population from 1800 to the present

a.

b.

c.

d.

87. *Height Reached by a Baseball* (Refer to Example 6.) A baseball is hit into the air, and its height h in feet after t seconds is given by $h(t) = -16t^2 + 64t + 2$.

(a) What is the height of the baseball when it is hit?

(b) After how many seconds does the baseball reach its maximum height?

(c) Determine the maximum height of the baseball.

88. *Height Reached by a Golf Ball* A golf ball is hit into the air, and its height h in feet after t seconds is given by $h(t) = -16t^2 + 128t$.

(a) What is the height of the golf ball when it is hit?

(b) After how many seconds does the golf ball reach its maximum height?

(c) Determine the maximum height of the golf ball.

89. *Height Reached by a Baseball* Suppose that a baseball is thrown upward with an initial velocity of 66 feet per second (45 miles per hour) and it is released 6 feet above the ground. Its height h after t seconds is given by

$$h(t) = -16t^2 + 66t + 6.$$

After how many seconds does the baseball reach a maximum height? Estimate this height.

90. *Throwing a Baseball on the Moon* (Refer to Exercise 89.) If the same baseball were thrown the same way on the moon, its height h above the moon's surface after t seconds would be

$$h(t) = -2.55t^2 + 66t + 6.$$

Does the baseball go higher on the moon or on Earth? What is the difference in these two heights?

91. *Concert Tickets* (Refer to Example 7.) An agency is promoting concert tickets by offering a group-discount rate. The regular price is $100 and for each ticket bought the price decreases by $1. (One ticket costs $99, two tickets cost $98 *each*, and so on.)

(a) A graph of the revenue received from selling x tickets is shown in the figure. Interpret the graph.

Tickets Sold

(b) What is the maximum revenue? How many tickets should be sold to maximize revenue?

(c) Write a formula for $y = f(x)$ whose graph is shown in the figure.

(d) Use $f(x)$ to determine symbolically the maximum revenue and the number of tickets that should be sold to maximize revenue.

92. *Maximizing Revenue* The regular price for a round-trip ticket to Las Vegas, Nevada, charged by an airline charter company is $300. For a group rate the company will reduce the price of each ticket by $1.50 for every passenger on the flight.

(a) Write a formula $f(x)$ that gives the revenue from selling x tickets.

(b) Determine how many tickets should be sold to maximize the revenue. What is the maximum revenue?

93. *Monthly Facebook Visitors* The number of *unique* monthly Facebook visitors in millions x years after 2006 can be modeled by

$$V(x) = 10.75x^2 - 24x + 35.$$

(a) Evaluate $V(1)$, $V(2)$, $V(3)$, and $V(4)$. Interpret your answer.

(b) Explain why numbers of Facebook visitors can not be modeled by a linear function.

94. *Cell Phone Complexity* Consumers often enjoy having certain features on their cell phones, such as e-mail and the ability to surf the Web. However, as phones become more and more complicated to operate, the benefits from the additional complexity start to decrease. The following parabola models this general situation. Interpret why a parabola is appropriate to model this consumer experience.

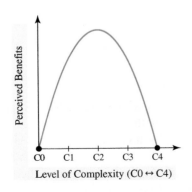

95. *Maximizing Area* A farmer is fencing a rectangular area for cattle and uses a straight portion of a river as one side of the rectangle, as illustrated in the figure. Note that there is no fence along the river. If the farmer has 1200 feet of fence, find the dimensions for the rectangular area that give a maximum area for the cattle.

96. *Maximizing Area* A rectangular pen being constructed for a pet requires 60 feet of fence.

(a) Write a formula $f(x)$ that gives the area of the pen if one side of the pen has length x.

(b) Find the dimensions of the pen that give the largest area. What is the largest area?

Exercises 97 and 98: Large-Screen Televisions (Refer to the introduction to this chapter.) Use the formula

$$S(x) = -0.227x^2 + 8.155x - 8.8,$$

where $6 \le x \le 16$, to estimate the recommended screen size in inches when viewers sit x feet from the screen.

97. $x = 8$ feet

98. $x = 12$ feet

99. *Carbon Emissions* Past and future carbon emissions in billions of metric tons during year x can be modeled by

$$C(x) = \frac{1}{300}x^2 - \frac{199}{15}x + \frac{39{,}619}{3},$$

where $1990 \le x \le 2020$. (*Source:* U.S. Department of Energy.)

(a) Evaluate $C(1990)$. Interpret your answer.

(b) Find the expected *increase* in carbon emissions from 1990 to 2020.

100. *Seedling Growth* In a study of the effect of temperature on the growth of melon seedlings, the seedlings were grown at different temperatures, and their heights were measured after a fixed period of time. The findings of this study can be modeled by

$$f(x) = -0.095x^2 + 5.4x - 52.2,$$

where x is the temperature in degrees Celsius and the output $f(x)$ gives the resulting average height in centimeters. (*Source:* R. Pearl, "The growth of *Cucumis melo* seedlings at different temperatures.")

 (a) Graph f in [20, 40, 5] by [0, 30, 5].
(b) Estimate graphically the temperature that resulted in the greatest height for the melon seedlings.
(c) Solve part (b) symbolically.

WRITING ABOUT MATHEMATICS

101. If $f(x) = ax^2 + bx + c$, explain how the values of a and c affect the graph of f.

102. Suppose that a quantity Q is modeled by the formula $Q(x) = ax^2 + bx + c$ with $a < 0$. Explain how to find the x-value that maximizes $Q(x)$. How do you find the maximum value of $Q(x)$?

6.2 Parabolas and Modeling

Vertical and Horizontal Translations ● Vertex Form ●
Modeling with Quadratic Functions (Optional)

A LOOK INTO MATH ▶

A taxiway used by an airplane to exit a runway often contains curves. A curve that is too sharp for the speed of the plane is a safety hazard. The scatterplot shown in Figure 6.20 gives an appropriate radius R of a curve designed for an airplane taxiing at x miles per hour. The data are nonlinear because they do not lie on a line. In this section we explain how a quadratic function may be used to model such data. First, we discuss translations of parabolas. (*Source:* FAA.)

NEW VOCABULARY

☐ Translations
☐ Vertex form
☐ Completing the square

Figure 6.20

Vertical and Horizontal Translations

The graph of $y = x^2$ is a parabola opening upward with vertex $(0, 0)$. Suppose that we graph $y_1 = x^2$, $y_2 = x^2 + 1$, and $y_3 = x^2 - 2$ in the same xy-plane, as calculated in Table 6.4 and shown in Figure 6.21. All three graphs have the same shape. However, compared to the graph of $y_1 = x^2$, the graph of $y_2 = x^2 + 1$ is shifted *upward* 1 unit and the graph of $y_3 = x^2 - 2$ is shifted *downward* 2 units. Such shifts are called **translations** because they do not change the shape of a graph—only its position.

Vertical Shifts of $y = x^2$

Figure 6.21

TABLE 6.4

x	$y_2 = x^2 + 1$	$y_1 = x^2$	$y_3 = x^2 - 2$
-2	5	4	2
-1	2	1	-1
0	1	0	-2
1	2	1	-1
2	5	4	2
↑	↑	↑ ↑	↑
The x-values do NOT change.	Add 1 to find the y-values.		Subtract 2 to find the y-values.

Next, suppose that we graph $y_1 = x^2$ and $y_2 = (x - 1)^2$ in the same xy-plane. Compare Tables 6.5 and 6.6. Note that the y-values are equal when the x-value for y_2 is 1 unit *larger* than the x-value for y_1. For example, $y_1 = 4$ when $x = -2$ and $y_2 = 4$ when $x = -1$. Thus the graph of $y_2 = (x - 1)^2$ has the same shape as the graph of $y_1 = x^2$ except that it is translated *horizontally to the right* 1 unit, as illustrated in Figure 6.22.

Horizontal Shift of $y = x^2$

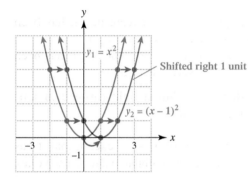

Figure 6.22

TABLE 6.5

x	$y_1 = x^2$
-2	4
-1	1
0	0
1	1
2	4

TABLE 6.6

x	$y_2 = (x - 1)^2$
-1	4
0	1
1	0
2	1
3	4

Add 1 to find the x-values.   The y-values do NOT change.

The graphs $y_1 = x^2$ and $y_2 = (x + 2)^2$ are shown in Figure 6.23. Note that Tables 6.7 and 6.8 show their y-values to be equal when the x-value for y_2 is 2 units *smaller* than the x-value for y_1. As a result, the graph of $y_2 = (x + 2)^2$ has the same shape as the graph of $y_1 = x^2$ except that it is translated *horizontally to the left* 2 units.

Horizontal Shift of $y = x^2$

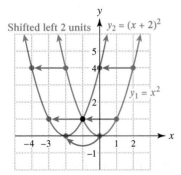

Figure 6.23

TABLE 6.7

x	$y_1 = x^2$
-2	4
-1	1
0	0
1	1
2	4

TABLE 6.8

x	$y_2 = (x + 2)^2$
-4	4
-3	1
-2	0
-1	1
0	4

Subtract 2 to find the x-values.   The y-values do NOT change.

These results are summarized as follows.

VERTICAL AND HORIZONTAL TRANSLATIONS OF PARABOLAS

Let h and k be positive numbers.

To graph	*shift the graph of $y = x^2$ by k units*
$y = x^2 + k$	upward.
$y = x^2 - k$	downward.

To graph	*shift the graph of $y = x^2$ by h units*
$y = (x - h)^2$	right.
$y = (x + h)^2$	left.

EXAMPLE 1   **Translating the graph $y = x^2$**

Sketch the graph of the equation and identify the vertex.

(a) $y = x^2 + 2$ **(b)** $y = (x + 3)^2$ **(c)** $y = (x - 2)^2 - 3$

Solution

(a) The graph of $y = x^2 + 2$ is similar to the graph of $y = x^2$ except that it has been translated *upward* 2 units, as shown in Figure 6.24(a). The vertex is $(0, 2)$.

(b) The graph of $y = (x + 3)^2$ is similar to the graph of $y = x^2$ except that it has been translated *left* 3 units, as shown in Figure 6.24(b). The vertex is $(-3, 0)$.

> **NOTE:** If you are thinking that the graph should be shifted right (instead of left) 3 units, try graphing $y = (x + 3)^2$ on a graphing calculator.

(c) The graph of $y = (x - 2)^2 - 3$ is similar to the graph of $y = x^2$ except that it has been translated downward 3 units *and* right 2 units, as shown in Figure 6.24(c). The vertex is $(2, -3)$.

(a)

(b)

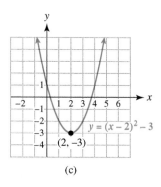
(c)

Figure 6.24

Now Try Exercises 15, 19, 27

Vertex Form

The graphs of $y = 2x^2$ and $y = 2x^2 - 12x + 20$ have *exactly* the same shape, as illustrated in Figures 6.25 and 6.26. However, the vertex for $y = 2x^2$ is $(0, 0)$, whereas the vertex for $y = 2x^2 - 12x + 20$ is $(3, 2)$.

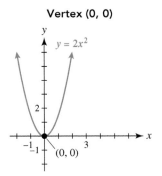

Vertex (0, 0)

Figure 6.25

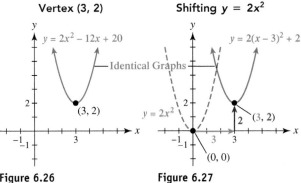

Vertex (3, 2)

Figure 6.26

Shifting $y = 2x^2$

Figure 6.27

When the graph of $y = 2x^2$ (in Figure 6.25) is shifted 3 units right and 2 units upward by graphing the equation

$$y = 2(x - 3)^2 + 2, \quad \text{Vertex form}$$

Shift 2 units upward

Shift 3 units right

CRITICAL THINKING

Expand $y = 2(x - 3)^2 + 2$ and combine like terms. What does it equal?

we get the graph in Figure 6.27, which is identical to the graph of $y = 2x^2 - 12x + 20$ in Figure 6.26. Thus $y = 2(x - 3)^2 + 2$ and $y = 2x^2 - 12x + 20$ are equivalent equations for the same parabola.

In general, the equation for any parabola can be written as either $y = ax^2 + bx + c$ or $y = a(x - h)^2 + k$, where the vertex is (h, k). The second form is sometimes called *vertex form*.

READING CHECK

Give the vertex form. Explain it with an example.

VERTEX FORM

The **vertex form** of the equation of a parabola with vertex (h, k) is

$$y = a(x - h)^2 + k,$$

where $a \neq 0$ is a constant. If $a > 0$, the parabola opens upward; if $a < 0$, the parabola opens downward.

NOTE: Vertex form is sometimes called **standard form for a parabola with a vertical axis**.

In the next three examples, we demonstrate graphing parabolas in vertex form, finding their equations, and writing vertex forms of equations.

EXAMPLE 2 | **Graphing parabolas in vertex form**

Compare the graph of $y = f(x)$ to the graph of $y = x^2$. Then sketch a graph of $y = f(x)$ and $y = x^2$ in the same xy-plane.

(a) $f(x) = \frac{1}{2}(x - 5)^2 + 2$ **(b)** $f(x) = -3(x + 5)^2 - 3$

Solution

(a) Compared to the graph of $y = x^2$, the graph of $y = f(x)$ is *translated 5 units right* and *2 units upward*. The vertex for $f(x)$ is $(5, 2)$, whereas the vertex of $y = x^2$ is $(0, 0)$. Because $a = \frac{1}{2}$, the graph of $y = f(x)$ *opens upward* and is *wider* than the graph of $y = x^2$. These graphs are shown in Figure 6.28(a) on the next page.

(b) Compared to the graph of $y = x^2$, the graph of $y = -3(x + 5)^2 - 3$ is *translated 5 units left* and 3 *units downward*. The vertex for $f(x)$ is $(-5, -3)$. Because $a = -3$, the graph of $y = f(x)$ *opens downward* and is *narrower* than the graph of $y = x^2$. These graphs are shown in Figure 6.28(b).

(a)

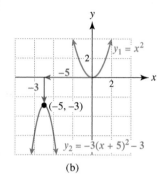

(b)

Figure 6.28

Now Try Exercises 35, 37

EXAMPLE 3   **Finding equations of parabolas**

Write the vertex form of a parabola with $a = 2$ and vertex $(-2, 1)$. Then express this equation in the form $y = ax^2 + bx + c$.

Solution

The vertex form of a parabola is given by $y = a(x - h)^2 + k$, where the vertex is (h, k). For $a = 2, h = -2$, and $k = 1$, the equation becomes

$$y = 2(x - (-2))^2 + 1 \quad \text{or} \quad y = 2(x + 2)^2 + 1.$$

To write $y = 2(x + 2)^2 + 1$ in the form $y = ax^2 + bx + c$, do the following.

$$
\begin{aligned}
y &= 2(x^2 + 4x + 4) + 1 && \text{Multiply } (x + 2)^2 \text{ as } x^2 + 4x + 4. \\
&= 2x^2 + 8x + 8 + 1 && \text{Distributive property} \\
&= 2x^2 + 8x + 9 && \text{Add.}
\end{aligned}
$$

The equivalent equation is $y = 2x^2 + 8x + 9$.

Now Try Exercise 41

In the next example, the vertex formula is used to write the equation of a parabola in vertex form.

EXAMPLE 4   **Using the vertex formula to write vertex form**

Find the vertex on the graph of $y = 3x^2 + 6x + 1$. Write this equation in vertex form.

Solution

We can use the vertex formula, $x = -\frac{b}{2a}$, to find the x-coordinate of the vertex with $a = 3$ and $b = 6$.

$$x = -\frac{b}{2a} = -\frac{6}{2(3)} = -1 \quad \text{x-coordinate of vertex}$$

To find the y-coordinate, let $x = -1$ in $y = 3x^2 + 6x + 1$.

$$y = 3(-1)^2 + 6(-1) + 1 = -2 \quad \text{Let } x = -1.$$

The vertex is $(-1, -2)$. We can now find the vertex form with $a = 3$, $h = -1$, and $k = -2$.

$$
\begin{aligned}
y &= a(x - h)^2 + k && \text{Vertex form} \\
y &= 3(x - (-1))^2 - 2 && \text{Substitute.} \\
y &= 3(x + 1)^2 - 2 && \text{Simplify.}
\end{aligned}
$$

The equations $y = 3x^2 + 6x + 1$ and $y = 3(x + 1)^2 - 2$ are equivalent, and their graphs represent the same parabola with vertex $(-1, -2)$.

| Now Try Exercise 53

Completing the Square

$$x^2 + 4x + 4 = (x + 2)^2$$

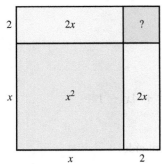

Figure 6.29

COMPLETING THE SQUARE TO FIND THE VERTEX The vertex of a parabola can be found by using a technique called **completing the square**. To complete the square for the expression $x^2 + 4x$, consider Figure 6.29.

Note that the blue and pink areas sum to

$$x^2 + 2x + 2x = x^2 + 4x.$$

The area of the small green square must be $2 \cdot 2 = 4$. Thus to *complete the square* for $x^2 + 4x$, we add 4. That is,

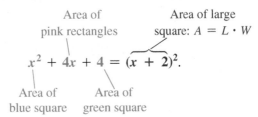

In the next example, we use the above result to complete the square and find the vertex on the graph of $y = x^2 + 4x$.

EXAMPLE 5 **Writing vertex form by completing the square**

Write the equation $y = x^2 + 4x$ in vertex form by completing the square. Identify the vertex.

Solution

As discussed, we must add 4 to $x^2 + 4x$ to complete the square. Because we are given an equation, we will add 4 *and* subtract 4 from the right side of the equation in order to keep the equation "balanced."

$$
\begin{aligned}
y &= x^2 + 4x. && \text{Given equation} \\
y &= x^2 + 4x + 4 - 4 && \text{Add and subtract 4 on the right.} \\
y &= (x^2 + 4x + 4) - 4 && \text{Associative property} \\
y &= (x + 2)^2 - 4 && \text{Perfect square trinomial}
\end{aligned}
$$

The vertex form is $y = (x + 2)^2 - 4$, and the vertex is $(-2, -4)$.

| Now Try Exercise 61

NOTE: Adding 4 and subtracting 4 from the right side of the equation in Example 5 is equivalent to adding 0 to the right side, which does not change the equation.

In general, to complete the square for $x^2 + bx$ we must add $\left(\frac{b}{2}\right)^2$, as illustrated in Figure 6.30. This technique is shown in Example 6.

READING CHECK

Use the figure to *complete the square* for $x^2 + 8x$.

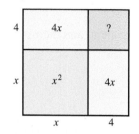

Completing the Square

$$x^2 + bx + \left(\frac{b}{2}\right)^2 = \left(x + \frac{b}{2}\right)^2$$

Figure 6.30

EXAMPLE 6   **Writing vertex form**

Write each equation in vertex form. Identify the vertex.
(a) $y = x^2 - 6x - 1$ (b) $y = x^2 + 3x + 4$ (c) $y = 2x^2 + 4x - 1$

Solution
(a) Because $\left(\frac{b}{2}\right)^2 = \left(\frac{-6}{2}\right)^2 = 9$, add *and* subtract 9 on the right side.

$$
\begin{aligned}
y &= x^2 - 6x - 1 & \text{Given equation} \\
&= (x^2 - 6x + 9) - 9 - 1 & \text{Add and subtract 9.} \\
&= (x - 3)^2 - 10 & \text{Perfect square trinomial}
\end{aligned}
$$

The vertex is $(3, -10)$.

(b) Because $\left(\frac{b}{2}\right)^2 = \left(\frac{3}{2}\right)^2 = \frac{9}{4}$, add *and* subtract $\frac{9}{4}$ on the right side.

$$
\begin{aligned}
y &= x^2 + 3x + 4 & \text{Given equation} \\
&= \left(x^2 + 3x + \frac{9}{4}\right) - \frac{9}{4} + 4 & \text{Add and subtract } \frac{9}{4}. \\
&= \left(x + \frac{3}{2}\right)^2 + \frac{7}{4} & \text{Perfect square trinomial}
\end{aligned}
$$

The vertex is $\left(-\frac{3}{2}, \frac{7}{4}\right)$.

(c) This equation is slightly different because the leading coefficient is 2 rather than 1. Start by factoring 2 from the first two terms on the right side.

$$
\begin{aligned}
y &= 2x^2 + 4x - 1 & \text{Given equation} \\
&= 2(x^2 + 2x) - 1 & \text{Factor out 2.} \\
&= 2(x^2 + 2x + 1 - 1) - 1 & \left(\frac{b}{2}\right)^2 = \left(\frac{2}{2}\right)^2 = 1 \\
&= 2(x^2 + 2x + 1) - 2 - 1 & \text{Distributive property: } 2 \cdot (-1) \\
&= 2(x + 1)^2 - 3 & \text{Perfect square trinomial}
\end{aligned}
$$

The vertex is $(-1, -3)$.

Now Try Exercises 65, 69, 73

Modeling with Quadratic Functions (Optional)

▶ **REAL-WORLD CONNECTION** In A Look Into Math for this section, we discussed airport taxiway curves designed for airplanes. The data previously shown in Figure 6.20 are listed in Table 6.9.

TABLE 6.9 Safe Taxiway Speed

x (mph)	10	20	30	40	50	60
R (ft)	50	200	450	800	1250	1800

Source: Federal Aviation Administration.

A second scatterplot of the data is shown in Figure 6.31. The data may be modeled by $R(x) = ax^2$ for some value a. To illustrate this relation, graph R for different values of a. In Figures 6.32–6.34, R has been graphed for $a = 2, -1$, and $\frac{1}{2}$, respectively. When $a > 0$ the parabola opens upward, and when $a < 0$ the parabola opens downward. Larger values of $|a|$ make a parabola narrower, whereas smaller values of $|a|$ make the parabola wider. Through trial and error, $a = \frac{1}{2}$ gives a good fit to the data, so $R(x) = \frac{1}{2}x^2$ models the data.

[−70, 70, 10] by [−2000, 2000, 500]

Figure 6.31

[−70, 70, 10] by [−2000, 2000, 500]

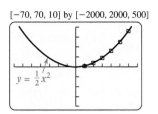

Figure 6.32 $a = 2$

[−70, 70, 10] by [−2000, 2000, 500]

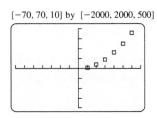

Figure 6.33 $a = -1$

[−70, 70, 10] by [−2000, 2000, 500]

Figure 6.34 $a = \frac{1}{2}$

CALCULATOR HELP

To make a scatterplot, see Appendix A (pages AP-3 and AP-4).

This value of a can also be found *symbolically*, as demonstrated in the next example.

EXAMPLE 7 ▶ **Modeling safe taxiway speed**

Find a value for the constant a so that $R(x) = ax^2$ models the data in Table 6.9. Check your result by making a table of values for $R(x)$.

Solution

From Table 6.9, when $x = $ **10** miles per hour, the curve radius is **50** feet. Therefore

$$R(10) = 50 \quad \text{or} \quad a(10)^2 = 50. \qquad R(x) = ax^2$$

Solving for a gives

$$a = \frac{50}{10^2} = \frac{1}{2}.$$

To be sure that $R(x) = \frac{1}{2}x^2$ is correct, make a table, as shown in Figure 6.35. Its values agree with those in Table 6.9.

X	Y1
0	0
10	50
20	200
30	450
40	800
50	1250
60	1800

Y1■.5X²

Figure 6.35

▌ Now Try Exercise 87

INCREASING AND DECREASING The concept of increasing and decreasing is frequently used when modeling data with functions. Suppose that the graph of the equation $y = x^2$ shown in Figure 6.36 represents a valley. If we walk from *left to right*, the valley "goes down" and then "goes up." Mathematically, we say that the graph of $y = x^2$ is *decreasing* when $x \leq 0$ and *increasing* when $x \geq 0$. In Figure 6.33, the graph of $y = -1x^2$ increases when $x \leq 0$ and decreases when $x \geq 0$, and in Figure 6.24(c) on page 430 the graph decreases when $x \leq 2$ and increases when $x \geq 2$.

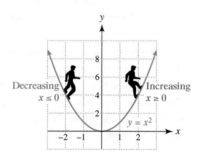

Figure 6.36

NOTE: When determining where a graph is increasing and where it is decreasing, we must "walk" along the graph *from left to right*. (We read English from left to right, which might help you remember.)

TABLE 6.10

Year	U.S. AIDS Cases
1981	425
1984	11,106
1987	71,414
1990	199,608
1993	417,835
1996	609,933

Source: Department of Health and Human Services.

▶ **REAL-WORLD CONNECTION** In 1981, the first cases of AIDS were reported in the United States. Table 6.10 lists the *cumulative* number of AIDS cases in the United States for various years. For example, between 1981 and 1990, a total of 199,608 AIDS cases were reported.

A scatterplot of these data is shown in Figure 6.37. To model these nonlinear and *increasing* data, we want to find (the right half of) a parabola with the shape illustrated in Figure 6.38. We do so in the next example.

Figure 6.37

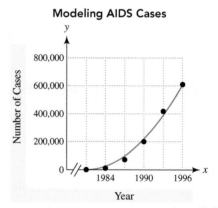

Figure 6.38

NOTE: From 1981 to 1996, the number of AIDS cases grew rapidly and can be modeled by a quadratic function. After 1996, the growth in AIDS cases slowed so a quadratic model is much less accurate. When modeling data with functions, it is important to remember that data can change character over time. As a result, the same modeling function may not be appropriate for every time period.

EXAMPLE 8   **Modeling AIDS cases**

Use the data in Table 6.10 to complete the following.
(a) Make a scatterplot of the data in [1980, 1997, 2] by [−10000, 800000, 100000].
(b) The lowest data point in Table 6.10 is (1981, 425). Let this point be the vertex of a parabola that opens upward. Graph $y = a(x - 1981)^2 + 425$ together with the data by first letting $a = 1000$.
(c) Use trial and error to adjust the value of a until the graph models the data.
(d) Use your final equation to estimate the number of AIDS cases in 1992. Compare it to the known value of 338,786.

Solution
(a) A scatterplot of the data is shown in Figure 6.39.

STUDY TIP

Sometimes we use only the right half or only the left half of a parabola to model data.

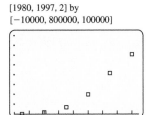

[1980, 1997, 2] by
[−10000, 800000, 100000]

Figure 6.39

[1980, 1997, 2] by
[−10000, 800000, 100000]

$y = 1000(x - 1981)^2 + 425$

Figure 6.40 $a = 1000$

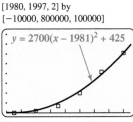

[1980, 1997, 2] by
[−10000, 800000, 100000]

$y = 2700(x - 1981)^2 + 425$

Figure 6.41 $a = 2700$

(b) A graph of $y = 1000(x - 1981)^2 + 425$ is shown in Figure 6.40. To have a better fit of the data, a larger value for a is needed.
(c) Figure 6.41 shows the effect of adjusting the value of a to **2700**. This value provides a reasonably good fit. (Note that you may decide on a slightly different value for a.)
(d) If $a = $ **2700**, the modeling equation becomes

$$y = 2700(x - 1981)^2 + 425.$$

To estimate the number of AIDS cases in 1992, substitute $x = $ **1992** to obtain

$$y = 2700(\mathbf{1992} - 1981)^2 + 425 = \mathbf{327{,}125}.$$

This number is about 12,000 less than the known value of **338,786**.

Now Try Exercise 91

6.2   Putting It All Together

CONCEPT	EXPLANATION	EXAMPLES
Translations of Parabolas	Compared to the graph $y = x^2$, the graph of $y = x^2 + k$ is shifted vertically k units and the graph of $y = (x - h)^2$ is shifted horizontally h units.	Compared to the graph of $y = x^2$, the graph of $y = x^2 - 4$ is shifted *downward* 4 units. Compared to the graph of $y = x^2$, the graph of $y = (x - 4)^2$ is shifted *right* 4 units and the graph of $y = (x + 4)^2$ is shifted *left* 4 units.
Vertex Form	The vertex form of the equation of a parabola with vertex (h, k) is $$y = a(x - h)^2 + k,$$ where $a \neq 0$ is a constant. If $a > 0$, the parabola opens upward; if $a < 0$, the parabola opens downward.	The graph of $y = 3(x + 2)^2 - 7$ has a vertex of $(-2, -7)$ and opens upward because $3 > 0$.

continued on next page

continued from previous page

CONCEPT	EXPLANATION	EXAMPLES
Completing the Square Method	To complete the square to obtain the vertex form, add *and* subtract $\left(\frac{b}{2}\right)^2$ on the right side of the equation $y = x^2 + bx + c$. Then factor the perfect square trinomial.	If $y = x^2 + 10x - 3$, then add *and* subtract $\left(\frac{b}{2}\right)^2 = \left(\frac{10}{2}\right)^2 = 25$ on the right side of this equation. $$y = (x^2 + 10x + 25) - 25 - 3$$ $$= (x + 5)^2 - 28$$ The vertex is $(-5, -28)$.

6.2 Exercises

MyMathLab Math XL PRACTICE WATCH DOWNLOAD READ REVIEW

CONCEPTS AND VOCABULARY

1. Compared to the graph of $y = x^2$, the graph of $y =$ _____ is shifted upward 2 units.

2. Compared to the graph of $y = x^2$, the graph of $y =$ _____ is shifted to the right 2 units.

3. The vertex of $y = (x - 1)^2 + 2$ is _____.

4. The vertex of $y = (x + 1)^2 - 2$ is _____.

5. A quadratic function f may be written either in the form _____ or _____.

6. The vertex form of a parabola is given by _____ and its vertex is _____.

7. The graph of the equation $y = -x^2$ is a parabola that opens _____.

8. The x-coordinate of the vertex of $y = ax^2 + bx + c$ is $x =$ _____.

9. Compared to the graph of $y = x^2$, the graph of $y = x^2 + k$ with $k > 0$ is shifted k units _____.
   a. upward   **b.** downward
   c. left   **d.** right

10. Compared to the graph of $y = x^2$, the graph of $y = (x - k)^2$ with $k > 0$ is shifted k units _____.
    a. upward   **b.** downward
    c. left   **d.** right

TABLES AND TRANSLATIONS

Exercises 11–14: Complete the table for each translation of $y = x^2$. State what the translation does.

11.

x	-2	-1	0	1	2
$y = x^2$					
$y = x^2 - 3$					

12.

x	-2	-1	0	1	2
$y = x^2$					
$y = x^2 + 5$					

13.

x					
$y = x^2$	4	1	0	1	4

x					
$y = (x - 3)^2$	4	1	0	1	4

14.

x					
$y = x^2$	16	4	0	4	16

x					
$y = (x + 4)^2$	16	4	0	4	16

GRAPHS OF PARABOLAS

Exercises 15–34: Do the following.
    (a) Sketch a graph of the equation.
    (b) Identify the vertex.
    (c) Compare the graph of $y = f(x)$ to the graph of $y = x^2$. (State any transformations used.)

15. $f(x) = x^2 - 4$ **16.** $f(x) = x^2 - 1$

17. $f(x) = 2x^2 + 1$ **18.** $f(x) = \frac{1}{2}x^2 + 1$

19. $f(x) = (x - 3)^2$ **20.** $f(x) = (x + 1)^2$

21. $f(x) = -x^2$ **22.** $f(x) = -(x + 2)^2$

23. $f(x) = 2 - x^2$ **24.** $f(x) = (x - 1)^2$

25. $f(x) = (x + 2)^2$ **26.** $f(x) = (x - 2)^2 - 3$

27. $f(x) = (x + 1)^2 - 2$ **28.** $f(x) = (x - 3)^2 + 1$

29. $f(x) = (x - 1)^2 + 2$

30. $f(x) = \frac{1}{2}(x + 3)^2 - 3$

31. $f(x) = 2(x - 5)^2 - 4$

32. $f(x) = -3(x + 4)^2 + 5$

33. $f(x) = -\frac{1}{2}(x + 3)^2 + 1$

34. $f(x) = 2(x - 5)^2 + 10$

Exercises 35–38: Compare the graph of $y = f(x)$ to the graph of $y = x^2$. Then sketch a graph of $y = f(x)$ and $y = x^2$ in the same xy-plane.

35. $f(x) = \frac{1}{2}(x - 1)^2 - 2$

36. $f(x) = 2(x + 2)^2 - 1$

37. $f(x) = -2(x + 1)^2 + 3$

38. $f(x) = -\frac{1}{2}(x - 2)^2 + 2$

 Exercises 39 and 40: Graph the equation in a window that shows the vertex and all intercepts.

39. $f(x) = -0.4x^2 + 6x - 10$

40. $f(x) = 3x^2 - 40x + 50$

VERTEX FORM

Exercises 41–44: (Refer to Example 3.) Write the vertex form of a parabola that satisfies the conditions given. Then write the equation in the form $y = ax^2 + bx + c$.

41. Vertex $(3, 4)$ and $a = 3$

42. Vertex $(-1, 3)$ and $a = -5$

43. Vertex $(5, -2)$ and $a = -\frac{1}{2}$

44. Vertex $(-2, -6)$ and $a = \frac{3}{4}$

Exercises 45–48: Write the vertex form of a parabola that satisfies the conditions given. Assume that $a = \pm 1$.

45. Opens upward, vertex $(1, 2)$

46. Opens downward, vertex $(-1, -2)$

47. Opens downward, vertex $(0, -3)$

48. Opens upward, vertex $(5, -4)$

Exercises 49–52: Write the vertex form of the parabola shown in the graph. Assume that $a = \pm 1$.

49.   **50.**

51.   **52.**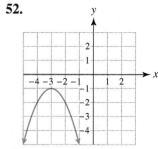

Exercises 53–58: (Refer to Example 4.) Do the following.
(a) Find the vertex on the graph of the equation.
(b) Write the equation in vertex form.

53. $y = 4x^2 - 8x + 5$

54. $y = 3x^2 - 12x + 15$

55. $y = -x^2 - 2x - 3$

56. $y = -x^2 - 4x - 5$

57. $y = -2x^2 - 4x + 1$

58. $y = 2x^2 - 16x + 27$

COMPLETING THE SQUARE

Exercises 59 and 60: Use the given figure to determine what number should be added to the expression to complete the square.

59. $x^2 + 2x$

	x	?
1		
x	x^2	x
	x	1

60. $x^2 + 6x$

	$3x$	?
3		
x	x^2	$3x$
	x	3

Exercises 61–78: (Refer to Example 6.) Write the equation in vertex form. Identify the vertex.

61. $y = x^2 + 2x$ **62.** $y = x^2 + 6x$

63. $y = x^2 - 4x$ **64.** $y = x^2 - 8x$

65. $y = x^2 + 2x - 3$ **66.** $y = x^2 + 4x + 1$

67. $y = x^2 - 4x + 5$ **68.** $y = x^2 - 8x + 10$

69. $y = x^2 + 3x - 2$ **70.** $y = x^2 + 5x - 4$

71. $y = x^2 - 7x + 1$ **72.** $y = x^2 - 3x + 5$

73. $y = 3x^2 + 6x - 1$ **74.** $y = 2x^2 + 4x - 9$

75. $y = 2x^2 - 3x$ **76.** $y = 3x^2 - 7x$

77. $y = -2x^2 - 8x + 5$ **78.** $y = -3x^2 + 6x + 1$

MODELING DATA

Exercises 79–82: Find a value for the constant a so that $f(x) = ax^2$ models the data. If you are uncertain about your value for a, check it by making a table of values.

79.

x	1	2	3
y	2	8	18

80.

x	−2	0	2
y	6	0	6

81.

x	2	4	6	8
y	1.2	4.8	10.8	19.2

82.

x	5	10	15	20
y	17.5	70	157.5	280

Exercises 83–86: Modeling Quadratic Data (Refer to Example 8.) Find a quadratic function expressed in vertex form that models the data in the given table.

83.

x	1	2	3	4
y	−3	−1	5	15

84.

x	−2	−1	0	1	2
y	5	2	−7	−22	−43

85.

x	1980	1990	2000	2010
y	6	55	210	450

86.

x	1990	1995	2000	2005
y	10	60	205	470

87. *Braking Distance* The table lists approximate braking distances D in feet for cars traveling at x miles per hour on dry, level pavement.

x	12	24	36	48
D	12	48	108	192

(a) Make a scatterplot of the data.
(b) Find a function given by $D(x) = ax^2$ that models these data.

88. *Health Care Costs* The table lists approximate *annual* percent increases in the cost of health insurance premiums between 1992 and 2000.

Year	1992	1994	1996	1998	2000
Increase	11%	4%	1%	4%	11%

Source: Kaiser Family Foundation.

(a) Describe what happened to health care costs from 1992 to 2000.
(b) Would a linear function model these data? Explain.
(c) What type of function might model these data? Explain.
(d) What might be a good choice for the vertex? Explain.
(e) Find a quadratic function C expressed in vertex form that models the data. (Answers may vary.)
(f) Graph C and the data.

89. *Sub-Saharan Africa* The table lists actual and projected real gross domestic product (GDP) per capita for selected years in Sub-Saharan Africa.

Year	1980	1995	2010	2025
Real GDP	$1000	$600	$1000	$2200

Source: IMF WEO, Standard Chartered Research.

(a) Describe what happens to the real GDP.
(b) Would a linear function model these data? Explain.
(c) What type of function might model these data? Explain.

(d) What might be a good choice for the vertex? Explain.

(e) Find a quadratic function C expressed in vertex form that models the data. (Answers may vary.)

(f) Graph C and the data.

90. *Tax Theory and Modeling* If a government wants to generate enough revenue from income taxes, then it is important to assess the correct tax rates. On the one hand, if tax rates are too low, then enough revenue may not be generated. On the other hand, if taxes are too high, people may work less and not earn as much money. Again, enough revenue may not be generated. The following parabolic graph illustrates this phenomenon.

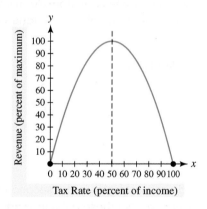

(a) The points (0, 0) and (100, 0) are on this graph. Explain why.

(b) Explain why a linear model is not suitable.

(c) According to *this* graph, what rate maximizes revenue?

91. *U.S. AIDS Deaths* (Refer to Example 8.) The table lists cumulative numbers of AIDS deaths *in thousands* for selected years.

Year	1982	1986	1990	1994
Deaths (thousands)	1	25	123	300

Source: Department of Health and Human Services.

(a) Determine $f(x) = a(x - h)^2 + k$, so that f models these data.

(b) Estimate the number of AIDS deaths in 1992 and compare it to the actual value of 202 thousand.

92. *Head Start Enrollment* The table lists numbers of students *in thousands* enrolled in Head Start for selected years.

Year	1966	1980	1995
Students (thousands)	733	376	750

(a) Determine $f(x) = a(x - h)^2 + k$, so that f models these data.

(b) Estimate Head Start enrollment in 1990 and compare it to the actual value of 541 thousand.

INCREASING AND DECREASING

Exercises 93–96: Use the graph of $y = f(x)$ to determine the intervals where f is increasing and where f is decreasing.

93.

94.

95.

96.

Exercises 97–102: Determine the intervals where $y = f(x)$ is increasing and where it is decreasing.

97. $y = 3x^2 - 4x + 1$ **98.** $y = 2x^2 - 5x - 2$

99. $y = -x^2 - 3x$ **100.** $y = -2x^2 + 3x - 4$

101. $y = 5 - x - 4x^2$ **102.** $y = 3 + x + x^2$

WRITING ABOUT MATHEMATICS

103. Explain how to find the vertex of $y = x^2 + bx + c$ by completing the square.

104. If $f(x) = a(x - h)^2 + k$, explain how the values of a, h, and k affect the graph of $y = f(x)$.

Checking Basic Concepts

1. Graph each quadratic function. Identify the vertex and axis of symmetry.
   (a) $f(x) = x^2 - 2$
   (b) $f(x) = x^2 - 2x - 2$

2. Compare the graph of $y_1 = 2x^2$ to the graph of $y_2 = -\frac{1}{2}x^2$.

3. Find the maximum y-value on the graph of the equation $y = -3x^2 + 12x - 5$.

4. Sketch a graph of $y = f(x)$. Compare this graph to the graph of $y = x^2$.
   (a) $f(x) = (x - 1)^2 + 2$
   (b) $f(x) = -(x + 3)^2$

5. Write the vertex form for each equation.
   (a) $y = x^2 + 14x - 7$
   (b) $y = 4x^2 + 8x - 2$

6.3　Quadratic Equations

Basics of Quadratic Equations ● The Square Root Property ● Completing the Square ● Solving an Equation for a Variable ● Applications of Quadratic Equations

A LOOK INTO MATH ▶

NEW VOCABULARY

☐ Quadratic equation
☐ Square root property

For many years, MySpace was the largest social network in the United States. However, during 2010 the number of unique monthly visitors fell dramatically from 70 million in January 2010 to 45 million in January 2011. Table 6.11 lists the number of unique visitors V to MySpace in millions x months after January 2010.

TABLE 6.11　**Unique MySpace Visitors (millions)**

x (months after Jan. 2010)	0	6	12
V (unique monthly visitors)	70	63	45

Source: comScore.

Decreased　Decreased
7 million　18 million

The number of unique visitors to MySpace decreased faster in the second half of 2010 than it did in the first half, so a linear function will *not* model these data. Instead, these data can be modeled by the *quadratic function*

$$V(x) = -\frac{25}{144}x^2 + 70. \qquad \text{Quadratic function}$$

If we want to determine the month when MySpace had **56** million unique visitors, then we could solve the *quadratic equation*

$$-\frac{25}{144}x^2 + 70 = 56. \qquad \text{Quadratic equation}$$

In this section we learn how to solve this and other quadratic equations. See Exercise 125.

Basics of Quadratic Equations

Any quadratic function f can be represented by $f(x) = ax^2 + bx + c$ with $a \neq 0$. Examples of quadratic functions include

$$f(x) = 2x^2 - 1, \, g(x) = -\tfrac{1}{3}x^2 + 2x, \text{ and } h(x) = x^2 + 2x - 1. \qquad \text{Quadratic functions}$$

Quadratic functions can be used to write quadratic equations. Examples of quadratic equations include

$$2x^2 - 1 = 0, \quad -\tfrac{1}{3}x^2 + 2x = 0, \quad \text{and} \quad x^2 + 2x - 1 = 0. \quad \text{Quadratic equations}$$

READING CHECK

How can you identify a quadratic equation?

QUADRATIC EQUATION

A **quadratic equation** is an equation that can be written as

$$ax^2 + bx + c = 0,$$

where a, b, and c are constants with $a \neq 0$.

Solutions to the quadratic equation $ax^2 + bx + c = 0$ correspond to x-intercepts of the graph of $y = ax^2 + bx + c$. Because the graph of a quadratic function is either $\cup$-shaped or $\cap$-shaped, it can intersect the x-axis zero, one, or two times, as illustrated in Figure 6.42. Hence a quadratic equation can have zero, one, or two real solutions.

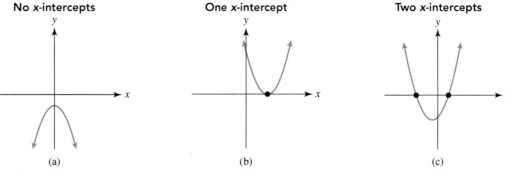

No x-intercepts	One x-intercept	Two x-intercepts
(a)	(b)	(c)

Figure 6.42

NOTE: Some quadratic equations may not have 0 on the right side of the equation, such as $4x^2 = 1$. To solve this quadratic equation graphically, we will sometimes rewrite it as $4x^2 - 1 = 0$ and graph $y = 4x^2 - 1$. Then solutions are x-intercepts, because $y = 0$ on the x-axis.

We have already solved quadratic equations by factoring, graphing, and constructing tables. In the next example we apply these three techniques to quadratic equations that have no real solutions, one real solution, and two real solutions.

EXAMPLE 1   **Solving quadratic equations**

Solve each quadratic equation. Support your results numerically and graphically.
(a) $2x^2 + 1 = 0$ (No real solutions)
(b) $x^2 + 4 = 4x$ (One real solution)
(c) $x^2 - 6x + 8 = 0$ (Two real solutions)

Solution
(a) *Symbolic Solution*

$$
\begin{aligned}
2x^2 + 1 &= 0 \qquad &&\text{Given equation} \\
2x^2 &= -1 \qquad &&\text{Subtract 1 from each side.} \\
x^2 &= -\frac{1}{2} \qquad &&\text{Divide each side by 2.}
\end{aligned}
$$

This equation has no real-number solutions because $x^2 \geq 0$ for all real numbers x.

Numerical and Graphical Solution The points in Table 6.12 for $y = 2x^2 + 1$ are plotted in Figure 6.43 and connected with a parabolic graph. The graph of $y = 2x^2 + 1$ has no x-intercepts, indicating that there are no real solutions.

TABLE 6.12

For all x, $y \neq 0$, so there are no solutions.

x	y
-2	9
-1	3
0	1
1	3
2	9

Figure 6.43

(b) *Symbolic Solution* Next, we solve $x^2 + 4 = 4x$.

$$x^2 + 4 = 4x \qquad \text{Given equation}$$
$$x^2 - 4x + 4 = 0 \qquad \text{Subtract } 4x \text{ from each side.}$$
$$(x - 2)(x - 2) = 0 \qquad \text{Factor.}$$
$$x - 2 = 0 \quad \text{or} \quad x - 2 = 0 \qquad \text{Zero-product property}$$
$$x = 2 \qquad \text{There is one solution.}$$

Numerical and Graphical Solution Because the given quadratic equation is equivalent to $x^2 - 4x + 4 = 0$, we let $y = x^2 - 4x + 4$. The points in Table 6.13 are plotted in Figure 6.44 and connected with a parabolic graph. The graph of $y = x^2 - 4x + 4$ has one x-intercept, **2**. Note that in Table 6.13, $y = 0$ when $x = 2$, indicating that the equation has one solution.

TABLE 6.13

One solution: **2**

x	y
0	4
1	1
2	**0**
3	1
4	4

Figure 6.44

(c) *Symbolic Solution* Next, we solve $x^2 - 6x + 8 = 0$.

$$x^2 - 6x + 8 = 0 \qquad \text{Given equation}$$
$$(x - 2)(x - 4) = 0 \qquad \text{Factor.}$$
$$x - 2 = 0 \quad \text{or} \quad x - 4 = 0 \qquad \text{Zero-product property}$$
$$x = 2 \quad \text{or} \quad x = 4 \qquad \text{There are two solutions.}$$

Numerical and Graphical Solution The points in Table 6.14 for $y = x^2 - 6x + 8$ are plotted in Figure 6.45 and connected with a parabolic graph. The graph of

$y = x^2 - 6x + 8$ has two x-intercepts, **2** and **4**, indicating two solutions. Note that in Table 6.14 $y = \mathbf{0}$ when $x = \mathbf{2}$ or $x = \mathbf{4}$.

TABLE 6.14

x	y
0	8
1	3
2	**0**
3	−1
4	**0**
5	3
6	8

Two solutions: **2** and **4**

Two Solutions

Two x-intercepts: **2** and **4**, so there are two solutions: **2** and **4**.

$y = x^2 - 6x + 8$

Figure 6.45

Now Try Exercises 29, 37, 39

READING CHECK

How many solutions can a quadratic equation have?

The Square Root Property

The **square root property** is used to solve quadratic equations that have no x-terms. The following is an example of the square root property.

$$x^2 = 25 \quad \text{is equivalent to} \quad x = \pm 5.$$

The equation $x = \pm 5$ (read "x equals plus or minus 5") indicates that either $x = 5$ or $x = -5$. Each value is a solution because $(5)^2 = 25$ and $(-5)^2 = 25$.

We can derive this result in general for $k \geq 0$.

$$x^2 = k \qquad \text{Given quadratic equation}$$
$$\sqrt{x^2} = \sqrt{k} \qquad \text{Take the square root of each side.}$$
$$|x| = \sqrt{k} \qquad \sqrt{x^2} = |x| \text{ for all } x.$$
$$x = \pm \sqrt{k} \qquad |x| = b \text{ implies } x = \pm b, b \geq 0.$$

This result is summarized by the *square root property*.

SQUARE ROOT PROPERTY

Let k be a nonnegative number. Then the solutions to the equation

$$x^2 = k$$

are given by $x = \pm \sqrt{k}$. If $k < 0$, then this equation has no real solutions.

Before applying the square root property in the next two examples, we review a quotient property of square roots. If a and b are positive numbers, then

$$\sqrt{\frac{a}{b}} = \frac{\sqrt{a}}{\sqrt{b}}.$$

For example, $\sqrt{\frac{25}{36}} = \frac{\sqrt{25}}{\sqrt{36}} = \frac{5}{6}$.

EXAMPLE 2 | **Using the square root property**

Solve each equation.
(a) $x^2 = 7$ **(b)** $16x^2 - 9 = 0$ **(c)** $(x - 4)^2 = 25$

Solution
(a) $x^2 = 7$ is equivalent to $x = \pm \sqrt{7}$ by the square root property. The solutions are $\sqrt{7}$ and $-\sqrt{7}$.

(b)

$16x^2 - 9 = 0$	Given equation
$16x^2 = 9$	Add 9 to each side.
$x^2 = \dfrac{9}{16}$	Divide each side by 16.
$x = \pm \sqrt{\dfrac{9}{16}}$	Square root property
$x = \pm \dfrac{3}{4}$	Simplify.

READING CHECK

When do you use the square root property to solve an equation?

The solutions are $\frac{3}{4}$ and $-\frac{3}{4}$.

(c)

$(x - 4)^2 = 25$	Given equation
$(x - 4) = \pm \sqrt{25}$	Square root property
$x - 4 = \pm 5$	Simplify.
$x = 4 \pm 5$	Add 4 to each side.
$x = 9$ or $x = -1$	Evaluate $4 + 5$ and $4 - 5$.

The solutions are 9 and -1.

▌ Now Try Exercises 51, 53, 57

▶ **REAL-WORLD CONNECTION** If an object is dropped from a height of h feet, its distance d above the ground after t seconds is given by

$$d(t) = h - 16t^2.$$

This formula can be used to estimate the time it takes for a falling object to hit the ground.

EXAMPLE 3 | **Modeling a falling object**

A toy falls 30 feet from a window. How long does the toy take to hit the ground?

Solution
The height h of the window above the ground is 30 feet, so let $d(t) = 30 - 16t^2$. The toy strikes the ground when the distance d above the ground equals 0.

$30 - 16t^2 = 0$	Equation to solve for t
$-16t^2 = -30$	Subtract 30 from each side.
$t^2 = \dfrac{30}{16}$	Divide each side by -16.
$t = \pm \sqrt{\dfrac{30}{16}}$	Square root property
$t = \pm \dfrac{\sqrt{30}}{4}$	Simplify.

Time cannot be negative in this problem, so the appropriate solution is $t = \frac{\sqrt{30}}{4} \approx 1.4$. The toy hits the ground after about 1.4 seconds.

▌ Now Try Exercise 115

Completing the Square

In Section 6.2 we used the *method of completing the square* to find the vertex of a parabola. This method can also be used to solve quadratic equations. Because

$$x^2 + bx + \left(\frac{b}{2}\right)^2 = \left(x + \frac{b}{2}\right)^2,$$

we can solve a quadratic equation in the form $x^2 + bx = d$, where b and d are constants, by adding $\left(\frac{b}{2}\right)^2$ to each side and then factoring the resulting perfect square trinomial.

In the equation $x^2 + 6x = 7$ we have $b = 6$, so we add $\left(\frac{6}{2}\right)^2 = 9$ to each side.

$x^2 + 6x = 7$	Given equation
$x^2 + 6x + 9 = 7 + 9$	Add 9 to each side.
$(x + 3)^2 = 16$	Perfect square trinomial
$x + 3 = \pm 4$	Square root property
$x = -3 \pm 4$	Add -3 to each side.
$x = 1$ or $x = -7$	Simplify $-3 + 4$ and $-3 - 4$.

The solutions are 1 and -7. Note that after completing the square, the left side of the equation is a perfect square trinomial. We show how to create one in the next example.

READING CHECK

Use the figure to *complete the square* for $x^2 + 6x$.

EXAMPLE 4 **Creating a perfect square trinomial**

Find the term that should be added to $x^2 - 10x$ to form a perfect square trinomial.

Solution
The coefficient of the x-term is -10, so we let $b = -10$. To complete the square we divide b by 2 and then square the result.

$$\left(\frac{b}{2}\right)^2 = \left(\frac{-10}{2}\right)^2 = 25$$

If we add 25 to $x^2 - 10x$, a perfect square trinomial is formed.

$$x^2 - 10x + 25 = (x - 5)^2$$

Now Try Exercise 67

EXAMPLE 5 **Completing the square when the leading coefficient is 1**

Solve the equation $x^2 - 4x + 2 = 0$.

Solution
Start by writing the equation in the form $x^2 + bx = d$.

$x^2 - 4x + 2 = 0$	Given equation
$x^2 - 4x = -2$	Subtract 2.
$x^2 - 4x + 4 = -2 + 4$	Add $\left(\frac{b}{2}\right)^2 = \left(\frac{-4}{2}\right)^2 = 4$.
$(x - 2)^2 = 2$	Perfect square trinomial; add.
$x - 2 = \pm\sqrt{2}$	Square root property
$x = 2 \pm \sqrt{2}$	Add 2.

The solutions are $2 + \sqrt{2} \approx 3.41$ and $2 - \sqrt{2} \approx 0.59$.

Now Try Exercise 73

EXAMPLE 6   **Completing the square when the leading coefficient is not 1**

Solve the equation $2x^2 + 7x - 5 = 0$.

Solution

Start by writing the equation in the form $x^2 + bx = d$. That is, add 5 to each side and then divide each side by 2 so that the leading coefficient of the x^2-term becomes 1.

$$2x^2 + 7x - 5 = 0 \qquad \text{Given equation}$$

$$2x^2 + 7x = 5 \qquad \text{Add 5 to each side.}$$

$$x^2 + \frac{7}{2}x = \frac{5}{2} \qquad \text{Divide each side by 2.}$$

$$x^2 + \frac{7}{2}x + \frac{49}{16} = \frac{5}{2} + \frac{49}{16} \qquad \text{Add } \left(\frac{b}{2}\right)^2 = \left(\frac{7}{4}\right)^2 = \frac{49}{16}.$$

$$\left(x + \frac{7}{4}\right)^2 = \frac{89}{16} \qquad \text{Perfect square trinomial; add.}$$

$$x + \frac{7}{4} = \pm \frac{\sqrt{89}}{4} \qquad \text{Square root property}$$

$$x = -\frac{7}{4} \pm \frac{\sqrt{89}}{4} \qquad \text{Add } -\frac{7}{4}.$$

$$x = \frac{-7 \pm \sqrt{89}}{4} \qquad \text{Combine fractions.}$$

The solutions are $\frac{-7 + \sqrt{89}}{4} \approx 0.61$ and $\frac{-7 - \sqrt{89}}{4} \approx -4.1$.

Now Try Exercise 81

CRITICAL THINKING

What happens if you try to solve

$$2x^2 - 13 = 1$$

by completing the square? What method could you use to solve this problem?

Solving an Equation for a Variable

We often need to solve an equation or formula for a variable. For example, the formula $V = \frac{1}{3}\pi r^2 h$ calculates the volume of the cone shown in Figure 6.46. Let's say that we know the volume V is 120 cubic inches and the height h is 15 inches. We can then find the radius of the cone by solving the equation for r.

Figure 6.46

$$V = \frac{1}{3}\pi r^2 h \qquad \text{Solve the equation for } r.$$

$$3V = \pi r^2 h \qquad \text{Multiply by 3.}$$

$$\frac{3V}{\pi} = r^2 h \qquad \text{Divide by } \pi.$$

$$\frac{3V}{\pi h} = r^2 \qquad \text{Divide by } h.$$

$$r = \pm \sqrt{\frac{3V}{\pi h}} \qquad \text{Square root property; rewrite.}$$

Because $r \geq 0$, we use the positive or *principal square root*. Thus for $V = 120$ cubic inches and $h = 15$ inches,

$$r = \sqrt{\frac{3(120)}{\pi(15)}} = \sqrt{\frac{24}{\pi}} \approx 2.8 \text{ inches.}$$

EXAMPLE 7 **Solving equations for variables**

Solve each equation for the specified variable.
(a) $s = -\frac{1}{2}gt^2 + h$ for t **(b)** $d^2 = x^2 + y^2$ for y

Solution

(a) Begin by subtracting h from each side of the equation.

$$s = -\frac{1}{2}gt^2 + h \qquad \text{Solve the equation for } t.$$

$$s - h = -\frac{1}{2}gt^2 \qquad \text{Subtract } h.$$

$$-2(s - h) = gt^2 \qquad \text{Multiply by } -2.$$

$$\frac{2h - 2s}{g} = t^2 \qquad \text{Divide by } g; \text{ simplify.}$$

$$t = \pm\sqrt{\frac{2h - 2s}{g}} \qquad \text{Square root property; rewrite.}$$

(b) Begin by subtracting x^2 from each side of the equation.

$$d^2 = x^2 + y^2 \qquad \text{Solve the equation for } y.$$

$$d^2 - x^2 = y^2 \qquad \text{Subtract } x^2.$$

$$y = \pm\sqrt{d^2 - x^2} \qquad \text{Square root property; rewrite.}$$

Now Try Exercises 105, 107

Applications of Quadratic Equations

▶ **REAL-WORLD CONNECTION** In Section 6.2 we modeled curves on airport taxiways by using $R(x) = \frac{1}{2}x^2$. In this formula x represented the airplane's speed in miles per hour, and R represented the radius of the curve in feet. This formula may be used to determine the speed limit for a curve with a radius of **650** feet by solving the *quadratic equation*

$$\frac{1}{2}x^2 = 650.$$

In the next example, we solve this quadratic equation. *(Source: FAA.)*

EXAMPLE 8 **Finding a safe speed limit**

Solve $\frac{1}{2}x^2 = 650$ and interpret any solutions.

Solution
Use the square root property to solve this problem.

$$\frac{1}{2}x^2 = 650 \qquad \text{Given equation}$$

$$x^2 = 1300 \qquad \text{Multiply by 2.}$$

$$x = \pm\sqrt{1300} \qquad \text{Square root property}$$

The solutions are $\sqrt{1300} \approx 36$ and $-\sqrt{1300} \approx -36$. The solution of $x \approx 36$ indicates that a safe speed limit for a curve with a radius of 650 feet is about 36 miles per hour. (The negative solution has no physical meaning in this problem.)

Now Try Exercise 113

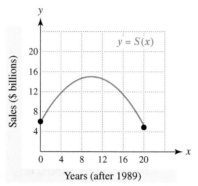

▶ **REAL-WORLD CONNECTION** From 1989 to 2009 there was a dramatic increase in compact disc and tape sales and then a dramatic decrease. Their global music sales S in billions of dollars x years after 1989 are modeled by

$$S(x) = -0.095x^2 + 1.85x + 6.$$

A graph of $S(x) = -0.095x^2 + 1.85x + 6$ is shown in Figure 6.47. (*Source:* RIAA, Bain Analysis.)

Global Music Sales from CDs and Tapes

Figure 6.47

When were sales equal to $12 billion? Because the graph is parabolic, it appears that there are two answers to the question: about 4 years and about 15 years after 1989. In the next example, we use graphical and numerical methods to find these years. In Section 6.4 (Exercise 113), you are asked to answer this question symbolically.

EXAMPLE 9 ▶ **Modeling global CD and tape sales**

Use each method to determine the years when global sales of CDs and tapes were $12 billion.
(a) Graphical   **(b)** Numerical

Solution

(a) *Graphical Solution* Graph $y_1 = -0.095x^2 + 1.85x + 6$ and $y_2 = 12$, as shown in Figures 6.48(a) and (b). Their graphs intersect near the points (4.11, 12) and (15.36, 12). Because x is years *after* 1989, sales were $12 billion dollars in about 1993 (1989 + 4) and about 2004 (1989 + 15).

CALCULATOR HELP

To find a point of intersection, see Appendix A (page AP-6).

Determining When Sales Were $12 Billion

Figure 6.48

(b) *Numerical Solution* Make a table of $y_1 = -0.095x^2 + 1.85x + 6$ and $y_2 = 12$, as shown in Figure 6.48(c). When $x = 4$, y_1 is approximately 12. Thus sales were $12 billion around 1993. If we were to scroll down in the table further, we would see that sales also equal $12 billion when $x \approx 15$, or in 2004. The graphical and numerical solutions agree.

Now Try Exercise 117

6.3 Putting It All Together

Quadratic equations can have no real solutions, one real solution, or two real solutions. Symbolic techniques for solving quadratic equations include factoring, the square root property, and completing the square. We discussed factoring in Chapter 3, so the following table summarizes only the square root property and the method of completing the square.

TECHNIQUE	DESCRIPTION	EXAMPLES
Square Root Property	If $k \geq 0$, the solutions to the equation $x^2 = k$ are $\pm \sqrt{k}$.	$x^2 = 100$ is equivalent to $x = \pm 10$ and $x^2 = 13$ is equivalent to $x = \pm \sqrt{13}$. $x^2 = -2$ has no real solutions.
Method of Completing the Square	To solve an equation in the form $x^2 + bx = d$, add $\left(\frac{b}{2}\right)^2$ to each side of the equation. Factor the resulting perfect square trinomial and solve for x by applying the square root property.	To solve $x^2 + 8x = 3$, add $\left(\frac{8}{2}\right)^2 = 16$ to each side. $x^2 + 8x + 16 = 3 + 16$ Add 16. $(x + 4)^2 = 19$ Perfect square trinomial $x + 4 = \pm \sqrt{19}$ Square root property $x = -4 \pm \sqrt{19}$ Add -4.

6.3 Exercises

CONCEPTS AND VOCABULARY

1. Give an example of a quadratic equation. How many real solutions can a quadratic equation have?

2. Is a quadratic equation a linear equation or a nonlinear equation?

3. Name three symbolic methods that can be used to solve a quadratic equation.

4. Sketch a graph of a quadratic function that has two x-intercepts and opens downward.

5. Sketch a graph of a quadratic function that has no x-intercepts and opens upward.

6. If the graph of $y = ax^2 + bx + c$ intersects the x-axis twice, how many solutions does the equation $ax^2 + bx + c = 0$ have? Explain.

7. Solve $x^2 = 64$. What property did you use?

8. To solve $x^2 + bx = 6$ by completing the square, what value should be added to each side of the equation?

Exercises 9–16: Is the given equation quadratic?

9. $x^2 - 3x + 1 = 0$

10. $2x^2 - 3 = 0$

11. $3x + 1 = 0$

12. $x^3 - 3x^2 + x = 0$

13. $-3x^2 + x = 16$

14. $x^2 - 1 = 4x$

15. $x^2 = \sqrt{x} + 1$

16. $\dfrac{1}{x - 1} = 5$

SOLVING QUADRATIC EQUATIONS

Exercises 17–20: Approximate to the nearest hundredth.

17. (a) $1 \pm \sqrt{7}$ (b) $-2 \pm \sqrt{11}$

18. (a) $\pm \dfrac{\sqrt{3}}{2}$ (b) $\pm \dfrac{2\sqrt{5}}{7}$

19. (a) $\dfrac{3 \pm \sqrt{13}}{5}$ (b) $\dfrac{-5 \pm \sqrt{6}}{9}$

20. (a) $\dfrac{2}{5} \pm \dfrac{\sqrt{5}}{5}$ (b) $-\dfrac{3}{7} \pm \dfrac{\sqrt{3}}{7}$

Exercises 21–24: A graph of $y = ax^2 + bx + c$ is given. Use this graph to solve $ax^2 + bx + c = 0$, if possible.

21.

22.

23.

24.

Exercises 25–28: A table of $y = ax^2 + bx + c$ is given. Use this table to solve $ax^2 + bx + c = 0$.

25.

X	Y1
-3	6
-2	0
-1	-4
0	-6
1	-6
2	-4
3	0

Y1≣X^2−X−6

26.

X	Y1
-6	0
-4	-16
-2	-24
0	-24
2	-16
4	0
6	24

Y1≣X^2+2X−24

27.

X	Y1
-2	9
-1.5	4
-1	1
-.5	0
0	1
.5	4
1	9

Y1≣4X^2+4X+1

28.

X	Y1
-4	-2.5
-3	0
-2	1.5
-1	2
0	1.5
1	0
2	-2.5

Y1≣−X^2/2−X+3/2

Exercises 29–40: Use each method to solve the equation.

(a) *Symbolic* **(b)** *Graphical* **(c)** *Numerical*

29. $x^2 - 4x - 5 = 0$ **30.** $x^2 - x - 6 = 0$

31. $x^2 + 2x = 3$ **32.** $x^2 + 4x = 5$

33. $x^2 = 9$ **34.** $x^2 = 4$

35. $4x^2 - 4x = 3$ **36.** $2x^2 + x = 1$

37. $x^2 + 2x = -1$ **38.** $4x^2 - 4x + 1 = 0$

39. $x^2 + 2 = 0$ **40.** $-4x^2 - 1 = 2$

Exercises 41–50: Solve by factoring.

41. $x^2 + 2x - 35 = 0$ **42.** $2x^2 - 7x + 3 = 0$

43. $6x^2 - x - 1 = 0$ **44.** $x^2 + 4x + 6 = -3x$

45. $4x^2 + 13x + 9 = x$ **46.** $9x^2 + 4 = 12x$

47. $25x^2 - 350 = 125x$ **48.** $20x^2 + 150 = 130x$

49. $2(5x^2 + 9) = 27x$ **50.** $15(3x^2 + x) = 10$

Exercises 51–62: Use the square root property to solve.

51. $x^2 = 144$ **52.** $4x^2 - 5 = 0$

53. $5x^2 - 64 = 0$ **54.** $3x^2 = 7$

55. $(x + 1)^2 = 25$ **56.** $(x + 4)^2 = 9$

57. $(x - 1)^2 = 64$ **58.** $(x - 3)^2 = 0$

59. $(2x - 1)^2 = 5$ **60.** $(5x + 3)^2 = 7$

61. $10(x - 5)^2 = 50$ **62.** $7(3x + 1)^2 = 14$

COMPLETING THE SQUARE

Exercises 63–66: To solve by completing the square, what value should you add to each side of the equation?

63. $x^2 + 4x = -3$ **64.** $x^2 - 6x = 4$

65. $x^2 - 5x = 4$ **66.** $x^2 + 3x = 1$

Exercises 67–70: (Refer to Example 4.) Find the term that should be added to the expression to form a perfect square trinomial. Write the resulting perfect square trinomial in factored form.

67. $x^2 - 8x$ **68.** $x^2 - 5x$

69. $x^2 + 9x$ **70.** $x^2 + x$

Exercises 71–86: Solve by completing the square.

71. $x^2 - 2x = 24$ **72.** $x^2 - 2x + \frac{1}{2} = 0$

73. $x^2 + 6x - 2 = 0$ **74.** $x^2 - 16x = 5$

75. $x^2 - 3x = 5$ **76.** $x^2 + 5x = 2$

77. $x^2 - 5x + 1 = 0$ **78.** $x^2 - 9x + 7 = 0$

79. $x^2 - 4 = 2x$ **80.** $x^2 + 1 = 7x$

81. $2x^2 - 3x = 4$ **82.** $3x^2 + 6x - 5 = 0$

83. $4x^2 - 8x - 7 = 0$ **84.** $25x^2 - 20x - 1 = 0$

85. $36x^2 + 18x + 1 = 0$ **86.** $12x^2 + 8x - 2 = 0$

Exercises 87–96: Solve by any method.

87. $3x^2 + 12x = 36$ **88.** $6x^2 + 9x = 27$

89. $x^2 + 4x = -2$ **90.** $x^2 + 6x + 3 = 0$

91. $3x^2 - 4 = 2$ **92.** $-2x^2 + 3 = 1$

93. $-6x^2 + 70 = 16x$

94. $-15x^2 + 25x + 10 = 0$

95. $-3x(x - 8) = 6$ **96.** $-2x(4 - x) = 8$

Exercises 97 and 98: Thinking Generally *Solve for x. Assume a and c are positive.*

97. $ax^2 - c = 0$ **98.** $ax^2 + bx = 0$

SOLVING EQUATIONS BY MORE THAN ONE METHOD

Exercises 99–104: Solve the quadratic equation

  (a) symbolically,
  (b) graphically, and
  (c) numerically.

99. $x^2 - 3x - 18 = 0$ **100.** $\frac{1}{2}x^2 + 2x - 6 = 0$

101. $x^2 - 8x + 15 = 0$ **102.** $2x^2 + 3 = 7x$

103. $4(x^2 + 35) = 48x$ **104.** $4x(2 - x) = -5$

SOLVING AN EQUATION FOR A VARIABLE

Exercises 105–112: Solve for the specified variable.

105. $x = y^2 - 1$ for y

106. $x = 9y^2$ for y **107.** $K = \frac{1}{2}mv^2$ for v

108. $c^2 = a^2 + b^2$ for b

109. $E = \dfrac{k}{r^2}$ for r **110.** $W = I^2R$ for I

111. $LC = \dfrac{1}{(2\pi f)^2}$ for f

112. $F = \dfrac{KmM}{r^2}$ for r

APPLICATIONS

113. *Safe Curve Speed* (Refer to Example 8.) Find a safe speed limit x for an airport taxiway curve with the given radius R by using $R = \frac{1}{2}x^2$.
  (a) $R = 450$ feet   **(b)** $R = 800$ feet

114. *Braking Distance* The braking distance y in feet that it takes for a car to stop on wet, level pavement can be estimated by $y = \frac{1}{9}x^2$, where x is the speed of the car in miles per hour. Find the speed associated with each braking distance. (*Source*: L. Haefner, *Introduction to Transportation Systems.*)
  (a) 25 feet   **(b)** 361 feet   **(c)** 784 feet

115. *Falling Object* (Refer to Example 3.) How long does it take for a toy to hit the ground if it is dropped out of a window 60 feet above the ground? Does it take twice as long as it takes to fall from a window 30 feet above the ground?

116. *Falling Object* If a metal ball is thrown *downward* with an initial velocity of 22 feet per second (15 mph) from a 100-foot water tower, its height h in feet above the ground after t seconds is modeled by

$$h(t) = -16t^2 - 22t + 100.$$

  (a) Determine symbolically when the height of the ball is 62 feet.
  (b) Support your result in part (a) either graphically or numerically.
  (c) If the ball is thrown *upward* at 22 feet per second, then its height is given by

$$h(t) = -16t^2 + 22t + 100.$$

  Determine when the height of the ball is 80 feet.

Exercises 117 and 118: Television Size (Refer to the introduction of this chapter.) The size S of the television screen recommended for a person who sits x feet from the screen ($6 \le x \le 15$) is given by

$$S(x) = -0.227x^2 + 8.155x - 8.8.$$

If a person buys a television set with a size S screen, how far from the screen should the person sit?

117. $S = 42$ inches   **118.** $S = 50$ inches

119. *Distance* Two athletes start jogging at the same time. One jogs north at 6 miles per hour while the second jogs east at 8 miles per hour. After how long are the two athletes 20 miles apart?

120. *Geometry* A triangle has an area of 35 square inches, and its base is 3 inches more than its height. Find the base and height of the triangle.

121. *Construction* A rectangular plot of land has an area of 520 square feet and is 6 feet longer than it is wide.
(a) Write a quadratic equation in the form $ax^2 + bx + c = 0$, whose solution gives the width of the rectangular plot of land.
(b) Solve the equation.

122. *Modeling Motion* The height y in feet of a tennis ball after x seconds is shown in the graph. Estimate when the ball was 25 feet above the ground.

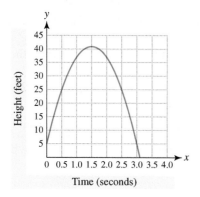

Time (seconds)

123. *Seedling Growth* (Refer to Exercise 100, Section 6.1.) The heights of melon seedlings grown at different temperatures are shown in the following graph. At what temperatures were the heights of the seedlings about 22 centimeters? (*Source:* R. Pearl, "The growth of *Cucumis melo* seedlings at different temperatures.")

Temperature (°C)

124. *U.S. Population* The three tables show the population of the United States in millions from 1800 through 2010 for selected years.

Year	1800	1820	1840	1860
Population	5	10	17	31

Year	1880	1900	1920	1940
Population	50	76	106	132

Year	1960	1980	2000	2010
Population	179	226	269	308

Source: U.S. Census Bureau.

(a) Without plotting the data, how do you know that the data are nonlinear?
(b) These data are modeled (approximately) by

$$f(x) = 0.0066(x - 1800)^2 + 5.$$

Find the vertex of the graph of f and interpret it.
(c) Estimate when the U.S. population reached 85 million.

125. *MySpace Visitors* (Refer to A Look Into Math at the beginning of this section.) The number of unique monthly visitors V in millions to MySpace x months after January 2010 can be modeled by

$$V(x) = -\frac{25}{144}x^2 + 70.$$

Determine the month when this number of visitors was 56 million.

126. *Federal Debt* The federal debt D in trillions of dollars held by foreign and international investors x years after 1970 can be modeled by

$$D(x) = \frac{1}{320}x^2 - \frac{3}{80}x,$$

where $15 \leq x \leq 40$.
(a) Evaluate $D(40)$ and interpret the result.
(b) Determine the year when the federal debt held by foreign and international investors first reached $500 billion ($0.5 trillion).

WRITING ABOUT MATHEMATICS

127. Suppose that you are asked to solve

$$ax^2 + bx + c = 0.$$

Explain how the graph of $y = ax^2 + bx + c$ can be used to find any real solutions to the equation.

128. Explain why a quadratic equation could not have more than two solutions. (*Hint:* Consider the graph of $y = ax^2 + bx + c$.)

Group Activity   Working With Real Data

Directions: Form a group of 2 to 4 people. Select someone to record the group's responses for this activity. All members of the group should work cooperatively to answer the questions. If your instructor asks for the results, each member of the group should be prepared to respond.

Personal Consumption Although there was an economic downturn in 2008, personal consumption has grown overall. Table 6.15 lists (approximate) personal consumption C in dollars for selected years x.

TABLE 6.15 **Personal Consumption (dollars)**

x	1959	1982	1990	1998	2009
C	$300	$2000	$4000	$6000	$10,000

Source: BEA.

 (a) Make a scatterplot of these data. Use the window [1955, 2010, 10] by [0, 12000, 2000].

(b) Find a quadratic function given by

$$C(x) = a(x - 1959)^2 + k$$

that models the data. Graph C and the data. (Answers may vary.)

(c) Estimate when personal consumption was $8000. Compare your answer to the actual value of 2005.

(d) Use your function C to predict consumption in 2020 to the nearest thousand dollars.

6.4   The Quadratic Formula

Solving Quadratic Equations ● The Discriminant ● Quadratic Equations Having Complex Solutions

A LOOK INTO MATH ▶

To model the stopping distance of a car, highway engineers compute two quantities. The first quantity is the *reaction distance*, which is the distance a car travels from the time a driver first recognizes a hazard until the brakes are applied. The second quantity is *braking distance*, which is the distance a car travels after a driver applies the brakes. *Stopping distance* equals the sum of the reaction distance and the braking distance. If a car is traveling x miles per hour, highway engineers estimate the reaction distance in feet as $\frac{11}{3}x$ and the braking distance in feet as $\frac{1}{9}x^2$. See Figure 6.49. (*Source:* L. Haefner, *Introduction to Transportation Systems.*)

NEW VOCABULARY

☐ Quadratic formula
☐ Discriminant

Figure 6.49 Stopping Distance

To estimate the total stopping distance d in feet, add the two expressions to obtain

$$d(x) = \frac{1}{9}x^2 + \frac{11}{3}x.$$

If a car's headlights don't illuminate the road beyond **500** feet, a safe nighttime speed limit x for the car can be determined by solving the quadratic equation

$$\frac{1}{9}x^2 \quad + \quad \frac{11}{3}x \quad = \quad 500. \qquad \text{Quadratic equation}$$

Braking Distance + Reaction Distance = Stopping Distance

In this section we learn how to solve this equation with the quadratic formula. (See Example 4 and Exercises 109–112.)

Solving Quadratic Equations

Thus far, we have solved quadratic equations by factoring, the square root property, and completing the square. In this subsection, we derive a formula that can be used to solve *any* quadratic equation. To do this, we solve the general quadratic equation $ax^2 + bx + c = 0$ for x by completing the square. The resulting formula is called the **quadratic formula**. We assume that $a > 0$ and derive this formula as follows.

$$ax^2 + bx + c = 0 \qquad \text{Quadratic equation}$$

$$ax^2 + bx = -c \qquad \text{Subtract } c.$$

$$x^2 + \frac{b}{a}x = -\frac{c}{a} \qquad \text{Divide by } a.$$

$$x^2 + \frac{b}{a}x + \frac{b^2}{4a^2} = -\frac{c}{a} + \frac{b^2}{4a^2} \qquad \text{Add } \left(\frac{b/a}{2}\right)^2 = \frac{b^2}{4a^2}.$$

$$\left(x + \frac{b}{2a}\right)^2 = -\frac{c}{a} + \frac{b^2}{4a^2} \qquad \text{Perfect square trinomial}$$

$$\left(x + \frac{b}{2a}\right)^2 = -\frac{c \cdot 4a}{a \cdot 4a} + \frac{b^2}{4a^2} \qquad \text{Multiply } -\frac{c}{a} \text{ by } \frac{4a}{4a}.$$

$$\left(x + \frac{b}{2a}\right)^2 = -\frac{4ac}{4a^2} + \frac{b^2}{4a^2} \qquad \text{Simplify.}$$

$$\left(x + \frac{b}{2a}\right)^2 = \frac{-4ac + b^2}{4a^2} \qquad \text{Add fractions.}$$

$$\left(x + \frac{b}{2a}\right)^2 = \frac{b^2 - 4ac}{4a^2} \qquad \text{Rewrite.}$$

$$x + \frac{b}{2a} = \pm\sqrt{\frac{b^2 - 4ac}{4a^2}} \qquad \text{Square root property}$$

$$x = -\frac{b}{2a} \pm \sqrt{\frac{b^2 - 4ac}{4a^2}} \qquad \text{Add } -\frac{b}{2a}.$$

$$x = -\frac{b}{2a} \pm \frac{\sqrt{b^2 - 4ac}}{2a} \qquad \text{Property of square roots}$$

$$x = \frac{-b \pm \sqrt{b^2 - 4ac}}{2a} \qquad \text{Combine fractions.}$$

QUADRATIC FORMULA

The solutions to $ax^2 + bx + c = 0$ with $a \neq 0$ are given by

$$x = \frac{-b \pm \sqrt{b^2 - 4ac}}{2a}.$$

NOTE: The quadratic formula can be used to solve *any* quadratic equation. It always "works."

EXAMPLE 1 **Solving a quadratic equation having two solutions**

Solve the equation $2x^2 - 3x - 1 = 0$. Support your results graphically.

Solution

Symbolic Solution Let $a = 2, b = -3$, and $c = -1$ in $2x^2 - 3x - 1 = 0$.

$$x = \frac{-b \pm \sqrt{b^2 - 4ac}}{2a} \qquad \text{Quadratic formula}$$

$$x = \frac{-(-3) \pm \sqrt{(-3)^2 - 4(2)(-1)}}{2(2)} \qquad \text{Substitute for } a, b, \text{ and } c.$$

$$x = \frac{3 \pm \sqrt{17}}{4} \qquad \text{Simplify.}$$

The solutions are $\frac{3 + \sqrt{17}}{4} \approx 1.78$ and $\frac{3 - \sqrt{17}}{4} \approx -0.28$.

Graphical Solution The graph of $y = 2x^2 - 3x - 1$ is shown in Figure 6.50. Note that the two x-intercepts correspond to the two solutions for $2x^2 - 3x - 1 = 0$. Estimating from this graph, we see that the solutions are approximately -0.25 and 1.75, which supports our symbolic solution. (You could also use a graphing calculator to find the x-intercepts.)

Two Solutions

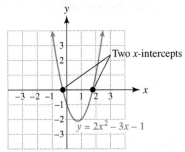

Figure 6.50

Now Try Exercise 9

CRITICAL THINKING

Use the equation and results from Example 1 to evaluate each expression mentally.

$$2\left(\frac{3 + \sqrt{17}}{4}\right)^2 - 3\left(\frac{3 + \sqrt{17}}{4}\right) - 1 \quad \text{and} \quad 2\left(\frac{3 - \sqrt{17}}{4}\right)^2 - 3\left(\frac{3 - \sqrt{17}}{4}\right) - 1 \quad \text{Both equal 0.}$$

EXAMPLE 2   **Solving a quadratic equation having one solution**

Solve the equation $25x^2 + 20x + 4 = 0$. Support your result graphically.

Solution

Symbolic Solution Let $a = 25, b = 20$, and $c = 4$ in $25x^2 + 20x + 4 = 0$.

$$x = \frac{-b \pm \sqrt{b^2 - 4ac}}{2a} \qquad \text{Quadratic formula}$$

$$= \frac{-20 \pm \sqrt{20^2 - 4(25)(4)}}{2(25)} \qquad \text{Substitute for } a, b, \text{ and } c.$$

$$= \frac{-20 \pm \sqrt{0}}{50} \qquad \text{Simplify.}$$

$$= \frac{-20}{50} = -0.4 \qquad \sqrt{0} = 0$$

There is one solution, -0.4.

Graphical Solution The graph of $y = 25x^2 + 20x + 4$ is shown in Figure 6.51. Note that the one x-intercept, -0.4, corresponds to the solution to $25x^2 + 20x + 4 = 0$.

Now Try Exercise 11

One Solution

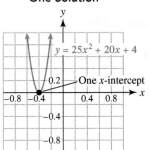

Figure 6.51

EXAMPLE 3 **Recognizing a quadratic equation having no real solutions**

Solve the equation $5x^2 - x + 3 = 0$. Support your result graphically.

Solution

Symbolic Solution Let $a = 5$, $b = -1$, and $c = 3$ in $5x^2 - 1x + 3 = 0$.

$$x = \frac{-b \pm \sqrt{b^2 - 4ac}}{2a} \qquad \text{Quadratic formula}$$

$$= \frac{-(-1) \pm \sqrt{(-1)^2 - 4(5)(3)}}{2(5)} \qquad \text{Substitute for } a, b, \text{ and } c.$$

$$= \frac{1 \pm \sqrt{-59}}{10} \qquad \text{Simplify.}$$

There are *no real solutions* to this equation because $\sqrt{-59}$ *is not a real number*. (Later in this section we discuss how to find complex solutions to quadratic equations like this one.)

Graphical Solution The graph of $y = 5x^2 - x + 3$ is shown in Figure 6.52. There are no x-intercepts, indicating that the equation $5x^2 - x + 3 = 0$ has no real solutions.

Now Try Exercise 13

No Real Solutions

$y = 5x^2 - x + 3$

No x-intercepts

Figure 6.52

▶ **REAL-WORLD CONNECTION** Earlier in this section we discussed how engineers estimate safe stopping distances for automobiles. In the next example we solve the equation presented in A Look Into Math.

EXAMPLE 4 **Modeling stopping distance**

If a car's headlights do not illuminate the road beyond 500 feet, estimate a safe nighttime speed limit x for the car by solving $\frac{1}{9}x^2 + \frac{11}{3}x = 500$.

500 feet

Solution

Begin by subtracting 500 from each side of the given equation.

$$\frac{1}{9}x^2 + \frac{11}{3}x - 500 = 0 \qquad \text{Subtract 500.}$$

To eliminate fractions, multiply each side by the LCD, which is 9. (This step is not necessary, but it makes the problem easier to work.)

$$x^2 + 33x - 4500 = 0 \qquad \text{Multiply by 9.}$$

Now let $a = 1$, $b = 33$, and $c = -4500$ in the quadratic formula.

$$x = \frac{-b \pm \sqrt{b^2 - 4ac}}{2a} \qquad \text{Quadratic formula}$$

STUDY TIP

The quadratic formula can be used to solve *any* quadratic equation.

$$= \frac{-33 \pm \sqrt{33^2 - 4(1)(-4500)}}{2(1)} \qquad \text{Substitute for } a, b, \text{ and } c.$$

$$= \frac{-33 \pm \sqrt{19{,}089}}{2} \qquad \text{Simplify.}$$

The solutions are

$$\frac{-33 + \sqrt{19{,}089}}{2} \approx 52.6 \quad \text{and} \quad \frac{-33 - \sqrt{19{,}089}}{2} \approx -85.6.$$

The negative solution has no physical meaning because negative speeds are not possible. The other solution is 52.6, so an appropriate speed limit might be 50 miles per hour.

▌ **Now Try Exercise 109**

The Discriminant

The expression $b^2 - 4ac$ in the quadratic formula is called the **discriminant**. It provides information about the number of solutions to a quadratic equation.

READING CHECK

How can you use the discriminant to determine the number of solutions to a quadratic equation?

THE DISCRIMINANT AND QUADRATIC EQUATIONS

To determine the number of solutions to the quadratic equation $ax^2 + bx + c = 0$, evaluate the discriminant $b^2 - 4ac$.

1. If $b^2 - 4ac > 0$, there are two real solutions.
2. If $b^2 - 4ac = 0$, there is one real solution.
3. If $b^2 - 4ac < 0$, there are no real solutions; there are two complex solutions.

GRAPHS AND THE DISCRIMINANT The graph of $y = ax^2 + bx + c$ can be used to determine the sign of the discriminant, $b^2 - 4ac$. Figure 6.53 illustrates several possibilities. For example, in Figure 6.53(a) neither graph with $a > 0$ or $a < 0$ intersects the x-axis. Therefore these graphs indicate that the equation $ax^2 + bx + c = 0$ has no real solutions and that the discriminant must be negative: $b^2 - 4ac < 0$. Figures 6.53(b) and (c) can be done similarly.

Figure 6.53

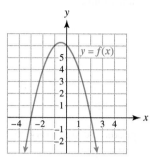

Figure 6.54

EXAMPLE 5

Analyzing graphs of quadratic functions

A graph of $f(x) = ax^2 + bx + c$ is shown in Figure 6.54.
(a) State whether $a > 0$ or $a < 0$.
(b) Solve the equation $ax^2 + bx + c = 0$.
(c) Determine whether the discriminant is positive, negative, or zero.

Solution
(a) The parabola opens downward, so $a < 0$.
(b) The graph of $f(x) = ax^2 + bx + c$ intersects the x-axis at -3 and 2. Therefore $f(-3) = 0$ and $f(2) = 0$. The solutions to $ax^2 + bx + c = 0$ are -3 and 2.
(c) There are two solutions, so the discriminant is positive.

▪ Now Try Exercise 33

EXAMPLE 6

Using the discriminant

Use the discriminant to determine the number of solutions to $4x^2 + 25 = 20x$. Then solve the equation, using the quadratic formula.

Solution
Write the equation as $4x^2 - 20x + 25 = 0$ so that $a = 4, b = -20$, and $c = 25$. The discriminant evaluates to

$$b^2 - 4ac = (-20)^2 - 4(4)(25) = 0.$$

Thus there is **one real solution**.

$$x = \frac{-b \pm \sqrt{b^2 - 4ac}}{2a} \qquad \text{Quadratic formula}$$

$$= \frac{-(-20) \pm \sqrt{0}}{2(4)} \qquad \text{Substitute.}$$

$$= \frac{20}{8} = 2.5 \qquad \text{Simplify.}$$

The only solution is 2.5.

▪ Now Try Exercise 39(a), (b)

Quadratic Equations Having Complex Solutions

The quadratic equation written as $ax^2 + bx + c = 0$ has no real solutions if the discriminant, $b^2 - 4ac$, is negative. For example, the quadratic equation $x^2 + 4 = 0$ has $a = 1, b = 0$, and $c = 4$. Its discriminant is

$$b^2 - 4ac = 0^2 - 4(1)(4) = -16 < 0,$$

so this equation has no real solutions. However, if we use complex numbers, we can solve this equation as follows.

$$x^2 + 4 = 0 \qquad \text{Given equation}$$

$$x^2 = -4 \qquad \text{Subtract 4.}$$

$$x = \pm\sqrt{-4} \qquad \text{Square root property}$$

$$x = \sqrt{-4} \quad \text{or} \quad x = -\sqrt{-4} \qquad \text{Meaning of } \pm$$

$$x = 2i \quad \text{or} \quad x = -2i \qquad \text{The expression } \sqrt{-a}$$

No x-intercepts

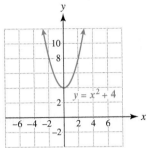

Figure 6.55

The solutions are $\pm 2i$. We check each solution to $x^2 + 4 = 0$ as follows.

$$(2i)^2 + 4 = (2)^2i^2 + 4 = 4(-1) + 4 = 0 ✓ \quad \text{It checks.}$$
$$(-2i)^2 + 4 = (-2)^2i^2 + 4 = 4(-1) + 4 = 0 ✓ \quad \text{It checks.}$$

The fact that the equation $x^2 + 4 = 0$ has only imaginary solutions is apparent from the graph of $y = x^2 + 4$, shown in Figure 6.55. This parabola does not intersect the x-axis, so the equation $x^2 + 4 = 0$ has no real solutions.

These results can be generalized as follows.

> ## THE EQUATION $x^2 + k = 0$
>
> If $k > 0$, the solutions to $x^2 + k = 0$ are given by $x = \pm i\sqrt{k}$.

NOTE: This result is a form of the *square root property* that includes complex solutions.

EXAMPLE 7 | **Solving a quadratic equation having complex solutions**

Solve $x^2 + 5 = 0$.

Solution
The solutions are $\pm i\sqrt{5}$. That is, $x = i\sqrt{5}$ or $x = -i\sqrt{5}$.

▮ **Now Try Exercise 57**

When $b \neq 0$, the preceding method cannot be used. Consider the quadratic equation $2x^2 + x + 3 = 0$, which has $a = 2$, $b = 1$, and $c = 3$. Its discriminant is negative.

$$b^2 - 4ac = 1^2 - 4(2)(3) = -23 < 0$$

This equation has two complex solutions, as demonstrated in the next example.

EXAMPLE 8 | **Solving a quadratic equation having complex solutions**

Solve $2x^2 + x + 3 = 0$. Write your answer in standard form: $a + bi$.

Solution
Let $a = 2$, $b = 1$, and $c = 3$.

CALCULATOR HELP

To set your calculator in $a + bi$ mode or to access the imaginary unit i, see Appendix A (page AP-7).

$$x = \frac{-b \pm \sqrt{b^2 - 4ac}}{2a} \qquad \text{Quadratic formula}$$

$$= \frac{-1 \pm \sqrt{1^2 - 4(2)(3)}}{2(2)} \qquad \text{Substitute for } a, b, \text{ and } c.$$

$$= \frac{-1 \pm \sqrt{-23}}{4} \qquad \text{Simplify.}$$

$$= \frac{-1 \pm i\sqrt{23}}{4} \qquad \sqrt{-23} = i\sqrt{23}$$

$$= -\frac{1}{4} \pm i\frac{\sqrt{23}}{4} \qquad \text{Property of fractions}$$

The solutions are $-\frac{1}{4} + i\frac{\sqrt{23}}{4}$ and $-\frac{1}{4} - i\frac{\sqrt{23}}{4}$.

▮ **Now Try Exercise 73**

CRITICAL THINKING

Use the results of Example 8 to evaluate each expression mentally.

$$2\left(-\frac{1}{4} + i\frac{\sqrt{23}}{4}\right)^2 + \left(-\frac{1}{4} + i\frac{\sqrt{23}}{4}\right) + 3 \quad \text{and} \quad 2\left(-\frac{1}{4} - i\frac{\sqrt{23}}{4}\right)^2 + \left(-\frac{1}{4} - i\frac{\sqrt{23}}{4}\right) + 3$$

Sometimes we can use properties of radicals to simplify a solution to a quadratic equation, as demonstrated in the next example.

EXAMPLE 9 **Solving a quadratic equation having complex solutions**

Solve $\frac{3}{4}x^2 + 1 = x$. Write your answer in standard form: $a + bi$.

Solution

Begin by subtracting x from each side of the equation and then multiply by 4 to clear fractions. The resulting equation is $3x^2 - 4x + 4 = 0$. Substitute $a = 3$, $b = -4$, and $c = 4$ in the quadratic formula.

$$
\begin{aligned}
x &= \frac{-b \pm \sqrt{b^2 - 4ac}}{2a} & \text{Quadratic formula} \\[2mm]
&= \frac{-(-4) \pm \sqrt{(-4)^2 - 4(3)(4)}}{2(3)} & \text{Substitute.} \\[2mm]
&= \frac{4 \pm \sqrt{-32}}{6} & \text{Simplify.} \\[2mm]
&= \frac{4 \pm 4i\sqrt{2}}{6} & \sqrt{-32} = i\sqrt{32} = i\sqrt{16}\sqrt{2} = 4i\sqrt{2} \\[2mm]
&= \frac{2}{3} \pm \frac{2}{3}i\sqrt{2} & \text{Property of fractions; simplify.}
\end{aligned}
$$

▌ **Now Try Exercise 79**

In the next example, we use completing the square to obtain complex solutions.

EXAMPLE 10 **Completing the square to find complex solutions**

Solve $x(x + 2) = -2$ by completing the square.

Solution

After applying the distributive property, we obtain the equation $x^2 + 2x = -2$. Because $b = 2$, add $\left(\frac{b}{2}\right)^2 = \left(\frac{2}{2}\right)^2 = 1$ to each side of the equation.

$$
\begin{aligned}
x^2 + 2x &= -2 & \text{Equation to be solved} \\
x^2 + 2x + 1 &= -2 + 1 & \text{Add 1 to each side.} \\
(x + 1)^2 &= -1 & \text{Perfect square trinomial; add.} \\
x + 1 &= \pm\sqrt{-1} & \text{Square root property} \\
x + 1 &= \pm i & \sqrt{-1} = i, \text{ the imaginary unit} \\
x &= -1 \pm i & \text{Add } -1 \text{ to each side.}
\end{aligned}
$$

The solutions are $-1 + i$ and $-1 - i$.

▌ **Now Try Exercise 91**

6.4   Putting It All Together

CONCEPT	EXPLANATION	EXAMPLES
Quadratic Formula	The quadratic formula can be used to solve *any* quadratic equation written as $ax^2 + bx + c = 0$. The solutions are given by $$x = \frac{-b \pm \sqrt{b^2 - 4ac}}{2a}.$$	For the equation $$2x^2 - 3x + 1 = 0$$ with $a = 2$, $b = -3$, and $c = 1$, the solutions are $$\frac{-(-3) \pm \sqrt{(-3)^2 - 4(2)(1)}}{2(2)} = \frac{3 \pm \sqrt{1}}{4} = 1, \frac{1}{2}.$$
The Discriminant	The expression $b^2 - 4ac$ is called the discriminant. 1. $b^2 - 4ac > 0$ indicates two real solutions. 2. $b^2 - 4ac = 0$ indicates one real solution. 3. $b^2 - 4ac < 0$ indicates no real solutions; rather, there are two complex solutions.	For the equation $$x^2 + 4x - 1 = 0$$ with $a = 1$, $b = 4$, and $c = -1$, the discriminant is $$b^2 - 4ac = 4^2 - 4(1)(-1) = 20 > 0,$$ indicating two real solutions.
Quadratic Formula and Complex Solutions	If the discriminant is negative $(b^2 - 4ac < 0)$, the two solutions are complex numbers that are not real numbers. If $k > 0$, the solutions to $x^2 + k = 0$ are given by $x = \pm i\sqrt{k}$.	Solve $2x^2 - x + 3 = 0$. $$x = \frac{-(-1) \pm \sqrt{(-1)^2 - 4(2)(3)}}{2(2)}$$ $$= \frac{1 \pm \sqrt{-23}}{4} = \frac{1}{4} \pm i\frac{\sqrt{23}}{4}$$ $x^2 + 7 = 0$ is equivalent to $x = \pm i\sqrt{7}$.

Three Ways to Solve $x^2 - x - 2 = 0$

Symbolic Solution

Solve $x^2 - x - 2 = 0$.

$$x = \frac{-(-1) \pm \sqrt{(-1)^2 - 4(1)(-2)}}{2(1)}$$

$$x = \frac{1 \pm 3}{2}$$

$$x = 2, -1$$

Solutions are -1 and 2.

Numerical Solution

$x^2 - x - 2 = 0$ when $x = -1$ or 2.

Graphical Solution

The x-intercepts are -1 and 2.

6.4   Exercises

MyMathLab   Math XL PRACTICE   WATCH   DOWNLOAD   READ   REVIEW

CONCEPTS AND VOCABULARY

1. What is the quadratic formula used for?

2. What basic algebraic technique is used to derive the quadratic formula?

3. Write the discriminant.

4. If the discriminant evaluates to 0, what does that indicate about the quadratic equation?

5. Name four symbolic techniques for solving a quadratic equation.

6. Does every quadratic equation have at least one real solution? Explain.

7. Solve $x^2 - k = 0$, if $k > 0$.

8. Solve $x^2 + k = 0$, if $k > 0$.

THE QUADRATIC FORMULA

Exercises 9–14: Use the quadratic formula to solve the equation. Support your result graphically. If there are no real solutions, say so.

9. $2x^2 + 11x - 6 = 0$ **10.** $x^2 + 2x - 24 = 0$

11. $-x^2 + 2x - 1 = 0$ **12.** $3x^2 - x + 1 = 0$

13. $-2x^2 + x - 1 = 0$ **14.** $-x^2 + 4x - 4 = 0$

Exercises 15–32: Solve by using the quadratic formula. If there are no real solutions, say so.

15. $x^2 - 6x - 16 = 0$ **16.** $2x^2 - 9x + 7 = 0$

17. $4x^2 - x - 1 = 0$ **18.** $-x^2 + 2x + 1 = 0$

19. $-3x^2 + 2x - 1 = 0$ **20.** $x^2 + x + 3 = 0$

21. $36x^2 - 36x + 9 = 0$ **22.** $4x^2 - 5.6x + 1.96 = 0$

23. $2x(x - 3) = 2$ **24.** $x(x + 1) + x = 5$

25. $(x - 1)(x + 1) + 2 = 4x$

26. $\frac{1}{2}(x - 6) = x^2 + 1$ **27.** $\frac{1}{2}x(x + 1) = 2x^2 - \frac{3}{2}$

28. $\frac{1}{2}x^2 - \frac{1}{4}x + \frac{1}{2} = x$ **29.** $2x(x - 1) = 7$

30. $3x(x - 4) = 4$ **31.** $-3x^2 + 10x - 5 = 0$

32. $-2x^2 + 4x - 1 = 0$

THE DISCRIMINANT

Exercises 33–38: A graph of $y = ax^2 + bx + c$ is shown.
  (a) State whether $a > 0$ or $a < 0$.
  (b) Solve $ax^2 + bx + c = 0$, if possible.
  (c) Determine whether the discriminant is positive, negative, or zero.

33.   **34.**

35.   **36.**

37. 38.

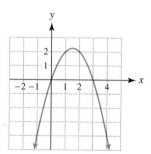

Exercises 39–46: Do the following for the given equation.
  (a) Evaluate the discriminant.
  (b) How many real solutions are there?
  (c) Support your answer for part (b) graphically.

39. $3x^2 + x - 2 = 0$ **40.** $5x^2 - 13x + 6 = 0$

41. $x^2 - 4x + 4 = 0$ **42.** $\frac{1}{4}x^2 + 4 = 2x$

43. $\frac{1}{2}x^2 + \frac{3}{2}x + 2 = 0$ **44.** $x - 3 = 2x^2$

45. $x(x + 3) = 3$

46. $(4x - 1)(x - 3) = -25$

Exercises 47–56: Use the quadratic formula to find any x-intercepts on the graph of the equation.

47. $y = x^2 - 2x - 1$ **48.** $y = x^2 + 3x + 1$

49. $y = -2x^2 - x + 3$ **50.** $y = -3x^2 - x + 4$

51. $y = x^2 + x + 5$ **52.** $y = 3x^2 - 2x + 5$

53. $y = x^2 + 9$ **54.** $y = x^2 + 11$

55. $y = 3x^2 + 4x - 2$ **56.** $y = 4x^2 - 2x - 3$

COMPLEX SOLUTIONS

Exercises 57–88: Solve the equation. Write complex solutions in standard form.

57. $x^2 + 9 = 0$ **58.** $x^2 + 16 = 0$

59. $x^2 + 80 = 0$ **60.** $x^2 + 20 = 0$

61. $x^2 + \frac{1}{4} = 0$ **62.** $x^2 + \frac{9}{4} = 0$

63. $16x^2 + 9 = 0$ **64.** $25x^2 + 36 = 0$

65. $x^2 = -6$ **66.** $x^2 = -75$

67. $x^2 - 3 = 0$ **68.** $x^2 - 8 = 0$

69. $x^2 + 2 = 0$ **70.** $x^2 + 4 = 0$

71. $x^2 - x + 2 = 0$ **72.** $x^2 + 2x + 3 = 0$

73. $2x^2 + 3x + 4 = 0$ **74.** $3x^2 - x = 1$

75. $x^2 + 1 = 4x$ **76.** $3x^2 + 2 = x$

77. $x(x + 1) = -2$ **78.** $x(x - 4) = -8$

79. $5x^2 + 2x + 4 = 0$ **80.** $7x^2 - 2x + 4 = 0$

81. $\frac{1}{2}x^2 + \frac{3}{4}x = -1$ **82.** $-\frac{1}{3}x^2 + x = 2$

83. $x(x + 2) = x - 4$ **84.** $x - 5 = 2x(2x + 1)$

85. $x(2x - 1) = 1 + x$ **86.** $2x = x(3 - 4x)$

87. $x^2 = x(1 - x) - 2$ **88.** $2x^2 = 2x(5 - x) - 8$

COMPLETING THE SQUARE

Exercises 89–94: Solve by completing the square.

89. $x^2 + 2x + 4 = 0$ **90.** $x^2 - 2x + 2 = 0$

91. $x(x + 4) = -5$ **92.** $x(8 - x) = 25$

93. $2x^2 - 4x + 6 = 0$ **94.** $2x^2 + 2x + 1 = 0$

YOU DECIDE THE METHOD

Exercises 95–108: Find exact solutions to the quadratic equation, using a method of your choice. Explain why you chose the method you did. Answers may vary.

95. $x^2 - 3x + 2 = 0$ **96.** $x^2 + 2x + 1 = 0$

97. $0.5x^2 - 1.75x = 1$ **98.** $\frac{3}{5}x^2 + \frac{9}{10}x = \frac{3}{5}$

99. $x^2 - 5x + 2 = 0$ **100.** $2x^2 - x - 4 = 0$

101. $2x^2 + x = -8$ **102.** $4x^2 = 2x - 3$

103. $4x^2 - 1 = 0$ **104.** $3x^2 = 9$

105. $3x^2 + 6 = 0$ **106.** $4x^2 + 7 = 0$

107. $9x^2 + 1 = 6x$ **108.** $10x^2 + 15x = 25$

APPLICATIONS

Exercises 109–112: Modeling Stopping Distance (Refer to Example 4.) Use $d = \frac{1}{9}x^2 + \frac{11}{3}x$ to find a safe speed x for the following stopping distances d.

109. 42 feet

110. 152 feet

111. 390 feet

112. 726 feet

113. *Global Music Sales* (Refer to Example 9, Section 6.3.) From 1989 to 2009, global music sales S of compact discs and tapes in billions of dollars can be modeled by $S(x) = -0.095x^2 + 1.85x + 6$, where x is years after 1989. Estimate symbolically when sales were $12 billion. (*Source: RIAA, Bain Analysis.*)

114. *Monthly Facebook Visitors* The number of *unique* monthly Facebook visitors in millions x years after 2006 can be modeled by

$$V(x) = 10.75x^2 - 24x + 35.$$

Assuming current trends continue, estimate symbolically when this number might reach 530 million.

115. *Groupon's Growth* Groupon negotiates coupons for items discounted 50–90% off by having thousands of subscribers. As a result, it experienced a dramatic increase in value from October 2010 to March 2011. The function

$$G(x) = 0.4x^2 + 1.8x + 6$$

approximates the company's value in billions of dollars x months after October 2010.
(a) Evaluate $G(0)$. Interpret the result.
(b) Determine when Groupon's value was about $15 billion.

116. *Foursquare Users* Foursquare provides a service that allows your friends to know your whereabouts by "checking in." From March 2010 to March 2011, it experienced amazing growth. The function

$$F(x) = \frac{1}{18}x^2 - \frac{1}{12}x + \frac{1}{2}$$

approximates Foursquare users in millions x months after March 2010.
(a) Evaluate $F(3)$. Interpret the result.
(b) Determine symbolically when Foursquare had 4.25 million users.

117. *U.S. AIDS Deaths* The cumulative numbers in thousands of AIDS deaths from 1984 through 1994 may be modeled by

$$f(x) = 2.39x^2 + 5.04x + 5.1,$$

where $x = 0$ corresponds to 1984, $x = 1$ corresponds to 1985, and so on until $x = 10$ corresponds to 1994. See the accompanying graph. Use the formula for $f(x)$ to estimate the year when the total number of AIDS deaths reached 200 thousand. Compare your result with that shown in the graph.

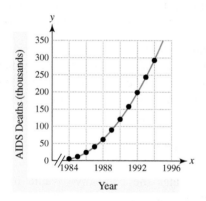

118. *Canoeing* A camper paddles a canoe 2 miles downstream in a river that has a 2-mile-per-hour current. To return to camp, the canoeist travels upstream on a different branch of the river. It is 4 miles long and has a 1-mile-per-hour current. The total trip (both ways) takes 3 hours. Find the average speed of the canoe in still water. (*Hint:* Time equals distance divided by rate.)

119. *Airplane Speed* A pilot flies 500 miles against a 20-mile-per-hour wind. On the next day, the pilot flies back home with a 10-mile-per-hour tail wind. The total trip (both ways) takes 4 hours. Find the speed of the airplane without a wind.

120. *Distance* Two cars leave an intersection, one traveling south and one traveling east, as shown in the figure at the top of the next column. After 1 hour the

two cars are 50 miles apart and the car traveling east has traveled 10 miles farther than the car traveling south. How far did each car travel?

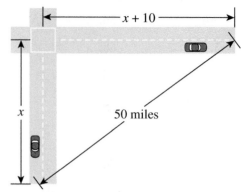

121. *Screen Dimensions* The width of a rectangular computer screen is 3 inches more than its height. If the area of the screen is 154 square inches, find its dimensions
(a) graphically,
(b) numerically, and
(c) symbolically.

122. *Sidewalk Dimension* A rectangular flower garden in a park is 30 feet wide and 40 feet long. A sidewalk around the perimeter of the garden is being planned, as shown in the figure. The gardener has enough money to pour 624 square feet of cement sidewalk. Find the width of the sidewalk.

123. *Modeling Water Flow* When water runs out of a hole in a cylindrical container, the height of the water in the container can often be modeled by a quadratic function. The data in the table show the height y in centimeters of water at 30-second intervals in a metal can that has a small hole in it.

Time	0	30	60	90
Height	16	11.9	6.4	5.3

Time	120	150	180
Height	3.1	1.4	0.5

These data are modeled by

$$f(x) = 0.0004x^2 - 0.15x + 16.$$

(a) Explain why a linear function would not be appropriate for modeling these data.

(b) Use the table to estimate the time at which the height was 7 centimeters.

(c) Use the quadratic formula to solve part (b).

124. *Hospitals* The general trend in the number of hospitals in the United States from 1945 through 2000 is shown in the graph and can be modeled by

$$f(x) = -1.38x^2 + 84x + 5865,$$

where $x = 5$ corresponds to 1945, $x = 10$ corresponds to 1950, and so on until $x = 60$ represents 2000.

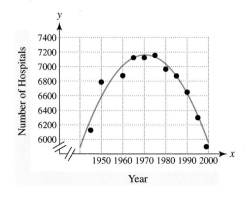

(a) Describe any trends in the numbers of hospitals from 1945 to 2000.

(b) What information does the vertex give?

(c) Use the formula for $f(x)$ to estimate the number of hospitals in 1970. Compare your result with that shown in the graph.

(d) Use the formula for $f(x)$ to estimate the year (or years) when there were 6300 hospitals. Compare your result with that shown in the graph.

WRITING ABOUT MATHEMATICS

125. Explain how the discriminant $b^2 - 4ac$ can be used to determine the number of solutions to a quadratic equation.

126. Let $f(x) = ax^2 + bx + c$ be a quadratic function. If you know the value of $b^2 - 4ac$, what information does this give you about the graph of f? Explain your answer.

Checking Basic Concepts

Sections 6.3 and 6.4

1. Solve the quadratic equation $2x^2 - 7x + 3 = 0$ symbolically and graphically.

2. Use the square root property to solve $x^2 = 5$.

3. Complete the square to solve $x^2 - 4x + 1 = 0$.

4. Solve the equation $x^2 + y^2 = 1$ for y.

5. Use the quadratic formula to solve each equation.
   (a) $2x^2 = 3x + 1$
   (b) $9x^2 - 24x + 16 = 0$
   (c) $x^2 + x + 2 = 0$

6. Calculate the discriminant for each equation and give the number of *real* solutions.
   (a) $x^2 - 5x + 5 = 0$
   (b) $2x^2 - 5x + 4 = 0$
   (c) $49x^2 - 56x + 16 = 0$

7. Solve each equation.
   (a) $x^2 + 5 = 0$
   (b) $x^2 + x + 3 = 0$

6.5 Quadratic Inequalities

Basic Concepts • Graphical and Numerical Solutions • Symbolic Solutions

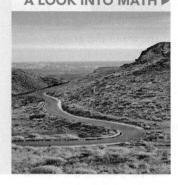

A LOOK INTO MATH ▶ Parabolas are frequently used in highway design. Sometimes it is necessary for engineers to determine where a highway is below a particular elevation. To do this, they may need to solve a *quadratic inequality*. (See Example 5.) In this section we discuss how to solve quadratic inequalities graphically, numerically, and symbolically.

Basic Concepts

If the equals sign in a quadratic equation is replaced with $>$, $\geq$, $<$, or $\leq$, a **quadratic inequality** results. Examples of quadratic inequalities include

$$x^2 + 4x - 3 < 0, \quad 5x^2 \geq 5, \quad \text{and} \quad 1 - z \leq z^2. \qquad \text{Quadratic inequalities}$$

Any quadratic equation can be written as

$$ax^2 + bx + c = 0, \quad a \neq 0, \qquad \text{Quadratic equation}$$

so any quadratic inequality can be written as

$$ax^2 + bx + c > 0, \quad a \neq 0, \qquad \text{Quadratic inequality}$$

where $>$ may be replaced with $\geq$, $<$, or $\leq$.

NEW VOCABULARY

☐ Quadratic inequality
☐ Test value

EXAMPLE 1 **Identifying a quadratic inequality**

Determine whether the inequality is quadratic.
(a) $5x + x^2 - x^3 \leq 0$ **(b)** $4 + 5x^2 > 4x^2 + x$

Solution
(a) The inequality $5x + x^2 - x^3 \leq 0$ is not quadratic because it has an x^3-term.
(b) Write the inequality as follows.

$$\begin{aligned}
4 + 5x^2 &> 4x^2 + x && \text{Given inequality} \\
4 + 5x^2 - 4x^2 - x &> 0 && \text{Subtract } 4x^2 \text{ and } x. \\
4 + x^2 - x &> 0 && \text{Combine like terms.} \\
x^2 - x + 4 &> 0 && \text{Rewrite.}
\end{aligned}$$

Because the inequality can be written in the form $ax^2 + bx + c > 0$ with $a = 1$, $b = -1$, and $c = 4$, it is a quadratic inequality.

Now Try Exercises 7, 11

Graphical and Numerical Solutions

Equality often is the boundary between *greater than* and *less than*, so a first step in solving an inequality is to determine the *x*-values where equality occurs. We begin by using this concept with graphical techniques.

A graph of $y = x^2 - x - 2$ has *x*-intercepts -1 and 2. See Figure 6.56. The solutions to $x^2 - x - 2 = 0$ are given by $x = -1$ or $x = 2$. Between the *x*-intercepts the graph dips **below** the *x*-axis and the *y*-values are **negative**. Thus solutions to $x^2 - x - 2 < 0$ satisfy $-1 < x < 2$. To support this result we select a **test value**. For example, 0 lies between -1 and 2. If we substitute $x = 0$ in $x^2 - x - 2 < 0$, it results in a true statement.

$$0^2 - 0 - 2 < 0 \quad \checkmark \qquad \text{True}$$

Visualizing Quadratic Inequalities

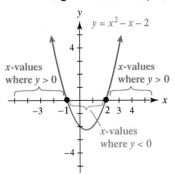

Figure 6.56

When $x < -1$ or $x > 2$, the graph lies **above** the x-axis and the y-values are **positive**. Thus the solutions to $x^2 - x - 2 > 0$ satisfy $x < -1$ or $x > 2$. For example, 3 is greater than 2 and -3 is less than -1. Therefore both 3 and -3 are solutions. We can verify this result by substituting **3** and -3 as test values in $x^2 - x - 2 > 0$.

$$3^2 - 3 - 2 > 0 \quad \checkmark \quad \text{True}$$
$$(-3)^2 - (-3) - 2 > 0 \quad \checkmark \quad \text{True}$$

In the next three examples, we use these concepts to solve quadratic inequalities.

EXAMPLE 2   **Solving a quadratic inequality**

Make a table of values for $y = x^2 - 3x - 4$ and then sketch the graph. Use the table and graph to solve $x^2 - 3x - 4 \leq 0$. Write your answer in interval notation.

Solution
The points calculated for Table 6.16 are plotted in Figure 6.57 and connected with a smooth ∪-shaped graph.

Numerical Solution Table 6.16 shows that $x^2 - 3x - 4$ equals 0 when $x = -1$ or $x = 4$. Between these values, $x^2 - 3x - 4$ is negative, so the solution set to $x^2 - 3x - 4 \leq 0$ is given by $-1 \leq x \leq 4$ or, in interval notation, $[-1, 4]$.

Graphical Solution In Figure 6.57 the graph of $y = x^2 - 3x - 4$ shows that the x-intercepts are -1 and **4**. Between these values, the graph dips **below** the x-axis. Thus the solution set is $[-1, 4]$.

STUDY TIP

Learn how to use a parabola to help solve a quadratic inequality.

TABLE 6.16

x	$y = x^2 - 3x - 4$
-2	6
-1	0
0	-4
1	-6
2	-6
3	-4
4	0
5	6

x-intercepts

Less than or equal to 0

Solving $x^2 - 3x - 4 \leq 0$
x-Intercepts: -1, 4

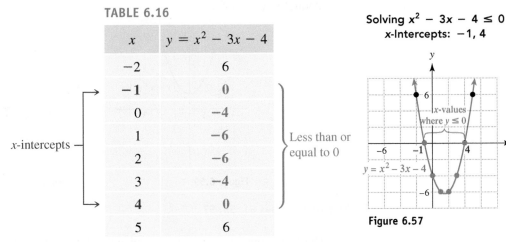

Figure 6.57

Now Try Exercises 19, 27

EXAMPLE 3

Solving a quadratic inequality

Solve $x^2 > 1$. Write your answer in interval notation.

Solution

First, rewrite $x^2 > 1$ as $x^2 - 1 > 0$. The graph of $y = x^2 - 1$ is shown in Figure 6.58 with x-intercepts -1 and 1. The graph lies **above** the x-axis and is shaded green to the left of $x = -1$ and to the right of $x = 1$. Thus the solution set is given by $x < -1$ or $x > 1$, which can be written in interval notation as $(-\infty, -1) \cup (1, \infty)$.

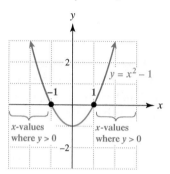

Figure 6.58

Now Try Exercise 49

EXAMPLE 4

Solving some special cases

Solve each of the inequalities graphically.
(a) $x^2 + 1 > 0$ (b) $x^2 + 1 < 0$ (c) $(x - 1)^2 \le 0$

Solution

(a) Because the graph of $y = x^2 + 1$, shown in Figure 6.59, is always above the x-axis, $x^2 + 1$ is always greater than 0. The solution set includes all real numbers, or $(-\infty, \infty)$.
(b) Because the graph of $y = x^2 + 1$, shown in Figure 6.59, never goes below the x-axis, $x^2 + 1$ is never less than 0. Thus there are no real solutions.
(c) Because the graph of $y = (x - 1)^2$, shown in Figure 6.60, never goes below the x-axis, $(x - 1)^2$ is never less than 0. When $x = 1$, $y = 0$, so **1** is the only solution to the inequality $(x - 1)^2 \le 0$.

Figure 6.59

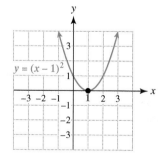

Figure 6.60

Now Try Exercises 51, 55, 57

The following chart summarizes visual solutions for several possibilities when solving quadratic equations and inequalities.

Visualizing Solutions to Quadratic Equations and Inequalities

Two x-Intercepts

Case 1: Upward Opening

Case 2: Downward Opening

Equation/Inequality	Solutions	Equation/Inequality	Solutions
$x^2 + x - 2 = 0$	$x = -2, 1$	$-x^2 - x + 2 = 0$	$x = -2, 1$
$x^2 + x - 2 < 0$	$-2 < x < 1$	$-x^2 - x + 2 < 0$	$x < -2$ or $x > 1$
$x^2 + x - 2 > 0$	$x < -2$ or $x > 1$	$-x^2 - x + 2 > 0$	$-2 < x < 1$

One x-Intercept

Case 1: Upward Opening

Case 2: Downward Opening

Equation/Inequality	Solutions	Equation/Inequality	Solutions
$(x - 1)^2 = 0$	$x = 1$	$-(x - 1)^2 = 0$	$x = 1$
$(x - 1)^2 < 0$	no solutions	$-(x - 1)^2 < 0$	$x < 1$ or $x > 1$
$(x - 1)^2 > 0$	$x < 1$ or $x > 1$	$-(x - 1)^2 > 0$	no solutions

No x-Intercepts

Case 1: Upward Opening

Case 2: Downward Opening

Equation/Inequality	Solutions	Equation/Inequality	Solutions
$x^2 + 1 = 0$	no solutions	$-x^2 - 1 = 0$	no solutions
$x^2 + 1 < 0$	no solutions	$-x^2 - 1 < 0$	all real numbers
$x^2 + 1 > 0$	all real numbers	$-x^2 - 1 > 0$	no solutions

▶ **REAL-WORLD CONNECTION** In the next example we show how quadratic inequalities are used in highway design, as discussed in A Look Into Math for this section.

EXAMPLE 5 **Determining elevations on a sag curve**

Parabolas are frequently used in highway design to model hills and sags (valleys) along a proposed route. Suppose that the elevation E in feet of a sag, or *sag curve*, is given by

$$E(x) = 0.00004x^2 - 0.4x + 2000,$$

where x is the horizontal distance in feet along the sag curve and $0 \le x \le 10{,}000$. See Figure 6.61. Estimate graphically the x-values where the elevation is 1500 feet or less. (*Source:* F. Mannering and W. Kilareski, *Principles of Highway Engineering and Traffic Analysis.*)

E

Figure 6.61

Solution

Graphical Solution We must solve the quadratic inequality

$$0.00004x^2 - 0.4x + 2000 \le 1500.$$

Let $y_1 = 0.00004x^2 - 0.4x + 2000$ be the sag curve and $y_2 = 1500$ be a line with an elevation of 1500 feet. Their graphs intersect at $x \approx 1464$ and $x \approx 8536$, as shown in Figure 6.62. The elevation of the road is less than 1500 feet between these x-values. Therefore the elevation is 1500 feet or less when $1464 \le x \le 8536$ (approximately).

Determining Where the Elevation is 1500 Feet

[0, 10000, 1000] by [0, 2500, 500] [0, 10000, 1000] by [0, 2500, 500]

(a)   (b)

Figure 6.62

CALCULATOR HELP

To find a point of intersection, see Appendix A (page AP-6).

Now Try Exercise 63

Symbolic Solutions

To solve a quadratic inequality symbolically, we first solve the corresponding equality. We can then write the solution to the inequality, using the following method.

SOLUTIONS TO QUADRATIC INEQUALITIES

Let $ax^2 + bx + c = 0$, $a > 0$, have two real solutions p and q, where $p < q$.

$ax^2 + bx + c < 0$ is equivalent to $p < x < q$ (see left-hand figure).

$ax^2 + bx + c > 0$ is equivalent to $x < p$ or $x > q$ (see right-hand figure).

Quadratic inequalities involving $\le$ or $\ge$ can be solved similarly.

READING CHECK

How can you distinguish a linear inequality from a quadratic inequality?

Solutions lie between p and q.   Solutions lie "outside" p and q.

One way to handle the situation where $a < 0$ is to multiply each side of the inequality by -1, in which case we must be sure to *reverse* the inequality symbol. For example, the inequality $-2x^2 + 8 \leq 0$ has $a = -2$, which is negative. If we multiply each side of this inequality by -1, we obtain $2x^2 - 8 \geq 0$ and now $a = 2$, which is positive.

EXAMPLE 6 | **Solving quadratic inequalities**

Solve each inequality symbolically. Write your answer in interval notation.
(a) $6x^2 - 7x - 5 \geq 0$ (b) $x(3 - x) > -18$

Solution

(a) Begin by solving $6x^2 - 7x - 5 = 0$.

$$6x^2 - 7x - 5 = 0 \qquad \text{Quadratic equation}$$
$$(2x + 1)(3x - 5) = 0 \qquad \text{Factor.}$$
$$2x + 1 = 0 \quad \text{or} \quad 3x - 5 = 0 \qquad \text{Zero-product property}$$
$$x = -\frac{1}{2} \quad \text{or} \quad x = \frac{5}{3} \qquad \text{Solve.}$$

Therefore solutions to $6x^2 - 7x - 5 \geq 0$ lie "**outside**" these two values and satisfy $x \leq -\frac{1}{2}$ or $x \geq \frac{5}{3}$. In interval notation the solution set is $\left(-\infty, -\frac{1}{2}\right] \cup \left[\frac{5}{3}, \infty\right)$.

(b) First, rewrite the inequality as follows.

$$x(3 - x) > -18 \qquad \text{Given inequality}$$
$$3x - x^2 > -18 \qquad \text{Distributive property}$$
$$3x - x^2 + 18 > 0 \qquad \text{Add 18.}$$
$$-x^2 + 3x + 18 > 0 \qquad \text{Rewrite.}$$
$$x^2 - 3x - 18 < 0 \qquad \text{Multiply by } -1 \text{ because } a < 0; \text{ reverse the inequality symbol.}$$

Next, solve $x^2 - 3x - 18 = 0$.

$$(x + 3)(x - 6) = 0 \qquad \text{Factor.}$$
$$x = -3 \quad \text{or} \quad x = 6 \qquad \text{Solve.}$$

Solutions to $x^2 - 3x - 18 < 0$ lie **between** these two values and satisfy $-3 < x < 6$. In interval notation the solution set is $(-3, 6)$.

Now Try Exercises 31, 37

CRITICAL THINKING

The graph of
$y = -x^2 + x + 12$ is a
parabola opening down-
ward with x-intercepts -3
and 4. Solve each inequality.
(a) $-x^2 + x + 12 > 0$
(b) $-x^2 + x + 12 < 0$

EXAMPLE 7 | **Finding the dimensions of a building**

A rectangular building needs to be 7 feet longer than it is wide, as illustrated in Figure 6.63. The area of the building must be at least 450 square feet. What widths x are possible for this building? Support your results with a table of values.

Figure 6.63

Solution

Symbolic Solution If x is the width of the building, $x + 7$ is the length of the build- ing and its area is $x(x + 7)$. The area must be at least 450 square feet, so the inequality $x(x + 7) \geq 450$ must be satisfied.

First solve the following quadratic equation.

$$x(x + 7) = 450 \qquad \text{Quadratic equation}$$

$$x^2 + 7x = 450 \qquad \text{Distributive property}$$

$$x^2 + 7x - 450 = 0 \qquad \text{Subtract 450.}$$

$$x = \frac{-7 \pm \sqrt{7^2 - 4(1)(-450)}}{2(1)} \qquad \begin{array}{l}\text{Quadratic formula: } a = 1, \\ b = 7, \text{ and } c = -450\end{array}$$

$$= \frac{-7 \pm \sqrt{1849}}{2} \qquad \text{Simplify.}$$

$$= \frac{-7 \pm 43}{2} \qquad \sqrt{1849} = 43$$

$$= \mathbf{18, -25} \qquad \text{Evaluate.}$$

Thus the solutions to $x(x + 7) \geq 450$ are $x \leq -25$ or $x \geq 18$. The width is positive, so the building width must be 18 feet or more.

Numerical Solution A table of values is shown in Figure 6.64, where $y_1 = x(x + 7)$ equals 450 when $x = 18$. For $x \geq 18$ the area is *at least* 450 square feet.

Figure 6.64

◼ **Now Try Exercise 67**

6.5 Putting It All Together

METHOD	EXPLANATION
Solving a Quadratic Inequality Symbolically	Let $ax^2 + bx + c = 0$, $a > 0$, have two real solutions p and q, where $p < q$. $ax^2 + bx + c < 0$ is equivalent to $p < x < q$. $ax^2 + bx + c > 0$ is equivalent to $x < p$ or $x > q$. *Examples:* The solutions to $x^2 - 3x + 2 = 0$ are 1 and 2. The solutions to $x^2 - 3x + 2 < 0$ satisfy $1 < x < 2$. The solutions to $x^2 - 3x + 2 > 0$ satisfy $x < 1$ or $x > 2$.
Solving a Quadratic Inequality Graphically	Given $ax^2 + bx + c < 0$ with $a > 0$, graph $y = ax^2 + bx + c$ and locate any x-intercepts. If there are two x-intercepts, then solutions correspond to x-values between the x-intercepts. Solutions to $ax^2 + bx + c > 0$ correspond to x-values "outside" the x-intercepts. See the box on page 471.
Solving a Quadratic Inequality Numerically	If a quadratic inequality is expressed as $ax^2 + bx + c < 0$ with $a > 0$, then we can solve $y = ax^2 + bx + c = 0$ with a table. If there are two solutions, then the solutions to the given inequality lie between these values. Solutions to $ax^2 + bx + c > 0$ lie before or after these values in the table.

6.5 Exercises

MyMathLab

  Math XL
PRACTICE

 WATCH

DOWNLOAD

READ

 REVIEW

CONCEPTS AND VOCABULARY

1. How is a quadratic inequality different from a quadratic equation?

2. Do quadratic inequalities typically have two solutions? Explain.

3. Is 3 a solution to $x^2 < 7$?

4. Is 5 a solution to $x^2 \geq 25$?

5. The solutions to $x^2 - 2x - 8 = 0$ are -2 and 4. What are the solutions to $x^2 - 2x - 8 < 0$? Write your answer as an inequality.

6. The solutions to $x^2 + 2x - 3 = 0$ are -3 and 1. What are the solutions to $x^2 + 2x - 3 > 0$? Write your answer as an inequality.

QUADRATIC INEQUALITIES

Exercises 7–12: Is the inequality quadratic?

7. $x^2 + 4x + 5 < 0$ **8.** $x > x^3 - 5$

9. $x^2 > 19$ **10.** $x(x - 1) - 2 \geq 0$

11. $4x > 1 - x$ **12.** $2x(x^2 + 3) < 0$

Exercises 13–18: Is the given value of x a solution?

13. $2x^2 + x - 1 > 0$ $x = 3$

14. $x^2 - 3x + 2 \leq 0$ $x = 2$

15. $x^2 + 2 \leq 0$ $x = 0$

16. $2x(x - 3) \geq 0$ $x = 1$

17. $x^2 - 3x \leq 1$ $x = -3$

18. $4x^2 - 5x + 1 > 30$ $x = -2$

GRAPHICAL SOLUTIONS

Exercises 19–24: The graph of $y = ax^2 + bx + c$ is given. Solve each equation or inequality.
  (a) $ax^2 + bx + c = 0$
  (b) $ax^2 + bx + c < 0$
  (c) $ax^2 + bx + c > 0$

19.   **20.**

21.   **22.**

23.   **24.**

 Exercises 25 and 26: Solve the inequality graphically to the nearest thousandth.

25. $\pi x^2 - \sqrt{3}x \leq \frac{3}{11}$ **26.** $\sqrt{5}x^2 - \pi^2 x \geq 10.3$

NUMERICAL SOLUTIONS

Exercises 27–30: A table for $y = ax^2 + bx + c$ is given. Solve each equation or inequality.
  (a) $ax^2 + bx + c = 0$
  (b) $ax^2 + bx + c < 0$
  (c) $ax^2 + bx + c > 0$

27. $y = x^2 - 4$

x	-3	-2	-1	0	1	2	3
y	5	0	-3	-4	-3	0	5

28. $y = x^2 - x - 2$

x	-3	-2	-1	0	1	2	3
y	10	4	0	-2	-2	0	4

29. $y = x^2 + 4x$

x	-5	-4	-3	-2	-1	0	1
y	5	0	-3	-4	-3	0	5

30. $y = -2x^2 - 2x + 1.5$

x	-2	-1.5	-1	-0.5	0	0.5	1
y	-2.5	0	1.5	2	1.5	0	-2.5

SYMBOLIC SOLUTIONS

Exercises 31–40: Solve the quadratic inequality symbolically. Write your answer in interval notation.

31. $x^2 + 10x + 21 \leq 0$ **32.** $x^2 - 7x - 18 < 0$

33. $3x^2 - 9x + 6 > 0$ **34.** $7x^2 + 34x - 5 \geq 0$

35. $x^2 < 10$ **36.** $x^2 \geq 64$

37. $x(6 - x) < 0$ **38.** $1 - x^2 \leq 0$

39. $x(4 - x) \leq 2$ **40.** $2x(1 - x) \geq 2$

YOU DECIDE THE METHOD

Exercises 41–44: Solve the equation in part (a). Use the results to solve the inequalities in parts (b) and (c).

41. (a) $x^2 - 4 = 0$ **42.** (a) $x^2 - 5 = 0$
    (b) $x^2 - 4 < 0$ (b) $x^2 - 5 \leq 0$
    (c) $x^2 - 4 > 0$ (c) $x^2 - 5 \geq 0$

43. (a) $x^2 + x - 1 = 0$
    (b) $x^2 + x - 1 < 0$
    (c) $x^2 + x - 1 > 0$

44. (a) $x^2 + 4x - 5 = 0$
    (b) $x^2 + 4x - 5 \leq 0$
    (c) $x^2 + 4x - 5 \geq 0$

Exercises 45–62: Solve the inequality by any method. Write your answer in interval notation when appropriate.

45. $x^2 + 4x + 3 < 0$ **46.** $x^2 + x - 2 \leq 0$

47. $2x^2 - x - 15 \geq 0$ **48.** $3x^2 - 3x - 6 > 0$

49. $2x^2 \leq 8$ **50.** $x^2 < 9$

51. $x^2 > -5$ **52.** $-x^2 \geq 1$

53. $-x^2 + 3x > 0$ **54.** $-8x^2 - 2x + 1 \leq 0$

55. $x^2 + 2 \leq 0$ **56.** $x^2 + 3 \geq -5$

57. $(x - 2)^2 \leq 0$ **58.** $(x + 2)^2 \leq 0$

59. $(x + 1)^2 > 0$ **60.** $(x - 3)^2 > 0$

61. $x(1 - x) \geq -2$ **62.** $x(x - 2) < 3$

APPLICATIONS

63. *Highway Design* (Refer to Example 5.) The elevation E of a sag curve, in feet, is given by

$$E(x) = 0.0000375x^2 - 0.175x + 1000,$$

where $0 \leq x \leq 4000$.
(a) Estimate graphically the x-values for which the elevation is 850 feet or less. (*Hint:* Use the window $[0, 4000, 1000]$ by $[500, 1200, 100]$.)
(b) For which x-values is the elevation 850 feet or more?

64. *Early Cellular Phone Use* The number of cellular subscribers in the United States in thousands from 1985 to 1991 can be modeled by

$$f(x) = 163x^2 - 146x + 205,$$

where x is the year and $x = 0$ corresponds to 1985, $x = 1$ to 1986, and so on. (*Source:* M. Paetsch, *Mobile Communication in the U.S. and Europe.*)
(a) Write a quadratic inequality whose solution set represents the years when there were 2 million subscribers or more.
(b) Solve this inequality.

65. *Heart Disease Death Rates* From 1960 to 2010, age-adjusted heart disease rates decreased dramatically. The number of deaths per 100,000 people can be modeled by

$$f(x) = -0.05107x^2 + 194.74x - 184{,}949,$$

where x is the year, as illustrated in the accompanying figure. (*Source:* Department of Health and Human Services.)

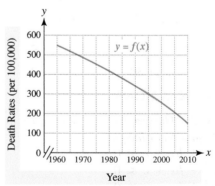

(a) Evaluate $f(1985)$, using both the formula and the graph. How do your results compare?
(b) Use the graph to estimate the years when this death rate was 500 or less.
(c) Solve part (b) by using the quadratic formula.

66. *Accidental Deaths* From 1910 to 2000 the number of accidental deaths per 100,000 people generally decreased and can be modeled by

$$f(x) = -0.001918x^2 + 6.93x - 6156,$$

where x is the year, as shown in the accompanying figure. Note that after 2000 these rates increased and are not modeled by $f(x)$. (*Source:* Department of Health and Human Services.)

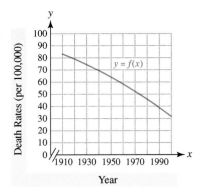

Year

(a) Evaluate $f(1955)$, using both the formula and the graph. How do your results compare?
(b) Use the graph to estimate when this death rate was 60 or more.
(c) Solve part (b) by using the quadratic formula.

67. *Dimensions of a Pen* A rectangular pen for a pet is 5 feet longer than it is wide. Give possible values for the width w of the pen if its area must be between 176 and 500 square feet, inclusively.

68. *Dimensions of a Cylinder* The volume of a cylindrical can is given by $V = \pi r^2 h$, where r is its radius and h is its height. See the accompanying figure. If $h = 6$ inches and the volume of the can must be 50 cubic inches or more, estimate to the nearest tenth of an inch possible values for r.

WRITING ABOUT MATHEMATICS

69. Consider the inequality $x^2 < 0$. Discuss the solutions to this inequality and explain your reasoning.

70. Explain how the graph of $y = ax^2 + bx + c$ can be used to solve the inequality

$$ax^2 + bx + c > 0$$

when $a < 0$. Assume that the x-intercepts of the graph are p and q with $p < q$.

6.6 Equations in Quadratic Form

Higher Degree Polynomial Equations • **Equations Having Rational Exponents** • **Equations Having Complex Solutions**

A LOOK INTO MATH ▶ Although many equations are *not* quadratic equations, they can sometimes be written in quadratic form. These equations are *reducible to quadratic form*. To express such an equation in quadratic form we often use substitution. In this section we discuss this process.

Higher Degree Polynomial Equations

Sometimes a fourth-degree polynomial can be factored like a quadratic trinomial, provided it does not have an x-term or an x^3-term. Let's consider the equation $x^4 - 5x^2 + 4 = 0$.

$x^4 - 5x^2 + 4 = 0$	Given equation
$(x^2)^2 - 5(x^2) + 4 = 0$	Properties of exponents

We use the substitution $u = x^2$.

$u^2 - 5u + 4 = 0$	Let $u = x^2$.
$(u - 4)(u - 1) = 0$	Factor.
$u - 4 = 0 \quad \text{or} \quad u - 1 = 0$	Zero-product property
$u = 4 \quad \text{or} \quad u = 1$	Solve each equation.

Because the given equation $x^4 - 5x^2 + 4 = 0$ uses the variable x, we must give the solutions in terms of x. We substitute x^2 for u in $u = 4$ and $u = 1$ and then solve to obtain the following four solutions.

$u = 4$	or	$u = 1$	Solutions in terms of u
$x^2 = 4$	or	$x^2 = 1$	Substitute x^2 for u.
$x = \pm 2$	or	$x = \pm 1$	Square root property

The solutions are $-2, -1, 1,$ and 2.

EXAMPLE 1 **Solving a sixth-degree equation by substitution**

Solve $2x^6 + x^3 = 1$.

Solution

Start by subtracting 1 from each side.

$2x^6 + x^3 - 1 = 0$	Subtract 1.
$2(x^3)^2 + (x^3) - 1 = 0$	Properties of exponents
$2u^2 + u - 1 = 0$	Let $u = x^3$.
$(2u - 1)(u + 1) = 0$	Factor.
$2u - 1 = 0$ or $u + 1 = 0$	Zero-product property
$u = \dfrac{1}{2}$ or $u = -1$	Solve.

Now substitute x^3 for u, and solve for x to obtain the following two solutions.

$x^3 = \dfrac{1}{2}$ or $x^3 = -1$	Substitute x^3 for u.
$x = \sqrt[3]{\dfrac{1}{2}}$ or $x = -1$	Take cube root of each side.

Now Try Exercise 3

Equations Having Rational Exponents

Equations that have negative exponents are sometimes reducible to quadratic form. Consider the following example, in which two methods are presented.

EXAMPLE 2 **Solving an equation having negative exponents**

Solve $-6m^{-2} + 13m^{-1} + 5 = 0$.

Solution

Method I Use the substitution $u = m^{-1} = \frac{1}{m}$ and $u^2 = m^{-2} = \frac{1}{m^2}$.

$-6m^{-2} + 13m^{-1} + 5 = 0$	Given equation
$-6u^2 + 13u + 5 = 0$	Let $u = m^{-1}$ and $u^2 = m^{-2}$.
$6u^2 - 13u - 5 = 0$	Multiply by -1.
$(2u - 5)(3u + 1) = 0$	Factor.
$2u - 5 = 0$ or $3u + 1 = 0$	Zero-product property
$u = \dfrac{5}{2}$ or $u = -\dfrac{1}{3}$	Solve for u.

Because $u = \frac{1}{m}$, $m = \frac{1}{u}$. Thus the solutions are given by $m = \frac{2}{5}$ or $m = -3$.

Method II Another way to solve this equation is to multiply each side by the LCD, m^2.

$$-6m^{-2} + 13m^{-1} + 5 = 0 \qquad \text{Given equation}$$
$$m^2(-6m^{-2} + 13m^{-1} + 5) = m^2 \cdot 0 \qquad \text{Multiply by } m^2.$$
$$-6m^2m^{-2} + 13m^2m^{-1} + 5m^2 = 0 \qquad \text{Distributive property}$$
$$-6 + 13m + 5m^2 = 0 \qquad \text{Add exponents.}$$
$$5m^2 + 13m - 6 = 0 \qquad \text{Rewrite the equation.}$$
$$(5m - 2)(m + 3) = 0 \qquad \text{Factor.}$$
$$5m - 2 = 0 \quad \text{or} \quad m + 3 = 0 \qquad \text{Zero-product property}$$
$$m = \frac{2}{5} \quad \text{or} \quad m = -3 \qquad \text{Solve.}$$

■ Now Try Exercise 5

In the next example we solve an equation having fractional exponents.

EXAMPLE 3 **Solving an equation having fractional exponents**

Solve $x^{2/3} - 2x^{1/3} - 8 = 0$.

Solution
Use the substitution $u = x^{1/3}$.

$$x^{2/3} - 2x^{1/3} - 8 = 0 \qquad \text{Given equation}$$
$$(x^{1/3})^2 - 2(x^{1/3}) - 8 = 0 \qquad \text{Properties of exponents}$$
$$u^2 - 2u - 8 = 0 \qquad \text{Let } u = x^{1/3}.$$
$$(u - 4)(u + 2) = 0 \qquad \text{Factor.}$$
$$u - 4 = 0 \quad \text{or} \quad u + 2 = 0 \qquad \text{Zero-product property}$$
$$u = 4 \quad \text{or} \quad u = -2 \qquad \text{Solve.}$$

Because $u = x^{1/3}$, $u^3 = (x^{1/3})^3 = x$. Thus $x = 4^3 = 64$ or $x = (-2)^3 = -8$. The solutions are -8 and 64.

■ Now Try Exercise 13

Equations Having Complex Solutions

Sometimes an equation that is reducible to quadratic form also has complex solutions. This situation is discussed in the next two examples.

EXAMPLE 4 **Solving a fourth-degree equation**

Find all complex solutions to $x^4 - 1 = 0$.

Solution

$$x^4 - 1 = 0 \qquad \text{Given equation}$$
$$(x^2)^2 - 1 = 0 \qquad \text{Properties of exponents}$$
$$u^2 - 1 = 0 \qquad \text{Let } u = x^2.$$
$$(u - 1)(u + 1) = 0 \qquad \text{Factor difference of squares.}$$
$$u - 1 = 0 \quad \text{or} \quad u + 1 = 0 \qquad \text{Zero-product property}$$
$$u = 1 \quad \text{or} \quad u = -1 \qquad \text{Solve for } u.$$

Now substitute x^2 for u, and solve for x.

$$u = 1 \quad \text{or} \quad u = -1 \qquad \text{Solutions in terms of } u$$

$$x^2 = 1 \quad \text{or} \quad x^2 = -1 \qquad \text{Let } x^2 = u.$$

$$x = \pm 1 \quad \text{or} \quad x = \pm i \qquad \text{Square root property}$$

There are four complex solutions: -1, 1, $-i$, and i.

■ **Now Try Exercise 25**

EXAMPLE 5 **Solving a rational equation**

Find all complex solutions to $\dfrac{1}{x} + \dfrac{1}{x^2} = -1$.

Solution

This equation is a rational equation. However, if we multiply through by the LCD, x^2, we clear fractions and obtain a quadratic equation with complex solutions.

$$\frac{1}{x} + \frac{1}{x^2} = -1 \qquad \text{Given equation}$$

$$\frac{x^2}{x} + \frac{x^2}{x^2} = -1x^2 \qquad \text{Multiply each term by } x^2.$$

$$x + 1 = -x^2 \qquad \text{Simplify.}$$

$$x^2 + x + 1 = 0 \qquad \text{Add } x^2.$$

$$x = \frac{-1 \pm \sqrt{1^2 - 4(1)(1)}}{2(1)} \qquad \text{Quadratic formula}$$

$$x = \frac{-1 \pm i\sqrt{3}}{2} \qquad \sqrt{-3} = i\sqrt{3}$$

$$x = -\frac{1}{2} \pm \frac{i\sqrt{3}}{2} \qquad \frac{a \pm b}{c} = \frac{a}{c} \pm \frac{b}{c}$$

■ **Now Try Exercise 31**

6.6 Putting It All Together

EQUATION	SUBSTITUTION	EXAMPLES
Higher Degree Polynomial	Let $u = x^n$ for some integer n.	To solve $x^4 - 3x^2 - 4 = 0$, let $u = x^2$. This equation becomes $$u^2 - 3u - 4 = 0.$$
Rational Exponents	Pick a substitution that reduces the equation to quadratic form.	To solve $n^{-2} + 6n^{-1} + 9 = 0$, let $u = n^{-1}$. This equation becomes $$u^2 + 6u + 9 = 0.$$ To solve $6x^{2/5} - 5x^{1/5} - 4 = 0$, let $u = x^{1/5}$. This equation becomes $$6u^2 - 5u - 4 = 0.$$

EQUATION	SUBSTITUTION	EXAMPLES
Equations Having Complex Solutions	Both polynomial and rational equations can have complex solutions. Use the fact that if $a > 0$, then $\sqrt{-a} = i\sqrt{a}$.	$$1 + \frac{1}{x^2} = 0$$ $$x^2 \cdot \left(1 + \frac{1}{x^2}\right) = 0 \cdot x^2$$ $$x^2 + 1 = 0$$ $$x^2 = -1$$ $$x = \pm i$$

6.6 Exercises

MyMathLab | Math XL PRACTICE | WATCH | DOWNLOAD | READ | REVIEW

EQUATIONS REDUCIBLE TO QUADRATIC FORM

Exercises 1–6: Use the given substitution to solve the equation.

1. $x^4 - 7x^2 + 6 = 0 \qquad u = x^2$

2. $2k^4 - 7k^2 + 6 = 0 \qquad u = k^2$

3. $3z^6 + z^3 - 10 = 0 \qquad u = z^3$

4. $2x^6 + 17x^3 + 8 = 0 \qquad u = x^3$

5. $4n^{-2} + 17n^{-1} + 15 = 0 \qquad u = n^{-1}$

6. $m^{-2} + 24 = 10m^{-1} \qquad u = m^{-1}$

Exercises 7–24: Solve. Find all real solutions.

7. $x^4 = 8x^2 + 9$

8. $3x^4 = 10x^2 + 8$

9. $3x^6 - 5x^3 - 2 = 0$

10. $6x^6 + 11x^3 + 4 = 0$

11. $2z^{-2} + 11z^{-1} = 40$

12. $z^{-2} - 10z^{-1} + 25 = 0$

13. $x^{2/3} - 2x^{1/3} + 1 = 0$

14. $3x^{2/3} + 18x^{1/3} = 48$

15. $x^{2/5} - 33x^{1/5} = -32$

16. $x^{2/5} - 80x^{1/5} = 81$

17. $x - 13\sqrt{x} + 36 = 0$

18. $x - 17\sqrt{x} + 16 = 0$

19. $z^{1/2} - 2z^{1/4} + 1 = 0$

20. $z^{1/2} - 4z^{1/4} + 4 = 0$

21. $(x + 1)^2 - 5(x + 1) - 14 = 0$

22. $2(x - 5)^2 + 5(x - 5) + 3 = 0$

23. $(x^2 - 1)^2 - 4 = 0$

24. $(x^2 - 9)^2 - 8(x^2 - 9) + 16 = 0$

EQUATIONS HAVING COMPLEX SOLUTIONS

Exercises 25–34: Find all complex solutions.

25. $x^4 - 16 = 0$

26. $\frac{1}{3}x^4 - 27 = 0$

27. $x^3 + x = 0$

28. $4x^3 + x = 0$

29. $x^4 - 2 = x^2$

30. $x^4 - 3 = 2x^2$

31. $\frac{1}{x} + \frac{1}{x^2} = -\frac{1}{2}$

32. $\frac{2}{x - 1} - \frac{1}{x} = -1$

33. $\frac{2}{x - 2} - \frac{1}{x} = -\frac{1}{2}$

34. $\frac{1}{x} - \frac{1}{x^2} = \frac{1}{2}$

WRITING ABOUT MATHEMATICS

35. Explain how to solve $ax^4 - bx^2 + c = 0$. Assume that the left side of the equation factors.

36. Explain what it means for an equation to be reducible to quadratic form.

SECTIONS 6.5 AND 6.6   **Checking Basic Concepts**

1. Solve the inequality $x^2 - x - 6 > 0$. Write your answer in interval notation.

2. Solve the inequality $3x^2 + 5x + 2 \le 0$. Write your answer in interval notation.

3. Solve $x^6 + 6x^3 - 16 = 0$.

4. Solve $x^{2/3} - 7x^{1/3} - 8 = 0$.

5. Find all complex solutions to $x^4 + 2x^2 + 1 = 0$.

CHAPTER 6   Summary

SECTION 6.1 ■ QUADRATIC FUNCTIONS AND THEIR GRAPHS

Quadratic Function Any quadratic function f can be written as

$$f(x) = ax^2 + bx + c \quad (a \neq 0).$$

Graph of a Quadratic Function Its graph is a parabola that is wider than the graph of $y = x^2$ if $0 < |a| < 1$, and narrower than the graph of $y = x^2$ if $|a| > 1$. The y-intercept is c.

Axis of Symmetry The parabola is symmetric with respect to this vertical line. The axis of symmetry passes through the vertex. Its equation is $x = -\frac{b}{2a}$.

Vertex Formula The x-coordinate of the vertex is $-\frac{b}{2a}$.

Example: Let $y = x^2 - 4x + 1$ with $a = 1$ and $b = -4$.

$$x = -\frac{-4}{2(1)} = 2 \quad \text{and} \quad y = 2^2 - 4(2) + 1 = -3. \text{ The vertex is } (2, -3).$$

SECTION 6.2 ■ PARABOLAS AND MODELING

Vertical and Horizontal Translations Let h and k be positive numbers.

To graph	**shift the graph of $y = x^2$ by k units**
$y = x^2 + k$	upward.
$y = x^2 - k$	downward.

To graph	**shift the graph of $y = x^2$ by h units**
$y = (x - h)^2$	right.
$y = (x + h)^2$	left.

Example: Compared to $y = x^2$, the graph of $y = (x - 1)^2 + 2$ is translated right 1 unit and upward 2 units.

Vertex Form Any quadratic function can be expressed as $f(x) = a(x - h)^2 + k$. In this form the point (h, k) is the vertex. A quadratic function can be put in this form by completing the square or by applying the vertex formula.

Example: $y = x^2 + 10x - 4$ Given equation
$= (x^2 + 10x + 25) - 25 - 4$ $\left(\frac{b}{2}\right)^2 = \left(\frac{10}{2}\right)^2 = 25$; complete the square.
$= (x + 5)^2 - 29$ Perfect square trinomial; add.
The vertex is $(-5, -29)$.

SECTION 6.3 ■ QUADRATIC EQUATIONS

Quadratic Equations Any quadratic equation can be written as $ax^2 + bx + c = 0$ and can have no real solutions, one real solution, or two real solutions. These solutions correspond to the x-intercepts for the graph of $y = ax^2 + bx + c$.

Example:
$$x^2 + x - 2 = 0$$
$$(x + 2)(x - 1) = 0$$
$$x = -2 \quad \text{or} \quad x = 1$$

The solutions are -2 and 1.
See the graph to the right.

x-intercepts: $-2, 1$

$y = x^2 + x - 2$

Completing the Square Write the equation in the form $x^2 + bx = d$. Complete the square by adding $\left(\frac{b}{2}\right)^2$ to each side of the equation.

Example:
$$x^2 - 8x = 3$$
$$x^2 - 8x + 16 = 3 + 16 \qquad \text{Add } \left(\frac{-8}{2}\right)^2 = 16 \text{ to each side.}$$
$$(x - 4)^2 = 19 \qquad \text{Perfect square trinomial}$$
$$x - 4 = \pm \sqrt{19} \qquad \text{Square root property}$$
$$x = 4 \pm \sqrt{19} \qquad \text{Add 4 to each side.}$$

SECTION 6.4 ■ THE QUADRATIC FORMULA

The Quadratic Formula The solutions to $ax^2 + bx + c = 0$ $(a \neq 0)$ are given by

$$x = \frac{-b \pm \sqrt{b^2 - 4ac}}{2a}.$$

Example: Solve $2x^2 + 3x - 1 = 0$ by letting $a = 2$, $b = 3$, and $c = -1$.

$$x = \frac{-3 \pm \sqrt{3^2 - 4(2)(-1)}}{2(2)} = \frac{-3 \pm \sqrt{17}}{4} \approx 0.28, -1.78$$

The Discriminant The expression $b^2 - 4ac$ is called the discriminant. If $b^2 - 4ac > 0$, there are two real solutions; if $b^2 - 4ac = 0$, there is one real solution; and if $b^2 - 4ac < 0$, there are no real solutions—rather there are two complex solutions.

Example: For $2x^2 + 3x - 1 = 0$, the discriminant is

$$b^2 - 4ac = 3^2 - 4(2)(-1) = 17 > 0.$$

There are two real solutions to this quadratic equation, as shown in the previous example.

Quadratic Equations with Complex Solutions A quadratic equation sometimes has no real solutions.

Example: $x^2 + 4 = 0$
$$x^2 = -4 \qquad \text{Subtract 4 from each side.}$$
$$x = \pm 2i \qquad \text{Square root property; two complex solutions}$$

SECTION 6.5 ■ QUADRATIC INEQUALITIES

Quadratic Inequalities When the equals sign in a quadratic equation is replaced with $<$, $>$, $\leq$, or $\geq$, a quadratic inequality results. For example,

$$3x^2 - x + 1 = 0$$

is a quadratic equation and

$$3x^2 - x + 1 > 0$$

is a quadratic inequality. Like quadratic equations, quadratic inequalities can be solved symbolically, graphically, and numerically. An important first step in solving a quadratic inequality is to solve the corresponding quadratic equation.

Examples: The solutions to $x^2 - 5x - 6 = 0$ are -1 and 6.

The solutions to $x^2 - 5x - 6 < 0$ satisfy $-1 < x < 6$.

The solutions to $x^2 - 5x - 6 > 0$ satisfy $x < -1$ or $x > 6$.

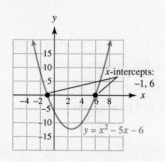

SECTION 6.6 ■ EQUATIONS IN QUADRATIC FORM

Equations Reducible to Quadratic Form An equation that is not quadratic, but can be put into quadratic form by using a substitution, is reducible to quadratic form.

Example: To solve $x^{2/3} - 2x^{1/3} - 15 = 0$, let $u = x^{1/3}$. This equation becomes

$$u^2 - 2u - 15 = 0.$$

Factoring results in $(u + 3)(u - 5) = 0$, so $u = -3$ or $u = 5$.
Because $u = x^{1/3}$, $x = u^3$ and $x = (-3)^3 = -27$ or $x = (5)^3 = 125$.

CHAPTER 6 Review Exercises

SECTION 6.1

Exercises 1 and 2: Identify the vertex, axis of symmetry, and whether the parabola opens upward or downward.

1.

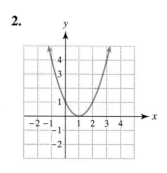

2.

Exercises 3–6: Do the following.
  (a) *Graph f.*
  (b) *Identify the vertex and axis of symmetry.*
  (c) *Evaluate $f(x)$ at the given value of x.*

3. $f(x) = x^2 - 2$, $x = -1$

4. $f(x) = -x^2 + 4x - 3$, $x = 3$

5. $f(x) = -\frac{1}{2}x^2 + x + \frac{3}{2}$, $x = -2$

6. $f(x) = 2x^2 + 8x + 5$, $x = -3$

7. Find the minimum y-value located on the graph of $y = 2x^2 - 6x + 1$.

8. Find the maximum y-value located on the graph of $y = -3x^2 + 2x - 5$.

Exercises 9–12: Find the vertex of the parabola.

9. $f(x) = x^2 - 4x - 2$ **10.** $f(x) = 5 - x^2$

11. $f(x) = -\frac{1}{4}x^2 + x + 1$ **12.** $f(x) = 2 + 2x + x^2$

SECTION 6.2

Exercises 13–18: Do the following.
 (a) Graph f.
 (b) Compare the graph of f with the graph of $y = x^2$.

13. $f(x) = x^2 + 2$ **14.** $f(x) = 3x^2$

15. $f(x) = (x - 2)^2$ **16.** $f(x) = (x + 1)^2 - 3$

17. $f(x) = \frac{1}{2}(x + 1)^2 + 2$

18. $f(x) = 2(x - 1)^2 - 3$

19. Write the vertex form of a parabola with $a = -4$ and vertex $(2, -5)$.

20. Write the vertex form of a parabola that opens downward with vertex $(-4, 6)$. Assume that $a = \pm 1$.

Exercises 21–24: Write the equation in vertex form. Identify the vertex.

21. $y = x^2 + 4x - 7$ **22.** $y = x^2 - 7x + 1$

23. $y = 2x^2 - 3x - 8$ **24.** $y = 3x^2 + 6x - 2$

Exercises 25 and 26: Find a value for the constant a so that $f(x) = ax^2 - 1$ models the data.

25.

x	1	2	3
$f(x)$	2	11	26

26.

x	-1	0	1
$f(x)$	$-\frac{3}{4}$	-1	$-\frac{3}{4}$

Exercises 27 and 28: Write $f(x)$ in the form given by $f(x) = ax^2 + bx + c$. Identify the y-intercept on the graph of f.

27. $f(x) = -5(x - 3)^2 + 4$

28. $f(x) = 3(x + 2)^2 - 4$

SECTION 6.3

Exercises 29–32: Use the graph of $y = ax^2 + bx + c$ to solve $ax^2 + bx + c = 0$.

29.   **30.**

31.   **32.**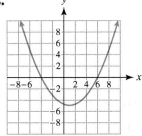

Exercises 33 and 34: A table of $y = ax^2 + bx + c$ is given. Solve $ax^2 + bx + c = 0$.

33.

X	Y1
-20	250
-15	100
-10	0
-5	-50
0	-50
5	0
10	100

Y1≣X^2+5X−50

34.

X	Y1
-.75	2
-.5	0
-.25	-1
0	-1
.25	0
.5	2
.75	5

Y1≣8X^2+2X−1

Exercises 35–38: Solve the quadratic equation
 (a) graphically and
 (b) numerically.

35. $x^2 - 5x - 50 = 0$ **36.** $\frac{1}{2}x^2 + x - \frac{3}{2} = 0$

37. $\frac{1}{4}x^2 + \frac{1}{2}x = 2$ **38.** $\frac{1}{2}x + \frac{3}{4} = \frac{1}{4}x^2$

Exercises 39–42: Solve by factoring.

39. $x^2 + x - 20 = 0$ **40.** $x^2 + 11x + 24 = 0$

41. $15x^2 - 4x - 4 = 0$ **42.** $7x^2 - 25x + 12 = 0$

Exercises 43–46: Use the square root property to solve.

43. $x^2 = 100$ **44.** $3x^2 = \frac{1}{3}$

45. $4x^2 - 6 = 0$ **46.** $5x^2 = x^2 - 4$

Exercises 47–50: Solve by completing the square.

47. $x^2 + 6x = -2$ **48.** $x^2 - 4x = 6$

49. $x^2 - 2x - 5 = 0$ **50.** $2x^2 + 6x - 1 = 0$

Exercises 51 and 52: Solve for the specified variable.

51. $F = \dfrac{k}{(R + r)^2}$ for R **52.** $2x^2 + 3y^2 = 12$ for y

SECTION 6.4

Exercises 53–58: Use the quadratic formula to solve.

53. $x^2 - 9x + 18 = 0$ **54.** $x^2 - 24x + 143 = 0$

55. $6x^2 + x = 1$ **56.** $5x^2 + 1 = 5x$

57. $x(x - 8) = 5$ **58.** $2x(2 - x) = 3 - 2x$

Exercises 59–64: Solve by any method.

59. $x^2 - 4 = 0$ **60.** $4x^2 - 1 = 0$

61. $2x^2 + 15 = 11x$ **62.** $2x^2 + 15 = 13x$

63. $x(5 - x) = 2x + 1$ **64.** $-2x(x - 1) = x - \frac{1}{2}$

Exercises 65–68: A graph of $y = ax^2 + bx + c$ is shown.
 (a) State whether $a > 0$ or $a < 0$.
 (b) Solve $ax^2 + bx + c = 0$.
 (c) Determine whether the discriminant is positive, negative, or zero.

65.

66.

67.

68.
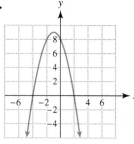

Exercises 69–72: Do the following for the given equation.
 (a) Evaluate the discriminant.
 (b) How many real solutions are there?
 (c) Support your answer for part (b) graphically.

69. $2x^2 - 3x + 1 = 0$ **70.** $7x^2 + 2x - 5 = 0$

71. $3x^2 + x + 2 = 0$

72. $4.41x^2 - 12.6x + 9 = 0$

Exercises 73–76: Solve. Write any complex solutions in standard form.

73. $x^2 + x + 5 = 0$ **74.** $2x^2 + 8 = 0$

75. $2x^2 = x - 1$ **76.** $7x^2 = 2x - 5$

SECTION 6.5

Exercises 77 and 78: The graph of $y = ax^2 + bx + c$ is shown. Solve each equation or inequality.
 (a) $ax^2 + bx + c = 0$
 (b) $ax^2 + bx + c < 0$
 (c) $ax^2 + bx + c > 0$

77.

78.
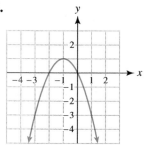

Exercises 79 and 80: A table of $y = ax^2 + bx + c$ is shown. Solve each equation or inequality.
 (a) $ax^2 + bx + c = 0$
 (b) $ax^2 + bx + c < 0$
 (c) $ax^2 + bx + c > 0$

79. $y = x^2 - 16$

x	-6	-4	-2	0	2	4	6
y	20	0	-12	-16	-12	0	20

80. $y = x^2 + x - 2$

x	-3	-2	-1	0	1	2	3
y	4	0	-2	-2	0	4	10

Exercises 81 and 82: Solve the equation in part (a). Use the results to solve the inequalities in parts (b) and (c).

81. (a) $x^2 - 2x - 3 = 0$
   (b) $x^2 - 2x - 3 < 0$
   (c) $x^2 - 2x - 3 > 0$

82. (a) $2x^2 - 7x - 15 = 0$
   (b) $2x^2 - 7x - 15 \leq 0$
   (c) $2x^2 - 7x - 15 \geq 0$

Exercises 83–88: Solve the quadratic inequality. Write your answer in interval notation.

83. $x^2 + 4x + 3 \le 0$ **84.** $5x^2 - 16x + 3 < 0$

85. $6x^2 - 13x + 2 > 0$ **86.** $x^2 \ge 5$

87. $(x - 1)^2 \ge 0$ **88.** $x^2 + 3 < 2$

SECTION 6.6

Exercises 89–92: Solve the equation.

89. $x^4 - 14x^2 + 45 = 0$

90. $2z^{-2} + z^{-1} - 28 = 0$

91. $x^{2/3} - 9x^{1/3} + 8 = 0$

92. $(x - 1)^2 + 2(x - 1) + 1 = 0$

Exercises 93 and 94: Find all complex solutions.

93. $4x^4 + 4x^2 + 1 = 0$ **94.** $\dfrac{1}{x - 2} - \dfrac{3}{x} = -1$

APPLICATIONS

95. *Construction* A rain gutter is being fabricated from a flat sheet of metal so that the cross section of the gutter is a rectangle, as shown in the accompanying figure. The width of the metal sheet is 12 inches.

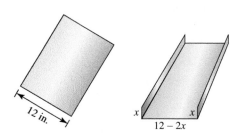

(a) Write a formula $f(x)$ that gives the area of the cross section.

(b) To hold the greatest amount of rainwater, the cross section should have maximum area. Find the dimensions that result in this maximum.

96. *Height of a Stone* Suppose that a stone is thrown upward with an initial velocity of 44 feet per second (30 miles per hour) and is released 4 feet above the ground. Its height h in feet after t seconds is given by

$$h(t) = -16t^2 + 44t + 4.$$

(a) When does the stone reach a height of 32 feet?

(b) After how many seconds does the stone reach maximum height? Estimate this height.

97. *Maximizing Revenue* Suppose that hotel rooms cost $90 per night. However, for a group rate the management is considering reducing the cost of a room by $3 for every room rented.

(a) Write a formula $f(x)$ that gives the revenue from renting x rooms at the group rate.

(b) Graph f in [0, 30, 5] by [0, 800, 100].

(c) How many rooms should be rented to receive revenue of $600?

(d) How many rooms should be rented to maximize revenue?

98. *Numbers* The product of two numbers is 143. One number is 2 more than the other.

(a) Write a quadratic equation whose solution gives the smaller number x.

(b) Solve the equation.

99. *Braking Distance* On dry pavement a safe braking distance d in feet for a car traveling x miles per hour is $d = \frac{x^2}{12}$. For each distance d, find x. (*Source:* F. Mannering, *Principles of Highway Engineering and Traffic Control.*)

(a) $d = 144$ feet   **(b)** $d = 300$ feet

100. *U.S. Energy Consumption* From 1950 to 1970 per capita consumption of energy in millions of Btu can be modeled by $f(x) = \frac{1}{4}(x - 1950)^2 + 220$, where x is the year. (*Source:* Department of Energy.)

(a) Find and interpret the vertex.

(b) Graph f in [1950, 1970, 5] by [200, 350, 25]. What happened to energy consumption during this time period?

(c) Use f to predict the consumption in 2010. Actual consumption was 321 million Btu. Did f provide a good model for 2010? Explain.

101. *Screens* A square computer screen has an area of 123 square inches. Approximate its dimensions to the nearest tenth of an inch.

102. *Flying a Kite* A kite is being flown, as illustrated in the accompanying figure. If 130 feet of string have been let out, find the value of x.

103. *Area* A uniform strip of grass is to be planted around a rectangular swimming pool, as illustrated in the accompanying figure on the next page. The swimming pool is 30 feet wide and 50 feet long. If there is only enough grass seed to cover 250 square feet, estimate the width x that the strip of grass should be.

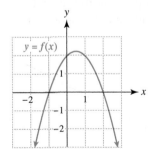

104. *Dimensions of a Cone* The volume V of a cone is given by $V = \frac{1}{3}\pi r^2 h$, where r is its base radius and h is its height. See the accompanying figure. If $h = 20$ inches and the volume of the cone must be between 750 and 1700 cubic inches, inclusively, estimate, to the nearest tenth of an inch, possible values for r.

CHAPTER 6 **Test** **CHAPTER Test Prep VIDEOS** Step-by-step test solutions are found on the Chapter Test Prep Videos available via the Video Resources on DVD, in *MyMathLab*, and on You Tube (search "RockswoldInterAlg" and click on "Channels").

1. Find the vertex and axis of symmetry for the graph of $f(x) = -\frac{1}{2}x^2 + x + 1$. Evaluate $f(-2)$.

2. Find the minimum y-value located on the graph of $y = x^2 + 3x - 5$.

3. Find the exact value for the constant a so that $f(x) = ax^2 + 2$ models the data in the table.

x	-2	0	2	4
$f(x)$	0	2	0	-6

4. Compare the graph of $y = f(x)$ to the graph of $y = x^2$. Then graph $y = f(x)$.
   (a) $f(x) = (x - 1)^2$ (b) $f(x) = x^2 - 2$
   (c) $f(x) = \frac{1}{2}(x - 3)^2 + 2$

5. Write $y = x^2 - 6x + 2$ in vertex form. Identify the vertex and axis of symmetry.

6. Use the graph of $f(x) = ax^2 + bx + c$ to solve $ax^2 + bx + c = 0$. Then evaluate $f(1)$.

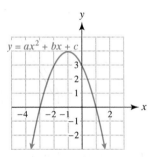

Exercises 7 and 8: Solve the quadratic equation.

7. $3x^2 + 11x - 4 = 0$ 8. $2x^2 = 2 - 6x^2$

9. Solve $x^2 - 8x = 1$ by completing the square.

10. Solve $x(-2x + 3) = -1$ by using the quadratic formula.

11. Solve $9x^2 - 16 = 0$.

12. Solve $F = \dfrac{Gm^2}{r^2}$ for m.

13. A graph of $y = ax^2 + bx + c$ is shown.
    (a) State whether $a > 0$ or $a < 0$.
    (b) Solve $ax^2 + bx + c = 0$.
    (c) Determine whether the discriminant is positive, negative, or zero.

14. Complete the following for $-3x^2 + 4x - 5 = 0$.
    (a) Evaluate the discriminant.
    (b) How many real solutions are there?
    (c) Support your answer for part (b) graphically.

Exercises 15 and 16: The graph of $y = ax^2 + bx + c$ is shown. Solve each equation or inequality.
    (a) $ax^2 + bx + c = 0$
    (b) $ax^2 + bx + c < 0$
    (c) $ax^2 + bx + c > 0$

15.

16.

17. Solve the quadratic equation in part (a). Use the result to solve the inequalities in parts (b) and (c) and write your answer in interval notation.
  (a) $8x^2 - 2x - 3 = 0$
  (b) $8x^2 - 2x - 3 \le 0$
  (c) $8x^2 - 2x - 3 \ge 0$

18. Solve $x^2 + 2x \le 0$.

19. Solve $x^6 - 3x^3 + 2 = 0$. Find all real solutions.

20. Solve $2x^2 + 4x + 3 = 0$. Write all complex solutions in standard form.

21. Solve $\sqrt{2} - \pi x^2 = 2.12x - 0.5\pi$ graphically. Round your answers to the nearest hundredth.

22. *Braking Distance* On wet pavement a safe braking distance d in feet for a car traveling x miles per hour is $d = \frac{x^2}{9}$. What speed corresponds to a braking distance of 250 feet? (*Source:* F. Mannering, *Principles of Highway Engineering and Traffic Control.*)

23. *Construction* A fence is being constructed along a 20-foot building, as shown in the accompanying figure. No fencing is used along the building.
  (a) If 200 feet of fence are available, find a formula $f(x)$ using only the variable x that gives the area enclosed.
  (b) What value of x gives the greatest area?

24. *Height of a Stone* Suppose that a stone is thrown upward with an initial velocity of 88 feet per second (60 miles per hour) and is released 8 feet above the ground. Its height h in feet after t seconds is given by

$$h(t) = -16t^2 + 88t + 8.$$

  (a) Graph h in [0, 6, 1] by [0, 150, 50].
  (b) When does the stone strike the ground?
  (c) After how many seconds does the stone reach maximum height? Estimate this height.

CHAPTER 6   Extended and Discovery Exercises

MODELING DATA WITH A QUADRATIC FUNCTION

1. *Survival Rate of Birds* The survival rate of sparrowhawks varies according to their age. The following table summarizes the results of one study by listing the age in years and the percentage of birds that survived the previous year. For example, 52% of sparrowhawks that reached age 6 lived to be 7 years old. (*Source:* D. Brown and P. Rothery, *Models in Biology.*)

Age	1	2	3	4	5
Percent (%)	45	60	71	67	67

Age	6	7	8	9
Percent (%)	61	52	30	25

  (a) Try to explain the relationship between age and the likelihood of surviving the next year.

  (b) Make a scatterplot of the data. What type of function might model the data? Explain.
  (c) Graph each function. Which of the following functions models the data better?

$$f_1(x) = -3.57x + 71.1$$
$$f_2(x) = -2.07x^2 + 17.1x + 33$$

  (d) Use one of these functions to estimate the likelihood of a 5.5-year-old sparrowhawk surviving for 1 more year.

2. *Photosynthesis and Temperature* Photosynthesis is the process by which plants turn sunlight into energy. At very cold temperatures photosynthesis may halt even though the sun is shining. In one study the efficiency of photosynthesis for an Antarctic species of grass was investigated. The following table lists results for various temperatures. The temperature x is in degrees Celsius, and the efficiency y is given as a percent. The purpose of the research was to determine the temperature at which photosynthesis is most efficient. (*Source:* D. Brown.)

x (°C)	−1.5	0	2.5	5	7	10	12
y (%)	33	46	55	80	87	93	95

x (°C)	15	17	20	22	25	27	30
y(%)	91	89	77	72	54	46	34

(a) Plot the data.
(b) What type of function might model these data? Explain your reasoning.
(c) Find a function f that models the data.
(d) Use f to estimate the temperature at which photosynthesis is most efficient in this type of grass.

TRANSLATIONS OF PARABOLAS IN COMPUTER GRAPHICS

Exercises 3 and 4: In older video games with two-dimensional graphics, the background is often translated to give the illusion that a character in the game is moving. The simple scene on the left shows a mountain and an airplane. To make it appear that the airplane is flying, the mountain can be translated to the left, as shown in the figure on the right. (Reference: C. Pokorny and C. Gerald, Computer Graphics.)

3. *Video Games* Suppose that the mountain in the figure on the left is modeled by $f(x) = -0.4x^2 + 4$ and that the airplane is located at the point $(1, 5)$.
   (a) Graph f in $[-4, 4, 1]$ by $[0, 6, 1]$, where the units are kilometers. Plot the point $(1, 5)$ to show the location of the airplane.
   (b) Assume that the airplane is moving horizontally to the right at 0.2 kilometer per second. To give a video game player the illusion that the airplane is moving, graph the image of the mountain and the position of the airplane after 10 seconds.

4. *Video Games* (Refer to Exercise 3.) Discuss how you could create the illusion of the airplane moving to the left and gaining altitude as it passes over the mountain. Try to perform a translation of this type. Explain your reasoning.

Exercises 5–8: Factoring and the Discriminant If the discriminant of the trinomial $ax^2 + bx + c$ with integer coefficients is a perfect square, then it can be factored. For example, on the one hand, the discriminant of $6x^2 + x - 2$ is

$$1^2 - 4(6)(-2) = 49,$$

which is a perfect square ($7^2 = 49$), so we can factor the trinomial as

$$6x^2 + x - 2 = (2x - 1)(3x + 2).$$

On the other hand, the discriminant for $x^2 + x - 1$ is

$$1^2 - 4(1)(-1) = 5,$$

which is not a perfect square, so we cannot factor this trinomial by using integers as coefficients. Similarly, if the discriminant is negative, the trinomial cannot be factored by using integer coefficients. Use the discriminant to predict whether the trinomial can be factored. Then test your prediction.

5. $10x^2 - x - 3$ 6. $4x^2 - 3x - 6$

7. $3x^2 + 2x - 2$ 8. $2x^2 + x + 3$

Exercises 9–14: Polynomial Inequalities The solution set for a polynomial inequality can be found by first determining the boundary numbers. For example, to solve $f(x) = x^3 - 4x > 0$ begin by solving $x^3 - 4x = 0$. The solutions (boundary numbers) are $-2, 0$, and 2. The function $f(x) = x^3 - 4x$ is either only positive or only negative on intervals between consecutive zeros. To determine the solution set, we can evaluate test values for each interval as shown below.

Interval	Test Value	$f(x) = x^3 - 4x$
$(-\infty, -2)$	$x = -3$	$f(-3) = -15 < 0$
$(-2, 0)$	$x = -1$	$f(-1) = 3 > 0$
$(0, 2)$	$x = 1$	$f(1) = -3 < 0$
$(2, \infty)$	$x = 3$	$f(3) = 15 > 0$

[−6, 6, 1] by [−4, 4, 1]

We can see that $f(x) > 0$ for $(-2, 0) \cup (2, \infty)$. These results are also supported graphically in the figure on the right above, where the graph of f is above the x-axis when $-2 < x < 0$ or when $x > 2$.

Use these concepts to solve the polynomial inequality.

9. $x^3 - x^2 - 6x > 0$

10. $x^3 - 3x^2 + 2x < 0$

11. $x^3 - 7x^2 + 14x \le 8$

12. $9x - x^3 \ge 0$

13. $x^4 - 5x^2 + 4 > 0$

14. $1 < x^4$

Exercises 15–20: Rational Inequalities Rational inequalities can be solved using many of the same techniques that are used to solve other types of inequalities. However, there is one important difference. For a rational inequality, the boundary between greater than and less than can be either an x-value where equality occurs or an x-value where a rational expression is undefined. For example, consider the inequality $f(x) = \frac{2-x}{2x} > 0$. The solution to the equation $\frac{2-x}{2x} = 0$ is 2. The rational expression $\frac{2-x}{2x}$ is undefined when $x = 0$. Therefore we select test values on the intervals $(-\infty, 0)$, $(0, 2)$, and $(2, \infty)$. The table in the next column reveals that $f(x) > 0$ for $(0, 2)$.

Interval	Test Value	$f(x) = \dfrac{2-x}{2x}$
$(-\infty, 0)$	$x = -0.5$	$f(-0.5) = -2.5 < 0$
$(0, 2)$	$x = 1$	$f(1) = 0.5 > 0$
$(2, \infty)$	$x = 2.5$	$f(2.5) = -0.1 < 0$

Note that $f(x)$ changes from negative to positive at $x = 0$, where $f(x)$ is undefined. These results are supported graphically in the figure on the right above.

Solve the rational inequality.

15. $\dfrac{3-x}{3x} \ge 0$

16. $\dfrac{x-2}{x+2} > 0$

17. $\dfrac{3-2x}{1+x} < 3$

18. $\dfrac{x+1}{4-2x} \ge 1$

19. $\dfrac{5}{x^2-4} < 0$

20. $\dfrac{x}{x^2-1} \ge 0$

CHAPTERS 1–6   Cumulative Review Exercises

1. Evaluate $F = \dfrac{5}{z^2 + 1}$ when $z = -2$.

2. Classify each number as one or more of the following: natural number, whole number, integer, rational number, or irrational number: $0.\overline{4}$, $\sqrt{7}$, 0, -5, $\sqrt[3]{8}$, $-\frac{4}{3}$.

3. Simplify each expression. Write the result using positive exponents.

  (a) $\left(\dfrac{x^2 y^6}{x^{-3}}\right)^2$ **(b)** $\dfrac{(xy^{-3})^2}{x(y^{-2})^{-1}}$

  (c) $(a^2 b)^2 (ab^3)^{-4}$

4. Write 9,290,000 in scientific notation.

5. Find $f(-2)$, if $f(x) = \sqrt{2 - x}$. What is the domain of f?

6. If $f(2) = 5$, then what point lies on the graph of f?

Exercises 7 and 8: Graph f by hand.

7. $f(x) = x^2 + 2x$ **8.** $f(x) = |2x - 4|$

9. Find the slope–intercept form of the line that passes through $(4, -1)$ and is parallel to the line passing through $(0, 1)$ and $(-2, 4)$.

10. Find the equation of a vertical line that passes through $(-3, 4)$.

11. Solve $2x - 3(x + 2) = 6$.

Exercises 12–14: Solve the inequality. Write your answer in interval notation.

12. $7 - x > 3x$ **13.** $|3x - 2| \le 1$

14. $-4 \le 1 - x < 2$

15. Solve the system.

$$-x - 4y = -3$$
$$5x + y = -4$$

16. Shade the solution set in the xy-plane.

$$3x + y \le 3$$
$$x - 3y \le 3$$

17. Solve the system.

$$x + y - z = 3$$
$$x - y + z = 1$$
$$2x - y - z = 1$$

Exercises 18–20: Multiply the expression.

18. $(3x - 2)(2x + 7)$ **19.** $3xy(x^2 + y^2)$

20. $(\sqrt{x} + 3)(\sqrt{x} - 3)$

Exercises 21 and 22: Factor the expression.

21. $x^3 - x^2 - 2x$ **22.** $4x^2 - 25$

Exercises 23 and 24: Solve each equation.

23. $x^2 - 3 = 0$ **24.** $x^2 + 1 = 2x$

Exercises 25 and 26: Simplify the expression.

25. $\dfrac{(x + 3)^2}{x + 2} \cdot \dfrac{x + 2}{2x + 6}$ **26.** $\dfrac{1}{x + 2} - \dfrac{1}{x}$

Exercises 27–30: Simplify the expression. Assume all variables are positive.

27. $\sqrt{16x^6}$ **28.** $16^{-3/2}$

29. $\dfrac{\sqrt[3]{81x}}{\sqrt[3]{3x}}$ **30.** $\sqrt{8x} + \sqrt{2x}$

31. Graph $f(x) = \sqrt{4x}$.

32. Find the distance between $(-1, 2)$ and $(4, 3)$.

33. Write $\dfrac{3 - i}{2 + i}$ in standard form.

34. Solve $3\sqrt{x + 1} = 2x$.

35. Solve the equation $2x = \sqrt{2.1 - x} + \sqrt[3]{0.1x}$ to the nearest hundredth.

36. Sketch a graph of $f(x) = x^2 - 2x + 3$.
   (a) Find the vertex.
   (b) Evaluate $f(-1)$.
   (c) What is the axis of symmetry?
   (d) Where is f increasing?

37. Write $f(x) = 2x^2 - 4x - 1$ in vertex form.

38. Compare the graph of $f(x) = 4(x + 1)^2 - 2$ to the graph of $y = x^2$.

39. Solve $x^2 + 6x = 2$ by completing the square.

40. Solve $2x^2 - 3x = 1$ by using the quadratic formula.

41. Solve $x(4 - x) = 3$.

42. The graph of $y = ax^2 + bx + c$ is shown in the next column. Solve each equation or inequality.

(a) $ax^2 + bx + c = 0$
(b) $ax^2 + bx + c \leq 0$

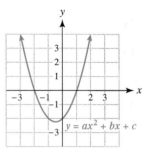

43. Solve $x^2 - 3x + 2 > 0$.

44. Solve $x^4 - 256 = 0$. Find all complex solutions.

Exercises 45–52: Thinking Generally *Match the graph (a.–h.) with its equation. Assume that a, b, and c are positive constants.*

45. $y = ax - b$ **46.** $y = b$

47. $y = -ax^2 + c$ **48.** $y = \dfrac{a}{x}$

49. $y = ax^3$ **50.** $y = |ax + b|$

51. $y = a\sqrt{x}$ **52.** $y = a\sqrt[3]{x}$

a.

b.

c.

d.

e.

f.

g.

h.
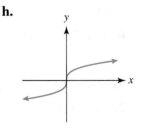

APPLICATIONS

53. *Calculating Water Flow*   Water is being pumped out of a tank. The gallons G of water in the tank after t minutes is shown in the figure, where $y = G(t)$.

(a) Evaluate $G(0)$. Interpret your answer.

(b) What is the t-intercept? Interpret your answer.

(c) What is the slope of the graph of G? Interpret your answer.

(d) Find a formula for $G(t)$.

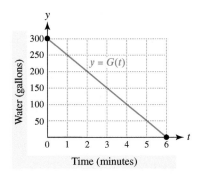

54. *Investment*   Suppose $4000 is deposited in three accounts paying 4%, 5%, and 6% annual interest. The amount invested at 6% is $1000 more than the amount invested at 5%. The interest after 1 year is $216. How much is invested at each rate?

55. *Maximizing Area*   There are 490 feet of fence available to surround the perimeter of a rectangular garden. On one side, there is a 10-foot gate that requires no fencing. What dimensions for the garden give the largest area?

56. *Height of a Tree*   A 6-foot-tall person casts a shadow that is 10 feet long while a nearby tree casts a 55-foot shadow. Find the height of the tree.

Overview of the Appendix

This appendix provides instruction for the TI-83, TI-83 Plus, and TI-84 Plus graphing calculators that may be used in conjunction with this textbook. It includes specific keystrokes needed to work several examples from the text. Students are advised to consult the *Graphing Calculator Guidebook* provided by the manufacturer.

Entering Mathematical Expressions

EVALUATING π To evaluate π, use the following keystrokes, as shown in the first and second lines of Figure A.1. (Do *not* use 3.14 or $\frac{22}{7}$ for π.)

$$\boxed{\text{2nd}}\,\boxed{\wedge[\pi]}\,\boxed{\text{ENTER}}$$

```
π
        3.141592654
√(200)
        14.14213562
10^4
             10000
```

Figure A.1

EVALUATING A SQUARE ROOT To evaluate a square root, such as $\sqrt{200}$, use the following keystrokes, as shown in the third and fourth lines of Figure A.1.

$$\boxed{\text{2nd}}\,\boxed{x^2[\sqrt{\,}]}\,\boxed{2}\,\boxed{0}\,\boxed{0}\,\boxed{)}\,\boxed{\text{ENTER}}$$

EVALUATING AN EXPONENTIAL EXPRESSION To evaluate an exponential expression, such as 10^4, use the following keystrokes, as shown in the last two lines of Figure A.1.

$$\boxed{1}\,\boxed{0}\,\boxed{\wedge}\,\boxed{4}\,\boxed{\text{ENTER}}$$

```
³√(64)
                 4
```

Figure A.2

EVALUATING A CUBE ROOT To evaluate a cube root, such as $\sqrt[3]{64}$, use the following keystrokes, as shown in Figure A.2.

$$\boxed{\text{MATH}}\,\boxed{4}\,\boxed{6}\,\boxed{4}\,\boxed{)}\,\boxed{\text{ENTER}}$$

SUMMARY: ENTERING MATHEMATICAL EXPRESSIONS

To access the *number* π, use $\boxed{\text{2nd}}\,\boxed{\wedge[\pi]}$.

To evaluate a *square root*, use $\boxed{\text{2nd}}\,\boxed{x^2[\sqrt{\,}]}$.

To evaluate an *exponential expression*, use the $\boxed{\wedge}$ key. To square a number, the $\boxed{x^2}$ key can also be used.

To evaluate a *cube root*, use $\boxed{\text{MATH}}\,\boxed{4}$.

```
(1/3)+(2/5)-(4/9
)▶Frac
             13/45
```

Figure A.3

Expressing Answers as Fractions

To evaluate $\frac{1}{3} + \frac{2}{5} - \frac{4}{9}$ in fraction form, use the following keystrokes, as shown in Figure A.3.

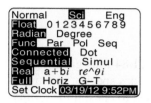

Figure A.4

Displaying Numbers in Scientific Notation

To display numbers in scientific notation, set the graphing calculator in scientific mode (Sci) by using the following keystrokes. See Figure A.4. (These keystrokes assume that the calculator is starting from normal mode.)

(MODE)(▷)(ENTER)(2nd)(MODE [QUIT])

In scientific mode we can display the numbers 5432 and 0.00001234 in scientific notation, as shown in Figure A.5.

Figure A.5

Entering Numbers in Scientific Notation

Numbers can be entered in scientific notation. For example, to enter 4.2×10^{-3} in scientific notation, use the following keystrokes. (Be sure to use the negation key $(-)$ rather than the subtraction key.)

(4)(.)(2)(2nd)(,[EE])((−))(3)

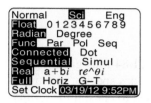

Figure A.6

This number can also be entered using the following keystrokes. See Figure A.6.

(4)(.)(2)(×)(1)(0)(^)(()((−))(3)())

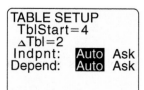

Figure A.7

Making a Table

Figure A.8

To make a table of values for $y = 3x + 1$ starting at $x = 4$ and incrementing by 2, begin by pressing (Y=) and then entering the formula $Y_1 = 3X + 1$, as shown in Figure A.7. (See Entering a Formula on page AP-4.) To set the table parameters, press the following keys. See Figure A.8.

(2nd)(WINDOW [TBLSET])(4)(ENTER)(2)

X	Y1	
4	13	
6	19	
8	25	
10	31	
12	37	
14	43	
16	49	

Y1◼3X+1

Figure A.9

These keystrokes specify a table that starts at $x = 4$ and increments the x-values by 2. Therefore, the values of Y_1 at $x = 4, 6, 8, \ldots$ appear in the table. To create this table, press the following keys.

$$\boxed{\text{2nd}}\ \boxed{\text{GRAPH [TABLE]}}$$

We can scroll through x- and y-values by using the arrow keys. See Figure A.9. Note that there is no first or last x-value in the table.

SUMMARY: MAKING A TABLE

1. Enter the formula for the equation using $\boxed{\text{Y =}}$.
2. Press $\boxed{\text{2nd}}\ \boxed{\text{WINDOW [TBLSET]}}$ to set the starting x-value and the increment between x-values appearing in the table.
3. Create the table by pressing $\boxed{\text{2nd}}\ \boxed{\text{GRAPH [TABLE]}}$.

Setting the Viewing Rectangle (Window)

ZOOM MEMORY
1:ZBox
2:Zoom In
3:Zoom Out
4:ZDecimal
5:ZSquare
6◼ZStandard
7↓ZTrig

Figure A.10

There are at least two ways to set the standard viewing rectangle of $[-10, 10, 1]$ by $[-10, 10, 1]$. The first involves pressing $\boxed{\text{ZOOM}}$ followed by $\boxed{6}$. See Figure A.10. The second method for setting the standard viewing rectangle is to press $\boxed{\text{WINDOW}}$ and enter the following keystrokes. See Figure A.11.

$$\boxed{(-)}\ \boxed{1}\ \boxed{0}\ \boxed{\text{ENTER}}\ \boxed{1}\ \boxed{0}\ \boxed{\text{ENTER}}\ \boxed{1}\ \boxed{\text{ENTER}}$$
$$\boxed{(-)}\ \boxed{1}\ \boxed{0}\ \boxed{\text{ENTER}}\ \boxed{1}\ \boxed{0}\ \boxed{\text{ENTER}}\ \boxed{1}\ \boxed{\text{ENTER}}$$

WINDOW
 Xmin=-10
 Xmax=10
 Xscl=1
 Ymin=-10
 Ymax=10
 Yscl=1
 Xres=1

Figure A.11

(Be sure to use the negation key $(-)$ rather than the subtraction key.) Other viewing rectangles can be set in a similar manner by pressing $\boxed{\text{WINDOW}}$ and entering the appropriate values. To see the viewing rectangle, press $\boxed{\text{GRAPH}}$.

SUMMARY: SETTING THE VIEWING RECTANGLE

To set the standard viewing rectangle, press $\boxed{\text{ZOOM}}\ \boxed{6}$. To set any viewing rectangle, press $\boxed{\text{WINDOW}}$ and enter the necessary values. To see the viewing rectangle, press $\boxed{\text{GRAPH}}$.

NOTE: You do not need to change "Xres" from 1.

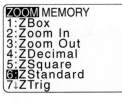

◼	L2	L3	1
1	4	------	
2	5		
3	6		
------	------		

L1={1, 2, 3}

Figure A.12

Making a Scatterplot or a Line Graph

To make a scatterplot with the points $(-5, -5)$, $(-2, 3)$, $(1, -7)$, and $(4, 8)$, begin by following these steps.

1. Press $\boxed{\text{STAT}}$ followed by $\boxed{1}$.
2. If list L1 is not empty, use the arrow keys to place the cursor on L1, as shown in Figure A.12. Then press $\boxed{\text{CLEAR}}$ followed by $\boxed{\text{ENTER}}$. This deletes all elements in the list. Similarly, if L2 is not empty, clear the list.
3. Input each x-value into list L1 followed by $\boxed{\text{ENTER}}$. Input each y-value into list L2 followed by $\boxed{\text{ENTER}}$. See Figure A.13.

L1	L2	L3	1
-5	-5	------	
-2	3		
1	-7		
4	8		
------	------		

L1(5) =

Figure A.13

Figure A.14

Figure A.15

[−10, 10, 1] by [−10, 10, 1]

Figure A.16

It is essential that both lists have the same number of values—otherwise, an error message appears when a scatterplot is attempted. Before these four points can be plotted, "STAT PLOT" must be turned on. It is accessed by pressing

$$\boxed{\text{2nd}}\,\boxed{\text{Y} = [\text{STAT PLOT}]},$$

as shown in Figure A.14.

There are three possible "STAT PLOTS," numbered 1, 2, and 3. Any one of the three can be selected. The first plot can be selected by pressing $\boxed{1}$. Next, place the cursor over "On" and press $\boxed{\text{ENTER}}$ to turn "Plot1" on. There are six types of plots that can be selected. The first type is a *scatterplot* and the second type is a *line graph*, so place the cursor over the first type of plot and press $\boxed{\text{ENTER}}$ to select a scatterplot. (To make the line graph, place the cursor over the second type of plot and press $\boxed{\text{ENTER}}$.) The x-values are stored in list L1, so select L1 for "Xlist" by pressing $\boxed{\text{2nd}}\boxed{1}$. Similarly, press $\boxed{\text{2nd}}\boxed{2}$ for the "Ylist," since the y-values are stored in list L2. Finally, there are three styles of marks that can be used to show data points in the graph. We will usually use the first because it is largest and shows up the best. Make the screen appear as in Figure A.15. Before plotting the four data points, be sure to set an appropriate viewing rectangle. Then press $\boxed{\text{GRAPH}}$. The data points appear as in Figure A.16.

REMARK 1: A fast way to set the viewing rectangle for any scatterplot is to select the "ZOOMSTAT" feature by pressing $\boxed{\text{ZOOM}}\boxed{9}$. This feature automatically scales the viewing rectangle so that all data points are shown.

REMARK 2: If an equation has been entered into the $\boxed{\text{Y} =}$ menu and selected, it will be graphed with the data. This feature is used frequently to model data.

SUMMARY: MAKING A SCATTERPLOT OR A LINE GRAPH

The following are basic steps necessary to make either a scatterplot or a line graph.

1. Use $\boxed{\text{STAT}}\boxed{1}$ to access lists L1 and L2.
2. If list L1 is not empty, place the cursor on L1 and press $\boxed{\text{CLEAR}}\boxed{\text{ENTER}}$. Repeat for list L2, if it is not empty.
3. Enter the x-values into list L1 and the y-values into list L2.
4. Use $\boxed{\text{2nd}}\boxed{\text{Y} = [\text{STAT PLOT}]}$ to select appropriate parameters for the scatterplot or line graph.
5. Set an appropriate viewing rectangle. Press $\boxed{\text{GRAPH}}$. Otherwise, press $\boxed{\text{ZOOM}}\boxed{9}$. This feature automatically sets the viewing rectangle and plots the data.

NOTE: $\boxed{\text{ZOOM}}\boxed{9}$ *cannot* be used to set a viewing rectangle for the graph of an equation.

Figure A.17

Figure A.18

Entering a Formula

To enter a formula, press $\boxed{\text{Y} =}$. For example, use the following keystrokes after "$Y_1 =$" to enter $y = x^2 - 4$. See Figure A.17.

Note that there is a built-in key to enter the variable X. If "$Y_1 =$" does not appear after pressing $\boxed{\text{Y} =}$, press $\boxed{\text{MODE}}$ and make sure the calculator is set in *function mode*, denoted "Func". See Figure A.18.

SUMMARY: ENTERING A FORMULA

To enter a formula, press $\boxed{\text{Y=}}$. To delete a formula, press $\boxed{\text{CLEAR}}$.

Graphing an Equation

[−10, 10, 1] by [−10, 10, 1]

Figure A.19

To graph an equation, such as $y = x^2 - 4$, start by pressing $\boxed{\text{Y=}}$ and enter $Y_1 = X^2 - 4$. If there is an equation already entered, remove it by pressing $\boxed{\text{CLEAR}}$. The equals signs in "$Y_1 =$" should be in reverse video (a dark rectangle surrounding a white equals sign), which indicates that the equation will be graphed. If the equals sign is not in reverse video, place the cursor over it and press $\boxed{\text{ENTER}}$. Set an appropriate viewing rectangle and then press $\boxed{\text{GRAPH}}$. The graph will appear in the specified viewing rectangle. See Figures A.17 and A.19.

SUMMARY: GRAPHING AN EQUATION

1. Use the $\boxed{\text{Y=}}$ menu to enter the formula.
2. Use the $\boxed{\text{WINDOW}}$ menu to set an appropriate viewing rectangle.
3. Press $\boxed{\text{GRAPH}}$.

Graphing a Vertical Line

Vertical -4

Figure A.20

Set an appropriate window (or viewing rectangle). Then return to the home screen by pressing

$$\boxed{\text{2nd}}\,\boxed{\text{MODE [QUIT]}}.$$

To graph a vertical line, such as $x = -4$, press

$$\boxed{\text{2nd}}\,\boxed{\text{PRGM [DRAW]}}\,\boxed{4}\,\boxed{(-)}\,\boxed{4}.$$

See Figure A.20. Pressing $\boxed{\text{ENTER}}$ will make the vertical line appear, as shown in Figure A.21.

[−6, 6, 1] by [−6, 6, 1]

Figure A.21

SUMMARY: GRAPHING THE VERTICAL LINE $x = h$

1. Set an appropriate window by pressing $\boxed{\text{WINDOW}}$.
2. Return to the home screen by pressing $\boxed{\text{2nd}}\,\boxed{\text{MODE [QUIT]}}$.
3. Draw a vertical line by pressing $\boxed{\text{2nd}}\,\boxed{\text{PRGM [DRAW]}}\,\boxed{4}\,\boxed{h}\,\boxed{\text{ENTER}}$.

Squaring a Viewing Rectangle

In a square viewing rectangle the graph of $y = x$ is a line that makes a 45° angle with the positive x-axis, a circle appears circular, and all sides of a square have the same length. An approximate square viewing rectangle can be set if the distance along the x-axis is 1.5 times the distance along the y-axis. Examples of viewing rectangles that are (approximately) square include

$$[-6, 6, 1] \text{ by } [-4, 4, 1] \quad \text{and} \quad [-9, 9, 1] \text{ by } [-6, 6, 1].$$

Square viewing rectangles can be set automatically by pressing either

$$\boxed{\text{ZOOM}}\,\boxed{4} \quad \text{or} \quad \boxed{\text{ZOOM}}\,\boxed{5}.$$

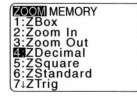

Figure A.22

ZOOM 4 provides a *decimal window*, which is discussed on page AP-11. See Figure A.22.

Figure A.23

Locating a Point of Intersection

To find the point of intersection for the graphs of

$$y_1 = 3(1 - x) \quad \text{and} \quad y_2 = 2,$$

start by entering Y_1 and Y_2, as shown in Figure A.23. Set the window, and graph both equations. Then press the following keys to find the intersection point.

(2nd)(TRACE [CALC])(5)

See Figure A.24, where the "intersect" utility is being selected. The calculator prompts for the first curve, as shown in Figure A.25. Use the arrow keys to locate the cursor near the point of intersection and press (ENTER). Repeat these steps for the second curve. Finally we are prompted for a guess. For each of the three prompts, place the free-moving cursor near the point of intersection and press (ENTER). The approximate coordinates of the point of intersection will be shown.

```
CALCULATE
1:value
2:zero
3:minimum
4:maximum
5:intersect
6:dy/dx
7:∫f(x)dx
```

Figure A.24

$[-6, 6, 1]$ by $[-4, 4, 1]$

```
Y1=3(1−X)
```

First curve?
X=.25531915 Y=2.2340426

Figure A.25

Shading Inequalities

To shade the solution set for one or more linear inequalities such as $2x + y \le 5$ and $-2x + y \ge 1$, begin by solving each inequality for y to obtain $y \le 5 - 2x$ and $y \ge 2x + 1$. Then let $Y_1 = 5 - 2X$ and $Y_2 = 2X + 1$, as shown in Figure A.26. Position the cursor to the left of Y_1 and press (ENTER) three times. The triangle that appears indicates that the calculator will shade the region below the graph of Y_1. Next locate the cursor to the left of Y_2 and press (ENTER) twice. This triangle indicates that the calculator will shade the region above the graph of Y_2. After setting the viewing rectangle to $[-15, 15, 5]$ by $[-10, 10, 5]$, press (GRAPH). The result is shown in Figure A.27.

Figure A.26

$[-15, 15, 5]$ by $[-10, 10, 5]$

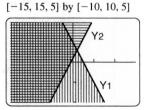

Figure A.27

SUMMARY: SHADING ONE OR MORE INEQUALITIES

1. Solve each inequality for y.
2. Enter each formula as Y_1 and Y_2 in the (Y=) menu.
3. Locate the cursor to the left of Y_1 and press (ENTER) two or three times to shade either above or below the graph of Y_1. Repeat for Y_2.
4. Set an appropriate viewing rectangle.
5. Press (GRAPH).

NOTE: The "Shade" utility in the DRAW menu can also be used to shade the region *between* two graphs.

Figure A.28

Setting $a + bi$ Mode

To evaluate expressions containing square roots of negative numbers, such as $\sqrt{-25}$, set your calculator in $a + bi$ mode by using the following keystrokes.

See Figures A.28 and A.29.

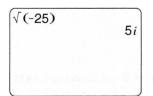

Figure A.29

SUMMARY: SETTING $a + bi$ MODE

1. Press (MODE).
2. Move the cursor to the seventh line, highlight $a + bi$, and press (ENTER).
3. Press (2nd)(MODE [QUIT]) and return to the home screen.

Evaluating Complex Arithmetic

Complex arithmetic can be performed much like other arithmetic expressions. This is done by entering

$$\boxed{\text{2nd}}\boxed{.\,[i]}$$

to obtain the imaginary unit i from the home screen. For example, to find the sum $(-2 + 3i) + (4 - 6i)$, perform the following keystrokes on the home screen.

Figure A.30

The result is shown in Figure A.30. Other complex arithmetic operations are done similarly.

SUMMARY: EVALUATING COMPLEX ARITHMETIC

Enter a complex expression in the same way as you would any arithmetic expression. To obtain the complex number i, use (2nd)(.[i]).

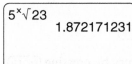

Figure A.31

Other Mathematical Expressions

EVALUATING OTHER ROOTS To evaluate a fifth root, such as $\sqrt[5]{23}$, use the following keystrokes, as shown in Figure A.31.

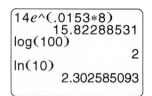

Figure A.32

EVALUATING THE NATURAL EXPONENTIAL FUNCTION To evaluate $14e^{0.0153(8)}$, use the following keystrokes, as shown in the first and second lines of Figure A.32.

EVALUATING THE COMMON LOGARITHMIC FUNCTION To evaluate $\log(100)$, use the following keystrokes, as shown in the third and fourth lines of Figure A.32.

(LOG)(1)(0)(0)())(ENTER)

EVALUATING THE NATURAL LOGARITHMIC FUNCTION To evaluate ln (10), use the following keystrokes, as shown in the last two lines of Figure A.32.

(LN)(1)(0)())(ENTER)

SUMMARY: OTHER MATHEMATICAL EXPRESSIONS

To evaluate a *kth root*, use (k)(MATH)(5).

To access the *natural exponential function*, use (2nd)(LN [eˣ]).

To access the *common logarithmic function*, use (LOG).

To access the *natural logarithmic function*, use (LN).

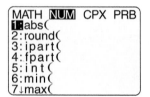

Figure A.33

Accessing the Absolute Value

To graph $y_1 = |x - 50|$, begin by entering $Y_1 = abs(X - 50)$. The absolute value (abs) is accessed by pressing

(MATH)(▷)(1).

See Figure A.33.

SUMMARY: ACCESSING THE ABSOLUTE VALUE

1. Press (MATH).
2. Position the cursor over "NUM".
3. Press (1) to select the absolute value.

Entering the Elements of a Matrix

The elements of the augmented matrix A given by

$$A = \left[\begin{array}{ccc|c} 1 & 1 & 2 & 1 \\ -1 & 0 & 1 & -2 \\ 2 & 1 & 5 & -1 \end{array} \right]$$

can be entered by using the following keystrokes on the TI-83 Plus or TI-84 Plus to define a matrix A with dimension 3×4. (*Note:* On the TI-83 the matrix menu is found by pressing (MATRX).)

(2nd)(x⁻¹ [MATRIX])(▷)(▷)(1)(3)(ENTER)(4)(ENTER)

Input the 12 elements of the matrix A, row by row. Finish each entry by pressing (ENTER). See Figure A.34. After these elements have been entered, press

(2nd)(MODE [QUIT])

Figure A.34

```
[A]
  [[1  1  2  1]
  [-1 0  1 -2]
  [2  1  5 -1]]
```

Figure A.35

to return to the home screen. To display the matrix *A*, press

(2nd)(x⁻¹ [MATRIX])(1)(ENTER).

See Figure A.35.

SUMMARY: ENTERING THE ELEMENTS OF A MATRIX *A*

1. Begin by accessing the matrix *A* by pressing (2nd)(x⁻¹ [MATRIX])(▷)(▷)(1).
2. Enter the dimension of *A* by pressing (m)(ENTER)(n)(ENTER), where the dimension of the matrix is *m* × *n*.
3. Input each element of the matrix, row by row. Finish each entry by pressing (ENTER). Use (2nd)(MODE [QUIT]) to return to the home screen.

NOTE: On the TI-83, replace the keystrokes (2nd)(x⁻¹ [MATRIX]) with (MATRX).

Reduced Row–Echelon Form

```
rref([A])
  [[1  0  0  1]
   [0  1  0  2]
   [0  0  1 -1]]
```

Figure A.36

To find the reduced row–echelon form of matrix *A* (entered above in Figure A.35), use the following keystrokes from the home screen on the TI-83 Plus or TI-84 Plus.

(2nd)(x⁻¹ [MATRIX])(▷)(ALPHA)(APPS [B])(2nd)(x⁻¹ [MATRIX])(1)( ))(ENTER)

The resulting matrix is shown in Figure A.36. On the TI-83 graphing calculator, use the following keystrokes to find the reduced row–echelon form.

(MATRX)(▷)(ALPHA)(MATRX [B])(MATRX)(1)( ))(ENTER)

SUMMARY: FINDING THE REDUCED ROW–ECHELON FORM OF A MATRIX

1. To make rref([A]) appear on the home screen, use the following keystrokes for the TI-83 Plus or TI-84 Plus graphing calculator.

(2nd)(x⁻¹ [MATRIX])(▷)(ALPHA)(APPS [B])(2nd)(x⁻¹ [MATRIX])(1)( ))

2. Press (ENTER) to calculate the reduced row–echelon form.
3. Use arrow keys to access elements that do not appear on the screen.

NOTE: On the TI-83, replace the keystrokes (2nd)(x⁻¹ [MATRIX]) with (MATRX) and (APPS [B]) with (MATRX [B]).

```
MATRIX[A]  3×3
[ 2    1    -1  ]
[ -1   3    2   ]
[ 4    -3   -5  ]
```

Figure A.37

Evaluating a Determinant

To evaluate the determinant of matrix *A* given by

$$A = \begin{bmatrix} 2 & 1 & -1 \\ -1 & 3 & 2 \\ 4 & -3 & -5 \end{bmatrix},$$

```
det([A])
                -6
```

Figure A.38

start by entering the 9 elements of the 3 × 3 matrix, as shown in Figure A.37. To compute det *A*, perform the following keystrokes from the home screen.

(2nd)(x⁻¹ [MATRIX])(▷)(1)(2nd)(x⁻¹ [MATRIX])(1)( ))(ENTER)

The results are shown in Figure A.38.

SUMMARY: EVALUATING A DETERMINANT OF A MATRIX

1. Enter the dimension and elements of the matrix A.
2. Return to the home screen by pressing (2nd)(MODE [QUIT]).
3. On the TI-83 Plus or TI-84 Plus, perform the following keystrokes.

(2nd)(x^{-1} [MATRIX]) (▷) (1) (2nd)(x^{-1} [MATRIX]) (1) ( )) (ENTER)

NOTE: On the TI-83, replace the keystrokes (2nd)(x^{-1} [MATRIX]) with (MATRX).

```
CALCULATE
1:value
2:zero
3:minimum
4:maximum
5:intersect
6:dy/dx
7:∫f(x)dx
```

Figure A.39

Locating an *x*-Intercept or Zero

To locate an *x*-intercept or *zero* of $f(x) = x^2 - 4$, start by entering $Y_1 = X^2 - 4$ into the (Y =) menu. Set the viewing rectangle to $[-9, 9, 1]$ by $[-6, 6, 1]$ and graph Y_1. Afterwards, press the following keys to invoke the zero finder. See Figure A.39.

(2nd)(TRACE [CALC]) (2)

The graphing calculator prompts for a left bound. Use the arrow keys to set the cursor to the left of the *x*-intercept and press (ENTER). The graphing calculator then prompts for a right bound. Set the cursor to the right of the *x*-intercept and press (ENTER). Finally, the graphing calculator prompts for a guess. Set the cursor roughly at the *x*-intercept and press (ENTER). See Figures A.40–A.42. The calculator then approximates the *x*-intercept or zero automatically, as shown in Figure A.43. The zero of -2 can be found similarly.

$[-9, 9, 1]$ by $[-6, 6, 1]$

Figure A.40

$[-9, 9, 1]$ by $[-6, 6, 1]$

Figure A.41

$[-9, 9, 1]$ by $[-6, 6, 1]$

Figure A.42

$[-9, 9, 1]$ by $[-6, 6, 1]$

Figure A.43

SUMMARY: LOCATING AN *x*-INTERCEPT OR ZERO

1. Graph the function in an appropriate viewing rectangle.
2. Press (2nd)(TRACE [CALC]) (2).
3. Select the left and right bounds, followed by a guess. Press (ENTER) after each selection. The calculator then approximates the *x*-intercept or zero.

```
Normal    Sci    Eng
Float 0123456789
Radian  Degree
Func  Par Pol Seq
Connected  Dot
Sequential  Simul
Real  a+bi  re^θi
Full  Horiz  G-T
Set Clock 03/19/12 9:54PM
```

Figure A.44

Setting Connected or Dot Mode

To set your graphing calculator in dot mode, press (MODE), position the cursor over "Dot," and press (ENTER). See Figure A.44. Graphs will now appear in dot mode rather than connected mode.

SUMMARY: SETTING CONNECTED OR DOT MODE

1. Press (MODE).
2. Position the cursor over "Connected" or "Dot". Press (ENTER).

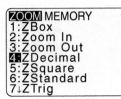

Figure A.45

Setting a Decimal Window

With a decimal window, the cursor stops on convenient x-values. In the decimal window $[-9.4, 9.4, 1]$ by $[-6.2, 6.2, 1]$ the cursor stops on x-values that are multiples of 0.2. If we reduce the viewing rectangle to $[-4.7, 4.7, 1]$ by $[-3.1, 3.1, 1]$, the cursor stops on x-values that are multiples of 0.1. To set this smaller window automatically, press (ZOOM)(4). See Figure A.45. Decimal windows are also useful when graphing rational functions with asymptotes in connected mode.

SUMMARY: SETTING A DECIMAL WINDOW

1. Press (ZOOM)(4) to set the viewing rectangle $[-4.7, 4.7, 1]$ by $[-3.1, 3.1, 1]$.
2. A larger decimal window is $[-9.4, 9.4, 1]$ by $[-6.2, 6.2, 1]$.

Finding Maximum and Minimum Values

To find a minimum y-value (or vertex) on the graph of $f(x) = 1.5x^2 - 6x + 4$, start by entering $Y_1 = 1.5X^2 - 6X + 4$ from the (Y =) menu. Set the viewing rectangle and then perform the following keystrokes to find the minimum y-value.

(2nd)(TRACE [CALC])(3)

Figure A.46

See Figure A.46.

The calculator prompts for a left bound. Use the arrow keys to position the cursor left of the vertex and press (ENTER). Similarly, position the cursor to the right of the vertex for the right bound and press (ENTER). Finally, the graphing calculator asks for a guess between the left and right bounds. Place the cursor near the vertex and press (ENTER). See Figures A.47–A.49. The minimum value is shown in Figure A.50.

Figure A.47

Figure A.48

Figure A.49

Figure A.50

A maximum of the function f on an interval can be found similarly, except enter

(2nd)(TRACE [CALC])(4).

The calculator prompts for left and right bounds, followed by a guess. Press (ENTER) after the cursor has been located appropriately for each prompt. The graphing calculator will display the maximum y-value. An example is shown in Figure A.51, where $f(x) = x(80 - 2x)$.

Figure A.51

SUMMARY: FINDING MAXIMUM AND MINIMUM VALUES

1. Graph the function in an appropriate viewing rectangle.
2. Press (2nd)(TRACE [CALC])(3) to find a minimum y-value.
3. Press (2nd)(TRACE [CALC])(4) to find a maximum y-value.
4. Use the arrow keys to locate the left and right x-bounds, followed by a guess. Press (ENTER) to select each position of the cursor.

Appendix B
The Midpoint Formula

▶ **REAL-WORLD CONNECTION** A common way to make estimations is to average data items. For example, in 2000 the average tuition and fees at public two-year colleges were about $1700, and in 2010 they were about $2700. (*Source: The College Board.*) To estimate tuition and fees in 2005, we could average the 2000 and 2010 amounts.

$$\frac{1700 + 2700}{2} = \$2200 \quad \text{Finding the average}$$

This technique predicts that tuition and fees were $2200 in 2005 and is referred to as finding the *midpoint*.

MIDPOINT FORMULA ON THE REAL NUMBER LINE The **midpoint** of a line segment is the unique point on the line segment that is an equal distance from the endpoints. For example, in Figure B.1 the midpoint M of -3 and 5 on the real number line is 1.

Figure B.1

We can calculate the value of M as follows.

$$M = \frac{x_1 + x_2}{2} = \frac{-3 + 5}{2} = 1$$

⤷ Average the x-values to find the midpoint.

MIDPOINT FORMULA IN THE xy-PLANE The midpoint of a line segment in the xy-plane can be found in a similar way. Figure B.2(a) shows the midpoint on the line segment connecting the points (x_1, y_1) and (x_2, y_2). The x-coordinate of M is equal to the average of x_1 and x_2, and the y-coordinate of M is equal to the average of y_1 and y_2. For example, the line segment with endpoints $(-2, 1)$ and $(4, -3)$ is shown in Figure B.2(b). The coordinates of the midpoint are

$$M = \left(\frac{-2 + 4}{2}, \frac{1 + (-3)}{2} \right) = (1, -1).$$

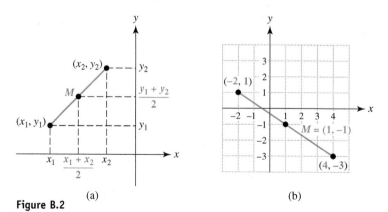

(a)   (b)

Figure B.2

This discussion is summarized as follows.

MIDPOINT FORMULA IN THE *xy*-PLANE

The midpoint of the line segment with endpoints (x_1, y_1) and (x_2, y_2) in the *xy*-plane is

$$\left(\frac{x_1 + x_2}{2}, \frac{y_1 + y_2}{2}\right).$$

EXAMPLE 1 **Finding the midpoint**

Find the midpoint of the line segment connecting the points $(-3, -2)$ and $(4, 1)$.

Solution
In the midpoint formula, let $(-3, -2)$ be (x_1, y_1) and $(4, 1)$ be (x_2, y_2).

$$M = \left(\frac{x_1 + x_2}{2}, \frac{y_1 + y_2}{2}\right) \qquad \text{Midpoint formula}$$

$$= \left(\frac{-3 + 4}{2}, \frac{-2 + 1}{2}\right) \qquad \text{Substitute.}$$

$$= \left(\frac{1}{2}, -\frac{1}{2}\right) \qquad \text{Simplify.}$$

The midpoint of the line segment is $\left(\frac{1}{2}, -\frac{1}{2}\right)$.

▌ Now Try Exercise 9

▶ **REAL-WORLD CONNECTION** In the next example we use the midpoint formula to estimate the divorce rate in the United States in 2005.

EXAMPLE 2 **Estimating the U.S. divorce rate**

The divorce rate per 1000 people in the year 2000 was 4.2 and in the year 2010 it was 3.4. (*Source:* Statistical Abstract of the United States.)

(a) Use the midpoint formula to estimate the divorce rate in 2005.
(b) Could the midpoint formula be used to estimate the divorce rate in 2003? Explain.

Solution
(a) In the midpoint formula, let $(2000, 4.2)$ be (x_1, y_1) and let $(2010, 3.4)$ be (x_2, y_2).

$$M = \left(\frac{x_1 + x_2}{2}, \frac{y_1 + y_2}{2}\right) \qquad \text{Midpoint formula}$$

$$= \left(\frac{2000 + 2010}{2}, \frac{4.2 + 3.4}{2}\right) \qquad \text{Substitute.}$$

$$= (2005, 3.8) \qquad \text{Simplify.}$$

The midpoint formula estimates that the divorce rate was 3.8 per 1000 people in 2005. (Note that the actual rate was 3.6.)
(b) No, the midpoint formula can be used to estimate data that are halfway between two given data points. Because the year 2003 is not halfway between 2000 and 2010, the midpoint formula cannot be used.

▌ Now Try Exercise 23

NOTE: An estimate obtained from the midpoint formula is equal to an estimate obtained from a linear function whose graph passes through the endpoints of the line segment. This fact is illustrated in the next example.

EXAMPLE 3 **Relating midpoints to linear functions**

The graph of a linear function f shown in Figure B.3 passes through the points $(-1, 3)$ and $(2, -3)$.

(a) Find a formula for $f(x)$.

(b) Evaluate $f\left(\frac{1}{2}\right)$. Does your answer agree with the graph?

(c) Find the midpoint M of the line segment connecting the points $(-1, 3)$ and $(2, -3)$. Comment on your result.

Solution

(a) The graph of function f is a line that passes through $(-1, 3)$ and $(2, -3)$. The slope m of the line is

$$m = \frac{-3 - 3}{2 - (-1)} = -\frac{6}{3} = -2,$$

and the y-intercept is 1. Thus $f(x) = -2x + 1$.

(b) $f\left(\frac{1}{2}\right) = -2\left(\frac{1}{2}\right) + 1 = 0$. Yes, they agree because the point $\left(\frac{1}{2}, 0\right)$ appears to lie on the graph of $y = f(x)$ in Figure B.3.

(c) The midpoint of the line segment connecting $(-1, 3)$ and $(2, -3)$ is

$$M = \left(\frac{-1 + 2}{2}, \frac{3 + (-3)}{2}\right) = \left(\frac{1}{2}, 0\right).$$

Finding the midpoint $M = \left(\frac{1}{2}, 0\right)$ of the line segment with endpoints $(-1, 3)$ and $(2, -3)$ is equivalent to evaluating the linear function f whose graph passes through $(-1, 3)$ and $(2, -3)$ at $x = \frac{1}{2}$.

Now Try Exercise 19

Figure B.3

B   Exercises

MyMathLab   Math XL PRACTICE   WATCH   DOWNLOAD   READ   REVIEW

Exercises 1–8: Find the midpoint of the line segment shown.

1.

2.

3.

4.

5.

6.

7.

8.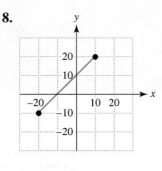

Exercises 9–18: Find the midpoint of the line segment connecting the given points.

9. $(-9, -3), (-7, 1)$

10. $(7, -2), (-5, 8)$

11. $\left(\frac{1}{2}, \frac{1}{3}\right), \left(-\frac{5}{2}, -\frac{2}{3}\right)$

12. $\left(-\frac{3}{5}, -\frac{1}{4}\right), \left(\frac{1}{10}, \frac{1}{2}\right)$

13. $(-0.3, 0.1), (0.7, 0.4)$

14. $(0.8, -0.4), (0.9, -0.1)$

15. $(2000, 5), (2010, 13)$

16. $(2005, 9), (2011, 3)$

17. Thinking Generally
$(a, -b), (3a, 5b)$

18. Thinking Generally
$(-a, b), (a, -b)$

Exercises 19–22: (Refer to Example 3.) The graph of a linear function f passes through the two given points.

(a) *Determine $f(2)$ by finding a formula for $f(x)$.*
(b) *Determine $f(2)$ by finding the midpoint of the line segment connecting the given points.*
(c) *Compare your answers for parts (a) and (b).*

19. $(0, 5), (4, -3)$

20. $(0, 2), (4, 10)$

21. $(-3, -1), (7, 3)$

22. $(-1, 3), (5, -5)$

Exercises 23–28: Use the midpoint formula to make the requested estimation.

23. *U.S. Life Expectancy* The life expectancy of a female born in 1990 was 78.8 years, and the life expectancy of a female born in 2010 rose to 80.8 years. Estimate the life expectancy of a female born in 2000. (*Source: Centers for Disease Control and Prevention.*)

24. *U.S. Life Expectancy* The life expectancy of a male born in 1990 was 71.8 years, and the life expectancy of a male born in 2010 rose to 75.6 years. Estimate the life expectancy of a male born in 2000. (*Source: Centers for Disease Control and Prevention.*)

25. *U.S. Population* The population of the United States in 1970 was 205 million, and in 2010 it was 308 million. Estimate the population in 1990. (*Source: U.S. Census Bureau.*)

26. *Distance Traveled* A car is moving at a constant speed on an interstate highway. After 1 hour the car passes the 103-mile marker and after 5 hours the car passes the 391-mile marker. What mile marker does the car pass after 3 hours?

27. *U.S. Median Income* In 1999 the median family income was $40,700, and in 2009 it was $49,800. Estimate the median family income in 2004.

28. *Estimating Fish Populations* In 2008 there were approximately 3200 large-mouth bass in a lake. This number increased to 3800 in 2012. Estimate the number of large-mouth bass in the lake in 2010.

Bibliography

Baker, S., with B. Leak, "Math Will Rock Your World." *Business Week*, January 23, 2006.

Battan, L. *Weather in Your Life.* San Francisco: W. H. Freeman, 1983.

Callas, D. *Snapshots of Applications in Mathematics.* Delhi, New York: State University College of Technology, 1994.

Eves, H. *An Introduction to the History of Mathematics,* 5th ed. Philadelphia: Saunders College Publishing, 1983.

Friedhoff, M., and W. Benzon. *The Second Computer Revolution: Visualization.* New York: W. H. Freeman, 1991.

Garber, N., and L. Hoel. *Traffic and Highway Engineering.* Boston, Mass.: PWS Publishing Co., 1997.

Grigg, D. *The World Food Problem.* Oxford: Blackwell Publishers, 1993.

Karttunen, H., P. Kroger, H. Oja, M. Poutanen, K. Donner, eds. *Fundamental Astronomy.* 2nd ed. New York: Springer-Verlag, 1994.

Lack, D. *The Life of a Robin.* London: Collins, 1965.

Lancaster, H. *Quantitative Methods in Biological and Medical Sciences: A Historical Essay.* New York: Springer-Verlag, 1994.

Miller, A., and R. Anthes. *Meteorology.* 5th ed. Columbus, Ohio: Charles E. Merrill Publishing Company, 1985.

Motz, L., and J. Weaver. *The Story of Mathematics.* New York: Plenum Press, 1993.

Nilsson, A. *Greenhouse Earth.* New York: John Wiley and Sons, 1992.

Paetsch, M. *Mobile Communications in the U.S. and Europe: Regulation, Technology, and Markets.* Norwood, Mass.: Artech House, Inc., 1993.

Pearl, R., T. Edwards, and J. Miner. "The growth of *Cucumis melo* seedlings at different temperatures." *J. Gen. Physiol.* 17: 687–700.

Pielou, E. *Population and Community Ecology: Principles and Methods.* New York: Gordon and Breach Science Publishers, 1974.

Pokorny, C., and C. Gerald. *Computer Graphics: The Principles behind the Art and Science.* Irvine, Calif.: Franklin, Beedle, and Associates, 1989.

Sharov, A., and I. Novikov. *Edwin Hubble, The Discoverer of the Big Bang Universe.* New York: Cambridge University Press, 1993.

Taylor, J. *DVD Demystified.* New York: McGraw-Hill, 1998.

Thomas, V. *Science and Sport.* London: Faber and Faber, 1970.

Varley, G., and G. Gradwell. "Population models for the winter moth." *Symposium of the Royal Entomological Society of London* 4: 132–142.

Wang, T. *ASHRAE Trans.* 81, Part 1 (1975): 32.

Wright, J. *The New York Times Almanac 1999.* New York: Penguin Group, 1998.

Zeilik, M., S. Gregory, and D. Smith. *Introductory Astronomy and Astrophysics.* 3rd ed. Philadelphia: Saunders College Publishers, 1992.

Answers to Selected Exercises

SECTION 1.1 (pp. 14–19)

1. function **2.** y equals f of x **3.** symbolic **4.** numerical
5. domain **6.** range **7.** one **8.** F
9. T **10.** $(3, 4)$; 3; 6 **11.** (a, b) **12.** d **13.** 1 **14.** equal
15. Yes **16.** Yes **17.** No **18.** No **19.** Yes **20.** No
21. -6; -2 **23.** 0; $\frac{3}{2}$ **25.** 25; $\frac{9}{4}$ **27.** 3; 3
29. 13; -22 **31.** $-\frac{1}{2}$; $\frac{2}{5}$
33. (a) $I(x) = 36x$ **(b)** $I(10) = 360$; There are 360 inches
in 10 yards. **35. (a)** $M(x) = \frac{x}{5280}$
(b) $M(10) = \frac{10}{5280} \approx 0.0019$; There is $\frac{10}{5280}$ mile in
10 feet. **37. (a)** $A(x) = 43,560x$ **(b)** $A(10) = 435,600$;
There are 435,600 square feet in 10 acres.
39. $f = \{(1, 3), (2, -4), (3, 0)\}$;
$D = \{1, 2, 3\}$; $R = \{-4, 0, 3\}$
41. $f = \{(a, b), (c, d), (e, a), (d, b)\}$;
$D = \{a, c, d, e\}$; $R = \{a, b, d\}$

43. **45.**

47. **49.**

51.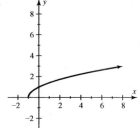

53. 3; -1 **55.** 0; 2 **57.** -4; -3 **59.** 5.5; 3.7
61. 26.9; in 1990 average fuel efficiency was 26.9 mpg.

63. Numerical:

x	-3	-2	-1	0	1	2	3
$y = f(x)$	2	3	4	5	6	7	8

Graphical:

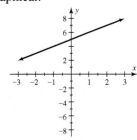

Symbolic: $y = x + 5$

65. Numerical:

x	-3	-2	-1	0	1	2	3
$y = f(x)$	-17	-12	-7	-2	3	8	13

Graphical:

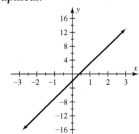

Symbolic: $y = 5x - 2$

67. Numerical   Graphical

[−10, 10, 1] by [−10, 10, 1]

69. Numerical   Graphical (Dot Mode)

[−10, 10, 1] by [−10, 10, 1]

71. Subtract $\frac{1}{2}$ from the input x to obtain the output y.
73. Divide the input x by 3 to obtain the output y.
75. Subtract 1 from the input x and then take the square root
to obtain the output y.
77. $f(x) = 0.50x$

Miles	10	20	30	40	50	60	70
Cost	$5	$10	$15	$20	$25	$30	$35

79. 1825; In 2011 there were 1825 billion, or 1.825 trillion, World Wide Web searches.
81. $D: -2 \le x \le 2; R: 0 \le y \le 2$
83. $D: -2 \le x \le 4; R: -2 \le y \le 2$
85. D: All real numbers; $R: y \ge -1$
87. $D: -3 \le x \le 3; R: -3 \le y \le 2$
89. $D = \{1, 2, 3, 4\}; R = \{5, 6, 7\}$
91. All real numbers **93.** All real numbers **95.** $x \ne 5$
97. All real numbers **99.** $x \ge 1$ **101.** All real numbers
103. $x \ne 0$ **105. (a)** 1726; 1726 whales were sighted in 2008. **(b)** $D = \{2005, 2006, 2007, 2008, 2009\}$, $R = \{649, 1265, 959, 1726, 1010\}$ **(c)** Increased every other year **107.** $D = \{1, 2, 3, \dots, 20\}$; $R = \{200, 400, 600, \dots, 4000\}$ **109.** No **111.** Yes
113. (a) 0.2 **(b)** Yes. Each month has one average amount of precipitation. **(c)** 2, 3, 7, 11 **115.** Yes. D: All real numbers; R: All real numbers **117.** No
119. Yes. $D: -4 \le x \le 4; R: 0 \le y \le 4$
121. Yes. D: All real numbers; $R: y = 3$ **123.** No
125. Yes. $D = \{-6, -4, 2, 4\}; R = \{-4, 2\}$ **127.** Yes
129. No **131.** The person walks away from home, then turns around and walks back a little slower.
133.

(4, 6000)

SECTION 1.2 (pp. 29–33)

1. $mx + b$ **2.** b **3.** line **4.** horizontal **5.** 7 **6.** 0 **7.** T
8. F **9.** Carpet costs $2 per square foot. Ten square feet of carpet costs $20. **10.** The rate at which water is leaving the tank is 4 gallons per minute. After 5 minutes the tank contains 80 gallons of water. **11.** Yes; $m = \frac{1}{2}, b = -6$ **13.** No
15. Yes; $m = 0, b = -9$ **17.** Yes; $m = -9, b = 0$
19. Yes **21.** No **23.** Yes; $f(x) = 3x - 6$ **25.** Yes; $f(x) = -\frac{3}{2}x + 3$ **27.** No **29.** Yes; $f(x) = 2x$
31. Yes; $f(x) = -4$ **33.** $-16; 20$ **35.** $\frac{17}{3}; 2$
37. $-22; -22$ **39.** $-2; 0$ **41.** $-1; -4$ **43.** 1; 1
45. $f(x) = 6x; 18$ **47.** $f(x) = \frac{x}{6} - \frac{1}{2}; 0$ **49.** d. **51.** b.

53.

55.

57.

59.

61.

63. $f(x) = \frac{1}{16}x$ **65.** $f(t) = 65t$ **67.** $f(x) = 24$ **69.** a

71. (a) f multiplies the input x by -2 and then adds 1 to obtain the output y.

73. (a) f multiplies the input x by $\frac{1}{2}$ and then subtracts 1 to obtain the output y.

(b)

x	-2	0	2
$y = f(x)$	5	1	-3

(b)

x	-2	0	2
$y = f(x)$	-2	-1	0

(c)

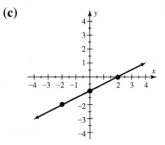

(c)

75. (a)

X	Y1
-3	.41421
-2	.74755
-1	1.0809
0	1.4142
1	1.7475
2	2.0809
3	2.4142

Y1=X/3+√(2)

(b) $[-6, 6, 1]$ by $[-4, 4, 1]$

77. (a)

X	Y1
-3	-.2
-2	0
-1	.2
0	.4
1	.6
2	.8
3	1

Y1=(X+2)/5

(b) $[-6, 6, 1]$ by $[-4, 4, 1]$

79. b. **81.** c. **83. (a)** $G(x) = \frac{X}{E}$ **(b)** $C(x) = \frac{3x}{E}$

85. (a) Symbolic: $f(x) = 70$
Graphical:

(b)

Hours	0	4	8	12	16	20	24
Temp. (°F)	70	70	70	70	70	70	70

(c) Constant
87. $D(t) = 60t + 50$
89. (a) $K(x) = 93x$ **(b)** $A(x) = x$ **(c)** 33,945; 365;
On average, someone under 18 sends 33,945 texts in 1 year
while someone over 65 sends 365 texts.   **91. (a)** 1.6 million
(b) 0.1 million   **(c)** $f(x) = 0.1x + 1.6$ **(d)** 2.2 million
93. (a) 563 million   **(b)** In 2006, there were about
123 million users.   **(c)** Users increased, on average, by 110
million per year.   **95. (a)** $V(T) = 0.5T + 137$
(b) 162 cm^3 **97.** $f(x) = 40x$; about 2.92 pounds
99. (a) 55%   **(b)** 4%   **(c)** $P(x) = 4x + 55$ **(d)** 67%

CHECKING BASIC CONCEPTS 1.1 & 1.2
(p. 33)

1. Symbolic: $f(x) = x^2 - 1$
   Graphical:

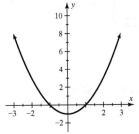

2. (a) $D: -3 \le x \le 3; R: -4 \le y \le 4$ **(b)** 0; 4
(c) No. The graph is not a line.
3. (a) Yes   **(b)** No   **(c)** Yes   **(d)** Yes
4. $f(-2) = 10$

5. $f(x) = \frac{1}{2}x - 1$ **6. (a)** 32.2; in 1990 the median age was
about 32 years.   **(b)** 0.225: the median age is increasing
by 0.225 years each year. 27.7: in 1970 the median age was
27.7 years.

SECTION 1.3 (pp. 43–47)

1. $y; x$ **2.** 0   **3.** rises   **4.** horizontal   **5.** vertical
6. slope–intercept   **7.** In 1999, $9 billion was spent on
pet health care.   **8.** Initially, the tank has 1000 gallons in it.
9. In 2006, 123 million people used Skype.   **10.** In 0 days
a person sends 0 texts.   **11.** 2   **13.** $-\frac{2}{3}$ **15.** 0   **17.** 2
19. $-\frac{2}{3}$ **21.** 0   **23.** Undefined   **25.** -10 **27.** $\frac{3}{5}$
29. $-0.\overline{21}$ **31.** $\frac{3b}{a}$ **33.** -1

35. (a) $-\frac{3}{4}$
(b)

(c) The graph falls 3 units
for every 4-unit increase in x

37. (a) $\frac{2}{3}$
(b)

(c) The graph rises 2 units
for every 3-unit increase in x

39.

41.

43.

45.

47. (a) 1; 2
(b)

49. (a) -3; 2
(b)

51. (a) $\frac{1}{3}$; 0
(b)

53. (a) 0; 2
(b)

55. (a) $-1; 3$
(b)

57. $y = -x + 4$ **59.** $y = 2$
61. $y = x - 2$ **63.** $y = 3x - 5$
65. $y = \frac{3}{2}x - \frac{3}{2}$ **67.** $2; -2$
69. $-7; 4$ **71. (a)** 3 **(b)** $f(x) = 2x - 1$
73. (a) 5 **(b)** $f(x) = \frac{3}{2}x + 5$ **75.** c.
77. b.   **79. (a)** $m_1 = 50, m_2 = 0, m_3 = 150$
(b) m_1: Water is being added at the rate of 50 gallons
per hour. m_2: The pump is neither adding nor removing
water. m_3: Water is being added at the rate of 150 gallons
per hour.   **(c)** The pool initially contained 100 gallons of
water. Water was added at the rate of 50 gallons per hour
for the first 4 hours. Then the pump was turned off for
2 hours. Finally, water was added at the rate of 150 gallons
per hour for 2 hours. The pool contains 600 gallons after
8 hours.
81. (a) $m_1 = 100, m_2 = 25, m_3 = -100$ **(b)** m_1: Water
is being added at the rate of 100 gallons per hour. m_2:
Water is being added at the rate of 25 gallons per hour.
m_3: Water is being removed at the rate of 100 gallons per
hour.   **(c)** The pool initially contained 100 gallons of
water. Water was added at the rate of 100 gallons per hour
for the first 2 hours. Then water was added at the rate of
25 gallons per hour for 4 hours. Finally, water was
removed at the rate of 100 gallons per hour for 2 hours.
The pool contains 200 gallons after 8 hours.
83. (a) $m_1 = 50, m_2 = 0, m_3 = -20, m_4 = 0$
(b) m_1: The car is moving away from home at the rate of
50 miles per hour. m_2: The car is not moving. m_3: The car
is moving toward home at the rate of 20 miles per hour.
m_4: The car is not moving.   **(c)** The car starts at home
and moves away from home at 50 miles per hour for
1 hour. Then the car does not move for 1 hour. The car
then moves toward home at the rate of 20 miles per hour
for 2 hours. Finally, the car stops and does not move for
1 hour. The car is 10 miles from home at the end of
the trip.
85.

87.

89. (a) \$13 billion, \$23 billion
(b)

(c) $\frac{10}{3}$ **(d)** Revenue increased on average by $\$3\frac{1}{3}$ billion
per year.
91. (a) 468,000   **(b)** 18.8, 299   **(c)** On average, the
number of finishers increased by 18,800 per year.
(d) In 2000, there were 299 thousand finishers.
93. 1500 gallons per hour   **95.** $m = 10$; the carpet costs
\$10 per square yard.   **97. (a)** $m = \frac{1}{3}$
(b) On average, spending on pet health care increased
by $\$\frac{1}{3}$ billion per year from 1984 to 2008.
99. (a) $m \approx 1470.6; b = 35,000$
(b) About \$49,700

SECTION 1.4 (pp. 59–64)

1. 1   **2.** 1.   **3.** $y = mx + b$ **4.** $y = m(x - x_1) + y_1$ or
$y - y_1 = m(x - x_1)$ **5.** $x = 5$ **6.** $y = 2$ **7.** $y = b$
8. $x = h$ **9.** $m_1 = m_2$ **10.** -1 **11.** $y = -\frac{3}{4}x - 3$
(answers may vary)   **12.** $y = \frac{4}{3}x + 2$ (answers may vary)
13. $x = 1$ (answers may vary)   **14.** $y = -5$
(answers may vary)   **15.** $y = -\frac{3}{4}x - \frac{1}{4}$ **17.** $y = \frac{1}{3}x + \frac{8}{3}$
19. Yes   **21.** No   **23.** d.   **25.** a.   **27.** f.
29. $y = -2(x - 2) - 3$
31. $y = 1.3(x - 1990) + 25$
33. $y = \frac{2}{3}(x - 1) + 3$ or $y = \frac{2}{3}(x + 5) - 1$
35. $y = 2(x - 1980) + 5$ or $y = 2(x - 2000) + 45$
37. $y = -\frac{2}{3}(x - 6) + 0$ or $y = -\frac{2}{3}(x - 0) + 4$
39.

$y = -\frac{1}{2}(x - 0) + 2$; yes

41. $y = 2x - 4$ **43.** $y = \frac{1}{2}x + 3$ **45.** $y = 22x - 43$
47. $y = -3x - 2$ **49.** $y = -\frac{3}{4}x - 2$ **51.** $y = -\frac{1}{3}x - 5$
53. $y = -x + 1$ **55.** $y = \frac{1}{3}x - \frac{2}{3}$ **57.** $y = -3x + 3$
59. $y = 4x - 1$ **61.** $y = -\frac{5}{3}x - 3$ **63.** $y = 3x + 14$
65. $y = \frac{9}{10}x - \frac{31}{20}$ **67.** $y = -\frac{1}{c}x + b$

69. (a) $y = -2x + 2$
(b)

71. (a) $y = \frac{1}{2}x + \frac{5}{2}$
(b)

(b) $m = 2.7$, $x_1 = 1980$, $y_1 = 227$ (answers may vary)
(c) 335 million (answers may vary)
117. (a) $f(x) = \frac{1}{3}(x - 1984) + 4$ **(b)** \$14 billion

CHECKING BASIC CONCEPTS 1.3 & 1.4 (pp. 64–65)

1. (a) $m = -3$; (5, 7) (answers may vary)
(b) $m = 0$; (1, 10) (answers may vary)
(c) m is undefined; $(-5, 0)$ (answers may vary)
(d) $m = 5$; (0, 3) (answers may vary)   **2. (a)** 2
(b) $y = 2(x - 2) - 4$ or $y = 2(x - 5) + 2$;
$y = 2x - 8$ **(c)** x-int: 4; y-int: -8 **3.** $x = -2$; $y = 5$
4. $y = 2x - 8$; $y = -\frac{1}{2}x - 3$ **5. (a)** Toward home
(b) -50; the car is moving toward home at 50 mph.
(c) x-int: 5, after 5 hours the driver is home; y-int: 250, the driver is initially 250 miles from home.
(d) $a = -50$, $b = 250$ **(e)** D: $0 \le x \le 5$;
R: $0 \le y \le 250$

73. (a) $y = 3x - 2$
(b)

75. (a) $y_1 = 2x$; $y_2 = -\frac{1}{2}x$ **(b)** $m_1 m_2 = 2\left(-\frac{1}{2}\right) = -1$
77. (a) $y_1 = -\frac{3}{2}x - 1$; $y_2 = \frac{2}{3}x - 1$
(b) $m_1 m_2 = -\frac{3}{2} \cdot \frac{2}{3} = -1$ **79.** $x = -1$
81. $y = -\frac{5}{6}$ **83.** $x = 4$ **85.** $x = -\frac{2}{3}$ **87.** Yes;
$y = 4x - 8$ **89.** No   **91. (a)** Leaving; 50 gal
(b) x-int: 8; y-int: 80; the tank is empty after 8 min and has 80 gal initially   **(c)** $y = -10x + 80$; water is leaving the tank at 10 gal per min.   **(d)** D: $0 \le x \le 8$; R: $0 \le y \le 80$
93. (a) Two acres have 100 people and 4 acres have 200 people.   **(b)** A zero-acre parcel has no people.
(c) $y = 50x$ **(d)** The land has 50 people per acre, on average.   **(e)** $P(x) = 50x$
95. (a)

(b) Horizontal   **97. (a)** $y = 2000x - 3,984,000$
(b) The cost is increasing by \$2000 per year.   **(c)** \$46,000
99. $f(x) = 0.6x - 1146$; 58.8 lb
101. $f(x) = 0.28x - 484.8$; 69.6 yr   **103.** $y = 4x - 3$
105. $y = -3.5x + 11.5$ **107.** $y = \frac{7}{60}x - 228.7$
109. $y = 0.09x - 173.8$ **111. (a)** $a = 0.30$, $b = 189.20$
(b) The fixed cost of owning the car for one month
113. (a) $R(c) = 4c - 14.6$ **(b)** About 10
115. (a)

CHAPTER 1 REVIEW (pp. 67–72)

1. -7; 0   **2.** -22; 2   **3.** -2; 1   **4.** 5; 5   **5. (a)** $P(q) = 2q$
(b) $P(5) = 10$; there are 10 pints in 5 quarts.
6. (a) $f(x) = 4x - 3$ **(b)** $f(5) = 17$; three less than four times 5 is 17.   **7.** (3, -2)   **8.** 4; -6
9.

10.

11.

12.

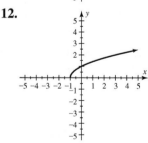

13. 1; 4   **14.** 1; -2 **15.** 7; -1
16. Numerical:

x	-3	-2	-1	0	1	2	3
$y = f(x)$	-11	-8	-5	-2	1	4	7

Symbolic: $f(x) = 3x - 2$
Graphical:

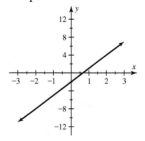

17. *D*: All real numbers; *R*: $y \leq 4$ **18.** *D*: $-4 \leq x \leq 4$;
R: $-4 \leq y \leq 0$ **19.** Yes **20.** No
21. $D = \{-3, -1, 2, 4\}$; $R = \{-1, 3, 4\}$; yes
22. $D = \{-1, 0, 1, 2\}$; $R = \{-2, 2, 3, 4, 5\}$; no
23. All real numbers **24.** $x \geq 0$ **25.** $x \neq 0$
26. All real numbers **27.** $x \leq 5$ **28.** $x \neq 2$
29. All real numbers **30.** All real numbers **31.** No
32. Yes **33.** Yes; $m = -4, b = 5$
34. Yes; $m = -1, b = 7$ **35.** No **36.** Yes; $m = 0, b = 6$
37. Yes; $f(x) = \frac{3}{2}x - 3$ **38.** No **39.** 1
40. $f(-2) = -3; f(1) = 0$

41.

42.

43.

44.

45. $H(x) = 24x$; $H(2) = 48$; there are 48 hours in 2 days.
46. (a) **(b)** Domain: $x \geq -2$

$[-10, 10, 1]$ by $[-10, 10, 1]$

47. -2 **48.** 0 **49.** $\frac{1}{3}$ **50.** Undefined **51.** $\frac{3}{2}$
52. $-\frac{3}{4}$ **53.** 0 **54.** Undefined
55. **56.** $-\frac{2}{3}; 0$

57. $y = -3x + 1$ **58.** $y = 2x + 2$ **59.** $-1; 1$
60. (a) $m_1 = 250, m_2 = 500, m_3 = 0, m_4 = -750$
(b) m_1: Water is being added to the pool at a rate of
250 gallons per hour. m_2: Water is being added to the pool
at a rate of 500 gallons per hour. m_3: No water is being added
or removed. m_4: Water is being removed from the pool at a
rate of 750 gallons per hour. **(c)** Initially the pool contains
500 gallons of water. For the first 2 hours water is added
to the pool at a rate of 250 gallons per hour until there are

1000 gallons in the pool. Then water is added at a rate of
500 gallons per hour for 1 hour until there are 1500 gallons
in the pool. For the next hour, no water is added or removed.
Finally, water is removed from the pool at a rate of 750 gallons
per hour for 1 hour until it contains 750 gallons.
61. **62. (a)** $\frac{1}{2}$; -2
(b)

63. Yes **64.** $-2; 2; 4$ **65.** $y = -3x + 7$
66. $y = -3(x + 2) + 3$; $y = -3x - 3$
67. $y = \frac{3}{2}x - 3$ **68.** $y = -2x + 2$ **69.** $y = 4x + \frac{13}{5}$
70. $y = -2x - 1$ **71.** $y = 2x - 5$ **72.** $y = \frac{2}{3}x + 1$
73. $y = -x + 2$ **74.** $y = 2x - 3$ **75.** No **76.** Yes
77. $x = -4$ **78.** $y = -\frac{7}{13}$ **79.** $y = 1$ **80.** $y = -8$
81. No **82.** Yes; $y = 2x + 5$
83. (a) $m_1 = 1.3, m_2 = 2.35, m_3 = 2.4, m_4 = 2.7$
(b) m_1: From 1920 to 1940 the population increased on
average by 1.3 million per year. The other slopes may be
interpreted similarly. **84.** For the first 2 minutes the inlet
pipe is open. For the next 3 minutes both pipes are open. For
the next 2 minutes only the outlet pipe is open. Finally, for
the last 3 minutes both pipes are closed.
85. (a) About 25.1
(b) Decreased

$[1885, 1965, 10]$ by $[22, 26, 1]$

(c) -0.0492; the median age decreased by about 0.0492
year per year.
86. (a) 2.2 million **(b)** The number of marriages each year
did not change. **87. (a)** $f(x) = 8x$ **(b)** 8
(c) The total fat increases at the rate of 8 grams per cup.
88. (a)

(b) $f(x) = -0.1675x + 350$ **(c)** About 15 per
1000 people (answers may vary)
89. (a) 113; in 1995 there were 113 unhealthy
days. **(b)** $D = \{1995, 1999, 2000, 2003, 2007\}$
$R = \{56, 87, 88, 100, 113\}$ **(c)** It decreased and then
increased.

90. (a) Linear

(b) $f(x) = \frac{9}{5}x + 32$; a 1°C change equals $\frac{9}{5}$¡F change.
(c) 68 °F
91. b. **92.** e. **93.** a. **94.** d. **95.** f. **96.** c.
97.

98. (a) $f(x) = 56{,}000(x - 2006) + 1{,}100{,}000$
(b) 1,604,000; total (cumulative) number of U.S. AIDS cases reported in 2015

CHAPTER 1 TEST (pp. 72–73)

1. 46, (4, 46) **2.** $C(x) = 4x$; $C(5) = 20$, 5 pounds of candy costs $20.
3. (a)

(b)

(c)

(d)

4. $0, -3$; $D: -3 \le x \le 3$, $R: -3 \le y \le 0$
5. Symbolic: $f(x) = x^2 - 5$
Numerical:

x	−3	−2	−1	0	1	2	3
$y = f(x)$	4	−1	−4	−5	−4	−1	4

Graphical:

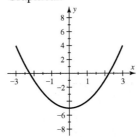

6. No, it fails the vertical line test.
7. (a) $D = \{-2, -1, 0, 5\}$ **(b)** All real numbers
(c) $x \ge -4$ **(d)** All real numbers **(e)** $x \ne 5$
8. It is. $f(x) = -8x + 6$ **9.** -1 **10.** $-\frac{1}{2}$
11. (a) $y = -2x - 4$ **(b)** $y = \frac{1}{2}x + \frac{9}{2}$
(c) $y = -\frac{7}{12}x - \frac{17}{12}$ **12.** $-2; 2; 4$ **13.** $y = -3x + 3$
14. $y = \frac{2}{3}x - 2$; $y = -\frac{3}{2}x$ **15.** $x = \frac{2}{3}$; $y = -\frac{1}{7}$
16. (a) $m_1 = 0.4$, $m_2 = 0$, $m_3 = -0.4$ **(b)** From 1970 to 1980, beneficiaries increased by 0.4 million per year. From 1980 to 1990, there was no change. From 1990 to 2000, beneficiaries decreased by 0.4 million per year; answers may vary slightly.
17.

18.

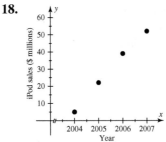

(b) $m = 15.67$, $x_1 = 2004$, $y_1 = 5$ (answers may vary)
(c) About 67.7 million

CHAPTERS 1 CUMULATIVE REVIEW (pp. 75–76)

1. Natural number: $\sqrt[3]{8}$; whole number: $\sqrt[3]{8}$; integer: -3, $\sqrt[3]{8}$; rational number: -3, $\frac{3}{4}$, -5.8, $\sqrt[3]{8}$; irrational number: $\sqrt{7}$
2. Natural number: $\frac{50}{10}$; whole number: 0, $\frac{50}{10}$; integer: 0, -5, $-\sqrt{9}$, $\frac{50}{10}$; rational number: 0, -5, $\frac{1}{2}$, $-\sqrt{9}$, $\frac{50}{10}$; irrational number: $\sqrt{8}$ **3.** Distributive property
4. Commutative property **5.** -2 **6.** $(x + 1)(x + 5)$
7. $-a + b$ **8.** $\frac{c}{a + b}$ **9.** $\frac{169}{126}$ **10. (a)** $\frac{81}{64}$ **(b)** $\frac{81x^5}{y^4}$
(c) $\frac{b^{12}}{a^8}$ **11.** 9.54×10^3 **12.** 34 **13.** $B = 18$

14. (a) $\{-3, 0, 2\}$ **(b)** $x \neq -6$ **(c)** $x \geq -4$

15.

16.

17.

18.

19.

20.

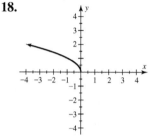

21. (a) Yes   **(b)** Both include all real numbers.
(c) $f(-1) = 1.5; f(0) = 1$ **(d)** x-intercept: 2; y-intercept: 1
(e) $-\frac{1}{2}$ **(f)** $f(x) = -\frac{1}{2}x + 1$ **22.** $y = -\frac{3}{2}x - 1$
23. $y = -\frac{1}{3}x + \frac{5}{3}$ **24.** $x = -2$ **25.** $m = -3$;
x-int: 1; y-int: 3   **26.** $y = -\frac{3}{2}x + \frac{3}{2}$
27. Commutative property for addition
28. 1600 cubic inches
29. (a) $f(x) = 0.2(x - 1970) + 4.7$ (answers may vary)
(b) 14.1%   **30.** The person earns $9 per hour.
31.

32. (a) Linear   **(b)** About 36.4; in 2005 the median age
was 36.4   **(c)** 0.243   **(d)** Each year the median age
increased by 0.243 year, on average.

33. (a) $f(x) = 10x$
(b)

(c) 10
(d) The total amount of fat
increases at a rate of 10 g of
fat per slice of pizza.

35. (a) 87.8 million tons
(b) [1960, 1995, 5] by [60, 220, 20]

(c) 3.4; solid waste increased by about 3.4 million tons
per year.
36. (a) $m_1 = -50, m_2 = 0, m_3 = -50$ **(b)** m_1: The
driver is traveling toward home at a rate of 50 miles per
hour. m_2: The car is not moving. m_3: The driver is traveling
toward home at a rate of 50 miles per hour.   **(c)** The car
started 300 miles from home and moved toward home at
50 mph for 2 hours to a location 200 miles from home.
The car was then parked for 1 hour. Finally, the car
moved toward home at 50 mph for 4 hours, at which point it
was home.

34. (a) $\frac{24}{25} = 0.96$ pint
(b)

(c) $\frac{4}{25} = 0.16$
(d) 0.16 pint of oil should
be added per gallon of
gasoline.

2   Linear Equations and Inequalities

SECTION 2.1 (pp. 89–93)

1. $ax + b = 0, a \neq 0$ **2.** One   **3.** Yes   **4.** Yes   **5.** 4
6. -2 **7.** An equals sign $(=)$ **8.** Numerical, graphical,
symbolic   **9.** 3   **10.** $ax + by = c$, a and b not both 0
11. $a + c = b + c$ **12.** $ac = bc$, for $c \neq 0$ **13.** T
14. T   **15.** F   **16.** F   **17.** No   **18.** Yes   **19.** Yes   **20.** No
21. Yes   **22.** Yes   **23.** 14   **25.** -2 **27.** $-\frac{3}{2}$ **29.** 3
31. -12 **33.** 5   **35.** 5   **37.** $\frac{16}{5}$ **39.** $\frac{6}{7}$ **41.** $-\frac{3}{2}$ **43.** $\frac{7}{4}$
45. $\frac{5}{2}$ **47.** $\frac{72}{53} \approx 1.36$ **49.** 11   **51.** 1983   **53.** $-\frac{1}{6}$
55. -5 **57.** 6   **59.** 2   **61.** 0.75   **63.** -12 **65.** $x = -\frac{b}{a}$
67. 2

x	1	2	3	4	5
$-4x + 8$	4	0	-4	-8	-12

69. -1

x	-2	-1	0	1	2
$4 - 2x$	8	6	4	2	0
$x + 7$	5	6	7	8	9

71. 10 **73.** 1 **75.** 1.5 **77.** −2 **79.** −1 **81.** −1 **83.** 0
85. −3 **87.** 2007 **89.** About 2.89 **91.** 7 **93.** 3
95. Contradiction **97.** Identity **99.** Identity
101. Conditional **103.** $(-2, 5)$
105. (a) x-int: 4; y-int: 4   **107. (a)** x-int: 5; y-int: 2
(b)   **(b)**

            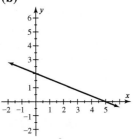

(c) $y = -x + 4$ **(c)** $y = -\frac{2}{5}x + 2$
109. (a) x-int: $\frac{9}{2}$; y-int: -3 **111. (a)** x-int: -3; y-int: -2
(b)   **(b)**

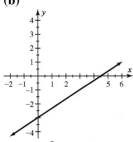

(c) $y = \frac{2}{3}x - 3$ **(c)** $y = -\frac{2}{3}x - 2$
113. (a) x-int: $\frac{7}{2}$; y-int: $\frac{7}{5}$
(b)

(c) $y = -\frac{2}{5}x + \frac{7}{5}$
115. (a) x-int: $-\frac{3}{5}$; y-int: $\frac{1}{2}$
(b)

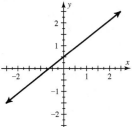

(c) $y = \frac{5}{6}x + \frac{1}{2}$
117. (a) $S(x) = 2.4(x - 1960) + 42$ **(b)** 138 million tons
(c) About 2027 **119. (a)** 2006 **(b)** 2006 **(c)** 2006
121. (a) $D(x) = 0.02x + 1.1$
(b) In 1970 $(x = 0)$ 1.1 million degrees were awarded.

(c) 2000 **(d)** 2000 **123. (a)** $37.645 billion; in 2008
revenue from newspaper ads was $37.645 billion.
(b) Online; online ad revenue is increasing while
newspaper ad revenue is decreasing **(c)** About 2011
(d) About 2011; yes
125. (a) 29.5%; In 2010 29.5% of mobile phone owners had
smartphones **(b)** In 2008 $(x = 0)$, 10% of mobile phone
owners had smartphones. **(c)** About 2012
127. About 1987 **129.** Using 1990 and 2005 data, about
1986 (answers will vary)

SECTION 2.2 (pp. 103–106)

1. $\frac{x}{2}$ **2.** $4x - 7$ **3.** $2W + 2L$ **4.** Read the problem
carefully. **5.** 0.431 **6.** 10 **7.** $y = -\frac{4}{3}x + 4$
9. $x = \frac{15}{8}y$ **11.** $b = \frac{S}{6a}$ **13.** $t = 14 - r$
15. $f(x) = 3x + 8$ **17.** $f(x) = \frac{2x}{\pi}$ **19.** $f(x) = \frac{8x}{3}$
21. $f(x) = \frac{-7x}{9}$ **23.** $f(x) = \frac{2x-20}{3}$ **25. (a)** $x + 2 = 12$
(b) 10 **27. (a)** $\frac{x}{5} = x + 1$ **(b)** $-\frac{5}{4}$ **29. (a)** $\frac{x + 5}{2} = 7$
(b) 9 **31. (a)** $\frac{x}{2} = 17$ **(b)** 34
33. (a) $x + (x + 1) + (x + 2) = 30$ **(b)** 9 **35.** 0.55
37. 0.0004 **39.** 3.41 **41.** −0.0167 **43.** 0.0025
45. (a) $L = \frac{P}{2} - W$ **(b)** 24 feet **47.** $h = \frac{A}{2\pi r}$
49. $C = \frac{5}{9}(F - 32)$ **51.** $h = \frac{2A}{b}$ **53.** 44, 45, 46
55. 23, 25, 27 **57.** 8 feet **59.** About 16 in. for the square;
12.5 in. for each circle **61.** 68 mph; 74 mph **63.** 4.5 liters
65. 2.5 hr at 74 mph; 1 hr at 63 mph **67.** 4 liters
69. $2200 at 6%; $2800 at 4% **71.** 38°, 66°, 76°
73. (a) 36,000 cubic feet per hour **(b)** 66 people
75. $2.80 **77.** 110,000 sq mi **79.** About $1.2 billion
81. 1500 people **83.** About 3.3

CHECKING BASIC CONCEPTS 2.1 & 2.2 (p. 107)

1. 1 **2.** $\frac{6}{11}$ **3. (a)** −2 **(b)** −2 **(c)** −2 Yes
4. 0.3 hour at 10 miles per hour; 0.9 hour at 8 miles per hour
5. x-int: 4; y-int: −5 **6. (a)** Identity **(b)** Contradiction
7. 23.5 ft by 17.5 ft

SECTION 2.3 (pp. 115–119)

1. $3x + 2 < 5$ (answers may vary) **2.** Yes; consider
$x + 2 > 2$. **3.** Yes **4.** Yes **5.** Yes; they have the same
solution set. **6.** No; $-4x < 8$ is equivalent to $x > -2$.
7. An equation has an equals sign, whereas an inequality has
an inequality symbol. **8.** Numerical, graphical, symbolic
9. $\{x \mid x < 6\}$ **10.** $\{x \mid x \geq -0.7\}$ **11.** Yes **12.** No
13. No **14.** Yes **15. (a)** $\{x \mid x = 2\}$ **(b)** $\{x \mid x < 2\}$
(c) $\{x \mid x > 2\}$ **17. (a)** $\{x \mid x = 3\}$ **(b)** $\{x \mid x > 3\}$
(c) $\{x \mid x < 3\}$ **19.** $\{x \mid x \leq 2\}$ **21.** $\{x \mid x > 36\}$
23. $\left\{x \mid x \geq \frac{14}{9}\right\}$ **25.** $\left\{x \mid x > \frac{17}{3}\right\}$ **27.** $\left\{x \mid x < \frac{27}{14}\right\}$
29. $\left\{x \mid x \geq \frac{2}{13}\right\}$ **31.** $\{x \mid x < 2010\}$ **33.** $\{x \mid x < 5\}$
35. $\{x \mid x \geq -6\}$ **37.** $\{z \mid z \leq -6\}$ **39.** $\left\{t \mid t \geq -\frac{7}{2}\right\}$
41. $\left\{x \mid x > -\frac{25}{3}\right\}$ **43.** $\left\{x \mid x > \frac{17}{9}\right\}$ **45.** $\left\{x \mid x \geq \frac{1}{2}\right\}$
47. $\left\{x \mid x \neq \frac{5}{2}\right\}$ **49.** $\left\{x \mid x \geq \frac{9}{5}\right\}$ **51.** $\left\{x \mid x > -\frac{1}{2}\right\}$

53. $\{x \mid x \geq 3\}$

x	1	2	3	4	5
$-2x + 6$	4	2	0	-2	-4

55. $\{x \mid x > 3\}$ **57.** $\{x \mid x \geq 2\}$ **59. (a)** $\{x \mid x = -1\}$
(b) $\{x \mid x < -1\}$ **(c)** $\{x \mid x > -1\}$ **61. (a)** $\{x \mid x = \frac{1}{2}\}$
(b) $\{x \mid x > \frac{1}{2}\}$ **(c)** $\{x \mid x < \frac{1}{2}\}$ **63.** $\{x \mid x \geq 1\}$
65. $\{x \mid x > 2\}$ **67. (a)** Car 1; the slope of the line for Car 1
is greater than the slope of the line for Car 2.   **(b)** 5 hours;
400 miles   **(c)** $x < 5$ **69. (a)** 1   **(b)** $\{x \mid x > 1\}$
(c) $\{x \mid x \leq 1\}$ **(d)** $\{x \mid x \geq 1\}$ **71.** $\{x \mid x < 1\}$
73. $\{x \mid x \geq 0\}$ **75.** $\{x \mid x \geq -2\}$ **77.** $\{x \mid x < -4\}$
79. $\{x \mid x < -3\}$ **81.** $\{x \mid x \leq 1991\}$
83. $\{x \mid x > 0.834\}$ **85.** $\{x \mid x < a\}$ **87.** After about 1975
89. $\{x \mid x < 2\}$ **91.** $\{x \mid x \leq 3\}$ **93. (a)** $\{x \mid x = 12\}$
(b) $\{x \mid x > 12\}$ **95. (a)** $\{x \mid x \leq -\frac{7}{3}\}$
(b) $\{x \mid x \geq -\frac{7}{3}\}$ **97. (a)** $\{x \mid x \leq -9\}$
(b) $\{x \mid x \geq -9\}$ **99. (a)** \$200   **(b)** \$5.00 each
(c) $P = 5x - 200$ **(d)** $x = 40$ DVDs
(e) $x > 40$ DVDs   **101.** $x < 10$ feet   **103. (a)** First car:
70 miles per hour; second car: 60 miles per hour
(b) When $x = 3.5$ hours   **(c)** Elapsed times after 3.5
hours   **105.** Below about 3.16 miles   **107.** Between 132
and 174 lb   **109. (a)** 2009 to 2012   **(b)** 2009 to 2012
(c) 2009 to 2012

SECTION 2.4 (pp. 127–131)

1. $x > 1$ and $x \leq 7$ (answers may vary)
2. $x \leq 3$ or $x > 5$ (answers may vary)   **3.** No   **4.** Yes
5. Yes   **6.** Numerically, graphically, symbolically
7. Yes, no   **8.** No, Yes   **9.** No, yes   **10.** Yes, no
11. No, yes   **12.** Yes, yes   **13.** [2, 10]   **15.** (5, 8]
17. $(-\infty, 4)$ **19.** $(-2, \infty)$ **21.** $[-2, 5)$ **23.** $(-8, 8]$
25. $(3, \infty)$ **27.** $(-\infty, -2] \cup [4, \infty)$
29. $(-\infty, 1) \cup [5, \infty)$ **31.** $(-3, 5]$ **33.** $(-\infty, -2)$
35. $(-\infty, 4)$ **37.** $(-\infty, 1) \cup (2, \infty)$
39. $\{x \mid -1 \leq x \leq 3\}$

41. $\{x \mid -2 < x < 2.5\}$

43. $\{x \mid x > 3\}$

45. $\{x \mid x \leq -1 \text{ or } x \geq 2\}$

47. All real numbers

49. $[-6, 7]$ **51.** $\left(\frac{13}{4}, \infty\right)$ **53.** $(-\infty, \infty)$
55. $\left(-\infty, -\frac{11}{5}\right) \cup (-1, \infty)$ **57.** No solutions
59. $[-6, 1)$ **61.** $\left[-\frac{1}{4}, \frac{11}{8}\right)$ **63.** $[-9, 3]$
65. $\left[-4, -\frac{1}{4}\right)$ **67.** $(-1, 1]$ **69.** $[-2, 1]$ **71.** $(0, 2)$
73. $(9, 21]$ **75.** $\left[\frac{12}{5}, \frac{22}{5}\right]$ **77.** $\left(-\frac{13}{3}, 1\right)$ **79.** $[0, 12]$
81. $[-1, 2]$ **83.** $(-1, 2)$ **85.** $[-3, 1]$
87. $(-\infty, -2) \cup (0, \infty)$

89. (a) Toward, because distance is decreasing
(b) 4 hours, 2 hours   **(c)** From 2 to 4 hours   **(d)** During the
first 2 hours   **91. (a)** 2   **(b)** 4   **(c)** $\{x \mid 2 \leq x \leq 4\}$
(d) $\{x \mid 0 \leq x < 2\}$ **93.** [1, 4]   **95.** $(-\infty, -2) \cup (0, \infty)$
97. [2002, 2010]   **99.** $(-\infty, 5]$
101. $(-\infty, -1) \cup (-1, \infty)$ **103.** $(0, \infty)$ **105.** [1, 3]
107. $(-\infty, \infty)$ **109.** $(-\infty, 1) \cup [3, \infty)$
111. $(c - b, d - b]$ **113. (a)** From 2006 to 2008
(b) From 2006 to 2008   **(c)** From 2006 to 2008
115. From 0.5 to 1.5 miles   **117.** From 5.$\overline{6}$ to 9 feet
119. From 1.5 to 2.5 miles   **121. (a)** $M(x) = 25x + 250$
(b) From 2002 to 2006

CHECKING BASIC CONCEPTS 2.3 & 2.4 (p. 131)

1. $\{x \mid x > \frac{8}{7}\}$ **2. (a)** $\{x \mid x = 2\}$ **(b)** $\{x \mid x < 2\}$
(c) $\{x \mid x \geq 2\}$ **3. (a)** Yes   **(b)** No   **4. (a)** $[-3, 1]$
(b) $(-\infty, -1) \cup [3, \infty)$ **(c)** $\left[-\frac{8}{3}, \frac{8}{3}\right)$

SECTION 2.5 (pp. 139–144)

1. $|3x + 2| = 6$ (answers may vary)
2. $|2x - 1| \leq 17$ (answers may vary)   **3.** Yes   **4.** Yes
5. Yes   **6.** No, it is equivalent to $-3 < x < 3$.   **7.** 2
8. 0   **9.** No, yes   **10.** Yes, no   **11.** No, yes   **12.** No, yes
13. Yes, yes   **14.** No, yes   **15.** 0, 4   **16.** $-2, 1$
17. $-3, 3$ **18.** $-5, 5$ **19.** $(-3, 3)$ **20.** $(-5, 5)$
21. $(-\infty, -3) \cup (3, \infty)$ **22.** $(-\infty, -5) \cup (5, \infty)$
23. $-7, 7$ **25.** No solutions   **27.** $-\frac{9}{4}, \frac{9}{4}$ **29.** $-4, 4$
31. $-6, 5$ **33.** 1, 2   **35.** $\frac{3}{4}$ **37.** $-8, 12$ **39.** No solutions
41. $-15, 18$ **43.** $-1, \frac{1}{3}$ **45.** $-5, \frac{3}{5}$ **47.** -6
49. (a) $-4, 4$ **(b)** $\{x \mid -4 < x < 4\}$
(c) $\{x \mid x < -4 \text{ or } x > 4\}$
51. (a) $\frac{1}{2}, 2$ **(b)** $\{x \mid \frac{1}{2} \leq x \leq 2\}$
(c) $\{x \mid x \leq \frac{1}{2} \text{ or } x \geq 2\}$ **53.** $[-3, 3]$
55. $(-\infty, -4) \cup (4, \infty)$ **57.** No solutions
59. $(-\infty, 0) \cup (0, \infty)$ **61.** $\left(-\infty, -\frac{7}{2}\right) \cup \left(\frac{7}{2}, \infty\right)$
63. $(-3, 5)$ **65.** $(-\infty, -9] \cup [-1, \infty)$ **67.** $\left[\frac{5}{6}, \frac{11}{6}\right]$
69. $[-10, 14]$ **71.** No solutions   **73.** $(-\infty, \infty)$
75. No solutions   **77.** $(-\infty, \infty)$
79. $(-\infty, -13] \cup [17, \infty)$ **81.** [0.9, 1.1]
83. $(-\infty, 9.5) \cup (10.5, \infty)$ **85. (a)** $-1, 3$ **(b)** $(-1, 3)$
(c) $(-\infty, -1) \cup (3, \infty)$ **87. (a)** $-1, 0$ **(b)** $[-1, 0]$
(c) $(-\infty, -1] \cup [0, \infty)$ **89.** $(-\infty, -1] \cup [1, \infty)$
91. $[-2, 4]$ **93.** $(-\infty, 1) \cup (3, \infty)$ **95.** $(2, 4.\overline{6})$
97. $(-\infty, \infty)$ **99.** $\{x \mid -3 \leq x \leq 3\}$
101. $\{x \mid x < 2 \text{ or } x > 3\}$ **103.** $|x| \leq 4$ **105.** $|y| > 2$
107. $|2x + 1| \leq 0.3$ **109.** $|\pi x| \geq 7$ **111.** two
113. (a) $\{T \mid 19 \leq T \leq 67\}$ **(b)** Monthly average
temperatures vary from 19°F to 67°F.
115. (a) $\{T \mid -26 \leq T \leq 46\}$ **(b)** Monthly average
temperatures vary from -26°F to 46°F.   **117. (a)** About
19,058 feet   **(b)** Africa and Europe   **(c)** South America,
North America, Africa, Europe, and Antarctica
(d) $|E - A| \leq 5000$ **119.** $\{d \mid 2.498 \leq d \leq 2.502\}$; the
diameter can vary from 2.498 to 2.502 inches.

121. $|d - 3.8| \leq 0.03$
123. Values between 19 and 21, exclusive

CHECKING BASIC CONCEPTS 2.5 (p. 144)

1. $-\frac{28}{3}, 12$ **2. (a)** $-\frac{2}{3}, \frac{14}{3}$ **(b)** $\left(-\frac{2}{3}, \frac{14}{3}\right)$
(c) $\left(-\infty, -\frac{2}{3}\right) \cup \left(\frac{14}{3}, \infty\right)$ **3.** $(0, 6); (-\infty, 0] \cup [6, \infty)$
4. (a) $1, 3$ **(b)** $[1, 3]$ **(c)** $(-\infty, 1] \cup [3, \infty)$

CHAPTER 2 REVIEW (pp. 147–150)

1. 2

x	0	1	2	3	4
$3x - 6$	-6	-3	0	3	6

2. 1

x	-1	0	1	2	3
$5 - 2x$	7	5	3	1	-1

3. Yes   **4.** 1   **5.** 2   **6.** 4   **7.** 14   **8.** $\frac{1}{2}$ **9.** $\frac{1}{7}$ **10.** $-\frac{1}{3}$
11. 10   **12.** $\frac{21}{8}$ **13.** 1972   **14.** $\frac{19}{5}$ **15.** 4   **16.** -9
17. Identity   **18.** Contradiction   **19.** x-int: 5, y-int: -4;
$y = \frac{4}{5}x - 4$ **20.** x-int: -3, y-int: -12; $y = -4x - 12$
21. $y = \frac{5}{4}x - 5$ **22.** $y = \frac{2}{3}x + 2$ **23.** $a = -3b$
24. $n = -\frac{2}{7}m$ **25.** $b = \frac{2A}{h} - a$ **26.** $h = \frac{3V}{\pi r^2}$
27. $f(x) = \frac{2}{3}x - \frac{8}{3}$ **28.** $f(x) = \frac{7}{27}x + \frac{1}{27}$
29. $f(x) = -\frac{3}{5}x + 2$ **30.** $f(x) = 3x$
31. $2x + 25 = 19; -3$ **32.** $2x - 5 = x + 1; 6$
33. $\{x \mid x > -1\}$ **34.** $\{x \mid x > 5\}$ **35.** $\{x \mid x \geq 2\}$
36. (a) $\frac{7}{4}$ **(b)** $\{x \mid x > \frac{7}{4}\}$ **(c)** $\{x \mid x < \frac{7}{4}\}$
37. $\{x \mid x \geq -1\}$ **38.** $\{x \mid x \leq -8\}$ **39.** $\{x \mid x > 1\}$
40. $\{x \mid x > \frac{4}{3}\}$ **41.** $\{t \mid t > \frac{16}{9}\}$ **42.** $\{x \mid x \geq 5\}$
43. $\{t \mid t \leq 2.1\}$ **44.** $\{z \mid z > -36.4\}$
45. $\{x \mid x \leq 1.840\}$ **46.** $\{x \mid x > 1.665\}$
47. $[-2, 2]$

48. $(-\infty, -3]$

49. $\left(-\infty, \frac{4}{5}\right] \cup (2, \infty)$

50. $(-\infty, \infty)$

51. $[-2, 1]$ **52. (a)** -4 **(b)** 2   **(c)** $[-4, 2]$ **(d)** $(-\infty, 2)$
53. (a) 2   **(b)** $(2, \infty)$ **(c)** $(-\infty, 2)$ **54. (a)** 4   **(b)** 2
(c) $(2, 4)$ **55.** $\left[-3, \frac{2}{3}\right]$ **56.** $(-6, 45]$ **57.** $\left(-\infty, \frac{7}{2}\right)$
58. $[1.8, \infty)$ **59.** $(-3, 4)$ **60.** $(-\infty, 4) \cup (10, \infty)$
61. $(-5, 5)$ **62.** $[8, 28]$ **63.** $(-9, 21)$ **64.** $[8, 28]$
65. $\left(-\frac{11}{5}, \frac{7}{5}\right]$ **66.** $[88, 138]$ **67.** No, no   **68.** No, yes
69. No, yes   **70.** No, yes   **71. (a)** $0, 4$ **(b)** $(0, 4)$
(c) $(-\infty, 0) \cup (4, \infty)$ **72. (a)** $-3, 1$ **(b)** $[-3, 1]$
(c) $(-\infty, -3] \cup [1, \infty)$ **73.** $-22, 22$ **74.** $1, 8$
75. $-26, 42$ **76.** $-\frac{23}{3}, \frac{25}{3}$ **77.** $0, 2$ **78.** $-3, \frac{9}{5}$
79. (a) $-8, 6$ **(b)** $[-8, 6]$ **(c)** $(-\infty, -8] \cup [6, \infty)$
80. (a) $-\frac{5}{2}, \frac{7}{2}$ **(b)** $\left[-\frac{5}{2}, \frac{7}{2}\right]$ **(c)** $\left(-\infty, -\frac{5}{2}\right] \cup \left[\frac{7}{2}, \infty\right)$
81. $(-\infty, -3) \cup (3, \infty)$ **82.** $(-4, 4)$ **83.** $[-3, 4]$

84. $\left(-\infty, -\frac{5}{2}\right] \cup [5, \infty)$ **85.** $[4.4, 4.6]$ **86.** $\left[\frac{3}{13}, \frac{7}{13}\right]$
87. $(-\infty, \infty)$ **88.** $\frac{3}{2}$ **89.** $(-\infty, -1.5] \cup [1.5, \infty)$
90. $[-2, 6]$ **91.** $|x| \leq 0.05$ **92.** $|5x - 1| > 4$
93. \$3500 at 5%; \$4200 at 7%   **94.** 0.6 hour at 8 miles per
hour; 0.8 hour at 10 miles per hour   **95.** About \$769,000
96. (a) $f(x) = -0.3125x + 10$ **(b)** About 5.9 million
97. (a) 3 hours   **(b)** 2 hours and 4 hours
(c) Between 2 and 4 hours, exclusive   **(d)** 20 miles per
hour   **98. (a)** Car 1; its graph has the steeper slope.
(b) 3 hours; 200 miles   **(c)** Before 3 hours
99. (a) About 31.8 inches   **(b)** Lengths less than 31.8
inches   **100. (a)** $T(x) = -19x + 60$ **(b)** Approximately
from 1.05 to 2.11 miles   **101. (a)** 1979   **(b)** Median age
increased, on average, by 0.238 year per year. In 1970
$(x = 0)$, the median age was 27.9.   **102.** 13 feet by 31 feet
103. $-44.\overline{4}°C$ to $41.\overline{6}°C$
104. $|L - 160| \leq 1; 159 \leq L \leq 161$
105. (a) $|A - 3.9| \leq 1.7$ **(b)** $2.2 \leq A \leq 5.6$
106. Values between 32.2 and 37.8, exclusive

CHAPTER 2 TEST (pp. 150–152)

1. Yes

2.

x	-2	-1	0	1	2
$2 - 3x$	8	5	2	-1	-4

$; \{x \mid x \geq 1\}$

3. -3 **4. (a)** 2   **(b)** $(-\infty, 2]$ **(c)** $[2, \infty)$ **5.** 1
6. (a) $\frac{7}{9}$ **(b)** $\frac{7}{13}$ **(c)** $\frac{10}{17}$ **7.** x-int: $-\frac{3}{2}$, y-int: 3; $y = 2x + 3$
8. $2 + 5x = x - 4; -\frac{3}{2}$ **9.** $f(x) = \frac{3}{2}x - 3$
10. $\left[-\frac{3}{5}, \infty\right)$ **11.** $(1.55, \infty)$
12.

13. $(-\infty, -2) \cup (1, \infty)$ **14. (a)** -5 **(b)** 5   **(c)** $[-5, 5]$
(d) $(-\infty, 5)$ **15.** $(-8, 0)$ **16.** $-12, 24$ **17. (a)** $[-5, 5]$
(b) $(-\infty, 0) \cup (0, \infty)$ **(c)** No solutions
(d) $(-\infty, -2) \cup (2, \infty)$ **(e)** $(-\infty, \infty)$ **(f)** $(-2, 8)$
18. (a) $-\frac{2}{5}, \frac{4}{5}$ **(b)** $\left[-\frac{2}{5}, \frac{4}{5}\right]$ **(c)** $\left(-\infty, -\frac{2}{5}\right] \cup \left[\frac{4}{5}, \infty\right)$
19. (a) 64 calories   **(b)** More than 64 calories
(c) Less than 64 calories   **(d)** Each gram of carbohydrates
corresponds to 4 calories.   **20. (a)** $f(x) = 0.4x + 75$
(b) 35 minutes   **21.** $g = \frac{2d}{t^2}$
22. \$3500 at 4%; \$1500 at 6%   **23.** $41°, 57°, 82°$ **24.** \$108
25. (a) From 1990 to 2000   **(b)** Numbers increased, on
average, by 190 per year; In 1980 $(x = 0)$ there were 6000
women marines.

CHAPTERS 1–2 CUMULATIVE REVIEW
(pp. 152–155)

1. Natural: $\frac{8}{2}$; whole: $0, \frac{8}{2}$; integer: $-7, 0, \frac{8}{2}$;
rational: $-7, -\frac{3}{5}, 0, \frac{8}{2}, 5.\overline{12}$; irrational: $\sqrt{5}$
2. Natural: $\sqrt{9}$; whole: $\frac{0}{9}, \sqrt{9}$; integer: $-\frac{6}{3}, \frac{0}{9}, \sqrt{9}$;
rational: $-\frac{6}{3}, \frac{0}{9}, \sqrt{9}, 4.\overline{6}$; irrational: π **3.** Distributive
4. Associative   **5.** 50   **6.** 693
7.

8. $5y + 4$ **9.** $\frac{3y^7}{x^5}$ **10.** $\frac{64b^9}{27a^6}$ **11.** 13

12. 5.9×10^{-5} **13.** 5   **14.** 30   **15.** (ii)
16. $D = \{-2, 0, 1, 3\}; R = \{0, 2, 4\}$
17. $(-2, 5), (-1, 3), (0, 1),$ **18.** $(-2, -2), \left(-1, \frac{3}{2}\right),$
$(1, -1), (2, -3)$ $(0, 2), \left(1, \frac{5}{2}\right), (2, 6)$

19.

20. $x \neq 0$ **21.** 2, -2 **22.** 2, -4
23. Yes; $m = -3, b = 11$ **24.** No   **25.** $f(x) = 4x + 3$
26.

27. 5; -4 **28.** -2
29.

30. $y = -\frac{1}{2}x - 1$ **31.** 3; -1; 3   **32.** $x = 5$
33. $y = 3x - 5$ **34.** $y = x + 3$ **35.** Yes   **36.** 1
37. $-\frac{2}{3}$ **38.** $\frac{1}{11}$ **39.** x-int: 2, y-int: -6; $y = 3x - 6$
40. x-int: -2, y-int: $\frac{5}{2}$; $y = \frac{5}{4}x + \frac{5}{2}$ **41.** $\{x \mid x > 0\}$
42. $(-\infty, -3]$ **43.** $(3, \infty)$ **44.** $(-\infty, 0]$
45. $(-1, 5]$

46. $\left(-\infty, -\frac{3}{2}\right) \cup [3, \infty)$

47. $[-2, 4]$ **48.** $[-16, 10]$ **49.** $(-\infty, -6) \cup \left(\frac{8}{3}, \infty\right)$
50. $[4, 7]$ **51.** (a) $-3, 1$ (b) $[-3, 1]$
(c) $(-\infty, -3] \cup [1, \infty)$ **52.** $-6, 18$ **53.** (a) 7004.25
(b) $14,741.05$ **54.** $d = 65t$ **55.** (a) $f(x) = 10x$
(b) 10   (c) The soda contains 10 mg of sodium per ounce.

56.

57. (a) Away; the slope of the line is positive.   (b) 3 hours
(c) From 0 to 3 hours (not including 3)
58. About 1992 to 2004

<table>
<tr><td>3</td><td>Polynomial Expressions and Functions</td></tr>
</table>

SECTION 3.1 (pp. 168–172)

1. $3x^2$ (answers may vary)   **2.** 3; -1 **3.** No; the powers must match for each variable.   **4.** $x^4 - 3x + 5$ (answers may vary)   **5.** No; the opposite is $-x^2 - 1$.   **6.** 96
7. No; a function has only one output for each input.
8. Yes, if the polynomial is linear.   **9.** 6   **10.** $3x^2$
11. $(f - g)(x) = x^2 + 12$ **12.** All but $3 - x^2$ **13.** Yes
15. No   **17.** Yes   **19.** No   **21.** No   **23.** x^2 **25.** πr^2
27. xy **29.** 7; 3   **31.** 7; -3 **33.** 6; -1 **35.** 2; 5
37. 3; $-\frac{2}{5}$ **39.** 5; 1   **41.** $5x^2$ **43.** $3y^4$ **45.** Not possible
47. $3x^2 + 3x$ **49.** $5x^2 + 9xy$ **51.** $5x^3y^7 + 13x$
53. $2x + 2$ **55.** $-2x^2 + 3x + 8$ **57.** $3x^3 + 5x^2 + 15$
59. $-7x^4 - 3x^2 + x - \frac{9}{2}$ **61.** $4r^4 + r^3 - 6r + 2$
63. $5y^2 - 4xy - 2x^2$ **65.** $-6x^5$ **67.** $-19x^5 + 5x^3 - 3x$
69. $7z^4 - z^2 + 8$ **71.** $3x - 7$ **73.** $6x^2 - 5x + 5$
75. $8x^4 + 14x^2 - 7$ **77.** $-3x - 11$ **79.** Yes; 4; fourth degree   **81.** No   **83.** No   **85.** Yes; 2; quadratic
87. -16 **89.** 24   **91.** 84   **93.** -1; 2   **95.** -4; 2   **97.** 12
99. 7   **101.** 5.8   **103.** 1   **105.** 0   **107.** 1.96   **109.** -6
111. $a^2 - 2a$ **113.** (a) 8   (b) -10 (c) $2x + 4$
(d) $4x - 6$ **115.** (a) -7 (b) -5 (c) $-2x^2 + 1$
(d) $-4x^2 - 1$ **117.** (a) 16   (b) 4   (c) $2x^3$ (d) $-4x^3$
119. (a) 23   (b) 3   (c) $5x^2 + x + 1$ (d) $-3x^2 - 5x + 1$
121. (a) 1300; 10,000   (b) 1300; 9924; they are similar.
(c) 8624   **123.** (a) 123 thousand, which is close to the actual value.   (b) 478.6 thousand, which is too high; AIDS deaths did not continue to rise as rapidly as the model predicts.
125. $5s^3$ **127.** $x^2 + \pi x^2$; $100 + 100\pi \approx 414.2$ square inches   **129.** From 4 to 8 minutes

t	3	4	5	6	7	8	9
$y = f(t)$	126.875	110	96.875	87.5	81.875	80	81.875

131. (i) $f(x)$ is the best, which can be determined from a table of values.   **133.** (a) $R(x) = 16x$
(b) $P(x) = 12x - 2000$ (c) 34,000; profit is $34,000 for selling 3000 DVDs.   **135.** (a) 130; it costs $130 thousand to make 100 notebook computers.   (b) The y-intercept for C is 100. The company has $100 thousand in fixed costs even if it makes 0 computers. The y-intercept for R is 0. If the company sells 0 computers, its revenue is $0.
(c) $P(x) = 0.45x - 100$ (d) 223 or more

SECTION 3.2 (pp. 181–184)

1. Distributive **2.** $3x, 2x - 7, x^2 - 3x + 1$ (answers may vary) **3.** x^8 **4.** $8x^3; x^6$ **5.** $a^2 - b^2$ **6.** $a^2 + 2ab + b^2$ **7.** $x^2 - x$ **8.** No, it equals $x^2 + 2x + 1$. **9.** F **10.** T **11.** d **12.** a **13.** x^{12} **15.** $-20y^8$ **17.** $-4x^4y^6$ **19.** $20x^2y^3z^6$ **21.** $5y + 10$ **23.** $-10x - 18$ **25.** $-6y^2 + 18y$ **27.** $27 - 12x$ **29.** $-a^3b + ab^3$ **31.** $-5mn^3 - 5m^2$ **33.** $x^2 + 3x + 2$; 42 square inches **35.** $2x^2 + 3x + 1$; 66 square inches **37.** $x^2 + 11x + 30$ **39.** $4x^2 + 4x + 1$ **41.** No, a square of a sum does not equal the sum of the squares. **43.** No **45.** Yes **47.** No **49.** $x^2 + 15x + 50$ **51.** $x^2 - 7x + 12$ **53.** $2z^2 + 3z - 2$ **55.** $y^2 - y - 12$ **57.** $-36x^2 + 43x - 12$ **59.** $-2z^2 + 7z - 6$ **61.** $z^2 - \frac{1}{4}z - \frac{1}{8}$ **63.** $2x^4 + x^2 - 1$ **65.** $x^2 - xy - 2y^2$ **67.** $4x^3 - 8x^2 - 12x$ **69.** $-x^5 + 3x^3 - x$ **71.** $6n^4 - 12n^3 + 3n^2$ **73.** $x^3 + 3x^2 - x - 3$ **75.** $-z^4 - 3z^3 - z^2 + 2z$ **77.** $4a^3b^2 - 2a^2b^3 + 6ab^4$ **79.** $6r^3 - 10r^2t - 6rt^2 + 4t^3$ **81.** $2^6 = 64$ **83.** $2z^{18}$ **85.** $25x^2$ **87.** $-8x^3y^6$ **89.** $16a^4b^6$ **91.** $x^2 - 16$ **93.** $9 - 4x^2$ **95.** $x^2 - y^2$ **97.** $x^2 + 4x + 4$ **99.** $4x^2 + 4x + 1$ **101.** $x^2 - 2x + 1$ **103.** $9x^2 - 12x + 4$ **105.** $3x^3 - 3x$ **107.** $3rt^3 - 12r^3t$ **109.** $a^4 - 4b^4$ **111.** $9m^6 + 30m^3n^2 + 25n^4$ **113.** $x^6 - 4x^3y^3 + 4y^6$ **115.** $x^2 - 6x - y^2 + 9$ **117.** $r^2 - t^2 - 4t - 4$ **119.** 9996 **121.** $0; x^2 - x - 2$ **123.** $-28; -5x^3 + 3x^2$ **125.** $27; 2x^4 + 2x^3 - 5x^2 + x - 3$ **127.** $x(x + 4)$; 480 square feet **129.** $(x + 3)^2$; 529 square feet **131.** **(a)** 30 thousand **(b)** $40p - \frac{1}{2}p^2$ **(c)** \$750 thousand **133.** **(a)** $\frac{1}{100}x^2 - 2x + 100$ **(b)** 43.56%; yes **(c)** If one serve is out of bounds 34% of the time, then two consecutive serves will be in bounds 43.56% of the time. **135.** **(a)** The average American used 1900 gallons of water daily in 1980, and this daily average is decreasing by 24 gallons each year. **(b)** $T(x) = -62.4x^2 - 580x + 437,000$ **(c)** 363,440; daily usage in 2010 was 363,440,000,000 gal. **137.** $x(x + 1) = x^2 + x$ **139.** $x(50 - x)$ or $50x - x^2$

CHECKING BASIC CONCEPTS 3.1 & 3.2 (p. 182)

1. **(a)** $3x^2 + 7x$ **(b)** $5x^3 + 2x^2 - 3x + 1$ **2.** $x(x + 120)$; 1300, when tickets cost \$10 each, the revenue will be \$1300. **3.** **(a)** 160 bpm **(b)** 92 bpm **4.** **(a)** $-5x + 30$ **(b)** $12x^5 - 20x^4$ **(c)** $2x^2 + 5x - 3$ **5.** **(a)** $25x^2 - 36$ **(b)** $9x^2 - 24x + 16$ **6.**

2	$2x$	8
x	x^2	$4x$
	x	4

SECTION 3.3 (pp. 192–195)

1. To solve equations **2.** Either $x = 0$ or $x - 3 = 0$; zero-product property **3.** Yes; because $2x$ is a factor of each term. **4.** No, because $4x^2$ is the greatest common factor. **5.** No; because $\frac{1}{2}(4) = 2$, and $\frac{1}{2} \neq 2$ and $4 \neq 2$.

6. Yes; by the zero-product property **7.** d **8.** b **9.** $5(2x - 3)$ **11.** $2(2x + 3y)$ **13.** $3(3r - 5t)$ **15.** $x(2x^2 - 5)$ **17.** $2a(4a^2 + 5)$ **19.** $6r^3(1 - 3r^2)$ **21.** $4x(2x^2 - x + 4)$ **23.** $3n(3n^3 - 2n + 1)$ **25.** $2t^2(3t^4 - 2t^2 + 1)$ **27.** $5x^2y^2(1 - 3y)$ **29.** $3a^2b^2(2a - 5b)$ **31.** $6mn^2(3 + 2mn)$ **33.** $5xy(3x + 2 - 5xy)$ **35.** $2a(2a - b + 3b^2)$ **37.** $-2(x^2 - 2x + 3)$ **39.** $-8z^3(z + 2)$ **41.** $-2mn(2mn^2 + 3n + 4)$ **43.** $m = 0$ or $n = 0$ **45.** $z = 0$ or $z = -4$ **47.** $r = 1$ or $r = -3$ **49.** $x = -2$ or $x = \frac{1}{3}$ **51.** $x = 0$ or $y = 6$ **53.** **(a)** $-3, 0$ **(b)** $-3, 0$ **(c)** $-3, 0$ **55.** **(a)** $0, 2$ **(b)** $0, 2$ **(c)** $0, 2$ **57.** **(a)** $-1, 1$ **(b)** $-1, 1$ **(c)** $-1, 1$ **59.** $0, 2$ **61.** $0, 1$ **63.** $-4, 0$ **65.** $0, 1$ **67.** $0, \frac{1}{5}$ **69.** $-\frac{1}{2}, 0$ **71.** $0, \frac{2}{3}$ **73.** $0, \frac{5}{2}$ **75.** $0, \frac{1}{2}$ **77.** $-2, 0$ **79.** $0, \frac{3}{2}$ **81.** $(2x + 3)(x + 2)$ **83.** $(x - 5)(x^2 - 2)$ **85.** $(x + 3)(x^2 + 2)$ **87.** $(3x - 2)(2x^2 + 3)$ **89.** $(x^2 + 1)(2x - 3)$ **91.** $(x^2 - 3)(x - 7)$ **93.** $(x - 5)(3x^2 + 5)$ **95.** $(y + 1)(x + 3)$ **97.** $(a + 2)(b - 3)$ **99.** b.; a. **101.** **(a)** After 8 seconds **(b)** After 8 seconds **(c)** Yes

t	3	4	5	6	7	8
$y = h(t)$	240	256	240	192	112	0

(d) 256 ft; 4 seconds **103.** 391; CO_2 concentration in 2010 was 391 ppm. **105.** $\frac{8}{\pi}$ **107.** **(a)** The function models the data quite well.

t	20	30	40	50	60	70	80
$y = f(t)$	4520	10,080	17,840	27,800	39,960	54,320	70,880

(b) About 54,000 feet **(c)** $-\frac{6}{11}, 0$; the shuttle is on the ground at time $t = 0$; the value $t = -\frac{6}{11}$ has no physical meaning. **109.** No; there are many possibilities, such as 9×24 and 8×27. **111.** Answers will vary.

SECTION 3.4 (pp. 203–206)

1. A polynomial with three terms; $x^2 - x + 1$ (answers may vary) **2.** Symbolic and graphical, grouping and FOIL (answers may vary) **3.** $a = 3, b = -1, c = -3$ **4.** Yes; it checks, using multiplication. **5.** $(x + 3)(x - 1)$ **6.** $(6x - 3)(x - 2)$ or $3(2x - 1)(x - 2)$ or $6\left(x - \frac{1}{2}\right)(x - 2)$ **7.** c **8.** d **9.** Yes **11.** No **13.** Yes **15.** No **17.** $(x + 2)(x + 5)$ **19.** $(x + 2)(x + 6)$ **21.** $(x - 9)(x - 4)$ **23.** $(x - 8)(x + 1)$ **25.** $(z - 8)(z + 9)$ **27.** $(t - 8)(t - 7)$ **29.** $(y - 12)(y - 6)$ **31.** $(m - 20)(m + 2)$ **33.** $(n - 30)(n + 10)$ **35.** $(x + 3)(2x + 1)$ **37.** $(2x + 1)(3x - 5)$ **39.** $(z + 4)(4z + 3)$ **41.** $(2t - 3)(3t - 4)$ **43.** $(2y + 3)(5y - 1)$ **45.** $(2m - 3)(3m + 4)$ **47.** $(6n + 5)(7n - 5)$ **49.** $(1 - x)(1 + 2x)$ **51.** $(5 - 2x)(4 + 3x)$ **53.** $5(y - 2)(y + 3)$ **55.** $2(z + 2)(z + 4)$ **57.** $z(z + 2)(z + 7)$ **59.** $t(t - 7)(t - 3)$ **61.** $m^2(m + 1)(m + 5)$ **63.** $x(x - 1)(5x + 6)$ **65.** $3x(x + 3)(2x + 1)$ **67.** $2x(x - 5)(x - 2)$ **69.** $10z(z + 4)(6z - 1)$ **71.** $2x^2(x + 3)(2x - 1)$ **73.** $(x + 2)(x + 3)$ **75.** $(x + a)(x + b)$ **77.** $-3; 2$ **79.** $f(x) = x + 1, g(x) = x + 2$ **81.** $f(x) = x + 2, g(x) = x - 4$ **83.** $(x - 2)(x - 4)$ **85.** $2(x + 1)(x - 2)$ **87.** $-(x - 2)(x + 1)$

89. $(x + 1)(x - 4)$ **91.** $2(x + 1)(x - 2)$
93. $(x - 2)(x + 5)$ **95.** $(x - 7)(x + 4)$
97. $2(x - 5)(x - 2)$ **99.** $5(x - 10)(x + 4)$
101. $4(x - 5)(2x - 1)$ **103. (a)** $(35 - x)(1200 + 100x)$
(b) $20 or $27   **105.** 7 by 13 feet   **107. (a)** 6 sec   **(b)** 6 sec

CHECKING BASIC CONCEPTS 3.3 & 3.4 (p. 206)

1. (a) $3x(x - 2)$ **(b)** $4x(4x^2 - 2x + 1)$
2. (a) $0, 2$ **(b)** $0, 9$ **3. (a)** $(x - 2)(x + 5)$
(b) $(x - 5)(x + 2)$ **(c)** $(2x + 3)(4x + 1)$
4. $-1, -2$ **5.** After 1 and 3 seconds

SECTION 3.5 (pp. 211–213)

1. $x^2 - 9$ (answers may vary)   **2.** $x^2 - 8x + 16$
(answers may vary)   **3.** $x^3 + 8$ (answers may vary)
4. $(a - b)(a + b)$ **5.** $(a + b)^2$
6. $(a - b)(a^2 + ab + b^2)$ **7.** c   **8.** b
9. Yes; $(x - 5)(x + 5)$ **11.** No; $(x + y)(x^2 - xy + y^2)$
13. $(x - 6)(x + 6)$ **15.** $(5 - z)(5 + z)$
17. Cannot be factored   **19.** $4(3x - 5)(3x + 5)$
21. $(7a - 8b)(7a + 8b)$ **23.** $z^2(8 - 5z)(8 + 5z)$
25. $5x(x - 5)(x + 5)$ **27.** Cannot be factored
29. $(4t^2 - r)(4t^2 + r)$ **31.** $(x - 4)(x + 6)$
33. $(14 - n)(6 + n)$ **35.** $(y - 2)(y + 2)(y^2 + 4)$
37. $(2x - y)(2x + y)(4x^2 + y^2)$ **39.** $(x - 1)(x + 1)^2$
41. $(2x - 1)(2x + 1)(x - 2)$ **43.** No   **45.** Yes; $(x + 4)^2$
47. Yes; $(2z - 1)^2$ **49.** No   **51.** $(x + 1)^2$ **53.** $(2x + 5)^2$
55. $(x - 6)^2$ **57.** $(3z - 4)^2$ **59.** $y^2(2y + 1)^2$
61. $z(3z - 1)^2$ **63.** $(3x + y)^2$ **65.** $(7a - 2b)^2$
67. $x^2(2x - y)^2$ **69.** $(x - 2)(x^2 + 2x + 4)$
71. $(y + z)(y^2 - yz + z^2)$ **73.** $(3x - 2)(9x^2 + 6x + 4)$
75. $(4z + 3t)(16z^2 - 12zt + 9t^2)$
77. $x(2x + 5)(4x^2 - 10x + 25)$
79. $y(3 - 2x)(9 + 6x + 4x^2)$
81. $(z^2 - 3y)(z^4 + 3z^2y + 9y^2)$
83. $(5z^2 + 2y^3)(25z^4 - 10z^2y^3 + 4y^6)$
85. $5(m^2 + 2n)(m^4 - 2m^2n + 4n^2)$
87. $(5x - 8)(5x + 8)$ **89.** $(x + 3)(x^2 - 3x + 9)$
91. $(8x + 1)^2$ **93.** $(x + 4)(3x + 2)$
95. $x(x + 2)(x^2 - 2x + 4)$
97. $8(2x + y)(4x^2 - 2xy + y^2)$ **99.** $2(r - 2t)(r + 2t)$
101. $a(a + 2b)^2$ **103.** $(x - 2)(x - 1)$
105. $(2z - 5)(2z + 5)$ **107.** $x^2(x + 8)^2$
109. $(z - 1)(z^2 + z + 1)$ **111.** $(t + 1)(3t - 8)$
113. $a(a + 3)(7a - 1)$
115. $(x + y)(x - y)(x^2 + xy + y^2)(x^2 - xy + y^2)$
117. $(10x - 1)(10x + 1)$
119. $(pq - 3)(p^2q^2 + 3pq + 9)$ **121.** $(x - 5)(x + 5)$

SECTION 3.6 (pp. 218–219)

1. Factor out the GCF.   **2.** $2x$ **3.** No; the sum of two
squares cannot be factored.   **4.** Grouping   **5.** $a(a - 1)$
7. $(a - 3)(a + 3)$ **9.** $(x - 1)^2$
11. $(x - a)(x^2 + ax + a^2)$ **13.** Not possible
15. $(x - 3)(x + 2)$ **17.** $(x + 2)(x^2 + 1)$ **19.** $2x(3x - 7)$
21. $2x(x - 3)(x + 3)$ **23.** $4(a - 2)(a + 2)(a^2 + 4)$
25. $x(x - 3)(6x + 5)$ **27.** $x^2(x - 5)(2x + 5)$
29. $(x^2 + 1)(2x^2 + 3)$ **31.** $(x^2 + 1)(x + 3)$

33. $5(x^2 + 2)(x - 1)$ **35.** $(a + b)(x - y)$
37. $2(3x + 1)^2$ **39.** $-4x(x - 3)^2$
41. $(2x - 3)(4x^2 + 6x + 9)$
43. $-x(x + 2)(x^2 - 2x + 4)$
45. $(x - 1)(x - 2)(x^2 + x + 1)$
47. $(r - 2)(r + 2)(r^2 + 4)$ **49.** $(5x - 2a)(5x + 2a)$
51. $2(x - y)(x + y)(x^2 + y^2)$ **53.** $3x(3x - 1)(x + 1)$
55. $(z - 5)(z + 1)$
57. $3(x + 1)(x^2 - x + 1)(x - 3)(x + 3)$
59. (a) $(x^2 + 2)(x - 390)$ **(b)** 390 ppm
61. (a) $x^3 - 3x^2 + 2x$ **(b)** $x^3 - 3x^2 + 2x = 6$ **(c)** 3 ft

CHECKING BASIC CONCEPTS 3.5 & 3.6 (p. 219)

1. (a) $(5x - 4)(5x + 4)$ **(b)** $(x + 6)^2$ **(c)** $(3x - 5)^2$
(d) $(x - 3)(x^2 + 3x + 9)$ **(e)** $(3x - 2)(3x + 2)(9x^2 + 4)$
2. (a) $(x^2 + 3)(x - 2)$ **(b)** $(x + 3)(x - 7)$
(c) $2x(2x - 1)(3x + 2)$

SECTION 3.7 (pp. 226–229)

1. It is used in solving polynomial equations (answers may
vary).   **2.** multiplying   **3.** Subtract 16 from each side.
4. No; the right side is not 0.   **5.** 1   **6.** No; it implies that
$x^2 = -4$.   **7.** $-1, 1$ **9.** $-2, 2$ **11.** $-1, 2$ **13.** $-8, 8$
15. $-\frac{1}{2}, \frac{1}{2}$ **17.** $-1, 4$ **19.** $-6, 2$ **21.** $-3, \frac{1}{2}$ **23.** $-4, 4$
25. -7 **27.** $\frac{1}{3}$ **29.** $-\frac{1}{5}, \frac{2}{3}$ **31.** $-\frac{4}{3}, \frac{3}{8}$ **33.** No solutions
35. $-3, 2$ **37.** $-2, 4$
39.   **41.**

43. $-3, 0, 3$ **45.** 0   **47.** $-2, 0, 5$ **49.** $-1, 0, 5$
51. $-7, -2, 2$ **53.** $-6, 2, 6$ **55.** $-3, 5$ **57.** $-\frac{1}{2}, 2$
59. $-5, -1$ **61.** $0, 2$ **63.** $-2, 2$ **65.** $-5, -1, 1, 5$
67. $-3, -2, 2, 3$ **69.** $-2, 2$ **71.** $-1, -\frac{2}{3}, \frac{2}{3}, 1$
73. 17 by 21 inches   **75.** $-1000, 1000$ **77.** 30 by 50 feet
79. (a) The ball is 2 feet above the ground when it is hit.
(b) After 2 sec (answers may vary)   **(c)** After 2 and
$\frac{17}{8} = 2.125$ sec   **(d)** Symbolic solutions can be more
accurate than reading a graph.   **81.** 33 mph
83. 0.6 by 2.4 by 4.1 in.   **85. (a)** The elevation begins at
500 feet, decreases, and then increases back to 500 feet.

x	0	300	600	900	1200	1500
$y = E(x)$	500	428	392	392	428	500

(b) 500 feet and 1000 feet

CHECKING BASIC CONCEPTS 3.7 (p. 229)

1. $-3, -1$ **2.** $-3, 3$ **3. (a)** 3   **(b)** No solutions
(c) $-\frac{5}{4}, \frac{2}{3}$ **4. (a)** 0   **(b)** $-3, 3$ **(c)** $-2, 2$ **(d)** $-7, -2, 7$

CHAPTER 3 REVIEW (pp. 232–235)

1. $x + 5, x^2 - 3x + 1$ (answers may vary)   **2.** $10xy^2$;
3200 cubic inches   **3.** $5; -4$ **4.** $3; 1$ **5.** $7; 5$ **6.** $10; -9$

7. $11x$ **8.** $4x^3 + x^2$ **9.** $14x^3y + x^3$ **10.** 19   **11.** 2; 5
12. 4; 2   **13.** $8x^2 + 3x - 1$ **14.** $23z^3 - 4z^2 + z$
15. $-x^2 + x$ **16.** $-5x^3 - x^2 - 3x + 6$ **17.** 7
18. -259 **19.** -4 **20.** $-11; 4x^2 - x - 1$
21. $15x - 20$ **22.** $-2x - 2x^2 + 8x^3$ **23.** x^8 **24.** $-6x^4$
25. $-42x^2y^8$ **26.** $60x^3y^5$ **27.** $x^2 + 9x + 20$
28. $x^2 - 15x + 56$ **29.** $12x^2 - 48x - 27$ **30.** $y^2 - \frac{1}{9}$
31. $8x^4 - 12x^3 - 4x^2$ **32.** $-4x - 5x^2 + 7x^3$
33. $16x^2 - y^2$ **34.** $x^2 + 6x + 9$ **35.** $4y^2 - 20y + 25$
36. $a^3 - b^3$ **37.** $25m^2 - 20mn^4 + 4n^8$
38. $r^2 - 2r + 1 - t^2$ **39.** $5x(5x - 6)$
40. $4x^2(3x^2 + 2x - 4)$ **41.** $-3, 0$ **42.** $-2, 0, 2$ **43.** $\frac{1}{2}, 1$
44. $-1, 3$ **45.** $(x + 1)(2x^2 - 3)$ **46.** $(z + 1)(z^2 + 1)$
47. $(a - b)(x + y)$ **48.** $5; x^2 - 2x - 3$ **49.** (a) 0, 3
(b) 0, 3   **(c)** 0, 3   **50. (a)** $-1, 2$ **(b)** $-1, 2$ **(c)** $-1, 2$
51. $(x + 2)(x + 6)$ **52.** $(x - 10)(x + 5)$
53. $(x + 3)(9x - 2)$ **54.** $2(x - 5)(2x - 1)$
55. $x(x - 3)(x - 1)$ **56.** $2x^2(x + 2)(x + 5)$
57. $5x^2(x - 3)(x + 6)$ **58.** $10x(x - 5)(x - 4)$
59. $(x + 3)(x - 5)$ **60.** $(x - 11)(x - 13)$
61. $(x + 7)(x - 4)$ **62.** 8, 13   **63.** $(t - 7)(t + 7)$
64. $(2y - 3x)(2y + 3x)$ **65.** $(x + 2)^2$ **66.** $(4x - 1)^2$
67. $(x - 3)(x^2 + 3x + 9)$
68. $(4x + 3)(16x^2 - 12xy + 9y^2)$
69. $10y(y - 1)(y + 1)$ **70.** $(2r^2 - t^3)(2r^2 + t^3)$
71. $(m - 2n)(m + 2n)(m^2 + 4n^2)$
72. $(n - 2)(n - 1)(n + 1)$ **73.** $(5a - 3b)^2$
74. $2r(r - 3t)^2$ **75.** $(a^2 + 3b)(a^4 - 3a^2b + 9b^2)$
76. $(2p^2 - q)(4p^4 + 2p^2q + q^2)$ **77.** $5x^2(x - 2)$
78. $-2x(x - 4)(x + 4)$ **79.** $(x - 2y)(x + 2y)(x^2 + 4y^2)$
80. $4x(x - 1)(x + 3)$ **81.** $-x(2x - 3)(x - 4)$
82. $(x^2 + 1)(x - 3)(x + 3)$
83. $(4a + b)(16a^2 - 4ab + b^2)$
84. $(2 - y)(y^2 + 2y + 4)$ **85.** $(z - 1)(z + 7)$
86. $x(x - 2)(x + 2)(x - 5)$ **87.** $-4, 4$ **88.** $-1, 3$
89. $\frac{7}{2}$ **90.** No solutions   **91.** $-1, \frac{5}{3}$ **92.** $-2, \frac{3}{4}$
93. $-1, 0, 1$ **94.** 1, 2, 3   **95.** $-9, 0, 8$ **96.** 0, 7, 8
97. $-2, 2$ **98.** $-2, 2$ **99. (a)** $R(x) = 15x$
(b) $P(x) = 12x - 9000$ **(c)** 39,000; profit is $39,000 for
selling 4000 DVDs.   **100. (a)** $x(x + 5)(x + 10)$
(b) $x(x + 5)(x + 10) = 168$ **(c)** 2 by 7 by 12 in.
101. 8 by 10 in.   **102.** $\frac{1}{2}x^2 - \frac{1}{2}x - 3$
103. (a) $73.6°\text{F}$ **(b)** July

X	Y₁
1	27.784
2	43.636
3	56.556
4	66.544
5	73.6
6	77.724
7	78.916
X=7	

(c) Temperatures increase from January through July and
then decrease from July through December.

[1, 12, 1] by [30, 90, 10]

104. (a) $100 - 2x + \frac{x^2}{100}$ **(b)** 9%

105. $(x - 2)(x - 1)(x) = x^3 - 3x^2 + 2x$
106.

	$2x$	14
x	x^2	$7x$

(left side marked 2 and x; bottom marked x and 7)

107. 9 feet by 16 feet   **108.** $25x - x^2$
109. (a) After $\frac{33}{8} = 4.125$ seconds   **(b)** After 1 second
and after $\frac{25}{8} = 3.125$ seconds
110. (a) $R(x) = (50 - x)(600 + 20x)$ **(b)** $40
111. $-1000, 1000$

CHAPTER 3 TEST (pp. 235–236)

1. $5x - 4x^2y^2$ **2.** $-7x^3 + x^2 - 7x + 11$ **3.** -8
4. -2 **5.** 4; 3   **6.** $8xyz$ **7.** -66 **8.** $66; -x^3 + 2x - 4$
9. $-4x^3 + 2x^2$ **10.** $14x^2y^8$ **11.** $10x^2 - 9x - 7$
12. $9x^2 - 30x + 25$ **13.** $25x^2 - 16y^2$
14. $-2x^4 + 6x^3 - 4x^2$ **15.** $x^3 - 8y^3$ **16.** $2x^4 - 2x^2$
17. $(x - 5)(x + 2)$ **18.** $2x(x^2 + 3)$ **19.** $(x + 4)(3x - 5)$
20. $5x^2(x - 1)(x + 1)$ **21.** $(2x + 1)(x^2 - 5)$
22. $(7x - 1)^2$ **23.** $(x + 2)(x^2 - 2x + 4)$
24. $4x^2y^2(y^2 + 2x^2)$ **25.** $(a - b)(a - 2b)$ **26.** 3; 1
27. c   **28.** $(x + 8)(x - 6)$ **29.** $x(x + 2) = x^2 + 2x$
30. 0, 3   **31.** $-5, \frac{1}{4}$ **32.** $-2, 0, 2$ **33.** $-1, 1$ **34.** $-1, 3$
35. (a) $x(x + 4) = 221$ **(b)** 13, -17; height is 13 inches.
(c) 60 inches   **36. (a)** About $57.5°\text{F}$ **(b)** The dew point
starts at about $30°\text{F}$ in January and increases to a maximum
of about $65°\text{F}$ in July. Then it decreases to $30°\text{F}$ by the end
of December.
37. $x^2 + 5x + 6$

	$2x$	6
x	x^2	$3x$

(left side marked 2 and x; bottom marked x and 3)

38. After 2 and 4 sec

CHAPTERS 1–3 CUMULATIVE REVIEW (pp. 237–238)

1. $\frac{15}{4}$ **2.** $\frac{b - a}{a}$ **3. (a)** $\frac{1}{x^6y^2}$ **(b)** $\frac{r^2}{81}$ **(c)** $\frac{a^3}{b^{11}}$
4. 58,590   **5.** -27 **6.** D: $x \geq 4$
7.   **8.**

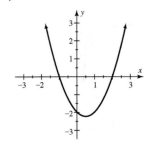

9. (a) Yes   **(b)** D: all real numbers; R: $y \geq -4$
(c) $-4, -3$ **(d)** $-1, 3$ **(e)** $-1, 3$
(f) $f(x) = (x + 1)(x - 3)$ **10.** $y = 2x + 9$
11. $f(x) = 2 - 5x$ **12.** $\frac{6}{11}$ **13.** $\left(-\infty, -\frac{5}{2}\right]$
14. $(-\infty, 1) \cup (3, \infty)$ **15.** $\left[0, \frac{4}{7}\right)$ **16.** $(2, 1)$

17. (a) $\{(x, y) \mid x + 2y = -5\}$ **(b)** $\left(2, \frac{1}{2}\right)$
18.

19. $(-4, -1, -3)$ **20.** $(2, 2, 2)$ **21.** -6 **22.** No solutions
23. $-2x^3 + 4x^2 - 10x$ **24.** $4a^2 - b^2$
25. $x^3 + 3x^2 - x - 3$ **26.** $8x^2 + 14x - 9$
27. $x^4 + 6x^2y^3 + 9y^6$ **28.** $2x^3 - 2x$
29. $(x + 3)(x - 11)$ **30.** $5x(2x - 1)(x + 7)$
31. $4(x - 5)(x + 5)$ **32.** $(7x - 5)^2$
33. $r(r - 1)(r^2 + r + 1)$ **34.** $(x + 2)(x^2 + 1)$
35. $-\frac{1}{2}, \frac{1}{2}$ **36.** $-5, \frac{1}{3}$ **37.** $0, 2$ **38.** $-1, 0, 1$ **39.** -1.1
40. $-2.1, 1.5$ **41.** \$2300 at 6%, \$1700 at 7%
42. (a) 10,550; in 1995 the car cost \$10,550 **(b)** The cost
increased, on average, by \$750 per year from 1990 to 2010.
43. 12 in. by 12 in. by 7 in. **44.** 80°, 60°, 40°

4 Rational Expressions and Functions

SECTION 4.1 (pp. 249–254)

1. A polynomial divided by a nonzero polynomial; $\frac{x^2 + 1}{3x}$
(answers may vary) **2.** $x = 4$ **3.** Multiply each side by
$x + 7$. **4.** No; the equation is undefined when $x = 5$.
5. No, it simplifies to $5 + x$. **6.** 1 **7.** a **8.** 0 **9.** c.
10. a. **11.** Yes **12.** Yes **13.** Yes **14.** No **15.** No
16. Yes **17.** $f(x) = \frac{x}{x + 1}$ **19.** $f(x) = \frac{x^2}{x - 2}$
21. $\{x \mid x \neq -2\}$ **23.** $\{x \mid x \neq \frac{1}{3}\}$
25. $\{t \mid t \neq -2, t \neq 2\}$ **27.** $\{x \mid x \neq 1, x \neq 2\}$
29. $\{x \mid x \neq -2, x \neq 0, x \neq 2\}$
31. $\{x \mid x \neq 1\}$ **33.** $\{x \mid x \neq 0\}$

35. $\{x \mid x \neq -2\}$ **37.** $\{x \mid -\infty < x < \infty\}$

39. $\left\{x \mid x \neq \frac{3}{2}\right\}$ **41.** $\{x \mid x \neq -1, x \neq 1\}$

43. $-\frac{1}{3}$ **45.** $\frac{1}{2}$ **47.** 3 **49.** 2, 0; $x = -1$
51. 0, undefined; $x = -2, x = 2$
53.

x	-2	-1	0	1	2
$f(x) = \frac{1}{x-1}$	$-\frac{1}{3}$	$-\frac{1}{2}$	-1	—	1

; undefined

55. $\frac{3}{5}$ **57.** 1 **59.** -2 **61.** 3 **63.** $-3, 1$ **65.** $-2, 1$
67. 0 **69.** No solutions **71.** -1 **73.** -4 **75.** -2
77. $-4, 1$ **79.** 0, 2 **81.** -1 **83.** 2 **85.** $-1.62, 0.62$
87. ab **89. (a)** 19 **(b)** -9 **(c)** 150 **(d)** 0 **91. (a)** 41
(b) -21 **(c)** 900 **(d)** Undefined **93. (a)** $2x + 3$
(b) -1 **(c)** $x^2 + 3x + 2$ **(d)** $\frac{x + 1}{x + 2}$ **95. (a)** $x^2 - x + 1$
(b) $1 - x - x^2$ **(c)** $x^2 - x^3$ **(d)** $\frac{1 - x}{x^2}$ **97.** c. **99.** d.
101. (a) 6.35; a curve with radius of 400 feet will have an
outer rail elevation of 6.35 inches.
(b) **(c)** It is halved. **(d)** 508 ft

103. (a) 75; the braking distance is 75 feet when the uphill
grade is 0.05. **(b)** 0.15 **105. (a)** 1; when cars are leaving
the lot at a rate of 4 vehicles per minute, the average wait
is 1 minute. **(b)** As more cars try to exit, the waiting time
increases; yes. **(c)** $4.\overline{6}$ vehicles per minute
107. (a) $P(1) = 0, P(50) = 0.98$; when there is only 1 ball,
there is no chance of losing. With 50 balls there is a 98%
chance of losing.
(b) [0, 100, 10] by [0, 1, 0.1]

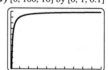

(c) It increases; yes, there are more balls without winning
numbers. **(d)** 40 balls

109. About 45% and 22%; after 1 day (3 days) students
remember 45% (22%) of what they have learned.
111. (a) $R(x) = \frac{350(x - 3)^2 + 50}{206(x - 3)^2 + 150}$ **(b)** Six years after
startup, Google's revenues were about 1.6 times more than
Facebook's revenues six years after startup.

SECTION 4.2 (pp. 263–265)

1. 1 **2.** -1 **3.** No, it is equal to $x + 1$. **4.** No; no
5. $\frac{2}{3}; \frac{7}{5}$ **6.** $\frac{ac}{bd}$ **7.** $\frac{ad}{bc}$ **8.** $\frac{a}{b}$ **9.** c. **10.** b. **11.** $\frac{2}{5}$ **13.** $-\frac{7}{2}$
15. $\frac{3}{4}$ **17.** $-\frac{1}{22}$ **19.** $\frac{2}{3}$ **21.** -18 **23.** $\frac{5}{x}$ **25.** 3 **27.** $\frac{2}{3}$
29. $x + 1$ **31.** $x - 2$ **33.** $\frac{x}{x + 1}$ **35.** $\frac{3x + 1}{5x - 2}$ **37.** $\frac{1}{x - 3}$

39. $\frac{x}{x+1}$ **41.** $\frac{3x+5}{x-5}$ **43.** $a+b$ **45.** m^2-mn+n^2
47. 1   **49.** -1 **51.** -1 **53.** $\frac{1}{4x}$ **55.** $\frac{5b}{2a}$ **57.** $\frac{5-x}{3-x}$
59. x^2+1 **61.** $\frac{2(x-1)}{3x^2}$ **63.** $\frac{(x-2)(x-3)}{x(x+4)}$ **65.** 1
67. 3   **69.** 3   **71.** $\frac{x+1}{x}$ **73.** $\frac{b^2+1}{(b+1)^2}$ **75.** $\frac{(x-1)(x+5)}{2(2x-3)}$
77. $3(n^2-3n+9)$ **79.** $\frac{n^2-3n+9}{4}$ **81.** $\frac{4}{xy}$
83. $\frac{y(x-1)}{2}$ **85.** $\frac{15}{4}$ **87.** $\frac{24b}{a}$ **89.** $2(n-1)$ **91.** $\frac{4}{b^3}$
93. $\frac{3a(3a+1)}{a+1}$ **95.** $\frac{x^2}{(x-5)(x^2-1)}$ **97.** $\frac{(x-2)(x-1)}{(x+2)^2}$
99. 1   **101.** $\frac{15}{y^2}$ **103.** $\frac{1}{x}$ **105.** $\frac{1}{x-2}$ **107.** $x-1$
109. (a) 54; it costs \$54, on average, to make each camera when 5000 are produced.   **(b)** $T(x)=50x+20,000$
(c) 270,000; it costs \$270,000 to make 5000 cameras.
111. (a) $5x+2$ **(b)** 32 ft   **113. (a)** $4x^2+4x+1$
(b) 21 by 21 by 10

CHECKING BASIC CONCEPTS 4.1 & 4.2 (p. 265)

1. (a) 2   **(b)** $\{x\,|\,x\neq 1\}$
(c) $x=1$

2. (a) $-\frac{1}{2}$ **(b)** $-1, 2$ **3.** $\frac{x-7}{x-1}$
4. (a) $\frac{x}{2(x-1)}$ **(b)** $\frac{x+3}{3}$

SECTION 4.3 (pp. 274–276)

1. 18   **2.** 18   **3.** $(x-5)(x+5)$ **4.** $(x-5)(x+5)$
5. A common denominator   **6.** A common denominator
7. $\frac{a+b}{c}$ **8.** $\frac{a-b}{c}$ **9.** b.   **10.** a.   **11.** 30   **13.** 102
15. $18a^2$ **17.** $50x^2(x-1)$ **19.** $(x-5)(x+1)^2$
21. $(x+y)(x-y)$ **23.** $\frac{5}{7}$ **25.** $\frac{7}{4}$ **27.** $-\frac{1}{5}$ **29.** $\frac{11}{8}$
31. $\frac{4}{x}$ **33.** $\frac{1-x}{x^2-4}$ **35.** $\frac{9}{x^2}$ **37.** $-\frac{3}{xy}$ **39.** 1   **41.** 1
43. $\frac{r}{t^2}$ **45.** $\frac{1}{t-3}$ **47.** $\frac{4b}{15a}$ **49.** $\frac{n+4}{(n-4)(n-2)}$
51. $\frac{-5x-4}{x(x+4)}$ **53.** $\frac{-4x^2+x+2}{x^2}$ **55.** $\frac{x^2+5x-34}{(x-5)(x-3)}$
57. $-\frac{4(n+6)}{(n-3)(n+3)}$ **59.** $\frac{x(5x+16)}{(x-3)(x+3)}$ **61.** $-\frac{1}{2}$
63. $\frac{6x^2-1}{(x-5)(3x-1)}$ **65.** $\frac{4x^2+4xy-9x+9y}{(x-y)(x+y)}$
67. $\frac{4x^2-x+3}{(x-2)(x-1)(x+1)}$ **69.** $\frac{x+15}{(x-3)(x+2)(x+3)}$
71. $\frac{4x-7}{(x-2)(x-1)^2}$ **73.** $\frac{3x^2-2x+3}{(x-1)^2(x+3)}$
75. $\frac{-2a^2+3b^2+4c^2}{abc}$ **77.** $\frac{5n^2+3n-168}{(n-6)(n+6)}$
79. $\frac{-2(x^2-4x+2)}{(x-5)(x-3)}$ **81.** $\frac{x^2+x+5}{(x+1)(2x-3)}$
83. $\frac{3}{(x-1)(x+1)}$ **85.** $\frac{2(a^2+b^2)}{(a+b)(a-b)}$
87. $1; \frac{1-x}{x+1}$ **89.** $\frac{2x}{(x-2)(x+2)}; \frac{-4}{(x-2)(x+2)}$
91. $C(x)=\frac{7x+1,500,000}{x}$ **93.** 60 years
95. $\frac{1200}{19}\approx 63.2$ ohms   **97.** $S\approx 0.101$ foot or about
1.2 inches   **99.** $\frac{16}{d^2}$ watts per square meter

SECTION 4.4 (pp. 285–288)

1. Multiply each side by $x+2$.   **2.** Multiply each side by
the LCD.   **3.** $\frac{1}{2}$ **4.** bc **5.** LCD   **6.** intersect   **7.** F
8. T   **9.** $5x$ **11.** x^2-1 **13.** $2(2x+1)(x-2)$
15. 1   **17.** 5   **19.** 4   **21.** $-\frac{7}{6}$ **23.** -3 **25.** 1   **27.** 6
29. No solutions   **31.** No solutions   **33.** $-\frac{1}{12}$ **35.** $1, -\frac{1}{2}$
37. $-1, 8$ **39.** 1   **41.** $-\frac{4}{15}, 3$ **43.** 3   **45.** -3 **47.** -10
49. $-\frac{1}{2}, \frac{1}{2}$ **51.** $\frac{a-b}{c}$ **53.** 1   **55.** 2   **57.** 3   **59.** $-3, 1$
61. 2.5   **63.** $-0.4, 0.67$ **65.** ± 1 **67.** 3   **69.** $-\frac{3}{2}, 1$
71. $-3.28, -0.90, 1.18$ **73.** $r=\frac{d}{t}$ **75.** $b=\frac{2A}{h}$
77. $a=\frac{b}{2}$ **79.** $R_1=\frac{RR_2}{R_2-R}$ **81.** $x=15-\frac{1}{T}$
83. $t=r-1$ **85.** $b=a(r-1)$ **87. (a)** 82 per hour
(b) The wait gets very long.   **89. (a)** $\frac{x}{5}+\frac{x}{2}=1$
(b) $\frac{10}{7}$ hours   **(c)** $\frac{10}{7}\approx 1.43$ hours
91. (a) 75; three testers found 75% of the glitches.   **(b)** 19
(c) As the number of testers becomes large, the percentage
of the total number of glitches found slowly nears 100%, but
never actually gets there.

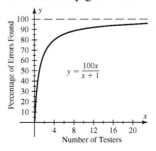

93. (a) 12.5; the number 36 pick receives 12.5% of the
number 1 pick's salary.   **(b)** Number 21
95. (a) $\frac{x}{40}+\frac{x}{70}=1$ **(b)** $\frac{280}{11}=25.\overline{45}$ hr
(c) $\frac{280}{11}=25.\overline{45}$ hr
97. Winner: 10 miles per hour; second place: 8 miles per
hour   **99.** 3 miles per hour   **101.** 250 miles per hour
103. 3 hr and 6 hr   **105.** 4 mph and 3 mph   **107.** 120 hr
109. Yes; slightly greater than 2

CHECKING BASIC CONCEPTS 4.3 & 4.4 (p. 289)

1. (a) $\frac{1}{x-1}$ **(b)** $-\frac{2(x-3)}{x(x-2)}$ **(c)** $\frac{3}{x(x+1)(x-1)}$
2. (a) 4   **(b)** 5   **(c)** $-\frac{1}{4}$ **3.** 8.4 minutes
4. $S=\frac{DF}{D-F}$

SECTION 4.5 (pp. 294–296)

1. $\frac{5}{7}\cdot\frac{11}{3}=\frac{55}{21}$ **2.** $\frac{a}{b}\cdot\frac{d}{c}$ **3.** Multiply numerator and
denominator by $x-1$ (answers may vary).
4. A rational expression with fractions in its numerator,
denominator, or both
5. $\dfrac{z+\frac{3}{4}}{z-\frac{3}{4}}$ **6.** $\dfrac{\frac{a}{b}}{\frac{a-b}{a+b}}$ **7.** $\frac{7}{20}$ **9.** 2   **11.** $\frac{32}{21}$ **13.** $\frac{2b}{3}$
15. $\frac{3}{4}$ **17.** $\frac{2(n-1)}{n+1}$ **19.** $\frac{2k+3}{k-4}$ **21.** $\frac{3}{z}$ **23.** $\frac{x}{x+4}$
25. $\frac{1}{x}$ **27.** $-\frac{x}{2x+3}$ **29.** $\frac{x+2}{3x-1}$ **31.** $\frac{3(x+1)}{(x+3)(2x-7)}$
33. $\frac{4x(x+5)}{(x-5)(2x+5)}$ **35.** $\frac{p+q}{q-p}$ **37.** $\frac{a+b}{a-b}$ **39.** $\frac{2x+1}{x}$
41. $\frac{5}{27}$ **43.** $\frac{mn^2-2m^2}{m^2n^2+1}$ **45.** $\frac{n}{n+1}$ **47.** $\frac{(x-1)(x+4)}{x^2-4}$

49. $\dfrac{P\left(1 + \frac{r}{12}\right)^{24} - P}{\frac{r}{12}}$ **51.** $R = \dfrac{R_1 R_2}{R_1 + R_2}$

53. (a) 5; after 11 practice trials this task can be completed in 5 sec. **(b)** $T(x) = \dfrac{100}{x + 9}$

SECTION 4.6 (pp. 306–310)

1. A statement that two ratios are equal **2.** $\frac{5}{6} = \frac{x}{7}$
3. It doubles. **4.** It is reduced by half. **5.** constant
6. constant **7.** kxy **8.** $kx^2 y^3$ **9.** Directly; if the number of people doubled, the food bill would double.
10. Inversely; increasing the number of painters would decrease the time needed to paint the building.
11. 10 **13.** 12 **15.** 72 **17.** $\frac{21}{20}$ **19.** $-\frac{5}{13}$ **21.** $-6, 6$
23. (a) $\frac{7}{9} = \frac{10}{x}$ **(b)** $x = \frac{90}{7}$ **25. (a)** $\frac{5}{3} = \frac{x}{6}$ **(b)** $x = 10$
27. (a) $\frac{78}{6} = \frac{x}{8}$ **(b)** $x = \$104$ **29. (a)** $\frac{2}{120} = \frac{5}{x}$
(b) $x = 300$ minutes **31. (a)** $k = 2$ **(b)** $y = 14$
33. (a) $k = 2.5$ **(b)** $y = 17.5$ **35. (a)** $k = -7.5$
(b) $y = -52.5$ **37. (a)** $k = 20$ **(b)** $y = 2$
39. (a) $k = 50$ **(b)** $y = 5$ **41. (a)** $k = 400$ **(b)** $y = 40$
43. (a) $k = 0.25$ **(b)** $z = 8.75$ **45. (a)** $k = 11$
(b) $z = 385$ **47. (a)** $k = 10$ **(b)** $y = 350$
49. (a) Direct **(b)** $y = 1.5x$
(c)

51. Neither **(b)** N/A **(c)** N/A
53. (a) Inverse **(b)** $y = \frac{210}{x}$
(c)

55. (a) Direct **(b)** $y = -2bx$ **57.** Direct; $k = 1$
59. Neither **61.** Direct; $k = 2$ **63.** Answers may vary.
65. About 23.1 ft **67.** 1.375 inches
69. About 67.0 million **71.** 2000 **73.** 75 ft

75. (a) $R = 0.012W$

(b) 38.4 pounds
77. (a) Direct; the ratios $\frac{D}{W}$ always equal 0.75.
(b) $D = 0.75W$ **(c)** 8.25 in.
79. (a) $F = \frac{1200}{L}$ **(b)** 60 pounds
81. \$797.50; k represents the cost per credit.
83. 1200 lb per square inch
85. (a) Direct **(b)** $y = -19x$ **(c)** Negative; for each 1-mile increase in altitude, the temperature decreases by $19°\text{F}$. **(d)** $66.5°\text{F}$ decrease **87.** About 1.43 ohms
89. $z = 0.5104 x^2 y^3$ **91.** About 133 pounds
93. About 35.2 pounds **95.** 750

CHECKING BASIC CONCEPTS 4.5 & 4.6 (p. 310)

1. $\frac{3x^2 - 1}{3x^2 + 1}$ **(b)** 1 **2. (a)** $k = 0.75$ **(c)** $y = 8.25$
3. (a) Direct; $y = 0.4x$ **(b)** Inverse; $y = \frac{120}{x}$

SECTION 4.7 (pp. 317–319)

1. term **2.** $\frac{a}{c} + \frac{b}{c}$ **3.** $5; 4; 1$ **4.** $3x - 5; x - 2; -2$
5. No; the divisor is not in the form $x - k$. **6.** The last number in the third row **7.** $2x - 3$ **9.** $2x^2 - 3$
11. $2 - \frac{1}{2x} + \frac{1}{2x^2}$ **13.** $3x^2 - 4x - 1$ **15.** $2a^2 - 3$
17. $\frac{4x^2}{3} - 2$ **19.** $ab - 4 + b$ **21.** $2m^2 n^2 + 1 - \frac{4}{m^2 n^2}$
23. $3x - 7$ **25.** $x^2 - 1 + \frac{1}{2x + 3}$ **27.** $10x + 10 + \frac{5}{x - 1}$
29. $4x^2 - 1$ **31.** $x^2 - 4x + 19 - \frac{80}{x + 4}$
33. $x^2 + 3x - 6 + \frac{1}{3x - 1}$ **35.** $a^3 - a$ **37.** $3x + 4$
39. $x + 1 + \frac{1}{x^2 - 1}$ **41.** $2a^2 - a + 3 - \frac{5}{a^2 - a + 5}$
43. $a^3 - b^3 + 1$ **45.** $x + 4 + \frac{3}{x - 1}$ **47.** $3x - 1$
49. $x^2 + 3x + 2$ **51.** $2x^2 + 5x + 10 + \frac{19}{x - 2}$
53. $2x^3 - 4x^2 + 11x - 22 + \frac{40}{x + 2}$
55. $b^3 + b^2 + b + 1$ **57.** $3x + 5$; 29 ft **59.** $x + 2$
61. (a) 0; 0 **(b)** 0; 0 **(c)** 1; 1 **(d)** 0; 0 **(e)** 35; 35
63. (a) 0; yes **(b)** 0; yes **(c)** -1; no **(d)** 0; yes
(e) -9; no

CHECKING BASIC CONCEPTS 4.7 (p. 319)

1. (a) $\frac{2}{x} - 1$ **(b)** $2a - 3 + \frac{5}{a}$ **2.** $5x - 3 + \frac{7}{2x + 1}$
3. (a) $2x^2 - 3x - 3 - \frac{4}{x - 1}$
(b) $2x^2 - 9x + 18 - \frac{37}{x + 2}$

CHAPTER 4 REVIEW (pp. 322–327)

1. $f(x) = \frac{1}{x-1}$ **2.** $f(x) = \frac{x-3}{x}$

3. $\{x \mid x \neq -2\}$

4. $\frac{1}{8}$; $x = \pm 1$ **5.** -3; 0.75 **6.** Undefined; 1.2

7. 3; 1; $x = 1$ **8.** 2; undefined; $x = -2$ **9.** 1 **10.** 2

11. No solutions   **12.** 2 **13.** (a) 12 (b) 27

14. (a) $x^2 - x$ (b) $x + 1$ **15.** $\frac{2}{3a^3}$ **16.** $\frac{x+2}{x+1}$

17. $x + 2$ **18.** $\frac{x-7}{2x-3}$ **19.** -1 **20.** 1 **21.** $\frac{y}{4}$

22. $\frac{x+2}{x+1}$ **23.** $\frac{x^2+1}{(x+1)^2}$ **24.** $\frac{x+1}{x-3}$ **25.** $3y^3$ **26.** $\frac{2}{3}$

27. $\frac{x}{x-5}$ **28.** $\frac{x+5}{x+3}$ **29.** $\frac{x(x+2)}{(2x-1)(x+3)}$

30. $\frac{(x+1)^2}{(x+2)(x+4)}$ **31.** 144 **32.** $4a^2b$ **33.** $18x^2y^3$

34. $(x-1)(x+2)$ **35.** $x(x-3)(x+3)$ **36.** $x^2(x-3)^2$

37. $\frac{4}{x+4}$ **38.** $\frac{x-1}{x}$ **39.** $\frac{1-x}{x+1}$ **40.** $\frac{2x-2}{x-2}$ **41.** $\frac{t-4}{t-1}$

42. $\frac{8}{(y-2)(y+2)}$ **43.** $\frac{4b^3-3a^3}{a^2b^2c}$ **44.** $\frac{r^3+t^3}{5r^2t^2}$

45. $-\frac{2(a-b-2)}{(a-b)(a+b)}$ **46.** $\frac{a^2+2ab-b^2}{(a-b)(a+b)}$

47. $\frac{2x}{(x-2)(x-1)(x+2)}$ **48.** $\frac{6}{(x-3)(x-2)(x+3)}$

49. $\frac{-x^2+x-2}{(x-2)(x+2)}$ **50.** $\frac{2x-2}{2x+1}$ **51.** 3 **52.** 11 **53.** $-2, 1$

54. -2 **55.** $-2, \frac{1}{2}$ **56.** $-\frac{5}{2}$ **57.** 0 **58.** $0, 1$ **59.** -1

60. -1 **61.** 2 **62.** $-2, 3$ **63.** $y_2 = m(x_2 - x_1) + y_1$

64. $a = T(b+2)$ **65.** $p = \frac{fq}{q-f}$ **66.** $b = \frac{2a}{aI-3}$

67. $\frac{39}{50}$ **68.** $\frac{2c}{a}$ **69.** $\frac{4n^2-1}{3n^2}$ **70.** $x + y$ **71.** $\frac{2x+3}{2x-3}$

72. $\frac{2(x+2)}{x-8}$ **73.** $\frac{4-5x}{x+1}$ **74.** $\frac{-3}{x-9}$ **75.** $\frac{9}{5}$ **76.** $\frac{77}{5}$

77. $\frac{3}{2}$ **78.** $\frac{31}{3}$ **79.** $\frac{7}{3}$ **80.** $\frac{88}{7} \approx 12.6$ **81.** $y = 28$

82. $y = 2$ **83.** $k = 3$ **84.** $z = 720$

85. Inverse; $y = \frac{200}{x}$ **86.** Direct; $y = 3x$

87. Direct; $k = \frac{1}{2}$ **88.** Inverse; $k = 6$ **89.** $2x + 3$

90. $2x + 1$ **91.** $2x - \frac{1}{2} + \frac{1}{x}$ **92.** $\frac{2a}{b} - \frac{3}{a}$

93. $2x - 3 + \frac{1}{x+1}$ **94.** $x^2 - x + 2 - \frac{3}{x+1}$

95. $2x^2 - x + 1 + \frac{1}{3x-2}$ **96.** $2x - 9 + \frac{25x-39}{x^2-2}$

97. $2x - 5 - \frac{2}{x-3}$

98. $3x^2 - 2x + 4 + \frac{3}{x+4}$

99. (a)

(b) It increases; as vehicles arrive at a faster rate, the wait in line increases.

100. (a) $D(0) = 166.\overline{6}$ feet, $D(0.1) = 242.\overline{42}$ feet; about 75.8 feet   (b) $x = 0.05\overline{3}$ or $5.\overline{3}\%$ **101.** (a) About 13 cars   (b) As x increases, the number of cars in line increases; yes.

102. (a) 5; initially there were 5000 fish in the lake.

(b) $[0, 6, 1]$ by $[0, 6, 1]$ (c) It decreases.   (d) After 2 years

103. (a) $\frac{x}{2} + \frac{x}{3} = 1$ (b) $\frac{6}{5} = 1.2$ hr   (c) $\frac{6}{5} = 1.2$ hr

104. 4 miles per hour   **105.** About 44 minutes

106. About 43.3 feet

107. (a) Inverse

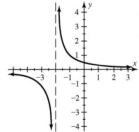

(b) $R = \frac{12,100}{W}$; $k = 12,100$ (c) $R = 220$ ohms

108. (a) $D = 0.06W$; $k = 0.06$ (b) 0.42 inch

109. $53°F$ **110.** (a) Direct   (b) $y = 3.5x$ (c) 8.05%

CHAPTER 4 TEST (pp. 327–328)

1. $f(x) = \frac{x}{x+2}$ **2.** (a) $\frac{1}{15}$ (b) $\left\{ x \mid x \neq \frac{1}{2}, x \neq -\frac{1}{2} \right\}$

3.

4. $\frac{a}{2}$ **5.** -1 **6.** $\frac{x-5}{2x-7}$ **7.** $\frac{x^2+4}{(x+2)^2}$ **8.** $2y^2$

9. $\frac{1}{x+5}$ **10.** $\frac{2x^2+3x+2}{(x-2)(x+2)}$ **11.** $\frac{5a^3-6b^4}{15ab}$

12. $\frac{x^3-2x^2+8}{x^2(x-2)}$ **13.** $\frac{x+1}{x-1}$ **14.** $\frac{4}{(z+4)^2}$ **15.** $\frac{3x+3}{x-17}$

16. $-\frac{2}{3}$ **17.** $-1, 2$ **18.** 5 **19.** $\frac{1}{4}$ **20.** No solutions

21. $\frac{1}{2}$ **22.** $m = \frac{Fr^2}{G}$ **23.** 0.47 **24.** 0; $\frac{1}{x-1}$ **25.** $\frac{35}{3}$

26. $\frac{80}{23}$ **27.** Inverse; $y = \frac{100}{x}$ **28.** Direct; $y = 1.5x$

29. $2a^2 + 5$ **30.** $3x^2 - x + 2 - \frac{6}{x+2}$ **31.** 21.9 feet

32. (a) $[0, 25, 5]$ by $[0, 2, 0.5]$

$x = 25$

(b) 24 vehicles per minute

33. (a) $\frac{x}{24} + \frac{x}{30} = 1$ (b) $\frac{40}{3} \approx 13.3$ hours

34. $41.75°F$

CHAPTERS 1–4 CUMULATIVE REVIEW
(pp. 330–332)

1. 9 **2.** 0 **3.** Natural: 1; whole: 0, 1; integer: $-\frac{12}{4}$, 0, 1; rational: $-\frac{12}{4}$, 0, 1, 2.$\overline{11}$, $\frac{13}{2}$; irrational: $\sqrt{3}$

4. a. **5.** $\frac{6y^6}{x^4}$ **6.** $\frac{9d^6}{4c^4}$ **7.** 6.73×10^{10}

8. $D = \{-3, -1, 0, 4\}$
$R = \{-2, 0, 1, 5\}$

9. $(-2, -7), (-1, -4),$
$(0, -1),(1, 2), (2, 5)$

10. $(-2, 0), \left(-1, \frac{3}{2}\right), (0, 2),$
$\left(1, \frac{3}{2}\right), (2, 0)$

11.

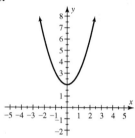

12. $\{x \mid x \neq 1\}$ **13.** $f(x) = 2x - 1$
14.

15. -3; 2 **16.** -3
17.

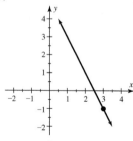

18. $y = -\frac{1}{2}x + 2$ **19.** $y = 2x + 2$ **20.** $y = -\frac{3}{2}x + 4$
21. 4 **22.** $-\frac{7}{29}$ **23.** 3 **24.** $\left(-\infty, -\frac{5}{6}\right]$ **25.** $(0, \infty)$
26. $(-3, 3]$

27. $(-\infty, 2] \cup (4, \infty)$

28. $-30, -6$ **29.** $(-4, 7)$ **30.** $(-\infty, -1] \cup [11, \infty)$
31. $(-8, -1)$
32.

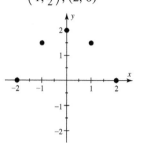

33. $\left(\frac{1}{2}, -\frac{1}{2}\right)$ **34.** $(6, 0)$ **35.** $R = 10$ **36.** $(1, 1, 2)$

37. $\begin{bmatrix} 1 & 1 & -1 & 4 \\ -1 & -1 & -1 & 0 \\ 1 & -2 & 1 & -9 \end{bmatrix}$; $(-1, 3, -2)$

38. 14 **39.** 8 in^2 **40.** $x = -1, y = 2$
41. $3x^5 + 15x^3 - 6x^2$ **42.** $2x^2 + x - 15$ **43.** $-2, 0$
44. $(3a - 1)(a^2 + 5)$ **45.** $(4x - 3)(x + 2)$
46. $3x(x - 2)(2x + 1)$ **47.** $(3a - 2b)(3a + 2b)$
48. $(4t + 3)(16t^2 - 12t + 9)$ **49.** $-\frac{1}{3}, 4$
50. $-5, 0, 6$ **51.** $\frac{x - 2}{x + 2}$ **52.** $x - 4$ **53.** $\frac{t - 4}{t^2 - 4}$
54. $\frac{4a^2c + 3b^3}{3a^2b^2c}$ **55.** $-\frac{7}{2}$ **56.** -3 **57.** $z = \frac{y}{J - 1}$
58. $\frac{4 + x}{4 - x}$ **59.** $\frac{1}{2}$ **60.** $x^2 - 2x + 6 - \frac{1}{x + 2}$
61. 3 **62.** $x - 1$
63. (a) Linear

(b) $f(x) = \frac{5}{9}(x - 32)$ (c) $40°$ C
64. 6, 6, and 10 inches **65.** Stair climber: $\frac{1}{2}$ hr; stationary bicycle: 1 hr **66.** 24 children, 6 adults **67.** 11 by 15 ft
68. (a) After 2.75 seconds (b) After 0.5 and 2.25 seconds
69. (a) $\frac{x}{15} + \frac{x}{10} = 1$ (b) 6 hours **70.** 48 feet

5 Radical Expressions and Functions

SECTION 5.1 (pp. 342–345)

1. ± 3 **2.** 3 **3.** 2 **4.** Yes **5.** b **6.** $|x|$ **7.** Undefined **8.** -3 **9.** d.

10. a.
11.
12.

13. $\{x \mid x \geq 0\}$ **14.** All real numbers   **15.** 3   **17.** 0.6
19. $\frac{4}{5}$ **21.** x **23.** 3   **25.** -4 **27.** $\frac{2}{3}$ **29.** $-x^3$ **31.** $4x^2$ **33.** 3
35. -3 **37.** Not possible   **39.** -2.24 **41.** 1.71
43. -1.48 **45.** 4   **47.** $|y|$ **49.** $|x - 5|$ **51.** $|x - 1|$ **53.** $|y|$
55. $|x^3|$ **57.** x **59.** 3, not possible   **61.** $\sqrt{6}$, not possible
63. $\sqrt{20}$ or $2\sqrt{5}$, $\sqrt{6}$ **65.** 1, 2   **67.** -2, 1   **69.** -1, $\sqrt[3]{-6}$ or
$-\sqrt[3]{6}$ **71.** 4   **73.** 5   **75.** $[-2, \infty)$ **77.** $[2, \infty)$ **79.** $[2, \infty)$
81. $(-\infty, 1]$ **83.** $(-\infty, \frac{8}{5}]$ **85.** $(-\infty, \infty)$ **87.** $\left(-\frac{1}{2}, \infty\right)$

89.
91.

Shifted 2 units left   Shifted 2 units upward

93.

Shifted 2 units left

95.

x	$\sqrt{x} + 1$
-1	—
0	1
1	2
4	3
9	4

$f(x) = \sqrt{x} + 1$

97.

x	$\sqrt[3]{3x}$
-1	—
0	0
$\frac{1}{3}$	1
$\frac{4}{3}$	2
3	3

$f(x) = \sqrt{3x}$

99.

x	$2\sqrt[3]{x}$
-8	-4
-1	-2
0	0
1	2
8	4

$f(x) = 2\sqrt[3]{x}$

101.

x	$\sqrt[3]{x-1}$
-7	-2
0	-1
1	0
2	1
9	2

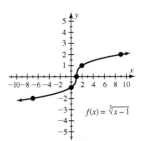

$f(x) = \sqrt[3]{x-1}$

103. $A = 6$ **105.** 1 sec   **107.** 122 mi
109. About $14 thousand; no
111. (a) $P(25,000) = \$71,246$; if \$25,000 is spent on equipment per worker, each worker will produce about \$71,246 worth of goods.
(b)

Productivity (dollars/worker) vs Physical Capital per Worker (dollars)

200,000
100,000
25,000 50,000 75,000

(c) \$26,197; \$20,102; an additional \$25,000 is spent on equipment per worker, but productivity levels off. There is a point where the business starts to lose money.

SECTION 5.2 (pp. 351–353)

1. 2   **2.** 2   **3.** $\frac{1}{2}$ **4.** $\frac{1}{2}$ **5.** $x^{1/2}$ **6.** $a^{4/3}$ **7.** $\sqrt[n]{a}$
8. $\left(\sqrt[n]{a}\right)^m$ or $\sqrt[n]{a^m}$ **9.** c.   **10.** f.   **11.** g.   **12.** h.   **13.** d.
14. e.   **15.** a.   **16.** b.   **17.** $\sqrt{7}$ **19.** $\sqrt[3]{a}$ **21.** $\sqrt[6]{x^5}$
23. $\sqrt{x + y}$ **25.** $\frac{1}{\sqrt[3]{b^2}}$ **27.** $t^{1/2}$ **29.** $(x + 1)^{1/3}$
31. $(x + 1)^{-1/2}$ **33.** $(a^2 - b^2)^{1/2}$ **35.** $x^{-7/3}$ **37.** 1.74
39. 1.71   **41.** 3.74   **43.** 0.55   **45.** $\sqrt{9}$; 3   **47.** $\sqrt[3]{8}$; 2
49. $\sqrt{\frac{4}{9}}$; $\frac{2}{3}$ **51.** $\sqrt[3]{(-8)^2}$ or $\left(\sqrt[3]{-8}\right)^2$; 4   **53.** $\sqrt[3]{8}$; 2
55. $\frac{1}{\sqrt[4]{16^3}}$ or $\frac{1}{\left(\sqrt[4]{16}\right)^3}$; $\frac{1}{8}$ **57.** $\frac{1}{\left(\sqrt[4]{4}\right)^3}$; $\frac{1}{8}$ **59.** $\sqrt[4]{z}$
61. $\frac{1}{\sqrt[5]{y^2}}$ **63.** $\sqrt[3]{3x}$ **65.** $y^{1/2}$ **67.** x **69.** $2x^{2/3}$
71. $\frac{7}{x^{1/6}}$ **73.** b^3 **75.** x^3 **77.** xy^2 **79.** $y^{13/6}$ **81.** $\frac{x^4}{9}$
83. $\frac{y^3}{x}$ **85.** $y^{1/4}$ **87.** $\frac{1}{a^{2/3}}$ **89.** $\frac{1}{k^2}$
91. $b^{3/4}$ **93.** $p^2 + p$ **95.** $x^{5/6} - x$ **97.** $\frac{3}{x^{1/6}}$
99. (a)

x	0	20	40	60	80
$A(x)$	0	27%	37%	44%	50%

(b) The abandonment rate levels off. The longer a person watches a video, the more likely he or she will continue to watch.   **101.** About 1 step/sec   **103. (a)** 400 in^2 **(b)** $A = 100W^{2/3}$ **105. (a)** 42.4 cm; 44.7 cm   **(b)** First year   **107.** Answers may vary.

CHECKING BASIC CONCEPTS 5.1 & 5.2 (p. 354)

1. (a) ± 7 **(b)** 7   **2. (a)** -2 **(b)** -3 **3. (a)** $\sqrt{x^3}$ or $\left(\sqrt{x}\right)^3$ **(b)** $\sqrt[3]{x^2}$ or $(\sqrt[3]{x})^2$ **(c)** $\frac{1}{\sqrt[5]{x^2}}$ or $\frac{1}{(\sqrt[5]{x})^2}$
4. $|x - 1|$ **5. (a)** 3   **(b)** 5   **(c)** About 1.37

SECTION 5.3 (pp. 361–362)

1. Yes   **2.** No   **3.** $\sqrt[3]{ab}$ **4.** $\frac{a}{b}$ **5.** $\frac{a}{b}$ **6.** $\frac{1}{3}$ **7.** No
8. Yes   **9.** No, since $1^3 \neq 3$ **10.** Yes; $4^3 = 64$
11. 3   **13.** 10   **15.** 4   **17.** $\frac{3}{5}$ **19.** $\frac{1}{4}$ **21.** $\frac{2}{3}$ **23.** x^3
25. $\frac{\sqrt[3]{7}}{3}$ **27.** $\frac{\sqrt[4]{x}}{3}$ **29.** $\frac{3}{z}$ **31.** $\frac{x}{4}$ **33.** 3   **35.** 4   **37.** 3
39. -2 **41.** a **43.** 3   **45.** $2x^2$ **47.** $-a^2\sqrt[3]{5}$
49. $2x\sqrt[4]{y}$ **51.** $6x$ **53.** $2x^2yz^3$ **55.** $\frac{3}{2}$ **57.** $\sqrt[3]{12ab}$
59. $5\sqrt{z}$ **61.** $\frac{1}{a}$ **63.** $\sqrt{x^2 - 16}$ **65.** $\sqrt[3]{a^3 + 1}$
67. $\sqrt{x + 1}$ **69.** 10   **71.** 2   **73.** 3   **75.** $10\sqrt{2}$ **77.** $3\sqrt[3]{3}$
79. $2\sqrt{2}$ **81.** $-2\sqrt[5]{2}$ **83.** $b^2\sqrt[3]{b}$ **85.** $2n\sqrt{2n}$
87. $2ab^2\sqrt{3b}$ **89.** $-5xy\sqrt[3]{xy^2}$ **91.** $5\sqrt[3]{5t^2}$ **93.** $\frac{3t}{r\sqrt[4]{5r^3}}$
95. $\frac{3\sqrt[3]{x^2}}{y}$ **97.** $\frac{7a\sqrt{a}}{9}$
99. $\left(\sqrt[mn]{a^m b^m}\right)^n = (a^m b^m)^{n/mn}$
$\qquad\qquad = (a^m b^m)^{1/m}$
$\qquad\qquad = a^{m/m} b^{m/m}$
$\qquad\qquad = ab$

101. $\sqrt[6]{3^5}$ **103.** $2\sqrt[12]{2^5}$ **105.** $3\sqrt[12]{3^{11}}$ **107.** $x\sqrt[12]{x}$
109. $\sqrt[12]{r^{11}t^7}$ **111. (a)** $S = 5\sqrt{M}$
(b) 50 miles per hour

SECTION 5.4 (pp. 373–375)

1. $2\sqrt{a}$ **2.** $3\sqrt[3]{b}$ **3.** like
4. Yes; $4\sqrt{15} - 3\sqrt{15} = \sqrt{15}$
5. No   **6.** $\frac{\sqrt{7}}{\sqrt{7}}$ **7.** $\sqrt{t} + 5$ **8.** $\frac{5 + \sqrt{2}}{5 + \sqrt{2}}$
9. Not possible   **11.** $\sqrt{7}, 2\sqrt{7}, 3\sqrt{7}$ **13.** $2\sqrt[3]{2}, -3\sqrt[3]{2}$
15. Not possible   **17.** $2\sqrt[3]{xy}, xy\sqrt[3]{xy}$ **19.** $9\sqrt{3}$ **21.** $6\sqrt[3]{5}$
23. Not possible   **25.** Not possible   **27.** Not possible
29. $5\sqrt[3]{2}$ **31.** $8\sqrt{2}$ **33.** $6\sqrt{11}$ **35.** $2\sqrt{x} - \sqrt{y}$
37. $2\sqrt[3]{z}$ **39.** $-5\sqrt[3]{6}$ **41.** $y^2 - y$ **43.** $9\sqrt{7}$ **45.** $6\sqrt[4]{3}$
47. $7\sqrt{x}$ **49.** $8\sqrt{2k}$ **51.** $-2\sqrt{11}$ **53.** $5\sqrt[3]{2} - \sqrt{2}$
55. $-\sqrt[3]{xy}$ **57.** $3\sqrt{x + 2}$ **59.** $\sqrt{x + 2}$
61. $(x - 1)\sqrt{x + 1}$ **63.** $4x\sqrt{x}$ **65.** $\frac{\sqrt[3]{7x}}{6}$ **67.** $\frac{3\sqrt{3}}{2}$
69. $\frac{71\sqrt{2}}{10}$ **71.** $2\sqrt{2}$ **73.** $(5x - 1)\sqrt[4]{x}$
75. $(8x + 2)\sqrt{x}$ or $2\sqrt{x}(4x + 1)$
77. $(3ab - 1)\sqrt[4]{ab}$ **79.** $(n - 2)\sqrt[3]{n}$
81. $(f + g)(x) = 3\sqrt{x} + 1$; $(f - g)(x) = 7\sqrt{x} - 5$
83. $(f + g)(x) = 4\sqrt[3]{x}$; $(f - g)(x) = 2$ **85.** $x - \sqrt{x} - 6$
87. 2   **89.** 119   **91.** $x - 64$ **93.** $ab - c$

95. $x + \sqrt{x} - 56$ **97.** $\frac{\sqrt{7}}{7}$
99. $\frac{4\sqrt{3}}{3}$ **101.** $\frac{\sqrt{5}}{3}$ **103.** $\frac{\sqrt{3b}}{6}$ **105.** $\frac{t\sqrt{r}}{2r}$
107. $\frac{3 + \sqrt{2}}{7}$ **109.** $\sqrt{10} - 2\sqrt{2}$ **111.** $\frac{11 - 4\sqrt{7}}{3}$
113. $\sqrt{7} + \sqrt{6}$ **115.** $\frac{z + 3\sqrt{z}}{z - 9}$ **117.** $\frac{a + 2\sqrt{ab} + b}{a - b}$
119. $\sqrt{x + 1} + \sqrt{x}$ **121.** $\frac{3\sqrt[3]{x^2}}{x}$ **123.** $\frac{\sqrt[3]{x}}{x}$
125. $12\sqrt{3} \approx 20.8$ cm   **127.** $2\sqrt{6}$ **129.** $120\sqrt{2}$ ft
131. $\sqrt{2x}$ ft

CHECKING BASIC CONCEPTS 5.3 & 5.4 (p. 375)

1. (a) $\frac{1}{8}$ **(b)** 10   **(c)** $-2x\sqrt[3]{xy}$ **(d)** $\frac{4b^2}{5}$ **2.** $\sqrt[6]{7^5}$
3. (a) 6   **(b)** 3   **(c)** $6x^3$ **4. (a)** $7\sqrt{6} + \sqrt{7}$
(b) $5\sqrt[3]{x}$ **(c)** $\sqrt{x}$ **5. (a)** $(y - x)\sqrt[3]{xy}$
(b) 14   **6.** $\frac{\sqrt{6}}{2}$ **7.** $\frac{\sqrt{5} + 1}{2}$

SECTION 7.5 (pp. 397–382)

1.   **2.**

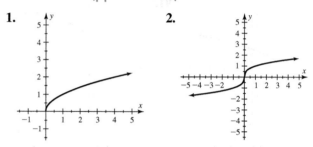

3. $\{x | x \geq 0\}$ **4.** All real numbers   **5.** $f(x) = x^p$,
p is rational.   **6.** $f(x) = \sqrt[n]{x}$, where n is an integer greater
than 1.   **7.** $\{x | x \geq 0\}$ **8.** All real numbers
9. $\sqrt{3} \approx 1.73$; undefined   **11.** $\sqrt[4]{6} \approx 1.57$; undefined
13. $\sqrt[5]{13} \approx 1.67$; 1   **15.** $\sqrt[3]{6} \approx 1.82$; -1 **17.** $f(x) = \sqrt{x}$
19. $f(x) = \sqrt[3]{x^2}$ **21.** $f(x) = \frac{1}{\sqrt[3]{x}}$ **23.** 32; 55.90
25. $-\frac{1}{128} \approx -0.01$; 0.04   **27.** 4; not possible   **29.** 4; 4
31. $[0, \infty)$ **33.** $(-\infty, \infty)$

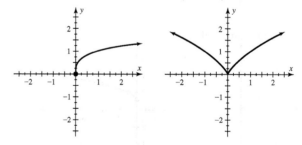

35. $g(x)$ is greater.   **37.** $f(x)$ is greater.
[0, 6, 1] by [0, 6, 1]   [0, 6, 1] by [0, 6, 1]

39. $x^p > x^q$ **41. (a)** 6   **(b)** $\sqrt{2x}$ **(c)** $4|x|$
(d) 2   **43.** b.   **45.** c.   **47.** d.   **49.** b.   **51.** 2877 in^2
53. About 35%   **55.** No, for $x \geq 10$ it is less than double.
57. (a) 6 yr   **(b)** The twin in the spaceship will be 4 years younger than the twin on Earth.

59. (a) [0, 5, 1] by [0, 0.5, 0.1]   **(b)** $k \approx 0.16$

(c) [0, 5, 1] by [0, 0.5, 0.1]; yes   **(d)** 0.295 m²

(answers may vary)

61. (a) $k \approx 0.91$ **(b)** [0, 1.5, 0.1] by [0, 1, 0.1]

It increases.

(c) About 0.808 m   **(d)** About 0.788; a bird weighing 0.65 kg has a wing span of about 0.788 m.

SECTION 5.6 (PP. 392–396)

1. Square each side.   **2.** Cube each side.   **3.** Yes
4. Check them in the given equation.   **5.** Finding an unknown side of a right triangle (answers may vary)   **6.** 5
7. $d = \sqrt{(x_2 - x_1)^2 + (y_2 - y_1)^2}$ **8.** $x^{1/2} + x^{3/4} = 2$
9. 2   **11.** x **13.** $2x + 1$ **15.** $5x^2$ **17.** 64   **19.** 81   **21.** 6
23. 48   **25.** 6   **27.** 3   **29.** 27   **31.** -2 **33.** 15   **35.** $\frac{1}{2}$
37. 0, 1   **39.** 2   **41.** -4 **43.** 9   **45.** 9   **47.** ± 7
49. ± 10 **51.** $-5, 3$ **53.** $-3, 7$ **55.** 4   **57.** -4 **59.** 1
61. $\frac{7}{5}$ **63.** ± 2 **65.** $\sqrt[5]{12}$ **67.** $-5, 1$ **69.** 3   **71.** 1.88
73. $-1, 0.70$ **75.** 1.79   **77.** -0.47 **79.** (a)–(c) 16
81. (a)–(c) 11   **83.** $L = \frac{8T^2}{\pi^2}$ **85.** $A = \pi r^2$ **87.** Yes
89. Yes   **91.** Yes   **93.** No   **95.** $\sqrt{32} = 4\sqrt{2}$ **97.** 7
99. $c = 5$ **101.** $b = \sqrt{61}$ **103.** $a = 14$
105. $\sqrt{20} = 2\sqrt{5}$ **107.** $\sqrt{4000} = 20\sqrt{10}$ **109.** $\sqrt{89}$
111. 5   **113.** 4   **115.** 2, 122   **117.** $W = 8$ pounds
119. About 81 sec   **121.** About 3 miles   **123.** About 269 feet
125. 19 inches   **127.** $h \approx 16.3$ inches, $d \approx 33.3$ inches
129. (a) 121 feet   **(b)** About 336 feet   **131. (a)** About 38 miles per hour; the vehicle involved in the accident was traveling about 38 miles per hour.   **(b)** About 453 feet
133. (a) It increases by a factor of 8.   **(b)** $v = \sqrt[3]{\frac{W}{3.8}}$
(c) 20 mph   **135.** $a\sqrt{2}$

CHECKING BASIC CONCEPTS 5.5 & 5.6 (p. 396)

1. (a)   **(b)**

$f(-1)$ is undefined. $f(-1) = -1$

(c)

$f(-1) = 1$

2. 3.2   **3.** $[4, \infty)$ **4. (a)** 4   **(b)** 28   **(c)** 3   **5.** 13   **6.** 9.6 in.
7. $-3, 1$

SECTION 5.7 (PP. 403–404)

1. $2 + 3i$ (answers may vary)   **2.** No; any real number a can be written as $a + 0i$.   **3.** i **4.** -1 **5.** $i\sqrt{a}$
6. $10 - 7i$ **7.** $a + bi$ **8.** $1 + 2i$ **9.** 4   **10.** -5 **11.** 0
12. pure   **13.** $i\sqrt{5}$ **15.** $10i$ **17.** $12i$ **19.** $2i\sqrt{3}$
21. $3i\sqrt{2}$ **23.** 3   **25.** $-8 + 7i$ **27.** $1 - 9i$
29. $-10 + 7i$ **31.** $-13 + 13i$ **33.** $20 - 12i$ **35.** 41
37. 20   **39.** $1 + 5i$ **41.** $3 + 4i$ **43.** $-2 - 6i$ **45.** -2
47. $a^2 + 9b^2$ **49.** $-i$ **51.** i **53.** -1 **55.** 1   **57.** $3 - 4i$
59. $6i$ **61.** $5 + 4i$ **63.** -1 **65.** $1 - i$ **67.** $-\frac{6}{29} + \frac{15}{29}i$
69. $2 + i$ **71.** $-1 + 6i$ **73.** $-1 - 2i$ **75.** $-\frac{3}{2}i$
77. $-\frac{1}{2} + \frac{3}{2}i$ **79.** $\frac{290}{13} + \frac{20}{13}i$ **81.** They are graphed using a real axis and an imaginary axis.

CHECKING BASIC CONCEPTS 5.7 (p. 405)

1. (a) $8i$ **(b)** $i\sqrt{17}$ **2. (a)** $3 - 4i$ **(b)** $-2 + 3i$
(c) $5 + i$ **(d)** $\frac{3}{4} + \frac{3}{4}i$

CHAPTER 5 REVIEW (pp. 409–411)

1. 2   **2.** 6   **3.** $3|x|$ **4.** $|x - 1|$ **5.** -4 **6.** -5 **7.** x^2
8. $3x$ **9.** 2   **10.** -1 **11.** x^2 **12.** $x + 1$ **13.** $\sqrt{14}$
14. $\sqrt[3]{-5}$ **15.** $\left(\sqrt{\frac{x}{y}}\right)^3$ or $\sqrt{\left(\frac{x}{y}\right)^3}$ **16.** $\frac{1}{\sqrt[3]{(xy)^2}}$ or $\frac{1}{(\sqrt[3]{xy})^2}$
17. 9   **18.** 2   **19.** 64   **20.** 27   **21.** z^2 **22.** xy^2 **23.** $\frac{x^3}{y^9}$
24. $\frac{y^2}{x}$ **25.** 8   **26.** -2 **27.** x^2 **28.** 2   **29.** $-\frac{\sqrt[3]{x}}{2}$ **30.** $\frac{1}{3}$
31. $4\sqrt{3}$ **32.** $3\sqrt{6}$ **33.** $\frac{3}{x}$ **34.** $4ab\sqrt{2a}$ **35.** $9xy$
36. $5z\sqrt[3]{z}$ **37.** $x + 1$ **38.** $\frac{2a\sqrt[4]{a}}{b}$ **39.** $2\sqrt[6]{x^5}$
40. $\sqrt[6]{r^5t^8}$ or $t\sqrt[6]{r^5t^2}$ **41.** $4\sqrt{3}$ **42.** $3\sqrt[3]{x}$ **43.** $-3\sqrt[3]{5}$

44. $-\sqrt[4]{y}$ **45.** $11\sqrt{3}$ **46.** $7\sqrt{2}$ **47.** $13\sqrt[3]{2}$
48. $3\sqrt{x+1}$ **49.** $(2x-1)\sqrt{x}$ **50.** $(b+2a)\sqrt[3]{ab}$
51. $5+4\sqrt{2}$ **52.** $7+7\sqrt{3}-\sqrt{5}-\sqrt{15}$ **53.** 3
54. 95   **55.** $a-2b$ **56.** $xy+\sqrt{xy}-2$ **57.** $\frac{4\sqrt{5}}{5}$
58. $\frac{r\sqrt{t}}{2t}$ **59.** $\frac{3-\sqrt{2}}{7}$ **60.** $\frac{5+\sqrt{7}}{9}$
61. $\sqrt{8}+\sqrt{7}$ **62.** $\frac{a-2\sqrt{ab}+b}{a-b}$

63.   **64.**

65. $f(x)=\sqrt{x}; 2$ **66.** $f(x)=\sqrt[4]{x^2}; \sqrt[4]{16}$
67.   **68.**

Shifted 2 units downward

Shifted 1 unit to the right

69. $[1, \infty)$ **70.** $(-\infty, 3]$ **71.** $(-\infty, \infty)$ **72.** $(-2, \infty)$
73. 2   **74.** 4   **75.** 9   **76.** 9   **77.** 8   **78.** $\frac{1}{4}$ **79.** 4.5
80. 1.62   **81.** $c=\sqrt{65}$ **82.** $b=\sqrt{39}$ **83.** $\sqrt{41}$
84. $\sqrt{52}=2\sqrt{13}$ **85.** ± 11 **86.** ± 4 **87.** $-3, 5$
88. 4   **89.** 3   **90.** 2   **91.** ± 4 **92.** -1 **93.** 1
94. $-2, 0$ **95.** -2 **96.** $-2+4i$ **97.** $5+i$ **98.** $1+2i$
99. $-\frac{14}{13}+\frac{5}{13}i$ **100.** $2-2i$ **101.** About 85 feet
102. $\sqrt{16,200}=90\sqrt{2}\approx 127.3$ feet   **103.** About 0.79
second   **104. (a)** 5 square units   **(b)** $5\sqrt{5}$ cubic units
(c) $\sqrt{10}$ units   **(d)** $\sqrt{15}$ units   **105.** About 0.82 foot
106. About 0.13 foot; the length of the pendulum is shorter.
107. $r=\sqrt[210]{\frac{281}{4}}-1\approx 0.02$; from 1790 through 2000 the
average annual percent growth rate was about 2%.
108. (a) About 43 miles per hour   **(b)** About 34 miles per
hour; a steeper bank allows for a higher speed limit; yes
109. $\sqrt{7}\approx 2.65$ feet

CHAPTER 5 TEST (pp. 411–412)

1. -3 **2.** $|z+1|$ **3.** $5x^2$ **4.** $2z^2$ **5.** $2xy\sqrt[4]{y}$ **6.** 1
7. $\sqrt[5]{7^2}$ or $(\sqrt[5]{7})^2$ **8.** $\sqrt[3]{\left(\frac{y}{x}\right)^2}$ or $\left(\sqrt[3]{\frac{y}{x}}\right)^2$ **9.** 16
10. $\frac{1}{216}$ **11.** $x^{4/3}$ **12.** $x^{7/10}$ **13.** $(-\infty, 4]$
14.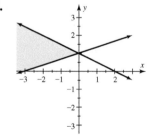

15. $8z^{3/2}$ **16.** $\frac{z}{y^{2/3}}$ **17.** 9   **18.** $\frac{y}{2}$ **19.** $4\sqrt{7}+\sqrt{5}$
20. $6\sqrt[3]{x}$ **21.** $14\sqrt{2}$ **22.** 2   **23. (a)** 27   **(b)** 7   **(c)** 3
(d) 17   **24. (a)** $\frac{2\sqrt{7}}{21}$ **(b)** $\frac{-1+\sqrt{5}}{4}$ **25.** 2.63
26. $\sqrt{120}\approx 10.95$ **27.** $\sqrt{8}=2\sqrt{2}$ **28.** $2-19i$
29. $-6+8i$ **30.** $\frac{5}{4}$ **31.** $\frac{4}{29}+\frac{10}{29}i$ **32. (a)** About 17.25 mi
(b) About 420 ft   **33.** 1.31 pounds

**CHAPTERS 1–5 CUMULATIVE REVIEW
(pp. 413–414)**

1. 36π **2.** $D=\{-1, 0, 1\}, R=(2, 4\}$ **3. (a)** $\frac{1}{a^3b^9}$
(b) x^4y^9 **(c)** r^8t^5 **4.** 4.3×10^{-4} **5.** $3; x\neq 2$
6. All real numbers
7.   **8.**

9.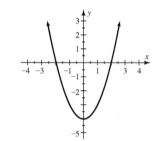

(a) D: all real numbers; R: $y\geq -4$ **(b)** 0   **(c)** $-2, 2$
(d) $-2, 2$ **10.** $y=\frac{1}{2}x+\frac{5}{2}$ **11.** $f(x)=1-3x$
12.

13. $\frac{6}{11}$ **14.** $(-\infty, 3]$ **15.** $[-1, 5]$ **16.** $\left[-\frac{5}{2}, 1\right]$
17. (a) $(4, 4)$ **(b)** No solutions
18.

19. $(3, 2, 1)$ **20.** 4   **21.** $-4x^4 + 16x$ **22.** $x^2 - 16$
23. $5x^2 - 7x - 6$ **24.** $16x^2 + 72x + 81$
25. $(3x - 4)(3x + 4)$ **26.** $(x - 2)^2$ **27.** $3x^2(5x - 3)$
28. $(4x - 3)(3x + 1)$ **29.** $(r - 1)(r^2 + r + 1)$
30. $(x - 3)(x^2 + 5)$ **31.** $1, 2$ **32.** $-2, 0, 2$ **33.** $2x + 4$
34. $\frac{7x - 5}{x^2 - x}$ **35.** $6x$ **36.** 4   **37.** $\frac{1}{64}$ **38.** 5   **39.** $4x$
40. $x^{3/4}$ or $\sqrt[4]{x^3}$ **41.** $2x$ **42.** $6\sqrt{3}x$ **43.** $2x^2 - \sqrt{3}x - 3$
44. $(-\infty, 1]$
45.

46. $\sqrt{10}$ **47.** $5 + i$ **48.** 13   **49.** 6   **50.** 28   **51.** $\frac{4}{9}, 4$
52. ± 3 **53.** 1.41   **54.** 4.06   **55.** The tank initially contains
300 gallons of water. Water is leaving the tank at 15 gal/min.
56.

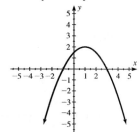

57. $1300 at 5%, $700 at 4%   **58.** 8 in. by 8 in. by 4 in.
59. 22.4 feet   **60.** $45°, 55°, 80°$

---

6 Quadratic Functions and Equations

SECTION 6.1 (pp. 426–430)

1. parabola   **2.** The vertex
3. axis of symmetry   **4.** $(0, 0)$
5.

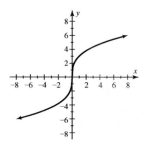

6. $-\frac{b}{2a}$ **7.** narrower   **8.** reflected   **9.** $ax^2 + bx + c$
with $a \neq 0$ **10.** vertex   **11.** T   **12.** F   **13.** F   **14.** T
15. $(2, -6)$ **17.** $(-3, 4)$ **19.** $(0, 3)$ **21.** $(1, 1.4)$
23. $(3, 9)$ **25.** $0, -4$ **27.** $-2, -2$ **29.** $(1, -2); x = 1;$
upward   **31.** $(-2, 3); x = -2;$ downward

33. (b)

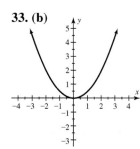

(a) $(0, 0); x = 0$
(c) $2; 4.5$

35. (b)

(a) $(0, -2); x = 0$
(c) $2; 7$

37. (b)

(a) $(0, 1); x = 0$
(c) $-11; -26$

39. (b)

(a) $(1, 0); x = 1$
(c) $9; 4$

41. (b)

(a) $(-2, 0); x = -2$
(c) $0; -25$

43. (b)

(a) $(-0.5, -2.25); x = -0.5$
(c) $0; 10$

45. (b)

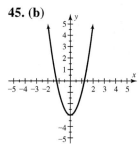

(a) $(0, -3); x = 0$
(c) $5; 15$

47. (b)

(a) $(1, 1); x = 1$
(c) $-8; -3$

49. (b)

(a) $(1, 1); x = 1$
(c) $-17; -7$

51. (b)

(a) $(2, 4); x = 2$
(c) $8; 4.25$

53. -2 **55.** $-\frac{25}{4}$ **57.** $-\frac{7}{2}$ **59.** 6 **61.** 4
63. $-\frac{39}{8}$ **65.** 10, 10

67.

69.

Reflected across the x-axis   Narrower

71.

Wider

73.

Reflected across the x-axis
and wider

75. (a) Upward; wider
(b) $x = -1; (-1, -2)$
(c) y-int: $-\frac{3}{2}$; x-int: $-3, 1$
(d)

77. (a) Downward; the same
(b) $x = 1; (1, 1)$
(c) y-int: 0; x-int: 0, 2
(d)

79. (a) Upward; narrower **(b)** $x = -\frac{1}{2}$; $\left(-\frac{1}{2}, -\frac{9}{2}\right)$
(c) y-int: -4; x-int: $-2, 1$
(d)

81. 3 slices **83.** d. **85.** a. **87. (a)** 2 feet **(b)** 2 seconds
(c) 66 feet **89.** $\frac{66}{32} \approx 2$ seconds; about 74 feet
91. (a) The revenue increases at first up to 50 tickets and
then it decreases. **(b)** $2500; 50 **(c)** $f(x) = x(100 - x)$

(d) $2500; 50 **93. (a)** $V(1) = 21.75, V(2) = 30,$
$V(3) = 59.75$, and $V(4) = 111$; in 2007 there were 21.75
million unique Facebook visitors in one month. Other values
can be interpreted similarly.
(b) The increases between consecutive years are 8.25 million, 29.75 million, and 51.25 million. A linear function
does not model the data because these three increases are
not equal (or nearly equal).
95. 300 feet by 600 feet **97.** 42 in.
99. (a) In 1990, emissions were 6 billion metric tons.
(b) 3 billion metric tons.

SECTION 6.2 (pp. 440–443)

1. $x^2 + 2$ **2.** $(x - 2)^2$ **3.** $(1, 2)$ **4.** $(-1, -2)$
5. $f(x) = ax^2 + bx + c; f(x) = a(x - h)^2 + k$
6. $y = a(x - h)^2 + k; (h, k)$ **7.** downward **8.** $-\frac{b}{2a}$
9. a. **10.** d.

11.

x	-2	-1	0	1	2
$y = x^2$	4	1	0	1	4
$y = x^2 - 3$	1	-2	-3	-2	1

Shifted 3 units downward

12.

x	-2	-1	0	1	2
$y = x^2$	4	1	0	1	4
$y = x^2 + 5$	9	6	5	6	9

Shifted 5 units upward

13.

x	-2	-1	0	1	2
$y = x^2$	4	1	0	1	4

x	1	2	3	4	5
$y = (x - 3)^2$	4	1	0	1	4

Shifted 3 units right

14.

x	-4	-2	0	2	4
$y = x^2$	16	4	0	4	16

x	-8	-6	-4	-2	0
$y = (x + 4)^2$	16	4	0	4	16

Shifted 4 units left

15. (a)

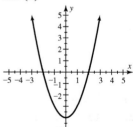

(b) $(0, -4)$
(c) Down 4 units

17. (a)

(b) $(0, 1)$
(c) Narrower and up 1 unit

19. (a)

(b) $(3, 0)$
(c) Right 3 units

21. (a)

(b) $(0, 0)$
(c) Reflected across the
x-axis

23. (a)

(b) $(0, 2)$
(c) Reflected across the
x-axis and up 2 units

25. (a)

(b) $(-2, 0)$
(c) Left 2 units

27. (a)

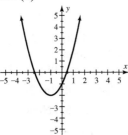

(b) $(-1, -2)$
(c) Left 1 unit and down
2 units

29. (a)

(b) $(1, 2)$
(c) Right 1 unit and up
2 units

31. (a)

(b) $(5, -4)$
(c) Narrower, right 5 units
and down 4 units

33. (a)

(b) $(-3, 1)$
(c) Wider, reflected
across the x-axis, left
3 units and up 1 unit

35. Translated 1 unit right,
2 units downward, and
is wider

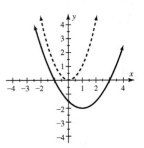

37. Translated 1 unit
left, 3 units upward,
opens downward, and
is narrower

39. [−20, 20, 2] by [−20, 20, 2]

41. $y = 3(x - 3)^2 + 4; y = 3x^2 - 18x + 31$
43. $y = -\frac{1}{2}(x - 5)^2 - 2; y = -\frac{1}{2}x^2 + 5x - \frac{29}{2}$
45. $y = (x - 1)^2 + 2$ **47.** $y = -(x - 0)^2 - 3$
49. $y = (x - 0)^2 - 3$ **51.** $y = -(x + 1)^2 + 2$
53. (a) $(1, 1)$ **(b)** $y = 4(x - 1)^2 + 1$ **55. (a)** $(-1, -2)$
(b) $y = -(x + 1)^2 - 2$ **57. (a)** $(-1, 3)$
(b) $y = -2(x + 1)^2 + 3$ **59.** 1
61. $y = (x + 1)^2 - 1; (-1, -1)$
63. $y = (x - 2)^2 - 4; (2, -4)$
65. $y = (x + 1)^2 - 4; (-1, -4)$
67. $y = (x - 2)^2 + 1; (2, 1)$
69. $y = \left(x + \frac{3}{2}\right)^2 - \frac{17}{4}; \left(-\frac{3}{2}, -\frac{17}{4}\right)$
71. $y = \left(x - \frac{7}{2}\right)^2 - \frac{45}{4}; \left(\frac{7}{2}, -\frac{45}{4}\right)$
73. $y = 3(x + 1)^2 - 4; (-1, -4)$
75. $y = 2\left(x - \frac{3}{4}\right)^2 - \frac{9}{8}; \left(\frac{3}{4}, -\frac{9}{8}\right)$
77. $y = -2(x + 2)^2 + 13; (-2, 13)$ **79.** $a = 2$
81. $a = 0.3$ **83.** $y = 2(x - 1)^2 - 3$
85. $y = 0.5(x - 1980)^2 + 6$
87. (a)   **(b)** $D(x) = \frac{1}{12}x^2$

89. (a) Decreases and then increases
(b) No, because the data decrease and then increase
(c) Quadratic; it can model data that decrease and increase.
(d) $(1995, 600)$; it has the minimum y-value.
(e) $C(x) = 1.8(x - 1995)^2 + 600$
(f) [1970, 2030, 10] by [0, 2500, 500]

91. (a) $f(x) = 2(x - 1982)^2 + 1$ (answers may vary)
(b) 201 thousand (answers may vary)   **93.** incr: $x \geq 2$,
decr: $x \leq 2$ **95.** incr: $x \leq 1$, decr: $x \geq 1$
97. incr: $x \geq \frac{2}{3}$, decr: $x \leq \frac{2}{3}$ **99.** incr: $x \leq -\frac{3}{2}$,
decr: $x \geq -\frac{3}{2}$ **101.** incr: $x \leq -\frac{1}{8}$, decr: $x \geq -\frac{1}{8}$

CHECKING BASIC CONCEPTS 6.1 & 6.2 (p. 444)

1. (a)

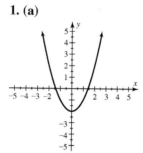

(b)

$(0, -2); x = 0$

$(1, -3); x = 1$

2. y_1 opens upward, whereas y_2 opens downward, y_1 is narrower than y_2.   **3.** 7

4. (a)

(b)

1 unit right, 2 units up

Reflected across the x-axis, 3 units left

5. (a) $y = (x + 7)^2 - 56$

(b) $y = 4(x + 1)^2 - 6$

SECTION 6.3 (pp. 453–456)

1. $x^2 + 3x - 2 = 0$ (answers may vary); it can have 0, 1, or 2 solutions   **2.** Nonlinear   **3.** Factoring, square root property, completing the square

4.

5.

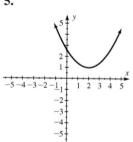

(answers may vary)

(answers may vary)

6. Two; the solutions are the x-intercepts.   **7.** ± 8; the square root property (answers may vary)   **8.** $\left(\frac{b}{2}\right)^2$
9. Yes   **10.** Yes   **11.** No   **12.** No   **13.** Yes   **14.** Yes
15. No   **16.** No   **17.** (a) $3.65, -1.65$ (b) $1.32, -5.32$
19. (a) $1.32, -0.12$ (b) $-0.28, -0.83$ **21.** $-2, 1$
23. No real solutions   **25.** $-2, 3$ **27.** -0.5 **29.** $-1, 5$
31. $-3, 1$ **33.** $-3, 3$ **35.** $-\frac{1}{2}, \frac{3}{2}$ **37.** -1 **39.** No real
solutions   **41.** $-7, 5$ **43.** $-\frac{1}{3}, \frac{1}{2}$ **45.** $-\frac{3}{2}$ **47.** $-2, 7$

49. $\frac{6}{5}, \frac{3}{2}$ **51.** ± 12 **53.** $\pm\frac{8}{\sqrt{5}}$ or $\pm\frac{8\sqrt{5}}{5}$ **55.** $-6, 4$
57. $-7, 9$ **59.** $\frac{1 \pm \sqrt{5}}{2}$ **61.** $5 \pm \sqrt{5}$ **63.** 4   **65.** $\frac{25}{4}$
67. 16; $(x - 4)^2$ **69.** $\frac{81}{4}$; $\left(x + \frac{9}{2}\right)^2$ **71.** $-4, 6$
73. $-3 \pm \sqrt{11}$ **75.** $\frac{3 \pm \sqrt{29}}{2}$ **77.** $\frac{5 \pm \sqrt{21}}{2}$
79. $1 \pm \sqrt{5}$ **81.** $\frac{3 \pm \sqrt{41}}{4}$ **83.** $\frac{2 \pm \sqrt{11}}{2}$
85. $\frac{-3 \pm \sqrt{5}}{12}$ **87.** $-6, 2$ **89.** $-2 \pm \sqrt{2}$
91. $\pm\sqrt{2}$ **93.** $-5, \frac{7}{3}$ **95.** $4 \pm \sqrt{14}$ **97.** $\pm\sqrt{\frac{c}{a}}$
99. $-3, 6$ **101.** $3, 5$ **103.** $5, 7$
105. $y = \pm\sqrt{x + 1}$ **107.** $v = \pm\sqrt{\frac{2K}{m}}$
109. $r = \pm\sqrt{\frac{k}{E}}$ **111.** $f = \pm\frac{1}{2\pi\sqrt{LC}}$ **113.** (a) 30 miles
per hour   (b) 40 miles per hour   **115.** About 1.9
seconds; no   **117.** About 8 feet   **119.** 2 hours
121. (a) $x^2 + 6x - 520 = 0$ (b) -26 or 20;
20 feet   **123.** About 23°C and 34°C   **125.** October 2010

SECTION 6.4 (pp. 465–469)

1. To solve quadratic equations that are written in the form
$ax^2 + bx + c = 0$ **2.** Completing the square
3. $b^2 - 4ac$ **4.** One solution   **5.** Factoring, square root
property, completing the square, and the quadratic
formula   **6.** No; not when $b^2 - 4ac < 0$ **7.** $\pm\sqrt{k}$
8. $\pm i\sqrt{k}$ **9.** $-6, \frac{1}{2}$ **11.** 1   **13.** No real solutions
15. $-2, 8$ **17.** $\frac{1 \pm \sqrt{17}}{8}$ **19.** No real solutions   **21.** $\frac{1}{2}$
23. $\frac{3 \pm \sqrt{13}}{2}$ **25.** $2 \pm \sqrt{3}$ **27.** $\frac{1 \pm \sqrt{37}}{6}$
29. $\frac{1 \pm \sqrt{15}}{2}$ **31.** $\frac{5 \pm \sqrt{10}}{3}$ **33.** (a) $a > 0$ (b)$-1, 2$
(c) Positive   **35.** (a) $a > 0$ (b) No real solutions
(c) Negative   **37.** (a) $a < 0$ (b) 2   (c) Zero   **39.** (a) 25
(b) 2   **41.** (a) 0   (b) 1   **43.** (a) $-\frac{7}{4}$ (b) 0   **45.** (a) 21
(b) 2   **47.** $1 \pm \sqrt{2}$ **49.** $-\frac{3}{2}, 1$ **51.** None   **53.** None
55. $\frac{-2 \pm \sqrt{10}}{3}$ **57.** $\pm 3i$ **59.** $\pm 4i\sqrt{5}$ **61.** $\pm\frac{1}{2}i$
63. $\pm\frac{3}{4}i$ **65.** $\pm i\sqrt{6}$ **67.** $\pm\sqrt{3}$ **69.** $\pm i\sqrt{2}$
71. $\frac{1}{2} \pm i\frac{\sqrt{7}}{2}$ **73.** $-\frac{3}{4} \pm i\frac{\sqrt{23}}{4}$ **75.** $2 \pm \sqrt{3}$
77. $-\frac{1}{2} \pm i\frac{\sqrt{7}}{2}$ **79.** $-\frac{1}{5} \pm i\frac{\sqrt{19}}{5}$ **81.** $-\frac{3}{4} \pm i\frac{\sqrt{23}}{4}$
83. $-\frac{1}{2} \pm i\frac{\sqrt{15}}{2}$ **85.** $\frac{1 \pm \sqrt{3}}{2}$ **87.** $\frac{1}{4} \pm i\frac{\sqrt{15}}{4}$
89. $-1 \pm i\sqrt{3}$ **91.** $-2 \pm i$ **93.** $1 \pm i\sqrt{2}$ **95.** $1, 2$
97. $-\frac{1}{2}, 4$ **99.** $\frac{5 \pm \sqrt{17}}{2}$ **101.** $-\frac{1}{4} \pm \frac{3}{4}i\sqrt{7}$ **103.** $\pm\frac{1}{2}$
105. $\pm i\sqrt{2}$ **107.** $\frac{1}{3}$ **109.** 9 miles per hour
111. 45 miles per hour   **113.** About 1993 and 2004
($x \approx 4.11, 15.36$)   **115.** (a) 6; in Oct. 2010 Groupon's
value was $6 billion.   (b) Jan. 2011   **117.** $x \approx 8.04$,
or about 1992; this agrees with the graph.
119. $130 + 5\sqrt{634} \approx 256$ mph   **121.** (a)–(c) 11 in. by
14 in.   **123.** (a) The rate of change is not constant.
(b) 75 seconds (answers may vary)   (c) 75 seconds

CHECKING BASIC CONCEPTS 6.3 & 6.4 (p. 469)

1. $\frac{1}{2}, 3$ **2.** $\pm\sqrt{5}$ **3.** $2 \pm \sqrt{3}$ **4.** $y = \pm\sqrt{1 - x^2}$

5. (a) $\frac{3 \pm \sqrt{17}}{4}$ **(b)** $\frac{4}{3}$ **(c)** $-\frac{1}{2} \pm i\frac{\sqrt{7}}{2}$ **6. (a)** 5; two real solutions **(b)** -7; no real solutions **(c)** 0; one real solution **7. (a)** $\pm i\sqrt{5}$ **(b)** $-\frac{1}{2} \pm i\frac{\sqrt{11}}{2}$

SECTION 6.5 (pp. 477–479)

1. It has an inequality symbol rather than an equals sign.
2. No, they often have infinitely many. **3.** No **4.** Yes
5. $-2 < x < 4$ **6.** $x < -3$ or $x > 1$ **7.** Yes **9.** Yes
11. No **13.** Yes **15.** No **17.** No **19. (a)** $-3, 2$
(b) $-3 < x < 2$ **(c)** $x < -3$ or $x > 2$ **21. (a)** $-2, 2$
(b) $-2 < x < 2$ **(c)** $x < -2$ or $x > 2$ **23. (a)** $-10, 5$
(b) $x < -10$ or $x > 5$ **(c)** $-10 < x < 5$
25. $[-0.128, 0.679]$ **27. (a)** $-2, 2$ **(b)** $-2 < x < 2$
(c) $x < -2$ or $x > 2$ **29. (a)** $-4, 0$ **(b)** $-4 < x < 0$
(c) $x < -4$ or $x > 0$ **31.** $[-7, -3]$
33. $(-\infty, 1) \cup (2, \infty)$ **35.** $(-\sqrt{10}, \sqrt{10})$
37. $(-\infty, 0) \cup (6, \infty)$
39. $(-\infty, 2 - \sqrt{2}] \cup [2 + \sqrt{2}, \infty)$ **41. (a)** $-2, 2$
(b) $-2 < x < 2$ **(c)** $x < -2$ or $x > 2$ **43. (a)** $\frac{-1 \pm \sqrt{5}}{2}$
(b) $\frac{-1 - \sqrt{5}}{2} < x < \frac{-1 + \sqrt{5}}{2}$
(c) $x < \frac{-1 - \sqrt{5}}{2}$ or $x > \frac{-1 + \sqrt{5}}{2}$ **45.** $(-3, -1)$
47. $(-\infty, -2.5] \cup [3, \infty)$ **49.** $[-2, 2]$ **51.** $(-\infty, \infty)$
53. $(0, 3)$ **55.** No real solutions **57.** 2
59. $(-\infty, -1) \cup (-1, \infty)$ **61.** $[-1, 2]$ **63. (a)** From
1131 feet to 3535 feet (approximately) **(b)** Before 1131 feet
or after 3535 feet (approximately) **65. (a)** About 383; they
agree (approx.). **(b)** About 1969 or after **(c)** About 1969
or after **67.** From 11 feet to 20 feet

SECTION 6.6 (p. 483)

1. $\pm 1, \pm \sqrt{6}$ **3.** $-\sqrt[3]{2}, \sqrt[3]{\frac{5}{3}}$ **5.** $-\frac{4}{5}, -\frac{1}{3}$ **7.** $-3, 3$
9. $-\sqrt[3]{\frac{1}{3}}, \sqrt[3]{2}$ **11.** $-\frac{1}{8}, \frac{2}{5}$ **13.** 1 **15.** $1, 32^5 = 33{,}554{,}432$
17. $16, 81$ **19.** 1 **21.** $-3, 6$ **23.** $-\sqrt{3}, \sqrt{3}$
25. $\pm 2, \pm 2i$ **27.** $0, \pm i$ **29.** $\pm\sqrt{2}, \pm i$
31. $-1 \pm i$ **33.** $\pm 2i$

CHECKING BASIC CONCEPTS 6.5 & 6.6 (p. 483)

1. $(-\infty, -2) \cup (3, \infty)$ **2.** $\left[-1, -\frac{2}{3}\right]$ **3.** $-2, \sqrt[3]{2}$
4. $-1, 8^3 = 512$ **5.** $\pm i$

CHAPTER 6 REVIEW (pp. 486–490)

1. $(-3, 4)$; $x = -3$; downward **2.** $(1, 0)$; $x = 1$; upward

3. (a)

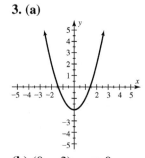

(b) $(0, -2)$; $x = 0$
(c) -1

4. (a)

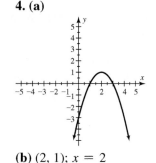

(b) $(2, 1)$; $x = 2$
(c) 0

5. (a)

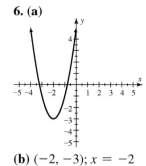

(b) $(1, 2)$; $x = 1$
(c) -2.5

6. (a)

(b) $(-2, -3)$; $x = -2$
(c) -1

7. $-\frac{7}{2}$ **8.** $-\frac{14}{3}$ **9.** $(2, -6)$ **10.** $(0, 5)$ **11.** $(2, 2)$
12. $(-1, 1)$

13. (a)

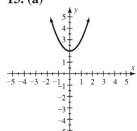

14. (a)

(b) Up 2 units

(b) Narrower

15. (a)

16. (a)

(b) Right 2 units

(b) Left 1 unit, down 3 units

17. (a)

18. (a)

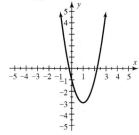

(b) Wider, left 1 unit,
up 2 units

(b) Narrower, right 1 unit,
down 3 units

19. $y = -4(x - 2)^2 - 5$ **20.** $y = -(x + 4)^2 + 6$
21. $y = (x + 2)^2 - 11$; $(-2, -11)$
22. $y = \left(x - \frac{7}{2}\right)^2 - \frac{45}{4}$; $\left(\frac{7}{2}, -\frac{45}{4}\right)$
23. $y = 2\left(x - \frac{3}{4}\right)^2 - \frac{73}{8}$; $\left(\frac{3}{4}, -\frac{73}{8}\right)$
24. $y = 3(x + 1)^2 - 5$; $(-1, -5)$ **25.** $a = 3$
26. $a = \frac{1}{4}$ **27.** $f(x) = -5x^2 + 30x - 41$; -41
28. $f(x) = 3x^2 + 12x + 8$; 8 **29.** $-2, 3$ **30.** -1
31. No real solutions **32.** $-4, 6$ **33.** $-10, 5$
34. $-0.5, 0.25$ **35.** $-5, 10$ **36.** $-3, 1$ **37.** $-4, 2$

38. $-1, 3$ **39.** $-5, 4$ **40.** $-8, -3$ **41.** $-\frac{2}{7}, \frac{2}{3}$
42. $\frac{4}{7}, 3$ **43.** ± 10 **44.** $\pm \frac{1}{3}$ **45.** $\pm \frac{\sqrt{6}}{2}$ **46.** No real
solutions   **47.** $-3 \pm \sqrt{7}$ **48.** $2 \pm \sqrt{10}$
49. $1 \pm \sqrt{6}$ **50.** $\frac{-3 \pm \sqrt{11}}{2}$ **51.** $R = -r \pm \sqrt{\frac{k}{F}}$
52. $y = \pm \sqrt{\frac{12 - 2x^2}{3}}$ **53.** $3, 6$ **54.** $11, 13$ **55.** $-\frac{1}{2}, \frac{1}{3}$
56. $\frac{5 \pm \sqrt{5}}{10}$ **57.** $4 \pm \sqrt{21}$ **58.** $\frac{3 \pm \sqrt{3}}{2}$
59. ± 2 **60.** $\pm \frac{1}{2}$ **61.** $\frac{5}{2}, 3$ **62.** $\frac{3}{2}, 5$ **63.** $\frac{3 \pm \sqrt{5}}{2}$
64. $\frac{1 \pm \sqrt{5}}{4}$ **65. (a)** $a > 0$ **(b)** $-2, 3$ **(c)** Positive
66. (a) $a > 0$ **(b)** 2 **(c)** Zero   **67. (a)** $a < 0$
(b) No real solutions   **(c)** Negative   **68. (a)** $a < 0$
(b) $-4, 2$ **(c)** Positive   **69. (a)** 1 **(b)** 2 **70. (a)** 144
(b) 2 **71. (a)** -23 **(b)** 0 **72. (a)** 0 **(b)** 1
73. $-\frac{1}{2} \pm i\frac{\sqrt{19}}{2}$ **74.** $\pm 2i$ **75.** $\frac{1}{4} \pm i\frac{\sqrt{7}}{4}$ **76.** $\frac{1}{7} \pm i\frac{\sqrt{34}}{7}$
77. (a) $-2, 6$ **(b)** $-2 < x < 6$ **(c)** $x < -2$ or $x > 6$
78. (a) $-2, 0$ **(b)** $x < -2$ or $x > 0$ **(c)** $-2 < x < 0$
79. (a) $-4, 4$ **(b)** $-4 < x < 4$ **(c)** $x < -4$ or $x > 4$
80. (a) $-2, 1$ **(b)** $-2 < x < 1$ **(c)** $x < -2$ or $x > 1$
81. (a) $-1, 3$ **(b)** $-1 < x < 3$ **(c)** $x < -1$ or $x > 3$
82. (a) $-\frac{3}{2}, 5$ **(b)** $-\frac{3}{2} \le x \le 5$ **(c)** $x \le -\frac{3}{2}$ or $x \ge 5$
83. $[-3, -1]$ **84.** $\left(\frac{1}{5}, 3\right)$ **85.** $\left(-\infty, \frac{1}{6}\right) \cup (2, \infty)$
86. $(-\infty, -\sqrt{5}\,] \cup [\sqrt{5}, \infty)$ **87.** $(-\infty, \infty)$
88. No solutions   **89.** $\pm \sqrt{5}, \pm 3$ **90.** $-\frac{1}{4}, \frac{2}{7}$
91. $1, 512$ **92.** 0 **93.** $\pm i\frac{\sqrt{2}}{2}$ **94.** $2 \pm i\sqrt{2}$
95. (a) $f(x) = x(12 - 2x)$ **(b)** 6 inches by 3 inches
96. (a) After 1 second and 1.75 seconds   **(b)** 1.375 seconds;
34.25 feet   **97. (a)** $f(x) = x(90 - 3x)$
(b) [0, 30, 5] by [0, 800, 100]

(c) 10 or 20 rooms   **(d)** 15 rooms
98. (a) $x(x + 2) = 143$ **(b)** $x = -13$ or $x = 11$; the
numbers are -13 and -11 or 11 and 13.
99. (a) $\sqrt{1728} \approx 41.6$ miles per hour   **(b)** 60 miles per hour
100. (a) (1950, 220); in 1950, the per capita consumption
was at a low of 220 million Btu.
(b) [1950, 1970, 5] by [200, 350, 25]

It increased.
(c) $f(2010) = 1120$; no; the trend represented by this
model did not continue after 1970.   **101.** About 11.1 inches
by 11.1 inches   **102.** 50 feet   **103.** About 1.5 feet
104. About 6.0 to 9.0 inches

CHAPTER 6 TEST (pp. 490–491)

1. $\left(1, \frac{3}{2}\right); x = 1; -3$ **2.** $-\frac{29}{4}$ **3.** $a = -\frac{1}{2}$
4. (a) Same as $y = x^2$ **(b)** Same as $y = x^2$ except
except shifted 1 unit right   shifted 2 units downward

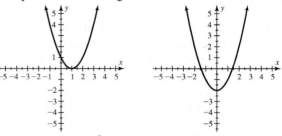

(c) Same as $y = x^2$ except it is wider, shifted right 3 units,
and shifted upward 2 units

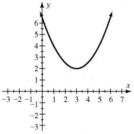

5. $y = (x - 3)^2 - 7; (3, -7); x = 3$ **6.** $-1, 2; 2$
7. $-4, \frac{1}{3}$ **8.** $-\frac{1}{2}, \frac{1}{2}$ **9.** $4 \pm \sqrt{17}$ **10.** $\frac{3 \pm \sqrt{17}}{4}$
11. $\pm \frac{4}{3}$ **12.** $m = \pm \sqrt{\frac{Fr^2}{G}}$ **13. (a)** $a < 0$ **(b)** $-3, 1$
(c) Positive   **14. (a)** -44 **(b)** No real solutions
(c) The graph of $y = -3x^2 + 4x - 5$ does not intersect the
x-axis.   **15. (a)** $-1, 1$ **(b)** $-1 < x < 1$
(c) $x < -1$ or $x > 1$ **16. (a)** $-10, 20$
(b) $x < -10$ or $x > 20$ **(c)** $-10 < x < 20$
17. (a) $-\frac{1}{2}, \frac{3}{4}$ **(b)** $\left[-\frac{1}{2}, \frac{3}{4}\right]$ **(c)** $\left(-\infty, -\frac{1}{2}\right] \cup \left[\frac{3}{4}, \infty\right)$
18. $[-2, 0]$ **19.** $\sqrt[3]{2}, 1$ **20.** $-1 \pm i\frac{\sqrt{2}}{2}$
21. $-1.37, 0.69$ **22.** $\sqrt{2250} \approx 47.4$ miles per hour
23. (a) $f(x) = (x + 20)(90 - x)$ **(b)** 35
24. (a) [0, 6, 1] by [0, 150, 50]

(b) After about 5.6 seconds
(c) 2.75 seconds; 129 feet

CHAPTERS 1–6 CUMULATIVE REVIEW
(pp. 493–495)

1. 1 **2.** Natural: $\sqrt[3]{8}$; whole: $0, \sqrt[3]{8}$; integer: $0, -5, \sqrt[3]{8}$;
rational: $0.\overline{4}, 0, -5, \sqrt[3]{8}, -\frac{4}{3}$; irrational: $\sqrt{7}$ **3. (a)** $x^{10}y^{12}$
(b) $\frac{x}{y^8}$ **(c)** $\frac{1}{b^{10}}$ **4.** 9.29×10^6 **5.** $2; x \le 2$ **6.** $(2, 5)$

7.

8.

9. $y = -\frac{3}{2}x + 5$ **10.** $x = -3$ **11.** -12 **12.** $\left(-\infty, \frac{7}{4}\right)$
13. $\left[\frac{1}{3}, 1\right]$ **14.** $(-1, 5]$ **15.** $(-1, 1)$

16.

17. $(2, 2, 1)$ **18.** $6x^2 + 17x - 14$ **19.** $3x^3y + 3xy^3$
20. $x - 9$ **21.** $x(x + 1)(x - 2)$ **22.** $(2x + 5)(2x - 5)$
23. $\pm\sqrt{3}$ **24.** 1 **25.** $\frac{x + 3}{2}$ **26.** $-\frac{2}{x(x + 2)}$ **27.** $4x^3$
28. $\frac{1}{64}$ **29.** 3 **30.** $3\sqrt{2x}$

31.

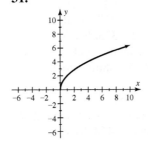

32. $\sqrt{26}$ **33.** $1 - i$ **34.** 3 **35.** 0.79

36.

(a) $(1, 2)$ **(b)** 6 **(c)** $x = 1$ **(d)** $x \geq 1$
37. $f(x) = 2(x - 1)^2 - 3$ **38.** Shifted 1 unit left, 2 units
downward; narrower   **39.** $-3 \pm \sqrt{11}$ **40.** $\frac{3 \pm \sqrt{17}}{4}$
41. $1, 3$ **42. (a)** $-2, 1$ **(b)** $-2 \leq x \leq 1$
43. $x < 1$ or $x > 2$ **44.** $\pm 4, \pm 4i$ **45.** c.   **46.** f.   **47.** g.
48. e.   **49.** d.   **50.** a.   **51.** b.   **52.** h.   **53. (a)** 300; initially,
the tank holds 300 gal. **(b)** 6; after 6 minutes the tank is empty.
(c) -50; water is pumped out at 50 gal/min.
(d) $G(t) = 300 - 50t$ **54.** $2200 at 6\%$, $1200 at 5\%$,
$600 at 4\%$ **55.** 125 ft by 125 ft   **56.** 33 feet

B	**The Midpoint Formula**

1. -1 **3.** $(-1, 0)$ **5.** $\left(-\frac{1}{2}, \frac{1}{2}\right)$ **7.** $(20, 0)$ **9.** $(-8, -1)$
11. $\left(-1, -\frac{1}{6}\right)$ **13.** $(0.2, 0.25)$ **15.** $(2005, 9)$ **17.** $(2a, 2b)$
19. (a) $f(x) = -2x + 5$; 1   **(b)** 1   **(c)** equal
21. (a) $f(x) = \frac{2}{5}x + \frac{1}{5}$; 1   **(b)** 1   **(c)** equal
23. 79.8 years   **25.** 256.5 million   **27.** $45,250

Photo Credits

Glossary

absolute value equation An equation that contains an absolute value.

absolute value function The function defined by $f(x) = |x|$.

absolute value inequality An inequality that contains an absolute value.

addition property of equality If a, b, and c are real numbers, then $a = b$ is equivalent to $a + c = b + c$.

annuity A sum of money from which regular payments are made.

arithmetic series The sum of the terms of an arithmetic sequence.

axis of symmetry for inverse functions The line $y = x$; f^{-1} can be sketched from the graph of $y = f(x)$ by reflecting the graph of f across the line $y = x$.

axis of symmetry of a parabola The line passing through the vertex of the parabola that divides the parabola into two symmetric parts.

base e If the base of an exponential expression is e (approximately 2.72), then we say this expression has base e.

basic principle of fractions When simplifying fractions, the principle which states $\frac{a \cdot c}{b \cdot c} = \frac{a}{b}$.

binomial A polynomial with two terms.

break-even point The point at which the cost of producing x items equals the revenue made from selling x items.

byte A unit of computer memory, capable of storing one letter of the alphabet.

center of a circle The point that is a fixed distance from all the points on a circle.

center of an ellipse The fixed point located exactly halfway between the two vertices.

change in x The value given by $x_2 - x_1$ if a line passes through two points (x_1, y_1) and (x_2, y_2).

change in y The value given by $y_2 - y_1$ if a line passes through two points (x_1, y_1) and (x_2, y_2).

circle The set of points in a plane that are a constant distance from a fixed point called the center.

clearing fractions The process of multiplying both sides of an equation by a common denominator to eliminate the fractions.

coefficient The numeric constant in a monomial.

common denominator A number or expression that each denominator can divide into *evenly* (without a remainder).

completing the square An important technique in mathematics that involves adding a constant to a binomial so that a perfect square trinomial results.

complex conjugate The complex conjugate of $a + bi$ is $a - bi$.

complex fraction A rational expression that contains fractions in its numerator, denominator, or both.

complex number A complex number can be written in standard form as $a + bi$, where a and b are real numbers and i is the imaginary unit.

composite function A function in which a quantity depends on a variable that depends on another variable; denoted $f(g(x))$.

composition Replacing a variable with an algebraic expression in function notation is called composition of functions.

compound inequality Two inequalities joined by the word *and* or the word *or*.

conditional equation An equation that is true for some, but not all, values of any of its variables.

conjugate The conjugate of $a + b$ is $a - b$.

constant function A linear function of the form $f(x) = b$, where b is a constant.

constant of proportionality (constant of variation) In the equation $y = kx$, the number k.

continuous growth Growth in a quantity that is directly proportional to the amount present.

contradiction An equation that is always false, regardless of the values of any variables.

cube root function The function defined by $g(x) = \sqrt[3]{x}$.

cubed A number or variable that has been raised to the third power has been cubed.

cubic function A polynomial function of degree 3.

cubic polynomial A polynomial of degree 3 that can be written as $ax^3 + bx^2 + cx + d$, where $a \neq 0$.

decimal form See standard (decimal) form.

degree of a monomial The sum of the exponents of the variables.

degree of a polynomial The degree of the monomial with highest degree.

dependent variable The variable that represents the output of a function.

determinant A real number associated with a square matrix.

diagrammatic representation A function represented by a diagram.

difference of two cubes Expression in the form $a^3 - b^3$, which can be factored as $(a - b)(a^2 + ab + b^2)$.

difference of two squares Expression in the form $a^2 - b^2$, which can be factored as $(a - b)(a + b)$.

directly proportional A quantity y is directly proportional to x if there is a nonzero number k such that $y = kx$.

discriminant The expression $b^2 - 4ac$ in the quadratic formula.

distance formula The distance between the points (x_1, y_1) and (x_2, y_2) in the xy-plane is $d = \sqrt{(x_2 - x_1)^2 + (y_2 - y_1)^2}$.

domain The set of all x-values of the ordered pairs in a relation.

equation of a line An equation whose graph is a line, such as point–slope form and slope–intercept form.

equivalent equations Two equations that have the same solution set.

even root The nth root, $\sqrt[n]{a}$, where n is even.

exponential equation An equation that has a variable as an exponent.

expression A term or sums and differences of terms; does not include an equals sign.

extraneous solution A solution that does not satisfy the given equation.

factoring by grouping A technique that uses the distributive property by grouping four terms of a polynomial in such a way that the polynomial can be factored even though its greatest common factor is 1.

factors In a multiplication problem, the two numbers multiplied.

FOIL A method for multiplying two binomials $(A + B)$ and $(C + D)$. Multiply **F**irst terms AC, **O**uter terms AD, **I**nner terms BC, and **L**ast terms BD; then combine like terms.

formula An equation that can be used to calculate one quantity by using a known value of another quantity.

function A relation where each element in the domain corresponds to exactly one element in the range.

function notation $y = f(x)$ is read "y equals f of x". This means that function f with input x produces output y.

general term (nth term) of a sequence a_n where n is a natural number in the domain of a sequence $a_n = f(n)$.

graphical factoring Using a graph to factor a polynomial by identifying the zeros of the polynomial.

graphical representation A graph of a function.

graphical solution A solution to an equation obtained by graphing.

greatest common factor (GCF) The term with the highest degree and largest coefficient that is a factor of all terms in the polynomial.

half-life The time it takes for a radioactive sample to decay to half its original amount.

horizontal line A line with zero slope.

hyperbola The set of points in a plane, the difference of whose distances from two fixed points is constant.

identity An equation that is always true regardless of the values of any variables.

imaginary number A complex number $a + bi$ with $b \neq 0$.

imaginary part The value of b in the complex number $a + bi$.

imaginary unit A number denoted i whose properties are $i = \sqrt{-1}$ and $i^2 = -1$.

independent variable The variable that represents the input of a function.

index The value of n in the expression $\sqrt[n]{a}$.

inequality When the equals sign in an equation is replaced with any one of the symbols $<$, $\leq$, $>$, or $\geq$, and inequality results.

infinity Values that increase without bound.

input An element of the domain of a function.

intersection Elements that belong to both sets A and B, denoted $A \cap B$.

interval notation A notation for number line graphs that eliminates the need to draw the entire line. A *closed interval* is expressed by the endpoints in brackets, such as $[-2, 7]$; an *open interval* is expressed in parentheses, such as $(-2, 7)$, and indicates that the endpoints are not included in the solution. A *half-open interval* has a bracket and a parenthesis, such as $[-2, 7)$.

inversely proportional A quantity y is inversely proportional to x if there is a nonzero number k such that $y = k/x$.

joint variation A quantity z varies jointly with x and y if there is a nonzero number k such that $z = kxy$.

leading coefficient In a polynomial of one variable, the coefficient of the monomial with highest degree.

least common denominator (LCD) The common denominator with the fewest factors.

least common multiple (LCM) The smallest number that two or more numbers will divide into evenly.

like radicals Radicals that have the same index and the same radicand.

like terms Two terms that contain the same variables raised to the same powers.

linear equation An equation that can be written in the form $ax + b = 0$, where $a \neq 0$.

linear function A function f represented by $f(x) = ax + b$, where a and b are constants.

linear inequality in one variable An inequality that can be written in the form $ax + b > 0$, where $a \neq 0$. (The symbol $>$ may be replaced with $\leq$, $<$, or $\geq$.)

linear inequality in two variables When the equals sign in a linear equation of two variables is replaced with $<$, $\leq$, $>$, or $\geq$, a linear inequality in two variables results.

linear polynomial A polynomial of degree 1 that can be written as $ax + b$, where $a \neq 0$.

linear system in three variables System of three equations in which each equation can be written in the form $ax + by + cz = d$; an ordered triple (x, y, z) is a solution to the system of equations if the values for x, y, and z make *all three* equations true.

lowest terms A fraction in lowest terms is one in which the numerator and the denominator have no common factors.

model A mathematical representation of a real-world application that can help explain phenomena or make predictions.

monomial A term whose variables have only nonnegative integer exponents.

multiplication property of equality If a, b, and c are real numbers with $c \neq 0$, then $a = b$ is equivalent to $ac = bc$.

name of the function In the function given by $f(x)$, we call the function f.

natural logarithm The base-e logarithm, denoted either $\log_e x$ or $\ln x$.

negative infinity Values that decrease without bound.

negative slope On a graph, the slope of a line that falls from left to right.

negative square root The negative square root is denoted $-\sqrt{a}$.

nonlinear data If data points do not lie on a (straight) line, the data are nonlinear.

nonlinear system of inequalities Two or more inequalities, at least one of which is nonlinear.

nth root The number b is an nth root of a if $b^n = a$, where n is a positive integer, and is denoted $\sqrt[n]{a} = b$.

numerical factoring Using a table of values to factor a polynomial by identifying the zeros of the polynomial.

numerical representation A table of values for a function.

numerical solution A solution often obtained by using a table of values.

odd root The nth root, $\sqrt[n]{a}$, where n is odd.

one-to-one function Two different inputs always result in two different outputs; that is, $x \neq y$ implies that $f(x) \neq f(y)$.

opposite of a polynomial The polynomial obtained by negating each term in a given polynomial.

order of operations The sequence in which calculations such as addition, subtraction, multiplication, etc., must be performed on an expression.

ordered triple Can be expressed as (x, y, z), where x, y, and z are numbers.

output An element of the range of a function.

parabola The $\cup$-shaped graph of a quadratic function.

parallel lines Two or more lines in the same plane that never intersect.

percent change When an amount A changes to a new amount B, then the percent change is calculated by $\frac{B-A}{A} \times 100$.

percent form To change to percent form take a number r in decimal form and multiply by 100.

percentage An amount in each hundred.

perfect cube An integer with an integer cube root.

perfect nth power The value of a if there exists an integer b such that $b^n = a$.

perfect square An integer with an integer square root.

perfect square trinomial A trinomial that can be factored as the square of a binomial, for example, $a^2 + 2ab + b^2 = (a + b)^2$.

perpendicular lines Two lines in a plane that intersect to form a right (90°) angle.

pixels The tiny units that comprise screens for computer terminals or graphing calculators.

point–slope form The line with slope m passing through the point (x_1, y_1) given by the equation $y = m(x - x_1) + y_1$ or, equivalently, $y - y_1 = m(x - x_1)$.

polynomial A monomial or a sum of monomials.

polynomials of one variable Polynomials that contain one variable.

positive slope On a graph, the slope of a line that rises from left to right.

power function A function that can be represented by $f(x) = x^p$, where p is a rational number.

principal nth root of a For an even positive integer n, if $b^n = a$ and b is positive, then b is a principal nth root of a and is denoted $\sqrt{a}, \sqrt[4]{a}, \sqrt[6]{a}, \ldots, \sqrt[n]{a}$.

properties of inequalities Rules for operations that can be performed on inequalities.

proportion A statement that two ratios are equal.

pure imaginary number A complex number $a + bi$ with $a = 0$ and $b \neq 0$ is called a pure imaginary number.

Pythagorean theorem If a right triangle has legs a and b with hypotenuse c, then $a^2 + b^2 = c^2$.

quadratic equation An equation that can be written as $ax^2 + bx + c = 0$, where a, b, and c are real numbers, with $a \neq 0$.

quadratic form An expression that is written in the form $ax^2 + bx + c$ after using substitution is in quadratic form.

quadratic formula The solutions to the quadratic equation, $ax^2 + bx + c = 0$, $a \neq 0$, are $x = (-b \pm \sqrt{b^2 - 4ac})/(2a)$.

quadratic function A function f represented by the equation $f(x) = ax^2 + bx + c$, where a, b, and c are real numbers with $a \neq 0$.

quadratic inequality If the equals sign in a quadratic equation is replaced with $>$, $\geq$, $<$, or $\leq$, a quadratic inequality results.

quadratic polynomial A polynomial of degree 2 that can be written as $ax^2 + bx + c$ with $a \neq 0$.

radical expression An expression that contains a radical sign.

radical sign The symbol $\sqrt{}$ or $\sqrt[n]{}$ for some positive integer n.

radicand The expression under the radical sign.

radius The fixed distance between the center and any point on a circle.

rate of change The value of a for the linear function given by $f(x) = ax + b$; slope can be interpreted as a rate of change.

rational equation An equation that involves a rational expression.

rational expression A polynomial divided by a nonzero polynomial.

rational function A function defined by $f(x) = p(x)/q(x)$, where $p(x)$ and $q(x)$ are polynomials and the domain of f includes all x-values such that $q(x) \neq 0$.

rationalizing the denominator The process of removing radicals from a denominator so that the denominator contains only rational numbers.

real part The value of a in the complex number $a + bi$.

reciprocal of a polynomial The reciprocal of a polynomial $p(x)$ is $\frac{1}{p(x)}$.

reciprocal of a rational expression The reciprocal of a rational expression $\frac{p(x)}{q(x)}$ is $\frac{q(x)}{p(x)}$.

reflection If the point (x, y) is on the graph of $y = f(x)$, then the point $(x, -y)$ is on the graph of its reflection across the x-axis.

remainder If a polynomial $p(x)$ can be written as $p(x) = d(x)q(x) + r(x)$, then $r(x)$ is the remainder when $p(x)$ is divided by $d(x)$.

rise The vertical change between two points on a line, that is, the change in the y-values.

root function In the power function $f(x) = x^p$, if $p = 1/n$, where $n \geq 2$ is an integer, then f is also a root function, which is given by $f(x) = \sqrt[n]{x}$.

run The horizontal change between two points on a line, that is, the change in the x-values.

scatterplot A graph of distinct points plotted in the xy-plane.

set-builder notation Notation to describe a set of numbers without having to list all of the elements. For example, $\{x \mid x > 5\}$ is read as "the set of all real numbers x such that x is greater than 5."

similar triangles Triangles that have equal corresponding angles and proportional corresponding sides.

slope The ratio of the change in y (rise) to the change in x (run) along a line. Slope m of a line equals $\frac{y_2 - y_1}{x_2 - x_1}$, where (x_1, y_1) and (x_2, y_2) are points on the line.

slope–intercept form The line with slope m and y-intercept b is given by $y = mx + b$.

solution A value for a variable that makes an equation a true statement.

solution set The set of all solutions to an equation.

solution to a system of equations An ordered pair (x, y), where the values for x and y satisfy both equations; could also be an ordered triple (x, y, z).

square root function The function given by $f(x) = \sqrt{x}$, where $x \geq 0$.

square root property If k is a nonnegative number, then the solutions to the equation $x^2 = k$ are $x = \pm\sqrt{k}$. If $k < 0$, then this equation has no real solutions.

squared A number or variable that has been raised to the second power has been squared.

standard equation of a circle The standard equation of a circle with center (h, k) and radius r is $(x - h)^2 + (y - k)^2 = r^2$.

standard (decimal) form A real number written with a decimal point or an assumed decimal point.

standard form of a complex number $a + bi$, where a and b are real numbers.

standard form of an equation for a line The form $ax + by = c$, where a, b, and c are constants with a and b not both 0.

standard form (for a system) A system of equations in two variables can be written in the form $ax + by = c$, $dx + ey = k$, where a, b, c, d, e, and k are constants.

subscript The expression x_1 has a subscript of 1; it is read "x sub one" or "x one".

substitution method A symbolic method for solving a system of equations in which one equation is solved for one of the variables and then the result is substituted into the other equation.

sum of two cubes Expression in the form $a^3 + b^3$, which can be factored as $(a + b)(a^2 - ab + b^2)$.

symbolic factoring Factoring a polynomial by hand, using a technique such as grouping or reverse FOIL.

symbolic representation Representing a function with a formula; for example, $f(x) = x^2 - 2x$.

symbolic solution A solution to an equation obtained by using properties of equations, and the resulting solution set is exact.

synthetic division A shortcut that can be used to divide $x - k$, where k is a number, into a polynomial.

table of values An organized way to display the inputs and outputs of a function; a numerical representation.

term A number, a variable, or a product of numbers and variables raised to powers.

terms of a sequence $a_1, a_2, a_3, \ldots, a_n, \ldots$ where the first term is $a_1 = f(1)$, the second term is $a_2 = f(2)$, and so on.

test point (for a system of inequalities) A point (x, y) that can be substituted into an inequality to determine the solution set.

test value A real number chosen to determine the solution set to an inequality.

three-part inequality A compound inequality written in the form $a < x < b$.

translation The shifting of a graph upward, downward, to the right, or to the left in such a way that the shape of the graph stays the same.

trinomial A polynomial with three terms.

varies directly A quantity y varies directly with x if there is a nonzero number k such that $y = kx$.

varies inversely A quantity y varies inversely with x if there is a nonzero number k such that $y = k/x$.

varies jointly A quantity z varies jointly with x and y if there is a nonzero number k such that $z = kxy$.

verbal representation A description, in words, of what a function computes.

vertex The lowest point on the graph of a parabola that opens upward or the highest point on the graph of a parabola that opens downward.

vertex (in a linear programming problem) The points where lines (boundaries) of the constraints intersect on the boundary of the region of feasible solutions.

vertex form of a parabola The vertex form of a parabola with vertex (h, k) is $y = a(x - h)^2 + k$, where $a \neq 0$ is a constant.

vertical asymptote A vertical asymptote typically occurs in the graph of a rational function when the denominator of the rational expression is 0 but the numerator is not 0; it can be represented by a vertical line in the graph of a rational function.

vertical line A line having an equation that can be written as $x = k$.

vertical line test If every vertical line intersects a graph at most once, then the graph represents a function.

vertical shift A translation of a graph upward or downward.

vertices of an ellipse The endpoints of the major axis.

vertices of a hyperbola The endpoints of the transverse axis.

x-intercept The x-coordinate of a point where a graph intersects the x-axis.

y-intercept The y-coordinate of a point where a graph intersects the y-axis.

Ymin Regarding the viewing rectangle of a graphing calculator, Ymin is the minimum y-value along the y-axis.

zero (of a polynomial) An x-value that makes a polynomial expression equal to zero.

zero-product property If the product of two numbers is 0, then at least one of the numbers must equal 0, that is, $ab = 0$ implies $a = 0$ or $b = 0$.

zero slope When a line passes through two points (x_1, y_1) and (x_2, y_2) where $y_1 = y_2$, the line has zero slope and is horizontal.

Index

SUPPLEMENT TO §2.1

1. Determine whether one quantity is a function of another within real life contexts by applying the definition of a function. Give your interpretation of the situation if you feel the description is vague.

   a. Is height a function of age?

   b. Is age a function of height?

   c. Is name a function of G# (i.e, PCC ID number)?

   d. Is G# a function of name?

   e. Is the cost per person a function of the number of people sharing a $20 pizza?

2. The value of a computer, in dollars, is given by $c(t) = 600 - 150t$, where t is the number of years since the computer was purchased.

   a. Find and interpret the vertical intercept of the function c.

   b. Find and interpret the horizontal intercept of the function c.

   c. Find the domain and range of c. State it using interval notation.

3. The function $y = p(x)$ is graphed in the below figure. Use it to determine the following values.

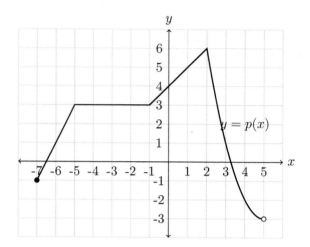

a. Find $p(0)$.

b. Find $p(1.5)$.

c. Find $p(5)$.

d. Find $p(-7)$.

e. Find $p(2)$.

f. Solve $p(x) = -2$.

g. Solve $p(x) = 1$.

h. Solve $p(x) = -4$.

i. Solve $p(x) = 3$.

j. Solve $p(x) = 0$.

k. State the domain of p in interval notaion.

l. State the range of p in interval notation.

m. Find all x for which $p(x) > 1$.

4. A group of rafters take a 15 day rafting trip down the Colorado River through the Grand Canyon. The distance, in miles, $K(t)$, that the group has floated is a function of the number of days traveled, t. The table below gives some data about the trip.

t	0	1	2	3	4	5	6	7	8	9	10	11	12	13	14	15
$K(t)$	0	20	35	45	58	75	100	125	135	145	158	175	211	230	258	277

a. Find and interpret $K(8)$.

b. Find and interpret $K(35)$.

c. Solve $K(t) = 125$ and interpret your answer.

d. Find the average rate of change between $t = 11$ and $t = 13$. Explain your answer

e. Find and interpret the vertical intercept of the function K.

f. What is the domain of the function K? Explain your answer.

g. What is the range of the function K? Explain your answer.

5. The historic Arlene Schnitzer Concert Hall originally opened in 1928 as the Portland Publix Theatre. The Theatre seated 2776 people and it cost 60 cents per ticket. Let $r(x)$ be the revenue, in dollars, from selling x tickets for an event at the Theatre.

    a. Find the algebraic formula for $r(x)$.

    b. Find the domain and range of r. Explain your answer.

6. Consider the linear function $f(x) = 4 - 0.5x$.

    a. Find and simplify the expressions for $y = f(x+6)$ and $y = f(x) + 6$.

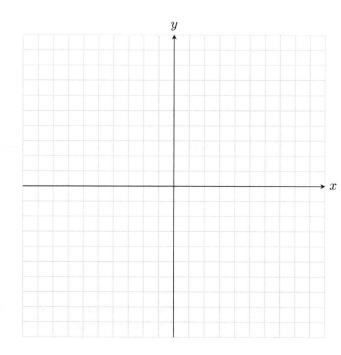

    b. Graph $y = f(x)$, $y = f(x+6)$, and $y = f(x) + 6$ on the same set of coordinate axes.

7. If $p(x) = x^2$, find and simplify expressions for $p(x+2)$ and $p(x) + 2$. Are the resulting expressions equivalent?

8. Let $j(x) = 4 - t + 2t^2$. Find and simplify the following expressions.

   a. $j(3t)$

   b. $j(3 - t)$

   c. $3j(t)$

   d. $3 - j(t)$

9. Suppse that $y = g(x)$ is a linear function and that $g(0) = -150$ and $g(50) = 2000$. Find the algebraic formula for $g(x)$.

10. Suppose that $y = h(x)$ is a linear function and that $h(-5) = 2$ and $h(5) = 20$. Find an algebraic formula for $h(x)$.

11. Suppose that $y = j(t)$ is a linear function and that $j(-6) = 5$ and $j(10) = -1$. Find an algebraic formula for $j(t)$.

SUPPLEMENT TO §6.1

1. State the domain and range of the functions shown below using interval notation and set notation.

a.

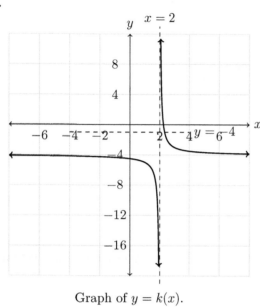

Graph of $y = k(x)$.

b.

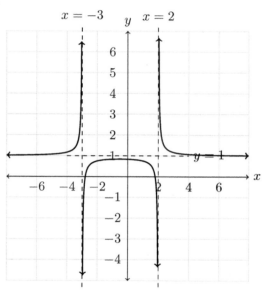

Graph of $y = j(x)$.

2. Let $f(x) = \dfrac{2x + 1}{5 - x}$. Simplify the following expressions.

   a. $f(x) + 2$

   b. $3f(x)$

c. $f(x+2)$ d. $f(3x)$

SUPPLEMENT TO §6.2

When we simplify the algebraic formula for a function we can lose information about the domain. We need to communicate hidden domain restrictions after we cancel factors in the denominator.

Example: Simplify the algebraic formula for $p(x) = \dfrac{3x + 3}{4x^2 - 4x - 8}$.

$$
\begin{aligned}
p(x) &= \frac{3x + 3}{4x^2 - 4x - 8} \\
&= \frac{3(x + 1)}{4(x^2 - x - 2)} \\
&= \frac{3(x + 1)}{4(x + 1)(x - 2)} \\
&= \frac{3\cancel{(x + 1)}}{4\cancel{(x + 1)}(x - 2)} \\
&= \frac{3}{4(x - 2)}, \quad x \neq -1
\end{aligned}
$$

(We write "$x \neq -1$" since the previous expression is not defined when $x = -1$ while this final expression is defined when $x = -1$. Thus they are only truly equal when $x \neq -1$.)

1. Simplify the expressions for the following rational functions. State any domain restriction necessary so that the expressions truly are equivalent.

   a. $f(x) = \dfrac{2x^2 + 6x}{3x + 9}$
                                          b. $T(x) = \dfrac{x^2 + 6x + 9}{x^2 - 9}$

c. $g(x) = \dfrac{2x^2 - x - 6}{x^2 + x - 6}$

e. $d(x) = \dfrac{x^2 - 16}{12 - 3x}$

d. $L(x) = \dfrac{x^3 - 4x^2 - 5x}{2x^2 - 13x + 15}$

f. $A(x) = \dfrac{12x^2 - 23x + 10}{12x^2 - 23x + 10}$

SUPPLEMENT TO §6.3

1. Let $S(x) = \dfrac{x+1}{x-3}$ and $R(x) = \dfrac{2}{x+2}$.

    a. If $a(x) = S(x) + R(x)$, find a simplified expression for $a(x)$ and state the domain of a using set notation.

    c. If $c(x) = S(x) \cdot R(x)$, find a simplified expression for $c(x)$ and state the domain of c using set notation.

    b. If $b(x) = S(x) - R(x)$, find a simplified expression for $b(x)$ and state the domain of b using set notation.

    d. If $d(x) = \dfrac{S(x)}{R(x)}$, find a simplified expression for $d(x)$ and state the domain of d using set notation.

SUPPLEMENT TO §7.1

1. Let $Y(x) = \sqrt{x-5} + 3$.

    a. Determine algebraically the domain of Y. State your conclusion using interval notation.

    b. Graph $y = Y(x)$ on your calculator and use it to determine the range of Y. State your conclusion using interval notation.

2. Let $Z(x) = \sqrt{7 - 2x} - 5$.

    a. Determine algebraically the domain of Z. State your conclusion using interval notation.

    b. Graph $y = Z(x)$ on your calculator and use it to determine the range of Z. State your conclusion using interval notation.

3. Let $U(t) = 2 - \sqrt{3 + 2t}$.

    a. Determine algebraically the domain of U. State your conclusion using interval notation.

    b. Graph $y = U(t)$ on your calculator and use it to determine the range of U. State your conclusion using interval notation.

4. Let $V(x) = \sqrt[3]{x+2}$.

   a. Determine algebraically the domain of V. State your conclusion using interval notation.

   b. Graph $y = V(x)$ on your calculator and use it to determine the range of V. State your conclusion using interval notation.

5. Let $T(k) = 3 - \sqrt[4]{3k-7}$.

   a. Determine algebraically the domain of T. State your conclusion using interval notation.

   b. Graph $y = T(k)$ on your calculator and use it to determine the range of T. State your conclusion using interval notation.

SUPPLEMENT TO §7.6

1. Let $f(x) = \sqrt{8 - 4x}$

    a. Evaluate $f(-2)$

    c. Solve $f(x) = 2$ and state your conclusion using set notation in a complete sentence.

    b. State the domain of f using set notation and interval notation.

2.   a. Solve the equation $1 + \sqrt{x} = \sqrt{3x - 3}$. State your conclusion using set notation in a complete sentence. Be sure to check the solutions you find to determine if there are any extraneous solutions.

    b. Solve the equation $1 + \sqrt{x} = \sqrt{3x - 3}$ by defining a function to represent each side of the equation and then using your calculator to graph both functions and find their intersection. Sketch the graphs in the provided space.

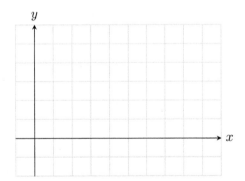

    c. What is the connection between what you found in part (a) in regards to extraneous solutions and the graphs in part (b)?

SUPPLEMENT TO §8.2

1. Use interval notation to express domain and range of the quadratic functions graphed below.

a.

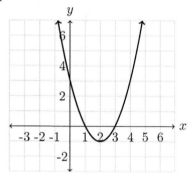

The graph of $y = m(x)$.

b.

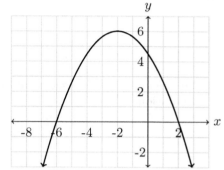

The graph of $y = n(x)$.

2. Graph the quadratic function $f(x) = -0.4x^2 + 5x + 15$ on your graphing calculator. Be sure to find a viewing window that allows you to see the vertex and all intercepts.

    a. Use either the min or max key to estimate the coordinates of the vertex of $y = f(x)$.

    d. Use the trace key and substitute $x = 0$ to find the vertical intercept of $y = f(x)$.

    b. Use function notation to state the vertex as an input and output in the function f.

    e. Use interval notation to express the domain and range of f.

    c. Use the calculator to determine the horizontal intercepts of $y = f(x)$.

SUPPLEMENT TO §8.3

1. The graph of $y = w(x)$ is given in the figure to the right. Use it to do the following exercises.

    a. Solve $w(x) < 1$.

    b. Solve $w(x) \geq -2$.

    c. Solve $-2 < w(x) \leq 6$.

    d. Solve $w(x) < -3$.

    e. Determine the domain and range of w. State your answer using interval notation.

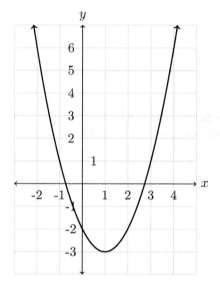

2. Use the graph of $y = f(x)$ to answer the following.

    a. Evaluate $f(-1)$.

    b. Solve $f(x) = 0$.

    c. Solve $f(x) > 0$.

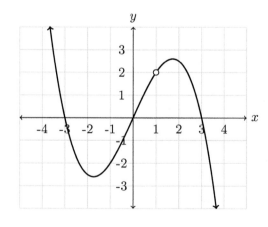

    d. Estimate solutions to $f(x) = 1$.

    e. What are the domain and range of f. Use interval notation.

3. Use the graph of $y = m(x)$ to answer the following questions.

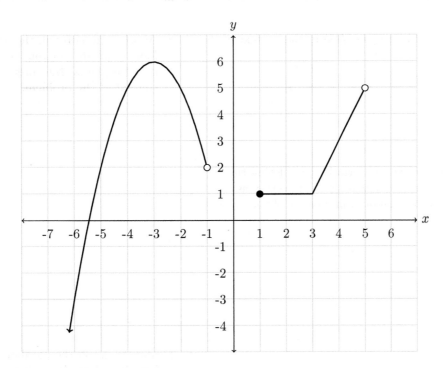

a. Evaluate $m(-5)$.

b. Evaluate $m(3)$.

c. Solve $m(x) = 2$.

d. Solve $m(x) = 6$.

e. Solve $m(x) > 0$.

f. Evaluate $m(-1)$.

g. Solve $m(x) = -3$.

h. Solve $m(x) = 3$.

i. Solve $m(x) \leq -3$.

j. Solve $m(x) > 5$.

k. State the domain and range of m using interval notation.

4. The function $f(t) = -t^2 + 2t + 3$ models the depth of water in feet in a large drainage ditch, where t is measured in hours and $t = 0$ corresponds to the moment that a summer storm has ended.

a. Evaluate and interpret $f(2)$ in the context of the real world function.

e. At what time(s) will the water in the ditch be 1 foot deep? Round your solutions to three decimal places. Interpret your solutions in the context of the problem.

b. Write $f(t)$ in vertex form by completing the square. State the meaning of the vertex as a maximum or minimum in context of the situation.

f. Make a graph the parabola $y = f(t)$ **on its implied domain** without using your calculator. Scale and label your axes.

c. Using the vertex form of $f(t)$ you found in part (b), solve the equation $f(t) = 0$ using the square root method.

d. What is the domain of and range of f in context of the situation? Write your answer in interval notation and explain your answer using a complete sentence.

5. A television is launched with a trebuchet. Suppose that the function $h(d) = -\dfrac{1}{100}d^2 + \dfrac{6}{5}d + 28$ models the television's height in feet above ground when its horizontal distance from the trebuchet is d feet.

a. Find and interpret the vertical intercept.

e. What are the horizontal distances at which the TV is 75 feet above the ground?

b. Find and interpret the horizontal intercept(s).

f. A six foot tall pole is positioned 130 feet from the trebuchet. How high above the pole is the TV as it passes over?

c. Find and interpret the vertex.

g. What is the domain based on the context of the problem? Explain your reasoning.

d. What are the horizontal distances at which the TV is 40 feet above the ground?

h. What is the range based on the context of the problem? Explain your reasoning.

ANSWERS TO SUPPLEMENT §2.1:

1. a. Answers may vary. You could answer, "Yes," since, at a particular time, you can only be one height. Or you could answer, "No," since, during a given year, you can grow and thus be more than one height at that age.

    b. No. You can be the same height for many years.

    c. Yes. Each G# is associated with only one name.

    d. No. There can be more than one person with the same name attending PCC, so there can be more than one G# associated with a particular name.

    e. Yes, if you split the cost evenly. The cost per person, c, can be a function of the number of people splitting the pizza, n, given by $c = f(n) = \dfrac{2}{n}$. For each positive integer number, n, the cost c will be unique.

2. a. The point $(0, 600)$ is the vertical intercept. It means that when the computer is brand new, it is worth $600.

    b. The point $(4, 0)$ is the horizontal intercept. It means that when the computer is 4 years old, it is worth nothing.

    c. The domain is $[0, 4]$. The range is $[0, 600]$.

3. a. $p(0) = 4$

    b. $p(1.5) = 5.5$

    c. $p(5)$ is undefined.

    d. $p(-7) = -1$

    e. $p(2) = 6$

    f. The solution set is $\{4\}$.

    g. The solutions set is $\{-6, 3\}$.

    h. The are no solutions. The solution set is $\{\}$.

    i. The solution set is $\{x| -5 \le x \le -1 \text{ or } x \approx 2.5\}$.

    j. The solution set is $\{x|x = -6.5 \text{ or } x \approx 3.2\}$.

    k. The domain is $[-7, 5)$.

    l. The range is $(-3, 6]$.

    m. $p(x) > 1$ for all x in the set $\{x| -6 < x < 3\}$.

4. a. $K(8) = 135$. After 8 days of rafting, the group has floated 135 miles down the Colorado River.

    b. $K(35)$ is undefined. The rafting trip was finished after 15 days, so the group was no longer rafting 35 days after starting the trip.

    c. The solution to $K(t) = 125$ is $t = 7$ since the group has floated down 125 miles of the Colorado River 7 days after starting the trip.

    d. The average rate of change is 27.5 miles per day. This means that each day between days 11 and 13 the rafting group traveled an average of 27.5 miles.

    e. The vertical intercept is $(0, 0)$, so the vertical and horizontal intercepts are the same. This point means that after 0 days of rafting, the group had floated 0 miles down the Colorado River.

    f. The domain is $[0, 15]$. The input values for this function represent the number of days of the rafting trip and the trip was 15 days long, so all time periods between and including 0 and 15 days must be in the domain.

    g. The range is $[0, 277]$. The rafters floated all 277 miles of the Grand Canyon so at some moment during the 15 day trip, the rafters had floated each unique distance between and including 0 and 277 miles, so all of these values must be in the range.

5. a. $r(x) = 0.6x$

    b. Domain: $\{0, 1, 2, ..., 2775, 2776\}$
        Range:
        $\{0.00, 0.60, 1.20, 1.80, ..., 1664.40, 1665.00, 1665.60\}$.

6. a. $y = f(x + 6) = 1 - 0.5x$ and
        $y = f(x) + 6 = 10 - 0.5x$

    b. Check your graph by graphing these functions on your graphing calculator.

7. $p(x + 2) = x^2 + 4x + 4$ while $p(x) + 2 = x^2 + 2$ which are not equivalent.

8. a. $j(3t) = 18t^2 - 3t + 4$

    b. $j(3 - t) = 2t^2 - 11t + 19$

    c. $3j(t) = 6t^2 - 3t + 12$

    d. $3 - j(t) = -2t^2 + t - 1$

9. $g(x) = 43x - 150$

10. $h(x) = \frac{9}{5}x + 11$

11. $j(x) = -\frac{3}{8}x + \frac{11}{4}$

ANSWERS TO SUPPLEMENT §6.1

1. a.   Domain $= \{x | x \neq 2\}$
                 $= (-\infty, 2) \cup (2, \infty)$
            Range $= \{y | y \neq -4\}$
                 $= (-\infty, -4) \cup (-4, \infty)$

    b.   Domain $= \{x | x \neq -3 \text{ and } x \neq 2\}$
                 $= (-\infty, -3) \cup (-3, 2) \cup (2, \infty)$
            Range $= \{y | y \neq 1\}$
                 $= (-\infty, 1) \cup (1, \infty)$

2. a. $f(x) + 2 = \dfrac{11}{5 - x}$

    c. $f(x + 2) = \dfrac{2x + 5}{3 - x}$

    b. $3f(x) = \dfrac{6x + 3}{5 - x}$

    d. $f(3x) = \dfrac{6x + 1}{5 - 3x}$

ANSWERS TO SUPPLEMENT §6.2

1.

a. $f(x) = \dfrac{2x}{3}$, $D = \{x | x \neq -3\}$

d. $L(x) = \dfrac{x(x+1)}{2x-3}$, $D = \{x | x \neq 5\}$

b. $T(x) = \dfrac{x+3}{x-3}$, $D = \{x | x \neq -3\}$

e. $d(x) = -\dfrac{x+4}{3}$, $D = \{x | x \neq 4\}$

c. $g(x) = \dfrac{2x+3}{x+3}$, $D = \{x | x \neq 2\}$

f. $A(x) = 1$, $D = \left\{ x \Big| x \neq \dfrac{5}{4}, \, x \neq \dfrac{2}{3} \right\}$

ANSWERS TO SUPPLEMENT §6.3:

1.

a. $a(x) = \dfrac{x^2 + 5x - 4}{(x+2)(x-3)}$,

$D = \{x | x \neq -2 \text{ and } x \neq 3\}$

b. $b(x) = \dfrac{x^2 + x + 8}{(x+2)(x-3)}$,

$D = \{x | x \neq -2 \text{ and } x \neq 3\}$

c. $c(x) = \dfrac{2(x+1)}{(x+2)(x-3)}$,

$D = \{x | x \neq -2 \text{ and } x \neq 3\}$

d. $d(x) = \dfrac{(x+1)(x+2)}{2(x-3)}$,

$D = \{x | x \neq 3 \text{ and } x \neq -2\}$

ANSWERS TO SUPPLEMENT §7.1

1. a. The domain of Y is $[5, \infty)$.

   b. The range of Y is $[3, \infty)$.

2. a. The domain of Z is $\left(-\infty, \dfrac{7}{2}\right]$.

   b. The range of Y is $[-5, \infty)$.

3. a. The domain of U is $\left[-\dfrac{3}{2}, \infty\right)$.

   b. The range of U is $(-\infty, 2]$.

4. a. The domain of V is $(-\infty, \infty)$.

   b. The range of V is $(-\infty, \infty)$.

5. a. The domain of T is $\left[\dfrac{7}{3}, \infty\right)$.

   b. The range of T is $(-\infty, 3]$.

ANSWERS TO SUPPLEMENT §7.6

1. a. $f(-2) = 4$ c. The solution set is $\{1\}$.

    b. The domain of f is $\{x | x \leq 2\} = (-\infty, 2]$.

2. a. The solution set is $\{4\}$. While it appears as though x could also equal 1, checking this as a solution in the original equation reveals that it is not actually a solution.

    b.
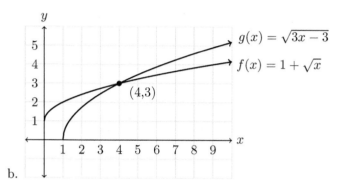

    The solution set is $\{4\}$.

    c. We see that the numbers which end up not being solutions to the problem when checked also do not show up as solutions when solving graphically.

ANSWERS TO SUPPLEMENT §8.2

1.   a. The domain of m is $(-\infty, \infty)$ and the range is $[-1, \infty)$.

b. The domain of n is $(-\infty, \infty)$ and the range is $(-\infty, 6]$.

2.   a. The vertex is $(6.25, 30.625)$.

d. The vertical intercept is $(0, 15)$.

b. $f(6.25) = 30.625$

e. The domain of f is $(-\infty, \infty)$ and the range is $(-\infty, 30.625]$.

c. The horizontal intercepts are $(-2.5, 0)$ and $(15, 0)$.

ANSWERS TO SUPPLEMENT §8.3

1. a. The solutions are in the interval $(-1, 3)$.

    b. The solutions are in the interval $(-\infty, 0] \cup [2, \infty)$.

    c. The solutions are in the interval $[-2, 0) \cup (2, 4]$.

    d. There are no solutions. The solution set is $\{\}$.

    e. The domain is $(-\infty, \infty)$ and the range is $[-3, \infty)$.

2. a. $f(-1) = -2$

    b. The solution set is $\{-3, 0, 3\}$.

    c. The solution set is $(-\infty, -3) \cup (0, 1) \cup (1, 3)$.

    d. The solution set is $\{x | x \approx -3.2 \text{ or } x \approx 0.5 \text{ or } x \approx 2.8\}$.

    e. The domain is $(-\infty, 1) \cup (1, \infty)$ and the range is $(-\infty, \infty)$.

3. a. $m(-5) = 2$

    b. $m(3) = 1$

    c. The solution set is $\{-5, 3.5\}$.

    d. The solution set is $\{-3\}$.

    e. The interval of solutions is $(-5.5, -1) \cup [1, 5)$.

    f. $m(-1)$ is not defined.

    g. The solution set is $\{-6\}$.

    h. The solution set is $\{x | x \approx -4.8 \text{ or } x \approx -1.3 \text{ or } x = 4\}$.

    i. The interval of solutions is $(-\infty, -6]$.

    j. The interval of solutions is $(-4, -2)$.

    k. The domain is $(-\infty, -1) \cup [1, 5)$. and the range is $(-\infty, 6]$.

4. a. $f(2) = 3$. Two hours after the storm ended, the water in the ditch was 3 feet deep.

    b. $f(t) = -(t-1)^2 + 4$. The vertex is $(1, 4)$. One hour after the storm ended, the water in the ditch reached its maximum depth of 4 feet.

    c. The solution set is $\{-1, 3\}$.

    d. The domain is $[-1, 3]$. Since one hour before the storm ended the ditch was empty and 3 hours after the storm ended, the ditch was empty again, having drained completely. The range is $[0, 4]$ since the minimum water depth is 0 feet and the maximum water depth is 4 feet deep.

    e. The water in the ditch will be 1 foot deep at approximately 0.732 hours before the storm ended and approximately 2.732 hours after the storm ended.

    f.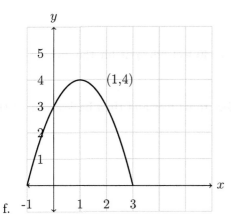

5. a. The vertical intercept is $(0, 28)$. The TV is 28 feet up in the air when at the point of launch.

    b. The horizontal intercepts are $(-20, 0)$ and $(140, 0)$. Only the second point makes sense in context and it represents the TV being 140 feet from the trebuchet when it hits the ground.

    c. The vertex is $(60, 64)$. The TV reaches its maximum height of 64 feet when it is 60 feet horizontally from the trebuchet.

    d. The TV is 40 feet above the ground when it is approximately 11.01 feet and approximately 108.99 feet horizontally away from the trebuchet.

    e. The TV never reaches 75 feet above the ground.

    f. The TV is 9 feet above the pole when it passes over it.

    g. The domain is $[0, 140]$ since the TV traveled from 0 feet to 140 feet where it hit the ground.

    h. The range is $[0, 64]$ since the TV's heights went from 28 feet to 64 feet and then back **down all the way** to 0 feet.

Real Math for the Real World

Astonishing Growth

Bamboo is rapidly becoming a popular building material because of its fast-growing, regenerative characteristics. In fact, bamboo is one of the fastest-growing plants on Earth, with some species growing up to 2 inches per hour under ideal conditions and reaching maturity in only 5 years. Learn how this rapid plant growth can be modeled using a linear function. See Example 6 on page 95.

Keeping Your Call from Being Dropped

Even though you might drive for many miles in your car, your cell phone doesn't drop your call. How does your cell phone company make it possible for your phone to access different cell phone towers across the country without losing its signal? Part of the reason that cell phones are reliable is because cell phone companies use systems of linear equations to send signals. See the Real World Connection and Example 10 on page 233.

Lurking or Participating in Social Networks

Have you ever noticed how a few very active people in a social network contribute almost all of the postings? Most people in a social network post almost nothing and spend most of their time "lurking." We can describe this phenomenon with a rational function. See the Real-World Connection on page 404 and Example 8 on page 405.

Going Green

Because of the high cost of energy, people are doing more construction with green building materials. As a result, sales of green building materials are predicted to increase at a constant rate in the near future. Using concepts from algebra, we can learn how to make predictions about future sales of these important materials. See the Section 2.2 A Look Into Math on page 89 and Example 7 on page 96.

Choosing Blockbuster or Netflix

More and more people are getting their movies via the mail or over the Internet, rather than going to the video store. This new phenomenon can be analyzed by using linear equations. See the Group Activity: Working with Real Data on page 263.

Crowding on an Island

It might be obvious that larger Pacific islands have a greater variety of tropical birds. However, if one island is 10 times larger than another, does the larger island have 10 times as many species of birds? It turns out that in order to understand nature, we need logarithms. See Example 8 on page 711.

Waiting, Waiting, Waiting

Nobody likes to wait in long lines. However, waiting in lines or in congested traffic has become a way of life. Some people spend as much as 3 years of their life waiting. To understand how long lines quickly form, we need to understand the concept of a rational function. See the Chapter 6 Opener on page 397 and Example 6 on page 439.

Giving Up on Online Videos

Today's viewers won't hesitate to click on a different online video if they aren't entertained right away. In fact, if the average online video has 100,000 viewers, then 20,000 of these viewers abandon the video within the first 10 seconds. With rational exponents, we can make predictions about people's behaviors regarding online videos. See the Section 7.2 A Look Into Math on page 503 and Example 3 on page 505.

Setting Yourself Up for SUCCESS in MATH

Make the Most of Class

☐ Attend class regularly.

☐ Bring your textbook and a notebook to every class.

☐ Take notes in class, and write down everything that is on the board.

☐ Ask questions. (You won't be the only one who wants to know the answer!)

☐ Study with others in your class.

Get Help When You Need it

☐ Find your instructor's office, and write down the number and office hours.

☐ Find the location and hours of the math tutor resources on campus.

☐ Try to solve the problems and write down your questions before you ask for help.

☐ Use the online resources, such as videos, that accompany this book.

Master the Exam

☐ Schedule a time and place to study every day instead of "cramming" before the exam.

☐ Watch the Chapter Test Prep Videos on YouTube to learn how an instructor solves the practice test problems.

☐ Read all your notes and go over your homework assignments to review important concepts.

☐ Pick a few problems from your assignments at random and try to solve them without help.

☐ Carefully write out all your work on the exam whenever possible.

Relax and Visualize doing well.
You CAN Learn Math.

Gary Rockswold has been a professor and teacher of mathematics, computer science, astronomy, and physical science for over 35 years. Not only has he taught at the undergraduate and graduate college levels, but he has also taught middle school, high school, vocational school, and adult education. He received his BA degree with majors in mathematics and physics from St. Olaf College and his PhD in applied mathematics from Iowa State University. He has been a principal investigator at the Minnesota Supercomputer Institute, publishing research articles in numerical analysis and parallel processing. He is currently an emeritus professor of mathematics at Minnesota State University–Mankato. He is an author for Pearson Education and has over 10 current textbooks at the developmental and precalculus levels. His developmental co-author and friend is Terry Krieger. They have been working together for over a decade. Making mathematics meaningful for students and professing the power of mathematics are special passions for Gary. In his spare time he enjoys sailing, doing yoga, and spending time with his family.

Terry Krieger has taught mathematics for over 20 years at the middle school, high school, vocational, community college, and university levels. His undergraduate degree in secondary education is from Bemidji State University in Minnesota, where he graduated summa cum laude. He received his MA in mathematics from Minnesota State University–Mankato. In addition to his teaching experience in the United States, Terry has taught mathematics in Tasmania, Australia, and in a rural school in Swaziland, Africa, where he served as a Peace Corps volunteer. Terry is currently teaching at Rochester Community and Technical College in Rochester, Minnesota. He has been involved with various aspects of mathematics textbook publication for more than 15 years and has joined his friend Gary Rockswold as co-author of a developmental math series published by Pearson Education. In his free time, Terry enjoys spending time with his wife and two boys, physical fitness, wilderness camping, and trout fishing.

Formulas from Geometry

Rectangle
$A = lw$
$P = 2l + 2w$

Triangle
$A = \frac{1}{2}bh$
$P = a + b + c$

Circle
$A = \pi r^2$
$C = 2\pi r$

Pythagorean Theorem
$a^2 + b^2 = c^2$

Trapezoid
$A = \frac{1}{2}(a + b)h$

**Sum of the Angles
in a Triangle**
$A + B + C = 180°$

Rectangular Prism
$V = lwh$
$S = 2lw + 2lh + 2wh$

Circular Cylinder
$V = \pi r^2 h$
$S = 2\pi rh + 2\pi r^2$

Sphere
$V = \frac{4}{3}\pi r^3$
$S = 4\pi r^2$

Cone
$V = \frac{1}{3}\pi r^2 h$
$S = \pi r\sqrt{r^2 + h^2} + \pi r^2$

Cube
$V = s^3$
$S = 6s^2$

Square-Based Prism
$V = \frac{1}{3}s^2 h$
$S = s^2 + 2sl$

Formulas from Algebra

Basic Properties
$a + b = b + a$

$ab = ba$

$(a + b) + c = a + (b + c)$

$(ab)c = a(bc)$

$a(b + c) = ab + ac$

$\dfrac{a}{c} + \dfrac{b}{c} = \dfrac{a + b}{c}$

$\dfrac{a}{b} \times \dfrac{c}{d} = \dfrac{ac}{bd}$

$\dfrac{a}{b} \div \dfrac{c}{d} = \dfrac{ad}{bc}$

Exponents
$a^m a^n = a^{m+n}$

$(a^m)^n = a^{mn}$

$(ab)^n = a^n b^n$

$\left(\dfrac{a}{b}\right)^n = \dfrac{a^n}{b^n}$

$\dfrac{a^m}{a^n} = a^{m-n}$

$a^{-n} = \dfrac{1}{a^n}$

$\dfrac{a^{-m}}{a^{-n}} = \dfrac{a^n}{a^m}$

$\left(\dfrac{a}{b}\right)^{-n} = \left(\dfrac{b}{a}\right)^n$

Logarithms
$\log_a x = k$ means $x = a^k$

$\log_a 1 = 0$ and $\log_a a = 1$

$\log_a m + \log_a n = \log_a mn$

$\log_a m - \log_a n = \log_a \dfrac{m}{n}$

$\log_a m^r = r \log_a m$

$\log_a a^x = x$

$a^{\log_a x} = x$

$\log_a x = \dfrac{\log_b x}{\log_b a}$ (change of base)

Radicals
$a^{1/n} = \sqrt[n]{a}$

$a^{m/n} = \sqrt[n]{a^m}$

$a^{m/n} = \left(\sqrt[n]{a}\right)^m$

$\sqrt[n]{ab} = \sqrt[n]{a} \cdot \sqrt[n]{b}$

$\sqrt[n]{\dfrac{a}{b}} = \dfrac{\sqrt[n]{a}}{\sqrt[n]{b}}$

Special Factoring
$a^2 - b^2 = (a - b)(a + b)$

$a^2 + 2ab + b^2 = (a + b)^2$

$a^2 - 2ab + b^2 = (a - b)^2$

$a^3 + b^3 = (a + b)(a^2 - ab + b^2)$

$a^3 - b^3 = (a - b)(a^2 + ab + b^2)$

Constants
$\pi \approx 3.141593$

$e \approx 2.718282$

$i = \sqrt{-1}$

$i^2 = -1$

Distance Formula
$d = \sqrt{(x_2 - x_1)^2 + (y_2 - y_1)^2}$

Midpoint Formula
$M = \left(\dfrac{x_1 + x_2}{2}, \dfrac{y_1 + y_2}{2}\right)$

Interval Notation
$x < 4$:	$(-\infty, 4)$
$1 < x \leq 6$:	$(1, 6]$
$x \geq 5$:	$[5, \infty)$

Slope of a Line
$m = \dfrac{\text{rise}}{\text{run}} = \dfrac{y_2 - y_1}{x_2 - x_1}$

Point–Slope Form
$y = m(x - x_1) + y_1$

$y - y_1 = m(x - x_1)$

Distance, rate, and time
$d = rt$

Vertical Line
$x = k$

Horizontal Line
$y = b$

Slope of Parallel Lines
$m_1 = m_2$

Slope of Perpendicular Lines
$m_1 \cdot m_2 = -1$, or

$m_1 = -\dfrac{1}{m_2}$

Quadratic Formula
$x = \dfrac{-b \pm \sqrt{b^2 - 4ac}}{2a}$

Vertex Formula
$x = -\dfrac{b}{2a}$

Vertex (Standard) Form
$y = a(x - h)^2 + k$

Slope–Intercept Form
$y = mx + b$

Standard Equation of a Circle
$(x - h)^2 + (y - k)^2 = r^2$